CONVERSION OF CUSTOMARY UNITS TO THE INTERNATIONAL SYSTEM OF UNITS (SI)

Length

1 angstrom	$= 0.1$ nm
1 astronomical unit	$= 149.6$ Gm
1 chain (66 feet)	$= 20.116\ 8$ m
1 ell (45 inches)	$= 1.143$ m
1 fathom	$= 1.828\ 8$ m
1 foot	$= 0.304\ 8$ m
1 foot (US survey, limited usage)	$= 0.304\ 800\ 6$ m
1 furlong	$= 0.201\ 168$ km
1 inch	$= 25.4$ mm
1 league (International nautical)	$= 5.556$ km
1 league (UK nautical)	$= 5.559\ 552$ km
1 league (US)	$= 4.828\ 032$ km
1 link (1/100 chain)	$= 0.201\ 168$ m
1 mile	$= 1.609\ 344$ km
1 mile (International nautical)	$= 1.852$ km
1 mile (UK nautical)	$= 1.853\ 184$ km
1 mile (US nautical)	$= 1.852$ km
1 mil (0.001 inch)	$= 25.4\ \mu m$
1 microinch	$= 25.4$ nm
1 parsec	$= 30.857$ Pm
1 light year	$= 9.4605$ Pm
1 perch	$= 5.029\ 2$ m
1 pica (printers)	$= 4.217\ 518$ mm
1 point (printers)	$= 0.351\ 459\ 8$ mm
1 pole	$= 5.029\ 2$ m
1 rod	$= 5.029\ 2$ m
1 yard	$= 0.914\ 4$ m

Mass

1 cental (100 lb)	$= 45.359\ 237$ kg
1 coal tub (100 lb. Newfoundland)	$= 45.359\ 237$ kg
1 drachm (apothecary)	$= 3.887\ 935$ g
1 dram (apothecary, US)	$= 3.887\ 935$ g
1 dram (avoirdupois)	$= 1.771\ 845$ g
1 grain	$= 64.798\ 91$ mg
1 hundredweight (100 lb)	$= 45.359\ 237$ kg
1 hundredweight (long 112 lb, UK)	$= 50.802\ 345$ kg
1 ounce (avoirdupois)	$= 28.349\ 523$ g
1 ounce (troy or apothecary)	$= 31.103\ 476\ 8$ g
1 metric carat	$= 200$ mg
1 pennyweight	$= 1.555\ 174$ g
1 pound (avoirdupois)	$= 0.453\ 592\ 37$ kg
1 pound (troy or apothecary)	$= 373.241\ 721\ 6$ g
1 quarter (28 lb, UK)	$= 12.700\ 58$ kg
1 scruple (apothecary, 20 grains)	$= 1.295\ 98$ g
1 slug	$= 14.593\ 9$ kg
1 stone (14 lb, UK)	$= 6.350\ 293$ kg
1 ton (2240 lb, UK)	$= 1.016\ 046\ 908\ 8$ t
1 ton (short, 2000 lb)	$= 0.907\ 184\ 74$ t
1 unified atomic mass	$= 1.660\ 44 \times 10^{-27}$ kg

Area

1 acre	$= 0.404\ 685\ 6$ ha
1 circular mil	$= 506.7\ \mu m^2$
1 legal subdivision (40 acres)	$= 0.161\ 874\ 2$ km^2
1 rood (1210 square yards)	$= 0.101\ 171\ 4$ ha
1 section (1 mile square, 640 acres)	$= 2.589\ 988$ km^2
1 square foot	$= 929.030\ 4$ cm^2
1 square inch	$= 645.16$ mm^2
1 square mile	$= 2.589\ 988$ km^2
1 square yard	$= 0.836\ 127\ 4$ m^2
1 township (36 sections)	$= 93.239\ 57$ km^2

Volume

1 acre foot	$= 1\ 233.482$ m^3
1 board foot	$= 2.359\ 737$ dm^3
1 cord (128 ft^3, 4 ft $\times$ 4 ft $\times$ 8 ft, stacked wood)	$= 3.624\ 6$ m^3
1 cubic foot	$= 28.316\ 85$ dm^3
1 cubic inch	$= 16.387\ 064$ cm^3
1 cubic yard	$= 0.764\ 555$ m^3
1 cunit (100 ft^3, solid timber)	$= 2.831\ 68$ m^3
1 Petrograd standard (165 ft^3, sawn timber)	$= 4.672\ 28$ m^3

Capacity

1 barrel (36 UK gallons)	$= 0.163\ 659$ m^3
1 barrel (US dry, 7056 in^3)	$= 0.115\ 627$ m^3
1 barrel (Oil, 42 US gallons)	$= 0.158\ 987\ 3$ m^3
1 barrel (US dry, cranberries, 5826 in^3)	$= 95.471$ dm^3
1 bushel	$= 36.368\ 72$ dm^3
1 bushel (UK)	$= 36.368\ 74$ dm^3
1 bushel (US dry, 2150.42 in^3)	$= 35.239\ 07$ dm^3
1 fluid dram	$= 3.551\ 633$ cm^3
1 fluid dram (US measure)	$= 3.696\ 691$ cm^3
1 fluid drachm (UK measure)	$= 3.551\ 634$ cm^3
1 fluid ounce	$= 28.413\ 062$ cm^3
1 fluid ounce (UK)	$= 28.413\ 08$ cm^3
1 fluid ounce (US)	$= 29.573\ 53$ cm^3
1 gallon*	$= 4.546\ 09$ dm^3
1 gallon (UK)†	$= 4.546\ 092$ dm^3
1 gallon (US)	$= 3.785\ 412$ dm^3
1 gill (UK)	$= 0.142\ 065$ dm^3
1 gill (US)	$= 0.118\ 294$ dm^3
1 minim (UK)	$= 59.193\ 9$ mm^3
1 minim (US)	$= 61.611\ 5$ mm^3
1 peck	$= 9.092\ 180$ dm^3
1 peck (UK)	$= 9.092\ 184$ dm^3
1 peck (US dry)	$= 8.809\ 768$ dm^3
1 pint	$= 0.568\ 261$ dm^3
1 pint (UK)	$= 0.568\ 262$ dm^3
1 pint (US dry)	$= 0.550\ 610$ dm^3
1 pint (US liquid)	$= 0.473\ 176$ dm^3
1 quart	$= 1.136\ 522$ dm^3
1 quart (UK)	$= 1.136\ 523$ dm^3
1 quart (US dry)	$= 1.101\ 221$ dm^3
1 quart (US liquid)	$= 0.946\ 353$ dm^3
1 ton (register)	$= 2.831\ 685$ m^3

* The Australian gallon is the same as the Canadian gallon. The term "Imperial gallon" is frequently used when the correct expression is "Canadian gallon" or simply "gallon" when from the context the intent is clear.

† Also referred to as the "Imperial gallon".

SOURCES: Metric Commission Canada, Box 4000, Ottawa, Ont. K1S 5G8; National Standard of Canada, CAN3 Z234.1-79, Canadian Metric Practice Guide

1989
CORPUS ALMANAC &
CANADIAN SOURCEBOOK

The Governor General, The Right Honourable Jeanne Sauvé.
Photo courtesy of the Governor General's Office.

1989

CORPUS ALMANAC &

CANADIAN SOURCEBOOK

24th annual edition

VOLUME 2

Gordon Sova,
Editor

Michael McVean,
Publisher

Corpus Information Services
A division of Southam Business Information
and Communications Group Inc.
1450 Don Mills Road, Don Mills, Ontario M3B 2X7

Staff:
Editorial:
Carol Douglas
Barbara Law

Contributors:
Dr. Roy Bishop
Susan Marshall
Charles Panksep

Our cover features the evening skyline of the city of Toronto, with the CN Tower, the world's tallest free-standing structure, at the left. Toronto is currently bidding to host the 1996 Summer Olympic Games. Photo courtesy of the Metropolitan Toronto Convention and Visitors Association.

ISBN 0-919217-50-8

ISSN 0823-1133

Printed and bound in Canada

NOTE FROM THE EDITOR

The cover of the 1989 *Corpus Almanac & Canadian Sourcebook* is an evening shot of the harbour and skyline of the city of Toronto. In 1988, Toronto hosted the Economic Summit of the seven western leaders. The city is also bidding to host the 1996 Summer Olympic Games. As well, construction of the SkyDome, a retractable dome stadium and future home of the Toronto Blue Jays, is scheduled to be completed this year.

The frontispiece for Volume 1 of this edition is of Vicki Keith of Kingston, Ont. who swam across all five Great Lakes to help raise money for Variety Village, a charitable organization that assists physically handicapped children.

With this edition, the Communications chapter has been improved through the use of two new and very reliable sources for the listings of names and addresses of cable, press and broadcasting outlets. MATTHEWS LIST and MATTHEWS CATV are Canada's oldest and best-respected media directories.

As always, there have been many changes to our government listings. Prime Minister Mulroney achieved his second mandate, and second PC majority, on Nov. 21 of last year. Premier John Buchanan's Conservatives won a slim majority in Nova Scotia, while Gary Filmon's PCs defeated the last NDP government in Canada in the Manitoba general election. (Complete and final results of all these elections can be found in Volume 2.) The year ended with the passage of the Free Trade Bill and Quebec's use of the "notwithstanding" clause to limit linguistic rights coming within days of each other in the final two weeks of the year.

Finally, an anticipation of possible changes for next year's edition. Research we have undertaken in the past has suggested that readers would prefer the *Sourcebook* in one volume rather than two. No material would be cut, and newly developed grades of paper would allow us to make the single volume much thinner than the two volumes together now are. We will be contacting *Sourcebook* buyers this summer to request feedback on this possibility. Anyone who has an opinion or a suggestion, pro or con, is urged to let the editors know.

April 20, 1989

Gordon Sova
Editor

Astronomy Consultant
Roy Bishop, M.Sc., Ph.D.
The Royal Astronomical Society of Canada
136 Dupont St., Toronto, ON M5R 1V2

Acknowledgment

The Editor wishes to acknowledge all those departments, individuals, companies and associations without whose help the information contained in this book could never have been gathered. Special thanks are given to Supply and Services Canada for permission to reprint from several of their publications and to Statistics Canada, from whose data many of the statistics in the *Sourcebook* were taken. Finally, we wish to mention the thousands of libraries, publishers and associations who took time to return our questionnaires, keeping the Sources of Information chapter as up-to-date as possible.

TABLE OF CONTENTS

For the convenience of the reader, a more detailed Table of Contents page precedes each chapter. Please refer to the Index at the back of each volume of the *Corpus Almanac & Canadian Sourcebook* when looking for a particular subject.

Volume 1

Current Events

Current Events 1-1

General Information

Sectional Table of Contents 2-1
The National Anthem 2-2
The National Coat of Arms, Flag and Emblems 2-2
Canadian Titles. 2-3
Table of Forms of Address 2-4
Holidays 2-8
Astronomy
    Description of the Universe 2-10
    Events of the months — 1989 (in E.S.T.) 2-17
    Time 2-20
Further Reading on Astronomy 2-22

Geography

Sectional Table of Contents 3-1
Geographical Structure 3-1
Political Regions 3-4
Physical Geography
    Geophysical regions of Canada 3-6
    Drainage basins and lakes 3-8
    Coastal waters and islands 3-9
Climate 3-10
Soils and Vegetation 3-12
Further Reading 3-13

Natural Resources

Sectional Table of Contents 4-1
Agriculture 4-2
Forestry 4-7
Fisheries 4-11

Fur Industry 4-14

Mineral Industry 4-14

Energy 4-17

Further Reading 4-20

The People

Sectional Table of Contents 5-1

Canada's Changing Population
   Population growth 5-1
   Population distribution 5-3
   Vital statistics 5-7

Demographic trends 5-7

Households and families 5-9

Labour force 5-11

Immigration 5-12

Further Reading 5-14

Religion

Sectional Table of Contents 6-1

Ecumenical Councils 6-2

Organized Denominations in Canada 6-3

Canadian Bible Colleges 6-16

Further Reading 6-18

Education

Sectional Table of Contents 7-1

Education in Canada
   General structure 7-2
   Provincial structure 7-3
   Federal government 7-4

Elementary-Secondary Level 7-6

Technical and Vocational Education 7-9

Post-Secondary Education
   Overview 7-10
   Universities and Colleges 7-12
   Community Colleges 7-45

Further Reading 7-54

Sources of Information

Sectional Table of Contents 8-1

Libraries and Archives
   Alberta library listings 8-7

British Columbia library listings 8-20
Manitoba library listings 8-28
New Brunswick library listings 8-34
Newfoundland library listings 8-38
Northwest Territories library listings 8-40
Nova Scotia library listings 8-42
Ontario library listings 8-45
Prince Edward Island library listings 8-79
Quebec library listings 8-80
Saskatchewan library listings 8-99
Yukon library listings 8-104

Book Publishers
Alphabetical listing of book publishers in Canada 8-105

Magazines
Business and Professional Periodicals (listed by subject) 8-120
Consumer Periodicals (listed by subject) 8-148
Farm Periodicals (listed alphabetically) 8-165
Religious Periodicals (listed alphabetically) 8-168
Scholarly Periodicals (listed alphabetically) 8-169
University and School Periodicals (listed alphabetically) 8-172

Associations and Societies (indexed alphabetically by name within subject categories) ... 8-177

Communications

Sectional Table of Contents 9-1

Telecommunications 9-1

Broadcasting 9-5

Postal Communications: Canada Post Corporation 9-9

Newspapers
English, French and bilingual newspapers 9-13
Ethnic Press 9-39

AM and FM radio listings 9-45

Television networks and stations 9-57

Transportation

Sectional Table of Contents 10-1

Federal Regulation of Transportation 10-1
Transport of dangerous goods 10-2

Rail Transport 10-2
Railway Safety Directorate 10-4
Railway companies in Canada 10-4

Road Transport 10-5

Water Transport 10-11

Civil Aviation 10-14

Further Reading 10-18

Labour

Sectional Table of Contents 11-1

Labour Legislation
    Division of legislative powers 11-1
    Labour unions 11-2
    Federal labour legislation 11-2
    Provincial labour legislation 11-3
    Payroll deductions 11-4
    Legislation prohibiting discrimination in employment 11-6

Trade Unions and Labour Organizations
    Central labour congresses 11-7
    International trade unions 11-9
    National and provincial trade unions 11-15

Further Reading 11-29

Law

Sectional Table of Contents 12-1

Canada's Legal System
    Common law and Quebec civil law 12-2
    Criminal law 12-2

Citizens' Rights 12-3

Courts and the Judiciary 12-6

Legal Services in Canada 12-8

Police Services in Canada
    General description 12-9
    Royal Canadian Mounted Police 12-9
    Ontario Provincial Police 12-9
    Sûreté du Québec 12-10

Crime and Delinquency 12-10

Further Reading 12-14

Banking, Finance & Insurance

Sectional Table of Contents 13-1

Banking
    Regulation of banking 13-2
    Bank of Canada 13-3
    Monetary system 13-5
    Foreign exchange 13-6
    Chartered banks 13-6
    Domestic chartered banks 13-8
    Foreign chartered banks 13-10
    Other banking institutions 13-14

Other Financial Institutions 13-15

Insurance 13-18

Investment Dealers 13-20

Equity Financing
    Securities regulation 13-21
    Stock exchanges 13-22

Commodity Exchange 13-33

Insolvency 13-34

Debt Financing 13-35

Further Reading 13-36

Business, Industry & Trade

Sectional Table of Contents 14-1

Overview of the Canadian Economy
  Summary of economic performance - 1988 14-1
  Prospects for 1989 14-3
  The Consumer Price Index 14-6

Industry Profiles
  Agriculture 14-7
  Forestry 14-8
  Fisheries 14-9
  Minerals 14-9
  Energy 14-10
  Manufacturing 14-10
  Steel 14-11
  Automobiles 14-11
  Textiles 14-12
  Technology 14-12
  Retailing 14-13
  Publishing 14-13
  Banking and Finance 14-13
  Real Estate 14-14
  Transportation 14-15
  Tourism 14-15

Regional Analysis of Industry 14-16

Canada's Trade Balance
  The trade surplus 14-19
  Summary of trade by industrial sector 14-21
  Current accounts balance 14-21
  Free trade 14-22

Further Reading 14-25

The Canadian Constitution

Sectional Table of Contents 15-1

Canada's System of Government
  Introduction 15-1
  Parliamentary government 15-2
  A federal state 15-3
  The rule of law and the courts 15-9
  The institutions of our federal government 15-9
  What goes on in Parliament 15-12
  Canada's political evolution 15-13

Royal Proclamation 15-16
Text of the *Canada Act*, the *Constitution Act, 1982*
  and the *Constitution Act, 1867* 15-16
Constitution Amendment, 1987 15-24

Further Reading 15-26

Index

Detailed index of both volumes 20-1

Volume 2

The Federal Government

Sectional Table of Contents 16-1

The Executive 16-5
   The Crown 16-5
   The Privy Council 16-6
   The Prime Minister 16-9
   The Cabinet 16-9
   Current inquiries of the Government of Canada 16-12

The Legislature 16-13
   The Parliament of Canada 16-13
   The Legislative Process 16-13
   The Senate 16-15
   Library of Parliament 16-17
   The House of Commons 16-17

Departments, Boards, Commissions and Corporations 16-28
   Organization chart, Government of Canada 16-29
   Federal government employment 16-30

Federal Departments and Ministries of State 16-32

Independent Agencies, Boards, Commissions, Crown Corporations
and Councils, reporting directly to the Government 16-128

Federal Judiciary and Judicial Officers 16-146
   The Supreme Court of Canada 16-146
   The Federal Court of Canada 16-146
   Court Martial Appeal Court of Canada 16-146
   Tax Court of Canada 16-147

Canadian Diplomatic and Trade Representatives Abroad 16-148

Foreign Ambassadors and High Commissioners to Canada 16-158

Consulates and Trade Commissions in Canada 16-163

Information for Canadians travelling abroad 16-175
   Canadian passports 16-175
   Travel regulations abroad 16-175
   Customs information for Canadian residents 16-177

The Canadian Armed Forces 16-179

Major World Organizations to which Canada belongs
   North Atlantic Treaty Organization (NATO) 16-184
   Other international organizations 16-185
   Canada's permanent missions 16-185
   Commonwealth of Nations 16-186

Canada and the Developing World 16-189

Provincial and Territorial Governments

Sectional Table of Contents 17-1

Province of Alberta
   Provincial profile 17-11
   Executive Council 17-13
   Legislative Assembly 17-13
   Government Departments and Senior Department Officials 17-15
   Independent Agencies, Boards, Commissions and Crown Corporations 17-52
   Judiciary and Judicial Officers 17-56

Province of British Columbia
Provincial profile 17-61
Executive Council 17-63
Legislative Assembly 17-63
Government Ministries and Senior Ministry Officials 17-65
Independent Agencies, Boards and Commissions 17-95
Judiciary and Judicial Officers 17-96

Province of Manitoba
Provincial profile 17-103
Executive Council 17-105
Legislative Assembly 17-105
Government Departments and Senior Department Officials 17-107
Independent Agencies, Boards, Commissions and Crown Corporations 17-138
Judiciary and Judicial Officers 17-142

Province of New Brunswick
Provincial profile 17-145
Executive Council 17-147
Legislative Assembly 17-147
Government Departments and Senior Department Officials 17-149
Independent Agencies, Boards, Commissions and Crown Corporations 17-163
Judiciary and Judicial Officers 17-168

Province of Newfoundland
Provincial profile 17-171
Executive Council 17-171
House of Assembly 17-174
Government Departments and Senior Department Officials 17-175
Independent Agencies, Boards, Commissions and Crown Corporations 17-191
Judiciary and Judicial Officers 17-194

The Northwest Territories
Territorial profile 17-197
Northwest Territories Executive 17-199
Legislative Assembly 17-201
Senior Department Officials 17-201
Independent Agencies, Boards and Councils 17-204
Federal Government Directory 17-210
Judiciary and Judicial Officers 17-211

Province of Nova Scotia
Provincial profile 17-213
Executive Council 17-215
Legislative Assembly 17-216
Government Departments and Senior Department Officials 17-217
Independent Agencies, Boards, Commissions and Crown Corporations 17-233
Judiciary and Court Officials 17-242

Province of Ontario
Provincial profile 17-247
Executive Council 17-249
Legislative Assembly 17-250
Government Ministries and Senior Ministry Officials 17-254
Independent Agencies, Boards and Commissions 17-303
Judiciary and Judicial Officers 17-304

Province of Prince Edward Island
Provincial profile 17-313
Executive Council 17-315
Legislative Assembly 17-315
Government Departments and Senior Department Officials 17-316
Independent Agencies, Boards, Commissions and Crown Corporations 17-322
Judiciary and Judicial Officers 17-327

Province of Quebec
Provincial profile 17-329
Conseil des ministres 17-331
Assemblée nationale 17-332
Government Ministries and Senior Ministry Officials 17-335

Independent Agencies 17-383
Judiciary and Judicial Officers 17-385

Province of Saskatchewan
   Provincial profile 17-393
   Executive Council 17-395
   Legislative Assembly 17-395
   Government Departments and Senior Department Officials 17-397
   Independent Agencies, Boards, Commissions and Crown Corporations 17-419
   Judiciary and Judicial Officers 17-425

The Yukon Territory
   Territorial profile 17-429
   Executive Council 17-431
   Legislative Assembly 17-432
   Senior Department Officials 17-432
   Federal Government Directory 17-438
   Judiciary and Judicial Officers 17-440

Intergovernmental Agencies

Sectional Table of Contents 18-1

Municipal Governments

Sectional Table of Contents 19-1

Alberta 19-1

British Columbia 19-6

Manitoba 19-10

New Brunswick 19-13

Newfoundland 19-15

Northwest Territories 19-18

Nova Scotia 19-19

Ontario 19-21

Prince Edward Island 19-29

Quebec 19-30

Saskatchewan 19-40

Yukon 19-43

Index

Detailed index of both volumes 20-1

Style and Abbreviations

In most matters of style, titles, form of postal addresses, capitalization, abbreviation, etc., the *Sourcebook* follows the Secretary of State's guidelines as set down in *The Canadian Style, A Guide to Writing and Editing*, Ottawa: Minister of Supply and Services, 1985; and in *Guide du rédacteur de l'administration fédérale*, Ottawa: Minister of Supply and Services, 1983. As a handier reference, the reader will find below a list of some of the more common English and French abbreviations used in the book.

English

A/	Acting	Inc.	Incorporated
AB	Alberta	Int'l.	International
Admin.	Administrative	Ltd.	Limited
Assn.	Association	Maj.	Major
Assoc.	Associate	MB	Manitoba
Asst.	Assistant	N.	North
Ave.	Avenue	Nat'l	National
BC	British Columbia	NB	New Brunswick
Bldg.	Building	NF	Newfoundland
Blvd.	Boulevard	NS	Nova Scotia
CAO	Chief Administrative Officer	NT	Northwest Territories
Cda.	Canada	ON	Ontario
Cdn.	Canadian	PE	Prince Edward Island
CEO	Chief Executive Officer	P.O.	Post Office
CFO	Chief Financial Officer	Prof.	Professional/Professor
COO	Chief Operating Officer	pubn.	publication
Co.	Company	Rd.	Road
c/o	care of	Rm.	Room
Col.	Colonel	R.R.	Rural Route
Corp.	Corporation	S.	South
Cres.	Crescent	Sec.	Secretary
Ct.	Court	SK	Saskatchewan
Dept.	Department	Sq.	Square
Div.	Division	Sr.	Senior
Dr.	Drive	St.	Saint/Street
E.	East	Ste.	Suite
Exec.	Executive	Stn.	Station
Flr.	Floor	Supt.	Superintendent
Gen.	General	W.	West
Hon.	Honourable	YT	Yukon Territory

French

adj.	adjoint(e)	hon.	honorable
a/s	au (bons) soins (de)	inc.	incorporée
assoc.	association/associé(e)	ltée.	limitée
av.	avenue	Me	maître
boul.	boulevard	P.-D.G.	président-directeur général
bur.	bureau	p.i.	par interim
cdn	canadien	pl.	place
cdne.	canadienne	prof.	professionnel(le)
ch.	chemin	prom.	promenade
C.P.	case postal	rte	route
dir.	directeur(trice)	St	Saint
ét.	étage	Ste	Sainte
gén.	général(e)	succ.	succursale

THE FEDERAL GOVERNMENT

(Government personnel listings are taken from *The Corpus Administrative Index*. It is updated four times a year, and therefore is always an accurate source of names and titles of federal government officials. Ask your reference librarian to show you the current copy. Subscription rate: $367/year, 4 issues. Available from: Southam Business Information and Communications Group Inc., 1450 Don Mills Rd., Don Mills, ON M3B 2X7.)

The Executive 16-5
  The Crown 16-5
    The Sovereign 16-5
    The Governor General 16-5
  The Privy Council 16-6
    Office of the President 16-7
    Privy Councillors 16-7
  The Prime Minister 16-9
  The Cabinet 16-9
    Cabinet committee system 16-10
    Privy Council Office 16-11
    Federal-Provincial Relations Office 16-12
  Current inquiries of the Government of Canada 16-12

The Legislature 16-13
  The Parliament of Canada 16-13
  The Legislative process 16-13
  The Senate 16-15
    Members of the Senate 16-15
    Remuneration of Members of the Senate 16-16
  Library of Parliament 16-17
  The House of Commons 16-17
    Officers of the House of Commons 16-17
    Party Leaders and Standings 16-18
    Remuneration of Members of the House of Commons 16-18
    Office of the Prime Minister 16-19
    Office of the Leader of the Official Opposition 16-18
    Office of the Leader of the New Democratic Party ... 16-19
    The Ministry (Cabinet) 16-19
    Cabinet Committees 16-19
    Parliamentary Secretaries 16-20
    Members of the House of Commons by Constituency 16-20
    Members of the House of Commons by Surname 16-23
    Standing, Special and Joint Committees 16-26
    Office of the Auditor General of Canada 16-26
    The Federal franchise 16-26
      Elections Canada 16-27
      Commissioner of Canada Elections 16-27

Departments, Boards, Commissions and Corporations 16-28
    Government of Canada, January 1989 16-29
  Federal government employment 16-30
    Table 1: Federal employees, by type of employment .. 16-30
    Table 2: Federal employees, by geographic area and sex 16-31

Federal Government Departments and Ministries of State
  Agriculture, Department of 16-32
  Auditor General, Office of the 16-38
  Communications, Department of 16-38
  Consumer and Corporate Affairs, Department of 16-51
  Employment and Immigration, Department of 16-52
  Energy, Mines and Resources, Department of 16-56
  Environment, Department of the 16-65
  External Affairs, Department of 16-68
  Finance, Department of 16-72

16

Financial Institutions, Office of the Superintendent of 16-73
Fisheries and Oceans, Department of 16-74
Forestry, Department of 16-76
Health and Welfare, Department of 16-77
Indian Affairs and Northern Development, Department of 16-82
Industry, Science and Technology, Department of 16-87
Justice, Department of 16-92
Labour, Department of 16-95
National Defence, Department of 16-97
Privatization and Regulatory Affairs, Department of 16-100
Public Service Commission 16-100
Public Works, Department of 16-101
Revenue, Department of 16-103
Science and Technology, Ministry of State for 16-107
Secretary of State of Canada, Department of the 16-107
Solicitor General, Department of the 16-110
Supply and Services, Department of 16-114
Transport, Department of 16-118
Treasury Board 16-124
Veterans Affairs, Department of 16-125
Western Industrial Diversification, Department of 16-128

Independent Commissions, Crown Corporations and
Councils reporting directly to the Government
Atlantic Canada Opportunities Agency 16-128
Canada Development Investment Corp. 16-129
Canada Lands Co. (Mirabel) Ltd. 16-129
Canada Lands Co. (Le Vieux-Port de Montréal) Ltd. 16-129
Canada Mortgage and Housing Corp. 16-129
Canada Post Corp. 16-131
Canadian Advisory Council on the Status of Women 16-131
Canadian Centre for Occupational Health and Safety 16-132
Canadian Commercial Corp. 16-132
Canadian International Development Agency 16-132
Canadian Patents and Development Ltd. 16-134
Commissioner of Official Languages 16-134
Economic Council of Canada 16-135
Export Development Corp. 16-135
International Development Research Centre 16-137
International Joint Commission 16-137
Medical Research Council of Canada 16-138
National Capital Commission 16-138
National Research Council of Canada 16-138
Natural Sciences and Engineering Research Council 16-140
Northern Pipeline Agency 16-140
Pension Appeals Board 16-141
Public Service Staff Relations Board 16-141
Science Council of Canada 16-141
Standards Council of Canada 16-142
Statistics Canada 16-142
Status of Women Canada 16-145

Federal Judiciary and Judicial Officers 16-146
The Supreme Court of Canada 16-146
The Federal Court of Canada 16-146
Court Martial Appeal Court of Canada 16-146
Tax Court of Canada 16-147

Canadian Diplomatic & Trade Representatives Abroad 16-148

Foreign Ambassadors & High Commissioners to Canada 16-158

Consulates & Trade Commissions in Canada 16-163

Information for Canadians travelling abroad
   Canadian passports 16-175
      Passport requirements 16-175
      Application for passport 16-175
   Travel regulations abroad 16-175
      Registration abroad 16-176
      Dual nationality 16-177
   Customs information for Canadian residents 16-177

The Canadian Armed Forces
   The Department of National Defence 16-179
   The Command structure of the Canadian Forces 16-179
   Liaison in other countries 16-181
   Training 16-182
   Canadian military colleges 16-183
   Canadian Forces bases 16-183

Major World Organizations to which Canada belongs
   North Atlantic Treaty Organization (NATO) 16-184
      North Atlantic Council 16-184
   Other International Organizations
      Canada-United States 16-185
      Colombo Plan 16-185
      Conservation 16-185
      Energy 16-185
      Inter-American 16-185
      Labour 16-185
   Canada's Permanent Missions
      Europe 16-185
      Organization of American States 16-186
      Organization for Economic Co-operation and Development 16-186
      United Nations 16-186
   Commonwealth of Nations 16-186
      Commonwealth Consultation and Co-operation 16-187
      Commonwealth Secretariat 16-188
      Canada's Role in the Commonwealth 16-188
   Canada and the Developing World 16-189

ACKNOWLEDGMENT

Portions of this section entitled "The Executive", "The Legislature", and "Departments, Boards, Commissions and Corporations" are based in part on material drawn from the *Canada Year Book,* Supply and Services Canada. Information has been reviewed and updated where necessary. The Editor also wishes to thank the following federal bodies which kindly co-operated in updating the text and statistical data: Machinery of Government, Privy Council Office; Federal-Provincial Relations Office; Table Research Branch, House of Commons; Office of the Chief Electoral Officer; Federal Identity Program, Treasury Board; Public Service Commission; Department of National Defence; Department of External Affairs; and other contributors of information too numerous to mention here.

The Prime Minister, The Right Honourable Brian Mulroney.
Photo courtesy of the Prime Minister's office.

THE FEDERAL GOVERNMENT OF CANADA

Seat of Government: Ottawa

The Canadian people are the ultimate source of political power, but jurisdiction over government activities is divided in the *Constitution Act, 1867* between the federal government and the provincial governments. At the federal level, the political power of the people is delegated by them to their elected representatives in the House of Commons, and to the appointed representatives in the Senate. In practice, effective legislative power is usually held by the largest party in the House of Commons and this party, in turn, puts executive authority into the hands of a group of its members, the Cabinet, led by the Prime Minister.

THE EXECUTIVE

THE CROWN

The *Constitution Act, 1867* provides that the executive government and authority of and over Canada is vested in the Queen. The functions of the Crown (that is, the formal executive represented by the Queen), substantially the same as those of the Crown in relation to the British government, are discharged in Canada by the Governor General.

The Sovereign

Since Confederation, Canada has had six sovereigns: Victoria, Edward VII, George V, Edward VIII, George VI and Elizabeth II. The present sovereign is not only Queen of Canada but is also head of state of other countries in the Commonwealth as well as being the formal head of the Commonwealth. Her title for Canada was approved by Parliament and established by a royal proclamation on May 28, 1953: "Elizabeth the Second, by the grace of God, of the United Kingdom, Canada and Her other Realms and Territories, Queen, Head of the Commonwealth, Defender of the Faith."

The Queen's participation in Canadian affairs includes frequent visits to Canada to take part in major events. The Queen also appoints the Governor General on the advice of the Canadian prime minister. The Governor General is her representative and carries out many official acts in the Queen's name. During royal visits, the Queen may participate in ceremonies and events as Queen of Canada, such as the opening of Parliament or the presentation of new colours to regiments.

In 1982, Her Majesty The Queen and His Royal Highness The Prince Philip, Duke of Edinburgh, came to Ottawa for the proclamation of the *Constitution Act* of Canada, at which Her Majesty officiated on Saturday, April 17, 1982, on the grounds of Parliament Hill. In 1987, she officiated at the opening of the Commonwealth Heads of Government Meeting when this took place in Victoria beginning on Oct. 13.

The Queen is also Sovereign of the Order of Canada and the Order of Military Merit. The Order of Canada recognizes outstanding achievement and service to Canada and to mankind in all fields of endeavour. The Order of Military Merit recognizes meritorious service by members of the Canadian Armed Forces. Members at all levels in both Orders are appointed by the Governor General on behalf of the Sovereign, and on the recommendation of advisory bodies appointed for the purpose. In the same manner, three Canadian decorations are conferred in recognition of acts of bravery.

In 1984, three additional medals for distinguished service were instituted for presentation to the members of certain high-risk professions. They are: the Police Exemplary Service Medal, the Corrections Exemplary Service Medal and the Fire Services Exemplary Service Medal. These decorations are awarded by the Governor General on the recommendation of ad hoc committees. The Meritorious Service Cross and the Special Service Medal, which are military decorations instituted in 1984, are awarded in the same manner.

The Governor General

The Governor General is the representative of the Crown in Canada. On Dec. 23, 1983, the Queen, on the recommendation of Prime Minister Trudeau, appointed the Rt. Hon. Jeanne Sauvé as Canada's twenty-third (and first woman) Governor General since Confederation. Her Excellency assumed office on May 14, 1984.

Constitutionally, the Queen of Canada is the Canadian head of state but the Governor General fulfills that role on her behalf. The letters patent revised and issued under the Great Seal of Canada on Oct. 1, 1947 authorized and empowered the Governor General, on the advice of his or her Canadian ministers, to exercise all powers and authorities lawfully belonging to the Sovereign in respect of Canada.

Following are the Governors General of Canada since Confederation, with dates of assumption of office:

The Viscount Monck of Ballytrammon,
   July 1, 1867
The Baron Lisgar of Lisgar and Bailieborough,
   Feb. 2, 1869
The Earl of Dufferin, June 25, 1872
The Marquess of Lorne, Nov. 25, 1878
The Marquess of Lansdowne, Oct. 23, 1883
The Baron Stanley of Preston, June 11, 1888
The Earl of Aberdeen, Sept. 18, 1893
The Earl of Minto, Nov. 12, 1898
The Earl Grey, December 10, 1904
Field Marshal HRH Prince Albert, The Duke of
   Connaught, Oct. 13, 1911
The Duke of Devonshire, Nov. 11, 1916
Gen. The Baron Byng of Vimy, Aug. 11, 1921
The Viscount Willingdon of Ratton, Oct. 2, 1926
The Earl of Bessborough, April 4, 1931
The Baron Tweedsmuir of Elsfield, Nov. 2, 1935
Maj.-Gen. The Earl of Athlone, June 21, 1940
Field Marshal The Viscount Alexander of Tunis,
   April 12, 1946
The Rt. Hon. Vincent Massey, Feb. 28, 1952
Gen. The Rt. Hon. Georges P. Vanier,
   Sept. 15, 1959
The Rt. Hon. Roland Michener, April 17, 1967
The Rt. Hon. Jules Léger, Jan. 14, 1974
The Rt. Hon. Edward Schreyer, Jan. 21, 1979
The Rt. Hon. Jeanne Sauvé, May 14, 1984

One of the most important responsibilities of the Governor General is to ensure that the country always has a government. If the office of the prime minister becomes vacant because of death or resignation, the Governor General must see that it is filled and that a new government is formed.

As the Queen's representative, the Governor General summons, prorogues and dissolves Parliament on the advice of the prime minister. They sign orders-in-council, commissions and other state documents, and give their assent to bills that have been passed in both houses of Parliament and which thereby become Acts of Parliament with the force of law. In virtually all cases they are bound by constitutional convention to carry out these duties in accordance with the advice of their responsible ministers. Should they not wish to accept this advice, and should the responsible ministers maintain that advice, their only alternative is to replace the existing government with a new government, but only if the principle of responsible government could be upheld. Thus, the Governor General's discretion in choosing another government is strictly limited to a situation in which a person other than the existing prime minister could command the confidence of the House of Commons.

Her Excellency the Governor General,
The Rt. Hon. Jeanne Sauvé

OFFICE OF THE SECRETARY TO THE GOVERNOR GENERAL
Government House, Ottawa, ON K1A 0A1
General inquiry: (613) 993-8200

Secretary to the Governor General, Secretary General of the Order of Canada and of the Order of Military Merit,
   Léopold Amyot
Deputy Secretary, Operations,
   Jean M. Sévigny
Deputy Secretary, Policy and Program,
   Anthony P. Smyth
Assistant Secretary and Director, Chancellery of Canadian Orders and Decorations,
   Lt.-Gen. F. Richard
Director, Finance, Personnel and Administration,
   Guy R. Brunet
Cultural Advisor, Jean-Noël Tremblay
Director, Orders and Decorations,
   David John
Chief Herald, Robert Watt
Director, Program Implementation, Health, Safety and Security,
   Maj. Colin Sangster, O.M.M., C.D.
Press Secretary, Marie Bender
Director, Information Services,
   Mary De Bellefeuille-Percy
Director, Policy and Program,
   Sharon Orr
Attaché, Liane Benoit
Director, Hospitality, Lola D'Ascanio
Director, Protocol and Ceremonial,
   Lucien L. Lemieux
Senior Aide-de-Camp,
   Capt. Peter Harrison
Aides-de-camp,
   Capt. Stéphane Nadeau
   Capt. Pierre Sergerie
Personal Asst. to the Governor General,
   Renée Langevin

QUEEN'S PRIVY COUNCIL FOR CANADA

The *Constitution Act, 1867* provides for a council to aid and advise the Government of Canada, called the Queen's Privy Council for Canada. The council that in fact advises the Queen's representative, the Governor General, is the committee of the Privy Council whose membership is identical to that of the cabinet.

Membership in the Privy Council is for life and includes cabinet ministers of the government of the day, former cabinet ministers, the chief justice of Canada and former chief justices, former speakers of the Senate and the House of Commons of Canada and, on occasion, members of the royal family, premiers of provinces, and a few other distinguished persons. As a condition of office, all ministers must first be sworn into the

Privy Council. A member is styled "Honourable" and may use the initials P.C. after his or her name. The Governor General, the Chief Justice of Canada and the Prime Minister of Canada automatically are given the title "Right Honourable" by royal warrant when they take office.

The Privy Council as a whole has met on only a few ceremonial occasions; its constitutional responsibilities to advise the Crown on government matters are discharged exclusively by the cabinet. The legal instruments through which executive authority is exercised are called orders-in-council. A number of ministers, acting as a committee of the Privy Council, make a submission to the Governor General for her approval which she is obliged to give in almost all circumstances; with this approval, the submission becomes an order-in-council.

The office of president of the Privy Council was formerly occupied, more often than not, by the prime minister; in recent years, it has been occupied by another minister who is usually the government leader in the House of Commons, that position having the broad responsibility of directing House business.

A list of members of the Privy Council of Canada is given below.

Office of the President of the Privy Council

Centre Block, House of Commons, Room 203-S
Ottawa, ON K1A 0A6

*President of the Queen's Privy Council
for Canada and Government House Leader,*
The Hon. Donald Mazankowski
Chief of Staff, Phil Evershed

Privy Councillors

(as of Jan. 31, 1989)

Name	Date Sworn In
The Hon. Paul J.J. Martin	Apr. 18, 1945
The Hon. G.-Edouard Rinfret	Aug. 25, 1949
The Hon. Walter E. Harris	Jan. 18, 1950
The Hon. J.W. Pickersgill	June 12, 1953
The Hon. Paul T. Hellyer	Apr. 26, 1957
The Hon. Howard C. Green	June 21, 1957
The Hon. George Hees	June 21, 1957
The Hon. Léon Balcer	June 21, 1957
The Hon. E. Davie Fulton	June 21, 1957
The Hon. Douglas S. Harkness	June 21, 1957
The Hon. Ellen L. Fairclough	June 21, 1957
The Hon. J. Angus MacLean	June 21, 1957
The Hon. Michael Starr	June 21, 1957
The Hon. William McLean Hamilton	June 21, 1957
The Hon. William J. Browne	June 21, 1957

Name	Date Sworn In
The Hon. Alvin Hamilton	Aug. 22, 1957
His Royal Highness Prince Philip, Duke of Edinburgh	Oct. 14, 1957
The Hon. David J. Walker	Aug. 20, 1959
The Hon. Pierre Sévigny	Aug. 20, 1959
The Hon. Jacques Flynn	Dec. 28, 1961
The Hon. Paul Martineau	Aug. 9, 1962
The Rt. Hon. Roland Michener	Oct. 15, 1962
The Hon. Marcel Lambert	Feb. 12, 1963
The Hon. Théogène Ricard	March 18, 1963
The Hon. Frank McGee	March 18, 1963
The Hon. Martial Asselin	March 18, 1963
The Hon. Mitchell Sharp	Apr. 22, 1963
The Hon. Azellus Denis	Apr. 22, 1963
The Hon. George J. McIllraith	Apr. 22, 1963
The Hon. Allan J. MacEachen	Apr. 22, 1963
The Hon. Hédard Robichaud	Apr. 22, 1963
The Hon. Roger Teillet	Apr. 22, 1963
The Hon. Charles M. Drury	Apr. 22, 1963
The Hon. Maurice Sauvé	Feb. 3, 1964
The Hon. Yvon Dupuis	Feb. 3, 1964
The Hon. Edgar J. Benson	June 29, 1964
The Hon. Léo A.J. Cadieux	Feb. 15, 1965
The Hon. Lawrence T. Pennell	July 7, 1965
The Hon. Jean-Luc Pepin	July 7, 1965
The Hon. Alan A. Macnaughton	Oct. 25, 1965
The Hon. Jean-Pierre Côté	Dec. 18, 1965
The Rt. Hon. John N. Turner	Dec. 18, 1965
The Rt. Hon. Pierre Elliott Trudeau	Apr. 4, 1967
The Hon. J.J. Jean Chrétien	Apr. 4, 1967
The Hon. Pauline Vanier	Apr. 11, 1967
The Hon. Louis J. Robichaud	July 5, 1967
The Hon. Dufferin Roblin	July 5, 1967
The Hon. Alexander B. Campbell	July 5, 1967
The Hon. Ernest C. Manning	July 5, 1967
The Hon. Joseph R. Smallwood	July 5, 1967
The Hon. Robert L. Stanfield	July 7, 1967
The Hon. Charles R. McKay Granger	Sept. 25, 1967
The Hon. Bryce Stuart Mackasey	Feb. 9, 1968
The Hon. Donald S. Macdonald	Apr. 20, 1968
The Hon. John Carr Munro	Apr. 20, 1968
The Hon. Gérard Pelletier	Apr. 20, 1968
The Hon. Jack Davis	Apr. 26, 1968
The Hon. Horace Andrew Olson	July 6, 1968
The Hon. Jean-Eudes Dubé	July 6, 1968
The Hon. Stanley Ronald Basford	July 6, 1968
The Hon. Eric William Kierans	July 6, 1968
The Hon. James A. Richardson	July 6, 1968
The Hon. Otto Emil Lang	July 6, 1968
The Hon. Herbert E. Gray	Oct. 20, 1969
The Hon. Robert Stanbury	Oct. 20, 1969
The Hon. Jean-Pierre Goyer	Dec. 22, 1970
The Hon. Alastair W. Gillespie	Aug. 12, 1971
The Hon. Martin P. O'Connell	Aug. 12, 1971
The Hon. Patrick M. Mahoney	Jan. 28, 1972
The Hon. Stanley Haidasz	Nov. 27, 1972
The Hon. Eugene F. Whelan	Nov. 27, 1972
The Hon. W. Warren Allmand	Nov. 27, 1972
The Hon. James Hugh Faulkner	Nov. 27, 1972
The Hon. André Ouellet	Nov. 27, 1972
The Hon. Marc Lalonde	Nov. 27, 1972
The Rt. Hon. Jeanne Sauvé	Nov. 27, 1972
The Hon. Lucien Lamoureux	June 10, 1974
The Hon. Raymond J. Perrault	Aug. 8, 1974
The Hon. Barnett J. Danson	Aug. 8, 1974
The Hon. J. Judd Buchanan	Aug. 8, 1974
The Hon. Roméo LeBlanc	Aug. 8, 1974
The Hon. Muriel McQueen Ferguson	Nov. 7, 1974
The Hon. Pierre Juneau	Aug. 29, 1975
The Hon. Marcel Lessard	Sept. 26, 1975

Name	Date Sworn In	Name	Date Sworn In
The Hon. Jack Cullen	Sept. 26, 1975	The Hon. Alfred Brian Peckford	Apr. 17, 1982
The Hon. Leonard S. Marchand	Sept. 15, 1976	The Hon. James Matthew Lee	Apr. 17, 1982
The Hon. John Roberts	Sept. 15, 1976	The Hon. Howard Russell Pawley	Apr. 17, 1982
The Hon. Monique Bégin	Sept. 15, 1976	The Hon. Sterling Rufus Lyon	Apr. 17, 1982
The Hon. Jean-Jacques Blais	Sept. 15, 1976	The Hon. David M. Collenette	Aug. 12, 1983
The Hon. Francis Fox	Sept. 15, 1976	The Hon. Céline Hervieux-Payette	Aug. 12, 1983
The Hon. Anthony C. Abbott	Sept. 15, 1976	The Hon. Roger Simmons	Aug. 12, 1983
The Hon. Iona Campagnolo	Sept. 15, 1976	The Hon. David Paul Smith	Aug. 12, 1983
The Hon. Joseph-Philippe Guay	Nov. 3, 1976	The Hon. Roy MacLaren	Aug. 17, 1983
The Hon. John Henry Horner	Apr. 21, 1977	The Rt. Hon. Brian Dickson	Apr. 19, 1984
The Hon. Norman A. Cafik	Sept. 16, 1977	The Hon. Robert B. Bryce	Apr. 19, 1984
The Hon. Gilles Lamontagne	Jan. 19, 1978	The Hon. Peter Michael Pitfield	Apr. 19, 1984
The Hon. John M. Reid	Nov. 24, 1978	The Rt. Hon. M. Brian Mulroney	May 7, 1984
The Hon. Pierre De Bané	Nov. 24, 1978	The Rt. Hon. Edward R. Schreyer	June 3, 1984
The Rt. Hon. Charles Joseph Clark	June 4, 1979	The Hon. Herb Breau	June 30, 1984
The Hon. Flora MacDonald	June 4, 1979	The Hon. J.R. Rémi Bujold	June 30, 1984
The Hon. James A. McGrath	June 4, 1979	The Hon. Jean-C. Lapierre	June 30, 1984
The Hon. Erik H. Nielsen	June 4, 1979	The Hon. Ralph Ferguson	June 30, 1984
The Hon. Allan F. Lawrence	June 4, 1979	The Hon. Douglas C. Frith	June 30, 1984
The Hon. John C. Crosbie	June 4, 1979	The Hon. Robert Carman Coates	Sept. 17, 1984
The Hon. David S.H. MacDonald	June 4, 1979	The Hon. Jack Burnett Murta	Sept. 17, 1984
The Hon. Lincoln Alexander	June 4, 1979	The Hon. Harvie Andre	Sept. 17, 1984
The Hon. Roch LaSalle	June 4, 1979	The Hon. Otto John Jelinek	Sept. 17, 1984
The Hon. Donald F. Mazankowski	June 4, 1979	The Hon. Thomas E. Siddon	Sept. 17, 1984
The Hon. Elmer M. MacKay	June 4, 1979	The Hon. Charles James Mayer	Sept. 17, 1984
The Hon. Arthur Jacob Epp	June 4, 1979	The Hon. William H. McKnight	Sept. 17, 1984
The Hon. John Allen Fraser	June 4, 1979	The Hon. Walter F. McLean	Sept. 17, 1984
The Hon. William Jarvis	June 4, 1979	The Hon. Thomas M. McMillan	Sept. 17, 1984
The Hon. Allan McKinnon	June 4, 1979	The Hon. Patricia Carney	Sept. 17, 1984
The Hon. Sinclair Stevens	June 4, 1979	The Hon. André Bissonnette	Sept. 17, 1984
The Hon. John Wise	June 4, 1979	The Hon. Suzanne Blais-Grenier	Sept. 17, 1984
The Hon. Ronald George Atkey	June 4, 1979	The Hon. Benoît Bouchard	Sept. 17, 1984
The Hon. Ramon John Hnatyshyn	June 4, 1979	The Hon. Andrée Champagne	Sept. 17, 1984
The Hon. David Crombie	June 4, 1979	The Hon. Michel Côté	Sept. 17, 1984
The Hon. Robert R. de Cotret	June 4, 1979	The Hon. James F. Kelleher	Sept. 17, 1984
The Hon. William H. Grafftey	June 4, 1979	The Hon. Robert E. Layton	Sept. 17, 1984
The Hon. Perrin Beatty	June 4, 1979	The Hon. Marcel Masse	Sept. 17, 1984
The Hon. J. Robert Howie	June 4, 1979	The Hon. Barbara J. McDougall	Sept. 17, 1984
The Hon. Steven E. Paproski	June 4, 1979	The Hon. Gerald S. Merrithew	Sept. 17, 1984
The Hon. Ronald Huntington	June 4, 1979	The Hon. Monique Vézina	Sept. 17, 1984
The Hon. Michael H. Wilson	June 4, 1979	The Hon. Maurice Riel	Nov. 30, 1984
The Hon. Renaude Lapointe	Nov. 30, 1979	The Hon. Cyril Lloyd Francis	Nov. 30, 1984
The Hon. Stanley H. Knowles	Nov. 30, 1979	The Hon. Saul Mark Cherniack	Nov. 30, 1984
The Hon. Hazen R. Argue	March 3, 1980	The Hon. Paule Gauthier	Nov. 30, 1984
The Hon. Gerald Regan	March 3, 1980	The Hon. Eugene Alfred Forsey	June 10, 1985
The Hon. Mark MacGuigan	March 3, 1980	The Hon. Lloyd Roseville Crouse	June 10, 1985
The Hon. Robert P. Kaplan	March 3, 1980	The Hon. Stewart McInnes	Aug. 20, 1985
The Hon. James S. Fleming	March 3, 1980	The Hon. Frank Oberle	Nov. 20, 1985
The Hon. William Rompkey	March 3, 1980	The Hon. G.F.J. Osbaldeston	Feb. 13, 1986
The Hon. Pierre Bussières	March 3, 1980	The Hon. Lowell Murray	June 30, 1986
The Hon. Charles Lapointe	March 3, 1980	The Hon. Paul Wyatt Dick	June 30, 1986
The Hon. Edward Lumley	March 3, 1980	The Hon. Pierre H. Cadieux	June 30, 1986
The Hon. Yvon Pinard	March 3, 1980	The Hon. Jean J. Charest	June 30, 1986
The Hon. Donald Johnston	March 3, 1980	The Hon. Thomas Hockin	June 30, 1986
The Hon. Lloyd Axworthy	March 3, 1980	The Hon. Monique Landry	June 30, 1986
The Hon. Paul Cosgrove	March 3, 1980	The Hon. Bernard Valcourt	June 30, 1986
The Hon. Judy Erola	March 3, 1980	The Hon. Gerry Weiner	June 30, 1986
The Hon. James A. Jerome	Feb. 16, 1981	The Hon. John W. Bosley	June 30, 1987
The Hon. Jacob Austin	Sept. 22, 1981	The Hon. Douglas G. Lewis	Aug. 27, 1987
The Hon. Charles L. Caccia	Sept. 22, 1981	The Hon. Pierre Blais	Aug. 27, 1987
The Hon. Serge Joyal	Sept. 22, 1981	The Hon. Gerry St. Germain	Mar. 31, 1988
The Hon. W. Bennett Campbell	Sept. 22, 1981	The Hon. Lucien Bouchard	Mar. 31, 1988
The Hon. R. Gordon Robertson	March 2, 1982	The Hon. John McDermid	Sept. 15, 1988
The Hon. Edward Broadbent	Apr. 17, 1982	The Hon. Shirley Martin	Sept. 15, 1988
The Hon. Richard B. Hatfield	Apr. 17, 1982	The Hon. Kim Campbell	Jan. 30, 1989
The Hon. William Grenville Davis	Apr. 17, 1982	The Hon. Mary Collins	Jan. 30, 1989
The Hon. Allan Emrys Blakeney	Apr. 17, 1982	The Hon. Jean Corbeil	Jan. 30, 1989
The Hon. E. Peter Lougheed	Apr. 17, 1982	The Hon. Gilles Loiselle	Jan. 30, 1989
The Hon. William R. Bennett	Apr. 17, 1982	The Hon. Alan Redway	Jan. 30, 1989
The Hon. John Buchanan	Apr. 17, 1982	The Hon. William Winegard	Jan. 30, 1989

THE PRIME MINISTER

The prime minister is the leader of the political party requested by the Governor General to form the government, which almost always means the leader of the party with the strongest representation in the Commons. His position is one of exceptional authority stemming in part from the success of the party at an election. The prime minister chooses his cabinet. When a member of cabinet resigns, the remainder of the cabinet is undisturbed; when the prime minister vacates his office, this act normally carries with it the resignation of the cabinet.

Part of the prime minister's authority lies in his power to recommend dissolution of Parliament. This right, which in most circumstances permits him to precipitate an election, is a source of considerable power both in his dealings with colleagues and with the opposition parties in the House. The prime minister is also responsible for organization of the cabinet and its committees; for the organization and functions of his own office, as well as the Privy Council Office and the Federal-Provincial Relations Office; and for the allocation of responsibilities between ministers.

Another source of the prime minister's authority derives from the appointments which he recommends, including privy councillors, cabinet ministers, lieutenant-governors of the provinces, provincial administrators, speakers of the Senate, chief justices of all courts, senators and certain senior executives of the public service. The prime minister also recommends the appointment of a new Governor General to the Sovereign, although this normally follows consultation with the cabinet.

Following are the prime ministers since Confederation, with dates of administrations:

Rt. Hon. Sir John Alexander Macdonald, July 1, 1867—Nov. 5, 1873
Hon. Alexander Mackenzie, Nov. 7, 1873—Oct. 9, 1878
Rt. Hon. Sir John Alexander Macdonald, Oct. 17, 1878—June 6, 1891
Hon. Sir John Joseph Caldwell Abbott, June 16, 1891—Nov. 24, 1892
Rt. Hon. Sir John Sparrow David Thompson, Dec. 5, 1892—Dec. 12, 1894
Hon. Sir Mackenzie Bowell, Dec. 21, 1894—April 27, 1896
Rt. Hon. Sir Charles Tupper, May 1, 1896—July 8, 1896
Rt. Hon. Sir Wilfrid Laurier, July 11, 1896—Oct. 6, 1911
Rt. Hon. Sir Robert Laird Borden, Oct. 10, 1911—Oct. 12, 1917
 (Conservative Administration)
Rt. Hon. Sir Robert Laird Borden, Oct. 12, 1917—July 10, 1920
 (Unionist Administration)
Rt. Hon. Arthur Meighen, July 10, 1920—Dec. 29, 1921
 (Unionist—National Liberal and Conservative Party)
Rt. Hon. William Lyon Mackenzie King, Dec. 29, 1921—June 28, 1926
Rt. Hon. Arthur Meighen, June 29, 1926—Sept. 25, 1926
Rt. Hon. William Lyon Mackenzie King, Sept. 25, 1926—Aug. 6, 1930
Rt. Hon. Richard Bedford Bennett, Aug. 7, 1930—Oct. 23, 1935
Rt. Hon. William Lyon Mackenzie King, Oct. 23, 1935—Nov. 15, 1948
Rt. Hon. Louis Stephen St-Laurent, Nov. 15, 1948—June 21, 1957
Rt. Hon. John George Diefenbaker, June 21, 1957—April 22, 1963
Rt. Hon. Lester Bowles Pearson, April 22, 1963—April 20, 1968
Rt. Hon. Pierre Elliott Trudeau, April 20, 1968—June 4, 1979
Rt. Hon. Joe Clark, June 4, 1979—March 3, 1980
Rt. Hon. Pierre Elliott Trudeau, March 3, 1980—June 30, 1984
Rt. Hon. John Napier Turner, June 30, 1984—Sept. 17, 1984
Rt. Hon. Martin Brian Mulroney, Sept. 17, 1984— . . .

THE CABINET

The cabinet's primary responsibility is to determine priorities among the demands brought to it and to define policies to meet those demands. The cabinet consists of all the ministers who are appointed on the recommendation of the prime minister, generally from among members of the House of Commons, although some cabinet ministers may be chosen from the Senate, including the leader of the government in the Senate. Ministers who are members of Parliament usually head government departments because the Constitution provides that measures for appropriating public funds or imposing taxes must originate in the Commons. If a senator heads a department, another minister in the Commons has to speak on his behalf on its affairs. *See also* the description of cabinet membership in the Canadian Constitution chapter, Volume 1.

Each cabinet minister usually assumes responsibility for one of the departments of government, although a minister may hold more than one portfolio at the same time or he may hold one or more portfolios and one or more acting portfolios. A minister without portfolio may be invited to join the cabinet because the prime minister wishes to have him or her in the cabinet without the heavy duties of running a department, or to provide a suitable balance of regional representation, or for any other reason that the prime minister sees fit. Because of Canada's cultural and geographical diversity, the prime minister gives close attention to geographic representation in the cabinet.

With the enactment of the *Ministries and Ministers of State Act (Government Organization Act, 1970)*, five categories of ministers of the Crown may be identified: departmental ministers, ministers with special parliamentary responsibilities, ministers without portfolio, and two types of ministers of state. Ministers of state for designated purposes may head a ministry of state created by proclamation. They are charged with developing new and comprehensive policies in areas of particular urgency and importance and have a mandate determined by the prime minister. They may have powers, duties and functions, and exercise supervision and control of elements of the public service, and may seek parliamentary appropriations to cover the cost of their staff and operations. Other ministers of state may be appointed to assist a departmental minister with his or her responsibilities. All ministers are appointed on the advice of the prime minister by commissions of office issued by the Governor General under the Great Seal of Canada, to serve and to be accountable to Parliament as members of the government and for any responsibility that might be assigned to them by law or otherwise.

In Canada, almost all executive acts of the government are carried out in the name of the Governor in Council. The cabinet, or a committee of ministers acting as a committee of the Privy Council, makes submissions to the Governor General for approval, and he or she is bound by the constitution in nearly all circumstances to accept them. A total of approximately 3,000 such orders-in-council were enacted in 1988, down from a high of 4,258 in 1984. Although some were routine and required little discussion in cabinet, others were of major significance and required extensive deliberation, sometimes covering months of meetings of officials, cabinet committees and the full cabinet.

The cabinet considers and approves the policy underlying each piece of proposed legislation. After proposed legislation is drafted it must be examined in detail. Between 40 and 60 bills are normally considered by cabinet during a parliamentary session. Policy to be adopted in fundamental constitutional changes or at a major international conference are among the issues which, on occasion, demand this extensive and detailed consideration.

The Cabinet Committee System

The nature and large volume of policy issues to be decided on by cabinet do not lend themselves to detailed discussion in each case by 40 ministers. Growing demands on the executive have stimulated delegation of some cabinet functions to its committees.

Cabinet committees provide a forum for thorough study of policy proposals, although the cabinet remains the prime focus of decision-making. Membership of cabinet committees is public but the same rules of secrecy that apply to cabinet deliberations apply to cabinet committees. The prime minister determines the establishment of cabinet committees, their membership and terms of reference. Ministers may invite one senior official as an advisor during cabinet committee for the discussion of issues directly related to their department's interests. The secretariats of the committees are provided by the Privy Council Office and the secretary of a cabinet committee is usually also an assistant secretary to the cabinet. Treasury Board, which is a cabinet committee and a committee of the Privy Council established by statute, is an exception; it has its own secretariat headed by a secretary who has the status of a deputy minister.

Under the direction of the prime minister, the secretary to the cabinet prepares agenda and refers memoranda to cabinet to the appropriate committee for study and report to the full cabinet. Except where the prime minister instructs otherwise, all memoranda to cabinet are submitted over the signature of the minister concerned.

The terms of reference of cabinet committees cover virtually the total area of government responsibility. All memoranda to cabinet are first considered by a cabinet committee, except when they are of exceptional urgency or when the prime minister directs otherwise, in which case an item may be considered immediately by the full cabinet.

There are currently four policy committees: economic; human resources, income support and health; foreign and defence; and operations. Four committees perform co-ordinating functions: priorities and planning, expenditure review, legislation and house planning, and the Treasury Board.

Additional standing committees of the cabinet are established from time to time and meet as required: the cabinet committees on communications, security and intelligence, and the special committee of council which considers many submissions to the Governor in Council.

Growing reliance on the cabinet committee system since World War II is evidence of its usefulness. The following is a brief outline of the involvement of cabinet and cabinet committees with a piece of legislation that the government ultimately introduces in the Commons or the Senate.

On the initiative of a minister a policy proposal is prepared, the implementation of which will require new legislation or the amendment of existing legislation. The proposal is addressed formally to cabinet, but is considered first by a policy committee concerned with the subject-matter in question; proposals with financial implications are considered by the responsible policy committee in the government's policy and expenditure management system. If approved, the proposal goes forward as a recommendation for confirmation or consideration by cabinet, or — if there are financial implications — the priorities and planning committee. If the committee's decision is confirmed, the justice department is instructed to prepare a draft bill expressing in legal terms the intent of the policy proposal. When the draft bill has the minister's approval, he or she submits it to the cabinet committee on legislation and house planning and it is examined from a legal rather than a policy point of view. Once this committee agrees that the bill is acceptable in all respects, or with modifications, and could be introduced in Parliament, it reports this to cabinet. If cabinet confirmation is given, the prime minister initials the bill and it is then introduced either in the Senate or the House of Commons, depending on constitutional and political considerations.

In a bid to reduce the deficit, Prime Minister Mulroney in January 1989 introduced two new cabinet committees to keep tighter control on government spending. The first is the Expenditure Review Committee, whose responsibility it will be to assure spending is limited to budgeted projects. The second is the Operations Committee, which will review the government's agenda and co-ordinate the handling of issues and the creation of new policies.

These two committees could exercise effective control over much of the policy of the government, either directly or through spending constraints. This is a formalization of the recent trend toward vesting real power in an "inner cabinet" rather than the large and awkward full cabinet.

In the same move, the membership of most of the committees was reduced from approximately 20 to less than a dozen. This is likely to streamline their operations even further.

The order and manner in which a bill is considered in Parliament is the responsibility of the government house leader who negotiates these matters with his counterparts in the opposition parties. If a bill is to be introduced in the Senate, the house leader will discuss questions such as timing and tactics with the leader of the government in the Senate, who in turn will negotiate consideration of the bill with the opposition leader in the Senate.

The Privy Council Office

Langevin Block, Ottawa, ON K1A 0A3

The Privy Council office provides support to the prime minister in his responsibilities as chairman of Cabinet and as head of government, and to the cabinet. For the purposes of the *Financial Administration Act* it is considered a government department. The prime minister is the minister responsible for the Privy Council Office. The work of the Privy Council Office is directed by a public servant known as the clerk of the Privy Council and secretary to the cabinet. He is the senior member of the public service of Canada.

Clerk of the Privy Council and Secretary to the Cabinet, Paul M. Tellier
Assoc. Secretary to the Cabinet, Deputy Clerk of the Privy Council and Senior Advisor, Personnel Management, Jack Manion
Asst. Secretary to the Cabinet, (Senior Personnel Management), M. Rochon
Asst. Secretary to the Cabinet, (Strategic Planning and Policy), Fred W. Gorbet
Intelligence and Security Co-ordinator, Blair Seaborn
Deputy Secretary to the Cabinet, (Plans), Leonard Good
Asst. Secretary to the Cabinet, (Priorities and Planning), R. Wright
Asst. Secretary to the Cabinet, (Machinery of Government), N. d'Ombrain
Asst. Secretary to the Cabinet, (Legislation and House Planning/Counsel), W.P.D. Elcock
Asst. Secretary to the Cabinet, (Communications), M.M. Gusella
Deputy Secretary to the Cabinet, (Operations), Ray Protti
Asst. Secretary to the Cabinet, (Economic and Regional Development Policy), Ronald Bilodeau
Asst. Secretary to the Cabinet, (Foreign and Defence Policy), E. Hébert
Asst. Secretary to the Cabinet, (Government Operations and Labour Relations), William A. Rowat
Asst. Secretary to the Cabinet, (Social Development), Dan E. Goodleaf
Cabinet Papers System Unit A/Supervisor, William J. Fleury
Asst. Clerk of the Privy Council, (Orders-in-Council), Henri Chassé

MANAGEMENT

Asst. Deputy Minister, Ginette Stewart
Operations
Co-ordinator and Commissions, W.E. Pratt
Co-ordinator, Access to Information and Privacy, T. Nicholson
Administration Division
Director, C.W. Dewar
Finance Division
Director, Vacant
Information Systems and Services
Director, A. Prakash
Personnel Management Division
Director, M. Garneau
Technical Services Division
A/Chief, S.A. Paterson
Legal Advisor, Senior General
Counsel, R.S.G. Thompson

Federal-Provincial Relations Office

59 Sparks St., Ottawa, ON K1A 0A3

The Federal-Provincial Relations Office was established on Jan. 15, 1975, by *An Act Respecting The Office of the Secretary to the Cabinet for Federal-Provincial Relations and Respecting the Clerk of the Privy Council.* The unit had previously functioned as the Federal-Provincial Relations Secretariat of the Privy Council Office. It is designated as a department of government under the prime minister, and it is headed by the secretary to the cabinet for federal-provincial relations who reports directly to the prime minister.

The Federal-Provincial Relations Office came into existence in response to the greatly increased inter-dependence of the federal and provincial levels of government. It developed as a co-ordinating and advisory agency designed to enable the federal government and the provinces to interact more effectively in serving the needs of the public. As one of its responsibilities in this respect, FPRO co-ordinates the development of policy proposals for the prime minister and provides administrative support for First Ministers' Conferences.

The FPRO's prime objective is to assist the prime minister, the cabinet, individual ministers and officials in examining the federal-provincial dimension of issues of current and long-term importance to the attainment of the government's goals and priorities.

The FPRO has a deputy secretary and five secretariats headed by assistant secretaries to cabinet (FPR) which work closely together with respect to the federal-provincial issues outlined above.

POLICY DEVELOPMENT
This secretariat takes the lead in such matters as constitutional renewal, overall strategies for constitutional negotiations, and longer term policies of fundamental importance to the federation.

LIAISON AND INTEGRATION
This secretariat acquires information, analyzes and reports on provincial and regional affairs, and identifies emerging issues affecting federal-provincial relations in each of the provinces. These functions provide other sections of FPRO and other federal agencies with more regionally based information, perceptions and advice respecting provincial and regional attitudes, aspirations and needs.

ECONOMIC POLICY AND PROGRAMS
SOCIAL POLICY AND PROGRAMS
These two secretariats are responsible for monitoring the policy and program activities of the relevant economic and social departments and agencies, providing advice on the federal-provincial relations aspects of these activities, and for co-ordinating the Office's views to the departments and agencies on the resolution of federal-provincial issues when they arise.

OFFICE OF ABORIGINAL CONSTITUTIONAL AFFAIRS
This Office was established by the prime minister following the government's commitment to hold, over the period 1982 to 1987, three First Ministers' Conferences on Aboriginal Constitutional Issues. The office is located in the Federal-Provincial Relations Office and is responsible for co-ordinating the development of policies, for ongoing negotiations with provinces and associations representing aboriginal peoples, and for advice, relating to the government's efforts toward eventual constitutional amendments in respect of aboriginal peoples.

Secretary to the Cabinet for Federal-Provincial Relations, Norman Spector
Deputy Secretary to the Cabinet, John E. Sinclair
Deputy Secretary to the Cabinet, (Constitutional Development), Vacant
Asst. Secretary to the Cabinet, (Liaison and Integration Secretariat), Florence Ievers
Asst. Secretary to the Cabinet, (Economic Policy and Programs), Peter Heap
Asst. Secretary to the Cabinet, (Social Policy and Programs), Martin Abrams
Asst. Secretary to the Cabinet, (Constitutional Affairs), D. Paget
Asst. Secretary to the Cabinet, (Policy Development), Vacant

MANAGEMENT
(See listing under Management, Privy Council Office)

CURRENT INQUIRIES OF THE GOVERNMENT OF CANADA

Royal Commission on the Future of the Toronto Waterfront
(P.C. 1988-586, March 30, 1988)

Commissioner: Hon. David Crombie
   171 Slater St., 11th Flr. Box 1527, Stn. B
   Ottawa, ON K1P 6P5
   (613) 990-3306

   207 Queen's Quay W., 5th Flr.
   Box 4111, Stn. A Toronto, ON M5W 2V4
   (416) 973-7185

Indian Commission of Ontario
(see Intergovernmental Agencies)

**Correctional Investigator—
Penitentiary Problems**
(P.C. 1977-3209, Nov. 15, 1977)

Commissioner: Ronald L. Stewart
   Journal Tower N., Rm. 520
   300 Slater St., Box 950, Stn. B
   Ottawa, ON K1P 5R1
   (613) 990-2689

THE LEGISLATURE

THE PARLIAMENT OF CANADA

The federal legislative authority is vested in the Parliament of Canada — the Queen, the Senate and the House of Commons. Bills may originate in either the Senate or the House of Commons, subject to Section 53 of the *Constitution Act, 1867,* which provides that bills for the appropriation of any part of the public revenue or the imposition of any tax or impost shall originate in the House of Commons. Bills must pass both Houses in identical form and receive Royal Assent before becoming law. In practice, most public bills originate in the House of Commons although the government may introduce some in the Senate in order that they may be dealt with there while the Commons is engaged in other matters, such as the debate on the speech from the throne. Private bills may originate in either the House of Commons or the Senate. Both the Senate and the House may postpone, amend or even refuse to pass bills sent to it from the other Chamber.

Section 91 of the *Constitution Acts, 1867* to *1975,* assigns to the Parliament of Canada legislative authority in very clearly specified areas. *These are discussed in the Canadian Constitution chapter which appears in Volume 1: see "Powers of the national and provincial governments."*

THE LEGISLATIVE PROCESS

If a bill is introduced and passed by the House of Commons, it then goes to the Senate and follows a similar procedure. Likewise, a bill first passed in the Senate goes to the House. There are two types of bills: public bills (affecting the populace in general and introduced by the ministry or by private members of Parliament) and private bills (seeking to exempt an individual or select group from the application of the law, and introduced by private members of Parliament). Note that this latter category is not the same as private member's bills, which are a type of public bill. All bills must pass through various stages before they become law. These stages provide Parliament with opportunities to examine and consider all bills both in principle and in detail. Each type is treated in a slightly different manner, and there are even differences in procedure when the House deals with government bills introduced pursuant to supply or ways and means motions on the one hand, and other government bills on the other. The following outline describes the procedure for a government bill introduced in the House of Commons.

The sponsoring minister gives notice that he or she intends to introduce a bill on a given subject. If the bill would require expenditure of money on the part of the government, it must also have the formal recommendation of the Governor General. Not less than 48 hours later he or she moves for leave to introduce the bill and for subsequent first reading and printing. This is normally granted automatically because this first step does not imply approval of any sort. It is only after first reading and printing that the bill is distributed among the members.

At a later sitting the minister moves that the bill be given second reading and be referred to a legislative committee of the House of Commons. A favourable decision on the motion for second reading represents general approval of the principle of the bill. There is often an extensive debate at this stage and, according to the procedures of the Commons, it should be confined to the basic purpose of the bill. At the conclusion of the debate, the motion for second reading is put to the House for its decision, which may or may not be determined by a recorded vote. If the decision of the House is in the affirmative, the bill is referred to a legislative committee of the House, where it is given clause-by-clause consideration. Unless the House otherwise orders, all bills, except those based on a supply motion, are referred to a legislative committee after second reading.

At the committee stage, expert witnesses and interested parties may be invited to give testimony pertaining to the bill, and the proceedings may cover many weeks. When the legislative committee has considered the bill, the committee reports it, with or without amendment, back to the House where, at the report stage, motions in amendment may also be considered. Any member may, on giving notice 24 hours before this stage begins, move an amendment to the bill. Such amendments are debated and decided upon by the House. Following that, a motion "that the bill be concurred in" or "that the bill, as amended, be concurred in," is put for the decision of the House.

After this report stage, the minister moves that the bill be given third reading and passage. The purpose of debate on this motion is to review the bill in its final form. Only certain amendments to the motion are permitted. If the bill passes, it is then transmitted to the Senate where there is a somewhat similar though not identical process, since each chamber has its own rules of procedure. After the bill has been passed by both Houses in identical form, it is given Royal Assent by the Governor General or by his or her deputy, one of the judges of the Supreme Court of Canada. The assent ceremony takes place in the Senate chamber in the presence of representatives of both Houses of Parliament. The bill comes into force on the day of assent, unless otherwise provided in the bill itself. Provision is sometimes made for coming into force on a certain day or a day fixed by the proclamation, and parts of the bill may come into force at different times.

The Legislative Process

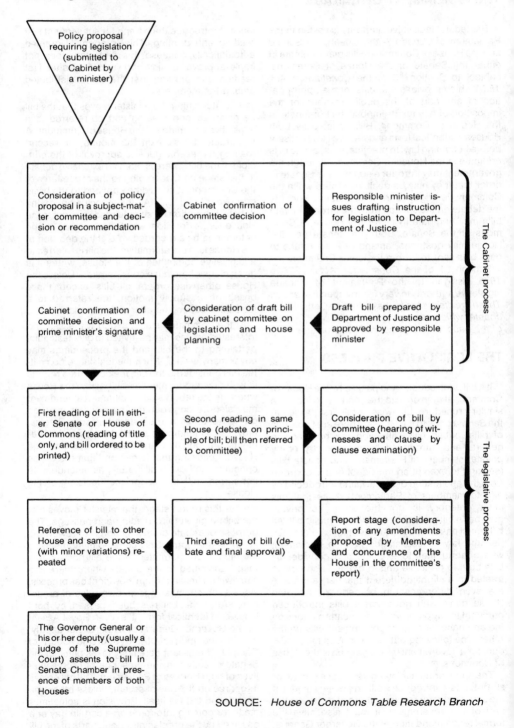

Policy proposal requiring legislation (submitted to Cabinet by a minister)

The Cabinet process

Consideration of policy proposal in a subject-matter committee and decision or recommendation

Cabinet confirmation of committee decision

Responsible minister issues drafting instruction for legislation to Department of Justice

Cabinet confirmation of committee decision and prime minister's signature

Consideration of draft bill by cabinet committee on legislation and house planning

Draft bill prepared by Department of Justice and approved by responsible minister

The legislative process

First reading of bill in either Senate or House of Commons (reading of title only, and bill ordered to be printed)

Second reading in same House (debate on principle of bill; bill then referred to committee)

Consideration of bill by committee (hearing of witnesses and clause by clause examination)

Reference of bill to other House and same process (with minor variations) repeated

Third reading of bill (debate and final approval)

Report stage (consideration of any amendments proposed by Members and concurrence of the House in the committee's report)

The Governor General or his or her deputy (usually a judge of the Supreme Court) assents to bill in Senate Chamber in presence of members of both Houses

SOURCE: *House of Commons Table Research Branch*

THE SENATE

Centre Block, Parliament Bldgs.
Ottawa, ON K1A 0A4

The Senate is responsible for the protection of the various provincial, minority and sectional interests in Canada. While the composition of the House of Commons is based on the principle of representation by population, Senate membership is based on the principle of equal regional representation.

This feature of the Senate is reflected in its make-up. The Senate has 104 seats distributed on a regional basis: Ontario, 24; Quebec, 24; the Maritime provinces, 24 (ten each from Nova Scotia and New Brunswick, and four from Prince Edward Island); Newfoundland, six; the Western provinces, 24 (six each from Manitoba, Saskatchewan, Alberta and British Columbia); and Yukon and Northwest Territories, one each.

Senators are appointed, in the Queen's name, by the Governor General on the advice of the prime minister. To qualify for appointment to the Senate, a person must be at least 30 years of age and own real property to the net value of at least $4,000 in the province for which he or she is appointed. In Quebec, senators are appointed for each of the original 24 electoral divisions in that province and they must reside, or have their property qualification, in the particular division for which they are appointed. Until 1965, senators were appointed for life; now the retirement age is 75.

The Senate performs three basic functions. In its legislative role, the Senate acts as a court of revision by reviewing Commons bills and frequently amending them. The amendments, often of a technical or clarifying nature, are usually concurred in by the Commons. Constitutionally, the Senate's legislative power is equal to that of the House of Commons. Any bill can be introduced in the Senate except a money bill. Although the Senate can reject any bill, it has rarely exercised this power.

Since 1971, it has been the practice to refer the subject-matter of major government bills to Senate committees before their formal introduction in the Senate. This has enabled the Senate to conduct thorough studies and, in some instances, to make recommendations for changes while a bill is still before the Commons.

In its deliberative role, the Senate provides a national forum for the discussion of public issues and the airing of regional concerns and grievances from all parts of Canada. On two days notice, a senator can start a debate, with no time limits, on any matter of regional or public concern.

Third is the Senate's investigative function. Inquiries into major social and economic issues by its standing and special committees have produced reports that have often been followed by remedial legislation or changes in government policy.

Representation in the Senate has grown from 72 at Confederation to its present total of 104 members, through the addition of members to represent new provinces and territories.

Speaker of the Senate,
  The Hon. Guy Charbonneau
Leader of the Government,
  The Hon. Lowell Murray, P.C.
Deputy Leader of the Government,
  The Hon. William Doody
Government Whip,
  The Hon. Orville Phillips
Leader of the Opposition,
  The Hon. Allan J. MacEachen, P.C.
Deputy Leader of the Opposition,
  The Hon. Royce Frith
Opposition Whip,
  The Hon. William Petten
Clerk of the Senate and
Clerk of the Parliaments,
  Charles A. Lussier
Asst. Clerk, Richard G. Greene
Law Clerk and Parliamentary Counsel,
  Raymond L. du Plessis, Q.C.
Gentleman Usher of the Black Rod,
  René Jalbert
Director of Committees, Gary W. O'Brien
Director of Personnel, Dale Jarvis
Director of Finance, Siroun Aghajanian

Members of the Senate

(Listed below alphabetically, by province. All Senators are entitled to the designation "The Honourable".)

POLITICAL AFFILIATIONS (as of Jan. 29, 1989):

Liberal (Lib)	56
Progressive Conservative (PC)	36
Independent (Ind)	5
Vacancies	7
Total Seats	104

Senator & Affiliation	Constituency
ALBERTA (6)	
Bielish, Martha P. (PC)	Lakeland
Fairbairn, Joyce (Lib)	Lethbridge
Hastings, Earl A. (Lib)	Palliser-Foothills
Hays, Daniel (Lib)	Calgary
Olson, H.A. (Lib)	Alberta South
(1 Vacancy)	
BRITISH COLUMBIA (6)	
Austin, Jack (Lib)	Vancouver South
Bell, Ann Elizabeth (Ind)	Nanaimo-Malaspina
Lawson, Edward M. (Ind)	Vancouver
Marchand, Leonard (Lib)	Kamloops-Cariboo
Perrault, Raymond (Lib)	North Shore-Burnaby
Van Roggen, George (Lib)	Vancouver-Point Grey
MANITOBA (6)	
Everett, Douglas (Lib)	Fort Rouge

Senator & Affiliation	Constituency
Guay, Joseph-Philippe (Lib)	St. Boniface
Molgat, Gildas L. (Lib)	Ste. Rose
Nurgitz, Nathan (PC)	Winnipeg North
Roblin, Duff (PC)	Red River
Spivak, Mira (PC)	Manitoba

NEW BRUNSWICK (10)

Anderson, Margaret (Lib)	Northumberland-Miramichi
Corbin, Eymard (Lib)	Grand-Sault
Leblanc, Roméo (Lib)	Beauséjour
McElman, Charles (Lib)	Nashwaak Valley
Robertson, Brenda (PC)	Riverview
Robichaud, Louis J. (Lib)	L'Acadie-Acadia
Sherwood, Cyril B. (PC)	Royal
Simard, Jean-Maurice (PC)	Edmundston
Thériault, L. Norbert (Lib)	Baie du Vin
(1 Vacancy)	

NEWFOUNDLAND (6)

Cochrane, Ethel (PC)	Newfoundland
Doody, C. William (PC)	Harbour Main-Bell Island
Lewis, Philip Derek (Lib)	St. John's
Marshall, Jack (PC)	Humber-St. George's-St. Barbe
Ottenheimer, Gerry (PC)	Waterford-Trinity
Petten, William J. (Lib)	Bonavista

NORTHWEST TERRITORIES (1)

Adams, Willie (Lib)	Northwest Territories

NOVA SCOTIA (10)

Graham, B. Alasdair (Lib)	The Highlands
Hicks, Henry D. (Lib)	The Annapolis Valley
Kirby, Michael (Lib)	South Shore
MacDonald, Finlay (PC)	Halifax
MacDonald, John M. (PC)	Cape Breton
MacEachen, Allan J. (Lib)	Highlands-Canso
Muir, Robert (PC)	Cape Breton-The Sydneys
Stewart, John B. (Lib)	Antigonish-Guysborough
(2 Vacancies)	

ONTARIO (24)

Atkins, Norman K. (PC)	Markham
Bélisle, Rhéal (PC)	Sudbury
Bosa, Peter (Lib)	York-Caboto
Cools, Anne C. (Lib)	Toronto Centre
Croll, David A. (Lib)	Toronto-Spadina
Davey, Keith (Lib)	York
Doyle, Richard (PC)	North York
Frith, Royce (Lib)	Lanark
Grafstein, Jerahmiel S. (Lib)	Metro Toronto
Haidasz, Stanley (Lib)	Toronto-Parkdale
Kelly, William M. (PC)	Port Severn
Kenny, Colin (Lib)	Rideau
Lang, Daniel (Ind)	South York
Marsden, Lorna (Lib)	Toronto-Taddle Creek
Murray, Lowell (PC)	Grenville-Carleton
Neiman, Joan (Lib)	Peel
Pitfield, Peter M. (Ind)	Ottawa-Vanier
Stanbury, Richard (Lib)	York Centre
Stollery, Peter (Lib)	Bloor/Yonge

Senator & Affiliation	Constituency
Thompson, Andrew E. (Lib)	Dovercourt
Turner, Charles (Lib)	London
Walker, David (PC)	Toronto
(2 Vacancies)	

PRINCE EDWARD ISLAND (4)

Bonnell, M. Lorne (Lib)	Murray River
Macquarrie, Heath (PC)	Hillsborough
Phillips, Orville Howard (PC)	Prince
Rossiter, Eileen (PC)	Prince Edward Island

QUEBEC (24)

Asselin, Martial (PC)	Stadacona
Bazin, Jean (PC)	De la Durantaye
Beaudoin, Gérald (PC)	Rigaud
Bolduc, Roch (PC)	Golfe
Chaput-Rolland, Solange (PC)	Mille-Iles
Charbonneau, Guy (PC)	Kennebec
Cogger, Michel (PC)	Lauzon
David, Paul P. (PC)	Bedford
De Bané, Pierre (Lib)	De la Vallière
Denis, Azellus (Lib)	La Salle
Flynn, Jacques (PC)	Rougemont
Gigantès, Philippe D. (Lib)	De Lorimier
Hébert, Jacques (Lib)	Wellington
Kolber, E. Leo (Lib)	Victoria
Leblanc, Fernand-E. (Lib)	Saurel
Lefebvre, Thomas Henri (Lib)	De Lanaudière
Molson, Hartland de M. (Ind)	Alma
Poitras, Jean-Marie (PC)	De Salaberry
Riel, Maurice (Lib)	Shawinigan
Rizzuto, Pietro (Lib)	Repentigny
Tremblay, Arthur (PC)	Les Laurentides
Watt, Charles W. (Lib)	Inkerman
Wood, Dalia (Lib)	Montarville
(1 Vacancy)	

SASKATCHEWAN (6)

Argue, Hazen (Lib)	Regina
Balfour, James (PC)	Regina
Barootes, E.W. (PC)	Regina-Qu'Appelle
Buckwold, Sidney L. (Lib)	Saskatoon
Sparrow, Herbert O. (Lib)	Saskatchewan
Steuart, David G. (Lib)	Prince Albert-Duck Lake

YUKON (1)

Lucier, Paul (Lib)	Yukon

Remuneration of Members of the Senate

(NOTE: Figures given below, effective Jan. 1, 1988, are subject to an annual cost-of-living adjustment. An increase of 1.69% was awarded for 1988 and 3% contemplated for 1989.

Members of the Senate:
$58,300 sessional allowance, plus $9,300 expense allowance (tax free) and travelling expenses between Ottawa, place of residence and destinations in Canada.

Speaker of the Senate:
$28,100 allowance, plus Member's Sessional

Allowance and expense allowance *(see above)*, plus $3,000 residence allowance and $1,000 vehicle allowance.

Leader of the Government in the Senate:
$44,500 under the *Salaries Act* if Member of the Cabinet and $2,000 vehicle allowance, or $31,700 annual allowance if not Member of the Cabinet; plus Member's Sessional Allowance and expenses *(see above)*.

Deputy Leader of the Government in the Senate:
$13,600 allowance, plus Member's Sessional Allowance and expense allowance *(see above)*.

Leader of the Opposition in the Senate:
$21,700 allowance, plus Member's Sessional Allowance and expense allowance *(see above)*.

Deputy Leader of the Opposition in the Senate:
$8,600 allowance, plus Member's Sessional Allowance and expense allowance *(see above)*.

Government Whip in the Senate:
$6,900 allowance, plus Member's Sessional Allowance and expense allowance *(see above)*.

Opposition Whip in the Senate:
$4,500 allowance, plus Member's Sessional Allowance and expense allowance *(see above)*.

LIBRARY OF PARLIAMENT

Parliament Bldgs., Ottawa, ON K1A 0A9

Members Responsible:
The Speaker of the House of Commons
The Speaker of the Senate

The Library of Parliament is established by the *Library of Parliament Act*, R.S.C. 1970 Chapter L-71. The Library was formed initially by the amalgamation of the legislative libraries of Upper and Lower Canada after these two provinces were united into the Province of Canada in 1841.

The direction and control of the Library of Parliament is vested in the speaker of the Senate and the speaker of the House of Commons. The parliamentary librarian and the associate parliamentary librarian are appointed by the Governor in Council. The parliamentary librarian holds the rank of a deputy minister.

The Library serves the Senate and the House of Commons in both a reference and research capacity.

Parliamentary Librarian, E.J. Spicer
Assoc. Parliamentary Librarian, R. Paré
Information and Technical Services Branch,
Director, Margot Montgomery
Research Branch
Director, H. Finsten

THE HOUSE OF COMMONS

Centre Block, Parliament Bldg.
Ottawa, ON K1A 0A6

The House of Commons, unless there are vacancies, is composed of 295 elected representatives of the people of Canada. These members of Parliament are elected from 295 electoral districts (or constituencies).

A Parliament may continue for no longer than five years following each general election (from the day of the return of the writs), subject to earlier dissolution by the Governor General. In the event of a vacancy occurring, by death of a member or otherwise, during the life of a Parliament, a writ for the holding of a by-election must be issued within six months of the receipt by the Chief Electoral Officer of a warrant for the issuance of such writ. Provision is made in the *Constitution Act, 1867* for a session of the Parliament of Canada at least once in every year "so that twelve months shall not intervene between the last sitting of the Parliament in one Session and its first sitting in the next Session".

The House of Commons has a speaker, a deputy speaker and chairman of committees of the whole house, a deputy chairman of committees of the whole house, and an assistant deputy chairman of committees of the whole house.

The presiding officer of the House of Commons is the speaker. He or she is elected by the members of that House by secret ballot while the speaker of the Senate is appointed by the Governor in Council. *See also "The Speakers" in the Canadian Constitution chapter, Volume 1.*

The deputy speaker of the House must possess full and practical knowledge of the official language which is not that of the speaker.

Officers of the House of Commons

Speaker of the House,
   The Hon. John A. Fraser
Deputy Speaker and Chairman of Committees of the Whole House, Marcel Danis
Deputy Chairman of Committees of the Whole House, The Hon. Steven E. Paproski
Asst. Deputy Chairman of Committees of the Whole House, The Hon. Andrée Champagne
Clerk of the House, R. Marleau
Deputy Clerk, M.A. Griffith
Clerk Assistant, P. Laundy
Law Clerk and Parliamentary Counsel,
   M.R. Pelletier
Director General of Operations,
   J. Sabourin
Sergeant-at-Arms, Maj.-Gen M. Gaston Cloutier
Deputy Sergeant-at-Arms, R.T. Hall
The Administrator, Edward Riedel

Party Leaders and Standings

34th Parliament, 1st Session
Date of last general election: Nov. 21, 1988

PRIME MINISTER:
　The Rt. Hon. M. Brian Mulroney
LEADER OF THE OFFICIAL
OPPOSITION:
　The Rt. Hon. John N. Turner
OTHER PARTY LEADER:
　The Hon. Edward Broadbent

Government House Leader:
　The Hon. Doug Lewis
Official Opposition House Leader:
　The Hon. Herb E. Gray
New Democratic Party House Leader:
　Nelson Riis
Chief Government Whip: Jim Hawkes
Chief Official Opposition Whip:
　Jean-Robert Gauthier
Chief New Democratic Party Whip:
　Rod Murphy

PARTY STANDINGS (as of Jan. 31, 1989):

Progressive Conservatives (PC)	168
Liberals (Lib)	83
New Democrats (NDP)	43
Vacant	1
Total No. of Seats	295

Remuneration of Members of the House of Commons

(NOTE: The figures given below, effective Jan. 1, 1988, are subject to an annual cost-of-living adjustment. An increase of 1.69% was awarded for 1988 and 3% is contemplated for 1989.)

Members of the House of Commons:
　$58,300 Member's Sessional Indemnity, travelling expenses between constituency and Ottawa (64 trips per year), plus a basic tax-free allowance of $19,400 (may be more, depending upon the constituency represented).
Prime Minister:
　$66,600, plus Member's Sessional Indemnity and expenses *(see above),* plus car provided.
Cabinet Ministers:
　$44,500, plus Member's Sessional Indemnity and expenses *(see above),* plus vehicle allowance.
Parliamentary Secretaries:
　$9,700, plus Member's Sessional Indemnity and expenses *(see above).*
Leader of the Opposition:
　$44,500, plus Member's Sessional Indemnity and expenses *(see above),* plus vehicle allowance.

Speaker of the House of Commons:
　$44,500 salary, plus Member's Sessional Indemnity and expenses *(see above),* plus allowance in lieu of residence and vehicle allowance.
Deputy Speaker of the House of Commons:
　$23,300 plus Member's Sessional Indemnity and expenses *(see above),* plus allowance in lieu of residence.
Deputy Chairman of Committees:
　$9,700, plus Member's Sessional Indemnity and expenses *(see above).*
Asst. Deputy Chairman of Committees:
　$9,700, plus Member's Sessional Indemnity and expenses *(see above).*
Leaders of Other Parties:
　$26,800, plus Member's Sessional Indemnity and expenses *(see above).*
Chief Government and Official Opposition Whips:
　$12,100, plus Member's Sessional Indemnity and expenses *(see above).*
Whips of Other Parties:
　$6,900, plus Member's Sessional Indemnity and expenses *(see above).*
Opposition House Leader:
　$21,700, plus Member's Sessional Indemnity and expenses *(see above).*

Office of the Prime Minister

Langevin Block, Ottawa, ON K1A 0A2

Prime Minister,
　The Rt. Hon. Martin Brian Mulroney
Exec. Secretary, Lisette Boucher
Principal Secretary, Peter G. White
Chief of Staff, Stanley Hartt
Deputy Chief of Staff, Marjory LeBreton
Communications
Director, Bruce Phillips
Press Secretary, Marc Lortie
Special Advisor, Policy and Planning,
Geoff Norquay

Office of the Leader of the Official Opposition

House of Commons, Ottawa, ON K1A 0A6

Leader of the Official Opposition,
　The Rt. Hon. John N. Turner
Principal Secretary, Douglas Richardson
Principal Secretary, Peter Connolly
Policy Advisor (Social), David Lockhart
Policy Advisor (Economic), Jacques Carrière
Legislative Advisor, Scott Sheppard
Director of Administration, Shirley Lauzon
Director of Correspondence, Judy Wood

Office of the Leader of the New Democratic Party

Centre Block, Room 629-C
House of Commons, Ottawa, ON K1A 0A6

Party Leader,
  The Hon. Edward Broadbent
Principal Secretary, Bill Knight
Chief of Staff, George Nakitsas
Press Secretary, Lyse Huot
Press Secretary, Bill Gillies
Director of Correspondence,
Wayne Harding
Research Director, George Nakitsas

The Ministry (Cabinet)

(according to precedence, as of
Jan. 31, 1989)

Prime Minister,
  The Rt. Hon. Martin Brian Mulroney
Secretary of State for External Affairs,
  The Rt. Hon. Charles Joseph Clark
Minister for International Trade,
  The Hon. John Carnell Crosbie
*Deputy Prime Minister, President of the
  Queen's Privy Council for Canada, Minister of
  Agriculture,*
  The Hon. Donald Frank Mazankowski
*Minister of Public Works and Minister for the
  purposes of the Atlantic Canada
  Opportunities Agency Act,*
  The Hon. Elmer MacIntosh MacKay
Minister of Energy, Mines and Resources,
  The Hon. Jake Epp
President of the Treasury Board,
  The Hon. Robert R. de Cotret
Minister of National Health and Welfare,
  The Hon. Henry Perrin Beatty
Minister of Finance,
  The Hon. Michael Holcombe Wilson
*Minister of Regional Industrial Expansion,
  Minister of State for Science and Technology,*
  The Hon. Harvie Andre
Minister of Revenue,
  The Hon. Otto John Jelinek
Minister of Fisheries and Oceans,
  The Hon. Thomas Edward Siddon
*Minister of State (Grains and Oilseeds) and
  Minister of Western Economic Diversification,*
  The Hon. Charles James Mayer
Minister of National Defence,
  The Hon. William Hunter McKnight
Minister of Transport,
  The Hon. Benoît Bouchard
Minister of Communications,
  The Hon. Marcel Masse
Minister of Employment and Immigration,
  The Hon. Barbara Jean McDougall

Minister of Veterans' Affairs,
  The Hon. Gerald S. Merrithew
*Minister of State (Employment and Immigration)
  and Minister of State (Seniors),*
  The Hon. Monique Vézina
Minister of State (Forestry),
  The Hon. Frank Oberle
*Leader of the Government in the Senate and
  Minister of State (Federal-Provincial
  Relations),*
  The Hon. Lowell Murray
Minister of Supply and Services,
  The Hon. Paul Wyatt Dick
*Minister of Indian Affairs and Northern
  Development,*
  The Hon. Pierre H. Cadieux
*Minister of State (Youth) and Minister of State
  (Fitness and Amateur Sport),*
  The Hon. Jean J. Charest
Minister of State (Small Businesses and Tourism),
  The Hon. Thomas Hockin
Minister for External Relations,
  The Hon. Monique Landry
Minister of Consumer and Corporate Affairs,
  The Hon. Bernard Valcourt
*Secretary of State and Minister of State
  (Multiculturalism and Citizenship),*
  The Hon. Gerry Weiner
*Minister of Justice and Attorney General of
  Canada,*
  The Hon. Doug Grinsdale Lewis
Solicitor General,
  The Hon. Pierre Blais
Minister of the Environment,
  The Hon. Lucien Bouchard
*Minister of State (Privatization and Regulatory
  Affairs),*
  The Hon. John McDermid
Minister of State (Transport),
  The Hon. Shirley Martin
*Minister of State (Indian Affairs and Northern
  Development),*
  The Hon. Kim Campbell
Associate Minister of National Defence,
  The Hon. Mary Collins
Minister of Labour,
  The Hon. Jean Corbeil
Minister of State (Finance),
  The Hon. Gilles Loiselle
Minister of State (Housing),
  The Hon. Alan Redway
Minister of State (Science and Technology),
  The Hon. William Winegard

Cabinet Committees*

(as of Jan. 31, 1989)

Communications
Chairman, Senator Lowell Murray

Cultural Affairs and National Identity
Chairman, Marcel Masse

Economic Policy
Chairman, The Hon. Robert R. de Cotret

Environment
Chairman, The Hon. Lucien Bouchard

Expenditure Review
Chairman, The Rt. Hon. Brian Mulroney

Federal-Provincial Relations
Chairman, The Hon. Lowell Murray

Foreign and Defence Policy
Chairman, The Rt. Hon. Joe Clark

Human Resources, Income Support, Health
Chairman, The Hon. Perrin Beatty

Legislation and House Planning
Chairman, The Hon. Doug Lewis

Operations
Chairman, The Hon. Donald Mazankowski

Priorities and Planning
Chairman, The Rt. Hon. Brian Mulroney

Trade Executive Committee
Chairman, The Hon. John Crosbie

Security and Intelligence
Chairman, The Rt. Hon. Brian Mulroney

Special Committee of Council
Chairman, The Hon. Donald Mazankowski

Treasury Board
Chairman, The Hon. Robert R. de Cotret

---

*N.B. The Deputy Prime Minister, Minister of Finance and President of the Treasury Board are *ex officio* members of the Cabinet Committees on Cultural Affairs and National Identity; Economic Policy; Environment; Federal-Provincial Relations; Foreign and Defence Policy; and Human Resources, Income Support and Health. All Ministers are free to attend meetings of these Committees.

Parliamentary Secretaries

The *Parliamentary Secretaries Act* of June 1959 provided for the appointment of 16 parliamentary secretaries from among the members of the Commons to assist ministers. That Act has been amended more recently by the *Government Organization Act, 1983*, which allows the number of parliamentary secretaries to equal the number of ministers who hold offices listed in sections 4 and 5 of the *Salaries Act*, that is, usually, ministers with departmental responsibilities, the prime minister, the leader of the government in the Senate and the president of the Privy Council. A parliamentary secretary works under direction of his minister, but has no legal authority in his association with the department, nor is he given acting responsibility or any of the powers, duties

and functions of a minister in his minister's absence or incapacity. Parliamentary secretaries are appointed by the prime minister and hold office for 12 months.

Parliamentary secretaries were not named in time for inclusion in the 1989 edition of the Sourcebook.

Members of the House of Commons by Constituency

34th Parliament, 1st Session
(as of Jan. 31, 1989)

Listed alphabetically by constituency within provincial boundaries.

Constituency	Member and Affiliation
ALBERTA	
Athabasca	Jack Shields (PC)
Beaver River	Vacant
Calgary Centre	The Hon. Harvie Andre (PC)
Calgary North	Al Johnson (PC)
Calgary Northeast	Alex Kindy (PC)
Calgary Southeast	Lee Richardson (PC)
Calgary Southwest	Barbara Sparrow (PC)
Calgary West	Jim Hawkes (PC)
Crowfoot	Arnold J. Malone (PC)
Edmonton East	Ross Harvey (NDP)
Edmonton North	The Hon. Steven E. Paproski (PC)
Edmonton Northwest	Murray W. Dorin (PC)
Edmonton Southeast	David Kilgour (PC)
Edmonton Southwest	James S. Edwards (PC)
Edmonton/ Strathcona	Scott Thorkelson (PC)
Elk Island	Brian O'Kurley (PC)
Lethbridge	Blaine Thacker (PC)
Macleod	Ken G. Hughes (PC)
Medicine Hat	Robert Porter (PC)
Peace River	Albert Cooper (PC)
Red Deer	Doug Fee (PC)
St. Albert	Walter Van De Walle (PC)
Vegreville	The Hon. Donald Mazankowski (PC)
Wetaskiwin	Willie Littlechild (PC)
Wild Rose	Louise Feltham (PC)
Yellowhead	The Rt. Hon. Joe Clark (PC)
BRITISH COLUMBIA	
Burnaby/Kingsway	Svend Robinson (NDP)
Capilano/Howe Sound	The Hon. Mary Collins (PC)
Cariboo/Chilcotin	David Worthy (PC)
Comox/Alberni	Robert E. Skelly (NDP)
Delta	Stan Wilbee (PC)
Esquimalt/Juan de Fuca	Dave Barrett (NDP)
Fraser Valley East	Ross Belsher (PC)
Fraser Valley West	Robert L. Wenman (PC)
Kamloops	Nelson A. Riis (NDP)
Kootenay East	Sid Parker (NDP)
Kootenay West/ Revelstoke	Lyle Kristiansen (NDP)
Mission/Coquitlam	Joy Langan (NDP)
Nanaimo/Cowichan	David D. Stupich (NDP)

Constituency	Member and Affiliation
New Westminster/ Burnaby	Dawn Black (NDP)
North Island/Powell River	Ray Skelly (NDP)
North Vancouver	Charles Cook (PC)
Okanagan Centre	Al Horning (PC)
Okanagan/ Shuswap	Lyle D. MacWilliam (NDP)
Okanagan/ Similkameen/ Merritt	Jack Whittaker (NDP)
Port Moody/ Coquitlam	Ian Waddell (NDP)
Prince George/ Bulkley Valley	Brian L. Gardiner (NDP)
Prince George/ Peace River	The Hon. Frank Oberle (PC)
Richmond	The Hon. Tom Siddon (PC)
Saanich/Gulf Islands	Lynn Hunter (NDP)
Skeena	Jim Fulton (NDP)
Surrey North	Jim Karpoff (NDP)
Surrey/White Rock	Benno Friesen (PC)
Vancouver Centre	The Hon. Kim Campbell (PC)
Vancouver East	Margaret Mitchell (NDP)
Vancouver Quadra	The Rt. Hon. John Turner (Lib)
Vancouver South	The Hon. John A. Fraser (PC)
Victoria	John F. Brewin (NDP)

MANITOBA

Brandon/Souris	Lee Clark (PC)
Churchill	Rod Murphy (NDP)
Dauphin/Swan River	Brian White (PC)
Lisgar/Marquette	The Hon. Charles Mayer (PC)
Portage/Interlake	Felix Holtmann (PC)
Provencher	The Hon. Jake Epp (PC)
Selkirk	David Bjornson (PC)
St. Boniface	Ronald Duhamel (Lib)
Winnipeg North	Rey Pagtakhan (Lib)
Winnipeg North Centre	David Walker (Lib)
Winnipeg South	Dorothy Dobbie (PC)
Winnipeg South Centre	The Hon. Lloyd Axworthy (Lib)
Winnipeg/St. James	John Harvard (Lib)
Winnipeg/ Transcona	Bill Blaikie (NDP)

NEW BRUNSWICK

Beauséjour	Fernand Robichaud (Lib)
Carleton/Charlotte	Greg Thompson (PC)
Fredericton	J.W. Bud Bird (PC)
Fundy/Royal	Robert Corbett (PC)
Gloucester	Douglas Young (Lib)
Madawaska/ Victoria	The Hon. Bernard Valcourt (PC)
Miramichi	Maurice Dionne (Lib)
Moncton	George S. Rideout (Lib)
Restigouche	Guy Arsenault (Lib)
Saint John	The Hon. Gerald Merrithew (PC)

NEWFOUNDLAND

Bonavista/Trinity/ Conception	Fred J. Mifflin (Lib)
Burin/St. George's	Roger Simmons (Lib)
Gander/Grand Falls	George Baker (Lib)
Humber/St. Barbe/ Baie Verte	Brian Tobin (Lib)
Labrador	The Hon. William Rompkey (Lib)
St. John's East	Ross Reid (PC)
St. John's West	The Hon. John C. Crosbie (PC)

Constituency	Member and Affiliation

NORTHWEST TERRITORIES

Nunatsiaq	Jack Iyerak Anawak (Lib)
Western Arctic	Ethel Blondin (Lib)

NOVA SCOTIA

Annapolis Valley/ Hants	Patrick Nowlan (PC)
Cape Breton/East Richmond	David Dingwall (Lib)
Cape Breton Highlands/Canso	Francis LeBlanc (Lib)
Cape Breton/The Sydneys	Russell MacLellan (Lib)
Central Nova	The Hon. Elmer MacKay (PC)
Cumberland/ Colchester	Bill Casey (PC)
Dartmouth	Ron MacDonald (Lib)
Halifax	Mary Clancy (Lib)
Halifax West	Howard E. Crosby (PC)
South Shore	Peter McCreath (PC)
South West Nova	Coline Campbell (Lib)

ONTARIO

Algoma	Maurice Foster (Lib)
Brampton	The Hon. John McDermid (PC)
Brampton/ Malton	Harry Chadwick (PC)
Brant	Derek Blackburn (NDP)
Bruce/Grey	Gus Mitges (PC)
Burlington	Bill Kempling (PC)
Cambridge	Pat Sobeski (PC)
Carleton/ Gloucester	Eugène Bellemare (Lib)
Cochrane/Superior	Réginald Bélair (Lib)
Durham	Ross Stevenson (PC)
Elgin	Ken Monteith (PC)
Erie	Girve Fretz (PC)
Essex/Kent	Jerry Pickard (Lib)
Essex/Windsor	Steven W. Langdon (NDP)
Glengarry/ Prescott/Russell	Don Boudria (Lib)
Guelph/Wellington	The Hon. William C. Winegard (PC)
Haldimand/Norfolk	Bob Speller (Lib)
Halton/Peel	Garth Turner (PC)
Hamilton East	Sheila Copps (Lib)
Hamilton Mountain	Beth Phinney (Lib)
Hamilton/Wentworth	Geoffrey Scott (PC)
Hamilton West	Stan Keyes (Lib)
Hastings/Fron- tenac/Lennox and Addington	Bill Vankoughnet (PC)
Huron/Bruce	Murray Cardiff (PC)
Kenora/Rainy River	Robert Nault (Lib)
Kent	Rex Crawford (Lib)
Kingston and the Islands	Peter Milliken (Lib)
Kitchener	John Reimer (PC)
Lambton/Middlesex	The Hon. Ralph Ferguson (Lib)
Lanark/Carleton	The Hon. Paul Dick (PC)
Leeds/Grenville	Jim Jordan (Lib)
Lincoln	The Hon. Shirley Martin (PC)
London East	Joe Fontana (Lib)
London/Middlesex	Terry Clifford (PC)
London West	The Hon. Thomas Hockin (PC)
Markham	William Attewell (PC)
Mississauga East	Albina Guarnieri (Lib)
Mississauga South	Don Blenkarn (PC)
Mississauga West	Bob Horner (PC)
Nepean	Beryl Gaffney (Lib)
Niagara Falls	Robert Nicholson (PC)
Nickel Belt	John R. Rodriguez (NDP)

Constituency	Member and Affiliation
Nipissing	Bob Wood (Lib)
Northumberland	Christine Stewart (Lib)
Oakville/Milton	The Hon. Otto Jelinek (PC)
Ontario	René Soetens (PC)
Oshawa	The Hon. Ed Broadbent (NDP)
Ottawa Centre	Mac Harb (Lib)
Ottawa South	John Manley (Lib)
Ottawa/Vanier	Jean-Robert Gauthier (Lib)
Ottawa West	Marlene Catterall (Lib)
Oxford	Bruce Halliday (PC)
Parry Sound/ Muskoka	Stanley Darling (PC)
Perth/Wellington/ Waterloo	Harry Brightwell (PC)
Peterborough	Bill Domm (PC)
Prince Edward/ Hastings	Lyle Vanclief (Lib)
Renfrew	Len D. Hopkins (Lib)
Sarnia/Lambton	Ken James (PC)
Sault Ste. Marie	Steve Butland (NDP)
Simcoe Centre	Edna Anderson (PC)
Simcoe North	The Hon. Doug G. Lewis (PC)
St. Catharines	Ken Atkinson (PC)
Stormont/Dundas	Bob Kilger (Lib)
Sudbury	Diane Marleau (Lib)
Thunder Bay/ Atikokan	Iain Angus (NDP)
Thunder Bay/ Nipigon	Joe Comuzzi (Lib)
Timiskaming	John MacDougall (PC)
Timmins/Chapleau	Cid Samson (NDP)
Victoria/Haliburton	Bill Scott (PC)
Waterloo	The Hon. Walter McLean (PC)
Welland/St. Cath- arines/Thorold	Gilbert Parent (Lib)
Wellington/Grey/ Dufferin/Simcoe	The Hon. Perrin Beatty (PC)
Windsor/Lake St. Clair	Howard McCurdy (NDP)
Windsor West	The Hon. Herb Gray (Lib)
York North	Maurizio Bevilacqua (Lib)
York/Simcoe	John E. Cole (PC)

Toronto (Metropolitan)

Beaches/Woodbine	Neil Young (NDP)
Broadview/ Greenwood	Dennis Mills (Lib)
Davenport	The Hon. Charles Caccia (Lib)
Don Valley East	The Hon. Alan Redway (PC)
Don Valley North	Barbara Greene (PC)
Don Valley West	The Hon. John Bosley (PC)
Eglinton/Lawrence	Joseph Volpe (Lib)
Etobicoke Centre	The Hon. Michael Wilson (PC)
Etobicoke/ Lakeshore	Patrick Boyer (PC)
Etobicoke North	Roy MacLaren (Lib)
Parkdale/High Park	Jesse Flis (Lib)
Rosedale	The Hon. David MacDonald (PC)
Scarborough/ Agincourt	Jim Karygiannis (Lib)
Scarborough Centre	Pauline Browes (PC)
Scarborough East	Bob Hicks (PC)
Scarborough/ Rouge River	Derek Lee (Lib)
Scarborough West	Tom Wappel (Lib)
St. Paul's	The Hon. Barbara McDougall (PC)
Trinity/Spadina	Dan Heap (NDP)
Willowdale	Jim Peterson (Lib)

Constituency	Member and Affiliation
York Centre	The Hon. Robert Kaplan (Lib)
York South/Weston	John V. Nunziata (Lib)
York West	Sergio Marchi (Lib)

PRINCE EDWARD ISLAND

Cardigan	Lawrence MacAulay (Lib)
Egmont	Joe McGuire (Lib)
Hillsborough	George Proud (Lib)
Malpeque	Catherine Callbeck (Lib)

QUEBEC

Abitibi	Guy St-Julien (PC)
Argenteuil/ Papineau	Lise Bourgault (PC)
Beauce	Gilles Bernier (PC)
Beauharnois/ Salaberry	Jean-Guy Hudon (PC)
Bellechasse	The Hon. Pierre Blais (PC)
Berthier/Montcalm	The Hon. Robert R. de Cotret (PC)
Blainville/Deux Montagnes	The Hon. Monique Landry (PC)
Bonaventure/ Îles-de-la Madeleine	Darryl Gray (PC)
Brome/Missisquoi	Gabrielle Bertrand (PC)
Chambly	Richard Grisé (PC)
Champlain	Michel Champagne (PC)
Charlesbourg	Monique B. Tardif (PC)
Charlevoix	The Rt. Hon. Brian Mulroney (PC)
Châteauguay	Ricardo Lopez (PC)
Chicoutimi	André Harvey (PC)
Drummond	Jean-Guy Guilbault (PC)
Frontenac	The Hon. Marcel Masse (PC)
Gaspé	Charles-Eugène Marin (PC)
Gatineau/La Lièvre	Mark Assad (Lib)
Hull/Aylmer	Gilles Rocheleau (Lib)
Joliette	Gaby Larrivée (PC)
Jonquière	Jean-Pierre Blackburn (PC)
Kamouraska/ Rivière-du-Loup	André Plourde (PC)
Lac-Saint-Jean	The Hon. Lucien Bouchard (PC)
Langelier	The Hon. Gilles Loiselle (PC)
La Prairie	Fernand Jourdenais (PC)
Laurentides	Jacques Vien (PC)
Lévis	Gabriel Fontaine (PC)
Longueuil	Nic Leblanc (PC)
Lotbinière	Maurice Tremblay (PC)
Louis-Hébert	Suzanne Duplessis (PC)
Manicouagan	Charles A. Langlois (PC)
Matapédia/Matane	Jean-Luc Joncas (PC)
Mégantic/Compton/ Stanstead	François Gérin (PC)
Montmorency/ Orléans	Charles Deblois (PC)
Pontiac/Gatineau/ Labelle	Barry Moore (PC)
Portneuf	Marc Ferland (PC)
Québec-Est	Marcel R. Tremblay (PC)
Richelieu	Louis Plamondon (PC)
Richmond/Wolfe	Yvon Côté (PC)
Rimouski/ Témiscouata	The Hon. Monique Vézina (PC)
Roberval	The Hon. Benoît Bouchard (PC)
Saint-Hubert	Pierrette Venne (PC)
Saint-Hyacinthe/ Bagot	The Hon. Andrée Champagne (PC)
Saint-Jean	Clément Couture (PC)
Saint-Maurice	Denis Pronovost (PC)

Constituency	Member and Affiliation
Shefford	The Hon. Jean Lapierre (Lib)
Sherbrooke	The Hon. Jean J. Charest (PC)
Témiscamingue	Gabriel Desjardins (PC)
Terrebonne	Jean-Marc Robitaille (PC)
Trois-Rivières	Pierre H. Vincent (PC)
Verchères	Marcel Danis (PC)

Island of Montréal and Île Jésus

Ahuntsic	Nicole Roy-Arcelin (PC)
Anjou/Rivière-des-Prairies	The Hon. Jean Corbeil (PC)
Bourassa	Marie Gibeau (PC)
Duvernay	Vincent Della Noce (PC)
Hochelaga/Maisonneuve	Allan Koury (PC)
Lachine/Lac Saint-Louis	The Hon. Robert Layton (PC)
LaSalle/Emard	Paul Martin (Lib)
Laurier/Sainte-Marie	Jean-Claude Malépart (Lib)
Laval	Guy Ricard (PC)
Laval-des-Rapides	Jacques Tetreault (PC)
Mercier	Carole Jacques (PC)
Mount-Royal	Sheila Finestone (Lib)
Notre-Dame-de-Grâce	The Hon. Warren Allmand (Lib)
Outremont	J. Pierre Hogue (PC)
Papineau/Saint-Michel	The Hon. André Ouellet (Lib)
Pierrefonds/Dollard	The Hon. Gerry Weiner (PC)
Rosemont	Benoît Tremblay (PC)
Saint-Denis	Marcel Prud'homme (Lib)
Saint-Henri/Westmount	David Berger (Lib)
Saint-Laurent	Shirley Maheu (Lib)
Saint-Léonard	Alfonso Gagliano (Lib)
Vaudreuil	The Hon. Pierre Cadieux (PC)
Verdun/St-Paul	Gilbert Chartrand (PC)

SASKATCHEWAN

Kindersley/Lloydminster	The Hon. William McKnight (PC)
Mackenzie	Vic Althouse (NDP)
Moose Jaw/Lake Centre	Rod Laporte (NDP)
Prince Albert/Churchill River	Ray Funk (NDP)
Regina/Lumsden	Les Benjamin (NDP)
Regina/Qu'Appelle	Simon DeJong (NDP)
Regina/Wascana	Larry Schneider (PC)
Saskatoon/Clark's Crossing	Chris Axworthy (NDP)
Saskatoon/Dundurn	Ron Fisher (NDP)
Saskatoon/Humboldt	Stan Hovdebo (NDP)
Souris/Moose Mountain	Len Gustafson (PC)
Swift Current/Maple Creek/Assiniboia	Geoff Wilson (PC)
The Battlefords/Meadow Lake	Len Taylor (NDP)
Yorkton/Melville	Lorne Nystrom (NDP)

YUKON TERRITORY

Yukon	Audrey McLaughlin (NDP)

Lib — Liberal
NDP — New Democrat
PC — Progressive Conservative

Members of the House of Commons by Surname

34th Parliament, 1st Session
(as of Jan. 31, 1989)

Member & Affiliation	Constituency
Allmand, The Hon. Warren (Lib)	Notre-Dame-de-Grâce
Althouse, Vic (NDP)	Mackenzie
Anawak, Jack Iyerak (Lib)	Nunatsiaq
Anderson, Edna (PC)	Simcoe Centre
Andre, The Hon. Harvie (PC)	Calgary Centre
Angus, Iain (NDP)	Thunder Bay/Atikokan
Arsenault, Guy H. (Lib)	Restigouche
Assad, Mark (Lib)	Gatineau/La Lièvre
Atkinson, Ken (PC)	St. Catharines
Attewell, Bill (PC)	Markham
Axworthy, Chris (NDP)	Saskatoon/Clark's Crossing
Axworthy, The Hon. Lloyd (Lib)	Winnipeg South Centre
Baker, George S. (Lib)	Gander/Grand Falls
Barrett, David (NDP)	Esquimalt/Juan de Fuca
Beatty, The Hon. Perrin (PC)	Wellington/Grey/Dufferin/Simcoe
Bélair, Réginald (Lib)	Cochrane/Superior
Bellemare, Eugène (Lib)	Carleton/Gloucester
Belsher, Ross (PC)	Fraser Valley East
Benjamin, Les (NDP)	Regina/Lumsden
Berger, David (Lib)	Saint-Henri/Westmount
Bernier, Gilles (PC)	Beauce
Bertrand, Gabrielle (PC)	Brome/Missisquoi
Bevilacqua, Maurizio (Lib)	York North
Bird, J.W. Bud (PC)	Fredericton
Bjornson, David (PC)	Selkirk
Black, Dawn (NDP)	New Westminster/Burnaby
Blackburn, Derek (NDP)	Brant
Blackburn, Jean-Pierre (PC)	Jonquière
Blaikie, Bill (NDP)	Winnipeg/Transcona
Blais, The Hon. Pierre (PC)	Bellechasse
Blenkarn, Don (PC)	Mississauga South
Blondin, Ethel (Lib)	Western Arctic
Bosley, The Hon. John (PC)	Don Valley West
Bouchard, The Hon. Benoît (PC)	Roberval
Bouchard, The Hon. Lucien (PC)	Lac Saint-Jean
Boudria, Don (Lib)	Glengarry/Prescott/Russell
Bourgault, Lise (PC)	Argenteuil/Papineau
Boyer, Patrick (PC)	Etobicoke/Lakeshore
Brewin, John F. (NDP)	Victoria
Brightwell, Harry (PC)	Perth/Wellington/Waterloo
Broadbent, The Hon. Edward (NDP)	Oshawa
Browes, Pauline (PC)	Scarborough Centre
Butland, Steve (NDP)	Sault Ste. Marie
Caccia, The Hon. Charles L. (Lib)	Davenport
Cadieux, The Hon. Pierre H. (PC)	Vaudreuil
Callbeck, Catherine (Lib)	Malpeque
Campbell, Coline (Lib)	South West Nova

Member & Affiliation	Constituency
Campbell, The Hon. Kim (PC)	Vancouver Centre
Cardiff, Murray (PC)	Huron/Bruce
Casey, Bill (PC)	Cumberland/Colchester
Catterall, Marlene (Lib)	Ottawa West
Chadwick, Harry (PC)	Brampton/Malton
Champagne, The Hon. Andrée (PC)	Saint-Hyacinthe/Bagot
Champagne, Michel (PC)	Champlain
Charest, The Hon. Jean J. (PC)	Sherbrooke
Chartrand, Gilbert (PC)	Verdun/Saint-Paul
Clancy, Mary (Lib)	Halifax
Clark, The Rt. Hon. Joe (PC)	Yellowhead
Clark, Lee (PC)	Brandon/Souris
Clifford, Terry (PC)	London/Middlesex
Cole, John E. (PC)	York/Simcoe
Collins, The Hon. Mary (PC)	Capilano/Howe Sound
Comuzzi, Joe (Lib)	Thunder Bay/Nipigon
Cook, Chuck (PC)	North Vancouver
Cooper, Albert (PC)	Peace River
Copps, Sheila (Lib)	Hamilton East
Corbeil, The Hon. Jean (PC)	Anjou/Rivière-des-Prairies
Corbett, Bob (PC)	Fundy/Royal
Côté, Yvon (PC)	Richmond/Wolfe
Couture, Clément (PC)	Saint-Jean
Crawford, Rex (Lib)	Kent
Crosbie, The Hon. John C. (PC)	St. John's West
Crosby, Howard (PC)	Halifax West
Danis, Marcel (PC)	Verchères
Darling, Stan (PC)	Parry Sound/Muskoka
De Blois, Charles (PC)	Montmorency/Orléans
de Cotret, The Hon. Robert (PC)	Berthier/Montcalm
de Jong, Simon (NDP)	Regina/Qu'Appelle
Della Noce, Vincent (PC)	Duvernay
Desjardins, Gabriel (PC)	Témiscamingue
Dick, The Hon. Paul (PC)	Lanark/Carleton
Dingwall, David (Lib)	Cape Breton/East Richmond
Dionne, Maurice A. (Lib)	Miramichi
Dobbie, Dorothy (PC)	Winnipeg South
Domm, Bill (PC)	Peterborough
Dorin, Murray (PC)	Edmonton Northwest
Duhamel, Ronald J. (Lib)	St. Boniface
Duplessis, Suzanne (PC)	Louis-Hébert
Edwards, James S. (PC)	Edmonton Southwest
Epp, The Hon. Jake (PC)	Provencher
Fee, Douglas (PC)	Red Deer
Feltham, Louise (PC)	Wild Rose
Ferguson, Ralph (Lib)	Lambton/Middlesex
Ferland, Marc (PC)	Portneuf
Finestone, Sheila (Lib)	Mount Royal
Fisher, Ron (NDP)	Saskatoon/Dundurn
Flis, Jesse (Lib)	Parkdale/High Park
Fontaine, Gabriel (PC)	Lévis
Fontana, Joe (Lib)	London East
Foster, Maurice (Lib)	Algoma
Fraser, The Hon. John A. (PC)	Vancouver South
Fretz, Girve (PC)	Erie
Friesen, Benno (PC)	Surrey/White Rock
Fulton, Jim (NDP)	Skeena
Funk, Ray (NDP)	Prince Albert/Churchill River
Gaffney, Beryl (Lib)	Nepean
Gagliano, Alfonso (Lib)	Saint-Léonard
Gardiner, Brian L. (NDP)	Prince George/Bulkley Valley
Gauthier, Jean-Robert (Lib)	Ottawa/Vanier
Gérin, François (PC)	Mégantic/Compton/Stanstead
Gibeau, Marie (PC)	Bourassa
Gray, Darryl L. (PC)	Bonaventure/Îles-de-la-Madeleine
Gray, The Hon. Herb (Lib)	Windsor West
Greene, Barbara (PC)	Don Valley North
Grisé, Richard (PC)	Chambly
Guarnieri, Albina (Lib)	Mississauga East
Guilbault, Jean-Guy (PC)	Drummond
Gustafson, Len (PC)	Souris/Moose Mountain
Halliday, Bruce (PC)	Oxford
Harb, Mac (Lib)	Ottawa Centre
Harvard, John (Lib)	Winnipeg/St. James
Harvey, André (PC)	Chicoutimi
Harvey, Ross (NDP)	Edmonton East
Hawkes, Jim (PC)	Calgary West
Heap, Daniel (NDP)	Trinity/Spadina
Hicks, Bob (PC)	Scarborough East
Hockin, The Hon. Thomas (PC)	London West
Hogue, J.-Pierre (PC)	Outremont
Holtmann, Felix (PC)	Portage/Interlake
Hopkins, Len D. (Lib)	Renfrew
Horner, Bob (PC)	Mississauga West
Horning, Al (PC)	Okanagan Centre
Hovdebo, Stan J. (NDP)	Saskatoon/Humboldt
Hudon, Jean-Guy (PC)	Beauharnois/Salaberry
Hughes, Ken G. (PC)	Macleod
Hunter, Lynn (NDP)	Saanich/Gulf Islands
Jacques, Carole (PC)	Mercier
James, Ken (PC)	Sarnia/Lambton
Jelinek, The Hon. Otto (PC)	Oakville/Milton
Johnson, Al (PC)	Calgary North
Joncas, Jean-Luc (PC)	Matapédia/Matane
Jordan, Jim (Lib)	Leeds/Grenville
Jourdenais, Fernand (PC)	La Prairie
Kaplan, The Hon. Robert (Lib)	York Centre
Karpoff, Jim (NDP)	Surrey North
Karygiannis, Jim (Lib)	Scarborough/Agincourt
Kempling, Bill (PC)	Burlington
Keyes, Stan (Lib)	Hamilton West
Kilger, Bob (Lib)	Stormont/Dundas
Kilgour, David (PC)	Edmonton Southeast
Kindy, Alex (PC)	Calgary Northeast
Koury, Allan (PC)	Hochelaga/Maisonneuve
Kristiansen, Lyle (NDP)	Kootenay West/Revelstoke
Landry, The Hon. Monique (PC)	Blainville/Deux-Montagnes
Langan, Joy (NDP)	Mission/Coquitlam
Langdon, Steven W. (NDP)	Essex/Windsor
Langlois, Charles A. (PC)	Manicouagan
Lapierre, The Hon. Jean (Lib)	Shefford
Laporte, Rod (NDP)	Moose Jaw/Lake Centre
Larrivée, Gaby (PC)	Joliette
Layton, The Hon. Bob (PC)	Lachine/Lac Saint-Louis
Leblanc, Francis G. (Lib)	Cape Breton Highlands/Canso
Leblanc, Nic (PC)	Longueuil
Lee, Derek (Lib)	Scarborough/Rouge River
Lewis, The Hon. Doug (PC)	Simcoe North

Member & Affiliation	Constituency
Littlechild, Willie (PC)	Wetaskiwin
Loiselle, The Hon. Gilles (PC)	Langelier
Lopez, Ricardo (PC)	Châteauguay
MacAulay, Lawrence (Lib)	Cardigan
Macdonald, The Hon. David (PC)	Rosedale
MacDonald, Ron (Lib)	Dartmouth
MacDougall, John A. (PC)	Timiskaming
MacKay, The Hon. Elmer M. (PC)	Central Nova
MacLaren, Roy (Lib)	Etobicoke North
MacLellan, Russell (Lib)	Cape Breton/The Sydneys
MacWilliam, Lyle Dean (NDP)	Okanagan/Shuswap
Maheu, Shirley (Lib)	Saint-Laurent
Malépart, Jean-Claude (Lib)	Laurier/Sainte-Marie
Malone, Arnold (PC)	Crowfoot
Manly, John (Lib)	Ottawa South
Marchi, Sergio (Lib)	York West
Marin, Charles-Eugène (PC)	Gaspé
Marleau, Diane (Lib)	Sudbury
Martin, Paul (Lib)	LaSalle/Emard
Martin, The Hon. Shirley (PC)	Lincoln
Masse, The Hon. Marcel (PC)	Frontenac
Mayer, The Hon. Charles (PC)	Lisgar/Marquette
Mazankowski, The Hon. Don (PC)	Vegreville
McCreath, Peter L. (PC)	South Shore
McCurdy, Howard (NDP)	Windsor/Lake St. Clair
McDermid, The Hon. John (PC)	Brampton/Georgetown
McDougall, The Hon. Barbara (PC)	St. Paul's
McGuire, Joe (Lib)	Egmont
McKnight, The Hon. Bill (PC)	Kindersley/Lloydminster
McLaughlin, Audrey (NDP)	Yukon
McLean, The Hon. Walter (PC)	Waterloo
Merrithew, The Hon. Gerald S. (PC)	Saint John
Mifflin, Fred J. (Lib)	Bonavista/Trinity/Conception
Milliken, Peter (Lib)	Kingston and the Islands
Mills, Dennis (Lib)	Broadview/Greenwood
Mitchell, Margaret (NDP)	Vancouver East
Mitges, Gus (PC)	Bruce/Grey
Monteith, Ken (PC)	Elgin
Moore, Barry (PC)	Pontiac/Gatineau/Labelle
Mulroney, The Rt. Hon. Brian (PC)	Charlevoix
Murphy, Rod (NDP)	Churchill
Nault, Robert D. (Lib)	Kenora/Rainy River
Nicholson, Rob (PC)	Niagara Falls
Nowlan, J. Patrick (PC)	Annapolis Valley/Hants
Nunziata, John (Lib)	York South/Weston
Nystrom, Lorne (NDP)	Yorkton/Melville
O'Kurley, Brian (PC)	Elk Island
Oberle, The Hon. Frank (PC)	Prince George/Peace River
Ouellet, The Hon. André (Lib)	Papineau/Saint-Michel
Pagtakhan, Rey (Lib)	Winnipeg North
Paproski, The Hon. Steven E. (PC)	Edmonton North
Parent, Gilbert (Lib)	Welland/St. Catharines/Thorold
Parker, Sid (NDP)	Kootenay East

Member & Affiliation	Constituency
Peterson, Jim (Lib)	Willowdale
Phinney, Beth (Lib)	Hamilton Mountain
Pickard, Jerry (Lib)	Essex/Kent
Plamondon, Louis (PC)	Richelieu
Plourde, André (PC)	Kamouraska/Rivière-du-Loup
Porter, Bob (PC)	Medicine Hat
Pronovost, Denis (PC)	Saint-Maurice
Proud, George (Lib)	Hillsborough
Prud'homme, Marcel (Lib)	Saint-Denis
Redway, The Hon. Alan (PC)	Don Valley East
Reid, Ross (PC)	St. John's East
Reimer, John (PC)	Kitchener
Ricard, Guy (PC)	Laval
Richardson, Lee (PC)	Calgary Southeast
Rideout, George S. (Lib)	Moncton
Riis, Nelson A. (NDP)	Kamloops
Robichaud, Fernand (Lib)	Beauséjour
Robinson, Svend J. (NDP)	Burnaby/Kingsway
Robitaille, Jean-Marc (PC)	Terrebonne
Rocheleau, Gilles (Lib)	Hull/Aylmer
Rodriguez, John R. (NDP)	Nickel Belt
Rompkey, The Hon. William (Lib)	Labrador
Roy-Arselin, Nicole (PC)	Ahuntsic
Samson, Cid (NDP)	Timmins/Chapleau
Schneider, Larry (PC)	Regina/Wascana
Scott, Bill (PC)	Victoria/Haliburton
Scott, Geoffrey (PC)	Hamilton/Wentworth
Shields, Jack (PC)	Athabasca
Siddon, The Hon. Tom (PC)	Richmond
Simmons, Roger (Lib)	Burin/St. George's
Skelly, Ray (NDP)	North Island/Powell River
Skelly, Robert E. (NDP)	Comox/Alberni
Sobeski, Pat (PC)	Cambridge
Soetens, René (PC)	Ontario
Sparrow, Barbara (PC)	Calgary Southwest
Speller, Bob (Lib)	Haldimand/Norfolk
St-Julien, Guy (PC)	Abitibi
Stevenson, Ross (PC)	Durham
Stewart, Christine (Lib)	Northumberland
Stupich, David D. (NDP)	Nanaimo/Cowichan
Tardif, Monique (PC)	Charlesbourg
Taylor, Len (NDP)	The Battlefords/Meadow Lake
Tetreault, Jacques (PC)	Laval-des-Rapides
Thacker, Blaine A. (PC)	Lethbridge
Thompson, Greg (PC)	Carleton/Charlotte
Thorkelson, Scott (PC)	Edmonton/Strathcona
Tobin, Brian (Lib)	Humber/St. Barbe/Baie Verte
Tremblay, Benoît (PC)	Rosemont
Tremblay, Marcel R. (PC)	Québec-Est
Tremblay, Maurice (PC)	Lotbinière
Turner, Garth (PC)	Halton/Peel
Turner, The Rt. Hon. John N. (Lib)	Vancouver Quadra
Valcourt, The Hon. Bernard (PC)	Madawaska/Victoria
Van De Walle, Walter (PC)	St. Albert
Vanclief, Lyle (Lib)	Prince Edward/Hastings
Vankoughnet, Bill (PC)	Hastings/Frontenac/Lennox & Addington
Venne, Pierrette (PC)	Saint-Hubert
Vézina, The Hon. Monique (PC)	Rimouski/Témiscouata
Vien, Jacques (PC)	Laurentides
Vincent, Pierre-H. (PC)	Trois-Rivières

Member & Affiliation	Constituency
Volpe, Joseph (Lib)	Eglinton/Lawrence
Waddell, Ian (NDP)	Port Moody/ Coquitlam
Walker, David (Lib)	Winnipeg North Centre
Wappel, Tom (Lib)	Scarborough West
Weiner, The Hon. Gerald (PC)	Pierrefonds/ Dollard
Wenman, Robert L. (PC)	Fraser Valley West
White, Brian (PC)	Dauphin/Swan River
Whittaker, Jack (NDP)	Okanagan/Simil-kameen/Merritt
Wilbee, Stan (PC)	Delta
Wilson, Geoff (PC)	Swift Current/Maple Creek/Assiniboia
Wilson, The Hon. Michael (PC)	Etobicoke Centre
Winegard, The Hon. William (PC)	Guelph/Wellington
Wood, Bob (Lib)	Nipissing
Worthy, Dave (PC)	Cariboo/Chilcotin
Young, Douglas (Lib)	Gloucester
Young, Neil (NDP)	Beaches/Woodbine

Lib — Liberal
NDP — New Democrat
PC — Progressive Conservative

Standing, Special and Joint Committees

Committees of the House of Commons are struck to do much of the work that would otherwise slow the business of the House. They are of three types and they are all created through the authority of the Standing Orders of the House of Commons. Standing committees generally correspond to a government department whose conduct they scrutinize. As well, there are several standing committees (private members' business and elections, privileges and procedures, for example) with special functions. Special committees are created to study problems and issues. Joint committees include senators in their membership.

Since their role was redefined in 1985, these committees have become smaller (seven to 10 members) and have been given more freedom in their choice of subjects for investigation. As well, they no longer have to study bills after second reading, a task now performed by special legislative committees struck for the purpose. At the end of the last Parliament, there were 27 standing committees, two special committees and two joint committees.

Members of standing, special and joint committees were not named in time for inclusion in the 1989 edition of the Sourcebook.

Office of the Auditor General of Canada

240 Sparks St., Ottawa, ON K1A 0G6

The Office of the Auditor General of Canada is responsible for examining the public accounts of Canada, including those relating to the Consolidated Revenue Fund, public property and various Crown corporations. The Auditor General performs comprehensive audits of departments, agencies and certain Crown corporations, and conducts government-wide studies of issues involving the management of financial, physical, and human resources of the federal government. The Auditor General reports annually to the House of Commons but may make a special report to the House on any matter that he feels should not be deferred until his annual report.

Auditor General, Kenneth M. Dye
Asst. Auditor General, E.F. McNamara

AUDIT OPERATIONS
Deputy Auditors General:
Raymond M. Dubois, D. Larry Meyers
Asst. Auditors General:
Douglas Deeks, W. Elwyn Dickson,
Robert R. Lalonde, David Marshall,
Jean-Guy Laliberté, Hector Millward,
William F. Radburn, Ron C. Thompson,
Paul D.M. Ward, Leonard M. McGimpsey
Donald Young

PROFESSIONAL SERVICES
Deputy Auditor General, Edward R. Rowe
Asst. Auditor General, Yvan Gaudette

ADMINISTRATIVE SERVICES
Deputy Auditor General, Ronald M. Warme

The federal franchise

The present federal franchise laws are contained in the *Canada Elections Act,* R.S.C. 1970 (1st Supp.), Chapter 14, as amended by the *Election Expenses Act,* S.C. 1973-74, Chapter 51. Generally, the franchise is conferred upon all Canadian citizens who have reached age 18 and ordinarily live in the electoral district on the date fixed for the beginning of the enumeration at the election. Persons denied the right to vote are: the chief electoral officer and the assistant chief electoral officer; judges appointed by the Governor in Council; the returning officer for each electoral district; persons whose liberty of movement is restricted or who are deprived of the management of their property because of mental disease (in some cases, these persons have successfully challenged this disenfranchisement under the *Charter of Rights and Freedoms);* and persons disqualified by law for corrupt or illegal practices.

The special voting rules set out in Schedule II to the *Canada Elections Act* prescribe voting procedures for members of the Canadian forces, for members of the federal public service posted abroad, and also for veterans receiving treatment or domiciliary care in certain institutions.

ELECTIONS CANADA

440 Coventry Road, Ottawa, ON K1A 0M6

The Chief Electoral Officer is responsible for the supervision of the administrative conduct of federal elections in Canada and for ensuring that all provisions of the *Canada Elections Act* are complied with and enforced. Major activities include the training of returning officers, the revision of polling division boundaries, the acquisition of election material and supplies, the maintenance of a registry of political parties and the certification of statutory payments to be made to auditors, political parties and candidates under the election expenses provisions of the Act.

Adjustment of electoral district boundaries. Pursuant to the *Electoral Boundaries Readjustment Act* and following each decennial census, the Chief Electoral Officer must calculate the number of electoral districts to be assigned to each province according to rules contained in section 51 of the *Constitution Act, 1867* and prepare population distribution maps for use by the 11 electoral boundaries commissions that are directly responsible for readjusting federal electoral district boundaries.

Once the Chief Electoral Officer has determined the number of seats to be allocated to each province, 11 commissions (one for each province and the Northwest Territories) work on the adjustments required in the electoral district boundaries and each submits a report on its deliberations. Normally they must complete this exercise in one year; however, the deadline may be extended by a period not to exceed six months. Each commission comprises three members, of which the chairman is appointed by the chief justice of the province and the other two members by the Speaker of the House of Commons.

The readjustment process takes place in three stages. The first consists of preparing a map of the province or the territory indicating the boundaries of the proposed constituencies (or electoral districts), the population figure for and the name of each constituency. The commission must then publish its proposals in at least one newspaper distributed generally throughout the province and hold public hearings, during which interested persons, acting either as individuals or in groups, may make appropriate representations.

For each commission, the second phase consists of reviewing its initial proposals in light of the representations which it has received during the public hearings, in order to make any changes which are considered appropriate. The report, together with the revised map, is then tabled in the House of Commons.

The third stage allows for a certain number of days to be set aside during which the members of the House of Commons may make known their opposition to one or more of the proposals. The proposals are then returned to the relevant commission with the comments of the members, in order that the final decision may be made. The process of readjustment ends with the proclamation of the "Representation Order".

A representation order becomes effective at the next dissolution of Parliament occurring at least one year after the date of the proclamation of the order. At least two and one half years must therefore elapse before all the requirements of the *Electoral Boundaries Readjustment Act* can be met.

Redistribution based on the 1981 Census took place on July 14, 1988 and the general election on Nov. 21 was carried out using the new electoral map. Thirteen new ridings were created to bring the total of seats in the House of Commons to 295. As well, six ridings disappeared and the boundaries were altered in 269 others.

In this round of redistribution, Alberta gained five seats, Ontario four and B.C. four. However, due to constitutional requirements and the sheer size of ridings, not all are of equal population. Nunatsiaq, in the Northwest Territories, contains 10,888 voters while York North near Toronto has 112,868. The average number of electors in P.E.I.'s four ridings is 21,768 in contrast to the 62,588 in the 23 on the Island of Montreal.

Chief Electoral Officer: J-M. Hamel
Asst. Chief Electoral Officer: R.A. Gould
General Counsel, Y. Tarte
Director of Operations: L. Lavoie
Asst. Director of Operations
    (Co-ordination & Planning): M. Villeneuve
Asst. Director of Operations
    (Redistribution & Revision): Mrs. A. Lortie
Election Financing and Registrar
    Director, F.B. Slattery
Administration & Personnel
    Director, C. Lesage
Communications
    Director, Ms. C. Jackson

COMMISSIONER OF CANADA ELECTIONS

440 Coventry Road, Ottawa, ON K1A 0M6

The Commissioner of Canada Elections, appointed under statutory authority by the Chief Electoral Officer, is responsible for ensuring compliance and enforcement of all provisions of the *Canada Elections Act* and the *Northwest Territories Elections Act.*

Commissioner, George Allen
Exec. Director, Y. Tarte

DEPARTMENTS, BOARDS, COMMISSIONS AND CORPORATIONS

In Canada, the work of government is conducted by federal departments, special boards, commissions and corporations owned or controlled by the Government of Canada, as well as several corporations in which the government holds a minority interest. Of the corporations owned by the Government of Canada, the Crown corporation mode of organization is the most common. The government has resorted to Crown corporations with increasing frequency to administer and manage public services, many of which require the combination of business enterprise and public accountability. The historical evolution of Crown corporations is described in the government's proposals on the control, direction and accountability of Crown corporations published in August 1977. Chapter I of that paper describes the historical and constitutional background of the Crown corporation form. Part XII of the *Financial Administration Act*, R.S.C. 1970, Chapter F-10, enacted by S.C. 1984, Chapter 31, came into force on Sept. 1, 1984. It provides a uniform system of financial and budgetary control and accountability, auditing and reporting for the majority of Crown corporations.

Departmental corporations. A departmental corporation is defined as a corporation that is a servant or agent of Her Majesty in right of Canada and is responsible for administrative, research, supervisory, advisory, or regulatory functions of a governmental nature. Departmental corporations are governed by the provisions of the *Financial Administration Act* that apply to departments generally. (They are listed in Schedule B to the *Financial Administration Act*.)

Crown corporations. A Crown corporation is either a parent or a wholly owned subsidiary. A parent Crown corporation is defined as a corporation which is directly owned by the Crown (i.e.: all outstanding shares are owned, directly or indirectly by, on behalf of, or in trust for the Crown or all directors are appointed by the Governor in Council or by a minister, with the approval of the Governor in Council), but does not include a departmental corporation. A wholly owned subsidiary is a corporation that is wholly owned directly or indirectly by one or more parent Crown corporations.

Parent Crown corporations and their subsidiaries are responsible for the management of trading or service operations on a quasi-commercial basis, for the management of procurement, construction or disposal activities on behalf of Her Majesty in right of Canada, for the management of lending or financial operations, or for the management of commercial or industrial operations involving the production of or dealing in goods and the supplying of services to the public.

Parent Crown corporations operating in a competitive environment and not ordinarily dependent on appropriations for operating purposes are listed in Schedule C-II of the *Financial Administration Act*. Other parent Crown corporations are listed in Schedule C-I.

Crown corporations are subject to the provisions of Part XII of the Act; if there is any inconsistency between its provisions and those of any other Act applicable to a corporation, the former prevail. This part provides for the conduct of corporate affairs and for the financial management and control. Among other things, it provides for the appointment of directors and officers and their duties; directions to a corporation by order-in-council; restrictions on incorporating new Crown corporations, on acquiring and selling shares of Crown corporations and on winding them up; approval of corporate plans and budgets; control of bank accounts and borrowing; turning over of surplus money to the Receiver General; keeping and auditing accounts; and preparation of financial statements and reports for submission to Parliament through the appropriate minister.

A further form of control is exercised by Parliament through the power to vote financial assistance to a corporation, which may secure financing through parliamentary grants, loans or advances, by the issue of capital stock to the government, or by borrowings from the capital markets, often with a government guarantee.

Unclassified corporations. Seven parent Crown corporations are not subject to the *Financial Administration Act* but are governed by their own special Act. They are: the Bank of Canada, the Canada Council, the Canadian Wheat Board, the National Arts Centre Corp., the International Development Research Centre, the Canadian Film Development Corp., and the Canadian Broadcasting Corp.

Other corporations. The federal government has established or assisted in the establishment of a number of corporations in which it holds a portion of the capital stock. In most cases, private sector investors hold the remaining shares; in several cases, shares are held by provincial or other governments. These corporations, known as mixed or joint enterprises, have been established either by a special Act of Parliament — for example, the Canada Development Corp. or Telesat Canada — or by letters patent or articles of incorporation — for example, Panarctic Oils Ltd. Such corporations are not listed in the schedules of the *Financial Administration Act* and are not subject to its provisions.

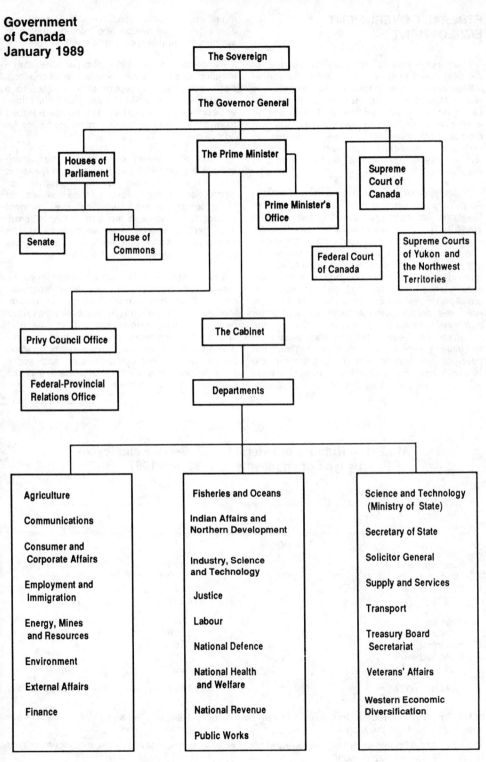

**Government
of Canada
January 1989**

The Sovereign

The Governor General

Houses of Parliament

The Prime Minister

Prime Minister's Office

Supreme Court of Canada

Senate

House of Commons

Federal Court of Canada

Supreme Courts of Yukon and the Northwest Territories

Privy Council Office

The Cabinet

Federal-Provincial Relations Office

Departments

Agriculture

Communications

Consumer and Corporate Affairs

Employment and Immigration

Energy, Mines and Resources

Environment

External Affairs

Finance

Fisheries and Oceans

Indian Affairs and Northern Development

Industry, Science and Technology

Justice

Labour

National Defence

National Health and Welfare

National Revenue

Public Works

Science and Technology (Ministry of State)

Secretary of State

Solicitor General

Supply and Services

Transport

Treasury Board Secretariat

Veterans' Affairs

Western Economic Diversification

FEDERAL GOVERNMENT EMPLOYMENT

Treasury Board (a statutory committee of cabinet) has overall responsibility for personnel management in the federal public service. It is responsible for development and application of personnel policies, systems and methods to ensure that the people needed to carry out programs effectively are obtained at competitive wages and put to efficient use with consideration for the individual and collective rights of employees.

Under provisions of the amended *Financial Administration Act* and the *Public Service Staff Relations Act,* both proclaimed in March 1967, Treasury Board is responsible for the development of policy guidelines, regulations, standards and programs in the areas of classification and pay, conditions of employment, collective bargaining and staff relations, official languages, human resources training, development and utilization, pensions, insurance and other employee benefits and allowances, and other personnel management matters affecting the public service. Treasury Board is also responsible for making recommendations on organization development, human resources planning, the determination and evaluation of training needs and education programs, and standards govern-ing health and safety. It advises departments and agencies on the design and implementation of systems to improve personnel management.

Responsibility for classification and the administration of salaries has, with a few exceptions, been delegated to departments, subject to a monitoring process. Benefit programs and allowance policies approved by the board are designed to give departments maximum responsibility for administration.

Under the system of collective bargaining established by the *Public Service Staff Relations Act,* Treasury Board is the employer for employees in the public service, except for separate employers such as the National Research Council and the National Film Board. The board negotiates collective agreements with unions representing bargaining units and advises departments on their administration.

The board develops policy guidelines for public service pension, insurance and related programs, co-ordinates their administration and recommends periodic revisions. It negotiates reciprocal pension transfer agreements with other public and private employers. It also studies and proposes means of ensuring compatibility between public service employee benefits and social security programs such as medicare and the Canada and Quebec pension plans.

TABLE 1 — Number of federal Public Service employees, by type of employment, 1986 and 1987

Type of employment	1986	1987
Full-time		
Indeterminate.	196,153	191,977
Seasonal	1,269	1,368
Specified term	14,870	16,300
TOTAL	212,292	209,645
Part-time		
Indeterminate.	3,989	4,055
Seasonal	68	71
Specified term	851	965
TOTAL	4,908	5,091
GRAND TOTAL	**217,223**	**214,930**

NOTE: Employees hired for periods of less than six months (11,845 in 1986 and 11,767 in 1987) have been excluded from the tables.

The sums of the figures do not equal the grand total because, in a number of cases, the documents did not specify type of employment.

SOURCE: Public Service Commission

TABLE 2 — Number and percentage of federal Public Service employees, by geographic area and sex, 1986 and 1987

Geographic area	1986				1987			
	Men	Women		Total	Men	Women		Total
		No.	%			No.	%	
Alberta	7,510	5,448	42.0	12,958	7,387	5,470	42.5	12,857
British Columbia	12,357	7,818	38.8	20,175	12,213	7,915	39.3	20,128
Manitoba	5,328	4,215	42.2	9,543	5,080	4,188	45.2	9,268
New Brunswick	4,580	2,810	38.0	7,390	4,493	2,886	39.1	7,379
Newfoundland	3,910	1,399	26.4	5,309	3,841	1,373	26.3	5,213
Northwest Territories	775	622	44.5	1,397	729	618	45.9	1,347
Nova Scotia	9,980	3,920	28.2	13,900	9,550	3,906	29.0	13,456
Ontario (except National Capital Region)	19,728	15,191	43.5	34,919	19,186	15,077	44.0	34,264
Ontario (National Capital Region)	28,045	24,191	46.3	52,236	27,485	24,036	46.7	51,521
Prince Edward Island	1,196	870	42.1	2,066	1,186	855	42.3	2,023
Quebec (except National Capital Region)	19,001	12,096	38.9	31,097	18,647	12,276	39.7	30,941
Quebec (National Capital Region)	9,347	8,767	48.4	18,114	9,270	8,930	49.1	18,200
Saskatchewan	3,103	2,529	44.9	5,632	2,986	2,518	45.7	5,504
Yukon	426	462	52.0	888	416	472	53.2	888
Outside Canada	1,198	375	23.8	1,573	1,207	393	24.6	1,600
TOTAL	**126,484**	**90,713**	**41.8**	**217,197**	**123,790**	**90,945**	**42.4**	**214,930**

SOURCE: Public Service Commission 1987 Annual Report

DEPARTMENT OF AGRICULTURE

Sir John Carling Bldg.
Carling Ave., Ottawa, K1A 0C5
General Inquiries: (613) 995-5222

MINISTER'S OFFICE
Rm. 203-S, Centre Blk.
House of Commons, Ottawa, K1A 0A6
Minister, The Hon. Don Mazankowski

OFFICE OF THE MINISTER OF STATE
(GRAINS AND OILSEEDS)
Rm. 175, E. Blk.
House of Commons, Ottawa, K1A 0A6
Minister, The Hon. Charles Mayer

OFFICE OF THE MINISTER OF STATE
(AGRICULTURE)
Rm. 446, Confederation Bldg.
Ottawa, K1A 0C6
Minister, The Hon. Pierre Blais

DEPUTY MINISTER'S OFFICE
Dep. Minister, Jean-Jacques Noreau
Sr. Asst. Dep. Minister, J.E. McGowan
Sr. Program Analyst, C.S. Lesslie-Jeffery

AUDIT AND EVALUATION BRANCH
A/Director Gen., G. Paterson
Program Evaluation Division
A/Director, C. Motuz
Internal Audit Division Director, P.G. Rowan
Emergency Planning Director, D. Puccini

Policy Branch
Asst. Dep. Minister, F. Claydon
FARM FINANCIAL PROGRAMS DIRECTORATE
Director Gen., Gilles Lavoie
Legislated Marketing Programs Division
A/Director, K. Trudel
Agricultural Stabilization Board
Sec.-Manager, A.E. Proulx
Crop Insurance Division
Director, T.E. Pender
Regional Managers:
East, J. Forget
West, W. Boddis
Central-Pacific, J.M. Ellis

FARM DEVELOPMENT POLICY DIRECTORATE
Director Gen., T. Richardson
Farm Finance and Taxation Division
Director, Dr. R.K. Eyvindson
Production Analysis Division
Director, Dr. K.J. McKenzie

COMMODITY CO-ORDINATION DIRECTORATE
Director Gen., Dr. C. L'Ecuyer

PLANNING, CO-ORDINATION AND ANALYSIS
DIRECTORATE
Director Gen., D.D. Hedley

Market Outlook and Analysis Division
Director, Z. Hasan
Food Markets Analysis Division
Director, H. Migie
PLANNING AND CO-ORDINATION
Exec. Director, Dr. J.K. Martin
Policy Planning Director, D.C. Loken

Corporate Management Branch
Asst. Dep. Minister, A. Lefebvre-Anglin
Sr. Advisor, B. Waters
Planning Officer, R. Fisher-Titus

REAL PROPERTY AND CORPORATE
ADMINISTRATION DIRECTORATE
Director Gen., M. Senécal
Departmental Services Division
Director, G.G. Esdale
Policy, Planning and Systems Division
Director, Vacant
Facilities Management Division
Director, R.C. Lee
Information Management Division
Director, H. Barrett

SYSTEMS AND CONSULTING DIRECTORATE
Director Gen., B. MacKenzie
Corporate Information Management Division
A/Director, V. Desroches
Client Services Division Director, H.W. Pearson
Planning and Development Division
Director, B. Gallant
Libraries Division Director, M.L. Morton

FINANCE AND RESOURCE MANAGEMENT
DIRECTORATE
Director Gen., S. Dixon
Accounting Division Director, G. White
Planning and Resource Management Division
Director, B. Mitchell
Financial Policies and Systems Division
Director, F.H. Crowe
REGIONAL OFFICES:

Atlantic Region
30 Highfield St., Box 6088
Moncton, NB E1C 8R2
A/Reg. Financial Manager, J. Snowdon
A/Reg. Admin. Manager, D.C. O'Brien
Systems and Consulting
A/Manager, T. Chafe

Quebec Region
Place Guy Favreau
200, boul. René-Lévesque ouest
Montréal, H2Z 1Y3
Finance and Resource Management
East Division Director, N. Hébert
Reg. Admin. Manager, P. Corriveau
Systems and Consulting Manager, N. Snow

Ontario Region
Penthouse #3, 4900 Yonge St.
Willowdale, M2N 6A4
Finance and Resource Management
A/Director, D. Collister
A/Reg. Admin. Manager, A. Deslauriers
Systems and Consulting Chief, A. Chok

Prairie Region
2nd Flr., 2212 Scarth St.
Box 8050, Regina, SK S4P 4E3
Reg. Financial Manager, D. Black
Systems and Consulting, H. Moen

Pacific Region
101, 620 Royal Ave.
Box 2521, New Westminster, BC V3L 5A8
Finance and Resource Management
Western Division
A/Manager, A. de Vries
Reg. Admin. Manager, S. Holland
Systems and Consulting Manager, T. Lund

PERSONNEL BRANCH
Director Gen., J.G. Soulière
Personnel Operations Division
Director, Vacant
Official Languages Division
Director, C.R. Desrochers
Classification and Organization Division
A/Director, P. Mills
Staff Relations Division
Director, J. Nolan
Health, Safety and Security Division
A/Director, C. Stern
Planning and Resource Management Division
Director, P. Scrivens
Training and Development Division
Director, M. Ledoux
Human Resources Planning
and Employment Equity
Director, R. Balson
Staffing Management Category Division
Director, Réjean Laplante

REGIONAL OFFICES
Atlantic Region
30 Highfield St., Box 6088
Moncton, NB E1C 8R2
Reg. Personnel Manager, B. Murray

Quebec Region
Place Guy Favreau, bur. 1002-P
200, boul. René-Lévesque ouest
Montreal, H2Z 1Y3
Reg. Personnel Manager, A. Dupont

Ontario Region
Penthouse #3, 4900 Yonge St.
Willowdale, M2N 6B9
Reg. Personnel Manager, Caroline Brown

Manitoba Region
401, 303 Main St., Winnipeg, R3C 3G7
Reg. Personnel Manager, E.W. Alexander

Alberta Region
Box 2914, Stn. M., Calgary, T2P 3C3
Reg. Personnel Manager, Mrs. R. Turner

British Columbia Region
Box 50, Rm. 201, 1161 Alberni St.
Vancouver, BC V6E 3W5
Reg. Personnel Manager, M.C. Oster

COMMUNICATIONS BRANCH
Director Gen., L. Neveu
Dep. Director Gen., D.J. Ros
Operations Director, F. Harding

Programs Director, Peter Hall
Sr. Advisor (Issues), D.J.R. Smithers
Media Relations Chief, Vacant

Agriculture Development Branch
Asst. Dep. Minister, R.C. Bailey
Priorities Management Strategies Division
Director, Margaret Bennett
Special Programs Division
Director, M. Comeau

COMMODITY PRODUCTION DEVELOPMENT
DIRECTORATE
Director Gen., C. Stoll
Livestock Development Division
Director, M. MacGregor
Food Development Division Director, L. Keen
Crop Development Division
Director, C. Paquette

REGIONAL DIRECTORS:
Box 1878, St. John's, NF A1C 5R4
Dr. T. Espie
Box 2949, Charlottetown, PE C1A 8C5
A/Director, H. Marshall
Box 698, 35 Commercial St.
Truro, NS B2N 5E5
Dr. D. Byers
209, 633 Queen St., Box 20280
Fredericton, NB E3B 1C3
L.P. Albert
5, parc Samuel-Champlain
Québec, (Québec) G1S 4S2
S. Thiboutôt
420, 102 Bloor St. W.
Toronto, ON M5S 1M8
F. Cullen
303-275 Portage Ave.
Winnipeg, MB R3B 2B3
William Breckman
310-2100 Broad St., Regina, SK S4P 4C7
J. Lowe
4th Flr., Corner Point Bldg.
10179-105th St., Edmonton, AB T5J 1E2
A/Director, T. Hayward
80-6th Ave., New Westminster, BC V3L 5B3
J. Berry

Food Production and Inspection Branch
Rm. 409, Sir John Carling Bldg.
Ottawa, K1A 0C5
Asst. Dep. Minister, Dr. B. Morrissey
Sr. Advisor, Dr. R. Reid

Special Investigations Division
2nd Flr., S.B.I. Bldg.
2323 Riverside Dr., Ottawa, K1A 0C5
Director, J. Brown

Race Track Division
62 Auriga Dr., Ottawa, K1A 0C5
Director, C. Lalonde

HEALTH OF ANIMALS DIRECTORATE
Director Gen., Dr. N.G. Willis
FOOD INSPECTION DIRECTORATE
Director Gen., Dr. M. Morissette

PLANT HEALTH DIRECTORATE
Director Gen., R. Roy
PESTICIDE DIRECTORATE
Director Gen., S.W. Ormrod
MANAGEMENT STRATEGIES AND PRIORITIES
DIRECTORATE
Director Gen., D. Hendrick

VETERINARY INSPECTION DIRECTORATE
Director Gen., Dr. G. Dittberner
REGIONAL OFFICES:
Atlantic
Terminal Plaza Bldg., 4th Flr.
Box 6088, 30 Highfield St.
Moncton, NB E1C 8R2
Reg. Director, Dr. D.M. Duplessis
Quebec
Place Guy Favreau, Tour est, bur. 1002-V
200, boul. René-Lévesque ouest
Montréal, H2Z 1Y3
Reg. Director, Dr. G. Meilleur
Ontario
Joseph Shepherd Bldg., Ste. 1210,
4900 Yonge St., Willowdale, M2N 6G7
Reg. Director, Dr. I.R. Sutherland
Manitoba
613 Federal Bldg., 269 Main St.
Winnipeg, R3C 1B2
Reg. Director, Dr. A.C. van Der Meulen
Saskatchewan
330, 2100 Broad St., Box 8070
Regina, S4P 4E5
Reg. Director, Dr. R. Clarke
Alberta
Harry Hayes Bldg., Ste. 751, 220-4th Ave. S.E.
Stn. M, Bag 2998, Calgary, T2P 3C3
Reg. Director, Dr. L.K. Anderson
British Columbia
801, 1001 W. Pender St.
Vancouver, V6E 2M7
Reg. Director, Dr. R.J. Marra

AGRICULTURAL INSPECTION DIRECTORATE
Director Gen., Dr. S. Thompson
REGIONAL OFFICES:
Atlantic
4th Flr., 30 Highfield St., Box 6088
Moncton, NB E1C 8R2
Reg. Director, R.A. Greene
Quebec
Place Guy Favreau, Tour est, bur. 1002-I
200, boul. René-Lévesque ouest
Montreal, H2Z 1Y3
Reg. Director, F. Planté
Ontario
Joseph Sheppard Bldg., Ste. 1220
4900 Yonge St., Willowdale, M2N 6G6
Reg. Director, R.L. Hillier
Manitoba
624 Federal Bldg., 269 Main St.
Winnipeg, R3C 1B2
Reg. Director, T.F. Wasylyshen
Saskatchewan
400, 2100 Broad St., Box 8060

Regina, S4P 4E3
Reg. Director, P. Amundson
Alberta
Rm. 831, Federal Bldg.
9820-107th St., Edmonton, T5K 1G2
Reg. Director, L.W. Outhwaithe
British Columbia
315, 80-6th St., New Westminster, V3L 5B3
Reg. Director, A. Oliver

International Programs Branch
240 Sparks St., 1G West
Ottawa, K1A 0C5
Exec. Director Gen., A. Gratias
International Market Development Division
Director, R. Stern
Overseas Projects Division
Director, J.P. Ferland
Multilateral Affairs Division
Director, W. Major
Bilateral Affairs Division
Director, Dr. D.W. Ware
Planning and Management Services
Director, J.A. Bonner
International Trade Directorate
Sir John Carling Bldg.
930 Carling Ave., Ottawa, K1A 0C5
Director Gen., K.R. Higham
Trade Access Management Division
Director, J. Lohoar
Trade Access Negotiations Division
Director, P. Stone

Research Branch
Asst. Dep. Minister, Dr. A.D. Olson
Management Services Division
Director, I. Wood
Central Region
Director Gen., Vacant
Eastern Region
Director Gen., Dr. Y. Martel
Western Region
Director Gen., Dr. W.L. Pelton

National Soil Conservation Program (NSCP)
1901 Victoria Ave., Regina, SK S4P 0R5
Exec. Director Gen., Dr. H.M. Hill
NSCP-West
Director, R.J. Wettlaufer
NSCP-East
32 Highfield St.
Box 6088, Moncton, NB E1C 8R2
Director, A.T. Watt
National Soil Conservation Program
Program Co-ordinator, L.B. Johnson

Grains and Oilseeds Branch
Sir John Carling Bldg.
930 Carling Ave., Ottawa, K1A 0C5

Assoc. Dep. Minister, Dr. H.F. Bjarnason
Executive Secretariat
Exec. Secretary, R.H.M. Cathcart
Management Services Directorate
Director, D. Normandeau

Priorities and Strategies Directorate
A/Director Gen., D. Fenety
Co-operatives Secretariat
Exec. Director, J. Arthur Leblanc
Director, K McCready
Grain Marketing Bureau
Director Gen., N.A. O'Connell

Grains and Oilseeds
610-360 Main St., Winnipeg, MB R3C 3Z3

Asst. Dep. Minister, Vacant
Western Grain Stabilization Administration
935, 303 Main St., Winnipeg, R3C 2P5
Director, G. Gorsky

AGENCIES, BOARDS, COMMISSIONS AND CROWN CORPORATIONS

Agricultural Products Board
Ottawa, K1A 0C5

The Agricultural Products Board was established under the authority of the *Agricultural Products Board Act,* R.S.C. 1970, Chapter A-5.

The Board's authority is to buy, sell, or import agricultural products. Generally, however, it deals with matters that are ancillary to agricultural commodity price support operations but not specifically under the authority of the *Agricultural Stabilization Act.* In recent years, the Board has supported such commodities as apples, cherries, grapes, potatoes, and turkeys.

In past programs, the Board has also supplied the World Food Program with canned turkey, dehydrated potatoes, canned beef loaf, and canned whole egg powder.

The members of the Board are usually the same as those of the Agricultural Stabilization Board.

Chairman, Gilles Lavoie
Vice-Chairman, Vacant
Member, L.P. Albert
Sec.-Manager, A.E. Proulx

Agricultural Stabilization Board
Ottawa, K1A 0C5

The Agricultural Stabilization Board was established by the *Agricultural Stabilization Act,* R.S.C. 1970, Chapter A-9, to stabilize the prices of agricultural commodities. Such stabilization ensures that producers realize fair returns for labour and investment and maintains a fair relationship between prices received and the costs of goods and services which farmers buy.

The Board makes annual calculations of support prices for 12 named commodities (and for any other agricultural commodity on the authority of the Governor in Council) and then makes payments to farmers when the average actual prices received fall below the support price calculated. The *Agricultural Stabilization Act* also provides authority to enter into agreements with provinces for tripartite cost-shared stabilization programs.

Chairman, Gilles Lavoie

Vice-Chairman, Vacant
Member, L.P. Albert
Sec.-Manager, A.E. Proulx
Agricultural Advisor, D. Karamchandani

Canadian Dairy Commission
Pebb Bldg., 2197 Riverside Dr.
Ottawa, K1A 0Z2
General Inquiries: (613) 998-9490

The Commission is a federal Crown corporation established by an Act of Parliament in October 1966. Its objectives are as follows:
- to enable efficient producers of milk and cream to obtain a fair return for their labour and investment, and
- to provide consumers with a continuous and adequate supply of dairy products of high quality.

The Commission administers a dairy support program which consists of an offer-to-purchase program for butter and skim milk powder and a federal subsidy on industrial and cream production. The Commission chairs the Canadian Milk Supply Management Committee, which administers the national supply management program for industrial milk and cream.

The Commission can purchase, package, process, store, ship, import, export, sell or otherwise dispose of any dairy product purchased by it, and is empowered to investigate relevant matters such as the cost of producing, processing or marketing any dairy product. Its role is also to initiate and assist in promoting the use of dairy products, in improving their quality and variety, and in disseminating information.

Annual financial transactions currently involve about $1.8 billion.

Chairman, Roch Morin
Vice-Chairman, Kenneth McKinnon
Commissioner, Dr. Cliff McIsaac
Sr. Policy Advisor, C. Birchard
Finance Director, P. Simard
Information Services Director, L. Champagne
Domestic Marketing Director, R.J. Lalonde
International Marketing Director, J. Comtois
Marketing Operations Director, L. Marcellus
Subsidy Operations Director, R. Labossiere
Legal Adviser, R. King

Canadian Grain Commission
600, 303 Main St., Winnipeg, R3C 3G8
General Inquiry: (204) 983-2770

Established in 1912 as the Board of Grain Commissioners, the Canadian Grain Commission is responsible to the Minister of State, Grains and Oilseeds, who in return reports to Parliament on its activities. The Commission administers the *Canada Grain Act,* which establishes standards of quality for Canadian grains and regulates grain handling in Canada.

Three commissioners, appointed by the Governor in Council, develop policies to meet the Commission's objectives. Six assistant commissioners, also appointed by the Governor in Council, deal with inquiries from producers and the grain industry. The four western assistant commissioners supervise the operations of licensed primary elevators.

Reporting to the Commission, the Supervisor of the Grain Futures Exchange supervises grain futures trading in Canada under the terms of the *Grain Futures Act*. The Chairman of the Grain Appeal Tribunal also reports to the Commission. The tribunal examines and rules upon appeals of grades assigned by a Commission inspector on the official inspection of a sample of grain.

Headquartered in Winnipeg, the Commission has offices across Canada. Operations are headed by the executive director, who plans, co-ordinates and administers the activities of the Commission's four operating divisions.

The Inspection Division maintains quality control of Canadian grains as they move through the handling system. It officially inspects grain at licensed terminal and transfer elevators, and supervises and controls the treatment of grain.

The Weighing Division supervises weighing of grain at licensed terminal and transfer elevators. It audits their physical stocks at regular intervals and investigates excessive overages and shortages in grain receipts or shipments.

The Grain Research Laboratory assesses the quality of new crops, conducts basic and applied research on Canadian grains and oilseeds and supplies technical assistance to marketers of Canadian grains and oilseeds.

The Economics and Statistics Division provides documentation to terminal and transfer elevators, conducts economic studies for the Commission and publishes statistics. It issues grain dealer and elevator licences and monitors security provisions related to licensees. It also administers the allocation of rail cars to producers who apply for this service.

Chief Commissioner, G.G. Leith
Commissioners:
R.A. Groundwater, M.E. Wakefield
Exec. Director, W.J. O'Connor
Information Services Head, L. Burch

Canadian Wheat Board
423 Main St., Box 816
Winnipeg, MB R3C 2P5

The Canadian Wheat Board was established in 1935 under the *Canadian Wheat Board Act*. The Board is responsible for marketing all wheat, oats and barley grown in Western Canada to the best advantage of producers and delivered into commercial facilities for sale in export markets or in domestic markets for human consumption. The Board also markets western wheat, oats, and barley to the domestic feed market in accordance with government policy.

In addition to marketing grain to the best advantage of producers, the Board ensures that western grain producers receive an initial guaranteed price for grain delivered to the Board and share equitably in pooled selling prices and

delivery opportunities. The Board plans and co-ordinates the optimum use of grain handling and transportation facilities. It also administers, on behalf of the federal government, the *Prairie Grain Advance Payments Act.*

The Board is composed of four commissioners appointed on a full-time basis by the federal government. The head office is in Winnipeg. Other offices are located in Vancouver, Montreal, and Tokyo, Japan. A producer advisory committee to the Board consists of 11 grain producers elected from across Western Canada.

Chief Commissioner, W.E. Jarvis
Asst. Chief Commissioner,
Dr. R.L. Kristjanson
Commissioners: F.M. Hetland,
W.H. Smith, R.H. Klassen

Farm Credit Corp.
434 Queen St., Box 2314, Stn. D
Ottawa, K1P 6J9
Information: (613) 996-6606

Farm Credit Corporation Canada was established as a Crown agency in 1959 with the primary objective to help Canadian farmers establish and develop sound farm enterprises through the use of long-term mortgage credit.

Under the *Farm Credit Act,* loans may be made to farmers individually or jointly and to farming corporations or co-operative farm associations. The maximum loan to a single farm business is $350,000 when there is one qualifying applicant and $600,000 when there is more than one. Loan funds may be used to purchase farm land, make permanent improvements, purchase breeding stock and farm equipment, pay debts, or in general to facilitate the efficient operation of the farm.

A borrower must be a Canadian citizen or a permanent resident and be of legal age to enter into a mortgage agreement. The applicant's management ability and the repayment capacity of the proposed operation are carefully assessed to determine eligibility for an FCC loan.

Under the *Farm Syndicates Credit Act,* the Corporation provides loans to groups or "syndicates" of farmers organized to share in the purchase and use of farm machinery, buildings and installed equipment.

Chairman, J.J. Hewitt
Secretary, L.J. Fooks
Vice-Chairman and CEO, C.G. Penney
Sr. Vice-President, Legal Counsel
and Corporate Secretary, T.S. Barton
Sr. Vice-President, Operations Director,
B.H. Strom
Sr. Vice-President, Finance, M. Pierce
Vice-President, Research and Planning
T. Kremenuik
Vice-President, Lending, D.G. Fraser
Vice-President, Corporate Audit
P. Laflamme
Vice-President, Administration, Vacant
Controller, J.J. Poirier

Treasurer, Thomas R. Robertson

REGIONAL OFFICES:

Atlantic Region
2nd Flr., Blvd. Plaza, Phase I
1133 St. George Blvd., Moncton, NB E1E 4E1
Reg. Vice-President, J. Van Abbema

Quebec Region
Edifice Champlain, bur. 2000
2700, boul. Laurier, Ste-Foy, G1V 4C7
Reg. Vice-President, J. Doran

Ontario Region
121, 450 Speedvale Ave. W., Guelph, N1H 7G7
Reg. Vice-President, R.G. Aumell

Manitoba Region
400, 5 Donald St., Winnipeg, R3L 2T4
Reg. Vice-President, M. Stachniak

Saskatchewan Region
500 South Broad Plaza, 2045 Broad St.
Regina, S4P 2B7
Reg. Vice-President, R.L. Holm

Alberta/B.C. Region
Ste. 1550, Continental Bank Bldg.
10250-101st St., Edmonton, AB T5J 3P4
Reg. Vice-President, G.M. Jones

Livestock Feed Board of Canada
5180, ch. Queen Mary, bur. 400
Montréal (Québec) H3W 3E7

The Livestock Feed Board of Canada is a Crown corporation reporting to Parliament through the Minister of Agriculture. It was established under the Livestock Feed Assistance Act in 1967 to deal with feed grain shortages and unstable prices outside the Prairie regions. Its objectives are to ensure: (a) the availability of feed grain in eastern Canada and B.C.; (b) the availability of adequate storage space in eastern Canada; and (c) the reasonable stability and fair equalization of feed grain prices in eastern Canada, B.C., Yukon and the Northwest Territories.

The Board administers the Feed Freight Assistance Program which pays a portion of the costs of transportation of feed grains. The Act also stipulates that it is the duty of the Board to make a continuing study of feed grain requirements and availability in these areas, as well as to study and make recommendations to the minister concerning requirements for additional feed grain storage facilities in eastern Canada.

It is also the duty of the Board to advise the government on all matters pertaining to the stabilization and fair equalization of feed grain prices to livestock feeders. It aims to consult and co-operate as much as possible with all departments, branches or other agencies of the Government of Canada or any province having duties, aims or objects related to those of the Board.

Chairman, D. Ethier
Program Co-ordination
Director Gen., G. René de Cotret
Director of Economic Research and
Secretary to the Board, A. Douglas Mutch
Transportation Director, John McAnulty
Finance Director, P.B. Morin

Members of the Board:
Gus Sonneveld, Wayne Everett,
Thomas G. Meredith, J.M. Tétrault

Advisory Committee
Chairman, William D. Swetnam

BRANCH OFFICES:
Ste. 3, 17655-57th Ave.
Surrey (Cloverdale), BC V3S 1H1
Director of Programs for British Columbia,
Malcolm B. Bryson
11 Princess St., Ste. 2, Amherst, NS B4H 1W5
Director of Programs for Atlantic Canada,
Vacant

National Farm Products Marketing Council
13th Flr., Martel Bldg., 270 Albert St.
Box 3430, Stn. D, Ottawa, K1P 6L4
Information: (613) 995-2297

The National Farm Products Marketing Council was established under the Farm Products Marketing Agencies Act in 1972 as the federal supervisory body for agencies set up to administer national marketing plans. There is a limitation in the Act whereby supply management controls are permitted only for poultry, eggs and, since November 1984, tobacco. At present, NFPMC is the watchdog over the Canadian Egg Marketing Agency, the Canadian Turkey Marketing Agency, the Canadian Chicken Marketing Agency, and the Canadian Broiler Hatching Egg Marketing Agency.

The Council's responsibilities include advising the Minister of Agriculture on all matters relating to the establishment, operation and performance of the agencies. It must ensure that the agencies promote competitive and efficient agriculture marketing and it must consult regularly with the provincial governments that have signed the plans authorizing the agencies.

The Council is made up of producer, agri-business, food industry and consumer representatives to enable it to balance the interests of these groups in all its activities.

Chairperson, R. Barrie
Vice-Chairman, L. Bergeron
Exec. Member, Glenn Flaten
Operations Director, Dr. G.A. Hiscocks
Commodity Manager and Co-ordinator,
Dr. Keith Wilkinson
Policy Co-ordination
Chief, Jacques N. Goulet
Management Services
Director, Jacques N. Goulet
Council Secretariat Chief, C. McWade
Administrative Services Head, Vacant
Public Information Chief, S. Leah
Legal Advisor, Daniel Gervais

Pest Management Advisory Board
Vanguard Bldg., Rm. 701
171 Slater St., Ottawa, K1A 0C5

The Pest Management Advisory Board was created in 1985 to bring greater public input into the pesticide regulation process. The Board aids in the solution of technical difficulties involved in the licensing of pest-control chemicals. It is also empowered to hear submissions from the general public and interested groups on the need for and safety of pesticides.

Chairman, H. Versteeg
Member, Dr. E.Y. Spencer
Member, W. Daman

Prairie Farm Rehabilitation Administration (PFRA)
Motherwell Bldg.
1901 Victoria Ave., Regina, SK S4P 0R5

The Prairie Farm Rehabilitation Administration was established in 1935 under the *Prairie Farm Rehabilitation Act,* to secure the rehabilitation of the drought and soil drifting areas in the provinces of Manitoba, Saskatchewan and Alberta, and to develop and promote within these areas systems of farm practice, tree culture, water supply, land utilization and land settlement.

The Agency operates irrigation projects, community pastures, an irrigation demonstration farm, a tree nursery facility and provides, in co-operation with the provinces, a major soil conservation planning service. It also provides technical and financial assistance for on-farm, group and small community wells, dugouts, dams, reservoirs, and pipelines, making water supplies available for municipal, domestic, livestock, and irrigation uses. Other services provided include the planning, investigation, and evaluation of development opportunities, and the design, construction, and maintenance of various works involving water development, irrigation, and community water infrastructure programs in the three Prairie provinces.

A/Director Gen., A.F. Lukey
Policy and Analysis Service
A/Director, G.G. Pearson
Administration Service
Director, W.F. Buhr
Soil and Water Conservation Service
Director, L.B. Chambers
Engineering Service
A/Director, D. Pollock
Personnel Manager, G. Picray

Manitoba Affairs
Century Plaza, 401, 1 Wesley Ave.
Winnipeg, MB R3C 4C6
A/Director, E. Caligiuri

Alberta Affairs
1620 Canada Place, 9700 Jasper Ave.
Edmonton, AB T5J 4C3
Director, R.T. Adam

AUDITOR GENERAL'S OFFICE
240 Sparks St., Ottawa, K1A 0G6
General Inquiries: (613) 995-3766

Auditor Gen., Kenneth M. Dye
Asst. Auditor Gen., E.F. McNamara

AUDIT OPERATIONS
Dep. Auditors Gen.:
Raymond M. Dubois, D. Larry Meyers
Asst. Auditors Gen.:
Douglas Deeks, W. Elwyn Dickson
Jean-Guy Laliberté, Robert R. Lalonde
David Marshall, Leonard M. McGimpsey
William F. Radburn, Ron C. Thompson
Paul D.M. Ward, Don Young, David Rattray

PROFESSIONAL SERVICES
Dep. Auditor Gen., Edward R. Rowe
Asst. Auditor Gen., Yvan Gaudette

ADMINISTRATIVE SERVICES
Dep. Auditor Gen., Ronald M. Warme

DEPARTMENT OF COMMUNICATIONS
Journal North Twr.
300 Slater St., Ottawa, K1A 0C8
Telex: 053-3342
Information Services: (613) 990-4900

MINISTER'S OFFICES
Rm. 209, Confederation Bldg.
Ottawa, K1A 0A6
Minister, The Hon. Marcel Masse

DEPUTY MINISTER'S OFFICE
Dep. Minister, Alain Gourd
Sr. Asst. Dep. Minister,
Corporate Policy, Ken Hepburn
Policy Sector Planning and Co-ordination
Director, Ruth Mayost

STRATEGY AND PLANS
Director Gen., Alain Desfossés
Fiscal Strategic Policy Analysis
Director, Peter Barnes
Social Policy Director, Dan Rainboth
Priority Planning and Government Business
Director, Lynn Elliot-Sherwood

INFORMATION SERVICES
Director Gen., Philip Kinsman
Publications and Creative Services
A/Director, Michael Holmes
Editorial Services
A/Director, Grace Brickell
Media and Public Relations
Director, Louise Lafleur
Exhibitions and Audio Visual Services
Director, Vacant

FEDERAL/PROVINCIAL RELATIONS
Director Gen., Eileen Sarkar
Cultural Policy and Liaison
A/Director, Manon Pelletier
Communications Policy and Liaison
Québec and East
A/Director, Louise Singer

Ontario and West
Director, Victor Banning
Corporate Liaison and Planning
Director, Vacant

INTERNATIONAL RELATIONS
Director Gen., G.I. Warren
International Informatics
Special Advisor, Dr. P. Robinson
Trade Policy and Canada/U.S.A.
Telecommunications
Director, Robert Tritt
Bilateral Telecommunications
Planning and Development
Director, Lucien Villeneuve
Multilateral Telecommunications
A/Director, Pierre Gagné
International Cultural Affairs
Director, Elisabeth Châtillon

Telecommunications and Technology

Asst. Dep. Minister, R.S. Stursberg
Management Systems and Plans
Director, Wendy Pride

TELECOMMUNICATIONS POLICY
A/Director Gen., Paul Racine
Industry Structure and Services
Director, Richard Simpson
Network Policy and Standards Management
A/Director, Gaston Dallaire
Financial and Regulatory Policy
A/Director, Larry Shaw
Spectrum and Orbit Policy
Director, Parke Davis

TECHNOLOGY POLICY AND PLANNING
Director Gen., Don MacLean
Strategic Planning Director, David Waung
Science, Technology and Social Policy
Nola Murray

INDUSTRY AND ECONOMIC DEVELOPMENT
A/Director Gen., David Mulcaster
Space/Telecommunications
Development Director, David Mulcaster
Technical Marketing Operations
A/Director, K. Chang
Information Industries and
Economic Development
Director, Jamie Hum
Communications Applications
Director, Terry Kerr

GOVERNMENT TELECOMMUNICATIONS
AGENCY
Journal North Twr.
300 Slater St., Ottawa, K1A 0C8
Director Gen., J.A. Gilbert
Finance and Administration
Director, H.B. Sullivan
Planning and Co-ordination
Director, R. Beauparlant

Development and Engineering
Director, D. Sum
Telecommunications Systems Management
Director, A. Keddy
Client Services Director, K. Shaw

BROADCAST TECHNOLOGIES RESEARCH
3701 Carling Ave.
Box 11490, Stn. H, Ottawa, K2H 8S2
Director Gen., Dr. W. Sawchuk
Systems and Networks Research
Director, Dr. Y.F. Lum
Information Processing Research
Director, Dr. Metin Akgun
Behavioral Research Director, Dr. D.A. Phillips

SPACE TECHNOLOGY RESEARCH
3701 Carling Ave.
Box 11490, Stn. H, Ottawa, K2H 8S2
Director Gen., Dr. Jack Chambers
Space Mechanics Director, F. Vigneron
Space Applications Director, N.G. Davies
David Florida Laboratory
Director, R. Mamen

COMMUNICATIONS TECHNOLOGIES
RESEARCH
3701 Carling Ave.
Box 11490, Stn. H, Ottawa, K2H 8S2
A/Director Gen., R.W. Breithaupt
Radio Propagation Director, Dr. J.S. Belrose
Radio Communications Technologies
Director Gen., Dr. McCormick
Satellite Communications Director, Bob Huck
MSAT Director, D. Buchanan

COMMUNICATIONS DEVICES AND
COMPONENTS RESEARCH
3701 Carling Ave.
Box 11490, Stn. H, Ottawa, K2H 8S2
Director Gen., Dr. M. Palfreyman
Components and Subsystems
Director, R.J.P. Douville
Advanced Devices and Reliability
Director, R.M. Kuley
Optical Communication Technologies
Director, K.O. Hill

*Canadian Workplace Automation Research
Centre (CWARC)*
1575, boul. Chomedey
Laval (Québec) H7V 2X2
Director Gen., René Guindon

**Spectrum Management and Regional
Operations**

Asst. Dep. Minister, R.A. Gordon
Sector Policy Planning and Assessment
Director, G. Rouleau
Engineering Programs
Director Gen., S.N. Ahmed
Broadcasting Regulation
Director Gen., R. Begley
Radio Regulation
Director Gen., R.W. Jones

Cultural Affairs and Broadcasting
Asst. Dep. Minister, Jeremy Kinsman
Sector Management Director, Michel Granger

MUSEUMS AND HERITAGE
Director Gen., Charles McGee
Museums Policy Working Group
Director, J. Thera
Movable Cultural Property
A/Manager, David A. Walden
Heritage Policy and Programs
A/Director, Robert Taylor

National Programmes
Asst. Secretary-Gen., R.W. Nichols
Programme Co-ordination Division
A/Director, S. O'Neil
Centennial Twrs., 8th Flr.
200 Kent St., Ottawa, K1A 0M8

CANADIAN CONSERVATION INSTITUTE
1030 Innes Rd., Ottawa, K1A 0M8
Director Gen., Charles G. Gruchy
Finance and Administration
Director, Sue Wilson
Conservation Research Services
Director, Dr. K.J. MacLeod
Conservation Services
A/Director, R. LaFontaine

MUSEUM ASSISTANCE PROGRAMMES
300 Slater St., 5th Flr., Ottawa, K1A 0M8
Director, Ronal Bourgeois
Programme Co-ordination
Asst. Director, Susan Murdock
Upgrading and Equipment Assistance
and Specialized Museums
Programme Co-ordinator,
Brian Laurie-Beaumont
Conservation Advisor, Murray Frost
Special Activities Assistance and Exhibitions
Assistance
Programme Co-ordinator, Vacant
Training Assistance
Programme Co-ordinator, Keith Wickens
National Exhibition Centres
Programme Co-ordinator, Vacant
REGIONAL OPERATIONS
A/Asst. Director, Deborah Robichaud
British Columbia and Yukon
Reg. Co-ordinator, Tara Douglas
Prairies
Reg. Co-ordinator, Neil Carleton
Ontario
Reg. Co-ordinator, Edna Foley
Quebec
Reg. Co-ordinator, Charles-H. Roy
Atlantic
Reg. Co-ordinator, Deborah Robichaud
Asst. Reg. Co-ordinator, Vacant

CANADIAN HERITAGE INFORMATION
NETWORK
365 Laurier Ave. W., Journal Twr. S.

12th Flr., Ottawa, K1A 0M8
Director, P. Homulos
Administration and Finance
Asst. Director, R. Rattray
Museum Services
Asst. Director, B. Rottenburg
Information Systems
Asst. Director, Vacant
Systems Development Chief, G. Eagen
Computer Operations Chief, C. Buckley
International Programme
Director, M. Couturier

BROADCASTING AND CULTURAL
INDUSTRIES POLICY AND PROGRAMS
Director Gen., Vacant
Broadcasting Policy
A/Director, Jean Guérette
Film, Video and Sound Recording
Policy and Programs
Director, John Watt
Publishing Policy and Programs
A/Director, Susan Katz
Public Interest and Access Policy
A/Director, Jean Guérette
Task Force on Broadcasting Strategy
Director, Mike Helm

ARTS AND POLICY PLANNING
A/Director Gen., Gaston Blais
Policy Planning, Research
and Special Projects
Director, Tom Caplan
Arts Policy Director, Don Stephenson
Cultural Initiatives Program
Director, Raynald Turgeon
Copyright Director, Denis Guay

Corporate Management
Asst. Dep. Minister, Michael Binder
Sector Management and
Departmental Co-ordination
Director, Jean Bélanger
Security and Communications Support Services
A/Director, C. Taylor

FINANCIAL MANAGEMENT
Director Gen., Barbara Bloor
Financial Planning and Resources Utilization
Director, Ron Simko
Financial Services
A/Director, Pat Gorbery
Accounting Operations and Policy
Director, Dan Audet
ADMINISTRATIVE AND TECHNICAL SERVICES
Director Gen., Brian Hepworth

HUMAN RESOURCES MANAGEMENT
Director Gen., Jean-Claude Bouchard
Personnel Operations Director, Wendy Pride
Staff Relations and Compensation
Director, Louis Brazeau
Human Resources Planning and Development
Director, Moira Law
Official Languages Director, Y. Lavallée

INFORMATICS MANAGEMENT
Director Gen., Frank Malick
Informatics Planning Director, James Tang
Client Services and Office Systems
Director, Fred Cook
Systems Development Director, Mel Fleming

REGIONAL OFFICES CANADA:

Atlantic
1222 Main St., Terminal Plaza Bldg.
Box 5090, Moncton, NB E1C 8R2
Director Gen., Pierre Boudreau

Quebec
295, rue St-Paul est, Montréal, H2Y 1H1
Director Gen., J.M. Pellerin

Canadian Workplace Automation Research Centre
1575, boul. Chomedey
Laval (Québec) H7V 2X2

Ontario
9th Flr., 55 St. Clair Ave. E.
Toronto, M4T 1M2
Director Gen., W.D. Lyon

Central
Manulife Bldg., Rm. 200
386 Broadway Ave., Winnipeg, MB R3C 3Y9
Director Gen., Roger Collet

Pacific
800 Burrard St., Rm. 1700
Vancouver, BC V6Z 2J7
Director Gen., J.A.W. Quigley

AGENCIES, BOARDS, COMMISSIONS AND CROWN CORPORATIONS

Canada Council
99 Metcalfe St., Box 1047, Ottawa, K1P 5V8
Inquiries: (613) 598-4365
Fax: (613) 598-4390
The Touring Office: (613) 598-4342

Atlantic Office
207 Robinson St., Ste. 11
Moncton, NB E1C 5C5
Inquiries: (506) 857-6090

The Canada Council was created by an Act of Parliament in 1957. Under the terms of the *Canada Council Act,* its purpose is "to foster and promote the study and enjoyment of, and the production of works in, the arts." It offers a wide-ranging program of financial assistance and special services to individuals and non-profit organizations in the arts. The Council also maintains the secretariat for the Canadian Commission for UNESCO and has some responsibility for promoting Canadian culture abroad.

The Council is headed by a 21-member board appointed by the Government of Canada. Its day-to-day operations are the responsibility of the Council staff, headed by the director. The Council and its staff rely heavily on the advice and co-operation of the disciplinary advisory committees, artists and arts-related professionals from all parts of Canada, who are consulted both individually and in juries and selection committees. The Council also works in close co-operation with federal and provincial cultural agencies and with the International Cultural Relations Bureau of the Department of External Affairs.

BOARD:
Chairman, Allan Gotlieb
Vice-Chairman, Jacques E. Lefebvre
Members: Julian D. Benson, Aubrey D. Browne, Edith Butler, Jacques Courtois, Ken Danby, Louise Dionne, H. Donald Guthrie, Martha Henry, Therese Lupien, Mary Pratt, Henry Purdy, Clément Richard, Nancy-Gay Rotstein, Lorraine Thorsrud
STAFF:
Director, Joyce Zemans
Assoc. Director, Robert Spickler
Sr. Asst. Director and Treasurer, Peter D.R. Brown
Asst. Director and Secretary to the Council, Jocelyn Harvey
Communications Service Head, Nadia Shafto
A/Head of the Policy Secretariat, Katherine Berg
Atlantic Office Representative, Thea Borlase
Arts Awards Service Head, Robert Kennedy
Dance Section A/Head, Barbara Laskin
Music and Opera Section Head, Vacant
Theatre Section Head, John Murrell
Touring Office Head, Yvan Saintonge
Writing and Publishing Section Head, Naïm Kattan
Public Lending Right Commission Exec. Secretary, Stéphane Dubois
Visual Arts Section Head, Edythe Goodridge
Art Bank Head, William Kirby
Media Arts Section Head, Glenn Lewis
Explorations Program Head, Helen Eriks
Killam Program Head, Mel MacLeod

Canadian Commission for UNESCO
Secretary-Gen., Francine Fournier

Canadian Broadcasting Corp.
CBC Bldg., 1500 Bronson Ave.
Box 8478, Ottawa, K1G 3J5
General Inquiry: (613) 724-1200
TDD: (613) 733-8868

The Canadian Broadcasting Corporation (CBC) is a publicly owned corporation which provides national broadcasting service in Canada in both official languages. It was established on Nov. 2, 1936 by an Act of the Canadian Parliament. Under this legislation, the CBC reports to Parliament each year through the Minister of Communications.

The CBC's funding is voted annually by Parliament. Supplementary revenue is obtained from commercial advertising on CBC television; CBC radio, however, is virtually free of commercial advertising.

The CBC operates several national services: a French television network, an English television network, and English and French AM radio and FM stereo networks. High levels of Canadian content are maintained in the 78 per cent range for television and even higher for radio. As well, the CBC operates the National Satellite Channel which makes the proceedings of the House of Commons available for viewing via cable.

Northern Service television began in 1967 as a tape delay rebroadcast service in 14 northern communities. Northern-based television production began in 1979 at Yellowknife. Today, Northern Service broadcasts on more than 100 northern television transmitters on two satellite channels across four time zones. Production facilities exist in Yellowknife, Whitehorse, Montreal and Ottawa. The service supplements network programs with shows produced by Northern Service, as well as programs procured from outside the Corporation. Northern Service also assists independent native broadcasters operating under the federal Northern Native Broadcast Access Program to distribute their programming over its television. Northern Service produces programs in English, Inuktitut, Slavey, Dogrib, Chipewyan, Loucheux, and Cree.

Radio Canada International (RCI), is a service of the CBC on shortwave — Canada's voice abroad. Broadcasting in 12 languages, RCI's information programming reflects Canada's political, economic, social and cultural spectrum to an international audience. RCI also produces programs for use by leading broadcasters in the world's major radio markets.

CBC transmission methods include leased channels on the Canadian space satellite Anik, plus more than 100,000 km of microwave and landline connections. Anik 1 started operation in 1973 and was the world's first synchronous domestic communications satellite.

President, Pierre Juneau
Exec. Vice-President, William T. Armstrong
Sr. Vice-President, Anthony S. Manera
Secretary-Gen., Marie P. Poulin
Gen. Counsel, Jacques Alleyn, Q.C.
Asst. Gen. Counsel, Gerald A. Flaherty, Q.C.
Planning and Corporate Affairs
Vice-President, John Shewbridge
Planning and Corporate Affairs
Asst. Vice-President, Alain Pineau
Engineering
Vice-President, Guy Gougeon
(Strategic Engineering and Capital Projects)
Asst. Vice-President, Brian D. Baldry
(Operations Engineering)
Asst. Vice-President, George N. Goossen
Human Resources
Vice-President, Pierre Racicot
Asst. Vice-President, Vacant
Finance
Vice-President, Stephen Cotsman
Asst. Vice-President, A. Normand Perron
Treasurer, Paul St. Pierre
Internal Auditor, Erik Peters
Regional Broadcasting Operations
Vice-President, Bill White
Assoc. Vice-President, Raymond Marcotte
Communications
Vice-President, Antonin Boisvert

Director, English Regional Broadcasting
Murray Weppler
Director, French Regional Broadcasting
Marcel Labelle
Gen. Manager, CBC Enterprises
Lyse Larouche
Management Information Systems
Exec. Director, Michael Hughes
Public Relations Director, Richard Chambers
Asst. Director, Guy Thériault

ENGLISH NETWORKS
1255 Bay St., Box 500, Stn. A
Toronto, M5W 1E6
Television
Vice-President, Denis Harvey
Network Television Director, Trina McQueen
Television Programming Director, Ivan Fecan
Dep. Director, Roman Melnyk
TV News and Current Affairs
Director, William (Bill) Morgan
Television Production and Operations
Director, David Martin
English Radio
Vice-President, Michael McEwen
Program Operations and
Regional Development
Director, Bill Terry
CBC Radio Program Director, Donna Logan
National Radio News
Man. Editor, Vince Carlin
Current Affairs—Radio
Head, Alex Frame

FRENCH NETWORKS
1400, boul. René-Lévesque est
C.P. 6000, Montréal (Québec) H3C 3A8
Vice-President, French Television
Franklin Delaney
Programming (General Television)
Gen. Manager, Andréanne Bournival
Television Operations
Gen. Manager, Jean-Baptiste Chardola
Planning (Telecasting and Resources)
Gen. Manager, Paul Rousseau
Programming (Information)
Gen. Manager, Pierre O'Neil
Marketing and TV Sales
Gen. Manager, Vacant
Vice-President, French Radio
Jean Blais
Program Director, Paul-Marie Lapointe

ENGINEERING
7925, ch. Côte-St-Luc
Montréal (Québec) H4W 1R5
Vice-President, Guy Gougeon
(Strategic Engineering and Capital Projects)
Asst. Vice-President, Brian D. Baldry
(Operations Engineering)
Asst. Vice-President, George N. Goossen

RADIO CANADA INTERNATIONAL
1055, boul. René-Lévesque est

C.P. 6000, Montréal (Québec) H3C 3A8
Director, Andrew Simon

REGIONAL OFFICES:
Newfoundland Region
95 University Ave., Box 12010, Stn. A
St. John's, NF A1B 3T8
English Services
Reg. Director, Jim Byrd
Maritime Region
5600 Sackville St.
Box 3000, Halifax, NS B3J 3E9
English Services
Reg. Director, Bill Donovan
Atlantic Provinces
250 Archibald St.
Box 950, Moncton, NB E1C 8N8
French Services
Reg. Director, Claude Bourque
Québec Region
1400, boul. René-Lévesque est
C.P. 6000, Montréal, H3C 3A8
English Services
Reg. Director, Nicole Bélanger
273, rue St-Jean-Baptiste ouest
Rimouski, G5L 4J8
French Services Director, François Raymond
2475, boul. Laurier
C.P. 10400, Ste-Foy, G1V 2X2
French Services Director, Jacques-D. Landry
Ontario Region
Box 500, Stn. A, Toronto, M5W 1E6
English Services
Annex, 372 Jarvis St., Toronto, M5W 1E6
Reg. Director, Don Goodwin
French Services
100 Carlton St., 2nd Flr., Toronto, ON M5B 1M3
Reg. Director, Claude Hurtubise
National Capital Region
250 Lanark Ave. (T.V.)
Château Laurier (Radio)
Box 3220, Stn. C, Ottawa, K1Y 1E4
A/Reg. Director, Doug Ward
Northern Service
250 Lanark Ave.
Box 3220, Stn. C, Ottawa, K1Y 1E4
Reg. Director, Brian Cousins
Manitoba Region
491 Portage Ave., Box 160
Winnipeg, R3C 2H1
English Services
Reg. Director, Donald Ferguson
French Services
Reg. Director, Gilbert Teffaine
Saskatchewan Region
2440 Broad St., Regina, S4P 4A1
English Services
Reg. Director, Ron Smith
French Services
Reg. Director, Lionel J. Bonneville
Alberta Region
Miller Bldg., 4990-92nd Ave.
Box 555, Edmonton, T5J 2P4
English Services
Reg. Director, Harold Redekopp

French Services
8861-75th St., Box 555
Edmonton, T5J 2P4
Reg. Director, L. Paul Dumaine
British Columbia Region
700 Hamilton St.
Box 4600, Vancouver, V6B 4A2
English Services
Reg. Director, Eric Moncur
French Services
Reg. Director, Michel Lacombe

Canadian Cultural Property Export Review Board
Rm. 500, 300 Slater St., Ottawa, K1A 0C8

The purpose of the *Cultural Property Export and Import Act* is to prevent the loss to Canada of cultural objects which are of outstanding significance to the country. This is accomplished through an export control system which requires that an export permit be obtained for any cultural object meeting certain age and value limits. Tax incentives are also provided to encourage owners of cultural property to donate or sell it to Canadian institutions, and grants and loans are available to Canadian institutions to patriate or repatriate important cultural objects.

Under the Act, the Cultural Property Export Review Board is responsible for reviewing applications for export permits and issuing cultural property tax certificates.

The Review Board also provides advice to the Minister of Communications on matters affecting the preservation of the Canadian heritage in movable cultural property. In particular, it makes recommendations regarding grants for the purchase of objects in respect of which export permits have been refused under the Act or for the purchase of cultural property situated outside Canada that relates to the national heritage. The grants and loans are made out of monies appropriated annually by Parliament.

Chairman, Colin B. Mackay
Secretary, David A. Walden
Asst. Secretary, Jennifer Hambridge

Canadian Radio-television and Telecommunications Commission
Central Bldg., Terrasses de la Chaudière
1, prom. du Portage, Hull, Qué.
MAILING ADDRESS: Ottawa, K1A 0N2
Telex: 053-4253; Fax: (819) 994-0218
General Information: (819) 997-0313
Complaints (Telecommunications):
(819) 997-0272
TTY (Visual Ear): (819) 994-0423

As a result of four major parliamentary examinations of broadcasting since the 1920's, Canadian law has come to regard publicly owned broadcasting, commercially based radio and TV, cable television and, more recently, pay-TV and specialty services as a "single system." This wording comes from the 1968 *Broadcasting Act,* which still provides the authority under which the

CRTC regulates the Canadian broadcasting system. Under the Act, the CRTC is responsible for implementing certain policy objectives: effective Canadian ownership and control of broadcasting facilities; a wide variety of programming which provides a reasonable, balanced opportunity for the expression of differing views on matters of public concern; availability of service in English and French to all Canadians; and programming of high standard that makes use of predominantly Canadian creative and other resources.

Under the *Railway Act,* the CRTC is required to ensure that all tolls, including rates or charges for telecommunications services, are just and reasonable. The Commission must ensure that carriers do not discriminate unjustly in rates, services, or facilities. The Act requires the Commission to approve any agreement entered into by carriers on the interchange of traffic or limitation of liability and, among other things, gives the Commission jurisdiction over interconnections between the telecommunications carriers.

CRTC decisions are made after public consultation in which Canadians are invited to participate.

The 1976 *CRTC Act* gave the Canadian Radio-television and Telecommunications Commission the authority to regulate and supervise all aspects of the Canadian broadcasting system and telecommunications carriers incorporated under federal legislation, namely Telesat Canada, Bell Canada, BC Tel, CNCP Telecommunications, Northwest Telecommunications and Terra Nova Telecommunications.

Chairman, Vacant
Vice-Chairman, (Broadcasting)
Monique Coupal
Vice-Chairman, (Telecommunications)
Louis R. (Bud) Sherman
Full-time Members: Rosalie Gower,
Beverly Oda, Adrian Burns, Paul E. McRae,
Frederic J. Arsenault, Edward A. Ross
Strategic Planning
A/Director Gen., Ken Katz
Research Analysis Director, Sjef Frenken

BROADCASTING
Cable, Pay and Specialty Services
A/Director Gen., Lisa de Wilde
Radio
A/Director Gen., Peter Fleming
Television
A/Director Gen., Robert Armstrong

Broadcast Operations
Cable
A/Operations Director, Eddy Trépanier
A/Policy Director, K. Spierkel
Radio
A/Operations Director, Diane Rhéaume
Television
A/Operations Director, Denis Ménard
A/Policy Director, Michel Tremblay

TELECOMMUNICATIONS
Exec. Director, Guido Henter
Sr. Planner, Vacant
Operations
Director Gen., Malcolm Andrew
Co-ordination, Complaints and Inquiries
Director, Paul Godin
Applications Director, Andrew Durocher
Sr. Operations Officer, Rachel Plouffe
Decisions
A/Director, Cynthia Stockley
Economic, Social and Technical Analysis
Director Gen., Terry Rochefort
Technical Analysis
Director, Robert Barry Reed
Rates and Service Costing
Director, Dave Bell
Economic and Regulatory Analysis
Director, Angus Oliver
Regulatory Analysis Chief, Michael Hennessy
Financial Analysis Director Gen., Don Donovan
Audit, Accounting and Statistics
Director, Louis Meduri
Efficiency Analysis Director, George Webber
Cost Inquiry Director, Fred Bigham

LEGAL
Gen. Counsel, A. Cohen
Broadcasting
Assoc. Gen. Counsel, Jean Doucet
Telecommunications
Assoc. Gen. Counsel, Greg van Koughnett

SECRETARIAT
Corporate Management
Exec. Director and Secretary-Gen.,
Fernand Bélisle
Secretariat Operations
Director Gen., Rosemary Chisholm
Public Hearings
Director, Jean-Maurice Olivier
Decisions Director, Mary Wilson
Information Services
A/Director Gen., Pierre Pontbriand
Correspondence and Complaints
Manager, Michel Blais
Technical Planning and Analysis
Director Gen., Andrew Kolada
Licensing
A/Director Gen., Brien Rodger
Corporate Analysis
A/Director Gen., Robert Tyre
Marketing Director, Vince Lee Chong
Financial and Corporate Affairs
Director, Douglas Wilson
Finance and Management Services
Director Gen., Jean Hurst
Corporate Audit and Evaluation
Director, William Weizenbach
Personnel
Director Gen., Joe Horan
Computer Services
Director, Jerry Olesnycky
Documentation and Library Services
Director, Martha Anschutz

REGIONAL OFFICES:

Halifax
Director Gen., Robert Oxner

Montreal
Director Gen., Roger Hébert

Winnipeg
Director Gen., Gerry Bergin

Vancouver
Director Gen., Virginia Krapiec

National Archives of Canada
395 Wellington St., Ottawa, K1A 0N3
General Information: (613) 995-5138

The National Archives of Canada is a research institution responsible for acquiring from any source all significant archival material of every kind, nature and description relating to all aspects of Canadian life and to the development of the country. It is also responsible for providing suitable research services and facilities to make this material available to the public.

The Historical Resources Branch is made up of the Manuscript Division, the Government Archives Division, the Cartographic and Architectural Records Division, the Documentary Art and Photography Division and the Moving Image and Sound Archives.

The Government Records Branch exercises a control function for federal records and provides a comprehensive service to government institutions in Ottawa and the larger metropolitan centres across Canada.

The Conservation Branch provides conservation and computer systems services to the National Archives and provides reproduction for both patrons and staff.

National Archivist, J-P. Wallot
Asst. National Archivist, M. Swift
Conservation Branch
Director Gen., K.F. Foster

HISTORICAL RESOURCES BRANCH
Director Gen., J. Atherton
Government Archives Division
Director, E. Frost
Moving Image and Sound Archives
A/Director, E. Dick
Manuscript Division
Director, Jacques Grimard
Cartographic and Architectural Archives
Director, Mrs. B. Kidd
Documentary Art and Photography Division
Director, L. Koltun

GOVERNMENT RECORDS BRANCH
Records Centre Bldg., Tunney's Pasture
Ottawa, K1A 0N3
Director Gen., L. McDonald
National Personnel Records Centre
Director, J. Paveling
Federal Records Centre
Director, T. Van Leyen
Records Management Services
Director, R. Westington

REGIONAL OFFICES:

Halifax Records Ctr.
131 Thornhill Rd., Dartmouth, NS B3B 1S2
Head, A. Cyr

Montreal Records Ctr.
665, montée de Liesse
Ville-St-Laurent (Québec) H4T 1P5
Head, R. Coté

Toronto Records Ctr.
190 Carrier Dr., Etobicoke, ON M9W 5R1
Head, C. Dwarka

Winnipeg Records Ctr.
201 Weston St., Winnipeg, MB R3E 3A4
Head, R. Weinholdt

Edmonton Records Ctr.
8707-51st Ave., Edmonton, AB T6E 5H0
Head, H. Christian

Vancouver Records Ctr.
3103 Thunderbird Cres.
Lake City Industrial Park
Burnaby, BC V5A 3G1
Head, H. Chapin

POLICY BRANCH
Director Gen., F. Houle
PUBLIC PROGRAMS BRANCH
Director Gen., Richard Huyda

National Arts Centre Corp.
Box 1534, Stn. B, Ottawa, K1P 5W1
General Inquiries: (613) 996-5051

The National Arts Centre is the largest performing arts organization in Canada. Home to the internationally acclaimed NAC Orchestra and a theatre department that produces plays in both English and French, the Centre also presents numerous visiting musical, theatre, dance and variety attractions from across Canada and abroad.

Conceived as the federal government's major centennial project in the National Capital Region, the NAC first opened to the public in June 1969. The maximum seating capacities for its four performance spaces are 2,236 for the Opera, 969 for the Theatre, 350 for the Studio, and 150 for the Salon. Each year some 900 performances are offered to audiences exceeding 700,000.

The Centre, a public corporation established by the Parliament of Canada, is governed by an independent board of trustees which reports to Parliament through the Minister of Communications. The NAC is funded through earned revenues, an annual appropriation from Parliament and a grant from the Regional Municipality of Ottawa-Carleton.

Chairman, Robert E. Landry
Vice-Chairman, Madeleine Panaccio
Director Gen., Yvon Desrochers
Advisor to the Director Gen., Ron Blackburn
ARTISTIC DIRECTION AND PROGRAMMING

Department of Music
Music Director and Conductor,
Gabriel Chmura
Principal Guest Conductor, Franco Mannino

Producer, Joanne Morrow
Theatre Department
Producer, Andis Celms
Artistic Director, French Theatre
André Brassard
Administrator, Suzanne Lefebvre
Dance Department
Producer, Jack Udashkin
Variety Department
Producer, Ted Demetre
COMMUNICATIONS
Director, Linda Oglov
OPERATIONS
Director of Operations, Carl Morrison
House Manager, Robert Asselin
Box Office Manager, Robert Cousineau
Production Manager, Ron Pollock
Supply and Services Manager, Yvon Dubé
Maintenance Project Manager, Gilles Landry
Restaurants
Exec. Chef, Kurt Waldele
Catering Manager, Ashok Dhawan
ADMINISTRATION
Financial Planning Director, Richard Lussier
Pay and Benefits Services
Manager, Bernard Brulé
Personnel Services Manager, Gary Taylor

National Film Board
150 Kent St., Ottawa, K1A 0M9
General Information: (613) 992-3615
OPERATIONAL HEADQUARTERS:
3155, ch. Côte de Liesse, St-Laurent (Québec)
MAILING ADDRESS:
C.P. 6100, Montréal, H3C 3H5
Inquiries: (514) 283-9000

The National Film Board of Canada (NFB) was founded in 1939 by an Act of Parliament. Its purpose is to initiate and promote the production and distribution of films for the national interest, with the primary object of interpreting Canada to Canadians and to other countries. Its board of trustees consists of nine members. Four of them, including the Government Film Commissioner, who is also chairman of the board, are from the public service, and five are prominent citizens representing the five major geographical regions of the country.

Since its inception, the Board has produced over 4,000 original films. In recent years production has averaged nearly 100 new titles annually, in both official languages. The NFB has maintained a high profile at international film festivals and has won almost 2,000 awards.

NFB documentary, animated and feature films are shown theatrically and televised. Individuals, educators and community associations also borrow, rent and purchase films and videocassettes from the network of NFB offices across the country. The board also produces slide sets, filmstrips and other materials for the educational sector.

In recent years, the NFB has placed increased emphasis on research and development into film and video technology, and has also established training programs for young filmmakers. The NFB has 12 audio-visual centres in the following Canadian cities: Vancouver, Edmonton, Winnipeg, Toronto, Moncton, Halifax, Montreal, St. John's, and Charlottetown. The first six of these, apart from Montreal, the NFB's headquarters, include production as well as marketing and distribution facilities.

The NFB also has offices in New York, London and Paris. These offices arrange the commercial distribution of NFB titles with private distributors, in addition to the direct sale of prints and videos. The international program operates both commercially and non-commercially. The non-commercial distribution of film is achieved in co-operation with the Department of External Affairs and diplomatic and trade posts around the world.

A/Government Film Commissioner and Chairman of the Board, Joan Pennefather
Secretary to Board of Trustees,
Jean-Claude Mahé
Vice-Government Film Commissioner and
Director of Corporate Affairs,
Joan Pennefather
English Program Branch
Director Gen., Barbara Emo
French Program Branch
Director Gen., Georges Dufaux
Services Division Director, Marcel Carrière
Administration, Finance and Personnel Division
Director, Gilles Roy
Communications Division
Director, Mireille Kermoyan
Equity Program Director, Suzanne Chevigny
REGIONAL CENTRES:
Halifax
1572 Barrington St., Halifax, NS B3J 1Z6
Head, Germaine Wong
Toronto
1 Lombard St., Toronto, ON M5C 1J6
Head, John Taylor
Winnipeg
245 Main St., Winnipeg, MB R3C 1A7
Head, Ches Yetman
Edmonton
Rm. 120, Place Canada
9700 Jasper Ave., Edmonton, AB T5J 4C3
Head, Graydon McCrea
Vancouver
Ste. 300, 1045 Howe St.
Vancouver, BC V6Z 2B1
Head, Barbara Janes
Montreal
Complex Guy-Favreau
200, boul. René-Lévesque ouest
Niveau 005, Montréal, H2Z 1X4
Reg. Manager, Maurice Vallée
OFFICES ABROAD:
New York
1251 Ave. of the Americas, 16th Flr.
New York, NY 10020
Representative, Rachelle Cournoyer
London
1 Grosvenor Sq.

London, England W1X 0AB
Representative, Hannah Kelson

Paris
15, rue de Berri, Paris 75008 France
Representative, Pierre Ducharme

National Library of Canada/Bibliothèque nationale du Canada
395 Wellington St., Ottawa, K1A 0N4
Telex: 053-4311, 053-4312
General Inquiries: (613) 995-9481

The National Library of Canada was established on Jan. 1, 1953 and is governed by the *National Library Act*, R.S.C. 1970, Chapter N-11. Its role is to preserve Canada's published heritage and promote Canadian studies, to foster the development of library resources throughout the country, and to support resource sharing on a national scale.

The National Librarian co-ordinates federal government library services and administers the legal deposit regulations, which require that two copies of current Canadian publications be deposited with the Library.

The Library acquires, maintains and preserves its comprehensive collection of Canadian materials and places special emphasis on music, rare books, literary manuscripts, newspapers, children's literature, and library science.

The Library publishes the national bibliography, *Canadiana*, which lists new publications relating to Canada; maintains and makes available union catalogues of books, periodicals, newspapers, and special format materials for disabled readers; offers interlibrary loan, reference and advisory service to libraries and to researchers; and supports the application of technological advances to library systems.

These collections and services enable the National Library to preserve and promote Canada's written and musical heritage and to encourage library service nationwide.

National Librarian, Marianne Scott
Assoc. National Librarian, Hope E.A. Clement
Internal Audit Director, H.W. Sainthill
External Relations Director, G. Evans
Federal Libraries Liaison Officer, M. Schryer
Public Programs Chief, M.J. Starr
Publications Chief, M. Wiper
Media Relations Chief, R. Carver

Planning and Policy Development
Sr. Planning Officer, J. Higginson
Planning Officer, J. Grassby

ACQUISITIONS AND BIBLIOGRAPHIC SERVICES BRANCH
Director, Dr. T. Delsey
Standards
Sr. Co-ordinator, R. Manning

Cataloguing
Asst. Director, A. Paul
Serials and Special Material
Cataloguing Division
A/Chief, E. McKeen

ISDS Canada Head, I. Bradley
Monograph Cataloguing Division
Chief, D. Murrell-Wright
Subject Analysis Division
A/Chief, J. Stegenga
National Services
Canadiana Editorial Division
Chief, D. Prentice
CIP Office Co-ordinator, L. Simard

Systems
Asst. Director, I. Parent

Acquisitions
Asst. Director, R.G. Lawless
Selection and Acquisition Division
Chief, M. Hood
Canadian Book Exchange Centre
Chief, E. Camlioglu
Canadiana Acquisitions Division,
Legal Deposit Office and ISBN Agency
A/Chief, M. Williamson
Canadian Theses Service
A/Head, H. Lussier-Tremblay

PUBLIC SERVICES BRANCH
Director, F.E. Patterson
Interlending
Asst. Director, R. Blair
Union Catalogue Division Chief, L. McQueen
Multilingual Biblioservice Chief, M. Zielinska
Interlibrary Loan Division
A/Chief, C. Lunau
Reading Room Division
A/Chief, K. Yates

Reference Services
A/Asst. Director, N. Brodie
Reference and Information
Services Division
A/Chief, P. McCormick
Reference Services
A/Head, R. Fox
Government Publications Specialist,
B. Deavy
Newspaper Specialist, S. Burrows
Library Documentation Centre
A/Chief, I. Heseltine
Music Division Chief, Dr. T. Maloney
Rare Books Division Chief, L. VanDerBellen
Literary Manuscripts Collection
Curator, C. LeMoine
Children's Literature Service Chief, I. Aubrey
Library Service for Disabled Persons
Chief, D. Guenter
Systems and Analysis
Sr. Advisor, C. Lunau

INFORMATION TECHNOLOGY SERVICES
A/Director, G. Saint-Pierre
Assoc. Director and Systems
Development Manager, L. Forget
Information Analysis and Standards
Manager, E. Buchinski
Information Technology Assessment
Manager, R. Duchesne
Policy and Planning Co-ordination
A/Manager, L. Forget

Systems Maintenance and Operation Manager, R. Webber
Systems and Telecommunications Support Manager, W. Newman
User Support A/Manager, P. Otto
Canadian MARC Office Chief, Y.H. Queinnec

FINANCIAL AND ADMINISTRATIVE SERVICES BRANCH
A/Director Gen., M. Gagnon
PERSONNEL SERVICES
Director Gen., M. Gagnon
CONSERVATION AND TECHNICAL SERVICES BRANCH
Director Gen., K.F. Foster

National Museums of Canada
Centennial Twrs., 8th Flr.
200 Kent St., Ottawa, K1A 0M8

The National Museums of Canada is a Crown corporation created in 1968 to assist in the accomplishment of the government's cultural objectives. Under the *National Museums Act,* augmented by appropriations voted to support the National Museum Policy of 1972, Parliament has given the NMC the mandate to enrich the lives of present and future generations through an understanding and enjoyment of the products of nature and culture with particular but not exclusive reference to Canada.

The NMC incorporates Canada's four National Museums: the National Gallery of Canada, including the Canadian Museum of Contemporary Photography; the Canadian Museum of Civilization, including the Canadian War Museum; the National Museum of Natural Sciences; and the National Museum of Science and Technology, including the National Aviation Museum and the Agriculture Museum. The National Museums are located in Ottawa-Hull but reach out to all Canadians through travelling exhibitions, loans of artworks and artifacts, publications, and educational activities in various media.

To complement the work of the four National Museums in Ottawa, a range of services as well as grants of financial assistance are offered to the museum community across Canada, under a fifth NMC component called National Programmes. These include: the Canadian Conservation Institute, providing research, advice, and skilled care to protect the national heritage; the Mobile Exhibits Programme; the computerized Canadian Heritage Information Network of museum objects; a program for the exchange of exhibitions between Canada and countries abroad; and the Museum Assistance Programmes, under which technical and financial aid is provided in the form of grants to hundreds of qualifying institutions.

Chairman, Dr. Sean Murphy
Secretary-Gen., John Edwards
Corporate Services
Asst. Secretary-Gen., Walter Kozar
Financial Services Director, Joe Geurts
Communications Advisor, Hélène Nantel

Personnel Services Director, Chris Laing
Planning and Management Services Director, Sharilyn J. Ingram

NATIONAL GALLERY OF CANADA
380 Sussex Dr., Ottawa, K1N 9N4
General Inquiries: (613) 990-1985
Director, Dr. Shirley Thomson
Dep. Director, Yves Dagenais
Collections and Research
Asst. Director, Brydon Smith
European Art Curator, Catherine Johnston
Canadian Art Curator, Charles Hill
Contemporary Art
Assoc. Curator, Diana Nemiroff
Video and Film Curator, Susan Ditta
European Prints and Drawings
Curator, Douglas E. Schoenherr
Canadian Prints and Drawings
Curator, Rosemarie Tovell
Curator of Photography, J. Borcoman
Registrar, André Fronton
Reference Library
Chief Librarian, Miss L.J. Hunter
Restoration and Conservation Laboratory
A/Head, Gregor Grant
Communications and Marketing
Asst. Director, Helen Murphy
Visitor Services Chief, Bodhanna Cmoc
Reproduction Rights Chief, Anne Hurley
Special Events Co-ordinator, Emily Tolot
Public Programmes
Asst. Director, G.V. Shepherd
Exhibitions Chief, Margaret Dryden
Publications Chief, Serge Thériault
Education Services
A/Head, Marie Currie
Museum Services
A/Asst. Director, Robert Caszanits
Protection Services Chief, J. Desjardins
Design and Technical Services
Chief, Craig Laberge
Accommodation Services
Chief, Robert Kaszanits
Comptroller, Dennis Moulding
Material Management
Chief, Bernard Pelletier
Finance, Nancy Lanthier
Personnel Chief, Monique Marleau
Records Management Chief, David Willson

NATIONAL MUSEUM OF NATURAL SCIENCES
Victoria Memorial Museum Bldg.
Metcalfe and McLeod Sts.
MAILING ADDRESS:
Box 3443, Stn. D, Ottawa, K1P 6P4
Director, Dr. Alan R. Emery
Dep. Director, Jacques Fournier
Collection and Research
Asst. Director, Dr. Stephen L. Cumbaa
Public Programmes
Asst. Director, Ridgeley Williams
Marketing and Communications
Asst. Director, Monique Doiron

Museum Operations
Asst. Director, Bruce Williams
Library Services, Arch Steward
Computer Services Chief, George Hickman
Architecture and Planning
Chief, Zoe Solomonesco
Protection Services Chief, Dennis Prince
Development Officer, Neil Carleton
Public Relations, Lise Laflamme
Zooarchaeological Identification Ctr.
491 Bank St., Ottawa, K1P 6P4
Head, Darlene Balkwill
Botany Division
1505 Laperrière Ave., Ottawa, K1P 6P4
Chief, Dr. Irwin M. Brodo
Zoology Division
2379 Holly Lane, Ottawa, K1P 6P4
Chief, Colin Eades
Paleobiology Division
921 St. Laurent Blvd., Ottawa, K1P 6P4
Chief, Dr. C.R. Harington
Mineral Sciences Division
1926 Merivale Rd., Ottawa, K1P 6P4
Chief, Dr. George Rebiuson
Exhibitions Division
2785 Riverside Dr., Ottawa, K1P 6P4
Chief, Barry Peers
Design and Technical Operations Division
2785 Riverside Dr., Ottawa, K1P 6P4
Chief, Greg Smith
Publishing Division
219 Argyle St., Ottawa, K1P 6P4
Chief, Bonnie Livingstone
Information and Resource Centre
Head, Nick Bélanger
Education Section
Victoria Memorial Museum Bldg.
Metcalfe and McLeod Sts.
Ottawa, K1A 0M8
Head, Mary-Anne Dancey
CANADIAN MUSEUM OF CIVILIZATION
Centre Asticou
241, boul. Cité-des-Jeunes, Hull
MAILING ADDRESS: Ottawa, K1A 0M8
DIRECTORATE:
Director, Dr. George MacDonald
Dep. Director, Jacques Ouellet
Public Programmes
Asst. Director, F. Corcoran
Marketing and Communications
Asst. Director, Michel Tremblay
Personnel Services
Asst. Director, Katherine Elliott
Management Services
Asst. Director, John Prok
New Building Project Director, Michael Carroll
Development Director, Brian Arthur
Finance Directorate Comptroller,
Jacques Gauthier
Collections and Research
A/Asst. Director, Paul Carpentier
Archaeological Survey of Canada
Chief, Ian Dyck
Canadian Ethnology Service
Chief, Dr. Andrea Laforêt

Canadian Centre for Folk Culture Studies
Chief, Dr. Stephen Inglis
History Division
Research Director, Dr. Dan Gallacher
Education and Cultural Affairs
A/Chief, Ron McRae
Communications Chief, Hélène Nantel
Exhibition Division Chief, Sylvie Morel
Design and Technical Services
Chief, R. Rodriguez
Conservation Service Division
Chief, T. Govier
Facilities Management Division
A/Chief, Guy Roy
Médiathèque Chief, Jacques Cinq-Mars
Material Management Chief, Alfred Dupuis
Administration
A/Chief, Denis O'Grady
Publishing
A/Chief, Jean-François Blanchette
Commercial Programs Division
Chief, Penny Trottier
Special Exhibition Programme
Chief, Sandra Gibb
Information Systems Division
Chief, Grant N. Boyd
Canadian War Museum
330 Sussex Dr., Ottawa, K1A 0M8
Director, W.J. Suthren
Curator of Collection, R.K. Malott
Communications, Faye Kert

NATIONAL POSTAL MUSEUM
Ottawa, K1A 0M8
Chief, Joanne LaRochelle
Curator of Collections, Susan McLeod-O'Reilly
Curator of Collections Management,
Roger Baird
Curator of Exhibits, Francine Brousseau
Communications Head, Monique Martin
Communications and Exhibits
Designer, Yves Paquin
Philatelic Counter, Irène Landry

NATIONAL MUSEUM OF SCIENCE AND
TECHNOLOGY
1867 St. Laurent Blvd., Ottawa, K1G 5A3
A/Director, Gordon Bruce
Dep. Director, Gordon Bruce

Public Programmes
Asst. Director, Jean-Pascal Souque
Education and Extension Chief, Marjorie Clark
Exhibition Development Manager, R. Tropea
Exhibits and Restoration Division
Chief, E. Russell
Electronics Head, C. Murray
Design Chief, Glenda Krusberg

Management Services
Asst. Director, L. Nadon
Administration Chief, J. Minnie
Computer Services Chief, Marc Fournier
Financial Services Chief, Graham Parsons
Facilities Services Chief, Robert Chartrand
Personnel Chief, Robert Mercier

Security Services Chief, Al Chapman

Collections and Research
Asst. Director, Dr. Paul F. Donahue
Agricultural Renewable Resources
Sr. Curator, T.A. Brown
Physical Sciences
A/Sr. Curator, Mary Grey
Communications and Space
Sr. Curator, E.A. DeCoste
Curator of Space, Doris Jelly
Energy and Natural Resources
Sr. Curator, Louise Trottier
Transportation
Sr. Curator, Vacant
Medical Technology
Curator, Dr. Sandra McRae
Graphic Arts Technology
A/Curator, D.G. Rider
Engineering and Industrial Technology
Sr. Curator, Dr. Norman Ball
Registrar, J. Johnston
Conservation/Restoration
A/Chief, Dave Elliott
Librarian, Hilary Perrott

Communications and Marketing
Asst. Director, Susan Spoke

National Aviation Museum
Rockcliffe, ON K1G 5A3
Director, R.W. Bradford
Curator, A.J. Shortt

Agricultural Museum
Central Experimental Farm
Curator, T.A. Brown

Social Sciences and Humanities Research Council of Canada
255 Albert St., Box 1610
Ottawa, K1P 6G4

Governed by a 22-member appointed council chosen from the academic community and other major interest sectors of society, the Social Sciences and Humanities Research Council is a grant-giving body whose funds are voted by Parliament. Its objective is to promote and assist research and scholarship in the social sciences and humanities.

● It supports independent research that in the judgment of scholars will best advance knowledge.

● It encourages research on subjects which the Council, in consultation with the academic community, considers to be of national importance.

● It facilitates communication among scholars in Canada and abroad, and stimulates dissemination of the results of research.

● It assists in and advises on maintaining and developing the national capacity for research.

In pursuit of these goals, the Council administers programs of fellowships for research training and research support, and grants for research, international scholarly exchanges, scholarly publishing and conferences.

President, Paule Leduc

Director Gen., Program Branch
Ralph Heintzman
Treasurer, Gaston Bouliane
A/Secretary, Gaston Bouliane
Information Division Director, Florentia Scott
Policy and Planning Unit
Director, Stephen Goban
Fellowships Division Director, Heather Steele
Research Grants Division
Director, Marion King
Strategic Grants Division
Director, Marion King
International Relations and
Research Communication Division
Director, Denis Croux
Finance and Administrative Services Division
Director, Pierre Chartrand
A/Chief, Suzanne Lavigne-Durocher
Personnel Division Chief, Vacant
Management Systems
Director, William T. Gordon

Telefilm Canada
Banque Nationale Twr.
600, rue de la Gauchetière ouest
Montréal (Québec) H3B 4L2
General Information: (514) 283-6383
Telex: 055-60998; Fax: (514) 283-8212

Telefilm Canada is a Crown corporation with a mandate to develop Canada's film, television and video industry.

Through Telefilm Canada, the Government of Canada provides support, as a partner, to the private sector for the production of film and broadcast material, either in the form of investment funds or through a variety of resources at Telefilm's disposal.

Telefilm Canada meets the diverse needs of this booming industry through a wide range of funds, participating in this way in over 300 projects in 1987/88. Support is available at all stages of the process, from screenplay development to final production and beyond to the distribution and marketing of the finished product in Canada and abroad.

Telefilm Canada's goal is to strengthen the competitive position of Canadian films, television programs and videos, as well as raising the export profile of Canadian companies, and to assist them in developing marketing and promotion strategies. Telefilm also co-ordinates Canada's participation in international festivals and administers a program of grants to Canadian festivals.

Telefilm Canada is responsible for managing the co-production agreements for film or television programs signed in Canada with a number of foreign countries. Among other provisions, the agreements stipulate that a co-production is treated exactly like a domestic production in each of the partner countries.

Telefilm Canada is a Crown corporation that reports to Parliament through the Minister of Communications. Its head office is in Montreal and it has offices in Toronto, Vancouver, Halifax, Los Angeles, Paris, and London.

BOARD OF DIRECTORS
Chairman, Jean Sirois, Q.C.
Vice-Chairman, Harvey A. Corn
Members: Nancy Jamieson, Nancy Morrison,
André Provost, Paulette Sonier-Rioux
Exec. Director, Pierre DesRoches
Marketing and International Affairs
Dep. Director, Louise Beaudoin
Co-productions Manager, Gilles Bériault
Festivals' Bureau Manager, Jean Lefebvre
Los Angeles
Manager, B. Good-Samsom
Paris Manager, Roland Ladouceur
London Manager, Robert Linnell
Production and Development
A/Director, Peter Katadotis
Ontario Operations Director, Vacant
Ontario Project Development
Manager, Bill Niven
Ontario Business Affairs Manager, Judy Watt
Quebec Operations Director, Vacant
Quebec Business Affairs
A/Manager, Danny Chalifour
Western Provinces Manager, Bill Gray
Eastern Provinces Manager, Ralph Holt
Financing and Administration
Director, Yves Beauchesne
Legal Affairs Director, Larry Pilon
Human Resources
A/Director, Marcel Choquette
Financial Controller, Lisa Scardocchio
Data Processing and Systems
Manager, Nam Trien
Planning and Policies
Director, Noel Cormier
Communications
Director, Denise Melillo
REGIONAL OFFICES:
Toronto
130 Bloor St. W., Ste. 901
Toronto, ON M5S 1N5
General Information: (416) 973-6436
Telex: 06-218344; Fax: (416) 973-8606
Halifax
Maritime Centre
1505 Barrington St., Ste. 1205
Halifax, NS B3J 3K5
General Information: (902) 426-8425
Telex: 019-21671; Fax: (902) 425-0314
Vancouver
1185 W. Georgia St., Ste. 1200
Vancouver, BC V6E 4E6
General Information: (604) 684-7262
Telex: 04-352-848; Fax: (604) 689-8380
OFFICES ABROAD:
Los Angeles
144 S. Beverly Dr., Ste. 400
Beverly Hills, CA 90212
Paris
15, rue de Berri, Paris 75008 France
London
55/59 Oxford St., 4th Flr.
London, England, W1R 1RD

DEPARTMENT OF CONSUMER AND CORPORATE AFFAIRS

50, rue Victoria, Place du Portage, Hull
Mailing Address: Ottawa, ON K1A 0C9
Telex: 053-3694
General Information: (613) 997-2938
TDD: (613) 994-0067

OFFICE OF THE MINISTER AND
REGISTRAR-GENERAL
Rm. 656, Confederation Bldg.
House of Commons, Ottawa, K1A 0A6

Minister and Registrar-Gen.,
The Hon. Bernard Valcourt

OFFICE OF THE DEPUTY MINISTER AND
DEPUTY REGISTRAR-GENERAL

Dep. Minister and Dep. Registrar-Gen.,
Ian D. Clark
Gen. Counsel, Michael Dambrot

Bureau of Policy Co-ordination

Asst. Dep. Minister, Mel Cappe
Planning Management Services
Director, S. Stimpson
Corporate Services and Research
Director, E. Carson
Legislative Review Director, D. Watters
Communications Branch
Director, Barbara Uteck

FINANCE AND ADMINISTRATION
Director Gen., H. McIlroy
Administration Services Branch
Director, L. Dagenais
Finance Branch Director, J. McCarthy
Information Systems Branch
Director, S.H. Talbert
Library and Records Services Branch
Director, C. MacLaurin
Internal Audit Branch Director, S. Dhingra

Personnel
Director Gen., Ann Midgley

Bureau of Competition Policy
Director of Investigation and Research,
Calvin S. Goldman, Q.C.
Sr. Dep. Director, H. Wetston
Compliance, Policy and
Management Co-ordination
Director Gen., Val Traversy
Compliance and Co-ordination
A/Director, J.A. Greig
Management Systems and Services
A/Director, John Read
Economics and Regulatory Affairs
Dep. Director, H. Chandler
Marketing Practices
Dep. Director, K. Decker
Resources and Manufacturing
Dep. Director, W. Critchley

Services
Dep. Director, I. Nielsen-Jones
Mergers
Assoc. Dep. Director, W. Lindsay

Bureau of Consumer Affairs
Asst. Dep. Minister, Wendy F. Porteous
Management Services Branch
Director, A. Johnston
Consumer Services Branch
Director, M. Wadsworth
Product Safety Branch Director, Jean Gariépy
Legal Metrology Branch Director, R. Knapp
Consumer Products Branch
Director, R. McKay
REGIONAL OFFICES:
Atlantic
Ste. 1500, 1489 Hollis St., Halifax, NS B3J 3M5
Reg. Director, R. Moir
Quebec
Place Guy Favreau, Tour est, bur. 502
200, boul. René-Lévesque ouest
Montréal, H2Z 1X4
Reg. Director, F. Sarrazin
Ontario
6th Flr., Federal Bldg.
4900 Yonge St., Willowdale, M2N 6B8
Reg. Director, R. Rusinek
Prairies
201, 260 St. Mary Ave.
Winnipeg, MB R3C 0M6
Reg. Director, W.A. Empke
Pacific
1400, 800 Burrard St.
Vancouver, BC V6Z 2H8
Reg. Director, M.Z. Brown

Bureau of Corporate Affairs
Asst. Dep. Minister, R. Gagnon
Management Systems Director, E. Zazulak
Corporations Branch Director, F. Sparling
Bankruptcy Branch
Director and Sup't, M.Y. Pigeon
Asst. Sup't, W. Clare
Commissioner of Patents, Director Gen.
of Intellectual Property and Registrar
of Trade Marks, J.H.A. Gariépy
Exec. Director, M. Leesti
Information and Technology Exploitation
Director, A. Lachance
Operational Planning and Research
Director, F. Adams
Automated Systems Director, R. Taylor
Patent Examination Director, A. McDonough
Patent Appeal Board
A/Chairman, Merle Brown
Trade Marks Examination
A/Director, Barbara Bova
Trade Marks Opposition Board,
Chairman, G. Partington
Copyright and Industrial Design
Director, L. Steingarten
Documentation and Registration
Director, D.V. Cummings

**Office of the Assistant Deputy
Registrar-General**
Trafalgar Bldg.,207 Queen St.
4th Flr., Ottawa, K1A 0C9
General Inquiries: (613) 995-0721

Asst. Dep. Registrar-Gen., J-P Kingsley
Conflict of Interest Advisory Group
A/Director, P. Lecomte
Management Registration and Trust
A/Director, A.D. LeVasseur
Chief of Registration, D. Kirchmayer
Place du Portage, Hull, K1A 0C9

AGENCIES, BOARDS AND COMMISSIONS

Competition Tribunal
Royal Bank Centre
90 Sparks St., Ste. 600
Ottawa, K1P 5B4
MAILING ADDRESS:
Box 1899, Stn. B, Ottawa, K1P 5R5
General Inquiries: (613) 957-3172

   The Competition Tribunal was created under
the *Competition Tribunal Act,* S.C. 1986, Chapter
26. It replaced the former Restrictive Trade
Practices Commission. It is made up of four
justices of the Federal Court, Trial Division and up
to eight lay members. As a rule, applications are
heard by between three and five members, of
whom at least one is a judge and one a lay
member.
   The Tribunal hears cases involving restrictive
business practices such as mergers, exclusive
dealing and tied selling. The Tribunal has the
power to issue either interim or final orders to deal
with these practices.

Chairman,
Hon. Madame Justice Barbara J. Reed
Members:
Hon. Mr. Justice Barry L. Strayer
Hon. Mr. Justice Leonard A. Martin
Hon. Mr. Justice Max M. Teitelbaum
Dr. Frank Roseman
Mme Marie-Hélène Sarrazin
Prof. M. Trebilcock
Registrar, Annaline Lubbe

Patented Medicine Prices Review Board
359 Kent St., Ottawa, K1A 0C9
General Inquiries: (613) 952-7360

Chairman, Dr. H.C. Eastman
Vice-Chairman, Dr. R. Goyer
Exec. Director, R. Atkinson
Sec.-Registrar, P. Sylvester
Compliance and Liaison Director, T. Brogan
Quantitative Analysis Director, G. Robertson
Communications Director, S. Massie

DEPARTMENT OF EMPLOYMENT AND IMMIGRATION
Phase IV, Place du Portage, Hull
MAILING ADDRESS: Ottawa, K1A 0J9

MINISTER'S OFFICE
W. Blk., House of Commons
Ottawa, K1A 0A6
Minister, The Hon. Barbara McDougall

OFFICE OF THE MINISTER OF STATE
(EMPLOYMENT AND IMMIGRATION)
Minister of State, The Hon. Monique Vézina

OFFICE OF THE MINISTER OF STATE
(YOUTH, FITNESS AND AMATEUR SPORT)
House of Commons, Ottawa, K1A 0A6
Minister of State, The Hon. Jean Charest

OFFICE OF THE MINISTER OF STATE
(SENIORS)
Minister of State, The Hon. Monique Vézina

DEPUTY MINISTER/CHAIRMAN'S OFFICE
Dep. Minister/Chairman, Vacant

ASSOCIATE DEPUTY
MINISTER/VICE-CHAIRMAN'S OFFICE
Assoc. Dep. Minister/ Vice-Chairman,
Nick Mulder

COMMISSIONERS:
Workers, Frank Boudreau
Employers, P. Doyle
Legal Services
Gen. Counsel, W. Black
Internal Audit Bureau
Exec. Director, G. Béland
Emergency Planning Director, W.J.H. Poole
Intergovernmental Affairs and External Liaison
Director, D. Medved
Public Rights Administration
Director, R. Rapley
Security Directorate and
Department/Commission Security Officer,
K. Williamson

IMMIGRATION
Exec. Director, J.B. Bissett
Immigration Policy Branch
Director Gen., A. Juneau
Refugee Affairs and Settlement Branch
Director Gen., R. Girard
Immigration Program Management Branch
Director Gen., L. Dubois
Adjudication Branch
A/Director, J. Beny-Madhu
Planning and Program Management Branch
A/Director Gen., L. Dubois
Operations Branch
Director Gen., E. Donagher
Policy and Program Development Branch
Director Gen., W.K. Bell
Settlement Branch Director, G. Barnett

CANADIAN JOBS STRATEGY
Exec. Director, P. Hicks
Special Advisor, I. Krupka

Program Development
Director Gen., N. St-Jacques
Operations
Director Gen., R. VanTongerloo
Planning and Monitoring
Director, Y. Timonin
Innovations
Director Gen., Louise Bourgault
Program Policy
A/Director Gen., N. St-Jacques

INSURANCE
Exec. Director, K. Wyman
Insurance Policy
Director Gen., J.J. Verbruggen
Control Branch
Director Gen., M. Nouvet
Insurance Services
Director Gen., W.J. McGee
Actuarial Services
Chief Actuary, J. Larose

EMPLOYMENT
A/Exec. Director, J. Hunter
Employment Operational Services
A/Director Gen., A. Pilon
Employment Equity Branch
Director Gen., M. Clarke
Worker Development
Director Gen., J. Stewart
Occupational and Career Information Branch
Director, L.G. Dixon
Planning and Co-ordination
Director, D. Neuman
Labour Market Services
Director Gen., S. Matthews
Employer Services Director, D. Crozier

SYSTEMS AND PROCEDURES
Exec. Director, B.K. Dertinger
Information Systems Directorate
Director Gen., S.J. Connolly
Computer Operations Directorate
Director Gen., J. Chartrand
Benefit Pay Systems and
Canadian Job Strategy Directorate
Director Gen., M. Robertson
Management Advisory Services Directorate
Director, M. Marta

PERSONNEL
Exec. Director, M. Hynna
Operations Personnel Services
Director, M.W. Reteff
Human Resources Development and
Planning Directorate
Director, G. Howard
Headquarters Personnel Services
Director, J. Lefebvre
Organization Development
Chief, J. Lindsay-Laberge
Personnel Management Systems and
Official Languages
Director, P.R. Johnston

FINANCE AND ADMINISTRATION
Exec. Director, P.J. Gauvin
Financial Services
Director Gen., H. Braiter
Services Administration
A/Director Gen., J. Mallen

Strategic Policy and Planning
Asst. Dep. Minister, B. Carin
Planning Branch
Director Gen., P. Fay
Program Evaluation Branch
Director Gen., I.H. Midgley
Policy and Program Analysis
A/Director Gen., P. Fay
Labour Market Outlook and Structural Analysis
Director Gen., G. Fletcher

PUBLIC AFFAIRS
Director Gen., R. Land
Corporate Affairs Directorate
Director, B. Mann
Labour Market Development and
Employment Services Information Directorate
Director, A.H. Sackman
Unemployment Insurance and
Immigration Directorate
A/Director, Ted Soroczan
Information Services Directorate
A/Director, F. Ianni

REGIONAL HEADQUARTERS:

Newfoundland
167 Kenmount Rd.
Box 12051, St. John's, A1B 3Z4
Director Gen., J.M. Duguay
Operations Director, G. Maher
Programs Director, D.E. Sellars
Immigration Director, P.V. Field
Personnel Manager, M.M. Lee
Financial Services Manager, P.W. Joudrey
Administrative Services Manager, E.J. Rogers
Economic Services Manager, B. Kenny
Public Affairs
A/Manager, E.S. King
Skill Development Manager, D.A. Cadigan
Planning and Co-ordination
A/Manager, C. Smith
Insurance Services Manager, R. Williams
Employment Operations
A/Manager, F. Brennan
Job Development/Job Entry
A/Manager, R. O'Neill
Regional Pay Centre Manager, W.S. Andrews
Adjustment Programs Manager, B.S. Wakelin
Planning and Analysis Manager, L.R. LeDrew
Youth Strategy Manager, R. Fifield

Nova Scotia
Box 1350, 99 Wyse Rd.
Dartmouth, B2Y 4B9
Director Gen., G.J. Everard
Public Affairs Manager, W.C. Boyle
Administrative Services Manager, J.R. King
Economic Services Manager, P.V. McNeill
Personnel Services Manager, B.H. Hale

Financial Services Manager, G.K. Oulton
Immigration Director, W.J. Marks
Programs Director, G. Laporte
Operations Director, H.J. Vaughan
Planning and Assessment
Manager, Mrs. K.L. MacInnis
Prince Edward Island
85 Fitzroy St., Box 8000
Charlottetown, C1A 8K1
Director Gen., O.N. Buffie
Planning and Economic Analysis
Manager, P.A. Johnstone
Operations Director, D.W. Gee
Administrative Services Manager, G.A. Linton
Personnel Services Manager, J.H. Tillman
Financial Services Manager, D. Miller
Programs Director, W.J. Power
Public Affairs Manager, G.C. Chapman
New Brunswick
975 Hanwell Rd., Box 2600
Fredericton, E3B 5V6
Director Gen., D.R. Demers
Operations Director, A.B. Ferguson
Programs Director, R.A. Bemrose
Immigration Director, D.D. Mesheau
Public Affairs
A/Manager, Roch Rollin
Administrative Services Manager, R.B. Porter
Planning and Co-ordination
Manager, Dave Easby
Employment Development
A/Manager, Pat Green
Employment Services Manager, Jeff MacLeod
Personnel Manager, Louise Branch
Planning and Analysis Manager, W. Holleran
Economic Services
A/Manager, Jim Taggart
1133 St. George St., Moncton, E1E 9G8
Financial Services Manager, R. Charron
Insurance Services
Manager, Norbert Robichaud
Computer Centre Manager, M. Estabrooks
975 Hanwell Rd., Box 2600
Fredericton, E3B 5V6
Labour Market Planning and Adjustment
Manager, Raelene Currie
120 Harbourview Blvd., Bathurst, E2A 4L8
National Services Director, L. Tremblay
Quebec
1441, rue St-Urbain, 9e ét.
Montréal, H2X 2M6
Exec. Director, T. Lacombe
Employment and Insurance
Director Gen., S. Bastien
Programs
Director Gen., Y. Poisson
Public Affairs Director, G. Parent
Financial Services Director, C. Lafontaine
Administrative Services Director, G. Guimond
Economic Services Director, F. Bertrand
Immigration Director, A. Gladu
Personnel Director, L. Bernier
Employment Development Branch
2001, rue University, Montréal, H3A 1K3
Director, J.A. Giroux

Ontario
4900 Yonge St., Ste. 700
North York, M2N 6A8
General Inquiries: (416) 224-4888
Exec. Director, D. Morley
Economic Services Director, G. Sperling
Personnel Director, N. Button
Operational Review Analysis and Services
Director, A. Mahmood
Administrative Services Director, Bob Barber
Financial Services Director, David Scott
Public Affairs Manager, T. Galasso
Operations
Director Gen., D.R. Brown
Programs
Director Gen., David Conn
Planning and Co-ordination
Director, B. Woodworth
Employment Skills Director, Dr. R. Taher
Insurance Services Director, J. Dutkiewicz
Box 4500, Belleville, K8N 5C1
Adjustment Programs Director, K. Gelok
Immigration
Director Gen., E. Harrigan
Facilitation, Enforcement and Control
Director, M. Best
Recruitment and Selection
Director, J. Klein
Priorities and Program Co-ordination
Director, P. Pirie
Settlement
A/Director, K. Reade
Manitoba
Rm. 710, Eaton Pl., 330 Graham Ave.
Winnipeg, R3C 4B9
Director Gen., B. Hill
Operations Director, G. Howarth
Programs Director, D. McCulloch
Immigration Director, R. Beirnes
Economic Services Manager, J. Treller
Personnel Manager, G. Twomey
Public Affairs Manager, W. Kennedy
Administrative Services Manager, E. Typa
Finance Manager, S. Bubbs
266 Graham Ave., Winnipeg, R3C 0J8
Computer Centre Manager, R. Thorpe
Saskatchewan
Financial Bldg., Rm. 600
2101 Scarth St., Regina, S4P 2H9
Director Gen., Allan Jacques
Operations Director, D.W. Murray
Programs Director, R.L. Torkelson
Economic Planning and Analysis
Director, F. Besier
Immigration Director, B. Harris
Administrative Services Manager, O. Blahut
Financial Services Manager, Paul Ready
Personnel Manager, J.M. Hooker
Public Affairs Manager, Susan Hogarth
Developmental Programs
Manager, David Goldsmith
Program Planning and Co-ordination
Manager, Jenny Speir
Investigation and Control
Manager, Dick Clarke

Insurance Services
Manager, Spence Partington
Adjustment Programs
Manager, Doug Robertson
Employment Services Manager, Ed Arndt

Alberta and the Northwest Territories
9925-109th St., Edmonton, T5K 2J8
Information: (403) 420-2431
Director Gen., R. Gates
Public Affairs Manager, W. Kennedy
Operations Director, R.E. Brown
Immigration Director, I. Wilson
Programs Director, M. Terris
N.W.T. Directorate
Director, C. Pilon
Services Administration
A/Manager, D. Pylypow
Economic Services Manager, K. Adams
Development and Programs Branch
A/Manager, E. Kowalec
External Relations Co-ordinator, R. Gagné
Financial Services Manager, S. Wawzonek
Personnel Manager, R. Bird
Planning and Analysis Manager, L. Madsen
Overpayment Recovery Division
Chief, B. Spelliscy

British Columbia and the Yukon
Box 11145, Royal Ctr.
1055 W. Georgia St., Vancouver, V6E 2P8
Director Gen., G. Botham
Employment and Insurance Operations
Director, W.D. Gardner
Immigration Operations
Director, L. Hanson
Secretariat
A/Manager, G. Jaques
Personnel Manager, P.M. Soucy
Administration Manager, A. St. Onge
Finance Manager, R. Boutin
Programs Director, S. Robertson

AGENCIES, BOARDS AND COMMISSIONS

Canada Employment and Immigration Advisory Council (CEIAC)
Ottawa, K1A 0J9
General Inquiries: (819) 994-2417

The CEIAC was created in August 1977 by an Act of Parliament. Its role is "to advise the Minister of Employment and Immigration on all matters to which his powers, duties and functions extend" and to present a yearly report of its activities to the minister. The minister is then required to table the report in Parliament.

The Council is composed of a chairman and fifteen to twenty-one other members. The Chairman's term is specified by the Governor in Council; the other members are appointed for terms not exceeding three years. One-third of members are appointed after consultation with organizations representative of employers and one-third after consultation with organizations representative of workers. No consultation is prescribed for the remaining third.

Chairman, Jacques Vasseur
Exec. Director, M.G. Lanctôt

Immigration and Refugee Board
116 Lisgar St., Ottawa, K1A 0K1
General Inquiries: (613) 995-6486

The Immigration and Refugee Board came into existence on Jan. 1, 1988 through amendments to the *Immigration Act* included in S.C. 1988, Chapter 35. The Board replaced the Immigration Appeal Board and the Refugee Status Advisory Committee.

The Board is made up of two divisions: the Convention Refugee Determination Division and the Immigration Appeal Division. The Refugee Division is made up of the Chairman of the Immigration and Refugee Board, a deputy chairman, up to seven assistant deputy chairmen, up to 65 full-time members, and part-time members as required. The Appeal Division includes the Chairman of the Board, a deputy chairman, up to five assistant deputy chairmen, up to 30 full-time members, and part-time members as required. All are appointed by the Governor in Council, the Chairman for seven years and all other members for five.

All persons claiming to be refugees according to the United Nations Convention are first interviewed by immigration officers. If their case is considered reasonable, the claim is placed before the Refugee Division. The Division then judges the merit of the claim and rules on whether the claimant may be considered a Convention refugee. The process is informal, the Division is not bound by normal legal rules of evidence and procedure. At least two members hear each claim.

The Appeal Division is a superior court of record. It hears appeals of deportation or removal orders made against those who have been refused landed immigrant or refugee status, or against permanent residents. It also hears appeals by the Minister of Employment and Immigration against decisions to grant landed immigrant or refugee status. Appeals to the Appeal Division are normally heard by at least three members.

Appeals, in limited circumstances, of decisions of the Refugee Division and, in questions of law, of decisions of the Appeal Division, may be made to the Federal Court of Canada.

Chairman, Gordon Fairweather
Deputy Chairmen:
Drasko Bubalo, Nurjehan N. Mawani
Exec. Director, Peter Harder
Legal Services Director, Mario Bouchard
Policy and Planning
Director Gen., Jerry Robbins
Documentation Centre
Director, Graham Howell
Finance, Administration and Personnel
Director, Terry R. Hickey
Refugee Hearing Officers
Director, Sam Laredo

Montreal Office
Place Guy Favreau, Tour est, bur. 110
200, boul. René-Lévesque ouest
Montréal, H2Z 1X4
Asst. Dep. Chairmen: Joseph S. Blumer,
Gisèle T. Morgan, Colette Savard
Reg. Director, Pierre Bourget

Toronto Office
1 Front St. W., 15th Flr.
Toronto, M5J 1A5
Asst. Dep. Chairmen:
Kathi I. Arkin, Dorothy Davey, Anna Ker
Reg. Director, Laurent Matte

Winnipeg Office
185 Carleton St., 3rd Flr.
Winnipeg, R3C 3J1
Asst. Dep. Chairman: Lila Goodspeed
Reg. Director, Jerry Kozubal

Calgary Office
510-12th Ave., Rm. 217, Calgary, T2R 0X5
Asst. Dep. Chairman: Elizabeth Bryant

Vancouver Office
800 Burrard St., Ste. 1600
Vancouver, V6Z 2J9
Asst. Dep. Chairmen:
Stanley B. Knight, Andrew Z. Wlodyka
Reg. Director, R. Gatland

Office of the Umpire
365 Laurier Ave. W., 18th Flr. N.
Box 8966, Ottawa, K1G 3J2

The Office of the Umpire was established to provide administrative support and services to umpires constituted under the *Unemployment Insurance Act*. This independent judicial authority hears appeals of decisions made by Boards of Referees on unemployment insurance matters. The Chief Umpire is the Associate Chief Justice of the Federal Court of Canada.
Registrar, Carol Hamelin

DEPARTMENT OF ENERGY, MINES AND RESOURCES
580 Booth St., Ottawa, K1A 0E4
(except where otherwise indicated)
Telex: 053-3117
General Inquiries: (613) 995-3065

MINISTER'S OFFICE
Rm. 607, Confederation Bldg.
House of Commons, Ottawa, K1A 0A6
Minister, The Hon. Jake Epp

DEPUTY MINISTER'S OFFICE
Dep. Minister, Bruce I. Howe

ASSOCIATE DEPUTY MINISTER'S OFFICE
Assoc. Dep. Minister, Pierre O. Perron

Corporate Policy and Communications Sector
Asst. Dep. Minister, Jocelyne Bourgon

STRATEGIC POLICY AND PLANS
Director Gen., Michel Bourdon
Sr. Policy Analysts: Peter Black,
Brian Calvert, Andrée Delagrave,
Patricia Smith, Jack Taylor

CABINET AFFAIRS
Director, Brian Johnson
Sr. Policy Advisor, Shirley Siegel
Policy Officers: Patrick Hollier,
Richard Clair, Marie Maher

CORPORATE AFFAIRS BRANCH
Director Gen., Alain Bénicy
Internal Audit Director, Marcel Gibeault
Program Evaluation Director, Alain Barbarie
Management Consulting Services
Director, Mary Macies-Lymburner
Executive Services
Asst. Director, Paul Meloche
Office of Environmental Affairs
Director, J.D. McTaggart-Cowan

COMMUNICATIONS BRANCH
Director Gen., Diana Monnet
Dep. Director Gen., A. Arbuckle
Client Services
Director (Energy), Marc Demers
Client Services (MESP)
A/Director, B. Adams
Strategic Analysis and Co-ordination
A/Director, Jacques Noel
Regional Communications Division
Director, G. Robinson
Creative Services Division
Director, P. Cheffins
Central Services Director, Alfred Tsang

Human Resources Sector
Asst. Dep. Minister, Jacques Y. Ranger
Personnel Programs Operations Branch
Director, L.E. LeBoldus
Management Category, Human
Resources Planning Programs
Director, N. Moodie

Finance and Administration Sector
Asst. Dep. Minister, Robert Giroux
Information Management
Director, V. Pettis

FINANCIAL MANAGEMENT
Director Gen., R.O. Sorenson
Financial Analysis and Planning
Director, G. Tardif
Financial Policy and Systems
Director, B.C. Bury
Accounting Director, F.A. Donnelly
Geological Survey of Canada
Finance Director, C. Bowstead
A/Financial Advisor, Mineral Policy, J. Parker
Surveys, Mapping and Remote Sensing
Director, A. Jansen

Mineral and Energy Technology
Director, C. Laberge
Administration Program
Director, Randy Burch
Energy Finance Director, D. Parr

INFORMATION TECHNOLOGY BRANCH
A/Director Gen., N. MacLeod
Consulting Services Division
Director, B. Wainwright
Computing Facilities Services Division
Director, C. Hughes
Policy, Planning and Co-ordination Division
Director, N. MacLeod
Security Director, D. Barton
Administrative Services
Director, Gérard Lebrun
Materiel Management
A/Asst. Director, G. Chambers
Property Planning and Management
Asst. Director, Donn Smith
Occupational Health and Safety
Asst. Director, M. Laurin
Graphics and Audio-Visual Support Services
Asst. Director, R. Rouleau
Headquarters Library Chief, B. Scollie

Mineral and Energy Technology
Asst. Dep. Minister, Dr. M.D. Everell
Program Advisor, M. Nobert
Mineral and Energy Technology
Special Advisor, Dr. E. Smith
Explosives Branch Director, R. Shaw
Office of Energy Research and Development
Director Gen., B.D. Cook

CANADA CENTRE FOR MINERAL AND
ENERGY TECHNOLOGY (CANMET)
555 Booth St., Ottawa, K1A 0G1
(except where otherwise noted)

CANMET—MINERAL TECHNOLOGY BRANCH
Director Gen., Dr. J.T. Jubb
Mineral Sciences Laboratories
Director, L.L. Sirois
Mining Research Laboratories
Bells Corners Complex
c/o CANMET, 555 Booth St.
Ottawa, K1A 0G1
Director, Dr. J.E. Udd
Elliot Lake Laboratory
Box 100, Elliot Lake, ON P5A 2J6
Manager, Dr. R. Tervo
Metals Technology Laboratories
568 Booth St., Ottawa, K1A 0G1
Director, Dr. W.H. Erickson

CANMET—ENERGY TECHNOLOGY BRANCH
Director Gen., Vacant
Energy Research Laboratories
Bells Corners Complex
c/o CANMET, 555 Booth St.
Ottawa, K1A 0G1
Director, Dr. D.A. Reeve

Coal Research Laboratories
P.O. Bag 1280, Devon, AB T0C 1E0
Director, Dr. T.D. Brown
Manager, Dr. H.A. Hamza

Coal Research Laboratory
210 George St., Sydney, NS B1P 1J3
Manager, G. Haslett

CANMET - POLICY, PLANNING AND
SERVICES BRANCH
Director Gen., J. Ferron
Administrative Services Director, J.K. Daly
Technology Marketing Division
Director, K. Belinko
Research Program Office Director, R. Sage
Library and Documentation Services Division
Director, Dr. J.E. Kanasy
Library: (613) 995-4162
Technical Inquiries: (613) 992-4121
Publications Distribution: (613) 992-6793
Fax: (613) 952-2587
Technical Services Division
556 Booth St., Ottawa, K1A 0G1
Director, J.M. Duchesne

Surveys, Mapping and Remote Sensing Sector
580 Booth St., Ottawa, K1A 0E4

Asst. Dep. Minister, J.H. O'Donnell
Planning, Co-ordination and
Cartographic Services
Director Gen., F.H.A. Campbell
Director of Finance, A. Jansen

Canada Centre for Mapping (Ottawa)
615 Booth St., Ottawa, K1A 0E9
Director Gen., L.J. O'Brien
Geographical Services Division
Director, R. Groot
Topographical Survey Division
Director, E.V. Schaubel

Canada Centre for Geomatics
2144, rue King ouest
Sherbrooke (Québec) J1J 2E8
Director, R. Gareau

Canada Centre for Surveying
615 Booth St., Ottawa, K1A 0E9
Director Gen., G. Babbage
Geodetic Survey Division
Dominion Geodesist and Director, J.D. Boal
International Boundary Commission
Canadian Section:
Commissioner, Dr. A.C. McEwen
Legal Surveys Division
Surveyor Gen. and Director, G. Raymond

REGIONAL OFFICES

(LEGAL SURVEYS DIVISION):

Atlantic
Government of Canada Bldg.
40 Havelock St., Box 368
Amherst, NS B4H 3Z5
Reg. Surveyor, J.C. Mitchell

Quebec
2144, rue King ouest, Sherbrooke, J1J 2E8
Reg. Surveyor, J. Sasseville

Ontario
25 St. Clair Ave. E., Toronto, M4T 1M2
Reg. Surveyor, D.H. Browne

Manitoba
Kensington Bldg., Rm. 305
275 Portage Ave., Winnipeg, R3B 2B3
Reg. Surveyor, G.W. Kitchen

Saskatchewan
1000, 2221 Cornwall St., Regina, S4P 2L1
Reg. Surveyor, D.A. Bouck

Alberta
Canada Pl., Ste. 610
9700 Jasper Ave., Edmonton, T5J 4C3
Reg. Surveyor, G.E. Olsson

British Columbia
1300, 800 Burrard St., Vancouver, V6Z 2J4
Reg. Surveyor, D.K. Nielsen

Yukon Territory
204 Range Rd., Rm. 208
Whitehorse, Y1A 3V1
Reg. Surveyor, D. Culham

Northwest Territories
50th St., Bellanca Bldg., 8th Flr.
Box 668, Yellowknife, X1A 2N5
Reg. Surveyor, Lorne E. McNeice

CARTOGRAPHIC INFORMATION AND
DISTRIBUTION CENTRE
615 Booth St., Ottawa, K1A 0E9
Man. Director, J.P. Raymond
Distribution Director, L.L. Aubrey

CANADA CENTRE FOR REMOTE SENSING
2464 Sheffield Rd., Ottawa, K1A 0Y7
Director Gen., Dr. L. Sayn-Wittgenstein
Dep. Director Gen., Dr. E. Shaw
Administrative Services
Chief Admin. Division, R.C. Bone
Personnel Advisor, R. Lachapelle
A/Comptroller, C. Bouvier
Planning and Technology Assessment
A/Chief, A.L. Whitney
Digital Methods Division
Director, Florian Guertin
Radarsat Project Office
Director, Dr. E. Langham
Data Acquisition Division
Limebank Rd., Ottawa, K1A 0Y7
Director, L. Bronstein
Applications Technology Division
1547 Merivale Rd., 4th Flr.
Ottawa, K1A 0Y7
Director, J.C. Henein
User Assistance, J. Game
Technical Information Service
Head, B. McGurrin

Geological Survey of Canada
601 Booth St., Ottawa, K1A 0E8
Asst. Dep. Minister, Dr. R.A. Price
580 Booth St., Ottawa, K1A 0E8
External Research Programs
Co-ordinator, G.D. Pearce
Financial Services Director, C.C. Bowstead

Polar Continental Shelf Project
344 Wellington St., Rm. 6146
Ottawa, K1A 0E4
A/Director, P. Lapointe

PROGRAMS, PLANNING AND SERVICES
BRANCH
A/Chief Scientist, Dr. R.P. Riddihough
Program Co-ordination and Planning Division
Director, Dr. J.E. Harrison
Geoscience Information Division
Director, Dr. R.G. Blackadar
Frontier Geoscience Program
Co-ordinator, Dr. D. Picklyck
Mineral Development Program Office
Co-ordinator, Dr. W.H. Poole
Administrative Services Director, Y. Claude
Special Projects Co-ordinator, Dr. T.E. Bolton

CONTINENTAL GEOSCIENCE AND MINERAL
RESOURCES BRANCH
Director Gen., Dr. D.C. Findlay
Lithosphere and Canadian Shield Division
Director, Dr. J.C. McGlynn
Mineral Resources Division
A/Director, Dr. G.M. Plant

GEOPHYSICS AND TERRAIN SCIENCES
BRANCH
Director Gen., Dr. J.S. Scott
Geophysics Division
1 Observatory Cres., Ottawa, K1A 0Y3
Director, Dr. M.J. Berry
Terrain Sciences Division
601 Booth St., Ottawa, K1A 0E8
Director, Dr. D. St-Onge

SEDIMENTARY AND MARINE GEOSCIENCE
BRANCH
580 Booth St., 20th Flr., Ottawa, K1A 0E4
Director Gen., Dr. C.R. Barnes
Institute of Sedimentary and
Petroleum Geology
3303-33rd St. N.W., Calgary, AB T2L 2A7
Director, Dr. W.W. Nassichuk
Atlantic Geoscience Centre
Box 1006, Dartmouth, NS B2Y 4A2
Director, Dr. M.J. Keen
Cordilleran and Pacific Geoscience Division
100 W. Pender St.
Vancouver, BC V6B 1R8
Director, D. Tempelman-Kluit
Pacific Geoscience Subdivision
9860 West Saanich Rd., Box 6000
Sidney, BC V8L 4B2
Head, Dr. L. Law

Mineral Policy Sector
Asst. Dep. Minister, Ron R. Sully
A/Finance Director, J. Parker
Advisor (Special Projects), R. Webster
Information and Management Systems Division
Management Processes
A/Director, J. Bureau

Information Systems Division
Director, J. Brennan

MINERAL AND METAL COMMODITIES
BRANCH
Director Gen., W. McCann
Strategic Issues Advisor, C.J. Cajka
Nonferrous Commodities Division
Director, G.E. Wittur
Rare and Minor Metals Director, A. Ignatow
Industrial Minerals Division
Director, J.Y. Tremblay
Coal and Iron Division
A/Director, E. Laver

ECONOMIC AND FINANCIAL POLICY
ANALYSIS BRANCH
Director Gen., Keith J. Brewer
Economic Policy Analysis Division
Director, D. Hull
National Mineral Inventory Division
Chief, A.G. Sozanski
Tax Policy Analysis Division
Director, W.D. Kitts
Financial and Corporate Analysis Division
Director, R.K. Jones
Mining Tax Legislation Interpretation Division
Director, D. Schell

MINERAL STRATEGY BRANCH
Director Gen., B. Lipsett
Mineral Policy and Planning Division
A/Director, G. Kendall
Regional and Intergovernmental
Affairs Division
A/Director, A. Clark
International Mineral Relations Division
Director, G.R. Peeling
Ocean Mining Division Director, D. Pasho

FINANCIAL AND MARKET ANALYSIS BRANCH
Director Gen., R. Erdmann
Dep. Director Gen., W. Wouters
Fiscal Analysis Division
A/Director, S. O'Dell
Project Analysis I Division
Director, Vacant
Project Analysis II Division
Director, R. Vani
Industry Analysis Division
A/Director, N. McIlveen
Energy Market Analysis Division
Director, W. Jarvis

INTERNATIONAL ENERGY RELATIONS
BRANCH
Director Gen., Vacant
Bilateral Energy Relations Division
Director, M. Sills
Multilateral Energy Relations
and Special Projects Division
Director, G. Winstanley
Energy Policy Co-ordination Branch
A/Sr. Advisor, Vacant

Programs Sector
Asst. Dep. Minister, J. Carruthers
Management Services Branch
Director, J. Desjardins
Co-ordination and Strategic Planning Branch
Director, G. McKenzie
Economic and Policy Analysis
Asst. Director, K. Cliffe

DEVELOPMENT AND MARKETING BRANCH
Director Gen., M. Ruel
Residential Energy Management Division
Director, M.A. MacKenzie
Business and Government Energy
Management Division
Director, C. Luckman

TECHNOLOGY BRANCH
Director Gen., Dr. D. Strange
Bioenergy Division Director, A. Dolenko
Solar Energy Division
Director, S. Pneumaticos

TRANSPORTATION ENERGY BRANCH
Director Gen., A.C. Taylor
Policy Analysis Director, Vacant
Technology and Programs
Director, P. Reilly-Roe

OPERATIONS BRANCH
Director Gen., C. Boucher
Planning and Systems Division
Director, T. Baba
Federal/Provincial/Territorial
Sr. Advisor, K. Doyle
REGIONAL OFFICES:
Newfoundland
Box 65, Atlantic Pl., Ste. 301
215 Water St., St. John's, A1C 6C9
Director, N. French
Nova Scotia
Bank of Montreal Twr., Ste. 503
5151 George St., Halifax, B3J 1M5
Director, B. Cook
New Brunswick
835 Champlain St., Dieppe, E1A 1P6
Director, J. Hutchinson
Prince Edward Island
Harbourside #1, Brecken-Yates Bldg.
Queen St., Charlottetown, C1A 8R4
Director, N. Hall
Quebec
Place Guy Favreau, Tour ouest, bur. 501
200, boul. René-Lévesque ouest
Montréal, H2Z 1X4
Director, T. Traynor
Ontario
55 St. Clair Ave. E., Rm. 606
Box 2009, Toronto, M4T 1M2
Director, W. Peden
Manitoba
Main Flr., 213 Notre-Dame Ave.
Winnipeg, R3B 1N3
Director, W. Bryant

Saskatchewan
S.J. Cohen Bldg., Ste. 706
119-4th Ave. S., Saskatoon, S7K 5X2
Director, L. Epp
Alberta
Grandin Park Plaza, Rm. 200
22 Sir Winston Churchill Ave.
St. Albert, T8N 1B4
Director, E. Kilotat
British Columbia
100 W. Pender St., Rm. 200
Vancouver, V6B 1R8
Director, G.W. Bartram
Yukon
2078-2nd Ave., Whitehorse, Y1A 1B1
Director, G.W. Bartram
Northwest Territories
Precambrian Bldg., 10th Flr.
4922-52nd St., Box 68, Yellowknife, X1A 2N1
Director, J. Cumming

INCENTIVES LEGISLATION AND AUDIT
BRANCH
Director Gen., R. Laureys
Legislation, Policy and Forecasting
Director, D. Cioccio
Appeals and Interpretation
Director, V. Desjardins

CALGARY OPERATIONS BRANCH
Reg. Director Gen., G. Currie
Operations
Dep. Director Gen., R. Charron
Interpretations and Rulings
Director, M. Cameron
Audit Director, P. Neilson
AEL Control
A/Director, J. Bradford
PIP Audit Director, G. Crawford
Assessment Director, A. Boiteau

Energy Sector
Asst. Dep. Minister, G.R.M. Anderson

PETROLEUM RESOURCES BRANCH
Director Gen., J.P. Hea
New Petroleum Supplies Division
Director, M.K. El-Defrawy
Conventional Resources Division
Director, H.L. Potts
Resource Evaluation Division
Director, R. Conn

OIL AND EMERGENCY PLANNING BRANCH
Director Gen., J.D. Oulton
Domestic Oil Supply Division
Director, G. Vollans
International Oil Supply Division
A/Director, J. Booth
Oil Pricing Market Analysis Division
Director, L. Mahoney
Downstream Petroleum Technology Division
Director, D. Black

Oil Emergency Planning
Dep. Director Gen., H. Honarvar
Allocation Division Director, Vacant
Rationing Division Director, J. Rajabalee
Planning, Evaluation and Systems Division
Director, R. Bentley
National Emergency Agency
for Energy Division
Director, M. Johnson

NATURAL GAS BRANCH
Director Gen., M. Musgrove
Gas Exports Division
A/Director, M. Schwarz
Domestic Gas Division Director, M. Tobin

ELECTRICAL BRANCH
Director Gen., C.B. Marriott
Electrical Energy Technology Division
Director, E.M. Warnes
Economic Analysis Division
Director, D. Burpee
Electrical Energy Policy Director, D. Penpraze

URANIUM AND NUCLEAR BRANCH
Director Gen., R.W. Morrison
Radiation and Nuclear
Asst. Advisor, Vacant
Nuclear Power Advisor, H.E. Thexton
Uranium Advisor, R.M. Williams

ENERGY STRATEGY BRANCH
Director Gen., B. Emmett
Energy Policy Planning Division
Director, R. Lyman
Economic and Policy Studies
Analysis Division Director, N. Marty

Canada Oil and Gas Lands Administration
355 River Rd., Ottawa, K1A 0E4
Administrator, M.E. Taschereau
ENVIRONMENTAL PROTECTION
Director Gen., V. Lafferty
Environmental Studies Research Fund
Director, Dr. O.H. Loken

POLICY ANALYSIS AND CO-ORDINATION
Director Gen., D. Whelan
Policy Co-ordination
A/Director, W. Greenall
Policy Analysis Director, B. MacDonald
OPERATIONS
Director Gen., G. Yungblut
Exploration Engineering Director, F. Lepine
Reservoir and Production Director, T. Baker

RIGHTS MANAGEMENT
Director Gen., J.W. Gallagher
Rights Issuance and Policy Director, L. Napert
Rights Administration Director, J. Barrett
Rights Registration and Transfers
Director, J. Charron
Public Lands Chief, K. Corbett

RESOURCE EVALUATION
Director Gen., G. Campbell

COGLA Nova Scotia Office
Cogswell Twr., Scotia Sq., Ste. 102
2000 Barrington St., Halifax, B3J 3K1
A/Director Gen., R. Bailey
COGLA Alberta Office
Box 2638, Stn. M, Calgary, T2P 3C1
Liaison Officer, T.B. Stalinski
COGLA Yellowknife Office
Bellanca Bldg., 6th Flr.
4914-50th St., Yellowknife, X1A 1R6
Reg. Engineer, M. Thomas

AGENCIES, BOARDS, COMMISSIONS AND CROWN CORPORATIONS

Atomic Energy Control Board
270 Albert St., Box 1046
Ottawa, K1P 5S9

The Atomic Energy Control Board is a federal Crown corporation established in 1946 by the *Atomic Energy Control Act.* The Board is the regulatory agency responsible for the control of the health, safety and security aspects of nuclear energy and radioactive materials in Canada. It achieves this control by means of regulations and a comprehensive licensing system administered with the co-operation of other federal and provincial government departments in the areas of health, environment, transport, labour and others.

The Board sets standards and imposes requirements that must be met and assesses licence applicants' capabilities, plans and programs. Once a licence is issued, it carries out compliance inspections to ensure adherence to licence conditions and the Atomic Energy Control Regulations. To ensure that Canada's national policies and international commitments relating to the non-proliferation of nuclear explosives are met, the Board controls all imports and exports of nuclear materials and equipment, in co-operation with other federal government agencies.

President, R.J.A. Lévesque
Secretary to the Board, P.E. Hamel
Publications, M. Fife
Office of Public Information
Chief, H.J.M. Spence
Legal Advisor, Paul J. Barker
Planning and Administration Branch
Director, R.W. Blackburn
Administration Division
Manager, J.G. Waddington
Planning and Co-ordination Division
Chief, L.L. Trudel
Information Management Section
Chief, W. Goodwin
A/Librarian, C.M. MacLean
Finance and Material Management Section
Chief, W. Gregory
Personnel Section Chief, B.R. Richard
Regulatory Research Branch
Director, J.W. Beare
Radiation Protection Division
Manager, R.M. Duncan

Health and Environmental Effects Section
Chief, H. Stocker
Safety and Safeguards Section
Chief, J.R. Coady

DIRECTORATE OF REACTOR REGULATION
Director Gen., Z. Domaratzki
Power Reactor Division-A
Manager, J.P. Marchildon
Power Reactor Division-B
Manager, J.D. Harvie
Operator Certification and
Research Facility Division
Manager, F. Davediuk
Safety Evaluation Division
A/Manager, P.H. Wigfull
Components and Quality Assurance Division
Manager, T.J. Molloy

DIRECTORATE OF FUEL CYCLE AND
MATERIALS REGULATION
Director Gen., W.D. Smythe
Uranium Mine Division Manager, A.B. Dory
Waste Management Division
Manager, G.C. Jack
Fuel and Heavy Water Plant Division
Manager, J.P. Didyk
Radioisotopes and Transportation Division
Manager, G.B. Knight
Compliance Services and
Laboratories Division Manager, L.C. Henry
Safeguards and Security Division
Manager, D.B. Sinden

Atomic Energy of Canada Ltd.
Canada Bldg.
344 Slater St., Ottawa, K1A 0S4

Atomic Energy of Canada Limited is a federal Crown corporation established in 1952 under the provisions of the *Companies Act*. It has the authority to develop, for the national benefit, the peaceful uses of atomic energy.

The Company employs about 5,500 persons at sites in Manitoba, Ontario, Quebec, Nova Scotia and British Columbia. The Corporation is organized into four operating companies controlled by a corporate office. The Research Company with head offices in Ottawa carries out pure and applied research in the field of nuclear energy. CANDU Operations, which has its head offices at Sheridan Park in Mississauga, Ont., designs and markets nuclear power stations, components and technology, provides nuclear engineering services to Canadian utilities and overseas customers and owns heavy water plants. The Radiochemical Company with head offices in Kanata, Ont., manufactures and markets a wide range of products employing radiation from radioisotopes and accelerators for medical and industrial applications. The Medical Products Division with head offices in Kanata, designs and manufactures cancer therapy units.
President and CEO, James Donnelly
Corporate Exec. Vice-President, M. Therrien

Human Resources
Corporate Vice-President, H.T. Hughes
Corporate Secretary and
Vice-President, Corporate Relations
R. Veilleux
Finance
Corporate Vice-President, Finance
and CFO, D.G. Cuthbertson
Gen. Counsel, T.A. Wardrop
Treasurer, E. Deslauriers
Asst. Corporate Secretary, Louise Carisse
QUEBEC OPERATIONS
1155, rue Metcalfe, 2e ét.
Montréal, H3B 2V6
CANDU OPERATIONS
Sheridan Park Research Community
Mississauga, ON L5K 1B2
President, D.S. Lawson
RESEARCH COMPANY
344 Slater St., 16th Flr., Ottawa, K1A 0S4
President, Dr. S.R. Hatcher

Sites:
Chalk River Nuclear Laboratories
Chalk River, ON K0J 1J0
Whiteshell Nuclear Research Establishment
Pinawa, MB R0E 1L0

Canada-Nova Scotia Offshore Oil and Gas Board
Cogswell Twr., Scotia Sq., 1st Flr.
2000 Barrington St., Halifax, B3J 3K1

On March 2, 1982, the Government of Canada and the Government of Nova Scotia agreed to a co-operative management system for the development of oil and natural gas in the offshore Nova Scotia area. As a result, the Canada-Nova Scotia Offshore Oil and Gas Board was set up. On Aug. 26, 1986, the governments of Canada and Nova Scotia signed the *Canada-Nova Scotia Offshore Petroleum Accord*, replacing the 1982 Agreement.

The current Board is responsible for the collection of royalties from the oil companies, making offshore resource management decisions and directing the activities of the Canada Oil and Gas Lands Administration (COGLA) in the offshore region. The Board is comprised of five members, three appointed by Canada and two by Nova Scotia. The chairperson, ex officio, is the administrator of COGLA.

COGLA is the agency responsible for regulating petroleum activities in the frontier regions on behalf of the federal government. COGLA's Halifax office provides technical support to the Canada/Nova Scotia Board.

One of the provisions of the 1986 Accord is the establishment of a new independent Canada-Nova Scotia Offshore Oil and Gas Board. This Board would administer and regulate all aspects of offshore oil and gas activities. The office and staff will be located in Nova Scotia. Until the new Board is operational, all questions on the Nova Scotia Offshore area should be directed to the Canada Oil and Gas Lands Administration Halifax office.

Federal (Bill C-75) and provincial (Bill 109) legislation to create the new Board has been passed and will come into effect on a date to be fixed by proclamation. The new independent Board will assume management responsibility for the Nova Scotia Offshore on the date of proclamation.

Chairman, M.E. Taschereau
355 River Rd., Ottawa, K1A 0E4
Secretary, W. Potter

Canadian Permanent Committee on Geographical Names
615 Booth St., Ottawa, K1A 0E9
General Inquiries: (613) 992-3892

This committee deals with all questions of geographical nomenclature affecting Canada and advises on research and investigation into the origin and use of geographical names. Its membership includes representatives of federal mapping agencies and other federal offices concerned with nomenclature and a representative appointed by each province and the two territories. The committee's functions were redefined in 1969 by Order-in-Council. The Order-in-Council recognizes that the provinces and territories have exclusive jurisdiction to make decisions on names in lands under their jurisdiction. However, the provinces and the territories have agreed not to make unilateral decisions regarding federal lands.

Chairman, J.H. O'Donnell

Energy Supplies Allocation Board
580 Booth St., Ottawa, K1A 0E4

The Board is responsible, in a national emergency, for the allocation of crude oil to refiners and for the allocation of refined products to wholesale petroleum users, and, if necessary, for administering a rationing program to reinforce the allocation programs. When there is no emergency, it maintains contingency plans and monitors trends in petroleum supply and demand to evaluate the need to recommend introduction of a mandatory allocation program as provided by the Energy Supplies Emergency Act, 1979.

Chairman, H.F. Stevenson
Board Secretary, R.D. Bentley

National Energy Board
Trebla Bldg., 473 Albert St.
Ottawa, K1A 0E5
Telex: 053-3791; Fax: (613) 990-7900
Inquiries: (613) 998-7204

Under the National Energy Board Act of 1959, as amended, the Board has two principal roles: to regulate specific matters concerning oil, gas and electricity in the public interest, and to advise the government on the development and use of energy resources.

The Board acts as a regulatory body in the issuing, with the approval of the Governor in Council, of certificates of public convenience and necessity for the construction of interprovincial and international pipelines and international power lines and such interprovincial power lines as may be designated by the Governor in Council, as well as the issuing of licences for the export or import of natural gas, the export of oil and of electrical power. In addition, the Board is charged with the implementation of adequate standards of construction and operation to ensure the safety of any pipeline facility it has certified. The Board also has the authority to regulate the tolls and tariffs of pipeline companies under its jurisdiction to ensure that the tolls are just and reasonable and that there is no unjust discrimination against any person or locality.

The Board also has responsibilities under the Northern Pipeline Act.

Chairman, R. Priddle
Vice-Chairman, J.-G. Fredette
Assoc. Vice-Chairman, Dr. L.M. Thur
Assoc. Vice-Chairman, A. Digby Hunt
Members: J.R. Jenkins, R.B. Horner,
W.G. Stewart, A.B. Gilmour
Exec. Director, R. Glass
Secretary, J.S. Klenavic
Communications
Asst. Secretary, N. Bourque
Regulatory
Asst. Secretary, G. Laing
Director Gen., Pipeline Regulation
K.W. Vollman
Director Gen., Energy Regulation
Dr. P.L. Miles
Economics Branch Director, M. Segal
Electric Power Branch Director, A. Karas
Energy Supply Branch Director, W.A. Hiles
Environment and Right-of-Way Branch
Director, P.A. Carr
Finance Branch Director, W. Ganim
Financial Regulatory Branch Director, H. Pau
Gas and Oil Branch Director, R. White
Information Technology Branch
Director, D. Emmens
Law Branch
Gen. Counsel, S.K. Fraser
Personnel Branch Director, J. Thompson
Pipelines Engineering/Operations Branch
Director, E.L.M. Gordon

Petro-Canada
HEAD OFFICE:
Petro-Canada Ctre. W.
150-6th Ave. S.W., Calgary, T2P 3E3
Petro-Canada Ctre. E.
111-5th Ave. S.W., Calgary, T2P 3E3
MAILING ADDRESS:
Box 2844, Calgary, T2P 3E3
(except where otherwise indicated)

Petro-Canada is a Crown corporation established by a special Act of Parliament on July 30, 1975. The purpose of this legislation was to establish, within the energy industries in Canada, a Crown-owned company with authority to explore for hydrocarbon deposits, to negotiate for and acquire petroleum and petroleum products from abroad to assure a continuity of supply for

Canada's needs, and to develop and exploit deposits of hydrocarbons within and without Canada.

With assets of over $8 billion and revenue of more than $5 billion, Petro-Canada ranked eleventh in the 1987 Financial Post 500 survey of the largest industrial corporations in the country. It is the largest Canadian-owned oil and gas company and one of four integrated energy companies in Canada that are national in scope.

Petro-Canada has two distinct business groups: Petro-Canada Products and Petro-Canada Resources. In addition, there is a corporate group that provides financial, administrative, legal and human resources support.

Chairman and CEO, W.H. (Bill) Hopper
President and COO, E.M. Lakusta
President, Petro-Canada Resources
J.M. Stanford
President, Petro-Canada Products
R.J. Mayo
Exec. Vice-President and Secretary,
Vacant

CHAIRMAN'S OFFICE
Public Affairs
Vice-President, Bob Foulkes
Products Public Affairs Director, Judy Wish
Resources Public Affairs
Director, Sheila O'Brien
Legal Division
Vice-President and Gen. Counsel,
R.W. McCaskill
Human Resources Division
Vice-President, C.L. Houde
Finance and Planning Division
Information Services and
Corporate Development
Vice-President, W. Twiss
Vice-President and Controller, W. Morrow
Administration
Vice-President, T.B. Simms
Vice-President and Treasurer, F.B. Grant

PETRO-CANADA RESOURCES DIVISION
President, J.M. Stanford
Exploration
Sr. Vice-President, Dr. P. Kaye
Canadian Exploration
Vice-President and Gen. Manager,
W.B. Thompson
Vice-President, International Exploration
R.A. Halpin
Engineering
Vice-President and Gen. Manager,
I.G. Bryden
Production
Sr. Vice-President, N.F. McIntyre
Production Operations
Vice-President and Gen. Manager,
R.T. McGrath
Natural Gas Marketing
Vice-President and Gen. Manager,
J.F. Bechtold
Vice-President, Joint Ventures

B.C. McDonald
Business Analysis and Support
Vice-President, Brant G. Sangster

PETRO-CANADA PRODUCTS
Box 2844, Calgary, T2P 3E3
President, R.J. Mayo
Eastern Region
1 Place Ville Marie
Montréal (Québec) H3B 4A9
Sr. Vice-President, G.N. Beauregard
Central Region
5140 Yonge St., Ste. 200
North York, ON M2N 6L6
Sr. Vice-President, J. Pantelidis
Western Region
Box 2844, Calgary, AB T2P 3E3
Sr. Vice-President, Barry D. Stewart
Refining and Technology
Vice-President, R.S. Vincent
Engineering Services
Sr. Director, S. Giannangelo
Marketing and Development
Vice-President, S. Ford Ralph
Planning and Business Analysis
Vice-President, S. Thompson
Divisional Controller, C.J. Smith
Supply
Vice-President, T. Matsushita
Human Resources
Sr. Director, R.C. Legge

**Petro-Canada International Assistance Corp.
(PCIAC)**
(PCIAC is a wholly owned subsidiary of Petro-Canada).
OTTAWA OFFICE
Ste. 1601, 360 Albert St., Ottawa, K1R 7X7
CALGARY OFFICE
150-6th Ave. S.W.
Box 2844, Calgary, T2P 3E3
General Inquiries: (403) 296-5554

Petro-Canada International Assistance Corporation (PCIAC) was established by the Government of Canada in 1981 to help oil-importing developing countries to find and develop their own oil and gas supplies with the help of Canadian goods and services.

Though a subsidiary of Petro-Canada, PCIAC receives its funding through an appropriation from the Canadian Parliament pegged at $60.5 million for 1988-89. Petro-Canada provides the personnel and services to assess and direct the aid projects on a non-profit cost-recovery basis to PCIAC.

The board of directors of PCIAC is made up of a representative of the Minister of Energy, Mines and Resources, of the Secretary of State for External Affairs, and three officers of Petro-Canada.

Chairman and C.E.O., Peter M. Towe
Policy and Planning
Vice-President, Yves Gagnon
Operations
Vice-President, W.R. Maiklem

Petroleum Monitoring Agency
580 Booth St., Ottawa, K1A 0E4

The Petroleum Monitoring Agency (PMA) — a fact-finding organization established in 1980 by Order-in-Council under the *Inquiries Act* — today derives its authority from the *Energy Monitoring Act.* The Agency's mandate is to monitor and report to the Minister of Energy, Mines and Resources on the financial position and performance of the oil and gas industry in Canada. The Agency reports semi-annually on production, revenue and profits, flow of funds, capital expenditures, ownership and control, and other results and measures of industry performance.

Chairman, P. Camu
Director, G.A. Reinecke
Asst. Director, P. Blitt

DEPARTMENT OF THE ENVIRONMENT
Terrasses de la Chaudière
10, rue Wellington, Hull
MAILING ADDRESS: Ottawa, K1A 0H3
Telex: 053-3608; Fax: (819) 997-1924
Departmental Inquiries: (819) 997-2800

MINISTER'S OFFICE
Rm. 511-S, Centre Blk.
House of Commons, Ottawa, K1A 0A6
Minister, The Hon. Lucien Bouchard

DEPUTY MINISTER'S OFFICE
Dep. Minister, Geneviève A. Sainte-Marie
Office of the Science Advisor
Science Advisor, Dr. E.F. Roots

COMMUNICATIONS DIRECTORATE
Director Gen., William Peters
Dep. Director Gen., Conrad Bastien
Policy and Planning Director, Maggie Grogan
Creative Services Director, Jim Shearon
Personnel Directorate
Director Gen., L. Pertus
REGIONAL DIRECTORS GENERAL:
Atlantic Region
45 Alderney Dr., Dartmouth, NS B2Y 2N6
Jim Vollmershausen
Quebec Region
2700, boul. Laurier
C.P. 10100, Ste-Foy, G1V 4H5
G. Lamoureux
Ontario Region
55 St. Clair Ave. E., 6th Flr.
Toronto, M4T 1M2
Elizabeth Dowdeswell
Western and Northern Region
2nd Flr., 4999-98th Ave.
Edmonton, AB T6B 2X3
Bev Burns
Pacific and Yukon Region
3rd Flr., Kapilano 100, Park Royal South

West Vancouver, V7T 1A2
Kirk Dawson

Finance and Administration Service
Asst. Dep. Minister, W. Evan Armstrong

SYSTEMS AND INFORMATICS DIRECTORATE
Director Gen., D.M. Brown
Application Software and Quantitative Methods
Director, A.W. Douglas
Computing Operations Director, B.J. Cabana
Informatics Management Director, K.M. Magar

FINANCE DIRECTORATE
A/Departmental Comptroller, Luc Desroches
Financial Systems and
Management Information Branch
Director, M. Hider
Financial Planning and
Resource Analysis Branch
A/Director, Nicole Chateauneuf
Financial Services Branch
Director, G. Pearson
Administration Program
Director, Nicole Bureau

DEPARTMENTAL MANAGEMENT SERVICES
Director Gen., François Pagé
Document, Text and Library Services
Director, Agatha Bystram
Materiel and Accommodation Management
Director, G. Touchette
Administrative Practices and Systems
Director, R. Allègre

INTERNAL AUDIT BRANCH
Director Gen., Vacant
Operational Audit
A/Manager, T.A. Foulkes
Financial and Administrative
Audit Program Manager, J.C. Carroll
Personnel—Administration Program
Director, R. Boisvenu

Environmental Conservation and Protection
Place Vincent Massey
351, boul. St-Joseph, Hull
MAILING ADDRESS: Ottawa, K1A 0H3
Asst. Dep. Minister, Lorette Goulet
Policy Branch Director, J. Maxwell
Management Information and
Accountability Branch
Director, J.-C. Dumesnil
Finance and Administration Branch
Director, G.A. Coates
Personnel Branch Director, M. Boudrias

INLAND WATERS
Director Gen., D.A. Davis
Program Analysis and Co-ordination Branch
A/Director, F. Guimont
Water Planning and Management Branch
Director, R.L. Pentland

Water Quality Branch Director, V.E. Niemela
Water Resources Branch Director, K. Kimmett
Management Services Branch
Director, A.M. Tippins
National Water Research Institute
Box 5050, Burlington, ON L7R 4A6
Reg. Director, Dr. D.L. Egar
National Hydrology Research Institute
11 Innovation Blvd., Saskatoon, SK S7N 3H5
Director, Dr. T. Milne Dick

ENVIRONMENTAL PROTECTION
Director Gen., P.M. Higgins
Management and Emergencies Branch
Director, G.M. Cornwall
C&P Toxic Chemicals Program
Special Advisor, Dr. H.R. Eisenhauer
Commercial Chemicals Branch
Director, G.A. Allard
Industrial Programs Branch
Director, V. Shantora
Technology Development and
Technical Services
Director, Vacant
Wastewater Technology Centre
Box 5050, 867 Lakeshore Rd.
Burlington, ON L7R 4A6
A/Reg. Director, B.E. Jank

CANADIAN WILDLIFE SERVICE
Director Gen., H.A. Clarke
Migratory Birds and
Wildlife Conservation Branch
A/Director, E.F. Lynch
Wildlife Toxicology and Surveys Branch
Director, J.A. Keith
Program Analysis and Co-ordination Branch
Director, D. Pollock
Sustainable Development Branch
A/Director, L. Whitby
State of the Environmental Reporting Branch
A/Director, A. Jolicoeur
REGIONAL OFFICES:
Pacific and Yukon Region
Kapilano 100, Park Royal S.
West Vancouver, V7T 1A2
Reg. Director Gen., E.D. Anthony
Protection
Reg. Director, B.A. Heskin
Inland Waters
Reg. Director, E.M. Clark
Canadian Wildlife Service
5421 Robertson Rd., Delta, BC V4K 3Y3
Reg. Director, A. Martell
Western and Northern Region
Twin Atria Bldg., No. 2, 2nd Flr.
4999-98th Ave., Edmonton, AB T6B 2X3
Reg. Director Gen., Bev Burns
Protection
Reg. Director, R.K. Lane
Canadian Wildlife Service
Reg. Director, G. Kerr
Inland Waters
1901 Victoria Ave., Saskatoon, S4P 3R4
Reg. Director, R.A. Halliday

Ontario Region
25 St. Clair Ave. E., Toronto, M4T 1M2
Reg. Director Gen., Elizabeth Dowdeswell
Protection
Reg. Director, K. Shikaze
Inland Waters
867 Lakeshore Rd., Box 5050
Burlington, L7R 4A6
Reg. Director, E. Tony Wagner
Canadian Wildlife Service
1725 Woodward Dr., Ottawa, K1A 0E7
Reg. Director, S.G. Curtis
Quebec Region
1141, rte de l'Eglise
C.P. 10100, Ste-Foy, G1V 4H5
Reg. Director Gen., J.-P. Gauthier
Inland Waters
Reg. Director, C. Triquet
Canadian Wildlife Service,
Reg. Director, Jean Cinq-Mars
Protection
1179, rue de Bleury, 2e ét.
Montréal, H3B 3H9
Reg. Director, R. Perrier
Atlantic Region
5th Flr., Queen Sq.
45 Alderney Dr., Dartmouth, B2Y 2N6
Reg. Director Gen., Jim Vollmershausen
Protection
Reg. Director, E.J. Norrena
Inland Waters
Reg. Director, S. Fenety
Canadian Wildlife Service
31 W. Main St., Box 1590
Sackville, NB E0A 3C0
Reg. Director, G. Finney

Atmospheric Environment Service
Headquarters
27th Flr., Terrasses de la Chaudière, Hull
MAILING ADDRESS: Ottawa, K1A 0H3
Asst. Dep. Minister, H.L. Ferguson
Policy, Planning and Assessment Directorate
Director Gen., Pierre Martel
Sr. Science Advisor, Dr. W.L. Godson
Scientific Programs Co-ordinator,
Dr. J.D. Reid
Liaison Meteorologist, Yvon Bernier
Administrative Office
4905 Dufferin St., Downsview, ON M3H 5T4
Finance and Administration Branch
Director, J. Boll
Atmospheric Research Directorate
Director Gen., Dr. A.J. Chisholm
Central Services Directorate
Director Gen., G.M. Shimizu
Weather Services Directorate
A/Director Gen., P.G. Aber
Canadian Climate Centre
Director Gen., Dr. D.K. Dawson
REGIONAL OFFICES:
Pacific Region
1200 W. 73rd Ave., Ste. 700
Vancouver, BC V6P 6H9
Reg. Director, P.J. Pender

Western Region
2nd Flr., Twin Atria Bldg.
4999-98th Ave., Edmonton, AB T6B 2X3
Reg. Director, Brian O'Donnell
Central Region
AES, Rm. 1000
266 Graham Ave., Winnipeg, MB R3C 3V4
Reg. Director, M. Balshaw
Ontario Region
25 St. Clair Ave. E., Toronto, M4T 1M2
A/Reg. Director, John Mills
Quebec Region
100, boul. Alexis-Nihon, 3e ét.
Ville-St-Laurent, H4M 2N6
Reg. Director, François Lemire
Atlantic Region
1496 Bedford Hwy., Bedford, NS B4A 1E5
Reg. Director, Dr. A.D.J. O'Neill
Canadian Meteorological Centre
2121, rte Trans-Canada, bur. 404
Dorval (Québec) H9P 1J3
Director, Hubert Allard
Meteorology and Oceanography
National Defence Headquarters
101 Colonel By Drive, 7th Flr.
Ottawa, K1A 0K2
A/Director, W.I. Pugsley

Parks

Asst. Dep. Minister, J.D. Collinson

PROGRAM MANAGEMENT
Director Gen., G.A. Yeates
Intergovernmental Affairs—Heritage
Chief, Jean Brown
Program Policy Group
Sr. Policy Advisor, H. Eidsvik
Finance and Administration
Comptroller, L.J. Brunette
National Parks Branch
A/Director Gen., Ian Rutherford
National Historic Parks and Sites Branch
Director Gen., Dr. Christina Cameron
REGIONAL OFFICES:
Atlantic Region
Historic Properties
Upper Water St., Halifax, NS B3J 1S9
Director Gen., W.C. Turnbull
Directors:
Policy Planning and Research, N. Munro
Administration, R. Orr
Operations, J. O'Brien
Quebec Region
3, rue Buade, C.P. 6060, succ. Haute-Ville
Québec, G1K 4V7
Director Gen., G. Desaulniers
Directors:
Operations, Henri Hubert
Programming and Development, L. Tremblay
Ontario Region
111 Water St. E.
Box 1359, Cornwall, K6H 6S3
Director Gen., J.C. Christakos
Asst. Directors:
Operations, G.M. Davison

Planning, Programming and Development,
Onno Kremers
Prairie Region
Confederation Bldg.
457 Main St., Winnipeg, R3B 1B4
Director Gen., W.D. Harper
Asst. Directors:
Operations, Mike Fay
Programming and Development, T. Heggie
Western Region
5th Flr., 220-4th Ave. S.E.
Box 2989, Stn. M, Calgary, T2P 3H8
Director Gen., Sandra B. Davis
Directors:
Operations, Randy Mitchell
Programming and Development, D.W. Street

ASSORTED SERVICES
Translation Director, Gilles Melanson
Legal Services
Director, Louise Sabourin-Hébert, Q.C.

AGENCIES, BOARDS AND COMMISSIONS

Canadian Environmental Advisory Council
Terrasses de la Chaudière
Ottawa, K1A 0H3

The Canadian Environmental Advisory Council (CEAC) was established in 1972 as a means of promoting communication and the understanding of environmental concerns among diverse interest groups in society, and between those groups and the Minister of the Environment. It serves as an independent advisory body to the minister. Members are appointed by the Minister, and represent a cross-section of the public who are knowledgeable and concerned about environment quality.

Chairman, Dr. R. Page
Environmental Centre
Trent University
Peterborough, ON K9J 7B8
Exec. Director, K. Ogilvie
Science Advisor, Dr. E.F. Roots

Federal Environmental Assessment Review Office
13th Flr., Fontaine Bldg.
Ottawa, K1A 0H3

The Federal Environmental Assessment Review Office (FEARO) administers the federal environmental assessment and review process (EARP). The process calls for departments to consider — early in the planning stages — the environmental and directly-related social impact of any proposals in which they are involved. FEARO provides advice and guidelines to departments on EARP, and manages public reviews of proposals that have potentially significant environmental impact. It also provides the secretariat for the Canadian Environmental Advisory Council (see above).

Exec. Chairman, R.M. Robinson

Policy and Administration
Director Gen., J.F. Herity
Central Region
Sr. Reg. Director, R.G. Connelly
Quebec Region
A/Director, Carol Martin
Atlantic Region Director, David Barnes
Pacific Western and Northern Region
Director, D.W. Marshall
Process Evaluation and Co-ordination
Director, C.D. Robertson
Canadian Environmental Assessment
Research Council
13th Flr., Fontaine Bldg., Ottawa, K1A 0H3
Manager, Dr. Elisabeth Marsollier

Historic Sites and Monuments Board of Canada
Terrasses de la Chaudière, Ottawa, K1A 0H3
Inquiries: (819) 997-4059

The Historic Sites and Monuments Board of Canada, which was established in 1919, is the statutory body appointed to advise the Minister of the Environment on the commemoration of the nation's historic sites. The *Historic Sites and Monuments Act* of 1953 provided the statutory base for the operation of the Board and defined its advisory role.

The Act now provides for a Board membership of seventeen, which is composed of: two representatives each from Ontario and Quebec and one each from the eight remaining provinces and from the Yukon and Northwest Territories, all of whom are appointed by the Governor in Council; a representative from the National Museums of Canada; the Dominion Archivist; and an officer from the Department of the Environment (this position has traditionally been left vacant).

The Board has established special committees of its members to expedite its work. The Committees work regularly throughout the year and report to the Board at its regular meetings. The Board generally meets twice yearly, with one meeting taking place in a different part of Canada each year.

Chairman, Prof. Thomas H.B. Symons
Secretary, Dr. Christina Cameron
Asst. Secretary, L. Friend

National Battlefields Commission
390, av. de Bernières
Quebec (Québec) G1R 2L7

The National Battlefields Commission was established in 1908 by *An Act respecting National Battlefields at Quebec.* The Commission, a departmental corporation, is responsible for the acquisition, restoration, and maintenance of the historic battlefields at Quebec that form the Quebec Battlefields Park.

Chairman, J. Villeneuve
Secretary, Michel Leullier
Commissioners: Louis-Philippe Bonneau,
Constance de Lottinville, François Lavoie,
Marc O'Neil, Roger Rochette,
Raymond Thivierge, Paul Thomassin

DEPARTMENT OF EXTERNAL AFFAIRS

Lester B. Pearson Bldg.
125 Sussex Dr., Ottawa, K1A 0G2
Fax: (613) 996-9103; Telex: 053-3745
General Inquiries: (613) 996-9134

OFFICE OF THE SECRETARY OF STATE FOR
EXTERNAL AFFAIRS
Rm. 165, E. Blk., House of Commons
Ottawa, K1A 0A6
Secretary of State for External Affairs,
The Rt. Hon. Joe Clark

OFFICE OF THE MINISTER FOR
INTERNATIONAL TRADE
418N, House of Commons, Ottawa, K1A 0A6
Minister, The Hon. John Crosbie

OFFICE OF THE MINISTER FOR EXTERNAL
RELATIONS AND INTERNATIONAL
DEVELOPMENT
256 Confederation Bldg.
House of Commons, Ottawa, K1A 0A6
Minister, The Hon. Monique Landry

OFFICE OF THE MINISTER OF STATE
(INTERNATIONAL TRADE)
350 Confederation Bldg.
House of Commons, Ottawa, K1A 0A6
Minister of State, The Hon. John McDermid

OFFICE OF THE UNDER-SECRETARY OF
STATE FOR EXTERNAL AFFAIRS
Under-Secretary of State
for External Affairs, James H. Taylor
Assoc. Under-Secretary of State
for External Affairs, Raymond Chretien
Assoc. Under-Secretary of State for External
Affairs and Dep. Minister for International
Trade, G. Shannon
Asst. Dep. Minister for Special Projects,
Michael R. Bell
Access to Information and Privacy
Co-ordinator, S.A. Wade
Canadian Submarine Acquisition Program
Co-ordinator, A. Blum
Chief Air Negotiator, R. Gherson

CORPORATE MANAGEMENT BUREAU
Director Gen., L.J. Edwards
Cabinet Liaison and Co-ordination Secretariat
A/Director, B. Cherkasky
Evaluation and Resource Review Division
Director, W.J. Van Staalduinen
Resource Management Division
Director, A.J. Stewart
Federal Provincial Relations
Sr. Advisor, F.M. Filleul
Inspector General
Inspector Gen., Wang Eb
Internal Audit Division
Director, Malcolm J. MacDonald

Trade Advisory Committee Secretariat
Sr. Advisor and Co-ordinator, Robert Noble

POLICY DEVELOPMENT BUREAU
Director Gen., J. Higginbotham
Economic and Trade Analysis Division
Director, F. de Kerckhove
Political and Strategic Analysis Division
Director, N. Etheridge

PROTOCOL
Chief of Protocol, T.J. Arcand
Dep. Chief, Pierrette Lucas
Diplomatic Corps Service
Director, Heidi Bennet

Africa and Middle East Branch

Asst. Dep. Minister, Marc Perron
Southern Africa Task Force
Chairman, John Schioler

AFRICA BUREAU
Director Gen., R.M. Middleton
Africa Trade Development Division
Director, B. Dussault
Anglophone Africa Relations Division
Director, Verona Edelstein
Francophone Africa and
Maghreb Relations Division
Director, M. Bujold

MIDDLE EAST BUREAU
Director Gen., A.P. Sherwood
Middle East Relations Division
Director, Andrew Robinson
Middle East Trade Development Division
Director, P. Dingledine
Africa and Middle East Programs Division
Director, W. Hammond

Asia and Pacific Branch

Asst. Dep. Minister, Jean C. McCloskey
Asia and Pacific Programs Division
Director, E.E. Allen

ASIA PACIFIC NORTH BUREAU
Director Gen., Arthur C. Perron
East Asia Trade Development Division
Director, D.D.H. Wright
North Asia Relations Division
Director, H. Balloch
Japan Trade Development Division
Director, C.S. Russel

ASIA PACIFIC SOUTH BUREAU
Director Gen., George W. Seymour
Asia Pacific South Relations Division
Director, H.G. Pardy
Asia Pacific South Trade Development Division
Director, R. Dery

Communications and Culture Branch

Asst. Dep. Minister, C. Peter Daniel

Communications Policy Division
Director, A.D. Morgan
Media Relations Director, C. Sarrazin
Communication Services Bureau
Director Gen., Peter Lloyd
Professional and Financial Services Division
Director, Vacant

FOREIGN POLICY AND GENERAL
COMMUNICATIONS BUREAU
Director Gen., Michael Phillips
Domestic Communications Division
Director, Len Mader
External Communications Division
Director, Valerie Raymond
Library Services Division
Director, Ruth M. Thompson

INTERNATIONAL CULTURAL RELATIONS
BUREAU
Director Gen., J.F. Tanguay
Academic Relations Division
Director, Janet W. Bax
Arts Promotion Division Director, D. Peacock

TRADE COMMUNICATIONS BUREAU
Director Gen., Alain Dudoit
Trade Communications Abroad Division
Special Advisor, N.R. Cumming
Trade Communications—Canada Division
Director, Paul Desbiens
Canadexport
French Editor, L. Kovacs
English Editor, D. Wright
Info. Export: (613) 993-6435
Toll Free Line: 1-800-267-8376
International Expositions Division
Director, R. Marceau

Economic and Trade Policy Branch

Asst. Dep. Minister, John L. Paynter

ECONOMIC POLICY BUREAU
Director Gen., David C. Elder
Economic Relations with
Developing Countries Division
Director, R. Grauer
Energy and Environment Division
Director, A.C. De Hoog
International Economic Relations Division
A/Director, Wallace Dowswell
International Financial and
Investment Affairs Division
Director, Mark E. Bailey

SPECIAL TRADE RELATIONS BUREAU
Director Gen., P. Gosselin
Data Processing Division Director, Vacant
Export Controls Division Director, D. Ryan
Import Controls Division — I
(Textiles and Clothing)
Director, C. Valle
Import Controls Division — II
Director, J. Cheh
Nuclear Division Director, Arsène Després

TRADE POLICY BUREAU
Director Gen., H.R. Wilson
Agriculture Trade Policy Division
Director, E.W. Stewart
GATT Affairs Division Director, B.E. Morrisey
Industrial Trade Policy Division
Director, Paul Lau
Resources and Commodity Trade
Policy Division
Director, P. Marsden-Dole
Services and General Trade Policy Division
Director, R.F. Andrigo

Europe Branch

Asst. Dep. Minister, Jacques S. Roy

WESTERN EUROPE BUREAU
Director Gen., Jean-Pierre Juneau
European Community Division
Director, M. Huber
Western Europe Programs Division
Director, G.E. Whitehead
Western Europe Relations Division
Director, I.M. Hall
Western Europe Trade Development Division
Director, A.N. Lever

U.S.S.R. AND EASTERN EUROPE BUREAU
Director Gen., A.P. McLaine
U.S.S.R. and Eastern Europe Programs Division
Director, A. Jurkovich
U.S.S.R. and Eastern Europe Relations Division
Director, W.M.M. Fairweather
U.S.S.R. and Eastern Europe Trade
Development Division
Director, R.C. Lee

Finance and Administration Branch

Asst. Dep. Minister, Roger J. Marsham

FINANCE AND HEADQUARTERS
ADMINISTRATIVE SERVICES BUREAU
Director Gen., R. Legros
Accounting and Financial Operations Division
Director, M.P. Eastman
Financial Planning, Analysis
and Reporting Division
Director, J.G. Séguin
Financial Policy and Systems Division
Director, D.W. Gordon
Headquarters Administrative Services Division
Director, John Harding

INFORMATION RESOURCE MANAGEMENT
BUREAU
Director Gen., D.G. Woods
COSICS Project Manager, R.J. MacPhee
Information Systems Division
Director, P.S. Dunseath
Records Information Management Division
Director, M. Hutton
Telecommunications Division
A/Director, R. Beill

PASSPORT BUREAU
6th Flr., Place du Centre
200, prom. du Portage Ottawa, K1A 0G3
Director Gen., R.J. Sutherland
Public Inquiries: (819) 994-3500
Other exchanges: 1-800-567-6844
Visual Ear: (819) 994-3560
Regional and Foreign Operations
Chief of Marketing, R. Dumouchel

PHYSICAL RESOURCES BUREAU
Director Gen., D.M. Stockwell
Materiel Procurement and
Transportation Division
Director, G.E. Saucier
Policy and Advisory Services Division
A/Director, J.D. Hughes
Property Acquisition and Development Division
Director, W. Graham

International Trade Development Branch

A/Asst. Dep. Minister, Reg H. Dorrett

AGRI-FOOD, FISH AND RESOURCE
PRODUCTS BUREAU
Director Gen., Robert Burchill
Agri-Food Products Division
Director, D.G. McNicol
Fisheries and Fish Products Division
Director, R.L. Ablett
Food Products Division Director, D.G. McNicol
Market Development Division
Director, D.A. Gibson

DEFENCE PROGRAMS AND ADVANCED
TECHNOLOGY BUREAU
Director Gen., J.E.G. Gibson
EXPORT DEVELOPMENT PROGRAMS AND
SERVICES BUREAU
Director Gen., Jon Swanson
Export And Investment Programs Division
Director, G. Bruneau
Export and Transportation Services Division
Director, I.G. Lochhead
Trade Development Policy and
Planning and WIN Exports Division
Director, M. Waine McQuinn
Science and Technology Division
Director, A.S. Poole
International Trade Centres and
Regional Operations Division
Director, Louise Fortin

INTERNATIONAL TRADE CENTRES

Charlottetown
134 Kent St., Ste. 400
Box 1115, Charlottetown, C1A 7M8
Sr. Trade Commissioner, F. Dickson

Edmonton
The Cornerpoint Bldg., Ste. 505
10179-105th St., Edmonton, T5J 3S3
Sr. Trade Commissioner, J. Kepper

Halifax
1496 Lower Water St.,
Box 940, Stn. M, Halifax, B3J 2V9
Sr. Trade Commissioner, Doug Rosenthal

Moncton
Assumption Pl., 770 Main St.
Box 1210, Moncton, E1C 8P9
Sr. Trade Commissioner, Guy-André Gélinas

Montreal
800, place Victoria, 38e ét.
C.P. 247, Montreal, H4Z 1E8
Sr. Trade Commissioner, Bruno Goulet

St. John's
90 O'Leary Ave., Box 8950
St. John's, A1B 3R9
Sr. Trade Commissioner, J. Harman

Saskatoon
6th Flr., 105-21st St. E., Saskatoon, S7K 0B3
Sr. Trade Commissioner, A.D.D. McEwen

Toronto
4th Flr., Dominion Public Bldg.
1 Front St. W., Toronto, M5J 1A4
Director Gen., Trade, Doug Sirrs

Vancouver
900, 650 W. Georgia St.
Box 11610, Vancouver, M5J 1A4
Sr. Trade Commissioner, Z. Burianyk

Winnipeg
Ste. 608, 330 Portage Ave.
Winnipeg, R3C 2V2
Trade Commissioner, Tony van Rosmalen

Latin America and Caribbean Branch

Asst. Dep. Minister, Louise Frechette
Roving Ambassador for Latin America and
Permanent Observer to the Organization of
American States, R.V. Gorham
Latin America and Caribbean
Programs Division
Director, M.A. Schellenberger

CARIBBEAN AND CENTRAL AMERICA
BUREAU
Director Gen., Dwight W. Fulford
Caribbean and Central America
Relations Division
Director, G. Longmuir
Caribbean and Central America Trade
Development Division
Director, M. Stolarik

SOUTH AMERICA BUREAU
Director Gen., D.J. Browne
South America Relations Division
Director, C. Anstis
South America Trade Development Division
Director, C. Hartman

**Legal, Consular and Immigration Affairs
Branch**

Legal Advisor and Asst. Dep. Minister,
E.G. Lee
Canada-France Maritime Affairs
Sr. Negotiator, Paul Lapointe

CONSULAR AND IMMIGRATION AFFAIRS
BUREAU
Director Gen., G.H. Stewart

Consular Operations Division
Director, Murio Lapointe
Consular Policy Division
Director, Marc Baudouin
Immigration Affairs Division
Director, J.L. Baker
Domestic Legal Services
Director, Nora O'Brien

LEGAL AFFAIRS BUREAU
Director Gen., F. Mathys
Economic and Trade Law Division
Director, P. Dubois
Legal Advisory Division
Director, B. Dickson
Legal Operations Division
Director, R. Rochon

Personnel Branch

Asst. Dep. Minister, Peter Walker
Official Languages Division
Director, B. Hutton
Personnel Policy and Planning Division
Director, C.D. Fogerty

PERSONNEL ADMINISTRATION BUREAU
Director Gen., B.T. Pflanz
Compensation and Benefits Policy Division
Director, John Groves
Staff Relations and Locally
Engaged Staff Abroad Division
Director, P. Scott
Posting Services Centre
Director, L. Giannetti

PERSONNEL OPERATIONS BUREAU
Director Gen., Bernard A. Gagosz
Employment Equity Program Head, S.J. Boles
International Appointments
Sr. Advisor, George Rejhon
Training and Development Programs Division
Director, F. McGuigan
Administrative Personnel Assignments
Director, Lucie Allaire
Trade Commissioner Service and
Development Assistance
Director, L.R. Kohler
Political, Economic and Social Affairs
Director, Anne Leahy

**Political and International Security Affairs
Branch**

Asst. Dep. Minister, Fred Bild
Ambassador for Disarmament, Douglas Roche
International Women's Equity Division
Director, Ahluwalia Rashim
International Institute for Human Rights and
Democratic Development
Special Advisor, V. Edelstein

FOREIGN INTELLIGENCE BUREAU
Director Gen., J.M. Fraser
Economic Intelligence Division
Director, G.A. MacKenzie

Intelligence Services Division
Director, G. Calkin
Interview Division Director, F. Haigh
Political Intelligence Division
Director, P.R. Anderson
Francophone Affairs and Summit
Federal Co-ordinator for La Francophonie,
Claude Laverdure

INTERNATIONAL ORGANIZATIONS BUREAU
Director Gen., C. Westdal
Commonwealth Division Director, S. Beattie
Human Rights and Social Affairs Division
Director, J.D. Livermore
United Nations Affairs Division
Director, C. Svoboda

INTERNATIONAL SECURITY AND ARMS
CONTROL BUREAU
Director Gen., John J. Noble
Arms Control and Disarmament Division
Director, R.J. Lysyshyn
Defence Relations Division
Director, J.R.D. Fowell

SECURITY SERVICES BUREAU
Director Gen., A.G. Vincent
Emergency Co-ordination Division
Director, P. McRae
Security Division Director, D. Martin Collacott

United States Branch
Asst. Dep. Minister, D.W. Campbell
Exec. Director Gen., P.T. Eastham

UNITED STATES RELATIONS BUREAU
Director Gen., Douglas Branion
U.S. General Relations
and Programmes Division
Director, Mark Moher
U.S. Transboundary Division
Director, B. Buckley

UNITED STATES TRADE AND ECONOMIC
RELATIONS BUREAU
Director Gen., D.G. Waddell
U.S. Economic Relations Division
Director, R. Clark
U.S. Trade Relations Division
Director, C.L. Bland

UNITED STATES TRADE, TOURISM AND
INVESTMENT DEVELOPMENT BUREAU
Director Gen., W.L. Clarke
U.S. Trade and
Investment Development Division
Director, B.A. Northgrave
U.S. Trade and Tourism Development Division
Director, T.W. Colfer

AGENCIES, BOARDS AND COMMISSIONS
Foreign Claims Commission
125 Sussex Dr., Ottawa, K1A 0G2

The Commission, established under the *Inquiries Act,* examines claims made by Canadian citizens against countries with which Canada has entered into agreements for compensation. It reports to the Secretary of State for External Affairs and Minister of Finance concerning individual claimants' eligibility for awards and the amounts they should be awarded. Where such an agreement is contemplated, the Commission may also, at the request of the Secretary of State for External Affairs, advise him as to the number of potentially valid claims and the estimated amount of such claims.
Commissioner, Peter Hargadon

Permanent Joint Board on Defence
Lester B. Pearson Bldg.
125 Sussex Dr., Ottawa, K1A 0G2

The Permanent Joint Board on Defence (PJBD) was formed between Canada and the United States on Aug. 18, 1940, during the Second World War. On Feb. 12, 1947, the two countries issued a joint statement that military co-operation would continue through the PJBD.

The Board is headed by two co-chairmen, each of whom reports directly to their own national leader. In addition, each country is represented in the PJBD by both military and diplomatic personnel. The PJBD functions in an advisory rather than an executive capacity. It meets three times a year: February in the United States, June in Canada, and the October meeting alternating between the two capitals.

The board's agenda has included almost all of the important defence measures — for example, it has been directly involved in the formation of the Distant Early Warning (DEW) Line, and, less directly, in the establishment of NORAD. The PJBD has no direct relationship with the North Atlantic Treaty Organization (NATO) or the United Nations. *See also the* Canadian Armed Forces *section in this chapter.*

Chairman, The Hon. Allan Lawrence
Secretary, Dennis Goresky

DEPARTMENT OF FINANCE
L'Esplanade Laurier, Ottawa, K1A 0G5
General Information: (613) 992-1573

MINISTER'S OFFICE
515-S, Ctr. Blk., Ottawa, K1A 0A6
Minister, The Hon. Michael Wilson

OFFICE OF THE MINISTER OF STATE
(FINANCE)
Rm. 625, Confederation Bldg.
Ottawa, K1A 0A6
Minister of State, The Hon. Gilles Loiselle

DEPUTY MINISTER'S OFFICE
Dep. Minister, Fred Gorbet

Assoc. Dep. Minister, Michel Caron
Assoc. Dep. Minister, Dr. Wendy Dobson
*Asst. Dep. Minister (Justice), Counsel to
the Dept. of Finance,* H. Calof
Asst. Dep. Minister, Consultations and
Communications, P. Liebel

Fiscal Policy and Economic Analysis Branch

Asst. Dep. Minister, C. Scott Clark
Gen. Director, D. Smee
Fiscal Policy Director, L. Langlois
Economic Studies and Policy Analysis
Director, P.H. Lapointe
Economic Analysis and Forecasting
Director, D. Drummond

Federal-Provincial Relations and Social Policy Branch

Asst. Dep. Minister, R. Robinson
Gen. Director, S. Serson
Federal Provincial Relations
Director, Anne Park
Social Policy Director, S. Peterson

Financial Sector Policy Branch

Asst. Dep. Minister, N. Lepan
Gen. Director, T. Kane
Debt Management Division
Director, G.W. King
Chief, R.G. Miller
Financial Institutions and Markets Division
Director, Vacant
Financial Flows Section Chief, F. Swedlove
Financial Analysis Division
Director, Michael Kelly
Monetary Analysis Section
Chief, J. Cockerline
Exchange Market Section
Chief, Jim McCollum

International Trade and Finance Branch

Asst. Dep. Minister, K. Lynch
Gen. Director, T. Bernes
Tariffs Director, W. McCloskey
International Economic Relations
Director, Vacant
International Finance and Development
Director, A. Burger

Tax Policy and Legislation Branch

Sr. Asst. Dep. Minister, David A. Dodge
Special Advisor, John Sargent
Gen. Director, Legislation, R.A. Short
Gen. Director, Analysis, J. Lynn
Gen. Director, Gen. Counsel, M. Jewett
Corporate and Resource Tax Analysis
Director, D. Holland
Tax Analysis and Commodity Tax
Director, D. MacDonald
Tax Policy/Legislation Director, Len Farber
Tax Measures and Evaluation
Director, D. Sewell

Economic Development Policy Branch

Asst. Dep. Minister, Ian E. Bennett
Gen. Director, M. Francino
Special Advisor, Myles Foster
Crown Corporations Directorate
Asst. Secretary, D. Patriquin
Economic Development Division
Director, S. Kennedy
Energy and Resource Policy Division
Director, R. Edwards

Administration Branch

Asst. Dep. Minister, E. Aquilina
Personnel Director, A. Lachapelle
Administrative Services Director, J. Eadie
Financial Services Director, D.D. Lusby
Systems Division Director, E. Warrysh

SUPERINTENDENT OF FINANCIAL INSTITUTIONS CANADA

255 Albert St., 16th Flr.
Ottawa, K1A 0H2
General Inquiries: (613) 990-7788
Minister responsible, The Hon. Michael Wilson
Rm. 515-S, Centre Blk.
House of Commons, Ottawa, K1A 0A6
Minister of State responsible,
The Hon. Gilles Loiselle

SUPERINTENDENT'S OFFICE
Sup't of Financial Institutions,
Michael Mackenzie

MANAGEMENT SERVICES
Exec. Director, Robert M. Emond
Personnel and Systems
Director, Peter G. Headley
Financial Services Director, H. Ross Urquhart

Regulatory Policy, Planning and Resources Sector

Dep. Sup't, Suzanne Labarge
Legislative Planning Division
A/Director, Karl Adamsons
Policy and Research
Director, Anthony S. Maxwell
Rulings Director, André Brossard
Planning and Professional Development
Director, Blaine Knapp
Communications and Public Affairs Division
Director, Nancy Murphy

Deposit-Taking Institutions Sector

Dep. Sup't, Donald M. Macpherson
Examinations
Director Gen., Jack W. Heyes
Toronto Operations Director, Andy Poprawa
Specialist Support Director, Brian M. Kogan
National Operations Director, Neville Grant
Registration and Investigations
Director, Keith Bell
Financial Analysis Director, Ian M.D. Ruxton

Insurance and Pensions Sector

Dep. Sup't, Robert M. Hammond
Asst. Dep. Sup't, George W. Poznanski
Pension Benefits
Director Gen., Vacant
Property and Casualty Insurance
Director Gen., Richard H. Mabee
Life Insurance
Director Gen., Donald A. McIsaac
Chief Actuary, Walter Riese
Canada Pension Plan
Director, Bernard Dussault
Government Services Division
Director, Pierre Treuil
Special Projects, K.B.L. Kohli

AGENCIES, BOARDS, COMMISSIONS AND CROWN CORPORATIONS

Bank of Canada
234 Wellington St., Ottawa, K1A 0G9
General Inquiries: (613) 782-8111

Canada's central bank, the Bank of Canada, began operations on March 11, 1935, under the terms of the *Bank of Canada Act.* This Act charges the Bank with the responsibility for regulating "credit and currency in the best interests of the economic life of the nation," a responsibility that is carried out through the formulation and implementation of monetary policy. *(See also the description in the Banking, Finance and Insurance chapter, Volume 1.)*

The Bank acts as fiscal agent for the government of Canada in respect of the management of both the public debt of Canada and the Exchange Fund Account. The sole right to issue paper money for circulation in Canada is vested in the Bank of Canada.

The Bank is under the management of a board of directors composed of the Governor, the Deputy Governor and twelve directors. The Governor and Deputy Governor are appointed for terms of seven years each by the directors, with the approval of the Governor in Council. The directors are appointed by the Minister of Finance, with the approval of the Governor in Council, for terms of three years each.

The head office of the Bank of Canada is in Ottawa. It has agencies in Halifax, Saint John, Montreal, Ottawa, Toronto, Winnipeg, Regina, Calgary and Vancouver and is represented in Edmonton.

Governor, John W. Crow
Sr. Dep. Governor, G.G. Thiessen
Dep. Governors:
A. Jubinville, J.N.R. Wilson
Director of Administration, W.A. McKay
Sr. Foreign Exchange Advisor,
Nicholas Close
Advisors: J.A. Bussières,
J.A.J.S. Vachon, F. Faure
C. Freedman, W.R. White, A.C. Lamb
Advisor and Secretary, T.E. Nöel

Montreal Office
901, Square Victoria, Montréal, H2Z 1R2
Assoc. Advisor, J. Clément

Canada Deposit Insurance Corp.
Place de Ville, Twr. A
320 Queen St., 22nd Flr.
Box 2340, Stn. D, Ottawa, K1P 5W5

The Canada Deposit Insurance Corporation was established in 1967 by the *Canada Deposit Insurance Corporation Act.* The prime purpose of this Corporation is to provide, for the benefit of persons having deposits with member institutions, deposit insurance against the loss, in whole or in part, of such deposits because of the insolvency of member institutions. The maximum insurance for each person in each member institution is $60,000. Member institutions include banks, trust companies and loan companies, and these institutions pay insurance premiums to the Corporation.

The Canada Deposit Insurance Corp. is a Crown corporation and reports to the Minister of Finance. The chairman of the Corporation is appointed by the Governor in Council for a term of five years. The other members of the Board are the Governor of the Bank of Canada, the Deputy Minister of Finance, the Superintendent and Deputy Superintendent of Financial Institutions and up to four private sector members.
Board of Directors: J.W. Crow, F.W. Gorbet,
M.A. Mackenzie, R.M. Hammond,
Private Sector Directors: H.M. Caron,
E.S. Evans, P.G. Morton, R.N. Robertson

Chairman, Ron McKinlay
President and CEO, Charles C. de Léry
Exec. Vice-President and COO, J.P. Sabourin
Corporate Secretary and Gen. Counsel,
L.T. Lederman
Vice-President, Insurance and
Risk Assessment, G. St. Pierre
Vice-President, Operations, B.C. Scheepers
Vice-President, Field Operations
H.J.W. Richards
Comptroller, J. Lanthier
Director of Public Relations D.E. Racine
Information Systems Director, K.R. Adam

DEPARTMENT OF FISHERIES AND OCEANS
Rm. 121, East Blk.
House of Commons, Ottawa, K1A 0A6
(except where otherwise indicated)
General Inquiries: (613) 993-0600

MINISTER'S OFFICE
Minister, The Hon. Tom Siddon

OFFICE OF THE DEPUTY MINISTER
Dep. Minister, Peter Meyboom
Sr. Asst. Dep. Minister, François Pouliot

ASSISTANT DEPUTY MINISTERS
Pacific and Freshwater Fisheries,
Pierre Asselin
International Fisheries, Dr. Victor Rabinovitch
Atlantic Fisheries, Wayne Shinners
Science, Bill Doubleday
Policy and Program Planning, David Good

MANAGEMENT
Legal Services Director, Marla Bryant
Communications Branch
Director Gen., Nicole Deschênes
Small Craft Harbours Branch
A/Director, M. Godin
Ship Branch Director, J.M. Cutts
A/Dominion Hydrographer, G.R. Douglas
REGIONAL OFFICES:

Newfoundland Region
Box 5667, St. John's, A1C 5X1
Reg. Director Gen., E. Dunne

Scotia-Fundy Region
Box 550, Halifax, B3J 2S7
Reg. Director Gen., J-E. Haché

Bedford Institute of Oceanography
Box 1006, Dartmouth, NS B2Y 4A2
Reg. Director of Science, S.B. MacPhee

Gulf Region
Box 5030, Moncton, NB E1C 9B6
Reg. Director Gen., E.J. Niles

Quebec Region
901, rue Cap Diamant
C.P. 15500, Québec, G1K 7Y7
Director Gen., D. Martin

Maurice Lamontagne Institute
850, rte de la Mer, C.P. 1000
Mont-Joli (Québec) G5H 3Z4
Director, J. Boulva

Central and Arctic Region
Freshwater Institute
501 University Cres., Winnipeg, MB R3T 2N6
Director Gen., P.H. Sutherland

Pacific Region
Ste. 400, 555 W. Hastings St.
Vancouver, BC V6B 5G3
Director Gen., P. Chamut

Institute of Ocean Sciences
Fisheries and Oceans Canada
9860 West Saanich Rd.
Box 6000, Sidney, BC V8L 4B2
Reg. Science Director, Dr. J.C. Davis

AGENCIES, BOARDS AND COMMISSIONS
Canadian Saltfish Corp.
Box 9440, St. John's, A1A 2Y3
General Inquiries: (709) 772-6080

The Canadian Saltfish Corporation was established by the *Saltfish Act,* R.S.C. 1970 (1st Supp.), Chapter 37, for the purpose of improving the earnings of primary producers of cured fish of the cod family. Its power is also based on supporting legislation from Newfoundland and Quebec.

The Corporation is the first buyer of cured fish and fish for curing in participating provinces. It is the sole marketing agent for specified salt fish products produced in these provinces. Initial prices are announced by the Corporation for each grade and size at the beginning of the fishing season. Any surplus funds remaining after sales of annual production may be distributed to each fisherman on the basis of his sales to the Corporation. Individuals or firms in the salt fish industry sign agreements to be agents of the corporation and perform functions such as collecting, drying, storing, and packing cod fish.

The Corporation consists of a board of directors composed of a chairman, a president, one director for each participating province, and not more than five other directors, each of whom is appointed by the Governor in Council to hold office for a term not exceeding five years.

Chairman, James Barnes
President, W.R. Moyse
Vice-President, Marketing, C.E. Wheeler
Vice-President, Production, B.K. Kennedy
Export Manager, I.J. Dower
Comptroller, G.P. Angel, Jr.

Fisheries and Oceans Research Advisory Council (FORAC)
Ste. 901, 1649 Hollis St., Halifax, NS B3J 1V8

The Fisheries and Oceans Research Advisory Council was created by the *Government Organization Act, 1979.* The Council advises the Minister of Fisheries and Oceans on all matters referred to it by the minister which relate to:
• fisheries research and the marine sciences, including technological developments in those fields;
• the scope and adequacy of the science policies and programs of the Department of Fisheries and Oceans, having regard to the duties and functions of that Department and the science policies and international obligations of the Government of Canada; and
• the co-ordination of research and development programs in the fields of fisheries research and marine sciences.

The Chairman of the Council is appointed by the Governor in Council and the twenty-four other members of the Council are appointed by the Minister of Fisheries and Oceans.

Chairman, G.N. Ewing

Fisheries Prices Support Board
200 Kent St., 13th Flr., Ottawa, K1A 0E6

The Fisheries Prices Support Board was established under the *Fisheries Prices Support Act,* R.S.C. 1970, Chapter F-23.

The legislation is designed to protect commercial fishermen against the impact of declines in raw-fish prices. The board is thus responsible for investigating the causes and effects of such declines and for recommending measures to stabilize fishery prices when appropriate.

The Board, subject to approval of the Governor in Council, is empowered to purchase fishery products at prescribed prices or to pay deficiency payments to producers of fishery products equal to the difference between a prescribed price and the average price at which such products were sold.

Chairman, Harold Collins
Vice-Chairman, Peter S. Hyndman
Members: Allan R. Billard,
Thomas Best, Beverley Cottrell
Exec. Director, John J. LeVert

Freshwater Fish Marketing Corp.
1199 Plessis Rd., Winnipeg, MB R2C 3L4

The Freshwater Fish Marketing Corporation was established by the *Freshwater Fish Marketing Act,* S.C. 1968-69, Chapter 21. The Corporation consists of a board of directors composed of a chairman, a president, one director for each participating province, and four other directors, each of whom is appointed by the Governor in Council.

The Corporation was established for the purpose of marketing and trading in fish, fish products, and fish by-products in and out of Canada. Except in accordance with the terms and conditions set forth in any licence that may be issued by it, the Corporation has the exclusive right to market and trade in fish in interprovincial and export trade, and exercise that right, either by itself or by its agents, with the object of: (a) marketing fish in an orderly manner; (b) increasing returns to fishermen; and, (c) promoting international markets for and increasing interprovincial and export trade in fish.

The Corporation may enter into and carry out arrangements with any government or person that the corporation deems necessary or desirable in furtherance of the purpose for which it was established, and may receive and exercise any grants, rights, franchises, privileges, and concessions that may be granted to or conferred upon it by any government or person.

Under federal-provincial agreements, the Corporation can perform on behalf of the provinces functions relating to intraprovincial trade in fish which are parallel to those performed under federal powers in interprovincial and export trade.

Chairman, John G. McFarlane
200 Kent St., 15th Flr., Ottawa, K1A 0E6
President, J.T. Dunn
Vice-President of Marketing, Peter R. Smith

DEPARTMENT OF FORESTRY
Place Vincent Massey
351, boul. St-Joseph, Hull
MAILING ADDRESS: Ottawa, K1A 1G5

MINISTER OF STATE (FORESTRY)
Rm. 580, Confederation Bldg.
House of Commons, Ottawa, K1A 0A6
Minister, The Hon. Frank Oberle

Assoc. Dep. Minister, Jean-Claude Mercier
Asst. Dep. Minister, Policy, Dr. J.S. Maini
Asst. Dep. Minister, Operations, T. Lee
Communications Director, N. Heseltine

FINANCE AND ADMINISTRATION DIRECTORATE
Director Gen., R. Bickerton
Materiel Management and Administration Director, C. Ménard
Finance Branch Director, G. Séguin

FOREST SCIENCE DIRECTORATE
Director Gen., C.H. Winget
Forest Research Director, Dr. L.W. Carlson
Forest Insect and Disease Services Director, Vacant

POLICY, PLANNING AND INTERNATIONAL FORESTRY
Director Gen., P. Hunt
Planning Director, Tim Bezanson
International Forestry Director, Dr. G. Steneker
Cabinet Liaison
Sr. Advisor, S. Ames
Economics Branch Director, D. Ketcheson
Industry and Trade Relations Branch
Director Gen., Warren Calow

FORESTRY DEVELOPMENT DIRECTORATE
Director Gen., A. Hughes
Federal Lands Director, Bob Woods
Labour Market Development Director, Mimsi Rodrigue
Development Director, Vacant
Forest Pest Management Institute
Box 490, Sault Ste. Marie, ON P6A 5M7
Director Gen., Dr. G.W. Green
Petawawa National Forestry Institute
Chalk River, ON K0J 1J0
Director Gen., Dr. F.C. Pollett
REGIONAL OFFICES:
Atlantic Region
Newfoundland Forestry Ctr.
Box 6028, St. John's, A1C 5X8
Director Gen., Dr. J. Munro
Maritimes Forestry Ctr., Box 4000, MacKay Dr.
Fredericton, NB E3B 5P7
A/Director Gen., H. Oldham
Quebec Region
Laurentian Forestry Ctr.
Box 3800, Ste-Foy, G1V 4C7
Director Gen., M.Y. Hardy
Ontario Region
Great Lakes Forestry Ctr.
Box 490, Sault Ste. Marie, P6A 5M7
A/Director Gen., B. Haig
Western and Northern Region
Northern Forestry Ctr.
5320-122nd St., Edmonton, AB T6H 3S5
Director Gen., D. Kiil
Pacific and Yukon Region
Pacific Forestry Ctr., 506 West Burnside Rd.
Victoria, BC V8Z 1M5
A/Director Gen., D.R. Dobbs

DEPARTMENT OF HEALTH AND WELFARE

Brooke Claxton Bldg., Ottawa, K1A 0K9
General Inquiries: (613) 957-2991

MINISTER'S OFFICE
Rm. 707, Confederation Bldg.
House of Commons, Ottawa, K1A 0K6
Minister, The Hon. Perrin Beatty

DEPUTY MINISTER'S OFFICE
Dep. Minister, Dr. Maureen Law
Status of Women
Sr. Advisor, Freda Paltiel

PERSONNEL ADMINISTRATION DIRECTORATE
Director Gen., Garth Corrigall
Staff Relations and Compensation
Director, Benoit Parisien
Classification and Organization
Director, L.A. Trecarten
Staffing Management
A/Chief, Karen Duncan
Human Resource Management Bureau
Director, Desmond O'Flaherty
Human Resource Planning and
Affirmative Action
Chief, Bride Lefebvre
Official Languages
A/Director, Luce Ratté

Corporate Management Branch
Jeanne Mance Bldg., Tunney's Pasture
Ottawa, K1A 0K9
Asst. Dep. Minister, Raymond Laframboise
Branch Financial Advisor, S. Harrison
Executive Secretariat and
Management Consulting Services
Director, B.I. Driscoll
Facilities Planning and Management Directorate
Director, L.P. Cousineau
Financial Administration Directorate
Director Gen., K. McCarthy
Departmental Administrative
Services Directorate
Brooke Claxton Bldg., Ottawa, K1A 0K9
Director, J. Butler
Informatics Directorate
Director Gen., Dr. J. Saha
Program Audit and Review Directorate
Director Gen., R.J. Allen
Departmental Correspondence and
Parliamentary Relations Division
Chief, R. Bisson

ASSOCIATED SERVICES
Legal Services
Gen. Counsel, S. Tucker-Parks, Q.C.
Sr. Counsel, Faye E. Campbell
Counsel: Stuart Archibald, Gaston Arseneault,
Theresa Brucker, Bonnie Braithwhite-Lee,
Lindsay Horwood, Debra Prupas,
Bernice Wilkinson, Danielle Laurent

Law Clerk, G. McClinton
Auditor General's Representative,
W. Rafuse

Policy, Communications and Information Branch
Asst. Dep. Minister, Ian C. Green
Planning and Management Services Division
Director, Richard McKendry

POLICY DEVELOPMENT DIRECTORATE
Director Gen., Kathy O'Hara
Income Policy Director, J. Kane
Health Policy Director, A. Thomson

INFORMATION SYSTEMS DIRECTORATE
Director Gen., David Beavis
Special Advisor, D.C. McNaught
Information Access and Co-ordination Division
Director, J.A. Schriel
Social Security Information Division
Director, R.J. Young
Health Information Division
Director, L. Rehmer
Access to Information/Privacy
Director, Vacant

COMMUNICATIONS DIRECTORATE
Brooke Claxton Bldg., Ottawa, K1A 0K9
Director Gen., Monique Plante-Boyd
Media and Public Relations
Director, C. Peacock
Planning and Operations Director, A. Verville
REGIONAL COMMUNICATIONS MANAGERS:
Jean Martinet
Place Guy Favreau, Tour est, bur. 206
200, boul. René-Lévesque ouest
Montréal (Québec) H2Z 1X4
Nes Lubinsky
Ste. 1110, 200 Town Ctr. Crt.
Scarborough, ON M1P 4X8
Blair Parkhurst
245 Sinclair Centre, 757 W. Hastings St.
Vancouver, BC V6C 1A1
Pat Brownlow
Ste. 304, The Brewery
1489 Hollis St., Halifax, NS B3J 1R9
Marc Desrosiers
Ste. 505, Eaton Place
330 Graham Ave., Winnipeg, MB R3C 4C8

Income Security Programs Branch (Canada Pension Plan, Family Allowances, Old Age Security)
Asst. Dep. Minister, Dr. D.E.L. Maasland
Programs, Policy, Appeals and Legislation
Director Gen., P. Fortier
Policy and Legislation
Asst. Director Gen., R. Hagglund
Pension Appeals Board
Registrar, Colette E. Poitras
Data Development and Analysis
A/Director, C. Goodman
Appeals and Ministerial Enquiries Division
Director, J. McCann

Operations
Director Gen., F.D. Kealey
Planning and Management
Information Services
Head, K. Rawley
Controls Program Director, B. Holloway
Asst. Director Gen., R.K. Stuart
International Operations Directorate
Director, P. Iannitti
Data Management and
Operational Support Services
A/Director, R. Rowe
Disability Advisory Division
Director, Dr. H. Mohamdee
Record of Earnings and
Contributor Information Services
Director, D. Walsh
National Benefits Director, D. Haney
CPP Disability Operations Director, D. Ulis
Financial Services
A/Director, D.M. Boyd
International Liaison Director, E. Tamagno
Communications, K. Bennett
ISP Systems Redesign
Exec. Director, G. Thomson
Systems Directorate
Asst. Director Gen., E. Wallace

AREA AND REGIONAL OFFICES AND CLIENT
SERVICE CENTRES:
WESTERN AREA
1230 Bank of B.C. Bldg.
10055-106th St., Edmonton, T5J 2Z6
Asst. Director Gen., D.J. Hopkinson
British Columbia Regional Office
Federal Bldg., 436, 1230 Government St.
Victoria, V8W 2P1
Reg. Director, N. Landucci
Alberta Regional Office
Ste. 715, 9700 Jasper Ave.
Edmonton, T5J 4C2
Reg. Director, A.W. Clark
Saskatchewan Regional Office
Dominion Government Bldg.
1975 Scarth St., Regina, S4P 3K4
Reg. Director, A.D. Clarke
Manitoba Regional Office
Eaton Place, Rm. 506, 330 Graham Ave.
Winnipeg, R3C 4C8
A/Reg. Director, J. Tkatchuk
ONTARIO AREA
Box 5100, Stn. D, Scarborough, M1R 5C8
Asst. Director Gen., M. Goldfinger
Southwestern Ontario Regional Office
Judy LaMarsh Bldg., 65 William St. S.
Box 2020, Chatham, N7M 4B2
Reg. Director, R.J. Hobbs
Northern Ontario Regional Office
70 Cedar St. S., Box 2013, Timmins, P4N 8C8
Reg. Director, D. Beauchamp
QUEBEC AREA
330, rue de la Gare-du-Palais,
Québec, G1K 7L5
Asst. Director Gen., G. Turbide

ATLANTIC AREA
West End Mall, Ste. 111
6960 Mumford Rd., Halifax, B3L 4P1
Asst. Director Gen., L.C. Russell
New Brunswick Regional Office
Box 250, 633 Queen St.
Fredericton, E3B 4Z6
Reg. Director, J.R. MacQuarrie
Nova Scotia Regional Office
1400 Barrington Twr., Rm. 1400, Scotia Sq.
Box 1687, Stn. M, Halifax, B3J 3J4
Reg. Director, M.J. Lane
Prince Edward Island Regional Office
Box 1238, Charlottetown, C1A 7M9
Reg. Director, V.E. McIntyre
Newfoundland Regional Office
310 Pleasantville, Box 9430
St. John's, A1A 2Y5
Reg. Director, P. Derrane

Social Service Programs Branch
Asst. Dep. Minister, J.G. Soar
Management Services
Manager, W. Bernard

COST-SHARED PROGRAMS
A/Director Gen., G.M. Camrass
Social Assistance and Services
A/Director, J. Patry
Program Finance
A/Director, L. Homulos
Field Operations
A/Director, K. Chapman

PROGRAM DEVELOPMENT DIRECTORATE
Director Gen., D.G. Ogston
Child Care Division Director, Debbie Jette
Family Violence Prevention Division
Director, Elaine Scott
Special Advisor, Child Sexual Abuse
R.G. Rogers
Policy, Liaison and Information Division
Director, D. Moodie

SOCIAL DEVELOPMENT DIRECTORATE
Director Gen., O. Marquardt
National Welfare Grants
A/Director, Dr. D. Thornton
New Horizons Director, E. Kwavnick
NEW HORIZONS REGIONAL OFFICES:
British Columbia
1525 West 8th Ave., Main Flr.
Vancouver, V6J 1T5
Reg. Manager, Heather Fraser
Alberta, N.W.T. and Yukon
10621-100th Ave., 203 Financial Bldg.
Edmonton, T5J 0B3
Reg. Manager, Don Mayne
Saskatchewan
Federal Bldg., 4th Flr.
1975 Scarth St., Regina, S4P 3K4
Reg. Manager, Norma Wallace

Manitoba
340 Graham Ave., Eaton Place
Winnipeg, R3C 4C2
A/Reg. Manager, Esther Korchynski

Ontario
2300 Yonge St., Ste. 1104, Toronto, M4P 1E4
Reg. Manager, F. Lozier

Quebec
Place Guy Favreau, Tour est, bur. 212
200, boul. René-Lévesque ouest
Montréal, H2Z 1X4
Reg. Manager, Roger B. Mondor

New Brunswick
1222 Main St., 3rd Flr., Terminal Plaza Bldg.
Moncton, E1C 1H6
Reg. Manager, Vacant

Nova Scotia
Halifax Insurance Bldg., 4th Flr.
5670 Spring Garden Rd., Halifax, B3J 1H6
Reg. Manager, Kevin Ryan

Prince Edward Island
3 Harbour Side, Ste. 101
Charlottetown, C1A 7M9
Reg. Representative, S. Gaudet

Newfoundland
Sir Humphrey Gilbert Bldg., Rm. 602
165 Duckworth St., St. John's, A1C 1G4
Reg. Manager, Harold House

Intergovernmental and International Affairs Branch

Asst. Dep. Minister, Norbert Préfontaine
Health Affairs Director, E.M. Aiston
Sr. Advisors:
J. Larivière, A. Moineau, N. Ritchie, P. Downie
Metric Conversion Unit
Program Officer, R. Bourgon
Social Affairs Director, P. Dionne
Sr. Advisors: M. Fillion,
G. Demers, A. Leblanc
Program Analyst, Claude Giroux
International Information and Planning
Director, Vacant
International Information Chief, P. Baird
Documentalist, N. Blondin
Management Practices
Chief, Jacques Bourassa
Fellowships/Visits
A/Co-ordinator, D. Quesnel

Health Services and Promotion Branch
Jeanne Mance Bldg.
Tunney's Pasture, Ottawa K1A 1B4

Asst. Dep. Minister, Dr. Peter Glynn
Canadian Blood Committee
A/Exec. Director, Dr. I. Henderson
Planning and Management Services
Director, B. Plant

HEALTH SERVICES
Director Gen., Dr. J. Hauser
Institutional and Professional Services
Director, D.F. Moffatt

Community Health Services Director, E. Glor
Mental Health
A/Director, C. Lakaski
Preventive Health Services
Director, Dr. H. Colburn
Health Human Resources
Director, Dr. J.A. Dupont
Design for Health Director, T. Ogrodnik

EXTRAMURAL RESEARCH PROGRAMS
Director Gen., Dr. R.A. Heacock
Research Administration Director, S. Lee

HEALTH PROMOTION
Director Gen., L. Pinder
A/Programs Director, B. Ouellet
Program Resources
A/Director, Dr. I. Rootman
Regional Services
A/Director, B. Bell

REGIONAL OFFICES:

Atlantic Region
Ste. 1122, Duke Twr., Scotia Square
5251 Duke St., Halifax, B3J 1P4
Reg. Director, M. Keddy

Quebec Region
Place Guy Favreau, Tour est, 2e ét.
200, boul. René-Lévesque ouest
Montreal, H2Z 1X4
Reg. Director, Clermont Racine

Ontario Region
2221 Yonge St., Ste. 605, Toronto, M4S 2B4
Reg. Director, Gale Barr

Prairies Region
Rm. 603, 213 Notre Dame Ave.
Winnipeg, R3B 1N3
A/Reg. Director, W. Fergus

Pacific Region
750 Cambie St., 4th Flr., Vancouver, V6B 4V5
Reg. Director, Rita Stern

HEALTH INSURANCE
Director Gen., Dr. D. Leclerc
Program Analysis Director, M. Snider
Program Administration Director, B. Davis

Health Protection Branch
Tunney's Pasture, Ottawa, K1A 0L2

Asst. Dep. Minister, Dr. A.J. Liston
Branch Exec. Director, J. Hopkins
Management Processes Director, F. Wong
Briefings and Correspondence
Chief, Y. Arvisais
Communications Executive, T. Baker
A/Media Officer, Bonnie Fox-McIntyre

FINANCE AND ADMINISTRATION
DIRECTORATE
Sir Frederick Banting Research Ctr.
Ross Ave., Tunney's Pasture
Ottawa, K1A 0L2
Director, M.T. McElrone

DRUGS DIRECTORATE
Director Gen., Dr. E. Somers
Bureau of Drug Research
Director, Dr. K. Bailey
Bureau of Human Prescription Drugs
A/Director, Dr. G. Johnson
Bureau of Nonprescription Drugs
Director, R.T. Ferrier
Bureau of Dangerous Drugs
Director, J.G. LeCavalier
Bureau of Biologics
Director, Dr. J. Furesz
Bureau of Veterinary Drugs
Director, Dr. J. Messier
Bureau of Pharmaceutical Surveillance
Director, L.B. Rowsell

FOOD DIRECTORATE
Director Gen., Dr. S.W. Gunner
Regulatory Affairs Division, Food
Chief, B.L. Smith
Bureau of Chemical Safety
Director, D. Kirkpatrick
Bureau of Microbial Hazards
Director, Dr. G. Harwig
Bureau of Nutritional Sciences
Director, Dr. L. Bradshaw
Food Statistics and Operational Planning
Chief, Dr. C.S. Shih

FIELD OPERATIONS DIRECTORATE
Jeanne Mance Bldg.
Tunney's Pasture, Ottawa, K1A 1B7
Director Gen., J.R. Elliot
Bureau of Field Operations
Director, J.F. Riou
REGIONAL OFFICES:

Atlantic
Ralston Bldg., 5th Flr.
1557 Hollis St., Halifax, B3J 1V5
Director, B. Wilson

Quebec
1001, boul. St-Laurent ouest
Longueil, J4K 1C7
Director, V. Bolduc

Ontario
2301 Midland Ave., Scarborough, M1P 4R7
Director, Dr. C. Broughton

Central
510 Lagimodière Blvd., Winnipeg, R2J 3Y1
Director, V.F. Warkentin

Pacific
3155 Willingdon Green
Burnaby, V5G 4P2
Director, J.M. Forbes

ENVIRONMENTAL HEALTH DIRECTORATE
Environmental Health Ctr.
Tunney's Pasture, Ottawa, K1A 0L2
A/Director Gen., J.R. Hickman
Scientific Advisor, Mark Richardson
Bureau of Chemical Hazards
A/Director, Dr. P. Toft

Radiation and Medical Protection Bureau
Brookfield Rd., Confederation Hts.
Ottawa, K1A 1C1
Director, Dr. E.G. Létourneau

LABORATORY CENTRE FOR DISEASE CONTROL
Tunney's Pasture, Ottawa, K1A 0L2
Director Gen., Dr. J.Z. Losos
Special Advisor, I. Hynie
Microbiology Director, Dr. K. Rozee
Chronic Disease Epidemiology
Director, Dr. J.W. Davies
Biometrics Chief, Dr. G. Wells
Bureau of Communicable Disease Epidemiology
A/Director, Dr. D. Kincloch

FEDERAL CENTRE FOR AIDS
Bonaventure Bldg., Ottawa, K1A 0L2
Director Gen., Dr. A. Clayton

Medical Services Branch
Jeanne Mance Bldg., Tunney's Pasture
Ottawa, Ont., K1A 0L3
Asst. Dep. Minister, J.D. Nicholson
Branch Secretariat
Exec. Director, I.C. Inglis
Asst. Director, H. Lindsay

PUBLIC SERVICE HEALTH DIRECTORATE
Director Gen., C.E. Tupper
Environmental Health Services
A/Director, Dr. D. Dimitroff
Occupational Health Unit
Director, Dr. J. Kirkbride
Occupational Medicine
Director, Dr. J. Cappon

INDIAN AND NORTHERN HEALTH SERVICES DIRECTORATE
Director Gen., Dr. G.I. Lynch
Hospitals and Health Facilities
Director, M. Fortier
Community Health Services
Director, Dr. R. D'Aeth
Non-Insured Health Benefits
Director, N. Chedore
National Native Alcohol and
Drug Abuse Program
A/Director, R. Scott
Nursing Division
A/Director, S. Osborne

HEALTH ADVISORY SERVICES DIRECTORATE
Director Gen., Dr. H. Murdoch
Immigration and Overseas Health
Director, Dr. B. Brett
Immigration Medical Assessment Unit
Asst. Director, Dr. M.J. Ferrari
Emergency Services Director, L. Davies
Medical Advisory Division
A/Chief, Dr. D. Ingram
Civil Aviation Medicine
Director, Dr. G.Y. Takahashi

**PROGRAM TRANSFER AND POLICY
DEVELOPMENT DIRECTORATE**
Director Gen., J. Moore
Intergovernmental and Health Sector Relations
Director, Dr. C. Carver
Transfer Policy, Planning and Implementation
Director, M. Keeley
Policy Development Director, Vacant
Transfer, Training and Support
Director, H. Beauchemin
Planning and Informatics Co-ordination
Director, P. Blais

FITNESS AND AMATEUR SPORT
Journal Bldg., S. Twr.
365 Laurier Ave. W., Ottawa, K1A 0X6

**OFFICE OF THE MINISTER OF STATE FOR
(FITNESS AND AMATEUR SPORT)**
Rm. 581, Confederation Bldg.
Wellington St., Ottawa, K1A 0A6
Minister of State, The Hon. Jean J. Charest
Asst. Dep. Minister, Lyle Makosky
Official Languages Consultant, Sandra Eddy
Sr. Personnel Advisor, Robert Rowan

SPORT CANADA
Director Gen., Abby Hoffman
High Performance Manager, Pat Reid
Athlete Assistance Program Manager, Vacant
Association Management
A/Chief, Greg Rokosh
Policy, Planning and Evaluation
Chief, Sue Neill
Fitness and Amateur Sport Women's Program
Manager, Diane Palmason

FITNESS CANADA
Director, Michel Bédard
Association Management Division
Chief, Jim Ball
Fitness Development Division
Chief, Barbara O'Brien-Jewett
Policy, Planning and Special Projects
Chief, Janet Connor

ADMINISTRATIVE SERVICES
Director, J.G. Peters
Branch Planning/Executive Asst.,
Huguette Routier
Electronic Information Systems
Manager, R. Brulé
Administrative Services Manager, J. Horricks

PROMOTION AND COMMUNICATIONS
Director, Lyle Cameron
Media Relations Officer, J.-P. Charbonneau
Fitness Promotion Officer, R. Bélanger
Production Officer, D. Porter

AGENCIES, BOARDS AND COMMISSIONS

National Advisory Council on Aging
Jeanne Mance Bldg., Tunney's Pasture
Ottawa, ON K1A 0K9

Established by a federal Order-in-Council on May 1, 1980, the 18-member National Advisory Council on Aging is charged with assisting and advising the Minister of Health and Welfare on matters relating to the quality of life of Canada's older citizens — a segment of the population which is growing rapidly.

Members are appointed because of their knowledge of various areas of aging and hold office for a term of two or three years, renewable once. They come from all provinces and territories of Canada.

The Council reviews the needs and problems of older people and recommends remedial action. It consults with national, provincial and local associations involved in aging, and increases public awareness of the problems of aging by publishing reports and stimulating discussion.

While the Council's secretariat and budget are provided by the Department of Health and Welfare, the Council is an autonomous group and has only an arms-length relationship.

The Council meets at least twice a year and its subcommittees convene more frequently.
Director, Suzanne Fletcher

National Advisory Council on Fitness and Amateur Sport
Journal Twr. S., 365 Laurier Ave. W.
Ottawa, K1A 0X6

The National Advisory Council on Fitness and Amateur Sport was established by the *Fitness and Amateur Sport Act,* R.S.C. 1970, Chapter F-25. It is an advisory body to the minister on matters of policy and program.

The Council may consist of up to 30 members, with at least one representative from each province and territory. Full Council meetings are held up to three times per year to review the studies prepared by Council committees on areas of particular concern to the minister or the FAS Branch.
Chairman, Dr. Bryce Taylor

National Council of Welfare
Rm. 566, Brooke Claxton Bldg.
Ottawa, K1A 0K9

The National Council of Welfare was established by the *Government Organization Act, 1969,* as a citizens' advisory body to the Minister of National Health and Welfare. Its mandate is to advise the minister on matters pertaining to welfare.

The Council consists of 21 members, drawn from across Canada and appointed by the Governor in Council. All are private citizens and serve in their personal capacities rather than as representatives of organizations or agencies. The membership of the Council includes past and present welfare recipients, public housing tenants and other low-income citizens, as well as lawyers, professors, social workers and others involved in voluntary service associations, private welfare agencies, and social work education.

Reports by the National Council of Welfare have

dealt with medicare, poverty statistics, income security, taxation, the working poor, children in poverty, single-parent families, social employment, social services, community organization, nutrition, legal aid/legal services, low-income consumers, poor people's groups and poverty coverage in the press.
Director, K. Battle

Sport Marketing Council
1600 James Naismith Dr.
Gloucester, K1B 5N4

The Council was established in February 1986 with federal government funding to assist national amateur sport and fitness associations to better market their properties and to sensitize the corporate community to the value of amateur sport as a vehicle for their marketing thrusts.

Activities of the Council include consulting services, research, and conducting workshops and seminars related to sport marketing. It also acts as a facilitator in bringing sport and fitness groups and the corporate sector together.

Chairman, John Esaw
President, Lou Lefaive
Marketing Director, Tom Ross

DEPARTMENT OF INDIAN AFFAIRS AND NORTHERN DEVELOPMENT
Terrasses de la Chaudière
10 Wellington St., N. Twr., Hull
MAILING ADDRESS: Ottawa, K1A 0H4

MINISTER'S OFFICE
Rm. 401, Confederation Bldg.
House of Commons, Ottawa, K1A 0A6
Minister, The Hon. Pierre H. Cadieux

OFFICE OF THE MINISTER OF STATE (INDIAN AFFAIRS AND NORTHERN DEVELOPMENT)
235 Queen St., Ottawa, K1A 0H5
Minister of State, The Hon. Kim Campbell

DEPUTY MINISTER'S OFFICE
Dep. Minister, Harry Swain
Assoc. Dep. Minister, F.R. Drummie

COMMUNICATIONS BRANCH
A/Director Gen., L. Long
Operations Directorate
A/Director, J.V. Bray
Creative Services Directorate
A/Director, K.C. Shindler

Economic Development
Asst. Dep. Minister, P. Harrison

POLICY DEVELOPMENT BRANCH
Director Gen., M. Sims
Economic Analysis Directorate
A/Director, P. Banerjee

Client, Industry and Government Co-ordination Directorate
Director, Vacant
Policy Co-ordination Director, G. Guay

PLANNING AND OPERATIONS BRANCH
Director Gen., J. Graham
Planning and Information Systems Directorate
Director, C. Cram
Economic Programs Directorate
Director, T. Henderson
Indian Minerals (East) Directorate
Director, J. Conduit

Indian Oil and Gas Canada
Gov't of Canada Bldg.
220-4th Ave. S.E.
Box 2924, Stn. M, Calgary, T2P 2M7
CEO, J. Eickmeier
Indian Minerals (West) Directorate
Rm. 300, 510-12th Ave. S. W.
Calgary, T2R 0X5
Manager, P. Coolen

EXECUTIVE SUPPORT SERVICES
Director Gen., R.G. Quiney
Exec. Director, N. Overend
Planning Director, W. McBride
Executive Secretariat Directorate
Director, M.A. Lamb
Evaluation Director, A. Winberg

Finance and Professional Services
Asst. Dep. Minister, J.B. Murray
Access to Information and Privacy Secretariat Co-ordinator, J. Holt
Quantitative Analysis and Solid-Demographic Research
Director, J. Hagey

MANAGEMENT SERVICES BRANCH
Director Gen., J.F. Phillips
Systems Planning, Co-ordination and Review Directorate
A/Director, B. Giffin
EDP Systems and Operations Directorate
Director, W.L. Taggart
Support Services Directorate
Director, J. Bilodeau

FINANCE BRANCH
Director Gen., A. Williams
Increased Ministerial Authority and Accountability Director, J. Dance
Financial Reporting Director, B. Handel
Financial Analysis and Program Review Director, A.H. Horner
Accounting Operations Directorate
A/Director, D. Luck

DIAND TECHNICAL SERVICES PUBLIC WORKS CANADA
Director Gen., S. Reid
Professional Services Director, Vacant
Technical Management Director, J. Benner

Contract Policy and Services
Director, L. Tranqui
Departmental Audit Branch
4th Flr., Rm. 400
Les Terrasses de la Chaudière
25 Eddy St., Hull, K1A 0H4
Director Gen., D.M. Cooke
Departmental Legal Services
A/Sr. Gen. Counsel, D.C. McGillis
Translation Services Director, A. Davignon

HUMAN RESOURCES
Director Gen., J.R. Dalzell
Personnel Services, NCR
A/Director, T. Paul
Employment Support Services
Director, Sharon Wood
Management Category Services
Director, P. Burkholder
Human Resources and Official Languages
Director, M. Bainbridge
Employee Relations and Compensation
A/Director, G.A.J. Hayes
Native Employment and Employment Equity
Director, G. Williams

Indian Services

Asst. Dep. Minister, J.S. Rayner
Exec. Director Gen., W. Van Iterson
Special Projects, D. Chatain
Alternative Funding Arrangement
A/Director, M. Fortier
Program Planning
A/Director, C. Milne

SOCIAL DEVELOPMENT BRANCH
Director Gen., S. Williams
Policy Director, N. Levasseur
Operations Director, H. McMorrow
Resource Allocation Management
and Information Systems
Director, S. Furlong

EDUCATION BRANCH
A/Director Gen., K. Kirby
Education Policy and Planning
Director, H.A. McCue
Education Program Operations
Director, Vacant
Resources and Management Systems
Director, M. VanWelter
Cultural/Educational Centres
Director, C. Aubin

BAND SUPPORT AND CAPITAL
MANAGEMENT BRANCH
Director Gen., G. Wouters
Housing
A/Director, I. Corbin
Band Support Director, R. Sterling
Capital Management Director, I. Howes
Transfer Payments Management
Director, F.J. Jetté

Lands, Revenues and Trusts

Asst. Dep. Minister, D.K. Goodwin

LANDS AND ENVIRONMENT BRANCH
Director Gen., J.L. Cochrane, Q.C.
Lands Director, G. Swan
Environment
A/Director, D. Kane
Manitoba Northern Flood Agreement Office
A/Director, R.N. Stewart

Lands, Revenues and Trusts Review
Exec. Director, Vacant

MEMBERSHIP, REVENUES AND BAND
GOVERNANCE BRANCH
Director Gen., G. MacIntosh
Estates Director, J. Flemming
Band Governance
A/Director, G. Pilon
Indian Moneys
A/Director, D. Boileau
Membership and Entitlement
Director, M. D'Avignon

PLANNING AND POLICY CO-ORDINATION
BRANCH
Planning
A/Director, R. Dowdall
Policy Director, B. Kilfoyle
Legal Liaison and Support Director, L. Clow
Lubicon Lake Band Litigation Support Group
A/Director, R. Coulter
Vancouver, B.C. Litigation Research
Manager, K. Copp
Specific Claims Director, M. Klein

Northern Affairs Program

Sr. Asst. Dep. Minister (North), R.J. Van Loon
Planning and Support Directorate
Director, J.M. Bellefontaine
Sr. Adviser, Oil and Gas, W.R. Durie

CONSTITUTIONAL DEVELOPMENT AND
STRATEGIC PLANNING BRANCH
Director Gen., J. Stagg
Constitutional Development and
Aboriginal Affairs Directorate
A/Director, C. Baker
Canadian Eskimo Art Council
Council Secretary, E. Schoeler
Circumpolar and Scientific Affairs
A/Director, H. Finkler
Strategic Planning Director, J.H. Berg

NATURAL RESOURCES AND ECONOMIC
DEVELOPMENT BRANCH
Director Gen., P.H. Beaubier
Resource Planning and Co-ordination
Director, G. Bangay
Renewable Resources
A/Director, Dr. J.I. Sneddon
Mining and Infrastructure
Director, Dr. J. Lazarovich

Economic Development
A/Director, R. Fosbrooke
Oil and Gas Management Director, P. Sullivan

Canada Oil and Gas Lands Administration
355 River Rd., Ottawa, K1A 0E4
Administrator, M.E. Taschereau
Policy Analysis, Benefits and Environment
Dep. Administrator, Vacant
Environmental Protection Branch
Director Gen., V. Lafferty
Physical Environment Director, G.K. Sato
Biological Environment
Director, F.R. Engelhardt
Environmental Studies Research Fund
Director, Dr. O.H. Loken
Policy Analysis and Co-ordination Branch
Director Gen., D. Whelan
Analysis Director, B. MacDonald
Policy Co-ordination Director, B. Moore
Operations Director, B. de Lotbinière-Harwood
Rights Management Branch
Director Gen., J.W. Gallagher
Rights Issuance and Policy Director, L. Napert
Rights Administration Director, J.A.S. Barrett
Transfers and Registration
Director, J. Charron
Engineering Branch
Director Gen., G. Yungblut
Exploration Engineering Director, F. Lépine
Reservoirs and Production Director, T. Baker
Resource Evaluation Branch
Director Gen., G. Campbell
REGIONAL OFFICES:
Nova Scotia Region
Cogswell Twr., Scotia Sq., Ste. 102
2000 Barrington St., Halifax, B3J 3K1
Director Gen., G. Yungblut
Northwest Territories
4914-50th St., Bellanca Bldg.
Yellowknife, X1A 1R6
Reg. Engineer, M. Thomas
Alberta Region
Box 2638, Stn. M, Calgary, T2P 3C1
Liaison Officer, T.B. Stalinski

Self-Government
Asst. Dep. Minister, R.J. Van Loon

SELF-GOVERNMENT NEGOTIATIONS BRANCH
Director Gen., L. Jamieson
Community Negotiations Director, G. Du Pont
Self-Government Development
A/Director, C. Asselin

POLICY AND IMPLEMENTATION BRANCH
Director Gen., Vacant
JBNQA Implementation Negotiations
25 Eddy St., Rm. 401B, Hull, J8X 4B5
Federal Negotiator, A. Croll
Implementation Director, P. Shafto
Operations Director, W. Clevette
Policy Director, S. McInnes

Constitution
Director, M. Whitaker
Indian Fishing Policy
Director Gen., D. Watson

COMPREHENSIVE CLAIMS BRANCH
Director Gen., I. Potter
Sr. Negotiator, N. Kenyon
CYI Claim
Sr. Negotiator, G. Lavoie
TFN Claim
Sr. Negotiator, B. Dewar
Dene/Métis Claim
Chief Negotiator, Land Selection, D. Murphy
Sr. Negotiator, N. Kenyon
CAM Claim
Sr. Negotiator, O. Gobeil
Newfoundland/Labrador Claims
Sr. Negotiator, A. Stewart
Nisga'a Claim (Vancouver Office)
Chief Federal Negotiator, F.J. Walchli

REGIONAL OFFICES
Atlantic Region
40 Havelock St., Box 160
Amherst, NS B4H 3Z3
Reg. Director Gen., R.C. Brant
Finance and Administration
Director, W. Draper
Human Resources Director, M. Paul
Regional Secretariat Director, L.J. Leblanc
Economic and Employment Development
A/Director, D.R. Macdonald
Lands, Revenues and Trusts
Director, R. Graves
Indian Services Director, G.H. Fotheringham
Socio-Economic Services
A/Director, D. MacDonald
Education Director, R. Pinney
Social Development Director, J. Paul
Band Support and Capital Management
A/Director, J. Brown
Indian Government Support
A/Director, P. Garrow
PWC-DIAND Technical Services
Reg. Manager, R. Korol
Quebec Region
320, rue St-Joseph est, C.P. 3725
Québec, G1K 7Y2
Reg. Director Gen., F. Vieni
Regional Secretariat Director, G. Ouellet
Legal Advisors:
Pierre Champagne, Yves Cazelais
Indian Services Director, Y. Savard
Band Support and Capital Management
Director, R. Perron
Education Director, C. Chamberland
PWC-DIAND Technical Services
A/Reg. Manager, S. Carpentier
Social Development
Director, N. Nadeau-Picard
Economic Development and Employment
Director, Y. Carier
Finance and Administration
Director, J-Y. Lepage

Lands, Revenues and Trusts
Director, G. Lemay
Human Resources Director, Y. Desilets

Ontario Region
25 St. Clair Ave. E., 5th Flr.
Toronto, M4T 1M2
Reg. Director Gen., G. Kerr
Indian Services Director, M.P Ivanski
Executive Secretariat Director, S. Patterson
Self-Government Director, B. Bennett
Economic and Employment Development
Director, J. Hébert
Social Development Director, T. Goff
Education
A/Director, J. Donnelly
PWC-DIAND Technical Services
Reg. Manager, M.J. Dewasha
Finance and Administration
A/Director, R. Shankar
Lands, Revenues and Trusts
Director, R. Hatfield
Band Support and Capital Management
A/Director, B. Garand
Human Resources Director, A. Yuile

Manitoba Region
1100, 275 Portage Ave.
Winnipeg, R3B 3A3
Reg. Director Gen., E. Korchinski
Indian Services Director, M. Morison
Regional Secretariat Director, M. Blais
Band Support and Capital Management
Director, A. Dighe
Economic and Employment Development
Director, J. Zyzneiwski
Social Development Director, C. Quast
Alternative Funding Arrangements
Director, D. Crellin
Education Director, G. Johnson
Lands, Revenues and Trusts
Director, L. Robinson
Human Resources Director, N. Rice
Finance and Administration
Director, W. Wright
PWC-DIAND Technical Services
Reg. Manager, B. McDonald
Communications Services
Director, M. Sizeland
Manitoba Resource Development
Impact Office
Director, R.N. Stewart

Saskatchewan Region
2221 Cornwall St., 3rd Flr.
Regina, S4P 2L1
Reg. Director Gen., W.R. Cooke
Finance and Administration
Director, L. Herback
Operations (Indian Services)
A/Director, Mel Smith
PWC-DIAND Technical Services
Reg. Manager, R. Filson
Human Resources Director, Vacant
Band Support and Capital Management
A/Director, A. Bemister
Economic Development Director, A. Hynd
Education Director, J. Hurnard

Executive Secretariat Director, A. Pinter
Lands, Revenues and Trusts
Director, C. Starr
Social Development Director, M. Buckle
Alternative Funding Arrangements
A/Director, A. Bemister

Alberta Region
9700 Jasper Ave., 6th Flr.
Edmonton, T5J 4G2
Reg. Director Gen., E. Turbayne
Indian Services Director, F. Jobin
Communications Services
Manager, K. Williams
Alternative Funding Arrangements
A/Director, D. Stephenson
Economic and Employment Development
Director, J. McIsaac
Social Development Director, Ron Dawson
Lands, Revenues and Trusts
Director, G. Throndson
Education Director, S. Carr-Stewart
Band Support and Capital Management
Director, J. Fleury, Jr.
PWC-DIAND Technical Services
A/Reg. Manager, L. Lechelt
Human Resources Director, W. Cockburn
Finance and Administration
Director, A. Oostendorp

British Columbia Region
Box 1000, 800 Burrard St.
Vancouver, V6Z 2J3
Reg. Director Gen., Dr. O.A. Anderson
Finance and Administration
Director, D.G. Sparks
Indian Services
A/Director, D. Mullins
Lands, Revenues and Trusts
Director, A.J. Gross
Band Support and Capital Management
A/Director, M. Fillion
PWC-DIAND Technical Services
Reg. Manager, D. Clegg
Human Resources Director, D.G. MacKay
Social Development Director, R. Frizell
Economic and Employment Development
Director, R. Alam
Education Director, R. Penner
Self-Government Director, M. Sakamoto
Executive Secretariat
A/Director, T. Swankey

Yukon Region
Indian and Inuit Affairs
Federal Bldg., Box 4100
Whitehorse, Y1A 3S9
Reg. Director, Dr. E.R. Daniels
Finance and Administration
A/Director, D.A. Steele
Program Planning Director, Vacant
Indian Services Director, A. McDiarmid
Communications Services Director, C. Yeo
PWC-DIAND Technical Services
Director, D. Ostapowich
Social Development Director, B. Brinley
Education Director, B. Fred

Economic Development
A/Director, W. Attwood
Lands, Revenues and Trusts
Director, P. Garrett
Administration
A/Chief, Contracts and Administration
G. Steers

Yukon Region
Northern Affairs
200 Range Rd., Whitehorse, Y1A 3V1
Reg. Director Gen., A.E. Ganske
Finance and Administration
Director, J. McLachlan
Renewable Resources and Environment
Director, L. Craig
Yukon Land Use Planning
Director, B. Chambers
Mineral Resources and Economic Analysis
Director, A.C. Ogilvy
Economic Development Director, R. Chambers
Communications Services Director, C. Yeo
Human Resources Director, M. Freibergs

Northwest Territories Region
Indian and Inuit Affairs
Box 2760, Yellowknife, X1A 1R6
Reg. Director, L. Tricoteux
Community Affairs Director, Vacant
Economic Development
Director, J.W.R. Metcalfe

Northwest Territories Region
Northern Affairs
Box 1500, Yellowknife, X1A 2R3
A/Reg. Director Gen., Dr. W. Stephen
Corporate Affairs
A/Director, J. Wilson
Finance and Administration
Director, C. McEwan
Renewable Resources and Environment
Director, Dr. W. Stephen
Northern Land Use Planning
Director, H. Mills
Mineral Resources and Economic Analysis
A/Director, P. Laporte
Human Resources
A/Director, P. Lizée
Communications Services
A/Director, L. Boyer

AGENCIES, BOARDS AND COMMISSIONS

Canadian Eskimo Arts Council
Box 2126, Stn. D, Ottawa, K1P 5Y1
Inquiries: (819) 997-0580

The Canadian Eskimo Arts Council is appointed by the Minister of Indian Affairs and Northern Development to advise him on all matters relating to the development and protection of Inuit art.

The Council, which includes Inuit representation, consists of eight members, appointed by the minister for a three-year term, and represents professions or activities related to the arts and fine crafts.

The Council may advise federal and territorial governments, co-operatives, and other organizations concerned with the production, marketing and distribution of Inuit arts and fine crafts, with particular reference to:
- the maintenance of high standards of quality in production and marketing;
- copyright protection and compensation;
- introduction and development of new techniques; and
- development of research facilities, collections, and exhibition programs.

Chair, Mary Sparling
Exec. Secretary, Ene Schoeler
Rm. 928, N. Twr.
Les Terrasses de la Chaudière
10 Wellington St., Hull, K1A 0H4

Beverly and Kaminuriak Caribou Management Board
3565 Revelstoke Dr., Ottawa, K1Y 7B9

The Beverly and Kaminuriak Caribou Management Board was established June 3, 1983 under an agreement between the governments of Canada, Manitoba, Saskatchewan and the Northwest Territories as a joint agency to co-ordinate the management of barren ground caribou herds migrating across provincial and territorial boundaries.

The Board has 13 members, eight of whom represent the traditional users of animals from the ranges of the Beverly and Kaminuriak barren ground caribou in Manitoba, Saskatchewan and the N.W.T., and five of whom represent departments of government with responsibilities for native people, caribou, and their habitat.

Under the terms of the inter-governmental agreement, the governments provide the Board with an annual operating budget of $75,000. They also provide additional funds to facilitate the active involvement of native people.

During 1987-88, the Board completed a long-term management plan of the caribou herds and established a scholarship to provide financial assistance to students pursuing further education in the management and conservation of caribou and their habitat.

Chairman, James Schaefer
Vice-Chairman, Ross Thompson
Exec. Secretary, Gunther Abrahamson

Northwest Territories Water Board
Box 1500, 4922-52nd St.
9th Flr., Precambrian Bldg.
Yellowknife, X1A 2R3

The N.W.T. Water Board provides for the conservation, development and utilization of the water resources of the Northwest Territories. Under the *Northern Inland Waters Act,* an application must be made to the Board for authorization or a licence to use water or dispose of wastes into the water. Domestic use of water is exempted from this regulation, as well as the use of water in emergency situations such as fire.

The Board has three to nine members

appointed by the Minister of Indian Affairs and Northern Development. Membership includes at least one member from each federal department that is directly concerned with the management of water resources in the N.W.T., and at least three persons named by the Commissioner in Council of the N.W.T.

Chairman, Dave Nickerson
Vice-Chairman, D'arcy Arden

Porcupine Caribou Management Board

Site 20, Comp. 116, R.R. #1
Whitehorse, YT Y1A 4Z6

The Porcupine Caribou Management Board was created by the In-Canada Porcupine Caribou Management Agreement signed in Old Crow, Yukon on Oct. 26, 1985. The Board consists of seven members appointed from the Council for Yukon Indians, the Inuvialuit Game Council, the Dene/Métis Assn. of the Northwest Territories, the Yukon Government, the Government of the N.W.T. and the federal government.

The Board is designed to permit full discussion of Porcupine Caribou herd management between subsistence users of the herd and bureaucrats who administer wildlife regulations. All aspects of herd management such as harvest levels, industrial impacts, research, and legislation are reviewed by the Board which, in turn, makes recommendations to the appropriate territorial or federal ministers. As well, the Board is responsible for maintaining communications between user communities and government concerning management of the caribou herd.

Chairman, Victor Mitander
76-11th Ave., Porter Creek, YT Y1A 4J2
Vice-Chairman, Stan Njootli
c/o Old Crow Band Office
Old Crow, YT Y0B 1N0

Yukon Territory Water Board

Ste. 302, 4114-4th Ave.
Whitehorse, Y1A 4N7

The Yukon Territory Water Board was established by the *Northern Inland Waters Act* which came into force in 1972. The Board consists of nine members — at least three members are nominated by federal government departments; and at least three others must be nominated by the Commissioner in Council. All members are appointed by the Minister of Indian Affairs and Northern Development.

"The objectives of the boards are to provide for the conservation, development and utilization of the water resources of the Yukon Territory and the Northwest Territories in a manner that will provide the optimum benefit therefrom for all Canadians and for the residents of the Yukon Territory and the Northwest Territories in particular" (*N.I.W.A.,* section 9).

The Board is responsible for licensing water users in the North. The water licences may contain terms and conditions which regulate the quantity of water to be used and the quality of wastes which may be returned to the environment.

The Board reports to the Minister of Indian Affairs and Northern Development.

Chairman, Diane Granger
Vice-Chairman, Mike Stutter
Licensing Officer, Angie Dornian

DEPARTMENT OF INDUSTRY, SCIENCE AND TECHNOLOGY

235 Queen St., Ottawa, K1A 0H5
(except where otherwise indicated)

MINISTER'S OFFICE
Rm 558, Confederation Bldg.
House of Commons, Ottawa, K1A 0A6
Minister, The Hon. Harvie Andre

OFFICE OF THE MINISTER OF STATE (SMALL BUSINESSES AND TOURISM)
235 Queen St., 11th Flr. E., Ottawa, K1A 0H5
Minister of State, The Hon. Thomas Hockin

OFFICE OF THE MINISTER OF STATE (SCIENCE AND TECHNOLOGY)
235 Queen St., 8th Flr. W., Ottawa, K1A 0M5
Rm. 558, Confederation Bldg.
House of Commons, Ottawa, K1A 0A6
Minister of State, The Hon. Harvie Andre

DEPUTY MINISTER'S OFFICE
Ottawa, K1A 0M4
Dep. Minister, H.G. Rogers
A/Corporate Secretary, Peter Sagar
A/Sr. Gen. Counsel, Vacant
Human Resources
Director Gen., M. Amoroso
Operations Audit Branch Director, E.M. Hahn

ASSOCIATE DEPUTY MINISTER'S OFFICE
235 Queen St., Ottawa, K1A 0H5
Assoc. Dep. Minister, Claude Lemelin

Native Economic Programs

235 Queen St., 6th Flr., W. Twr.
Ottawa, K1A 0H6
Asst. Dep. Minister, H.A. Reynolds
REGIONAL OFFICES:
Central Region — Winnipeg
9th Flr., 330 Portage Ave.
Box 3130, Winnipeg, R3C 4E6
NEDB Chairman, Kenneth C. Thomas
Reg. Director, H.S. Schultz
Western Region — Vancouver
Box 49275, Ste. 1964, Bentall Twr. IV
1055 Dunsmuir St., Vancouver, V7X 1L3
A/Reg. Director, Don Hannah
Eastern Region — Montreal
800, Square Victoria, bur. 2604
C.P. 289, Montréal, H4Z 1E8
A/Reg. Director, R. Pesner

FEDERAL ECONOMIC DEVELOPMENT
CO-ORDINATORS:

Québec
800, Square Victoria, bur. 1200
Montréal, H4Z 1J2
Federal Economic Development
Co-ordinator, Normand Plante

Ontario
1 Front St. W., 4th Flr.
Toronto, M5X 1A4
Federal Economic Development
Co-ordinator, George Post

REGIONAL OFFICES:

Newfoundland Region
Parsons Bldg., 90 O'Leary Ave.
Box 8950, St. John's, A1B 3R9
A/Exec. Director, F.J. Nolan
International Trade and Marketing
Director, J.J. Harman
Industry, Technology and Investment
A/Director, K. Powell
A/Comptroller, D.G. Wells
Communications Manager, E.J. Coady

Prince Edward Island Region
Confederation Twr., 134 Kent St.
Box 1115, Charlottetown, C1A 7M8
Exec. Director, Hugh W. Plant
Development and Operations
Director, W.S. Shepherd
Trade Development
Manager, G. Fraser Dickson
Tourism Development Director, R.W. Young
Communications and Special Projects
Manager, J.C. Wells

Nova Scotia Region
Box 940, Stn. M,
1489 Hollis St., Halifax, B3J 2V9
Exec. Director, Robert Russell
Industry and Technology
A/Director, R. Sherwood
Tourism Manager, Anne Thompson
International Trade Centre
Sr. Trade Commissioner, D. Rosenthal
Policy and Corporate Services
A/Director, W. Savin
Finance and Administration
A/Manager, M.A. Jeffries
Communications Advisor, Valerie Bachynsky
Capital and Industrial Goods
Manager, Richard Miles
Consumer Goods and Services
Manager, Donald MacNeill
Small Business Programs
Manager, Ted Withers

New Brunswick Region
770 Main St., Assumption Pl.
Box 1210, Moncton, NB E1C 8P9
A/Reg. Exec. Director,
Yvon A. Lavallée

Quebec Region
800, Square Victoria, C.P. 247
Montréal, H4Z 1E8

Reg. Exec. Director, G. Haack
Communications and Co-ordination
Director, G. Bouchard
Consumer Goods, Services and
Resource Industries
Director Gen., Pierre Lebeault
Capital and Industrial Goods
Director Gen., G. Voyer
Regional and Industrial Programs
Director Gen., G. Simard
Market Development
A/Director Gen., B. Goulet
Tourism Director, L. Germain
Planning Analysis and Evaluation
A/Director, D. Chicoine
Controller, D. McCraw

Ontario Region
Dominion Public Bldg., 4th Flr.
1 Front St. W., Toronto, M5J 1A4
Reg. Exec. Director, W.W. Cram
Tourism Director, Wayne St. John
Industry Development
Director Gen., G.V. Kelly
Policy, Planning and Analysis
Director Gen., David C. Dallimore
Trade, Technology and Investment
Director Gen., Doug Sirrs

*Federal Economic Initiative for Northern
Ontario (FEDNOR)*
Queencentre, Ste. 106
473-477 Queen St. E.
Sault Ste. Marie, P6A 1Z5
Director Gen., H. McGonigal

Manitoba Region
608, 330 Portage Ave.
Winnipeg, R3C 2V2
A/Reg. Exec. Director, Rainer Andersen
Trade and Investment Director, R.P.W. Mason
Industry and Trade Development
A/Director, Gary Hosea
Regional Programs Director, E. Heinicke
Communications Director, Wayne Hanna
Information Centre
A/Manager, Shannon Coughlin
Reg. Comptroller, R.W. Stalker

Saskatchewan Region
6th Flr., 105-21st St. E.
Saskatoon, S7K 0B3
Exec. Director, William A. Reid
Program Operations Branch
Special Agricultural and
Rural Development Agreement (SARDA)
Manager, R. Lagimodière
Northern Economic Development
Subsidiary Agreement (NEDSA)
Manager, E. Thomas
Advanced Technology Subsidiary Agreement
Manager, D. Tamney
Planning, Analysis and Evaluation Branch
Director, G. Arundel
Sr. Trade Commissioner, A.D.D. McEwen
Trade Manager, R. McLeod
Communications Manager, D. Allen

Alberta Region
Ste. 505, Cornerpoint Bldg.
10179-105th St., Edmonton, T5J 3S3
Reg. Exec. Director, W. Collett
Operations Director, Glenn Fields
Trade and Investment Director, Jack Kepper
Economic Analysis Planning and Evaluation
Manager, J.F. (Joe) Guinan
Communications and Business Services
Manager, Ron Selin

British Columbia Region
Scotia Twr., 900, 650 W. Georgia St.
Box 11610, Vancouver, V6B 5H8
Reg. Exec. Director, Victor G. Loots
Industry and Technology Services
Director, Tom A. Turner
Policy, Planning and Corporate Services
A/Director, B.R. Anderson
Trade Director, Z. Burianyk
Communications
A/Manager, B. Goodyer

GOVERNMENT OF CANADA BUSINESS INFORMATION CENTRES

Quebec
800, Square Victoria, bur. 4328
C.P. 247, Montréal, H4Z 1E8
Chief, M. Kaspy

Ontario
Business Counselling Group
Ste. 4840, 1 First Canadian Pl.
Box 98, Toronto, M5X 1B1
Manager, R. MacPherson

COMMUNICATIONS BRANCH
Director Gen., Bill Grogan
Planning and Services
A/Director, F. Girard

Finance, Personnel and Administration
Asst. Dep. Minister, John D. McLure
Comptroller, John McCrea
Resource Management Directorate
Director, Robin Butler
Accounting and Financial Control Directorate
A/Director, B.D. Booth
Financial Policy and
Systems Development Directorate
A/Director, D. Kelso
Contribution Verification Advisory Division
Director, J. Leduc
Access to Information and Privacy Office
Sr. Departmental Advisor, P. Trottier

INFORMATION MANAGEMENT BRANCH
Director Gen., Colin Campbell
Administrative Services Branch
Director Gen., M.W. Eustace
Human Resources Branch
Director Gen., M. Amoroso

Policy and Evaluation
Asst. Dep. Minister, R.G. Blackburn

Economic and Statistical Analysis Branch
A/Director Gen., R. Henry
Economic Analysis
Sr. Analyst, B. Kaufmann
Statistical Analysis Director, R. Sharma

CORPORATE PLANNING AND EVALUATION BRANCH
A/Director Gen., R. Chartrand
Policy Management Directorate
Director, Vacant
Evaluation Directorate
Director, J. Butler

INDUSTRIAL AND TRADE POLICY
Director Gen., R. Knox
Industrial Policy Directorate
Director, R. Smith
Trade Policy Directorate
A/Director, D. McCulla
Economic Development Policy Directorate
Director, M. Jenkin
Industrial Horizons
Director Gen., C. Taylor

Small Businesses
Asst. Dep. Minister, Vacant
Advocacy and Policy
Director Gen., Bruce Deacon
Product and Business Development
Director Gen., Claude Parent
Small Business Policy Development
Director, Vacant
Advocacy and Co-ordination
Director, Norman Levesque

Development Programs and Investments
Asst. Dep. Minister, Claude Huot
Policy, Planning and Services
Director, D. Hoye
Program Affairs
Director Gen., R. Haack
International Affairs
Director Gen., R. Bower
Business Services and Marketing
Director Gen., D. Graham
Regional Affairs
A/Director Gen., D. Hoye
Crown Investments and Guarantees
Director Gen., Norm Fraser

Industry Marketing
Asst. Dep. Minister, J.C. Mackay

AEROSPACE, DEFENCE AND INDUSTRIAL BENEFITS
Director Gen., T. Garrard
Aircraft Propulsion and Missile Systems
Director, R. Delvecchio
Planning and Analysis Director, T. Wright
Marine and Land Defence Systems
Director, Y. Moisan
Defence, Electronics and Space Systems
Director, B. Burns

INFORMATION TECHNOLOGIES INDUSTRIES
Director Gen., Ron C. Watkins
Technology Applications Director, Vacant
Industry Development
Director, Andrew Siman
Programs and Planning Manager, G. Lebrun
Microelectronics Technology Office
Director, D. Williams
Resource and Service Industries
Manager, A. Dubois

PLANNING, CO-ORDINATION AND CONTROL
Director Gen., D. Lane
Policy Co-ordination Director, T.C. Leung
Technology Liaison Director, E. Payne
Planning and Central Services
Director, F.C. Pim

RESOURCE PROCESSING INDUSTRIES
Director Gen., L. Bradet
Health Care and Biotechnology
Director, E. Dickson
Chemicals and Investments
Director, R. Harper
Planning and Co-ordination
Manager, R. Domokos
Metals and Minerals Director, F. Morissette
Advanced Industrial Materials
Director, A. Stone
Forest Products Director, J. Wansbrough

SERVICE INDUSTRIES AND CONSUMER
GOODS
Director Gen., D.P. DeMelto
Planning and Analysis Manager, R. Bandzierz
Commercial Service Industries
A/Director, C. Charette
Program Operations (CIRB)
A/Manager, C.B. Billing
Food Products Director, Sandra Humber
Consumer Products
A/Director, A. Leduc
Textiles, Clothing and Footwear
Director, R. Pageau

SPECIAL PROJECTS
Director Gen., J. Howe
Financial Economic Analysis
Director, F. Bennett
Strategic Analysis Director, J. Van Loon
Project Analysis Director, G. Nash

SURFACE TRANSPORTATION AND
MACHINERY
Director Gen., John Banigan
Machinery Director, R. Samarcq
Programs, Analysis and Co-ordination
Manager, D. Pidduck
Automotive Director, S. Skorupinski
Electrical and Energy Equipment
Director, W.H. Terry
Marine, Urban and Rail Directorate
Director, A. Lafond

Construction and Capital Projects
Director, J.B. Wickes

Tourism Canada
235 Queen St., Ottawa, K1A 0H6
General Inquiries: (613) 954-3854
Asst. Dep. Minister, Allan Cocksedge

RESEARCH
Director Gen., B.F. Stevens
Special Research Projects Manager, Vacant
Research Program Manager, P. Chau
Commercial Intelligence Program
Manager, P. Villemaire
Data Centre Head, G. Kolk

MANAGEMENT SERVICES AND LIAISON
Director Gen., Vacant
Liaison Program Manager, Vacant
Secretariat Head, M. Villemaire
Information Program Manager, B. Goodyer
Administrative Services Chief, B.D. Cook

PRODUCT DEVELOPMENT
Director Gen., Guy Bédard
Program Development
Director, R.B. Duncombe
Products and Services Director, J. Chretien
Policy Director, Vacant

MARKET DEVELOPMENT
Director Gen., Doug Fyfe
Advertising Director, M. Amendola
Public Relations and Promotions
Director, K. de Bellefeuille-Percy
Planning and Program Development
Director, R. Desjardins
REGIONAL OFFICES—CANADA
Alberta
The Cornerpoint Bldg., Ste. 505
10179-105th St., Edmonton, T5J 3S3
Industrial Development and Regional Benefits
Director, Glenn Fields
Tourism Development
Manager, Georgine Ulmer

British Columbia
900, 650 West Georgia St.
Box 11610, Vancouver, V6B 5H8
Industry and Technology Services
Director, Tom Turner
Manitoba
330 Portage Ave., 8th Flr.
Winnipeg, R3C 2V2
Industry and Trade Development
Director, R. Andersen
New Brunswick
770 Main St., Box 1210, Moncton, E1C 8P9
Industrial and Sector Development
Manager, Eric Robichaud
Newfoundland
90 O'Leary Ave., Box 8950
St. John's, A1B 3R9
Sr. Tourism Development Officer
Ed Jamieson

Nova Scotia
1446 Lower Water St.
Box 940, Stn. M, Halifax, B3J 2V9
Tourism Manager, Anne Thompson

Ontario
Dominion Public Bldg.
1 Front St. W., Toronto, M5J 1A4
Tourism Director, Wayne St. John

Prince Edward Island
Confederation Court Twr., Ste. 400
134 Kent St., Box 1115
Charlottetown, C1A 7M8
Tourism Development Manager, R. Young

Quebec
Stock Exchange Twr.
800, Square Victoria, bur. 3800
C.P. 247, Montréal, H4Z 1E8
Tourism Branch Director, L. Germain

Saskatchewan
105-21st St. E., 6th Flr., Saskatoon, S7K 0B3
Trade and Tourism Director, A.D.D. McEwen

Yukon
Ste. 301, 108 Lambert St.
Whitehorse, Y1A 1Z2
Director, Larry Bagnell
Tourism Program Officer, Dermot Flynn

Northwest Territories
Precambrian Bldg., Box 6100
Yellowknife, X1A 1C0
Director, Paul J. Berthelet
Tourism Development Officer, Rae Bradford

AGENCIES, BOARDS, COMMISSIONS AND CROWN CORPORATIONS

Federal Business Development Bank
800, Square Victoria, C.P. 335
Montréal, H4Z 1L4
Inquiries: (514) 283-5904

The Federal Business Development Bank (FBDB) extends financial assistance to new or existing businesses in Canada for which funds are not available on reasonable terms and conditions. Assistance may be in the form of term loans, loan guarantees, equity financing or any combination of these, according to the particular needs of a business. With 88 branches and a portfolio of $1.5 billion, FBDB is a major source of financing in Canada.

FBDB's counselling program, CASE, utilizes the expertise of more than 1,400 retired business people to assist small firms in improving their methods of doing business. For a nominal fee, experienced counsellors provide advice in all areas of business management including accounting, marketing, production and personnel. It is not necessary to be a borrower from FBDB to obtain CASE services.

The Management Services division of the FBDB is able to provide initial information and refer clients to proper departments for applicable government programs — federal and provincial. Management Services conducts one-day man-agement seminars in towns and cities throughout Canada, covering a range of topics from book-keeping, taxation, marketing to personnel. Other training available through FBDB to help small Canadian businesses to improve their manage-ment skills includes: the "Minding your own Business" series of booklets and library services, Management Clinics, and Owner/Manager Courses.

Chairman of the Board, William J. McAleer
President, Guy A. Lavigueur
Sr. Vice-Presidents:
Finance, J.P.W. Charbonneau
Management Systems and Control,
F.P. Urbanski
Loans and Management Services,
K.E. Neilson
Venture Capital Division, M.C. Vaillancourt
Vice-Presidents:
Loans, Y. Milette
Human Resources and Administration,
A. Millette
Government Relations, M. Azam
Planning, H.P. Carmichael
Inspection and Special Projects, G.W. Kyte
Controller's Department
Corporate Controller, J.G. Langlais
Field Support Services Director, Vacant
Financial Analysis and Control
Director, R.C. Morris
Economics Department
Asst. Vice-President, D. Layne
Human Resources
Corporate Personnel Services
Director, Y. Zacios
Compensation and Benefits
Director, A.L. Thibodeau
Organizational Planning and Development
Director, G. Corbeil
Premises and Supply Director, A. Mackie
Information Systems Director, E.G. Jopling
Internal Audit Manager, J. Santoni
Legal Services and Corporate Secretariat
Gen. Counsel and Corporate
Secretary, J.W. Hercus
Asst. Gen. Counsel, C.G. Winslow
Loans Department
Asst. Vice-President, F.T. Watters
Asst. Vice-President, G. Kirkwood
Management Services
Asst. Vice-President, J.J.R. Leduc
Director, J. McNulty
Administration and Funding Director, Vacant
Training Products Director, M. Boucher
Public Affairs
Communications Director, K. Cavanagh
Treasury Department
Capital Markets Director, C. Albert
REGIONAL OFFICES:
Atlantic
Cogswell Tower, Ste. 1400, Scotia Sq.
Halifax, B3J 2Z7
Vice-President and Reg.
Gen. Manager, J.J. Ryan

Quebec
800, Square Victoria, bur. 4600
Montréal, H4Z 1C8
Vice-President and Reg.
Gen. Manager, J. Lagacé

Ontario
777 Bay St., 29th Flr., Toronto, M5G 2C8
Vice-President and Reg.
Gen. Manager, J.H. Miller

Prairie and Northern
155 Carlton St., Ste. 1200
Winnipeg, R3C 3H8
Vice-President and Reg.
Gen. Manager, E.A. Duddle

British Columbia and Yukon
900 W. Hastings St., Vancouver, V6C 1E7
Vice-President and Reg.
Gen. Manager, D.A. Kerley

Investment Canada
240 Sparks St., Box 2800, Stn. D
Ottawa, K1P 6A5
Investment Inquiries: (613) 995-0465
Personnel Inquiries: (613) 995-9639
Access to Information/Privacy: (613) 995-8875

Investment Canada, an agency established under the *Investment Canada Act*, has a three-fold mandate: to promote and facilitate investment in Canada by Canadians and non-Canadians alike; to undertake research and analysis, as well as to provide policy advice to ensure Canada's investment climate is as open and hospitable as possible; and to ensure that significant investments by non-Canadians are of net benefit to Canada.

The *Investment Canada Act* was passed on June 30, 1985 and replaces the *Foreign Investment Review Act*. Under the new Act, the government's regulatory function is limited in scope. Only a small proportion of investments is subject to review and for these investments the review process has been simplified. Special consideration has been given under the new Act to cultural industries, such as book publishing and film production.

President, Paul Labbé
Corporate Secretary, F. Matte
Vice-President, J.A. Downer
Investment Review Division
Vice-President, G.H. Dewhirst
Investment Development Division
Vice-President, Vacant
Investment Research and Policy Division
Vice-President, J. Church
Corporate Services Division
Director, C.E. Hitsman

Native Economic Development Advisory Board
Bank of Montreal Bldg., Ste. 1103
330 Portage Ave., Box 3130
Winnipeg, MB R3C 4E6

The Department of Industry, Science and Technology co-ordinates federal government efforts concerning aboriginal economic development through this Board. Assistance is available to Inuit, Métis, status Indians and non-status Indians.

The program includes three types of financial aid:
- to native financial institutions to foster development in their communities;
- to community leaderships to carry out planning as a basis for sound investments; and
- to individuals and groups to establish or expand native ventures.

Chairman, Kenneth C. Thomas

DEPARTMENT OF JUSTICE
Justice Bldg., Wellington and Kent Sts.
Ottawa, K1A 0H8
Fax: (613) 996-9916
Departmental Inquiries Centre: (613) 957-4222
TDD: (613) 992-4556
Access to Information and Privacy Office
Co-ordinator, P. Lordon

MINISTER OF JUSTICE AND ATTORNEY GENERAL OF CANADA'S OFFICE
135 East Blk., House of Commons
Ottawa, K1A 0A6
Minister, The Hon. Doug Lewis

DEPUTY MINISTER AND DEPUTY ATTORNEY GENERAL'S OFFICE
Dep. Minister, John C. Tait, Q.C.

ASSOCIATE DEPUTY MINISTERS
Litigation, D.J.A. Rutherford, Q.C.
Sr. Gen. Counsel, Vacant
Civil Law, A.M. Trahan, Q.C.
Sr. Gen. Counsel, Frank J.E. Jordan, Q.C.

ASSISTANT DEPUTY MINISTERS
Legal Services, S.J. Skelly, Q.C.
Public Law, M.E. Dawson, Q.C.
Policy, Programs and Research,
D.C. Préfontaine, Q.C.
Legal Services (Commercial and Property Law)
R.L. Evans, Q.C.
Legal Services (Finance), H. Calof, Q.C.
Administration and Corporate Legal Counsel,
J.C. Demers, Q.C.

ASSISTANT DEPUTY ATTORNEYS GENERAL
Admiralty and Maritime, P.M. Troop, Q.C.
Civil Litigation, T.B. Smith, Q.C.
Criminal Law, Julius A. Isaac, Q.C.
Tax Law, D. Lefebvre, Q.C.

A/CHIEF LEGISLATIVE COUNSEL
P.E. Johnson, Q.C.
Chief General Counsel, E.A. Bowie, Q.C.
Chief Counsel (Corporate Policy and Co-ordination), J.N. LaBarre

HEADQUARTERS SECTIONS
Legal Services
Gen. Counsel, J.S. Milligan
Corporate Services Directorate
Sr. Counsel, P. Lordon
Bureau of Programme Evaluation
and Internal Audit
Director Gen., R.J. Wilson
Corporate Planning Directorate
Director Gen., G. Webster
Liaison and Federal Provincial
Relations Directorate
Director, M.A. Laniel
Communications and Public Affairs
Director Gen., Y.P. Roy
Federal Regulatory Offences Project
Gen. Counsel, L.S. Fairbairn
Criminal Law Review
Co-ordinator, E.A. Tollefson, Q.C.
Programs and Research
Director, Y. Dandurand
Criminal Law Policy and Amendments
Sr. Gen. Counsel, R.G. Mosley
Civil Litigation
Gen. Counsel, D.F. Friesen, Q.C.
Criminal Prosecutions
Gen. Counsel, W.H. Corbett, Q.C.
Tax Litigation
Gen. Counsel, I.S. MacGregor
Sr. Gen. Counsel: D.H. Aylen, Q.C.,
J.R. Power, Q.C., I. Whitehall, Q.C.
Gen. Counsel, L.P. Chambers, Q.C.
Advisory and Administrative Law
Gen. Counsel, H.L. Molot
Constitutional and International Law
Gen. Counsel, C. Verdon
Native Law
Sr. Counsel, M. Freeman
Privy Council Office
Sr. Gen. Counsel, R.S.G. Thompson
Legislation
Gen. Counsel, R. Bergeron, Q.C.
Statute Revision Commission
Secretary and Project Director, L. Levert
Human Rights Law
Sr. Gen. Counsel, D.M. Low
Civil Law (Quebec)
Gen. Counsel, P.R. Coderre, Q.C.
Information Law and Privacy
Sr. Counsel, H. Harris
Commercial Law Section
Gen. Counsel, J. Gauthier

ADMINISTRATION BRANCH
Sr. Counsel, Y. Roy
Sr. Counsel, W.S. Regan, Q.C.
Personnel Administration Director, Vacant
Financial Services Director, D. LeMoullec
Security Director, J.P.I. Aubrey
Informatics Director, W.A. Cholowski
Administrative Policies and Services
Exec. Director, M. Gervais
Administrative Services, S. Link
Library Services Director, S. Jackson

Official Languages Program
Director, A. Taschereau
Legal Contracts Support Unit
Chief, A. Brennan
Central Divorce Registry
Registrar, Ms. C.C. Perrin
Family Law Enforcement Assistance System
Inquiries: (613) 990-8197
REGIONAL OFFICES:
Nova Scotia
Royal Bank Bldg., 4th Flr.
5161 George St., Halifax, B3J 1M7
Gen. Counsel, J.D. Bissell
Quebec
Place Guy Favreau, Tour est, 9e ét.
200, boul. René-Lévesque ouest
Montréal, H2Z 1X4
Sr. Gen. Counsel, J. Letellier, Q.C.
Ontario
Box 57, 24th Flr.
Toronto Dominion Ctr.
Toronto, M5K 1E7
Sr. Gen. Counsel, J.E. Thompson
Manitoba
301 Centennial House
310 Broadway Ave., Winnipeg, R3C 0S6
Gen. Counsel, D.G. Frayer, Q.C.
Saskatchewan
Churchill Bldg., Rm. 301
229-4th Ave. S., Saskatoon, S7K 4E4
Gen. Counsel, B.D. Collins, Q.C.
Alberta
Rm. 928, Royal Trust Tower
Edmonton Ctr., Edmonton, T5J 2Z2
Gen. Counsel, B. MacFarlane
British Columbia
2800, 1055 W. Georgia St., Royal Ctr.
Vancouver, V6E 3P9
Gen. Counsel, G. Donegan, Q.C.
Yukon Territory
Financial Plaza, 204 Lambert St.
Box 1076, Whitehorse, Y1A 1Z4
Sr. Counsel, M.D. Gates
Northwest Territories
Precambrian Bldg., 11th Flr.
Box 8, Yellowknife, X1A 2N1
Sr. Counsel, G.M. Bickert

AGENCIES, BOARDS AND COMMISSIONS

Canadian Human Rights Commission
Royal Bank Ctr., 4th Flr., 90 Sparks St.
Ottawa, K1A 1E1
Public Information: (613) 995-1151

The Canadian Human Rights Commission's aim is to promote social change leading to equal opportunity for all. The Commission, an independent federal agency, administers the anti-discrimination provisions of the *Canadian Human Rights Act,* passed unanimously by the Parliament of Canada in July 1977.

On July 1, 1983, amendments to the Act were proclaimed and became effective immediately. Family status and disability (mental or physical) are now among the prohibited grounds of discrimination, as is differential treatment because of pregnancy and childbirth. It is also illegal to treat someone unfairly because of a previous or existing dependence on alcohol or a drug.

Since October 15, 1985, due to amendments to the Act, the Commission no longer appoints the human rights tribunals. Instead, the position of president of the tribunal was created. The president appoints a tribunal when the Commission asks for further inquiry into a complaint. The amendments also removed the word "substantiate" from Commission decisions and introduced a judicial procedure for issuing search warrants.

As before, the Commission continues to offer redress to those who have been the victims of discriminatory practices based on race, national or ethnic origin, colour, religion, age, sex, marital status and conviction for which a pardon has been granted. Harassment on all prohibited grounds is illegal.

Furthermore, the Act prohibits an employer from establishing or maintaining wage differences between male and female employees performing work of equal value in the same establishment, and sets out the criteria to be applied to measure the value of the work.

The Act applies to federal government departments and agencies, and Crown corporations and to business and industry under federal jurisdiction such as banks, broadcasting outlets, airline and railway companies.

The Commission is composed of members appointed by the Governor in Council. It is assisted by a staff located in seven regional offices across Canada — Halifax, Montreal, Ottawa, Toronto, Winnipeg, Edmonton and Vancouver — in addition to the headquarters office in Ottawa.

Chief Commissioner, Maxwell Yalden
Dep. Chief Commissioner,
Michelle Falardeau-Ramsay
Secretary-Gen., John Hucker
Gen. Counsel, Jocelyne Bessette-Aubry
Policy and Communications
Director Gen., Stuart Beaty
Public Programs Director, Vacant
Employment and Pay Equity
Director, Hanne Jensen
Complaints Procedure Director, Glenys Parry
Research and Policy Director, Debra Young
Corporate Services Director, Thérèse Gervais
Regional Operations
A/Director, Ajit Mehat
Tribunal Secretariat Head, Mike Glynn
REGIONAL OFFICES:
Atlantic Region
Rm. 300, 5670 Spring Garden Rd.
Halifax, B3J 1H1
Director, Hugh McKervill
Quebec Region
1253, av. McGill College, bur. 330
Montréal, H3B 2Y5
Director, Gilles Pépin

National Capital Region
915, 270 Albert St., Ottawa, K1P 5W3
A/Director, Charles Théroux
Ontario Region
Arthur Meighen Bldg., Ste. 623
55 St. Clair Ave. E., Toronto, M4T 1M2
A/Director, Michel Pitre
Prairie Region
Kensington Bldg., Ste. 718
275 Portage Ave., Winnipeg, R3B 2B3
Director, David Hosking
Alberta and Northwest Territories Region
Liberty Bldg., Rm. 401
10506 Jasper Ave., Edmonton, T5J 2W9
Director, Marinus Begieneman
Western Region
600, 609 W. Hastings St.
Vancouver, V6B 4W4
Director, Paul Leroux

Canadian Judicial Council
Varette Bldg., 130 Albert St.
Ottawa, K1A 0W8

The Canadian Judicial Council's aims, pursuant to its mandate under the *Judges Act*, are to promote efficiency, uniformity and improved judicial service in superior and county courts and in the Tax Court of Canada. It organizes seminars for the continuing education of judges, and approves the attendance of judges at seminars. It may conduct inquiries into allegations of misconduct against federally appointed judges. The Council consists of chief and associate chief justices and judges of superior and county courts and of the Tax Court of Canada. It is chaired by the Chief Justice of Canada.
Secretary to the Council, Jeannie Thomas

Commissioner for Federal Judicial Affairs
110 O'Connor St., 11th Flr., Ottawa, K1A 1E3

The Commissioner for Federal Judicial Affairs is appointed under the *Judges Act,* R.S.C. 1970, Chapter J-1, as amended. The Office oversees administrative matters respecting the Federal Court of Canada, the Tax Court of Canada, the Canadian Judicial Council and all federally appointed judges other than those of the Supreme Court of Canada.

Commissioner, Pierre Garceau, Q.C.
Dep. Commissioner, A. Laframboise

Information Commissioner
Twr. B, Place de Ville, 3rd Flr.
Ottawa, K1A 1H3
General Inquiry: 1-800-267-0441

The Information Commissioner is an independent officer of Parliament appointed for a seven-year term to investigate complaints from individuals who believe they have been denied access rights as set out in the *Access to Information Act. (See the Citizens' Rights section of the Law chapter for details.)*

The Commissioner may examine all records in

federal government files (except those designated confidences of the Queen's Privy Council) to ensure that complainants receive all the material to which the Act entitles them. Following investigation, the Commissioner reports to the complainant, and may report to the head of the government institution, depending on her findings.

The Commissioner may appear on a complainant's behalf (with his/her consent or as a party) to seek a federal court review of an institution's denial of access. She reports annually to Parliament through the speakers of the Senate and the House of Commons, and may submit special reports at any time.

Information Commissioner, Inger Hansen, Q.C.
Asst. Information Commissioners:
D.W. (Bill) McGibbon, Bruce Mann
A/Director Gen., Operations, Jim Duthie
A/Director, Investigations, Kevan Flood
Gen. Counsel, Paul Tetro

Law Reform Commission of Canada
Varette Bldg., 130 Albert St., 7th Flr.
Ottawa, K1A 0L6

The Law Reform Commission was established by the *Law Reform Commission Act,* which came into force on June 1, 1971. The statute was amended by Parliament in 1975, and in 1981, to provide for a Commission composed of a president, a vice-president and three other full-time commissioners, all appointed by the Governor in Council, each for a term not exceeding seven years.

The Law Reform Commission of Canada is a continuing organization whose objects are to study and to keep under review the federal laws of Canada, with a view to making recommendations for their improvement, modernization and reform. This includes, but is not limited to, removing anachronisms and anomalies in the law, reconciliation of differences and discrepancies in the law arising out of the concepts and institutions of the common and civil legal systems, elimination of obsolete laws, and development of new approaches and concepts of the law in keeping with the changing needs of society.

President, Mr. Justice Allen M. Linden
Vice-President, Gilles Létourneau
Commissioners: Joseph Maingot, Q.C.,
John P. Frecker,
Her Hon. Judge Michèle Rivet
Secretary to the Commission,
François Handfield
Operations Director, R.A. Rochon
Information Services
Director, Rolland Lafrance

Privacy Commissioner
112 Kent St., Ottawa, K1A 1H3
General Inquiry: (613) 995-2410
Toll-Free: 1-800-267-0441

The Privacy Commissioner is an independent officer of Parliament appointed for a seven-year term. He investigates complaints under the *Privacy Act* and audits how federal government institutions collect, keep, use and dispose of personal information in their files. *(See Citizens' Rights section in the Law chapter for details.)*

The Commissioner and his investigators may examine all material (except confidences of the Queen's Privy Council) in personal information banks — including exempted material in open banks and files in the closed investigation and national security banks.

Following investigation the Commissioner may find the complaint not justified and dismiss it, or he may find it justified and recommend that the head of the institution take any necessary steps to resolve the matter.

The Commissioner does not have the power to order an institution to comply with his recommendations, but he may go to court if he is dissatisfied with its handling of the complaint, or if he considers the matter significant enough to require a legal decision.

Complainants denied access to personal information, and not satisfied with the Privacy Commissioner's findings, may ask the Federal Court to review the institution's refusal.

The Commissioner reports annually to Parliament, and at any other time when he considers a matter sufficiently urgent or important.

Privacy Commissioner, John W. Grace
Exec. Director, Alan Leadbeater
Legal Advisor, Gerry van Berkel
Director of Complaints, Julien Delisle
Director of Compliance, Barry Baker
Information Officer, Sally Jackson

DEPARTMENT OF LABOUR
2 Place du Portage, Hull
MAILING ADDRESS: Ottawa, K1A 0J2
Telex: 053-3640; Fax: (819) 997-1664
General Inquiries: (819) 997-2617

MINISTER'S OFFICE
Minister, The Hon. Jean Corbeil

DEPUTY MINISTER'S OFFICE
Dep. Minister, Jennifer McQueen
Workplace Hazardous Materials
Information System (WHMIS)
Federal Co-ordinator, J.W. McLellan
Communications Directorate
Director Gen., Hugues Lacombe
Personnel
Director Gen., A. Andrews
Legal Services
Gen. Counsel, P. Sorokan

Federal Mediation and Conciliation Service
Assoc. Dep. Minister, Vacant
Mediation and Conciliation Branch
Director Gen., Michael McDermott

Technical Support and
Operational Research Branch
Director, John Fuchs
Arbitration Services Branch
Director, Gérard Chartrand
Legislative and Special Projects
Director, Elizabeth MacPherson

Policy

Asst. Dep. Minister, Greg Traversy

WOMEN'S BUREAU
Director Gen., Linda Geller-Schwartz
Policy Director, Paula Bennett
Chief, Blanch Borkovic
Federal-Provincial Relations
Exec. Director, Gloria Kunka
Office of International Affairs
Exec. Director, L. Caron
Policy and Strategic Analysis
Exec. Director, A. Piché

LABOUR ADJUSTMENT, INFORMATION AND
OUTREACH DIRECTORATE
Director Gen., R. Gordon
Bureau of Labour Information
Exec. Director, Lorne Kenney
Data Collection and Analysis
Chief, Bernard Fortin
Client Services Division
Chief, Akivah Starkman
Industrial Relations Information Services
A/Manager, G. Lalonde
Collective Bargaining Reports Unit
Manager, H. Beaufort
Product Development Division
Asst. Director and Chief, Sally Luce
Older Worker Adjustment Branch
Director, E. van Snellenberg
Labour Outreach Secretariat
Director, H. Lemieux
Client Consultations
Director, Gregg Murtagh

Operations

Asst. Dep. Minister, Herman P. Hansen
Program Services and Systems
Director, Carol Chauvin
Employment Relations and Conditions of Work
Director, Doug Baldwin
Occupational Safety and Health
Director Gen., Jean Trudeau
Fire Prevention and
Fire Commissioner of Canada
Director, Tom Dunfield
REGIONAL OFFICES:
Capital Region
S.B.I. Bldg., 7th Flr., Billings Bridge Plaza
2323 Riverside Dr., Ottawa, K1H 8L5
Reg. Director, G.R. McKnight
Atlantic Region
Professional Arts Building
100 Arden St., 4th Flr.
Box 2967, Stn. A, Moncton, NB E1C 8T8
Reg. Director, G. Blanchard

St. Lawrence Region
Place Guy Favreau, bur. 101, Tour ouest
200, boul. René-Lévesque ouest
Montréal, H2Z 1X4
Reg. Director, B.A. LeBlanc
Great Lakes Region
4211 Yonge St., 3rd Flr., Ste. 325
Willowdale, ON M2P 2A9
Reg. Director, Brigitte E. Hohn
Central Region
Canadian Grain Commission Bldg.
303 Main St., Rm. 400, Winnipeg, R3C 3G7
Reg. Director, W. Guthrie
Mountain Region
750 Cambie St., 7th Flr.
Vancouver, BC V6B 2P2
Reg. Director, Renée Godmer

MANAGEMENT SYSTEMS AND SERVICES
Director Gen. and Departmental
Security Officer, C.J. Helmes
Informatics Director, M. Bonnell
Financial and Administrative Services
Director, A.C. Chu
Corporate Services Director, Denise Roberge

AGENCIES, BOARDS AND COMMISSIONS

Canada Labour Relations Board
C.D. Howe Bldg., 4th Flr. W.
240 Sparks St., Ottawa, K1A 0X8

The Canada Labour Relations Board is an administrative tribunal with quasi-judicial functions in the application of Part I of the Canada Labour Code. Its main functions relate to the granting or termination of bargaining rights based on the wishes of the majority of employees in appropriate bargaining units; and dealing with complaints of unfair labour practices and applications for Board orders to terminate unlawful strikes or lock-outs.

In addition, the board has many other functions relating to the promotion of sound industrial relations. It interprets and applies provisions of the statute regarding such aspects as technological change, the possible imposition of first collective agreements, the regulation of hiring hall procedures, the access to employees in remote locations by union officials, the access to financial statements by union members and members of employers' organizations, and the obligation of bargaining agents to represent employees fairly.

The Board consists of a chairman, four vice-chairmen and a number of Board members appointed by the Governor in Council for specific terms. The Board conducts hearings in all parts of Canada and is supported by staff at headquarters and at regional offices in Vancouver, Winnipeg, Toronto, Montreal and Dartmouth. The staff includes labour relations officers who investigate applications and report to the Board and the parties, and also engage in mediation to assist the parties to settle complaints of unfair labour practice and unlawful strike or lock-out situations which may be developing.

The Board also determines appeals against decisions by safety officers under Part II of the Code and deals with complaints of discrimination against employees for exercising their rights under the safety provisions.

Industrial relations are primarily in the provincial jurisdiction, but the Board has jurisdiction in regard to some 700,000 employees engaged in federal works, undertakings, and businesses, which include interprovincial transportation (air, land and water), broadcasting, banking, grain-handling, longshoring, enterprises which are beyond the exclusive jurisdiction of a provincial legislature, and, in the Yukon and Northwest Territories, most employees who would normally fall under provincial jurisdiction.

Chairman, Marc Lapointe, Q.C.
Vice-Chairmen: Thomas M. Eberlee,
Hugh Jamieson, Serge Brault
MEMBERS: J. Abson, Linda Parsons,
V.E. Gannon, Calvin Davis, J. Alary,
E. Bourassa, G. Gosselin, R. Cadieux
Director of Administration, David Craig
Operational Services/Registrar
Director, Gérard Legault
Director of Planning and
Program Development, Jim Callon
REGIONAL DIRECTORS AND REGISTRARS
Atlantic
Queen Sq., 6th Flr., 45 Alderney Dr.
Dartmouth, NS B2Y 2N6
Director, John Vines
Quebec
Place Guy Favreau, bur. 1202
200, boul. René-Lévesque ouest
Montréal, H2Z 1X4
Director, Debra Robinson
Ontario
350 Bay St., 4th Flr., Toronto, M5H 2S6
Director, Jack Stanton
Central Region
One Lakeview Sq., Ste. 300
155 Carlton St., Winnipeg, R3C 3H8
Director, Gordon Keeler
Western Region
800 Burrard St., Ste. 1600
Vancouver, V6Z 2G7
Director, Phil Kirkland

Labour Adjustment Review Board
Phase II, Place du Portage, 8th Flr.
Ottawa, K1A 0J2

The Labour Adjustment Review Board certifies persons laid off from designated industries as eligible to apply for labour adjustment benefits where it decides that their lay-off meets the criteria established in the *Labour Adjustments Benefits Act.*

Chairman, Joseph Morris, C.C.

Merchant Seamen Compensation Board
2 Place du Portage, Hull, K1A 0J2

The members of the Merchant Seamen Com-pensation Board are appointed by the Governor in Council pursuant to the *Merchant Seamen Compensation Act.* The Act provides for a chairman, vice-chairman and one other member.

The *Merchant Seamen Compensation Act* provides benefits to seamen employed on ships registered in Canada or chartered by demise to a person resident in Canada or having his principal place of business in Canada. The Act applies to seamen who are not covered under any provincial workers' compensation legislation or the *Government Employees Compensation Act* while the ship on which they are engaged is on a foreign or home-trade voyage as described in the *Canada Shipping Act.*

Chairman, Herman P. Hansen
Vice-Chairman, Capt. J.G. Daniels
Member, Dr. H.T. Sellers

DEPARTMENT OF NATIONAL DEFENCE

101 Colonel By Dr., Ottawa, K1A 0K2
Telex: 053-4218
Inquiries: (613) 992-4581

MINISTER'S OFFICE
Rm. 401, Confederation Bldg.
House of Commons, Ottawa, K1A 0A6
Minister, The Hon. William McKnight

ASSOCIATE MINISTER'S OFFICE
Assoc. Minister, The Hon. Mary Collins

DEPUTY MINISTER'S OFFICE
Dep. Minister, D. Bevis Dewar

CHIEF OF THE DEFENCE STAFF'S OFFICE
Chief of the Defence Staff, Gen. Paul Manson
Vice-Chief of the Defence Staff,
Lt.-Gen. A.J.G.D. de Chastelain
Communications Security Establishment
Chief, P.R. Hunt

JUDGE ADVOCATE GENERAL
Brig.-Gen. R.L. Martin

EXECUTIVE SECRETARIAT
Director Gen., C.J. Gauthier
National Defence Headquarters Secretariat
Director, Col. M.W. Drapeau
National Defence Inquiries Director, Vacant
Departmental Administration
Director, J.A. Larkin

INFORMATION
Director Gen., Brig.-Gen. A.L. Geddry
Information Services
Director, Lt.-Col. L.D. Dent
Exhibitions and Displays
Director, Lt.-Col. G.K. Hogan

INTELLIGENCE AND SECURITY
Chief, Maj.-Gen. R.P. Pattee
Intelligence
Director Gen., Cmdre J.B. O'Reilly
Defence Intelligence
Director, Lt.-Col. W.D.M. Hamilton
Foreign Liaison Director, Col. B.J. Fegarty
Scientific and Technical Intelligence
Director, Dr. L.A. Kuehn
Security
Director Gen., Col. W.J. McCullough

Policy
Asst. Dep. Minister, Robert R. Fowler
Assoc. Asst. Dep. Minister,
Maj.-Gen. D. Huddleston
Policy Operations
Director Gen., Brig.-Gen. R.A. Cimon
Policy Planning
Director Gen., Dr. K. Colder
Policy Co-ordination
A/Director Gen., N. Wildgoose

OPERATIONAL RESEARCH AND ANALYSIS
ESTABLISHMENT
Chief, Vacant
General Analysis
Director Gen., K.R. Kavanagh
Strategic Analysis Director, Dr. E. Gilman
Social and Economic Analysis
Director, Dr. J.S. Finan
Mathematics and Statistics
Director, Dr. M.A. Weinberger
Manpower Analysis Director, T.A. Ewashko
Logistics Analysis Director, G. Lafond
Operational Research
Director Gen., P.R. Anderson
Land Operational Research
Director, A.G. Boothroyd
Maritime Operational Research
Director, M.D.F. Boulton
Air Operational Research
Director, Dr. R.C. Brereton
Administration Director, M.G. Kenny

Personnel
Asst. Dep. Minister,
Vice-Adm. W.B. Hotsenpiller
Assoc. Asst. Dep. Minister, D.J. Lindley
Official Languages
Director Gen., G. DesBecquets
Personnel Relations
Director Gen., D. Candline
Personnel Services
Director Gen., Cmdre H.A. Cooper
Compensation and Benefits
Director Gen., B.J. Berryman
Personnel Co-ordination
Director Gen., S.P. Hunter

PERSONNEL DEVELOPMENT
Chief, Maj.-Gen. F.J. Sutherland
Personnel Research and Development
Director Gen., W.M. Ritchie

Recruiting, Education and Training
Director Gen., Brig.-Gen. G.S. Clements
Personnel Careers and Senior Appointments
Chief, Maj.-Gen. J.C. Gervais
Personnel Careers Officers
Director Gen., Brig.-Gen. S.A. Hellstrom
Personnel Careers Other Ranks
Director Gen., Brig.-Gen. J.J.R. Parent
Chaplain Gen. (P), Brig.-Gen. S.H. Clarke
Manpower Utilization
Director Gen., Brig.-Gen. K.G. Troughton
Chaplain Gen. (RC), Brig.-Gen. C.J. Campbell
Classification
Director Gen., C.P. Barrett
Civilian Human Resources Management
Director Gen., P. Conroy
Surgeon Gen., Rear Adm. C.J. Knight
Dep. Surgeon Gen., Brig.-Gen. J.P. Morisset
Dental Services
Director Gen., Brig.-Gen. J.F. Begin

PERSONNEL SERVICES
Chief, Maj.-Gen. G.S. Kells
Combat-Related Employment of Women
Director Gen., Brig.-Gen. D.E. Munro

Deputy Chief of the Defence Staff
Vice-Adm. H.M.D. MacNeil
Operational Plans and Force Development
A/Chief, Brig.-Gen. W.R. Dobson
Maritime Doctrine and Operations
Chief, Rear Adm. J.C. Slade
Air Doctrine and Operations
Chief, Maj.-Gen. R. Morton
Land Doctrine and Operations
Chief, Maj.-Gen. H.R. Wheatley
Reserves and Cadets
Chief, Rear Adm. W.N. Fox-Decent
Military Plans and Operations
A/Director Gen., Col. D.T. Carney
Reserves and Cadets
Director Gen., Brig.-Gen. J.E.L. Gollner
Military Engineering Operations
Director Gen., Col. A.J. Tattersall
Communications and Electronics Operations
Director Gen., Capt.(N) J.E. Croft

Materiel
Asst. Dep. Minister, E.J. Healey
Assoc. Asst. Dep. Minister,
Maj.-Gen. G. MacFarlane
Material Administration and Programs
Director Gen., Brig.-Gen. W.E.R. Little
International Programs
Director Gen., Don Bell

ENGINEERING AND MAINTENANCE
Chief, Maj.-Gen. P.E. Woods
Maritime Engineering and Maintenance
Director Gen., Cmdre D.R. Boyle
Aerospace Engineering and Maintenance
Director Gen., Brig.-Gen. R.M. Ramsbottom
Land Engineering and Maintenance
Director Gen., Brig.-Gen. J.I. Hanson

Communications, Electronic Engineering
and Maintenance
Director Gen., W.R. Oldford

SUPPLY
Chief, R. Gillespie
Supply Systems
Director Gen., Brig.-Gen. G.B. Glenn
Procurement and Supply
Director Gen., R.N. Sturgeon
Transportation
Director Gen., Col. A.B. Thompson
Quality Assurance
Director Gen., D.W. Wilson

CONSTRUCTION AND PROPERTIES
Chief, Maj.-Gen. J.E. Woods
Quartering
Director Gen., Brig.-Gen. D.H. Smith
Construction
Director Gen., R.H. Walsworth
Works
Director Gen., Col. D.W. Edgecombe
Properties and Utilities
Director Gen., C.J. Crowe

RESEARCH AND DEVELOPMENT
Chief, Dr. D. Schofield
Assoc. Chief, Dr. R.M. Heggie
Operations
Director Gen., P. Solnoky
Policy
Director Gen., P.N. Brookes
Services
A/Director Gen., D.L. Blakley

Finance
Asst. Dep. Minister, L.E. Davies
Assoc. Asst. Dep. Minister,
Maj.-Gen. R.D. Leech

FINANCIAL SERVICES
Chief, Maj.-Gen. R.D. Leech
Financial Policy and Procedures
Director Gen., E.F. McTaggart
Financial Administration
Director Gen., Cmdre P.C. Martin

AUTOMATED INFORMATION SERVICES
Chief, Maj.-Gen. I. Alleslev
Management Services
Director Gen., Brig.-Gen. P.N. Fischer
Automated Data Processing Services
Director Gen., N. Inglis

DEFENCE RESEARCH ESTABLISHMENT
OTTAWA
Department of National Defence
Ottawa, K1A 0Z4
Chief, Dr. G.L. Nelms
Administration Division
Director, Janis Pelletier
Electronics Division Director, Dr. J.L. Pearce

Electronic Warfare Division
Director, A. Sewards
Protective Sciences Division
A/Director, Dr. B. Harrison
Radar Division Director, D. Mabey
Program Support/Telecomliaison Division
A/Director, A.R. Abercrombie

AGENCIES, BOARDS AND COMMISSIONS

Defence Construction (1951) Ltd.
Sir Charles Tupper Bldg.
Riverside Dr., Ottawa, K1A 0K3
Telex: 053-3726, 053-3727
Inquiries: (613) 998-9548

Defence Construction (1951) Limited, a Crown corporation of the Government of Canada, is the contracting and construction supervisory agency for the major construction and maintenance projects of the Department of National Defence. In addition to its legal title, the company has been assigned the applied title — Defence Construction Canada.

Defence Construction Canada performs a specialized role within the general field of construction management. Its principal functions are to obtain tenders, make recommendations on proposed awards, and award and administer construction and maintenance contracts. In addition, at the request of the Department of National Defence, the Company engages architectural and consulting engineering firms to prepare plans and specifications in accordance with the requirements of the department.

The head office is located in Ottawa and branch offices are in Halifax, Montreal, Toronto, Victoria, Winnipeg, and Lahr, West Germany.

During 1987-88 the Company awarded contracts including amendments, with a value of over $272 million. For the same period, the value of contract expenditures was in excess of $398 million.

President, Lorne Atchison

Emergency Preparedness Canada
122 Bank St., 2nd Flr.
Jackson Bldg., Ottawa, K1A 0W6

Emergency Preparedness Canada co-ordinates the peace and wartime emergency planning activities of federal departments, agencies and Crown corporations, and promotes emergency preparedness in other levels of government.

A Joint Emergency Preparedness Program provides financial assistance for selected projects carried out in concert with the provinces. Courses, conferences and seminars on emergency planning and preparedness are presented at the Canadian Emergency Preparedness College in Arnprior, Ont. EPC provides information to the public on emergency preparedness, participates in national and international exercises, and sponsors research into the nature of emergencies. In the wake of a disaster, EPC administers disaster financial assistance arrangements whereby the federal government absorbs an escalating proportion of the provinces' expenditure for disaster relief, according to a formula based on the population of the affected province.

The executive director of Emergency Preparedness Canada represents Canada on NATO's Senior Civil Emergency Planning Committee.
Exec. Director, T. D'arcy Finn, Q.C.
Operations
Director Gen., D.W. Hall
Emergency Operations Co-ordination
Director, Dave Peters
Public Information Director, Lesley Lynn
Plans
Director Gen., E.L. Shipley
Corporate Programs
Director, Bill Sutherland

OFFICE OF PRIVATIZATION AND REGULATORY AFFAIRS
Heritage Pl., 155 Queen St.
Ottawa, K1A 1J2

MINISTER'S OFFICE
Rm. 558, Confederation Bldg.
House of Commons, Ottawa, K1A 0A6
Minister, The Hon. John McDermid

DEPUTY MINISTER'S OFFICE
Dep. Minister, Janet Smith
Administration and Executive Services
Director, C. Downes
Policy and Co-ordination
Director, C. McQuillan
Communications Director, D. Rennie
Gen. Counsel, D. Lewis

Regulatory Affairs
Asst. Dep. Minister, A. Campbell
Director, L. Blackwell
Privatization
Head, K. Stein
Director, D. McLean

PUBLIC SERVICE COMMISSION
L'Esplanade Laurier
300 Laurier Ave. W., Ottawa, K1A 0M7
Chairman, Huguette Labelle
Commissioners: Gilbert Scott, Peter Lesaux
Secretary-Gen., Lise Pigeon
Official Languages Secretariat
Director, V. McLay

STAFFING PROGRAMS BRANCH
Exec. Director, E.J. Baker
Business/Government Executive Exchange
Special Advisor, J.J. Tennier
Interchange Canada Director, D. Beckman
Program Control and Resource Enhancement
Director, A. Knights

Management Category Programs Directorate
Director Gen., M. Ouellon
Operations and Special Projects Division
A/Director, J.M. Robichaud
Office of External Recruitment
Director, Barbara Billings
Economic Development Portfolio
Director, D. Dolan
Social Development Portfolio
Director, J.G. Léger
Transportation, Environment
and Defence Portfolio
Director, S. Beaudoin
Government Operations Portfolio
Director, L. Holmes
External Affairs and
International Programs Portfolio
Director, B. Watson
Asst. Dep. Minister Secretariat
Visiting Asst. Dep. Minister, J. Cyr
Women's Career Counselling
and Referral Bureau
Director, M.A. Derikx
Career Assignment Program
Director, D. McLewin
Policy, Monitoring and Information Directorate
Director Gen., G. Létourneau
Analysis and Information Management
Director, Vacant
Policy Development, Interpretation
and Consultation
Director, R. McMahon
Program Development (Staffing)
Director Gen., L.W. Slivinski
Recruitment Referral and
New Entrance Programs
Exec. Co-ordinator, L. Pearson
Employment Equity Program Development
Director Gen., L. Pederson

REGIONAL OFFICES
Atlantic
7th Flr., Brunswick Bldg.
1888 Brunswick St., Halifax, B3J 1M8
Reg. Director, B. Lopes
Quebec
Place Guy Favreau, Tour ouest, 8ᵉ ét.
200, boul. René-Lévesque ouest
Montréal, H2Z 1X4
Reg. Director, J. Pelletier
Ontario
1 Front St. W., 3rd Flr.
Toronto, M5G 2R5
Reg. Director, T. Johnson
Manitoba and Saskatchewan
4th Flr., Revenue Canada Bldg.
391 York Ave., Winnipeg, R3C 4G8
Reg. Director, J. Charrette
Alberta and the Northwest Territories
830, 9700 Jasper Ave., Canada Pl.
Edmonton, T5J 4G3
Reg. Director, L. Bazinet
Pacific and Yukon
500, 757 West Hastings St.
Vancouver, V6C 3G4

Reg. Director, J. Hickey
National Capital Regional Office
Vanguard Bldg., 7th Flr.
171 Slater St., Ottawa, K1A 0M7
Director, C.P. Stewart

TRAINING PROGRAMS BRANCH
A/Exec. Director, G.R. Gauthier
Canadian Centre for Management Development
Principal, J.L. Manion
Vice Principal, R. Bertrand
Orientation Program
Exec. Director, C.E. Caron
Finance and Administration
Career Assignment Program
Director, Yvon Bordua
Language Training Program
Director Gen., N. Charette
Staff Training Program
A/Director Gen., J.M. Westover
Comptroller, L. Ladouceur
Quality Assurance Program
Director, I. Jackson
Policy Analysis and Co-ordination
Chief, Vacant
Operations Support Directorate
Director, R. Sauvé
Language Training Directorate (NCR)
Director, D. Côté
French Programs Director, G. Jean
NCR-Language Training Directorate
Director, M. Allaire
Language Training Directorate
Management Category
Director, R. Mareschal
Course Development Directorate
A/Director, H. Woods
General Management Training
A/Director, A. Michel
Professional and Technical Training
Director, H. Proulx
Consulting and Quality Control
Director, F. Laurin
Teaching Operations Services Division
A/Chief, M. Gobeil
Personnel Services Manager, L. Séguin
Policy, Analysis and Co-ordination
A/Chief, D. Langevin
Audit Branch
Director Gen., Robert Jelking

APPEALS AND INVESTIGATIONS BRANCH
Exec. Director, Robert Cousineau
A/Registrar and Information, F. Bessette
Appeals Directorate
A/Director Gen., G. Carbonneau
Investigations Directorate
Director Gen., F.M. Lalonde
Branch Systems and Services
Director, Dawn Cavanagh

CORPORATE SYSTEMS AND SERVICES
BRANCH
Exec. Director, Mary J. Murphy

Personnel Services Director, Vacant
Financial Services Director, G.A. Wright
Administrative Services Director, J.P. Groulx
Public Affairs Director, S. Boissonneault
EDP Services Director, Vacant
Review Directorate
Director Gen., A. Lazar
Corporate Management Systems
Director, R. Power
Branch Management and Regional Services
Director, P.J. Marchand

DEPARTMENT OF PUBLIC WORKS
Sir Charles Tupper Bldg.
Riverside Dr., Ottawa, K1A 0M2
Telex: 053-4235
General Inquiries: (613) 998-7724

MINISTER'S OFFICE
Rm. 707, Confederation Bldg., W. Blk.
House of Commons, Ottawa, K1A 0A6
Minister, The Hon. Elmer MacKay

DEPUTY MINISTER'S OFFICE
Dep. Minister, Robert J. Giroux
Corporate Policy and Administration
A/Gen. Director, Mike Nurse
Corporate Communications
Director Gen., Terry Keleher
PUBLIC WORKS REGIONAL OFFICES:
Atlantic
Box 2247, Stn. M, Halifax, B3J 3C9
A/Reg. Director Gen., Gerry Westland
Quebec
200, boul. René-Lévesque ouest
Montréal, H2Z 1X4
Reg. Director Gen., G. Wolfe
National Capital
Place du Portage IV, Hull
Director Gen., P. Letellier
Ontario
4900 Yonge St., Willowdale, M2N 6A6
Reg. Director Gen., Susanne Borup
Western
Ste. 1000, Canada Pl.
9700 Jasper Ave., Edmonton, P5J 4E2
Reg. Director Gen., E. Bauckman
Pacific
1166 Alberni St., Vancouver, V6E 3W5
Reg. Director Gen., N. Hoyt

Architectural and Engineering Services
Asst. Dep. Minister, N. Freeman
Transportation
Gen. Director, J.E. Coke
Air Transportation
A/Director Gen., M.A. Stairs
Land Transportation
A/Director Gen., J.C. Beauchamp
Marine Transportation
Director Gen., M. Girgrah

Architectural Services
Gen. Director, J.E. Langford
A & ES (INAC)
Director Gen., S. Reid
Buildings
Director Gen., W. Rankin
A & ES (Env. Can.)
Director Gen., P.J. Choquette
A & ES Strategic Services
Gen. Director, F. Almeda
Technology
Director Gen., J. Davison

Corporate Management

Sr. Asst. Dep. Minister, B.J. Veinot
Corporate Policy and Administration
A/Gen. Director, Michael G. Nurse
Corporate Finance
Director Gen., H.G. Richards
Financial Services
Director Gen., J.-G. Hébert
Informatics Services
Director Gen., D. Snedden
Contract Policy and Administration
Director Gen., J.C. Morin
Planning Process
Performance and Productivity Assessment
A/Director, J. Lendvay-Zwickl
Make or Buy Methodology
A/Manager, C. Toussaint
Crown Corporations
Director, M. Charlebois-McKinnon
Administration Policy and Services
Director, B. Eardley
Public Rights and Executive Committee Support
Director, J. Dickinson
Claims Review and Analysis
Director Gen., A.C. Boughner
Administrative Policy and Services
A/National Director, H. Nadler
Legal Director, R. Gaulin

Realty Services

Asst. Dep. Minister, R.S Lafleur
Strategic Issues
A/Director, C. Beaupré

REAL ESTATE SERVICES
Director Gen., Jacques Roy
Acquisition, Leasing and Disposal
Director, A. Miller
Property Development and
Legal Land Surveys
A/Director, G. Abson
Municipal Grants Director, J. Piché

PROPERTY MANAGEMENT SERVICES
Director Gen., F.J. Brazeau
Operations Director, U. Ruppert
Policies Director, D. Patton

FACILITIES MAINTENANCE SERVICES
Director Gen., E.J. Newman

Facilities Operations and Maintenance
Director, O. Ward
Facilities Maintenance Resources
Director, R. Bégin
Facilities Maintenance Management
A/Director, R. Marleau

REALTY BUSINESS MANAGEMENT
Director Gen., A.C. Wade
Realty Business Planning and Administration
A/Director, K. Wyonch
Realty Systems
A/Director, P. Allen
Client Services Director, M. Lefebvre

Accommodation

Asst. Dep. Minister, J.M. Dunphy
Director Gen., P. Migus
Assets Investment (Capital)
Director, H. Wood
Leasing Investment Director, R. Hébert
Crown Properties Director, C. Beal
Appropriated Programs Director, G. Duncan
Emergency Preparedness Director, K. Farrell
Accommodation Control
A/Director, M. Ballantine

CORPORATE POLICY AND ADMINISTRATION
BRANCH
A/Gen. Director, Michael G. Nurse
Corporate Policy and Strategic Planning
Director, R. Swann
Management Practices
A/Director Gen., V. Hambly
Corporate Projects and
Management Improvements
Director, Vacant

CORPORATE COMMUNICATIONS
Director Gen., Terry Keleher
Operations Director, S. Axam

Human Resources

Asst. Dep. Minister, L.G. Potvin
HQ Region
Special Advisor, M. Turcotte
H.Q. Director, G. Lawlor
Corporate Classification Director, A. Caro
Corporate Staffing Director, L. Gaucher
Staff Relations
A/Director, S. Collis
Official Languages
A/Director, M.-C. Decourcelles
Education, Training and Development
Director, G. Blache
Employment Equity, Human
Resource Planning and Systems
A/Director, G. Curran
Employee Assistance Programme
Manager, P. Prud'homme

DEPARTMENT OF REVENUE
Ottawa, K1A 0L5

MINISTER'S OFFICE
707 Confederation Bldg.
House of Commons, Ottawa, K1A 0A6
Minister, The Hon. Otto Jelinek

CUSTOMS AND EXCISE
Connaught Bldg., Mackenzie Ave.
Ottawa, K1A 0L5

DEPUTY MINISTER'S OFFICE
Dep. Minister, Ruth Hubbard
Departmental and International Affairs
A/Director, B. Hebert

Customs Programs
Asst. Dep. Minister, Sheila K. Batchelor
Legislative Affairs Director, Christiane Ouimet
Assessment Programs
Director Gen., B. Brimble
Tariff Programs
Director Gen., Phil E. Zerr
Management Systems and Services
Director, G.B. Greene
Adjudications Director, R.F. Thompson
FTA Task Force
Director Gen., Rob Tait
Valuation Division
A/Director, Mike Jordan

Excise
Asst. Dep. Minister, R.F. Fulford
Excise Appeals
Director Gen., R.B. Burke
Excise Operations
Director Gen., K.H. McCammon
Excise Programs
Director Gen., M. Burpee
Commodity Tax Review
Director, S.F. Watson
Excise Commercial System
Director Gen., G.F. Kirkpatrick
Planning and Administration
Director, R.G. Thompson

Customs Operations
Asst. Dep. Minister, J.C.Y. Charlebois
Travellers and Enforcement
Director Gen., H.J. Giles
Commercial Directorate
Director Gen., E.D. Warren
Investigations Director, J.F. Johnston
Port Administration Director, D. Tucker
Human Resources Division
A/Chief, M. Wright
Interdiction Director, V. Castonguay
Intelligence Director, G. Rochon
Travellers Director, J. Walsh
Planning and Budgeting Division
Director, B. Cleveland

Systems Operation Director, P. Emond
Cargo and Release Director, J.F. Shearer
Project Management Director, P. Emond
Licensing Director, L. Klump
Entry, Postal and Appraisal Director, F. Light

Corporate Management
Asst. Dep. Minister, G. Bélec
Systems Planning and Development
Director Gen., T.R. Young
Corporate Planning
Director Gen., M.M. David
Administration Director, R.M. Hébert
Laboratory and Scientific Services
Director, W. Morris
Finance Director, K. Kerr
Capital Assets Program
Director, R. Lévesque
Audit and Evaluation
Director Gen., C.V. Veinotte
Personnel Administration
Director Gen., R.K. Cox
Communications
Director Gen., L. Gordon
Operations Director, B. Yolkouskie
Legal Services
Sr. Counsel, L. Holland, Q.C.
REGIONAL EXCISE OFFICES:
Atlantic
2nd Flr., 6169 Quinpool Rd.
Box 1658, Halifax, B3J 2Z8
Reg. Director, R.J. Young
Quebec
410, boul. Charest est, 7e ét.
C.P. 2117, Québec, G1K 7M9
Reg. Director, P. Gagnon
Montreal
400, place d'Youville, 7e ét.
C.P. 6072, Montréal, H2Y 3N4
Reg. Director, R. Tittley
Ottawa
360 Coventry Rd., Box 8257
Ottawa, K1G 3H7
Reg. Director, R.A. Gagné
Toronto
4th Flr., 25 St. Clair Ave. E.
Box 100, Stn. Q, Toronto, M4T 2L7
Reg. Director, L.J. Kluger
Southwestern Ontario
3rd Flr., Dominion Public Bldg.
457 Richmond St., Box 5548
London, N6A 4R3
Reg. Director, Norma Earl
Central
Revenue Bldg., Rm. 410, 391 York Ave.
Box 1022, Winnipeg, R3C 2W2
A/Reg. Director, B. Cook
Alberta
Harry Hays Bldg., 220-4th Ave. S.E.
Box 2525, Stn. M, Calgary, T2P 3B7
Reg. Director, C.K. Taylor
Pacific
4664 Lougheed Hwy., Rm. 201
Burnaby, V5C 6C2
Reg. Director, L.R. Hawtin

REGIONAL CUSTOMS OFFICES:
Atlantic
6169 Quinpool Rd., Ste. 203
Box 3080, Halifax, B3J 3G6
Reg. Collector, R.J. King
Quebec
130, rue Dalhousie, C.P. 2267
Québec, G1K 7P6
Reg. Collector, R.J. Falardeau
Montréal
400, place d'Youville
C.P. 400, succ. A, Montréal, H2Y 2C2
Reg. Collector, J.H. Noël
Ottawa
360 Coventry Rd., Ottawa, K1K 2C6
A/Reg. Collector, André Villeneuve
Toronto
1 Front St. W., Box 10, Stn. A
Toronto, M5W 1A3
Reg. Collector, J.G. MacDonald
Hamilton
10 John St. S., Box 989, Hamilton, L8N 3V8
Reg. Collector, Gloria Reid
Southwestern Ontario
1st Flr., 420 Devonshire Rd.
Windsor, N8Y 4T6
Reg. Collector, R.K. Watt
Central
Federal Bldg., 269 Main St.
Winnipeg, R3C 1B3
Reg. Collector, W. LeDrew
Alberta
220-4th Ave. S.E.
Box 2910, Stn. M, Calgary, T2P 2M7
Reg. Collector, A.L. Lentz
Pacific
1001 W. Pender St., Vancouver, V6E 2M8
Reg. Collector, G.T. Segodnia

TAXATION
875 Heron Rd., Ottawa, K1A 0L8

DEPUTY MINISTER'S OFFICE
Dep. Minister, Pierre Gravelle, Q.C.

Policy and Systems Branch
Asst. Dep. Minister, R. Roy

ASSESSING AND ENQUIRIES DIRECTORATE
Director Gen., G. Venner
Returns Processing Division
Director, J.M. Legault
Examination Division Director, W.E. Moore
Enquiries and Taxpayer Assistance Division
Director, Pauline McNally

COLLECTIONS AND ACCOUNTING
DIRECTORATE
Director Gen., D.S. Brown
Source Deductions Division
Director, L. Mancino
Revenue Programs Division
Director, A. Bissonnette
Collections Division Director, B. Kimmons

AUDIT PROGRAMS DIRECTORATE
Director Gen., G. Venner
Audit Programs and Assessment Division
Director, K. McLean
E.D.P. Audit Applications Division
Director, H. Beaulac
International Audits Division
Director, J.A. Calderwood
Audit Applications Division
A/Director, J. Daman
Special Audits Division Director, E. Gauthier

SYSTEMS DIRECTORATE
Director Gen., H.J. Lagasse
Computer Services Director, N. Epp
Individual Tax Systems Division
Director, D. Green
Business Tax Systems Division
Director, A. Landsberg
Informatics Support Division
Director, D. McLeod

COMPLIANCE RESEARCH AND
INVESTIGATIONS DIRECTORATE
Director Gen., J.R. Robertson
Compliance Research Division
Director, R.S. Hall
Investigations (Atlantic and Quebec)
Reg. Director, R. Davis
Investigations (Ontario and Central)
Reg. Director, R.W. Moore
Investigations (West)
Reg. Director, E. Kucher

**Legislative and Intergovernmental Affairs
Branch**
A/Asst. Dep. Minister, Robert Read
Finance, Personnel and Administration
Chief, Carol Waite
Fiscal Policy and Technical Interpretations
Chief, R.M. Beith

SPECIALTY RULINGS DIRECTORATE
Director Gen., R.J.L. Read
Reorganization and Non-Resident
Director, M. Hiltz
Small Business and General
Director, B. Dath

RULINGS DIRECTORATE
Director Gen., Vacant
Bilingual Services and Resources
Director, C. Gouin-Toussaint
Financial Industries Director, Brian Darling
Provincial and International Relations
Director, R.G. D'Aurelio
Technical Interpretations Director, A. Cockell

LEGISLATIVE AFFAIRS DIRECTORATE
Director Gen., C.D. McDonald
Current Amendments and Regulations
A/Director, B. Bryson
Publications Director, R. Shultis
Tax Reform Legislation
Special Advisor, Don Joy

REGISTRATION DIRECTORATE
Director Gen., B. Darling
Registered Pensions and
Deferred Income Plans
Director, S. Kotlar
Charities Director, G. Murray
Statistical Services Director, F. Hostetter
Legal Services
Gen. Counsel, Charles MacNab

Communications and Corporate Development Branch
Asst. Dep. Minister, John Rama
Communications Directorate
Director, Carla Gilders
Corporate Projects and Strategic Planning
Director, B. Anderson
Corporate Secretariat
Director, Lynn MacFarlane

INTERNAL AUDIT AND EVALUATION
Director Gen., M. LeBlond
Program Evaluation Director, W. Baker
Internal Audit Division Director, D. Newman

Management Services Branch
Asst. Dep. Minister, M.J. Cardinal
Planning and Program Services
Officer, N. St-Onge
Centre for Career Development
Director, Maureen Griffin

PERSONNEL DIRECTORATE
Director Gen., G. Leblond
Human Resources Director, Art Lawless
Employee Relations and Services
Director, J.C. Cloutier
Classification and Organization Division
Director, T. Pincombe

SECURITY DIRECTORATE
A/Director, Ron Twolan
OFFICE POLICY AND TECHNOLOGY
DIRECTORATE
Director, R. Dudding
TAX FORMS DIRECTORATE
Director, L.A. Donnelly

FINANCE DIRECTORATE
Director Gen., E.T. Parker
Financial Policy, Systems and Accounting
Director, M. Thurlbeck
Revenue Reporting and Tax Analysis
Director, B. Pink
Financial Analysis and Resource Allocation
Director, J. Kowalski

Appeals Branch
Asst. Dep. Minister, R.A. D'Avignon
Appeals and Referrals
Director, E. Noël de Tilly
Policy and Programs Director, G. Arsenijevic

Atlantic Region
2000 Barrington St., Ste. 800
Halifax, B3J 3K1
Asst. Dep. Minister, P.W. Kierstead
Newfoundland
Atlantic Place, Box 5968, St. John's, A1C 5X6
Director, A. Shields
St. John's Taxation Ctr.
Freshwater and Empire St.
St. John's, A1B 3Z1
Director, G.J. Brown
Prince Edward Island
90 Richmond St., Charlottetown, C1A 8L3
A/Director, H. Terris
Nova Scotia
Ralston Bldg., 1557 Hollis St., Halifax, B3J 2T5
Director, N.B. Squires
Federal Bldg., 60 Dorchester St.
Box 1300, Sydney, B1P 6K3
Director, M. Fitzgerald
New Brunswick
65 Canterbury St., Saint John, E2L 4H9
Director, R.D. Léger

Quebec
200, boul. René-Lévesque ouest
Montréal, H2Z 1X4
Asst. Dep. Minister, Serge Mercille
Quebec
165, rue de la Pointe-aux-Lièvres sud
Québec, G1K 7L3
Director, Gilles Guy
Sherbrooke
50, place de la Cité, C.P. 1300
Sherbrooke, J1H 5L8
Director, Marcel Ricard
Montreal
National Revenue Bldg.
305, boul. René-Lévesque ouest
Montréal, H2Z 1A8
Director, R. Doré
Laval
3131, boul. St-Martin ouest, bur. 100
Laval, H7T 2A7
Director, Georges Cloutier
St. Hubert
5245, boul. Cousineau, bur. 200
St-Hubert, J3Y 7Z7
Director, Marc Blanchard
Rouyn-Noranda
11, rue Terminus est
Rouyn-Noranda, J9X 3B5
Director, M. Morel
Shawinigan-Sud Taxation Centre
4695, Douzième av.
Shawinigan-Sud, G9N 7S6
Director, P.E. Moreau
Jonquière Taxation Centre
2251, boul. de la Centrale, Jonquière, G7S 5J1
Director, E. Tanguay

Central Ontario
38 Auriga Dr., Nepean, K2E 8A5
Asst. Dep. Minister, W.J. Clarke

Ottawa District Office
Century Bldg., 360 Lisgar St., Ottawa, K1A 0L9
Director, P.E. Séguin
Scarborough District Office
200 Town Centre Crt., Ste. 1053
Scarborough, M1P 4Y3
Director, G.J. Baronette
Toronto District Office
Mackenzie Bldg., 36 Adelaide St. E.
Toronto, M5C 1J7
Director, Ron Giles
Mississauga District Office
Box 8000, 36 Adelaide St. E.
Toronto, M5C 2T4
Director, G.R. Mohr
North York District Office
Box 7057, 36 Adelaide St. E.
Toronto, M5C 2V4
Director, P. Middlestead
Ottawa Taxation Centre
875 Heron Rd., Rm. 9088B, Ottawa, K1A 1A2
Director, T.S. Blanchard

Ontario
451 Talbot St., Ste. 1114, London, N6A 6E5
Asst. Dep. Minister, Ron Marshall
Belleville
New Federal Bldg., 11 Station St.
Belleville, K8N 2S3
Director, L. Myers
Hamilton
National Revenue Bldg., 150 Main St. W.
Hamilton, L8N 3E1
Director, Sherman Lee
Kingston
358 Princess St., Kingston, K7L 1C1
Director, L. Myers
Kitchener
National Revenue Bldg.
166 Frederick St., Kitchener, N2H 2M4
Director, B.B. Lowe
St. Catharines
Federal Bldg., 32-46 Church St.
St. Catharines, L2R 3B9
Director, Larry Schmidt
London
451 Talbot St., London, N6A 5E5
Director, P.E. Broder
Windsor
185 Ouellette Ave., Windsor, N9A 5S8
Director, Rod Mercer
Sudbury
Federal Bldg., 19 Lisgar St. S.
Sudbury, P3E 3L5
Director, D. Luciuk
Thunder Bay
Revenue Bldg., 201 N. May St.
Thunder Bay, P7C 3P5
Director, S. Stapleton
Sudbury Taxation Centre
1050 Notre Dame St., Sudbury, P3A 5C1
Director, J. Langlois

Western
Box 2939, Stn. M, Calgary, T2P 2M7
Asst. Dep. Minister, H.G. Ladd

Winnipeg
Revenue Bldg., 391 York Ave.
Winnipeg, MB R3C 0P5
Director, John Purda
Regina
Income Tax Bldg., 1955 Smith St.
Regina, SK S4P 2N9
Director, A. Kellett
Saskatoon
C.I.B.C. Bldg., 201-21st St. E.
Saskatoon, SK S7K 0A8
Director, S. Cochrane
Calgary
Harry Hays Bldg., 220-4th Ave. S.E.
Calgary, AB T2G 0L1
Director, A. Stubel
Edmonton
Canada Place, 9700 Jasper Ave.
Edmonton, AB T5J 4C8
Director, H. Lee
Penticton
Federal Bldg., 277 Winnipeg St.
Penticton, BC V2A 1N6
Director, K. Ritcey
Vancouver
1166 W. Pender St., Vancouver, BC V6E 3H8
A/Director, S. McKenzie
Victoria
1415 Vancouver St., Victoria, BC V8V 3W4
Director, R. Frolek
Winnipeg Taxation Cte.
66 Stapon Rd., Winnipeg, MB R3C 3M2
Director, Reid Corrigall
Surrey Taxation Cte.
9755 King George Hwy., Surrey, BC V3T 5E1
Director, B. Bergen

AGENCIES, BOARDS AND COMMISSIONS
Canadian International Trade Tribunal
19th Flr., Journal Twr. S.
365 Laurier Ave. W., Ottawa, K1A 0G5

The Canadian International Trade Tribunal was established in 1988 under the authority of the *Canadian International Trade Tribunal Act,* S.C. 1988, Chapter 56. It replaced the Tariff Board, the Textile and Clothing Board, and the Canadian Import Tribunal. The Tribunal, an independent, statutory, quasi-judicial court of record, makes formal inquiry as to whether the importation of goods is causing material injury to Canadian industry or is retarding the establishment of production in Canada, and determines appropriate action.

It protects Canadian manufacturers and producers from two important forms of unfair competition originating in foreign countries:
- exporting goods to Canada at lower prices than they would be sold at in their home market. This is referred to as "dumping"; and
- exporting goods to Canada which have been produced with the benefit of substantial foreign government subsidies. This is referred to as "subsidization".

Protection is provided if it is established to the

satisfaction of the Canadian International Trade Tribunal that dumped or subsidized imports have caused or threaten to cause material injury to the Canadian production of like goods. If material injury is established, anti-dumping or countervailing duties may be levied on these imports to offset the price advantage caused by the dumping or subsidization.

The process usually starts by a complaint from Canadian manufacturers to the Deputy Minister, National Revenue, Customs and Excise, alleging dumping or subsidization as well as injury from imported goods. Once satisfied that there is evidence of dumping or subsidization as well as material injury, the National Revenue officials start a formal investigation. Exporters and importers of the goods are placed on notice and their transactions are investigated by customs officials.

On receipt of a preliminary determination of dumping or subsidization from the Deputy Minister, the Canadian Import Tribunal begins an inquiry to determine whether the domestic producer or group of producers has suffered material injury or retardation as a consequence of the dumping or subsidization.

The Act provides that the Tribunal shall consist of a chairman, two vice-chairmen and six regular members appointed by the Governor in Council for five-year terms. It is supported by a secretariat which provides support services and by a research unit which conducts economic studies.

Chairman, John C. Coleman
Vice-Chairman, Robert J. Bertrand, Q.C.
Member, A.B. Trudeau
Secretary, Robert J. Martin
Dep. Secretary, R. Noël
Exec. Director, Ronald Erdmann

Machinery and Equipment Advisory Board
Connaught Bldg., Mackenzie Ave.
Ottawa, K1A 0L5

The Department of National Revenue's Machinery Program is administered by this Board. The Program fosters the expansion and efficiency of Canadian manufacturing by providing a reasonable measure of tariff protection to machinery producers. It also enables machinery users to acquire capital equipment at the lowest possible cost through remission of duty on imported equipment not available from Canadian producers.

Chairman, Phil E. Zerr
Dir.-Secretary, H.L. Jones

MINISTRY OF STATE FOR SCIENCE AND TECHNOLOGY
C.D. Howe Bldg., W. Twr.
240 Sparks St., Ottawa, K1A 1A1

OFFICE OF THE MINISTER
Confederation Bldg., Rm. 576
House of Commons, Ottawa, K1A 0A6
Minister, The Hon. William Winegard

OFFICE OF THE SECRETARY OF THE MINISTRY
Secretary and Chief Science Advisor to the Government, Bruce Howe
Corporate Secretary, Lynne Ree

Government and Universities Sector
Dep. Secretary, Roberto Gualtieri
Federal Research Branch
Director Gen., A. Doerr
University and Research Councils Branch
Director Gen., Alan Cobb

Industry and Intergovernmental Relations Sector
Dep. Secretary, Brian Salley
Intergovernmental Relations
Director Gen., Dr. David Henderson
Industrial Support and
Strategic Technologies Programs
Director Gen., Dr. Henri Rothschild
International Relations
Director, Sonia Saumier-Finch

Space Policy Sector
A/Dep. Secretary, Mac Evans
A/Director Gen., Dr. Jocelyn Ghent
Communications Branch
A/Director Gen., M. Chetcuti
Corporate Services Branch
Director Gen., Susan Vorner Kirby

DEPARTMENT OF THE SECRETARY OF STATE
Ottawa, K1A 0M5
(except where otherwise noted)
General Information: (819) 997-0055
Access to Information/Privacy: (819) 997-4311

MINISTER'S OFFICE
Jules Léger Bldg., 12th Flr.
Les Terrasses de la Chaudière
15, rue Eddy, Hull, K1A 0M5
Secretary of State, The Hon. Gerry Weiner

MINISTER OF STATE (MULTICULTURALISM AND CITIZENSHIP)
House of Commons
533 Confederation Bldg.
Ottawa, K1A 0A6
Minister of State, The Hon. Gerry Weiner

OFFICE OF THE UNDER-SECRETARY OF STATE
Under-Secretary of State, Jean T. Fournier

OFFICE OF THE ASSOCIATE UNDER-SECRETARY OF STATE
Associate Under-Secretary of State,
Dr. Noel A. Kinsella

PERSONNEL ADMINISTRATION BRANCH
Director Gen., J. Robert Joubert
Employee Assistance Program
Co-ordinator, Johanne Lavoie
Classification and Official Languages
Staff Relations and Pay and Benefits
Director, Diane Gorman
Human Resources Director, Benoît Duguay
Personnel Services
Chief, Division "A", Michel Brazeau
Chief, Division "B", Gérard Mathieu
Office Services Chief, Marie C. Cayer

Corporate Policy and Public Affairs
Asst. Under-Secretary of State,
Richard G.T. Clippingdale

CORPORATE POLICY BRANCH
Director Gen., Richard Berger
Legal Services
Gen. Counsel, Alain Bisson
Program Evaluation Directorate
Director, Kerry Johnston
State Ceremonial Branch
Director Gen., Harris D. Boyd
Corporate Secretariat
Director, Ginette Gloutier

COMMUNICATIONS BRANCH
Director Gen., Doug Christensen
Planning and Co-ordination
A/Dep. Director Gen., Marion Brown
Creative Services
A/Director, Jean-Claude Paradis

Management Practices
Asst. Under-Secretary of State, Robert Legros

INFORMATICS AND ADMINISTRATIVE
POLICIES AND SERVICES BRANCH
Director Gen., Ronald Désormeaux
Security and Facilities Management Directorate
Director, Jacques Grenier
Computer Systems Directorate
Director, Bernard Abela
Services Contracts Directorate
Director, Michel Bérubé
Information Resources Services Directorate
Director, E.W. Aumand
Management Improvement Directorate
Director, Claire Lavoie

FINANCE BRANCH
Director Gen., Jean-Pierre Breton
Financial Planning and Management Reporting
Director, Ginette Bergeron
Financial and Operational Planning
Asst. Director, André Couture
Accounting Operations, Financial
Policies and Systems Directorate
Director, John S. Klimczak
Financial Advisory Services,
Grants and Contributions
Director, Agathe Frappier

Internal Audit Directorate
Director, Carole Jolicoeur

Multiculturalism
Asst. Under-Secretary of State, Shirley Serafini
Policy Analysis and Research
Director, Greg Gauld
Multiculturalism Secretariat
A/Exec. Director, Michal Ben-Gara
Sector Management and Co-ordination
A/Director, Johanne C. Lamarre
Programs Branch
Director Gen., Lizzy Fraikin
Community Support and Participation Programs
Director, Manuel Da Costa
Community Development
A/Asst. Director, Judy Young
Race Relations and Cross
Cultural Understanding Program
A/Director, John Samuel
Japanese Canadian Redress Secretariat
A/Director, Anne Scotton

Citizenship
Asst. Under-Secretary of State, Richard Dicerni

POLICY CO-ORDINATION, ANALYSIS AND
MANAGEMENT SYSTEMS BRANCH
Director Gen., Catherine Lane
Policy and Planning Director, Vacant
Social Trends Analysis Director, Vacant
Secretariat and Systems
Chief, Margaret Regan
Women's Program Director, Judy Wright
Native Citizens Directorate
Director, Roy Jacobs
Status of Disabled Persons Secretariat
A/Exec. Director, Nancy Lawand
Disabled Persons Participation Program
A/Director, Suzanne Potter

CITIZENS' PARTICIPATION BRANCH
Director Gen., Jérôme Lapierre
Human Rights Directorate
Director, Jean Chartier
Voluntary Action Directorate
A/Director, Brigid Hayes
Youth Participation
Director, Pageen Walsh
National Literacy Secretariat
A/Exec. Director, Richard Nolan
Sr. Citizenship Judge
Judge Elizabeth Willcock
Citizenship Registration
Registrar, Eva Kmiecic

CITIZENSHIP REGISTRATION BRANCH
Operations Sydney, Box 7000
Sydney, NS B1P 6V6
Director, B. Hudson

Education Support
Asst. Under-Secretary of State,
Stewart Goodings

POLICY, ANALYSIS AND LIAISON
Director Gen., Lise Brisson-Noreau
Policy and Analysis
Director, Nigel Chippindale
International Liaison
A/Director, Gilles Jasmin
Canadian Studies Director, James E. Page

STUDENT ASSISTANCE
Director, Mary Meloshe
Policy, Intergovernmental and
Institutional Arrangements
Director, F.B. Woyiwada
A/Programs Director, Phillip Lavigne
Comptroller, Marie Piette
Canada Student Loans
Inquiries: (819) 994-1844
Official Languages in Education
Director, Hilaire Lemoine

TRANSLATION BUREAU
Information Services: (819) 997-2193
Terminological Information: (819) 997-4363
Foreign Languages: (819) 997-7707

Official Languages and Translation
Asst. Under-Secretary of State, Alain Landry

PLANNING MANAGEMENT AND
TECHNOLOGY BRANCH
Director Gen., Ming Tsui
Planning and Policy Directorate
Director, François Dumas
Management and Management Information
Director, Vacant
Technology Co-ordinator, Denise Charron

PROMOTION OF OFFICIAL LANGUAGES
BRANCH
Director Gen., Mark Goldenberg
Liaison and Programs Director, Gérard Finn
Policies, Analysis and
Inter-Governmental Operations
Director, Pierre Gaudet
Official Languages Secretariat
Director, Paul-Émile Leblanc

TERMINOLOGY AND LINGUISTIC SERVICES
BRANCH
Director, Malcolm Williams
Promotion and Client Services Directorate
A/Director, Monique Larichelière
Linguistic Services Directorate
A/Director, Robert Aubut

TRANSLATION OPERATIONS BRANCH
Director Gen., Germain Asselin
Departmental Translation and
Interpretation Services
Dep. Director Gen., Michel Robichaud
Strategic Planning and Communications
Director, C. Tremblay
Management Services Director, P. Danis
Human Resources Director, H. Brisson

Parliamentary Services Director, A. Morissette
Multilingual Translation Director, John McKee
Central Services Director, Jean Gordon
Quebec Translation Services
Director, Hélène DeCorwin

REGIONAL OPERATIONS—TRANSLATION
Nova Scotia Region
5281 Duke St., Halifax, B3J 3M1
Asst. Reg. Director, Ronald Bourque
New Brunswick Region
Rm. 100, 236 St. Georges St.
Moncton, E1C 1W1
A/Provincial Director, Romain Godbout
P.E.I. Region
25 University Ave., 3rd Flr.
Box 7700, Charlottetown, C1A 8M9
Provincial Director, Romain Godbout
Ontario Region
Ste. 210, 55 St. Clair Ave. E.
Toronto, M4T 1M2
Asst. Reg. Director, Sarah Cummins
Manitoba Region
Rm. 407, 391 York Ave., Winnipeg, R3C 0P4
Asst. Reg. Director, Raymond Arcand
Alberta/N.W.T. Regions
Rm. 254, 220-4th Ave. S.E., Calgary, T2P 3C1
Translator, Geneviève Wright
Pacific Region
Rm. 102, 1525 West 8th Ave.
Vancouver, V6J 1T5
Asst. Reg. Director, Sylvie Gilbert

Regional Operations
Asst. Under-Secretary of State,
Georges Proulx

POLICY DEVELOPMENT AND
CO-ORDINATION
Chief, Bernard Deschênes
Planning and Systems
Chief, Michel Régimbald
Administration Chief, Sylvie Mayer
Information, Pierre Boulanger
REGIONAL OFFICES:
Newfoundland Region
Box 75, Atlantic Pl.
215 Water St., St. John's, A1C 6C9
Reg. Director, Elmer Hynes
Nova Scotia Region
5281 Duke St., Halifax, B3J 3M1
Reg. Director, Joanne Linzey
New Brunswick and P.E.I. Region
Ste. 504, 860 Main St., Moncton, NB E1C 1G2
Reg. Director, J.-B. Lafontaine
Quebec Region
Place Guy-Favreau, Tour ouest, 10e ét.
200, boul. René-Lévesque ouest
Montréal, H2Z 1X4
Reg. Director, Norma Passaretti
Ontario Region
Ste. 200, 25 St. Clair Ave. E.
Toronto, M4T 1M2
Reg. Director, James R. MacDonald

Manitoba Region
303 Main St., Rm. 201, Winnipeg, R3C 3G7
Reg. Director, Michel Lagacé

Saskatchewan Region
200, 2101 Scarth St., Regina, S4P 2H9
Reg. Director, André Nogue

Alberta and N.W.T. Region
Canada Pl., 9700 Jasper Ave.
Rm. 200, Edmonton, T5K 4C3
Reg. Director, Marc Arnal

Pacific Region
1525 West 8th Ave., Rm. 207
Vancouver, V6J 1T5
Reg. Director, Wendy Carter

AGENCIES, BOARDS AND COMMISSIONS

Canadian Multiculturalism Advisory Council Secretariat

The Canadian Multiculturalism Council, formerly named the Canadian Consultative Council on
Multiculturalism, was established in 1973. The
Council is an advisory body to the Minister of State
for Multiculturalism. It is the single official advisory mechanism created specifically to assist the
minister to implement the multiculturalism policy
of the Government of Canada.

Multiculturalism policy is designed to encourage the preservation and development of the
many cultures found in Canadian society; to
promote sharing and cross-cultural awareness;
and to ensure that Canadians of every heritage
have equal opportunity to participate in the
cultural development of this country.

The members of the CMC are appointed by the
minister and are drawn from a cross-section of
Canada's many ethnocultural communities and
from all sectors of Canadian society. Their
selection is on the basis of their ability to draw
upon their own experience, interests, and wisdom
in the multiculturalism field.

The Council has a national chairperson and an
executive committee of 15 members. Within the
executive committee are five chairpersons who
head five regional committees that meet quarterly.

Chairman, Dr. Louis C. Melosky
British Columbia and Yukon Regions
Vice-Chairman, Dr. Wallace Chung
Prairies Region and Northwest Territories
Vice-Chairman, Dr. David Bai
Ontario Region
Vice-Chairman, Dr. Orest Rudzik
Quebec Region
Vice-Chairman, Dr. André Arcelin
Atlantic Region
Vice-Chairman, Peter McCreath
Exec. Director, Michael Leigh

DEPARTMENT OF THE SOLICITOR GENERAL

Sir Wilfrid Laurier Bldg.
340 Laurier Ave. W., Ottawa, K1A 0P8

SOLICITOR GENERAL'S OFFICE
452 Confederation Bldg.
Ottawa, K1A 0A6
Solicitor Gen. of Canada,
The Hon. Pierre Blais

DEPUTY SOLICITOR GENERAL
Dep. Solicitor Gen. of Canada,
Joseph S. Stanford, Q.C.

Police and Security Branch
Asst. Dep. Solicitor Gen., D. Ian Glen, Q.C.

Corrections Branch
Asst. Dep. Solicitor Gen., C. Nuttall
Communications Group
Director Gen., D. Davidson

Planning and Management Branch
Asst. Dep. Solicitor Gen., J. Filion
REGIONAL DIRECTORS:
Atlantic
Daniel F. Stote
1222 Main St., Terminal Plaza Bldg.
Moncton, NB E1C 1H6
Quebec
Odette Gravel-Dunberry
Place Guy-Favreau
200, boul. René-Lévesque ouest
Montréal, H2Z 1X4
Ontario
Ruth Pitman
60 St. Clair Ave. E., Ste. 600
Toronto, M4T 1N5
Prairies
Dianne MacDonald (acting)
Cumberland Sq., Unit 28
1501-8th St. E., Saskatoon, SK S7H 5J6
Pacific
John Konrad
Ste. 1320, 800 Burrard St.
Vancouver, V6Z 2J5
Alberta—Northwest Territories
Allan Phibbs
Hillsborough Place, Ste. 260
10149-109th St., Edmonton, T5J 3M4

OFFICE OF THE INSPECTOR GENERAL,
CANADIAN SECURITY INTELLIGENCE
SERVICE
Inspector Gen., Richard G. Thompson
340 Laurier Ave. W., Ottawa, K1A 0P8

LEGAL SERVICES
A/Sr. Gen. Counsel, Daniel A. Bellemare

CORRECTIONAL INVESTIGATOR
Ronald L. Stewart

AGENCIES, BOARDS AND COMMISSIONS

Canadian Security Intelligence Service (CSIS)
Box 9732, Ottawa Postal Terminal
Ottawa, K1G 4G4

The Canadian Security Intelligence Service

(CSIS) was legislated by Parliament to collect and analyse information and intelligence on threats to Canada's national security, and to inform the Government therewith. The Service may also provide security assessments to the departments of the Government of Canada. CSIS offices are located in most Canadian cities.

Director, Reid Morden
Communications Branch
Director Gen., Gerry Cummings

The Correctional Service of Canada

Sir Wilfrid Laurier Bldg.
340 Laurier Ave. W., Ottawa, K1A 0P9
General Inquiries: (613) 992-5891

The Correctional Service of Canada is an agency within the federal Department of the Solicitor General. Its role is to administer the sentence of the courts with respect to convicted offenders sentenced to two years or more, and certain provincial inmates who have been transferred to federal institutions under the provisions of Exchange of Services Agreements between the Government of Canada and the provincial jurisdictions. It is also responsible for the supervision of inmates who have been granted conditional release (day parole, parole, and mandatory supervision) under the authority of the National Parole Board.

The legislative and constitutional framework which guides the Correctional Service of Canada is set out by the *Constitution Act, 1867,* the *Criminal Code of Canada,* the *Penitentiary Act* and Regulations, the *Parole Act,* as well as various international agreements such as the United Nations Standard Minimum Rules with regard to the treatment of prisoners, and the International Covenant on Civil and Political Rights.

The Correctional Service is headed by a Commissioner of Corrections who has management responsibility for about 10,000 staff, an operating budget in excess of $795 million, and the custody and control of over 12,000 inmates as well as the supervision of about 7,500 offenders on parole or under mandatory supervision.

The Service has a national headquarters in Ottawa and five regional headquarters situated in Abbotsford, B.C. (Pacific Region), Saskatoon, Sask. (Prairie Region), Kingston, Ont. (Ontario Region), Laval, Que. (Quebec Region), and Moncton, N.B. (Atlantic Region).

The Correctional Service maintains 62 institutions, of the following classification levels: 10 maximum security; 16 medium security; 11 minimum security; 21 community correctional centres; three medical psychiatric centres; and one prison for women. In addition, there are about 75 parole offices across Canada to provide the necessary community supervision.
(See also the Law chapter, Volume 1, for further information.)

COMMISSIONER'S OFFICE
Commissioner of Corrections, Ole Ingstrup

Dep. Commissioner, J. Phelps
Asst. Commissioner, P.A. St-Aubin
Offender Policy and Program Development
Dep. Commissioner, J. Phelps
Health Care Services
Director Gen., R. Préfontaine
Offender Programs
Director Gen., D. Kane
Correctional Operations
Director Gen., P. Viau
Construction Policy and Services
A/Sr. Director, H.K. Chaudhry
Administrative Policy and Services
Asst. Commissioner, P.A. St-Aubin
Finance
Director Gen., A. Lepage
Materiel Management and Administration
Director Gen., G. Hooper
Personnel
Director Gen., Sandy Davis
Systems
Director Gen., Nancy Corbett
Corporate Policy and Planning
Asst. Commissioner, Mario Dion
Corporate Planning
A/Director, D. Borrowman
Corporate Policy and Strategic Planning
A/Director, D. Connor
Evaluation and Research
A/Director, P. Lamothe
Intergovernmental Affairs Director, D. Hawe
Inspector Gen., W.J.T. Rankin
Inmate Affairs Director, L. Gosselin
Public Affairs Director, J. Vandoremalen
Correspondence and Ministerial Liaison
Chief, A. Sierolawski

REGIONAL HEADQUARTERS OFFICES:
Atlantic Region
1222 Main St., 2nd Flr., Moncton, NB E1C 1H6
Dep. Commissioner, W. Gibbs
Quebec Region
3, place Laval, Laval, H7N 1A2
Dep. Commissioner, Jean-Claude Perron
Ontario Region
440 King St. W., Box 1174, Kingston, K7L 4Y8
Dep. Commissioner, A. Graham
Prairie Region
2002 Quebec Ave., Box 9223
Saskatoon, SK S7K 3X5
Dep. Commissioner, M.J. Duggan
Pacific Region
32315 South Fraser Way
Box 4500, Abbotsford, BC V2T 4M8
Dep. Commissioner, Art Trono

ATLANTIC REGION
DISTRICT PAROLE OFFICES
NB/PEI District Office
95 Foundry Pl., Ste. 311
Moncton, NB E1C 5H7
District Director, John Gillis
Nova Scotia District Office
1888 Brunswick St., Ste. 605
Halifax, B3J 2G7
District Director, Vince MacDonald

Newfoundland District and Area Office
102 Churchill Ave.
St. John's, A1A 1N1
District Director, Brendan Devine

QUEBEC REGION
DISTRICT PAROLE OFFICES:
District Montreal-Metropolitan
1851, rue Sherbrooke est, bur. 704
Montréal, H2K 4L5
Director, Louise Bellefeuille
District est/ouest de Québec
Edifice Fédéral
380 rue Labelle, 2ᵉ ét., St-Jérôme, J7Z 5L3
Director, Gilles Thibault

ONTARIO REGION
DISTRICT PAROLE OFFICES:
Eastern Ontario District Office
1440 Princess St., Princess Sq.
Kingston, K7M 3E5
A/District Director, Giles Martin
Central Ontario District Office
180 Dundas St. W., Toronto, M5G 1Z8
District Director, M. Provan

PRAIRIE REGION
DISTRICT PAROLE OFFICES:
Northern Alberta/NWT District Office
Liberty Bldg., 2nd Flr.
9530-101st Ave., Edmonton, T5H 0B3
District Director, J. Christian
Saskatchewan District Office
450, 2550-15th Ave., Regina S4P 1A5
A/District Director, G. Graceffo
Manitoba/NW Ontario District Office
2nd Flr., 472 Notre Dame Ave.
Winnipeg, R3G 3J5
District Director, G. Holloway

PACIFIC REGION
DISTRICT PAROLE OFFICES:
Abbotsford District Office
Box 6000, Abbotsford, BC V2S 2C1
District Director, Paul Jacks
Vancouver District Office
300, 112 East 3rd Ave., Vancouver, V5T 4J9
District Director, R. Bishop
Victoria District Office
Rm. 323, 816 Government St.
Victoria, V8W 1W9
A/District Director, R. Brown

National Parole Board
Sir Wilfrid Laurier Bldg.
340 Laurier Ave. W., Ottawa, K1A 0R1

The National Parole Board is composed of 31 full-time members appointed for a period of up to 10 years by Cabinet upon the recommendation of the Solicitor General. One of the members is designated chairman and chief executive officer and another member serves as vice-chairman. Temporary members may also be appointed to assist the Board in its duties. Community Board Members are appointed by the Solicitor General to the regional offices of the Board. They act as regular members when the National Parole Board is considering the release of inmates serving life for murder or serving sentences of preventive detention as dangerous offenders, dangerous sexual offenders or habitual criminals.

The National Parole Board, as part of the criminal justice system, makes independent, quality conditional release decisions and pardon recommendations. The Board, by facilitating the timely re-integration of offenders as law-abiding citizens, contributes to the protection of society.

The Board has exclusive jurisdiction and absolute discretion to grant, deny or revoke day parole and full parole for inmates in both federal and provincial prisons, except for cases under the jurisdiction of provincial parole boards. The Board is ultimately responsible for the granting of unescorted temporary absences; however, in some instances the Board delegates its authority to the directors of the institutions. The Board also has the authority to revoke mandatory supervision (MS). MS refers to the automatic release of inmates, after two-thirds of their sentence, for good behaviour.

Parole may be granted, according to the *Parole Act,* when:
- the requirement of the law or regulations as to the sentence time that must be served before becoming eligible for parole has been met (one-sixth for day parole, one-third for full parole);
- the reform or rehabilitation of the inmate will be aided by the granting of parole;
- the release of the inmate on parole would not constitute an undue risk to society; and
- in the case of full parole, the inmate has derived the maximum benefit from imprisonmnent.

Under the Act, the Board has authority to impose the conditions under which the parolee or offender under mandatory supervision will live in the community.

The Board is also required, when requested by the Solicitor General, to make enquiries in connection with the exercise of the Royal Prerogative of Mercy.

In addition, the Board has the responsibility, under the *Criminal Records Act,* to make recommendations concerning applications for pardon.

Each application is considered on its merits and the Board rules on a case after a full investigation has been made by officers of the Correctional Service of Canada.

Chairman, Fred E. Gibson
Special Advisor, M. Charbonneau
Vice-Chairman, R. Labelle
Sr. Legal Counsel, L. Younger
Director of Communications, M. Hale
MEMBERS: M. Benson, G. Depratto,
G. Valade, N. Stableforth
Exec. Director, J. Siberry
Policy, Planning and Research
Director Gen., P. Cummings

Financial and Administration Services
Director, R.P. Simms
Human Resources Services
Director, B. Cloutier
Clemency Division Director, P. Connolly
Information Systems and Services
Director, A. Simard

REGIONAL OFFICES:
Atlantic Region
1222 Main St., 4th Flr., Moncton, NB E1C 1H6
Sr. Member, J. Trevors
Members: D.H. MacKeen, C.M. Ryan
Reg. Director, E. Williams
Quebec Region
200, boul. René-Lévesque ouest, 2e ét.
Montréal, H2Z 1X4
Sr. Member, P. Young
Members: L. Laporte, G. Tremblay-Côté,
P. Harel, Anne-Marie Asselin
Reg. Director, Serge Lavallée
Ontario Region
86 Clarence St., Kingston, K7L 4X1
Sr. Member, F. Baines
Members: R. Drummond, M. Stienburg,
J.A. MacDonald, T. Lamothe, G. Piché
Reg. Director, S. Ferguson
Prairie Region (incl. N.W.T.)
Churchill Bldg., 6th Flr.
229-4th Ave. S., Saskatoon, SK S7K 4K3
Sr. Member, G. Bellavance
Members: K. Howland, A.F. Grier,
M. Clark, A.R. Steen
Reg. Director, N. Fagnou
Pacific Region (incl. Yukon)
32315 South Fraser Way, Rm. 305
Abbotsford, BC V2T 1W6
Sr. Member, K. Louis
Members: E.W. Chang,
R. Boucher, N.G. Harrison
Reg. Director, F. Simmons

Royal Canadian Mounted Police
1200 Vanier Parkway, Ottawa, K1A 0R2

The Royal Canadian Mounted Police consists of 14 divisions. There are 13 operational divisions divided into 47 subdivisions and 719 detachments. Specialized support is offered to operational divisions by Air and Marine Services.

The other division is "Depot", located at Regina, where recruits receive their basic training at the Academy. Centralized administrative services are provided at the national headquarters in Ottawa. The RCMP Band, Musical Ride and Canadian Police College are located in Rockcliffe Park, a suburb of Ottawa.

As a federal police organization, the RCMP is present in all provinces to enforce those federal statutes for which it has a policing responsibility. In addition, through agreements, it provides provincial and municipal police services to eight provinces, Yukon, the Northwest Territories and 185 municipalities. *(See also the RCMP description in the Law chapter, Volume 1.)*

SENIOR EXECUTIVE:

Commissioner, N.D. Inkster
Dep. Commissioners: J.M. Shoemaker,
H. Jensen, R.G. Moffatt, J.L.G. Favreau
Chief Financial Officer,
Asst. Commissioner G.D. Hurry
COMMISSIONER'S SECRETARIAT
Exec. Officer, Insp. F.M.J. Hummel
Communications and Media Relations
Director and Chief Sup't, J.R. Bentham
Commissioner's Audit Branch
Audit Directorate Director,
Asst. Commissioner P.E.J. Banning
Corporate Services Director,
Asst. Commissioner S.H. Schultz
Staffing and Personnel Branch (Officers)
Officer in charge, Chief Sup't G.R. Crosse
Internal Communications Officer,
Insp. E. Proteau
Personnel Director,
Asst. Commissioner J.A.D. Lagassé
Public Service Personnel Directorate
Director, C.O. Morissette
Training Directorate Director,
Asst. Commissioner G.L. McCully
Academy at "Depot"
Box 6500, Regina, S5P 3J7
Chief Sup't R.G. Bell
Budget and Accounting Systems Directorate
Director, Insp. J.L. Healey
Enforcement Services Directorate
Director, Asst. Commissioner R.D. Crerar
Drug Enforcement Directorate
Director, Asst. Commissioner J.J.M. Coutu
Economic Crime Directorate
Asst. Commissioner, R.T. Stamler
Information Access Directorate
Director, Chief Sup't D.J. McCormick
Protective Policy (Departmental Security)
Dep. Director, Sup't J.E. Religa
Health Services Directorate
A/Director, Dr. A. Trottier
Identification Services Directorate
Director, Chief Sup't B.W. King
Professional Standards Directorate
Director, Sup't J.W.M. Thivierge
Financial Control and Authorities Directorate
Director, Chief Sup't R.A. Welke
Forensic Laboratories Services Directorate
Director, Asst. Commissioner R.A. Bergman
Foreign Services Directorate
Director, Sup't L. Généreux
Official Languages Directorate
Director, Chief Sup't M. Robert
Protective Policing Directorate
Director, Asst. Commr. J.P.R. Murray
Criminal Intelligence Services Canada
Director, Sup't D.H. Egan
Services and Supply Directorate
Director, Chief Sup't J.G.A. Roy
Technical Security Directorate
Director, Chief Sup't A.G. Barkhouse
Informatics Directorate
Director, Asst. Commissioner P.M. McLellan

Air Services Directorate
Director, Chief Sup't N.M. Melsness
Canadian Police College Directorate
Director, Chief Sup't N.A. Doucette
Administrative Services, Headquarters
Director, Chief Sup't J.E.A. Yelle

RCMP DIVISIONS AND COMMANDING OFFICERS

"A" Division
Chomley Bldg.
400 Cooper St., Ottawa, K1A 0R4
Asst. Commissioner G.W. Allen

"B" Division
Box 9700, Stn. B, St. John's, NF A1A 3T5
Chief Sup't R.C. Currie

"C" Division
4225, boul. Dorchester ouest
C.P. 559, Westmount (Québec) H3Z 2T4
Asst. Commissioner J.A.M. Breau

"D" Division
1091 Portage Ave., Winnipeg, MB R3C 3K2
Asst. Commissioner J.B.D. Henry

"E" Division
657 W. 37th St., Vancouver, BC V5Z 1K6
Dep. Commissioner D.K. Wilson

"F" Division
Box 2500, Regina, SK S4P 3K7
Asst. Commissioner C.I.C. MacDonell

"G" Division
Bag 5000, Yellowknife, NT X1A 2R3
Chief Sup't E.R. Wilson

"H" Division
Box 2286, 3139 Oxford St.
Halifax, NS B3J 3E1
Chief Sup't G.G. Leahy

"J" Division
Box 3900, Fredericton, NB E3B 4Z8
Chief Sup't J.D. Farrell

"K" Division
Box 1320, 11140-109th St.
Edmonton, AB T5J 2N1
Asst. Commissioner, G.J. Greig

"L" Division
Box 1360, 450 University Ave.
Charlottetown, PE C1A 7N1
Chief Sup't H.R. Armstrong

"M" Division
4100-4th Ave., Whitehorse, YT Y1A 1H5
Chief Sup't A.J. Toews

"O" Division
Box 519, Adelaide P.O.
225 Jarvis St., Toronto, ON M5C 2M3
Asst. Commissioner R.M. Culligan

DEPARTMENT OF SUPPLY AND SERVICES

Place du Portage, Phase III, Hull
MAILING ADDRESS: Ottawa, K1A 0S5
(except where otherwise indicated)
Telex: 053-3703
General Inquiries: (819) 997-6363
Public Affairs: (819) 956-2300

Supplier Relations: (819) 997-2686
Govt. of Canada Publications: (819) 997-2560
Personnel Records: (819) 956-0350
Superannuation: 1-800-561-7930

MINISTER'S OFFICE
Minister and Receiver Gen.
for Canada, The Hon. Paul Dick

OFFICE OF THE DEPUTY MINISTER
Dep. Minister and Dep. Receiver Gen.
for Canada, Georgina Wyman

PUBLIC AFFAIRS DIRECTORATE
Director Gen., Geneviève O'Sullivan
Operations Director, T.R.W. Farr

HUMAN RESOURCES DIRECTORATE
Director Gen., J. Stern
Personnel Operations Branch
Director, B.G. Bartley
Career and Human Resources Planning Branch
Director, J.-G. Savoie
Classification Branch Director, D. Rombough
Staffing and Management Category Branch
Director, D. Normoyle
Staff Relations and Compensation Branch
Director, M. Bujold
Management Services Branch
Director, A. Trépanier

LEGAL SERVICES
Gen. Counsel, F. Brodie

Corporate Policy and Planning Sector
Asst. Dep. Minister, R.D. Weese
Operations Support Group
Manager, B.J. Chopra
Increased Ministerial Authority and
Accountability (IMAA)
Director, C. Panasuk
D.S.S. Internal Audit
Director Gen., J.J. Corr
Corporate Secretary, N. Fontaine
Access to Information
Manager, Pierre Beaudry
Policy Development and Analysis Directorate
Director Gen., M.J. Mercier-Savoie
Evaluation Branch
A/Director, J.E. Stewart
Policy Review and Implementation Branch
A/Director, P. Green
Policy Development Branch
Director, C. Blain
Contract Quality Assurance Branch
Director, J.J. Silverman

PLANNING AND PROGRAM DEVELOPMENT
DIRECTORATE
Director Gen., Jean Archambault
Defence Industries and Emergency Planning
A/Director, G.M. Kerr
Corporate Planning Branch
Director, R. Kane

Program Planning Branch
Director, Vacant
Research and Analysis Branch
Director, R.D. Irvine

Supply Operations Sector
Asst. Dep. Minister, L. Stedman
Supply Operations
Gen. Director, M. Desjardins-Chase
Supply Management Branch
Director, M.B. Skinner

AEROSPACE, MARINE AND ELECTRONICS
SYSTEMS DIRECTORATE
Director Gen., H.T. Webster
Aerospace and Electronics
Procurement Branch
Director, R.L. Spickett
Marine and Armament Procurement Branch
Director, A. Archambault
Management Services Branch
A/Director, C. Stewart
Canadian Patrol Frigate (CPF) Project
Director, A.E. Dumas
8th Flr., 190 O'Connor St., Ottawa, K1A 1G8
Canadian Airspace Systems (CASP) Project
Director, J. Holinsky
8th Flr., 110 O'Connor St., Ottawa, K1A 0S5
*Canadian Submarine Acquisition Project
(CASAP)*
Director, M. Fisher
Low Level Air Defence (LLAD) Project
Director, B. Fletcher
15th Flr., Journal Twr. S.
365 Laurier Ave. W., Ottawa, K1A 0S5
Polar 8 Icebreaker Project
Director, A. Rumstein
18th Flr., Twr. A, Place de Ville
Albert St., Ottawa, K1A 0N7

COMMUNICATIONS SERVICES DIRECTORATE
45, boul. Sacré-Coeur, Hull, K1A 0S7
Director Gen. and Queen's Printer,
N. Manchevsky
Communications Professional Services
Director, I. St. Pierre
Canadian Government Printing Services
Director, G.P. Franche
Canadian Government Publishing Centre
Director, P. Horner
Canadian Government Expositions
and Audio Visual Centre
Director, C. Stone
440 Coventry Rd., Ottawa, K1A 0T1
Management and Engineering
Services Branch
Director. L.A. Scott

OFFICE AUTOMATION, SERVICES AND
INFORMATION SYSTEMS DIRECTORATE
Director Gen., B.H.E. Maynard
Operations Support Branch
Director, E. Fournier
Procurement Operations Branch
Director, G. Westcott

Canadian Forces Supply System (CFSS)
Director, H.B. Harland
Intelligence and Security Complex
Director, G.M. Edwards
Canadian On-Line Secure Information
and Communications Systems (COSICS)
Director, T.C. Bartello

INDUSTRIAL AND COMMERCIAL PRODUCTS
DIRECTORATE
Director Gen., G.J. Brown
Industrial and Commercial Products Support
Director, C.E. Deveoght
Scientific, Electrical, Mechanical
and Construction Products Branch
A/Director, D.A. Davignon
Consumer Products and Traffic Management
Director, J. Nadon
Military Operational and Support Trucks
Director, R.W. Miller

SCIENCE AND PROFESSIONAL SERVICES
DIRECTORATE
Director Gen., N. Bhumgara
Financial and Management Services Branch
A/Director, R. Tutt
Science Programs Branch
Director, Jean Lacelle
Science Branch Director, D. Coxon
Professional Services Branch
Director, S. Turner

Management and Operational Services Sector
Asst. Dep. Minister, Alan G. Ross

ACCOUNTING, BANKING AND
COMPENSATION DIRECTORATE
Director Gen., J.C. Stobbe
Central Accounting and Reporting Branch
Director, G.G. Beaudry
Banking and Cash Management Branch
Director, J. Weinman
Departmental Products Branch
Director, J. Catterson
Personnel Products Branch
Director, M.J. Posen
Cheque Redemption and Control Branch
Director, C. Dupuis
C.P. 1000, Matane (Québec) G4W 3P7
Management Services Branch
A/Director, P. Gingras
Intergovernmental Taxation Centre
Director, F. Labelle
Public Service Compensation
Administration Project
Director, G. Downs

INFORMATION SYSTEMS DIRECTORATE
Director Gen., P.P. Janega
Compensation and Personnel Systems Branch
Director, Vacant
Financial and Socio-Economic Systems Branch
Director, D.W. Orr

Information Processing Facilities Branch
Director, A.G. Hurd
Planning and Management Services Branch
Director, M. Balfour
OAS/CPP Redesign Income Security Program
Director, G. Hunter

BUREAU OF MANAGEMENT CONSULTING
Journal Bldg. S.
365 Laurier Ave. W., Ottawa, K1A 0S5
Director Gen., S. Isenberg
Finance and Management Science Branch
Director, Dr. H. Johri
General Management Consulting Branch
Director, R. Sweetman
Management Information Systems Branch
Director, B. Whalley
Project Management Research Centre
A/Director, R. Sweetman
International Development Support Centre
A/Director, H. John
Information Technology Centre
A/Director, B. Whalley

AUDIT SERVICES BUREAU
Jackson Bldg., 122 Bank St., 8th Flr.
Ottawa, K1A 0S5
Director Gen., R. Salmon
Professional Practices Branch
Director, Vacant
Planning and Management Services Branch
Director, R. Proulx
Contract Audits Branch Director, H. Lane
Contribution and Special Audits Branch
Director, V.F. Abboud
Internal Audits Branch Director, J.J. Raymond
Informatics and Management Audits Branch
Director, N. Loftus
Regional Offices Co-ordination
Director, H. Desautels
REGIONAL OFFICES
Atlantic Region
West End Mall, 2nd Level
6960 Mumford Rd., Halifax, B3L 4P1
Director, J.A. MacDonald
Quebec Region
Place Guy Favreau, Tour ouest, bur. 505
200, boul. René-Lévesque ouest
Montréal, H2Z 1X4
Director, J. Leroux
1040, av. Belvedère, bur. 310, Sillery, G1S 3G3
Director, J. Leroux
Toronto Region
4900 Yonge St., Willowdale, M2N 6A4
Director, M. Vrana
Prairie Region
700, 266 Graham Ave., Winnipeg, R3C 3W6
Director, Clarence Lefko
Pacific Region
101, 2425 Quebec St., Vancouver, V5T 4L6
Director, Frank W. Weipert
270 Hillsborough Place
10145-109th St., Edmonton, T5G 3M4
Director, Frank W. Weipert

CLIENT OPERATIONAL SERVICES
DIRECTORATE
Director Gen., B. Ferguson
Resource Programs and Policy Development
Director, D.A.W. Richards
Software Exchange Pilot Project
Director, H. Sagan
Services Management Branch
Director, L.K. Larke
Client Services Directors: B. Howatt,
G. Richardson, J. Oakes, C. Flower, S. Harper

REGIONAL OPERATIONS
European Region
Director, B.J. McNally
MacDonald House, 1 Grosvenor Sq.
London, England, W1X 0AB
Washington Region
Director, B. Crossfield
Canadian Embassy
2450 Massachusetts Ave. N.W.
Washington, DC, 20008 U.S.A.

ATLANTIC DIRECTORATE
Director Gen., S.J. Hammond
Box 2252, Halifax, B3J 3C8
Nova Scotia Region
Director, G. Girard
2 Morris Dr., Burnside Industrial Park
Dartmouth, B3B 1S6
Newfoundland Region
A/Director, J. Thorsteinson
Box 1314, St. John's, A1C 5N5
New Brunswick Region
Director, E.C. Léger
Box 746, Moncton, E1C 8M9
Superannuation Branch
Director, M.J. Dempster
Box 5010, Moncton, E1C 8Z5
Prince Edward Island Region
Director, A. Hammond
Box 5000, Charlottetown, C1A 7V6

QUEBEC DIRECTORATE
Director Gen., P. Comeau
Place Guy Favreau, Tour est, 3e ét.
200, boul. René-Lévesque ouest
Montréal, H2Z 1X4
Western Quebec Region
Director, J.R. Lacombe
800, ch. Golf, Ile des Soeurs
Montréal, H3E 1G9
Eastern Quebec Region
A/Director, L. Vadeheneoeur
1040, av. Belvedère, 3e ét., Québec, G1S 4N1

CENTRAL DIRECTORATE
Director Gen., P.A. Fournier
Place du Portage, Phase III, 7A1
11, rue Laurier, Hull, K1A 0S5
Capital Region Supply Centre
Director, B. McLean
1010 Somerset St. W., Ottawa, K1A 0T4

Capital Region Services Branch
Director, G. Lafrenière
3rd Flr., 350 King Edward Ave.
Ottawa, K1A 0S5

Ontario Region
Director, F.J. Pincock
295 The West Mall, Ste. 200
Etobicoke, M9C 5A4

WESTERN DIRECTORATE
Director Gen., R.J. Neville
Harry Hayes Bldg., Rm. 584, 220-4th Ave. S.E.
Box 2950, Stn. M, Calgary, T2P 4C3

Manitoba Region
Director, R.V. McKinnon
00 Otter St., Winnipeg, R3T 0M8

Saskatchewan Region
Director, E. Routledge
783 Hamilton St., Rm. 1601
Regina, S4P 4H3

Alberta/N.W.T. Region
Director, T.A. Simper
Cornerpoint Bldg., Ste. 805
10179-105th St., Edmonton, T5J 3N1

PACIFIC DIRECTORATE
A/Director Gen., G.M. Suffidy
133 Melville St., 8th Flr., Vancouver, V6E 4E5

British Columbia/Yukon Region
A/Director, Vacant

Vancouver Island Region
A/Director, F.D. Jeffries

Finance and Administration Sector
Asst. Dep. Minister, S.E. Whiteley
Operations Support Group
Manager, K. Francis

COMPTROLLER
Comptroller, Vacant
Contractual Cost and Financial Review
Director, R.R. Moore
Resource Analysis Director, G.J. Charron
Accounting Services Director, C.B. Bhatia
Financial Policy Director, L. Lamadeleine

ADMINISTRATIVE SERVICES DIRECTORATE
Director Gen., R. Piché
Telecommunications, Materiel and
Tenant Services Branch
Director, J. deVries
Administrative Services Branch
Director, M.L. McLeod
Management and Technical Support Branch
Director, W.R. Dexter

CORPORATE SYSTEMS DIRECTORATE
Director Gen., J. Belcher
Management and Technical Services Branch
Director, P. Constantine
Management and Office Automation Systems
Director, R. Lapensée
Supply and Regional Systems Branch
Director, B. Lane

Contracts Settlement Board
Chairman, R. Wayne
Procurement and Acquisitions Support Systems
Director, B.P. Grier
Industrial and Corporate Security Branch
Director, E.J. Snyder
Statistical Information and Data Management
Director, C. Donnelly

AGENCIES, BOARDS, COMMISSIONS AND CROWN CORPORATIONS

Canadian General Standards Board (CGSB)
Phase III, 9C1 Place du Portage, Hull, K1A 1G6

Created in 1934 under the authority of the *National Research Council Act* as the Canadian Government Purchasing Standards Committee, this inter-departmental agency's name was changed in 1948 to Canadian Government Specifications Board and, again, in 1980, to the Canadian General Standards Board.

In 1965, the responsibility for the CGSB's operation was transferred by Order-in-Council to the Department of Defence Production, now part of the Department of Supply and Services. In 1978, membership of the Board was changed to include nominees from federal, provincial and municipal governments, national associations, and members-at-large appointed by the minister.

The role of the CGSB is to provide voluntary standards and qualification/certification listing of products and services to the public and private sectors. Standardization projects in more than 100 subject areas are maintained in support of procurement, consumer requirements, legislation, technical practices, test procedures and international trade. Over 1500 standards are currently on issue and available in both official languages. Standardization committees, of which there are over 300, are comprised of representatives from governments, producers, consumers, research and testing agencies, educational institutions, and professional, technical and trade societies. The CGSB has been accredited as a national standards writing organization by the Standards Council of Canada. The CGSB is a very active component of the national standards system.
Exec. Director, P. Cameron
Secretary, P.D. Curran
Qualification and Certification Listing Branch
Director, J.G. Deutekom
Standards and Specifications Branch
Director, P.M. Jones

Royal Canadian Mint
320 Sussex Dr., Ottawa, K1A 0G8
General Inquiries: (613) 993-3500

The Ottawa Mint was originally established in 1908 by Royal Proclamation as a branch of the Royal Mint, London, under the provisions of the *United Kingdom Coinage Act* of 1870. In 1931, by an Act of the Canadian Parliament, the Royal Canadian Mint was established as a branch of the

Department of Finance of Canada.

In 1969, the Mint was converted into a Crown corporation by the *Government Organization Act* of 1969 with the objects of minting coins in anticipation of profit and carrying out other related activities. It now operates under authority of the *Royal Canadian Mint Act*, R.S.C. 1970, Chapter R-8.

The corporate powers of the Mint are as follows:
- to produce and arrange for the production and supply of the coins of the currency of Canada;
- to produce coins of the currency of countries other than Canada;
- to melt, assay and refine gold, silver and other metals;
- to buy and sell gold, silver and other metals;
- to assay, refine, store and otherwise deal with gold, silver and other metals for the account of Her Majesty and others;
- to prepare and store shipments of coins, gold, silver and other metals, and to move such shipments to or from the Mint;
- to make medals, plaques and other devices;
- to borrow or lease precious metals that it requires for the purposes of its operations; and
- to perform other functions conducive to the attainment of the objectives and the enforcement of the powers of the Mint.

The Royal Canadian Mint has two plants located in Ottawa and Winnipeg. As a Crown agency, the Royal Canadian Mint reports to Parliament through the Minister of Supply and Services.

Chairman, James Corkery
Master and President, Maurice Lafontaine
Administration and Finance
Vice-President, John Uberig
Marketing
Vice-President, Jack Julien
Manufacturing
Vice-President, Denis Cudahy
Human Resources
Vice-President, Diana J. Beattie
Ottawa Plant
320 Sussex Dr., Ottawa, K1A 0G8
Reg. Director, Brian Gates
Winnipeg Plant
520 Lagimodière Blvd.
Winnipeg, R2J 3E7
Reg. Director, Derek Smith

SUPREME COURT OF CANADA
(See listings under Federal Judiciary in this chapter.)

DEPARTMENT OF TRANSPORT
Transport Canada Bldg.
Place de Ville, Ottawa, K1A 0N5
General Inquiries: (613) 990-2309

MINISTER'S OFFICE
Rm. 418-M, Centre Blk.
House of Commons, Ottawa, K1A 0A6
Minister, The Hon. Benoît Bouchard

OFFICE OF THE MINISTER OF STATE
(TRANSPORT)
25th Flr., Transport Canada Bldg.
Place de Ville, Ottawa, K1A 0N5
Minister of State, The Hon. Shirley Martin

DEPUTY MINISTER'S OFFICE
Dep. Minister, Glen Shortliffe

SECURITY AND EMERGENCY PLANNING
Director Gen., J. Rodocanachi
Security, Policy, Plans and
Legislative Programs
Director, Vacant
Security Operations Director, R. Roy
T.C. Bldg., Place de Ville, Ottawa, K1A 0N5
Intelligence COMSEC and Security Training
Director, C.A. Webster
Transportation Safety
Inspector Gen., D. Pratt
Marine Casualty Investigation
Chief, B.D. Thorne
Transport Canada Airport Authority Model
Transition Manager, N. Van Duyvendyk

Policy and Co-ordination
Asst. Dep. Minister, K.A. Sinclair
Assoc. Asst. Dep. Minister, M. Brennan
Regional Directors:
Vancouver, B. Pavlov
Edmonton, P. Bowes
Montreal, R. Imbeault
Winnipeg, Vacant
Toronto, J. Knight
Moncton, D. Sweet
St. John's, D. Oldford
Co-ordination
Director Gen., E.R. Cherrett
Departmental Secretariat
Director, P. Renart
Strategic Policy
Director Gen., J.R. Miller
Strategic Planning and Policy
Director, B. Butler
Research and Development
Director Gen., R.R. Mayes
Research Planning and Co-ordination
Director, W.F. Johnson
Research Program Development
Director, M. Brenckmann
Marine Policy
Director Gen., A. Pageot
Air Policy
Director Gen., G. Pokotylo
Surface Policy
Director Gen., S. Hurtubise
Economic Analysis
Director Gen., Vacant

Transport Canada Research and
Development Centre
200, boul. René-Lévesque ouest, bur. 601
Montréal, H2Z 1X4
Exec. Director, N.E. Rudback

Review
Asst. Dep. Minister, R.A.S. Jackson
Program Evaluation Director, N. Steinberg
Internal Audit and Review Director, A. Bolduc
Policy Planning, Methodology and Control
Chief, D. St-Louis
Program Control Board Secretariat
Exec. Director, D. Dickson

Personnel
Asst. Dep. Minister, C. Bernier
Management Category Programs
Director, I. Leclerc
Regional Personnel Operations
A/Director Gen., R. Bisaillon
N.C.R. Personnel
A/Reg. Manager, L. Cox
Operations Co-ordination Chief, G. Stewart
Personnel Policy and Planning
Director Gen., J. Read
Personnel Policy Director, G. Tessier
Staff Relations
Director Gen., G.M. Allan
Training
Director Gen., E. Hossack
Transport Canada Training Institute
1950 Montreal Rd., Cornwall, ON K6H 1B1
Director, A. Fracassi
George A. Scott Centre for
Transport Management Studies
1950 Montreal Rd., Cornwall, ON K6H 1B1
A/Director, F. Boire-Carriere
Canadian Coast Guard College
Box 4500, Sydney, NS B1P 6L1
Director, E. Kelly

PUBLIC AFFAIRS
Director Gen., D. Bell
LEGAL
Departmental Gen. Counsel, R. Williams

Finance
Asst. Dep. Minister, V. Malizia
Financial Administration Director, J.P. Paré
Administrative Services
Director, R.A. Dodunski
Materiel and Contracting Services
A/Director, W. Beazley
Financial Planning and Programming
Director Gen., Vacant
Communications and Informatics
Director Gen., M. Plouffe
Cost Recovery and Economic Evaluation
Director Gen., J.A.A. Lovink

Surface Group
Canada Bldg.
344 Slater St., Ottawa, K1A 0N5

Asst. Dep. Minister, V. Barbeau
Transport Dangerous Goods
Director Gen., J.A. Read
Regulations Director, J.R. Monteith
CANUTEC
Information: (613) 957-6275
Emergencies: (613) 957-6272
Road Safety and Motor Vehicle Regulation
Director Gen., C. Wilson
Rail Safety
Director Gen., C. Churcher

Aviation
Transport Canada Bldg.
Place de Ville, Ottawa, K1A 0N8
Asst. Dep. Minister, C.A. LaFrance
Aviation Safety Program Director, J. Stewart
Flight Services
Director Gen., D. Spruston
Flight Operations Director, R.R. Davidson
Technical Services Director, F.A. Levasseur
Special Projects and Operational Planning
Director, H.J. Layden
Training Director, L.J. Harker
Planning and Resource Management
Director Gen., F. Mousseau
Resource Administration Director, S. Milotay
Aviation Regulation
Director Gen., W. Newton
Enforcement and Legislation
Director, G. Mazowita
Licensing and Certification
Director, W. Slaughter
Aviation Medicine
Director, Dr. G.Y. Takahashi
Airworthiness Director, J.A. Torck
Program Analysis and Review Chief, B. Fraser
Air Navigation
Director Gen., B.D. Blair
Aeronautical Program Review and Analysis
A/Director, G.W. McElree
Air Navigation System Requirements
Director, G. Rodrigue
Air Traffic Services Director, P.J. Proulx
Technical Services
Exec. Director, J.C. McDonald
Air Operations Contingencies
Exec. Officer, G.S. Parslow

AIRPORTS AUTHORITY GROUP
Exec. Director, D.C. McAree
Sr. Director Gen., D.L. Gerrie
Airports Management Working Group
Exec. Director, A. Douglas
Airport Professional and Technical Services
Director, H.W.R. Smith
Airport Marketing
Director Gen., L. McCoomb
Corporate Management
Director Gen., I. Henderson
Commercial Development
Director Gen., G. Berigan
Airport Operations
Director Gen., P. Champagne

REGIONAL DIRECTORS GENERAL
Atlantic Region
Heritage Court, 95 Foundry St.
Box 42, Moncton, NB E1C 8K6
Reg. Director Gen., R.M. Lane
Quebec Region
Montreal International Airport
C.P. 5000, Dorval, H4Y 1B9
Reg. Director Gen., J. Wagner
Ontario Region
Ste. 300, 4900 Yonge St., Willowdale, M2N 6A5
Reg. Director Gen., R.S. Binnie
Central Region
333 Main St., Box 8550, Winnipeg, R3C 0P6
Reg. Director Gen., H.J. Bell
Western Region
Federal Bldg., 9820-107th St.
Edmonton, T5K 1G3
Reg. Director Gen., C. Tackaberry
Pacific Region
800 Burrard St., Box 220, Vancouver, V6Z 2J8
Reg. Director Gen., M. Duncan

Marine Group
Canada Bldg., Ottawa, K1A 0N7
Asst. Dep. Minister, R.A. Quail
Canarctic Shipping Co. Ltd.
350 Sparks St., Ste. 809, Ottawa, K1R 7S8
Exec. Vice-President, M.P. Luce

HARBOURS AND PORTS DIRECTORATE
Director Gen., D.N. Morrison
HARBOUR COMMISSIONS
Fraser River Harbour Commission
713 Columbia St., Ste. 505
New Westminster, BC V3M 1B2
Chairman, William M. Vogel
Port Manager, R.C. Pearce
Hamilton Harbour Commission
605 James St. N., Hamilton, ON L8L 1J9
Chairman, J. Agro, Q.C.
Port Director, Bob Hennessy
Lakehead Harbour Commission
Box 2266, Thunder Bay, ON P7B 5E8
Chairman, D. Johnson
Port Manager, P.R. Cook
Nanaimo Harbour Commission
104 Front St., Box 131, Nanaimo, BC V9R 5R4
Chairman, D. Beaton
Port Manager, Lloyd L. Bingham
North Fraser Harbour Commission
2020 Airport Rd., Richmond, BC V7B 1C6
Chairman, Glen MacRae
Port Manager, G.W. Colquhoun
Oshawa Harbour Commission
1050 Farewell St., Box 492
Oshawa, ON L1H 6N6
Chairman, Ray Lunn
Port Manager, Donna Taylor
Port Alberni Harbour Commission
2750 Harbour Rd., Box 99
Port Alberni, BC V9Y 7M6
Chairman, Hugh A. Anderson
Port Manager, Capt. D. Brooks

Toronto Harbour Commission
60 Harbour St., Toronto, M5J 1B7
Chairman, Fred Eisen
Gen. Manager, I. Brown
Windsor Harbour Commission
Canada Sq., 500 Riverside Dr. W.
Windsor, ON N9A 5K6
Chairman, Fred Quenneville
Port Manager, David Cree

CANADIAN COAST GUARD
Commissioner, R.A. Quail
Dep. Commissioner, M.A.H. Turner
Aids and Waterways
A/Director Gen., T.J. Stephen
Ship Safety Branch
Director Gen., M. Hubbard
Fleet Systems
Director Gen., P. Boisvert
Telecommunications and Electronics
Director Gen., B. Borodchak
Resource Management Director, N. Tiessen
Executive Services
A/Director, F. Sherwin
Coast Guard Northern
Director, C.S. Stephenson
Search and Rescue
A/Director, A. Mountain
Emergencies Chief, M.S. Greenham
REGIONAL OFFICES
Newfoundland Region
Box 1300, St. John's, A1C 6H8
Director Gen., L.C. Humphries
Maritimes Region
Twin Towers, Royal Bank Bldg.
46 Portland St., Box 1013
Dartmouth, NS B2Y 4K2
Director Gen., K.C. Curren
Maritime Command Headquarters
Rm. 116, HMC Dockyard, Halifax, B3K 2X0
Laurentian Region
104, rue Dalhousie
Québec Terminus, Québec, G1K 4B8
Director Gen., J.E. Clavelle
Central Region
Toronto Star Bldg., 20th Flr.
One Yonge St., Toronto, M5E 1E5
Director Gen., D.I. McMinn
Western Region
224 West Esplanade
North Vancouver, BC V7M 3J7
Director Gen., G.R. Stewart

PILOTAGE AUTHORITIES
Great Lakes Pilotage Authority Ltd.
Box 95, Cornwall, ON K6H 5R9
Chairman, R.G. Armstrong
Atlantic Pilotage Authority
Ste. 1203, 5151 George St.
Halifax, B3J 1M5
Chairman, Capt. C.R. Worthington
Laurentian Pilotage Authority
1080, côte du Beaver Hall, bur. 1804
Montréal, H2Z 1S8
Chairman, J. Chouinard

Pacific Pilotage Authority
Ste. 300, 1199 W. Hastings St.
Vancouver, V6E 4G9
Chairman, R.J. Smith

AGENCIES, BOARDS, COMMISSIONS AND CROWN CORPORATIONS

Canada Harbour Place Corp.
Corporate Office:
999 Canada Place, Ste. 600
Vancouver, V6C 3C1

Canada Harbour Place Corporation is a Crown corporation established in June 1982, to design and construct Canada Place. Canada Place was established as the site for the Canada Pavilion at Expo '86. Wholly funded by the Government of Canada, the Canada Pavilion was converted into the Vancouver Trade and Convention Centre in 1987. Canada Place, the second largest such facility in the country, includes a cruise-ship terminal, a luxury hotel with more than 500 rooms, a world trade centre office complex, and a range of exhibition and meeting rooms, as well as restaurants, shops and an IMAX theatre.

Chairman, Thomas G. Rust
Public Affairs and Administration
Vice-President and Corporate Secretary,
Annette Antoniak
Finance Director, Bill Watson

Canada Ports Corp.
99 Metcalfe St., Ottawa, K1A 0N6
Telex: 053-4127; Fax: (613) 996-9629
Inquiries: (613) 957-6787

Ports Canada describes a federal system of 15 ports which handles nearly half of all Canadian waterborne cargo. Its principal business is to provide an efficient national port system to facilitate Canada's trade objectives. This is based on the principle of responsible management within a private sector discipline, and a high degree of autonomy in the administration of ports within the system. Reporting to Parliament through the Minister of Transport, Ports Canada is a Schedule C-2 Crown corporation.

Ports legislation gives power to establish local port corporations at any of the Ports Canada ports. They are established at Vancouver, Prince Rupert, Montreal, Quebec City, Saint John, Halifax, and St. John's. Non-corporate ports include Belledune, N.B.; Sept-Iles, Chicoutimi, Baie-des-Ha!-Ha! and Trois-Rivières, Que.; and Port Colborne and Prescott, Ont.

Ports Canada has a 17-member board with a chairman and vice-chairman, all serving part-time, together with a full-time president and chief executive officer.

Chairman of the Board,
The Hon. A. Ronald Huntington
President and CEO, Jean Michel Tessier
Exec. Vice-President, Dr. Hassan Ansary
Sr. Port Manager, T.A. Lauzon

Finance and Administration
Vice-President, C. Guérin
PORTS
St. John's Port Corp.
Box 6178, St. John's, A1C 5X8
Port Manager and CEO, D.J. Fox
Halifax Port Corp.
Box 336, Halifax, B3J 2P6
President and CEO, David F. Bellefontaine
Port of Belledune
c/o National Office, 99 Metcalfe St.
Ottawa, K1A 0N6
Manager, T. Lauzon
Saint John Port Corp.
Box 6429, Stn. A, Saint John, NB E2L 4R8
Gen. Manager and CEO, Ken Krauter
Port of Sept-Iles
C.P. 280, Sept-Iles (Québec) G4R 4K5
Gen. Manager, Jean-Maurice Gaudreau
Port of Chicoutimi
C.P. 760, Chicoutimi (Québec) G7H 5E1
Gen. Manager, Serge Tremblay
Port of Quebec Corp.
C.P. 2268, Québec, G1K 7P7
President and CEO, Ross Gaudreault
Port of Trois-Rivières
C.P. 999, Trois-Rivières (Québec) G9A 5K2
Gen. Manager, P. Alain
Montreal Port Corp.
Port of Montréal Bldg., Wing 1
Cité du Havre, Montréal, H3C 3R5
Gen. Manager and CEO, Dominic Taddeo
Port of Prescott
Box 520, Prescott, ON K0E 1T0
Port Colborne Port Corp.
c/o National Office
99 Metcalfe St., Ottawa K1A 0N6
Manager, T. Lauzon
Port of Churchill
Box 217, Churchill, MB R0B 0E0
Operations Manager, G. Johnson
Vancouver Port Corp.
1900, 200 Granville St., Vancouver, V6C 2P9
Port Manager and CEO, F.J. MacNaughton
Prince Rupert Port Corp.
110-3rd Ave. W., Prince Rupert, BC V8J 1K8
Gen. Manager and CEO, Bob Tytaneck

Canadian Aviation Safety Board
Box 9120, Alta Vista Terminal
Ottawa, K1G 3T8
General Inquiries: (613) 994-3741

The Canadian Aviation Safety Board was established on May 1, 1984, by an Act of Parliament, as an independent agency reporting to Parliament through a designated Minister.

The mandate of the Board is the advancement of aviation safety, which is achieved by:
a) identifying safety deficiencies as evidenced by aviation occurrences, such as accidents, incidents and hazardous situations;
b) by conducting independent investigations and if necessary, public inquiries into aviation occurrences; and

c) by reporting publicly on its investigations and public inquiries, and making recommendations designed to eliminate or reduce safety deficiencies.

The Board has approximately 200 employees, with its head office in Place du Centre, Hull, and six regional offices across Canada which conduct the bulk of the occurrence investigations.

Chairman, K.J. Thorneycroft
BOARD MEMBERS:
Norman Bobbitt, Dr. Les Filotas,
Bill MacEachern, David Mussallem,
Arthur Portelance, Bruce Pultz,
Ross Stevenson, Frank Thurston
Exec. Director, Ken Johnson

Canadian National Railways
935, rue de la Gauchetière ouest
C.P. 8100, Montréal, H3C 3N4

The Canadian National Railways operates one of the largest freight railways in North America, with a 46,000-km Canadian rail network. Through the Grand Trunk Corp., it also serves 28 states of the U.S.

CN is also active in real estate, international consulting and contracting, and oil production and exploration.

CN is committed to providing its customers with the type of flexible, economic and efficient transportation and distribution services they require to ensure their own competitiveness.

In keeping with this objective, the company continues to reinforce its own strengths, shed excess capacity, and streamline operations.

A core-line rail system provides intermodal service from six strategically located hub centres in Moncton, Montreal, Toronto, Winnipeg, Edmonton, and Vancouver. Key satellite terminals are located at Halifax, Windsor, Saskatoon, and Calgary.

A/Chairman, Brian Gallery
President and CEO, R.E. Lawless
Sr. Vice-President and COO,
John H.D. Sturgess
Sr. Vice-President and CFO, Yvon H. Masse
Sr. Vice-President (Western Canada),
R.A. Walker
10004-104th Ave., Edmonton, T5J 0K2
Vice-President and Secretary, H.J.G. Pye
Vice-President, Accounting and Comptroller
R.D. McGrath
Treasurer, G.C. Church
Vice-President, Public Affairs and Advertising,
B.E. Ducey
Vice-President, Government Affairs, D.E. Todd
President and CEO, CN Investment Division
T. Cedraschi
Sr. Vice-President, Operations, J.P. Kelsall
Sr. Vice-President, Marketing, P.A. Clarke
Vice-President, Intermodal, A.J. Gillies
Vice-President, Purchases and Materials,
P.J. Foliot
Vice-President, Finance and Planning
J. Horrocks

Vice-President, Employee Relations
J.P. Laroche
Vice-President, Law, R. Boudreau
Vice-President, Strategic Direction
D. MacKinnon
Vice-President, Financial Planning
I.G. MacDonald
Vice-President, Planning and Co-ordination,
E. Horsman
Vice-President, Information Systems
A.R. Pozniak
Vice-President, Internal Audit, G. Maroulis
Vice-President, Atlantic Region
M.A. Blackwell
CN Terminal Bldg., Moncton, NB E1C 1H7
Vice-President, St. Lawrence Region
J.R. Lagacé
800, boul. René-Lévesque ouest
Montréal, H3C 3N3
Vice-President, Great Lakes Region
Allan E. Deegan
Union Station, Rm. 424, Toronto, M5J 1E7
Vice-President, Prairie Region, F.D. Campbell
CN Station, Rm. 300, Winnipeg, R3C 2P8
Group Vice-President, W.H. Morin
Terra Transport
Water St. W., St. John's, A1C 5K1
President and Gen. Manager, J.H. Easton
CANAC International Inc.
Chairman, Brian Gallery
President and CEO, M.L. De Pellegrin
CN Communications
151 Front St. W., Toronto, M5J 1G1
President, Vacant
CN Real Estate
President, H.D. Tipple
CN Exploration
Chairman, E. Demkiw
President, W.H. Waddell

Grain Transportation Agency
135 Lombard Ave., Winnipeg, R3B 0T4

The following is an abbreviated description of the objectives of the Grain Transportation Agency:

• to allocate the car fleet, including the CN/CP grain-dedicated fleet, Canadian government cars, Canadian Wheat Board cars, and industry-owned railway cars; and to determine the requirements and seek to ensure that the required fleet is available;

• to ensure that Prairie grain moves to domestic consumption and export positions in a prompt, efficient and orderly manner;

• to secure the co-operation and participation of the industries concerned in providing the required transportation and handling services and facilities;

• to carry out the required planning and to implement the changes necessary to make the forwarding system operate more efficiently and effectively; and

• to keep all parties and the public fully informed about system operations.

Administrator, Peter Thomson

A/Dep. Administrator, Gordon Miles
Planning, Development and Evaluation
Exec. Director, Paul Earl
Operations
Exec. Director, Vacant
Car Allocations
Co-ordinator, Richard Wansbutter
Transportation Programs
Co-ordinator, Van McLean
Transportation, Planning and Evaluation
Co-ordinator, Michael Shumsky
Finance and Administration
Director, Claire Warszycki
Director, Janet Daniels
VANCOUVER OFFICE
Ste. 1836, 1055 W. Georgia St.
Vancouver, V6E 3P3
Ports Co-ordinator, Western
W.G. Hopkins
THUNDER BAY OFFICE
Rm. 311, 33 S. Court St.
Box 2174, Thunder Bay, ON P7B 5E8
Ports Co-ordinator, Eastern
A.N. Kaplanis

Marine Atlantic Inc.
100 Cameron St., Moncton, NB E1C 5Y6

Marine Atlantic is an independent Crown corporation operating passenger, auto, and freight ferry services throughout Atlantic Canada and to the State of Maine. Year-round service is offered between Yarmouth and Bar Harbor, Maine; Digby and Saint John; Cape Tormentine, N.B. and Borden, P.E.I.; and North Sydney and Port-aux-Basques, Nfld. As well, a seasonal service is operated between North Sydney and Argentia, Nfld. and local runs along the coast of Newfoundland and Labrador.

Marine Atlantic carries more than 2 million passengers and one million vehicles annually. Revenue from paying customers is in excess of $65 million and federal subsidies are approximately $130 million for 1988/89.

President and CEO, R.J. Tingley
Vice-President, Law, J.L. Brean
Vice-President, Marine Services
P.A. Healthcote
Vice-President, PEI and Fundy Services
C.R. Kelley
Vice-President, Newfoundland, D.G. Newman
Human Resources and Administration
Director Gen., G.J. James
Finance and Administration
Director Gen., D.J. Weaver
Public Relations Director, T.G. Bartlett
External Relations Director, M.R. Gushue
Vessel Services Director, R.G.A. Lawrence
Official Languages Director, M. McLaughlin
Operations Co-ordination and Marketing
Manager, R.J. Arsenault

National Transportation Agency
Ottawa, K1A 0N9
Telex: 053-4254; Fax: (819) 997-6727
General Inquiries: (819) 997-6567

The National Transportation Agency (NTA) was established through the *National Transportation Act* which came into force on Jan. 1, 1988. The objective of the Act is to encourage a safe, economic, efficient and adequate system to serve the needs of shippers and travellers.

The NTA is responsible for the economic regulation of transportation in Canada. It is also responsible for rail safety pending Parliament's consideration of legislation that would transfer much of this responsibility to Transport Canada. The NTA replaces the Canadian Transport Commission which had been in existence for 20 years under the *National Transportation Act, 1967.*

The NTA is an independent agency that reports to Parliament through the Minister of Transport.

The Agency has all the powers, rights and privileges of a superior court in Canada. The Agency has its headquarters in the National Capital Region. Under the legislation, the Agency may establish regional offices: to date a western one has been located in Saskatoon and an Atlantic one in Moncton.

Chairman,
The Hon. Erik Nielsen, P.C., Q.C.
Exec. Director, Keith Thompson
Communications Director, Karen Laughlin
Legal Services
Gen. Counsel, Marie-Paule Scott
Management Services Branch
Director Gen., A.M. Barr
Dispute Resolution Branch
Director Gen., Margaret Bloodworth
Market Entry and Analysis Branch
Director Gen., Amelita Armit
Transportation Subsidies Branch
Director Gen., David Smith
Western Regional Office (Saskatoon)
Reg. Director, John Kimpinski
Atlantic Regional Office (Moncton)
Reg. Director, Maurice Cormier
Management Services Branch
Director Gen., Archie Barr

St. Lawrence Seaway Authority
360 Albert St., Ottawa, K1R 7X7
General Inquiries: (613) 598-4600

The St. Lawrence Seaway Authority was constituted as a Crown corporation by an Act of Parliament in 1954. Its purpose is to operate and maintain the Canadian locks and canals between Montreal and Lake Erie that allow navigation by vessels of 79.25 decimetres draft. The 15 locks of the waterway allow the passage of vessels not exceeding 222.5 metres in length or 23.16 m in breadth. The revenues of the Authority are derived from the St. Lawrence Seaway Tariff of Tolls, based on the type of cargo carried by vessels. *(See also the description in the Transportation chapter, Volume 1.)*

President, W.A. O'Neil
Vice-President, G. Laniel
Member, W.F. Blair
Secretary, V.C. Durant

CORNWALL HEADQUARTERS
202 Pitt St., Cornwall, ON K6J 3P7
Personnel and Administration
Director, C.G. Trépanier
Comptroller and Treasurer, R.J. Forgues
Operations and Maintenance
Director, J.M. Kroon
REGIONAL OFFICES:
Eastern Region
Box 97, St-Lambert (Québec) J4P 3N7
Vice-President, J.P. Patoine
Western Region
Box 370, St. Catharines, ON L2R 6V8
Vice-President, J.B. McLeod
Seaway International Bridge Corp. Ltd.
Box 836, Cornwall, ON, K6H 5T7
Manager, C.J. Maguire
Jacques Cartier and Champlain Bridges Inc.
1000, rue de Sérigny
Longueuil (Québec) J4K 5B1
Gen. Manager, M.L. Lesage

Via Rail Canada Inc.
2 Place Ville-Marie, #400
Montréal, H3B 2G6

Established in 1977, Via Rail Canada Inc. is a fully independent Crown corporation responsible for transcontinental and intercity passenger rail in Canada. VIA's mandate is to operate efficient and attractive passenger rail services within a cost-effective system.

The VIA Rail network extends over 18,500 km of track in eight Canadian provinces. In 1987, VIA Rail operated 106 trains daily and carried an average of 16,068 passengers per day.

VIA Rail provides all customer service from information, reservations and ticketing to on-board services such as dining and sleeping facilities, and is responsible for routes, fares and schedules.

VIA headquarters is in Montreal and the company is divided into four regions: VIA Ontario is based in Toronto; VIA West in Winnipeg; VIA Quebec in Montreal; and VIA Atlantic in Moncton.

Chairman, Lawrence Hanigan
President and CEO, Denis de Belleval
Marketing and Sales
Vice-President, Murray A. Jackson
Vice-President and Chief of
Transportation, R.J. Guiney
Development
Vice-President, R. Béchamp
Finance and Administration
Vice-President, Nicole Beaudoin-Sauvé
Human Resources
Vice-President, Jean-Roch Boivin
Equipment Maintenance
A/Vice-President, R. Bechamp
Corporate Planning
Vice-President, Jim Roche
Customer Services
Vice-President, R. Arnold
Public Affairs
Sr. Director, Marc-André Charlebois

Customer Services
Gen. Manager, Dave Carmichael
Special Examination Director, M. Huart
VIA Atlantic
Marketing and Sales
Reg. Director, Preston Beaumont
Customer Services
Reg. Director, C. Gaudet
VIA Quebec
Marketing and Sales
Reg. Director, A. Kyffin
Customer Services
Reg. Director, N. Lenoir
VIA Ontario
Marketing and Sales
Reg. Director, D.T. Carmichael
Customer Services
Reg. Director, C. Muggeridge
VIA West
Marketing and Sales
Reg. Director, Bill Funk
Customer Services
Reg. Director, R. DeFreitas

TREASURY BOARD

L'Esplanade Laurier, Ottawa, K1A 0R5
General Inquiries: (613) 957-2400

PRESIDENT'S OFFICE
9th Flr., Esplanade Laurier, Ottawa, K1A 0R5
President, The Hon. Robert de Cotret

OFFICE OF THE SECRETARY
Secretary of the Treasury Board,
Gérard Veilleux
Corporate Policy Unit
Asst. Secretary, David Brown
Communications Division
Director, Jean-Pierre Villeneuve

TREASURY BOARD SECRETARIAT

Official Languages Branch
Dep. Secretary, Georges Tsaï
Public Sector Operations Division
Director, D. Cobb
Policy Division Director, Louis Reynolds
Management Information and Services Division
Director, Gaston Guénette
Program Assessment Division
Director, M. Hotz
Liaison Division Director, Robert Desjardins

Program Branch
Dep. Secretary, A.J. Darling
Asst. Secretary, Perry Anglin
Asst. Secretary, S. Gershberg
Asst. Secretary, Mireille Badour
Asst. Secretary, B. Lacombe
Industry, Science and
Natural Resources Division
Director, Rolfe Cooke

General Government Services Division
Director, David Miller
External Affairs, Defence, Environment and
Culture Division
Director, W. Crandall
Social, Employment, Housing
and Secretary of State Division
Director, J. Kent
Estimates Division Director, Stephen O'Connor
Expenditure Analysis Division
Director, Dennis Kam
Crown Corporations Directorate
A/Asst. Secretary, Peter Middleton
Operations and Liaison Division
Director, Peter Middleton
Policy and Corporate Information Division
Director, H. Baumann

Administrative Policy Branch

Dep. Secretary, David McEachran
Information Management Division
Asst. Secretary, Vacant
Information Technology Management
Director, Jacques Thérien
Information Management Practices
Director, Gerry Bethell
Administrative Management Division
Sr. Asst. Secretary, R. Paton
Planning and Evaluation Division
A/Director, Jean-Guy Haché

Personnel Policy Branch

Dep. Secretary, G.G. Capello
Classification, Pay and Human Resources
Information Systems Division
Asst. Secretary, Lise Ouimet
General Personnel Management Division
Asst. Secretary, J. Thivierge
Human Resources Division
Asst. Secretary, Kristina Liljefors
Planning, Evaluation and
Policy Development Division
Asst. Secretary, David Brown
Pension and Special Projects
A/Asst. Secretary, Jean Martin

Staff Relations Branch

Dep. Secretary, L.M. Tenace
Consultation Officer, Guy Landriault
Policy and Co-ordination Director, Don Love
Negotiations and Adjudication
Director, D.J. Fowler
Information and Analysis
Director, Jean Bourdeau

COMPTROLLER GENERAL OF CANADA

OFFICE OF THE COMPTROLLER GENERAL
OF CANADA
Comptroller Gen. of Canada,
J. Andrew Macdonald
Corporate Management Division
A/Director, Evelyn Levine
Professional Development Division
A/Director, John Ferguson

**Financial Management Information and
Systems**

Dep. Comptroller Gen., Bernie A. Gorman
Financial Management Systems
Director, T.G. Buttigieg
Central Information and Classification
Director, Laura Talbot-Allen
Reporting Standards and Practices
Director, G. Willis
Strategy and Co-ordination
Director, J. Thoppil

Accounting and Costing Policy Branch

Dep. Comptroller Gen., James McCrindell
Government Accounting Policy
Director, J. Hodgins
Authorities and Internal Control
Director, W. Boston
Cash Management
A/Director, P. Nephin

Program and Review Branch

Dep. Comptroller Gen., David Roth
Audit Policy and Planning
A/Director, D. Wood
Operations Division Directors:
M. Abrahams, A. Whitla, D. Mooers

Program Evaluation Branch

Dep. Comptroller Gen., Guy Leclerc
Evaluation Policy Director, J. Mayne
Evaluation Operations Director, M. Ulrich

BUREAU OF REAL PROPERTY MANAGEMENT
Exec. Director, Lawrence J. O'Toole
Policy and Services Directorate
Director, Al Clayton
Portfolio Management Directorate
Director, William G. Roberts

DEPARTMENT OF VETERANS' AFFAIRS

East Memorial Bldg.
Lyon and Wellington Sts., Ottawa, K1A 0P4
Daniel J. MacDonald Bldg., 161 Grafton St.
Box 7700, Charlottetown, C1A 8M9
General Inquiries: (902) 566-8195

MINISTER'S OFFICE
Killeany Bldg., 460 O'Connor
13th Flr., Ottawa, K1A 5H3
Minister, The Hon. Gerald Merrithew

DEPUTY MINISTER'S OFFICE
Dep. Minister, David Broadbent
Audit
Director Gen., Gordon Harper

Field Operations
Asst. Dep. Minister, David Steele

COMMUNICATIONS DIVISION
Director Gen., Barbara Stewart Campbell
Public Relations Director, V.J. Murphy
Communications (Charlottetown)
Director, Chris Brittain

Administration
Asst. Dep. Minister, D.N. Rive
Access to Information
Co-ordinator, Sue LeMaistre

FINANCIAL MANAGEMENT
Director Gen., R. Bray
Benefit Delivery Director, Ron Herbert
Accounting Services
A/Director, D.P. Bruce
Planning and Evaluation
A/Director, W. Durling
Financial Policy and Internal Control
Director, B.H. Foster

PERSONNEL MANAGEMENT
Director Gen., Sam Mombourquette
Affirmative Action Director, Gerald Dénis
Human Resources Management
A/Director, C. Gavard
Official Languages Director, Gerald Dénis
Personnel Operations Director, A. Puxley

CORPORATE SERVICES
Director Gen., R.W. Hughes
Information Services Director, P. Sorensen
Administrative Services Director, R. Matthews
Legal Branch (Justice) Directorate
Gen. Counsel, Gordon Davidson

Veterans Land Administration
Asst. Dep. Minister, I. MacRae
Property Management Division
Director Gen., D.R. Bell

Programs
Asst. Dep. Minister, D. Ferguson

HEALTH CARE PROGRAMS
Director Gen., Gordon Parker
Director, G. Steele
Departmental Medical Director,
Dr. W.B.C. Robertson
Departmental Nursing Director,
A.R.G. McNaught
Departmental Gerontological Advisor,
Vacant
Departmental Dental Services Advisor,
Dr. J. Tsafaroff
Institutional Care Director, W. Holloway
Community Programs Directorate
Sr. Director, Carole Fahie
Health Programs Delivery Director, Joe Kiley
Health Programs Development
Director, Duncan Conrad
Veterans Independence Program (V.I.P.)
Director, Bob Bentley

DISABILITY PENSIONS DIVISION
Director Gen., Doris Boulet
Adjudication Support and
Non-Medical Benefits
Director, P. Dick
A/Chief Medical Advisor, N. Urie
Benefit Delivery Services
Director, Ron Herbert
Pension Services Director, J. Derry

ECONOMIC AND PROGRAM SUPPORT
DIVISION
Director Gen., Darragh Mogan
Income Support Director, Marie Williams
Program Support
A/Director, Bob Bentley
Corporate Planning
Director Gen., H. Adderley
REGIONAL OFFICES:

Atlantic
Reg. Director Gen., R. Witt
Box 1002, 45 Alderney Dr.
Dartmouth, NS B2Y 3Z7

Quebec
Reg. Director Gen., J.-P. Tétrault
4545, ch. Queen Mary, Montréal, H3W 1W4

Ontario
Reg. Director Gen., N.F. Corcoran
4900 Yonge St., Ste. 500
Willowdale, M2N 6B2

Prairie
Reg. Director Gen., W. Shead
610-330 Graham Ave., Box 6050
Winnipeg, MB R3C 4G1

Pacific
Reg. Director Gen., J.W. Liutkus
400, 1185 W. Georgia St.
Vancouver, BC V6E 4J5

AGENCIES, BOARDS AND COMMISSIONS

Army Benevolent Fund
Veterans' Affairs Bldg., Ottawa, K1A 0P4

The Army Benevolent Fund was formed in 1947 by an Act of Parliament to spend funds accumulated from army messes and canteens during World War II, and to assist army veterans of that conflict and their dependants where help is not available through veterans' legislation or other social sources. The Army Benevolent Fund also administers other Funds: the Canadian Welfare Fund — which assists members and ex-members of the Canadian Army who served between October, 1946 and February, 1968; and the Canadian Forces Personnel Assistance Fund — which assists serving members and ex-members of Canada's Armed Forces.

National Secretary, H. Graham Ball
Central Committee Secretary, W.T. (Bill) Love
Treasurer, B.W. Hanright
General Inquiries:
(613) 992-4144/5103; 996-1188/6722

Bureau of Pensions Advocates
Box 7700, Charlottetown, C1A 8M9

Prior to 1971, pensions advocates were members of the Veterans Bureau, which was part of the Department of Veterans Affairs. Part II of the *Pension Act*, added by the amendments of 1971, established the Bureau of Pensions Advocates as an independent agency under the Minister of Veterans' Affairs. By statute, the Bureau is not part of the Department, but it reports to the minister as he may direct from time to time.

The Bureau, upon request, provides legal counselling, assistance and representation to applicants and pensioners with respect to applications, hearings and appeals under the *Pension Act*. The relationship between the Bureau and an applicant or pensioner requesting its assistance is that of solicitor and client. Its services cover all claims adjudicated under the *Pension Act, Civilian War Pensions and Allowances Act* and allied statutes and orders.

An amendment to the *War Veterans Allowance Act* in 1984 authorized the Bureau to represent applicants under that Act on appeals to the War Veterans Allowance Board.

Chief Pensions Advocate, A. Lemieux
A/Dep. Chief Pensions Advocate, E.R. Elkin
Finance, Personnel and Administration
A/Director, J.B. Johnston
Administrative Services
A/Chief, M. Campbell
Sr. Area Advocate, R.C. MacLeod
Area Advocates: J. Beckett, B.J. Butler,
R.J. Ridlington, C. Duguay, A. Sheridan,
M. MacKinnon, M.A. Burke-Matheson
Operational Support Chief, Vacant

Canadian Pension Commission
Daniel J. MacDonald Bldg.
Box 9900, Charlottetown, C1A 8V6

The Canadian Pension Commission, established in 1933, reports to Parliament through the Minister of Veterans' Affairs. The Commission is responsible for adjudication under the *Pension Act* on claims for death or disability resulting from service in the Canadian Forces during the First World War, the Second World War, Special Force service and military service during peacetime. The Commission also adjudicates under various other Acts, regulations and orders on allied claims such as disability or death arising out of civilian service directly related to the war effort in the Second World War, service in the Royal Canadian Mounted Police or with respect to compensation for having been a prisoner of war. The authorization and payment of monetary grants accompanying certain awards for gallantry are also the responsibility of the Canadian Pension Commission, as is the administration of various trust funds established by private individuals for the benefit of veterans and their dependants.

Chairman, J.P. Wolfe
Dep. Chairman, M.L. MacFarlane

Commissioners: C.F. Bark, Y. Caron,
M. Chartier, A. Chatwood, S. Cheevers,
J.C. Chiasson, R.W. Cleary, C. Douglas,
R.L. Ford, R.C. Forest, D.J. Gogan,
G. Henderson, R.G. Jones, J.M. Lee,
C. McCabe, W.L. Morrison, E. Poirier,
J.G. Rivard, O.E. Rolfe, G.V. Sinclair,
J.M. Smith, P.J. Walsh, M.J. Wood

Special Advisors to the Commissioners:
N. Craig, J.W.C. Ferguson
Sr. Clinical Advisor on Special
Awards, Dr. R.B. Mitchell
Policy and Planning Support Chief, R. Hyde
Support Services Chief, Vacant
Commission Counsel, B.W. Chambers
Policy and Reference Library
A/Custodian, M. MacAulay

Commonwealth War Graves Commission (Canada)
Veterans Affairs Bldg.
Wellington St., Ottawa, K1A 0P4

The Commonwealth War Graves Commission was established by Royal Charter on May 21, 1917. Its duties are to mark and maintain the graves of the members of the Commonwealth forces who died in the two World Wars, to build memorials to the dead whose graves are unknown, and to keep records and registers.

The Canadian agency is responsible for carrying out these duties in respect of 14,300 war burials and 4,070 commemorations of the missing in North America. In addition, it provides information to the public concerning the 1,695,000 war burials or commemorations world wide.

The cost of the work is shared by the participating governments — United Kingdom, Canada, Australia, New Zealand, South Africa and India — in proportion to the numbers of their graves.

By an Instrument executed under Royal Charter, the Minister of Veterans' Affairs is the Commission's Canadian Agent. The secretary-general of the Canadian Agency is appointed by the Commission.
Secretary-Gen., S.M. Newell
Asst. Secretary-Gen., J.A. Gardam

Veterans Appeal Board
Box 7700, Charlottetown, C1A 8M9

The Veterans Appeal Board is an independent, quasi-judicial tribunal reporting to Parliament through the Minister of Veterans' Affairs. It was established under the *Veterans Appeal Board Act* on Sept. 14, 1987 and replaced the Pension Review Board and the War Veterans Allowance Board.

The Board is composed of a chairman, deputy chairman and four other members. Additional members are appointed by the Governor in Council when the workload so requires. There is a staff of thirty-one.

The Board provides a system of appeals to ex-members of the Armed Forces and of the RCMP, to certain civilians, and/or to their dependents, of decisions rendered by the Canadian Pension Commission and the Department of Veterans' Affairs under the *Pension Act*, the *Civilian War Pensions and Allowances Act* and the *War Veterans Allowance Act*, as well as other related statutes. The Board also interprets the legislation and is the final appeal level within the Veterans' Affairs portfolio. All hearings are public and are held at the offices of the Board in Charlottetown.

Chairman, Justice P. Letellier
Dep. Chairman, Norman A. Pimlott
Members:
Twila M. Whalen, J. Brendon McGinn,
Bernard R. Cormier, J. Roger Pichette,
André Roy, John H. Brehaut,
John R. Diamond, George A. MacKay,
Brian J. McKenna, Robert R. MacArthur,
Robert D. Campbell, K. McCorkell
Exec. Director, Jacques A. Boisvert
Legal Advisor, Jean C. Dixon
Program Support, Personnel and Finance
Chief, Trudy Molyneaux

DEPARTMENT OF WESTERN ECONOMIC DIVERSIFICATION

Ste. 604, Cornerpoint Bldg.
10179-105th St., Edmonton, T5J 3N1

MINISTER'S OFFICE
Minister, The Hon. Charles Mayer

DEPUTY MINISTER'S OFFICE
Dep. Minister, Bruce Rawson
Asst. Dep. Minister, Alberta, Brian Salley
Director Gen., Energy, Jack McPhee
Director Gen., High Technology, Gary Cooper
Director Gen., Program Operations
Gary Webster
Director Gen., Public Affairs, Don Carlson
REGIONAL OFFICES:
British Columbia
9th Flr., W. Pender St., Vancouver, V6C 2T8
Asst. Dep. Minister, Robin Dodson
Director Gen., Transportation, Frank Came
Saskatchewan
Ste. 601, S.J. Cohen Bldg., 119-4th Ave. S.
Box 2025, Saskatoon, S7K 3S7
Asst. Dep. Minister, Ian de la Roche
Director Gen., Agriculture, Doug Maley
Manitoba
Ste. 712, Cargill Bldg.,
240 Graham Ave., Winnipeg, R3C 0J7
Asst. Dep. Minister, Dennis Wallace
Director Gen., Trade, Randy Harrold

INDEPENDENT AGENCIES, BOARDS, COMMISSIONS, CROWN CORPORATIONS AND COUNCILS

Atlantic Canada Opportunities Agency

Box 6051, Moncton, NB E1C 9J8
General Inquiries: (506) 857-6523
Fax: (506) 857-7403

The Atlantic Canada Opportunities Agency, a federal development agency, was established on June 6, 1987 in order to increase opportunity for economic development in Atlantic Canada and, more particularly, to enhance the growth of earned incomes and employment in the region.

With its head office in Moncton, and regional offices in St. John's, Fredericton, Halifax, Charlottetown, Sydney and Ottawa, the Agency implements development programs for small and medium-sized businesses through advocacy, co-ordination, direct business support and co-operation.
Minister responsible, The Hon. Elmer MacKay
HEAD OFFICE:
770 Main St., 10th Flr., Moncton, NB E1C 9J8
President, Don McPhail

Newfoundland
Ste. 805, Atlantic Pl., 215 Water St.
St. John's, A1C 6C9
Co-ordinator, Gordon C. Slade

Prince Edward Island
Confederation Twr., Ste. 503
134 Kent St., Charlottetown, C1A 8R8
Co-ordinator, Leo Walsh

Nova Scotia
Ste. 3000, The Brewery, 1489 Hollis St.
Halifax, B3J 3M5
Co-ordinator, Jaffray Wilkins

New Brunswick
590 Brunswick St., Box 578
Fredericton, E3B 5A6
Co-ordinator, Frank Swift

Goose Bay District Office
217 Hamilton Rd., Box 730, Stn. A
Goose Bay, Labrador, A0P 1S0
Manager, S. Peyton

Corner Brook District Office
Herald Twr., Ste. 505, 4 Herald Ave.
Corner Brook, A2H 4B4
Manager, J. Tibbitts

Enterprise Cape Breton
15 Dorchester St., Box 2001
Sydney, NS B1P 6K7
Exec. Director, Ken MacVicar

Cape Breton Development Corp.
Box 2500, Sydney, NS B1P 6K9
Chairman, Dr. Teresa MacNeil
President and CEO, Vacant
Vice-President (Legal Services), Frank Elman

Vice-President (Finance), Keith Eldridge
Vice-President (Marketing), Vacant
Vice-President (Human Resources),
Terry Lineker
Organization Effectiveness and Training
Director, Don McCroome
Safety and Occupational Health
Director, Ralph Hoffman
Corporate Affairs Director, Wayne Antler

MINING OPERATIONS
Vice-President, R. Cooper
Prince Colliery
Gen. Manager, R. MacIntyre
Lingan Colliery
Gen. Manager, Peter Jones
Phalen Colliery
Gen. Manager, G. White
Mine Engineering Director, Roy MacLean

SURFACE OPERATIONS
Vice President, Walter MacKenzie
Coal Preparation
Gen. Manager, Allan McNeil
Transportation
Gen. Manager, Bill MacLellan

ENGINEERING
Vice-President, Ron Nicholson
Engineering Services Director, James Martin
Process Technology Director, Adrian White

INDUSTRIAL DEVELOPMENT DIVISION
Box 1750, Sydney, NS B1P 6T7
Vice-President, Keith Brown

Canada Development Investment Corp.

1 First Canadian Pl., Ste. 4520
Box 138, Toronto, M5X 1A4
General Inquiries: (416) 864-0333

The Canada Development Investment Corporation was incorporated under the *Canada Business Corporations Act* in May 1982 as a holding company to manage the federal government's investments in the business sector, to privatize these holdings where feasible, to advise the government on issues of industrial assistance when that advice is sought, and to be available to the government as a vehicle to hold, manage and privatize possible future investments. It will manage the federal government's investments in Eldorado Nuclear Ltd. following the sale of assets of Eldorado Nuclear Ltd., and manages government shares in Varity Corp. and Massey Combines Corp.
Minister responsible,
The Hon. Barbara McDougall

Chairman, Darcy McKeough
Vice-Chairman, Pierre Des Marais II
Exec. Vice-President, Michael Carter
Corporate Secretary, W. Kenneth McCarter

Eldorado Nuclear Ltd.

(Also Eldorado Resources Ltd. and Eldor Resources Ltd.)
700-360 Albert St., Ottawa, K1R 7X7

Chairman and CEO, G.N.M. Currie
President and COO, Nicholas M. Ediger
Vice-President (Finance), Thomas J. Gorman
Vice-President (Marketing), George Boyce
Vice-President (Resources and Technology),
Dr. A.W. Ashbrook
Corporate Secretary and Legal Advisor,
Louis R. Kohn

Canada Lands Co. (Mirabel) Ltd./ Société immobilière du Canada (Mirabel) ltée

9850, rue Belle-Rivière
C.P. 180, Ste-Scholastique
Mirabel (Québec) J0N 1S0

Canada Lands Company (Mirabel) Limited is a subsidiary to the Canada Lands Co. Ltd. It was duly incorporated under the *Canada Business Corporations Act* in 1981.

Under the jurisdiction of the Minister of Public Works, the Corporation is responsible for administering the Mirabel Airport peripheral land and selling the properties declared surplus to requirements while safeguarding the airport operations.

President and Director Gen., Pierre Hardy

Canada Lands Co. (Le Vieux Port de Montréal) Ltd.

333, rue de la Commune ouest
Montréal, H2Y 2E2

Canada Lands Company (Le Vieux-Port de Montréal) Limited, has the responsibility of implementing the master plan for the redevelopment of the Vieux-Port de Montréal.

Chairman, Roger L. Beaulieu
Exec. Director, Pierre Emond
Finance Director, Dany Bleau
Operations Director, Robert Simard
Planning and Construction
Director, Gilles Blais
Legal Services Director, Roger Coulombe
Communications,
A/Director, Camille Perrault

Canada Mortgage and Housing Corp.

682 Montreal Rd., Ottawa, K1A 0P7
General Inquiries: (613) 748-2000

Canada Mortgage and Housing Corporation (CMHC) is the housing agency of the government of Canada, charged with the administration of the *National Housing Act*. It is a Crown corporation with a board of directors appointed by Governor in

Council. CMHC is one of the largest financial institutions in Canada with responsibilities to the government of Canada for the administration of loans, grants, contributions and subsidies, the provision of advice to government on housing and related matters, and ensuring an adequate supply of mortgage funds, thus making housing accessible to Canadians.

The Corporation's activities are grouped into three components: government programs, administered funds, and asset administration.

In administering the government programs, CMHC encourages homeowners and owners of rental accommodation to maintain and conserve the existing housing stock, and improves access to homeownership and housing accommodation for low-income households. The Corporation is involved in research, development and demonstration, and the dissemination of information regarding housing activities and related matters.

The administered funds comprise the Mortgage Insurance Fund, the Home Improvement Loan Insurance Fund, the Rental Guarantee Fund, and the Mortgage-Backed Securities Fund established in 1987, all of which are administered as separate accounts within the Corporation.

Asset administration comprises the administration of mortgages, real estate and investments as well as services to others. CMHC also provides services to other government agencies or departments on a user-pay basis, and expertise in housing-related areas, including fee-for-service inspections and mortgage administration for government departments.

Chairman, Robert E. Jarvis
President, George Anderson
Corporate Secretary, C. Rump
Corporate Relations Director, C. Williams
Gen. Counsel, D. Bélisle-Horner
Legal Division Director, C. Poirier-Defoy
Employment Equity Manager, C. Paschal
Access to Information and Privacy Office
Co-ordinator, L. Oler

CORPORATE RESOURCES
Sr. Vice-President, Gaylen A. Duncan
Treasurer, G. Hendela
Controller, D.A. Whitelaw
Management Information Systems Directorate
Exec. Director, A.G. Walshe
Human Resources and Administration
Vice-President, Joyce Potter
Human Resources Centre
Director, J. Beaupré
Administration Division Director, R. Dreja

POLICY, RESEARCH AND PROGRAMS
Sr. Vice-President, E.A. Flichel
Research Division Director, D. Stewart
Strategic Planning and
Policy Development Division
Director, R. Lajoie
Project Implementation Division
Director, L. Finley

Statistical Services Division Director, P. Fuller
Programs
Vice-President, R.D. Warne
Program Planning and Analysis Division
Director, D. Cluff
Program Operations Division
Director, B. Lusk
Program Portfolio Management Division
Director, T. Gloyn

INSURANCE AND ASSET ADMINISTRATION
Professional Standards Division
Exec. Director, L. Lithgow
Insurance Sector
Vice-President, Gilles E. Girard
Underwriting Division Director, Denis St-Onge
Asset Management Director, F.N. Johnson
Operations Review
Exec. Director, F. Cameron
Operations Audit Director, M. Camelon
Program Evaluation Director, P. Brown
REGIONAL OFFICES:
Atlantic Region
Box 7320, Stn. A, Saint John, NB E2L 4S7
Gen. Manager, M. Daley

Quebec Region
1010, rue de la Gauchetière ouest
Montréal, H3B 2N2
Gen. Manager, C.A. D'Amour

Ontario Region
2255 Sheppard Ave. E., Atria North, Ste. E222
Willowdale, M2J 4Y1
Gen. Manager, J.T. Lynch

Prairie and NWT Region
410-22nd St. E., Ste. 300
Saskatoon, SK S7K 5T6
Gen. Manager, P.D. Anderson

B.C. and Yukon Region
Crown Life Place, Ste. 800
1500 W. Georgia St., Vancouver, V6G 3A1
Gen. Manager, V. Garland

Harbourfront Corp.
410 Queen's Quay W., Ste. 500
Toronto, M5V 2Z3

Harbourfront is a 37-hectare lakefront revitalisation project located in downtown Toronto. Harbourfront Corporation is a corporation chartered in the province of Ontario. Its only shareholder is the federal government. The Minister of Public Works appoints a board of directors drawn from the community and business, and includes representatives of the City of Toronto and Metropolitan Toronto. A Toronto-based management staff is responsible to the board for the day-to-day operation of the site and for the planning and development of Harbourfront's future.

Chairman, C. Di Nino
A/President and Gen. Manager,
Frank Mills
Communications Director, Marcia McClung
Public Programs Director, William Boyle

Planning and Development
Director, Frank Mills
Finance and Administration
Director, Leonard Golberg
Corporate Planning and Operations
Director, Robert Kanee

Canada Post Corp.

Sir Alexander Campbell Bldg.
Confederation Hts., Ottawa, K1A 0B1
Telex: 053-4387

Canada Post is a complex blend of public service and business enterprise. As a public service, its mandate is to "establish and operate a postal service for the collection, transmission and delivery of messages, information, funds and goods both within Canada and between Canada and places outside Canada." As a business enterprise, the Canada Post Corp. competes freely in the marketplace.

The Corporation employs more than 62,000 full-time employees who move seven billion pieces of mail a year through 8,000 postal facilities scattered across Canada from coast to coast. These facilities range in size from tiny one-person operations to giant mechanized postal plants as large as several football fields. Mail is delivered to households and businesses by a network of full-time and part-time letter carrier services serving urban, suburban, and rural routes as well as post office lock boxes and general delivery, and by certain specific services for bulk and other business mail. The Corporation, in partnership with the common carriers, uses surface and satellite electronic links, as well as air, road, rail, and water transport, to convey its traffic for both domestic and international communications.

The Canada Post Corp. offers four major classes of mail as well as special postal services. A philatelic branch serves the needs of the collector. Details of all the services can be obtained from any post office or from Canada Post Corp. at the above address. (See also the Communications chapter, Volume 1.)
Minister responsible, The Hon. Harvie Andre
Rm. 558, Confederation Bldg.
House of Commons, Ottawa, K1A 0A6

OFFICE OF THE CHAIRMAN

Chairman of the Board, Sylvain Cloutier
Corporate Secretary, N. Roger Gauthier
Board of Directors: Micheline Bouchard,
Jackson Chernoff, Anne Chippendale,
Sylvain Cloutier, William Dalton,
A. Ernest Downs, Irving Gerstein,
Donald H. Lander, Terry E. Yates,
Pierre Roy, Daniel Scanlan, Orland Tropea

OFFICE OF THE PRESIDENT

President and CEO, Donald H. Lander
Government Liaison Manager, Jim Stanton

Finance and Administration

Exec. Vice-President, Kenneth Harry
Corporate Finance and Planning Secretariat
Exec. Director, Jean Walker
Vice-President, Planning, Hank Klassen

Corporate Development

Exec. Vice-President, Stewart Cooke
Corporate Development Director, Bob Labelle
Corporate Representation
Vice-President, Elisabeth Kriegler
Corporate Affairs and Audit
Vice-President, Georges C. Clermont
Personnel and Administration
Vice-President, Bill Kennedy
Field Operations and Sales
Vice-President, John E. Aiken
Information Technology
Vice-President, Dr. Ken Tucker
Systems and Engineering
Vice-President, Jacques Sincennes
REGIONAL OFFICES
Atlantic Division
Box 1689, Halifax, B3J 2B1
Divisional Gen. Manager, G. Roy
Montreal Division
715, rue Peel, Montréal, H3C 4H6
Divisional Gen. Manager, Robert Favreau
Quebec Division
1535, ch. Ste.-Foy, Québec, G1S 1V6
Divisional Gen. Manager, André Villeneuve
York Division
21 Front St. W., Toronto, M5J 1A1
Divisional Gen. Manager, Bob Johnson
Rideau Division
Alta Vista Postal Stn., Ottawa, K1A 0C1
Divisional Gen. Manager, Marc l'Anglais
Huron Division
955 Highbury Ave., London, N5Y 1A3
Divisional Gen. Manager, Ray Jones
Mid West Division
266 Graham Ave., Winnipeg, R3C 0K1
Divisional Gen. Manager, George Wilton
Foothills Division
9828-104th Ave., Edmonton, T5J 2T7
A/Divisional Gen. Manager, Andy Varjas
Pacific Division
Box 2110, Vancouver, V6B 4Z3
Divisional Gen. Manager, Mike Gormick

Canadian Advisory Council on the Status of Women

110 O'Connor St., 9th Flr.
Box 1541, Stn. B, Ottawa, K1P 5R5

The Canadian Advisory Council on the Status of Women was established in 1973 by the federal government, upon recommendation of the Royal Commission on the Status of Women. The Council's mandate is to advise the federal government on women's issues and to promote public awareness of those issues. It is composed of a president, two vice-presidents and 27 part-time members appointed for three-year terms, from all the provinces and territories.

The Council addresses itself to the concerns of all Canadian women. The 30 members bring to the Council the particular problems of their regions. Research and background material provide the base upon which Council recommendations are made, following deliberation by members at general meetings. Recommendations for change in legislation and for other measures to improve the status of women are presented to the government through the Minister responsible for the Status of Women. As an autonomous agency, the Council retains the right to publish without ministerial consent. Council publications and activities — briefs, speeches, responses to current events, open communication with the public — maintain an awareness of the inequities facing women in Canadian society today.

Council meetings are held at least four times a year.

President, Sylvia Gold
Sr. Advisor, Judith Nolté
Director of Administration, Lise Benoit
Director of Research, Eliane Silverman
Director of Publications, Marguerite Alexander
Director of Public Affairs, Anne Marie Smart

Montreal Office
2021, av. Union, bur. 875, Montréal, H3A 2S9
Vice-President, Clarisse Codère

Calgary Office
220-4th Ave. S.E., Rm. 270
Box 1390, Stn. M, Calgary, T2P 2L6
Vice-President, Pat Cooper

Canadian Centre for Occupational Health and Safety

250 Main St. E., Hamilton, ON L8N 1H6
Inquiries: (416) 572-2981

The Centre is the national information resource in occupational health and safety, created by an Act of Parliament in 1987 "to promote the fundamental right of Canadians to a healthy and safe work environment." It is funded by the federal government and reports to Parliament through the Minister of Labour. It is governed by a council representative of government, labour, and employers.

The Centre provides occupational health and safety information through responses to inquiries, publications, and CCINFO — its computerized information service. The computerized information is available online (CCINFOline), on CD-ROM (CCINFOdisk), and on videotex (CCINFOimage). The Centre holds workshops on issues in occupational health and safety on request. These workshops bring together people from labour and government, employers, and professionals to discuss the issues and to establish common ground which can lead to accepted principles.

The objective of the Centre is to provide useful and easily understood occupational health and safety information. Services are provided in both English and French and the identity of inquirers is kept confidential.

Chairman, Martin O'Connell
President and CEO, Gordon Atherley
Finance, Publishing and
Administrative Services
Director, Kash Manchuk
Information Systems Services
Director, P.K. Abeytunga
Information Response Services
Director, Wendy Newman
Technical Services Director, William Louch

Canadian Commercial Corp.

50 O'Connor St., 11th Flr., Ottawa, K1A 0S6
Telex: 053-4359
Inquiries: (613) 996-0034

Canadian Commercial Corporation (CCC) is a Crown corporation wholly owned by the Government of Canada. It was established in 1946 to "assist in the development of trade between Canada and other nations". Its board of directors includes both business executives and senior public officials. CCC reports to Parliament through the Minister for International Trade.

The Corporation's business involves tying together the requirements of foreign governments and international agencies with the supply capabilities of Canadian producers of goods and services.

When a government-to-government transaction is requested by foreign buyers, or if a Canadian exporter believes such an arrangement will improve his chances for a sale, CCC acts as prime contractor, serving as a packager and catalyst to stimulate export of individual goods and services. Co-ordinating its activity with other government agencies, the Corporation alerts Canadian suppliers to bidding opportunities and concludes government-to-government contracts with a commitment to deliver a product, service or project package to a foreign governmental customer, with a back-to-back obligation from Canadian sources.

Minister responsible,
The Hon. John C. Crosbie
President, H.J. Mullington
Exec. Vice-President, O.I. Matthews
Vice-President, Corporate Affairs
P.A. Théberge
Vice-President, U.S. Group, Norman McIntosh
Secretary and Gen. Counsel,
Jean-Pierre Cloutier
Comptroller, F.O. Kelly

Canadian International Development Agency

200, prom. du Portage, Hull, K1A 0G4
Telex: 053-4140
General Inquiries: (819) 997-5006

Canada provided $2.7 billion of official development assistance in 1987-88 to more than 50 countries in Africa, Asia and the Americas.

The Canadian International Development Agency (CIDA) plans and administers about three-quarters of this aid. CIDA's president reports directly to the Minister for External Relations and International Development and the Secretary of State for External Affairs, who is responsible to Parliament in matters of international development.

CIDA delivers assistance through two main programs. The National Initiatives Program, which covers country-to-country assistance, and the Partnership Program, in which CIDA works with its partners in the volunteer, private, and international sectors involved in international development work.

CIDA recently released a Charter that specifies Canada's principles and priorities in development assistance. The principles are: putting poverty first, helping people to help themselves, letting development priorities prevail, and using partnership as the key approach to development. Shipments of food aid and other commodities are sent, Canadian advisors serve overseas, and Third World people are trained in Canada, in their own countries, or at "third country" training centres, usually in another part of their region of the world.

President, Margaret Catley-Carlson
Personnel Asst., Carol Chénier
Sr. Vice-President, Douglas Lindores

ASIA
Vice-President, David Holdsworth
Sr. Country Program Director, Julian Payne
Programming and Systems
Director, Roger Dumelie
Country Program Directors:
(Bangladesh, Burma), David Spring
(China), A.C.H. Smith
(India, Nepal), M. Esselmont
(Indonesia), A. Volkoff
(Pakistan), Joe Knockaert

ANGLOPHONE AFRICA
Vice-President, Charles Bassett
Programming and Systems
Director, John Sinclair
Sr. Country Program Director
(South Africa), J. Copeland
Country Program Directors:
(East Africa), R.W. Farrington
(East Africa), Art Labrecque
(N. Africa, Middle East), E. Yendall
(West Africa), Brian Ross

AMERICAS
Vice-President, John Robinson
Programming and Systems
Director, John Wood
South America Region
Director, Domingos Donida

Central America Region
Director, Nancy Stiles
Country Program Director
(Haiti) Jules Savaria
Caribbean Region
Director, F. Livingston

FRANCOPHONE AFRICA
Vice-President, Pierre Racicot
Programming and Systems
Director, Claude Francoeur
Sr. Country Program Director
(Sahel), André Gingras
Country Program Directors:
(Cameroon, Ivory Coast), D. Briand
(Zaire-Rwanda), Rosaline Murray
(Senegal, Guinea), Roger Couture
(Regional), Jean-Pierre Bolduc

MULTILATERAL PROGRAMS BRANCH
Vice-President, Noble Power
International Financial Institutions Division
Director Gen., Paul Krukowski
Dep. Director Gen., Ian Wright
Multilateral Technical Co-operation
Director Gen., Nicole Sénécal
Food Aid Co-ordination and Evaluation Centre
Director, Dianne Spearman
International Humanitarian Assistance
Director, François Arseneault

SPECIAL PROGRAMS BRANCH
Vice-President, Lewis Perinbam
International Non-Governmental Organizations
Director, Ronald Léger
Non-Governmental Organizations
Director Gen., Rick Ward
Institutional Co-operation and
Development Services Division
Director Gen., Aubrey Morantz
Programming, Planning and
Evaluation Division
Director, Jack Kuhns
Public Participation Program
Director, Ruth Groberman
Management for Change Program
Director, Iain Thomson

BUSINESS CO-OPERATION BRANCH
Vice-President, Denis Bélisle
Industrial Co-operation Division
Director Gen., Nick Hare
Policy and Systems Division
Director Gen., Marcel Bélanger
Consultant and Industrial Relations
A/Director, Lucienne Tremblay

POLICY BRANCH
Vice-President, François Pouliot
Director Gen., Marc Faguy
Strategic Planning Division
Director, Peter Houliston
Policy Co-ordination and Development Division
Director, Marcel Messier

Corporate Information and Economic Analysis
Director, Michel Goualt
Program Evaluation Division
Director, Jean Quesnel

PROFESSIONAL SERVICES BRANCH
Vice-President, Danielle Wetherup
Programing and Systems
Director, David Spring
Consultant Selection Secretariat
Director, Donald Burke
Infrastructure Division
Director Gen., Vacant
Natural Resources Division
Director Gen., Gilles Lessard
Social and Human Resource
Development Division
Director Gen., Pierre Beemans

OPERATIONS SERVICES BRANCH
Director Gen., Janet Zukowsky
Procurement Division Director, Bruno Hébert
Area Co-ordination Group
Director, Michael Lawrance
Contracts Division Director, Claude Latulippe
Gen. Counsel, A. Foster

COMPTROLLER'S BRANCH
Vice-President, Richard Herring
Dep. Comptroller, Jack O'Neil
Corporate Management Systems
Director, Raymond Prud'homme
Financial Management
Director, John Redmond
Financial Systems and Operations
Director, André Plante
Financial Policy and Systems
Director, André Plante
Accounting Operations
Director, Colette Turmel
Informatics and Telecommunications Services
Director Gen., N. Subramani
Systems Decentralization
Director, P. Finnegan
Informatics Services Director, R.N.P. Morris
Information Management
A/Director, G.K. Sutherland
Internal Audit Division
Director Gen., J.L. Plourde
Audit Operations Director, G. Kopil
Director, André Savard
Internal Financial Audit Director, R. Goulding

PERSONNEL AND ADMINISTRATION BRANCH
Director Gen., Ms. Claude Bernier
Personnel Operations Division
Director, Mike Williams
Organization, Planning and
Development Division
Director, E. Brian Legris
Official Languages Division
A/Director, Vacant
External Affairs Director, Pierre Giroux
Planning and Systems
Director, André Plouffe

Administrative Services Division
Director, Edgar Marengère

PUBLIC AFFAIRS BRANCH
Director Gen., Ruth Cardinal
Dep. Director Gen., André Champagne

Canadian Patents and Development Ltd.
275 Slater St., Ottawa, K1A 0R3

Canadian Patents and Development Limited, a Crown corporation reporting to Parliament through the Minister of Industry, Science and Technology, was established to assess, patent and license the industrial and intellectual property arising from research conducted in the laboratories of the federal government, provincial institutes and universities.

Chairman of the Board, J.A. Léger
Dep. Chairman of the Board, W.F. Graydon
President, Normand Plante
Vice-President, D.C. Cryderman
Sec.-Treasurer, L. Lipke
Marketing and Licensing Chief, K.F. Crowe
Patent Branch Chief, A.A. Thomson
Business Development Chief, E. Rymek

Commissioner of Official Languages
110 O'Connor St., 14th Flr.
Ottawa, K1A 0T8
General Inquiries: (613) 996-6368

The Commissioner is an Officer of Parliament whose appointment must be approved by both Houses and who can be dismissed only by a resolution of both Houses. He is independent of the government of the day, and reports directly to the Speakers of the House and Senate rather than through a minister.

The Commissioner has three main roles: as an *ombudsman* who takes complaints from the public when their linguistic rights have not been respected; as an *auditor* who examines the linguistic competence and performance of government departments and agencies; and as a *spokesperson* on language questions whose purpose is to gain greater acceptance for Canada's two official languages and to promote greater understanding between the two major linguistic groups.

The three main areas of interest of the Commissioner and his staff are to ensure that adequate service can be provided to the public in both languages, that as a general rule public servants can work in the official language of their choice, and that there is equitable representation of the two major linguistic groups in the public service of Canada.

In carrying out their duties the Commissioner and his staff not only work in conjunction with federal departments and agencies, but are also in contact with provincial institutions, with minority groups and their representatives and with the private sector.

Commissioner, D'Iberville Fortier
Dep. Commissioner, Peter L. Rainboth
Complaints and Audits Branch
Director, Jean-Claude Nadon
Regional Operations Branch
Director, Patrick McDonald
Policy Branch
A/Director, Marc Thérien
Communications Branch
Director, Patrick Doyle
Resource Management Branch
Director, Pierre de Blois

Economic Council of Canada

112 Kent St., Vanier, Ont.
MAILING ADDRESS:
Box 527, Ottawa, K1P 5V6
General Inquiries: (613) 952-1711

The Economic Council of Canada is an economic research and policy advisory agency, created in 1963 by an Act of Parliament.

The Council's research and advisory functions have three dimensions. First, a body of research and analysis has been developed that enables the Council to present periodic reviews of the actual performance of the economy and a broad "economic blueprint" for the medium-term future. From time to time, the Council undertakes special studies, either on its own initiative or at the request of the government. Second, through participation by its members from labour, business, agriculture and other interests across the country, the Council tries to influence public policy on important national issues. Third, this attempt to gain agreement about national objectives is furthered by means of public education, expressed primarily through widespread dissemination of the Council's consensus reports. The Council also publishes various background research studies.

The advisory function basically involves recommending "how Canada can achieve the highest possible levels of employment and efficient production in order that the country may enjoy a high and consistent rate of economic growth and that all Canadians may share in rising living standards."

Chairman, Judith Maxwell
Dep. Chairman, Caroline Pestieau
Dep. Chairman, Harvey Lazar
MEMBERS: Miller H. Ayre, Diane Bellemare, Jalynn H. Bennett, Alan A. Borger, Jacques Bougie, Dian Cohen, Thomas J. Courchene, Léon Courville, Alix Granger, Yves Guérard, Chester A. Johnson, Raymond Koskie, William Mackness, Raymond J. Nelson, Constantine E. Passaris, Marcel Pepin, Bartlett B. Rombough, Steve A. Stavro, Ken W. Stickland, Norman E. Wale, H. Graham Wilson

Export Development Corp.

Head Office: 151 O'Connor St.,
Box 655, Ottawa, K1P 5T9
Telephone: (613) 598-2500
Telex: 053-4136; Fax: (613) 237-2690

The Export Development Corporation (EDC) is Canada's official export credit agency, responsible for providing export credit insurance, loans, guarantees, and other financial services to promote Canadian export trade.

The Corporation insures:
- exporters against non-payment of foreign accounts receivable as a result of political or commercial risks, or both, with special policies available for U.S. sales and sales of bulk agricultural products;
- exporters who post bid or performance instruments on foreign sales;
- members of an exporting consortium against the call of a performance instrument due to the non-performance of one or more members of the consortium;
- domestic surety companies that provide performance instruments to exporters on foreign sales;
- exporters supported by EDC financing for the production risk from the effective date of financing until disbursement is made;
- subsuppliers on EDC-supported transactions against non-payment as a result of the inability or unwillingness of the buyer or exporter-of-record to make payment;
- exporters against political risks or actions by a foreign government that result in the loss of effective control over equipment on a foreign jobsite; and
- Canadians who invest abroad against expropriation, inability to repatriate earnings, and war or revolution.

The Corporation guarantees banks that 1) purchase notes issued to exporters by foreign buyers on sales of goods and services; 2) provide performance instruments on behalf of exporters; 3) provide non-recourse financing for exports of agricultural products sold on credit terms of up to three years when warranted by international competition; 4) provide loans to foreign buyers of Canadian goods and services; and, 5) extend lines of credit to foreign banks, which in turn finance purchases of Canadian goods and services sold on short-term credit.

The Corporation provides export financing for up to 85 per cent of the Canadian content of sales of Canadian capital goods, equipment and services to foreign buyers. Financing is available at both fixed and floating rates of interest, and funds are disbursed directly by EDC to Canadian exporters on behalf of the borrower — in effect providing the exporter with a cash sale. There are eight financing programs: loans, multiple disbursement agreement loans, protocols, lines of credit, note purchase agreements, forfeiting, simplified note purchase agreements, and specialized credits. The latter provides financing to

Canadian buyers for goods purchased in Canada for use or lease outside Canada.

Chairman, Edward Daughney
President and CEO, R.L. Richardson

FINANCE GROUP
Sr. Vice-President, Finance and Treasurer, B.A. Culham
Cash Management Department
Asst. Treasurer, C. Marshall
Corporate Finance Department
Asst. Treasurer, I. Gillespie
Claims and Recoveries Division
Gen. Manager, F. Werlen

EXPORT FINANCING GROUP
Sr. Vice-President, M.D. Bakker
Export Finance Policy and Services Division
Gen. Manager, D. Mackey
Latin America Division
Gen. Manager, D. Curtis
Mexico and Central America Department
Manager, D. Leonard
South America Department
Manager, W. James
OECD and Europe Division
A/Gen. Manager, E. Siegel
Central and Eastern Europe Department
Manager, A. Coles
OECD Department
A/Manager, J. Brockbank
Asia and Pacific Division
Gen. Manager, P. Foran
Pacific and North Asia Department
Manager, T. Macdonald
South Asia Department Manager, J. Balint
Africa and Middle East Division
Gen. Manager, M.G. McLean
North and West Africa Department
Manager, D. Delahousse
Middle East and East Africa Department
Manager, K. Hamp

EXPORT INSURANCE GROUP
Sr. Vice-President, B.R. King
Short Term Insurance Division
Gen. Manager, R. Doyle
Global Insurance Department
Manager, G. Bourbonnais
Agricultural Insurance Services
Manager, G. Kittleson
Medium Term Insurance Division
Gen. Manager, Vacant
Eastern Region Manager, A. Paiement
Western Region Manager, K. Dunn
Foreign Investment Insurance Department
Manager, R. Rendall
Short Term Credit Analysis Division
Gen. Manager, R. Lane
Quebec Department Manager, M. Carrière
Ontario Department Manager, J. Curley
Atlantic and Western Department
Manager, I. Miller

Services Development Department
Manager, J. Graves

MARKETING GROUP
Sr. Vice-President, R. Pruneau
Marketing and Communications Division
Gen. Manager, R. Fothergill
Corporate Communications Department
Manager, J.F. Cloutier
Marketing Department Manager, D. Neish
Country Assessment, Market and Economic Analysis Division
Chief Economist, F.P. Jeanjean
Market and Economic Analysis Department
Asst. Chief Economist, J. Olts
Country Assessment Department
Asst. Chief Economist, P. Bailey

HUMAN RESOURCES AND ADMINISTRATION GROUP
Vice-President, W. Musgrove

CORPORATE SECRETARIAT AND LEGAL SERVICES GROUP
Vice-President and Secretary, G. Ross

REGIONAL OFFICES:

British Columbia and Yukon Region
Ste. 1030, One Bentall Ctr.
505 Burrard St., Vancouver, V7X 1M5
Vice-President, K. O'Brien
Gen. Manager, J.G. Siddon
Business Development Department
Manager, R. Johnson

Prairie and Northern Region
Ste. 2140, Bow Valley Sq. III
255-5th Ave. SW, Calgary, T2P 3G6
Gen. Manager, M. Shaw
Toll-free: 1-800-661-8638
District Manager, W. Hutchings

Ontario Region
Ste. 810, National Bank Bldg.
Box 810, 150 York St., Toronto, M5H 3S5
Vice-President and Gen. Manager, D.B. Modin
Business Development Department
Manager, D. Summers
Client Services Department
Asst. Manager, K. Milloy

Quebec Region
800, Square Victoria, bur. 2724
C.P. 124, succ. Tour de la Bourse
Montréal, H4Z 1C3
Gen. Manager, H. Souquières
Business Development Department
Manager, P. D'Avignon
Client Services Department
Asst. Manager, S. Rubsoff

Atlantic Region
Toronto-Dominion Bank Bldg., Ste. 1003
1791 Barrington St., Halifax, B3J 3L1
Gen. Manager, P. Kavanagh
Business Development Department
Manager, C. Wood

London District
Ste. 303, 451 Talbot St., London, ON N6A 5C9
District Manager, B. Stanton

Ottawa District
Box 655, 151 O'Connor St., Ottawa, K1P 5T9
District Manager, J. Beaulieu

Manitoba/Saskatchewan District
330 Portage Ave., Ste. 707
Winnipeg, R3C 0C4
District Manager, D. Gyles

International Development Research Centre

250 Albert St., Box 8500, Ottawa, K1G 3H9

The International Development Research Centre was established in 1970 as a corporation to stimulate and support research for the benefit of developing countries. Its headquarters are in Ottawa, and it has regional offices for Southeast and East Asia (Singapore), South Asia (New Delhi), Eastern and Southern Africa (Nairobi), West and Central Africa (Dakar), Latin America and the Caribbean (Bogota), and the Middle East and North Africa (Cairo).

Research supported by IDRC is directed at improving the well-being of people in developing countries by adapting and applying science and technology to their needs. IDRC also promotes programs that will help developing regions bring the methods of scientific enquiry to bear for the solution of their own problems.

IDRC supports research in fields that directly affect the day-to-day lives of people, for example: agriculture, nutrition, education, health services, the impact of technological change on traditional society, population, tropical diseases, water supplies, information sciences, earth and engineering sciences, training, and implementation of research results. The great majority of IDRC-supported projects are aimed at improving the quality of life in the rural areas of developing countries. Three-quarters of the people of the world live in these areas, yet they are usually the last to benefit from the advances of science and technology. Some research support is also extended to urban areas, particularly when rural-urban problems are combined: the reasons for rural-urban migration patterns, the improvement of low-cost housing, and sanitation technology for squatter settlements are some of the subjects under study.

In 1980, the IDRC established co-operative programs to promote collaboration between research groups in the developing countries and their counterparts in the Canadian scientific community. The programs can provide support for specific research activities in any field that is of demonstrated importance to developing countries and in which there is recognized Canadian research capability.

President, Ivan L. Head
Vice-President (Program), James Mullin
Vice-President (Resources), Raymond Audet

Information Sciences Director, Martha Stone
Communications Director, David Nostbakken
Agriculture, Food and Nutrition Sciences
Director, Geoffrey Hawtin
Social Sciences Director, Anne Whyte
Health Sciences Director, Richard Wilson
Earth and Engineering Sciences
Director, Mousseau Tremblay
Fellowships and Awards
Director, Gerald Bourrier
Treasurer, Antoine Hawara
Human Resources Director, Allan Rix
Secretary and Gen. Counsel, Robert Auger
Planning and Evaluation
Director, Doug Daniels

International Joint Commission (United States—Canada)

Canadian Section
18th Flr., Berger Bldg.
100 Metcalfe St., Ottawa, K1P 5M1
General Inquiries: (613) 995-2984

The International Joint Commission is a unitary bi-national body, formally established in 1912 to carry out the provisions of the 1909 Canada-United States *Boundary Waters Treaty.*

The Commission approves certain uses, obstruction and diversion of boundary waters and rivers crossing the boundary between Canada and the U.S. In addition, when requested by the governments, the Commission carries out extensive investigations and provides recommendations on questions arising between the Canadian and U.S. governments along the "common frontier".

The Commission also assists in the implementation of the Canada-United States *Great Lakes Water Quality Agreement* and reports to the governments and the public with advice and recommendations.

The International Joint Commission consists of six members, three appointed by the Governor in Council and three appointed by the President of the United States.

Chairman, P. André Bissonnette, Q.C.
Special Asst., C. Cyr
Commissioners:
The Hon. E.D. Fulton, P.C., Q.C.
Robert S.K. Welch, Q.C.
Commission Secretary, Philip Slyfield
Advisors: E.A. Bailey, M. Clamen, A. Hamilton, R. Koop, G. Thornburn, M. Vechsler
Public Information Officer, A. Clarke

GREAT LAKES REGIONAL OFFICE
100 Ouellette Ave., Windsor, N9A 6T3
Director, A. Duda
Information Officer, S. Cole-Misch
Water Quality Board
Secretary, Dr. M. Bratzel, Jr.
Science Advisory Board
Secretary, Peter Boyer

Medical Research Council of Canada

Jeanne Mance Bldg., Tunney's Pasture
Ottawa, K1A 0W9
General Information: (613) 954-1812

The Medical Research Council of Canada was established in 1960 by the *Medical Research Council Act,* R.S.C. 1970, Chapter M-9, to promote, assist and undertake basic, applied and clinical research in Canada in the health sciences. The Council operates no laboratories of its own: the research it supports is carried out mainly in the health professional schools of Canadian universities and their affiliated institutions.

Applications for support are accepted in three main categories: grants in aid of research, personnel awards, and research promotion. Approximately 82 per cent of the Council's funds are used for its grants programs, which are designed either to offset the direct costs of research projects recommended to Council by its expert grants committees, or to support interdisciplinary and collaborative research programs and develop research in areas where it is not yet adequate. A further 17 per cent of Council's funds are spent on fellowships and studentships, offered in competition to those undertaking full-time research training in the Health Sciences at the post-doctoral or pre-doctoral level, and the salary support of a limited number of essentially full-time researchers in Canadian universities. The remainder of Council's funds are devoted to the support of symposia and workshops and other programs oriented to the promotion of research in the health sciences.

The full-time president, and the 21 part-time members of Council who serve without remuneration, are appointed by the Governor-General in Council. There is a full-time secretariat of 54.

President, Dr. Pierre Bois
Secretary to Council, M.E. Lipke
Scientific Advisor to the President,
Dr. G. Hetenyi
Program Operations Director, Dr. L. Slotin
Corporate Management Director, A. Belliveau
Scientific Evaluation Director, Dr. F. Rollesto
University—Industry Programs
Director, G. Beauchemin
Communications Director, D. Saint-Jean

National Capital Commission

161 Laurier Ave. W., Ottawa, K1P 6J6
Inquiries: (613) 996-1811, 239-5000
Toll-Free: 1-800-267-0450
Hull: (819) 778-2222, 994-6141

The National Capital Commission is a Crown corporation, successor to the Ottawa Improvement Commission (1899-1927) and to the Federal District Commission (1927-1959). The *National Capital Act,* which was proclaimed Feb. 6, 1959, created the National Capital Commission (NCC), an agency that has the mandate to prepare plans for and co-ordinate the development, conservation and improvement of the National Capital in accordance with its national significance as the seat of the Canadian government.

The National Capital Region is an area of 4,662 km^2 in Ontario and Quebec which surrounds and includes the cities of Ottawa and Hull. Here, through the NCC, the federal government seeks to achieve a capital that is:

• a well-functioning centre for the political and administrative demands of the government;
• an increasingly attractive physical and cultural setting that will be a source of pride for all Canadians;
• a meeting place where Canadians can participate in events that reflect their culture and heritage; and
• a dynamic symbol of Canada's linguistic and cultural values.

The Commission is composed of twenty members appointed by the Governor in Council. The Commissioners are selected from the residents of each province of Canada, the cities of Hull and Ottawa, and other municipalities within the National Capital Region.

Chairman, Jean E. Pigott
Exec. Vice-President and
Gen. Manager, Graeme M. Kirby
Sr. Counsel, P. Legault
Vice-Presidents:
Policy, G.M. Gyton
Public and Intergovernmental Relations,
E. MacKenzie
National Programming, A.J. Schouten
Capital Planning, R. McLemore
Realty and Official Residences, A. Jaouich
Information Services, R. Young
Controller, C. Wood
Human Resources, A. Call
Real Estate Development, A. Bonin
Environmental and Land Management,
A. Capling

National Research Council Canada

Montreal Rd., Ottawa, K1A 0R6
General Inquiries: (613) 993-9101

The National Research Council, Canada's leading science and technology agency, helps Canadian firms improve productivity, develop new products, and solve technical problems.

With a staff of 3,000 and a budget of $450 million, the NRC, with a dozen laboratory divisions and installations coast to coast, develops in-depth knowledge and practical know-how from its own basic and directed research programs aimed at improving Canada's economic competitiveness.

The NRC provides thousands of Canadian firms with a wide range of services, facilities, technology transfer programs, and collaborative research opportunities. Its Industrial Research Assistance Program alone — Canada's most effective technology network — creates thousands of jobs annually and generates billions of dollars in sales.

In addition, the NRC brings world-class electronic databanks of scientific and technical information to the fingertips of clients in industry, universities, and government through the Canadian Institute for Scientific and Technological Information (CISTI).

The NRC is especially active in providing for communication and collaboration among the many diverse industrial, university, federal, and provincial government science and technology agencies.

President, Dr. Larkin Kerwin
Exec. Vice-President and
Vice-President (Marketing), Dr. R.F. Pottie
Asst. Vice-President (Marketing),
Dr. W.M. Coderre
Vice-President (Technology Transfer),
K. Glegg
Vice-President (Personnel and
Administrative Services), B.D. Leddy
Vice-President (Science), Dr. Clive Willis
Vice-President (Engineering), E.H. Dudgeon
Vice-President (Senior Laboratory
and Biotechnology), Dr. M. Brossard
Comptroller, Dr. J.K. Pulfer
Vice-President (External Relations),
Dr. B.A. Gingras
Secretary-Gen., Dr. C.T. Bishop
Public Relations and Information Services
Exec. Manager, John Wildgust

LABORATORY DIVISIONS:
Institute for Marine Dynamics
Box 12093, Stn. A., St. John's, NF A1C 6B7
Director, N.E. Jeffrey
Asst. Director, Dr. D.C. Murdey
Atlantic Research Laboratory
1411 Oxford St., Halifax, B3H 3Z1
Director, Dr. R.A. Foxall
Division of Biological Sciences
Director, Dr. I.C.P. Smith
Biotechnology Research Institute
6100, av. Royalmount, Montréal, H4P 2R2
Director, Dr. B. Coupal
Institute for Research in Construction
Director, George Seaden
Space Division
Exec. Director, Dr. G.M. Lindberg
Division of Chemistry
Director, Dr. D.M. Wiles
Assoc. Director, Dr. K.U. Ingold
Division of Electrical Engineering
Director, S.A. Mayman
Asst. Director, Dr. M. Collins
Biomedical Engineering Laboratory
Head, O.Z. Roy
Informatics Division
Director, Dr. Roger Taylor
Herzberg Institute of Astrophysics
Director, Dr. D.C. Morton
Asst. Director, Dr. Bryan Andrew
Industrial Materials Research Institute
75, boul. Mortagne
Boucherville (Québec) J4B 6Y4
Director, G. Bata

Division of Mechanical Engineering
Director, J. Ploeg
National Aeronautical Establishment
Director, Dr. G.F. Marsters
Division of Physics
Director, Dr. M.J. Laubitz
Assoc. Director, Dr. H. Preston-Thomas
Plant Biotechnology Institute
110 Gymnasium Rd.
Saskatoon, SK S7N 0W9
Director, Dr. W.F. Steck

OBSERVATORIES:
Algonquin Radio Observatory
Algonquin Park, ON K0A 2L0
Dominion Astrophysical Observatory
Victoria, BC V8X 3X3
Director, Dr. J.E. Hesser
Dominion Radio Astrophysical Observatory
Penticton, BC V2A 6K3
Head, Dr. L.A. Higgs
Meteorite Observation and Recovery Project
Saskatoon, SK S7N 0W0
Head, A.T. Blackwell
Springhill Meteor Observatory
Springhill, ON K1A 0R6
Ottawa River Solar Observatory
Shirley's Bay, ON K1A 0R6

PERSONNEL AND ADMINISTRATIVE
SERVICES
Vice-President, B.D. Leddy
Administrative Services and
Property Management Branch
Exec. Manager, M.R.M. Proulx
Personnel Branch
Exec. Manager, R.W. Dolan
Gen. Manager, R. Lavallée
Comptroller, Dr. J.K. Pulfer
Management Services Branch
Director, Lucie Lapointe-Shaw
Financial Services Branch
Chief, M.K. Pawlowski
International Relations
Vice-President, Dr. B.A. Gingras
Director, Dr. J.M.R. Stone
Government Sector Advisors:
Loris Racine, C. Gauvreau, D.J. DeCoff

INDUSTRY DEVELOPMENT OFFICE
Vice-President, K. Glegg
Industry Development Office
Exec. Director, S. Abela
IDO Advisory Board, Dr. K. Bell
Industry Policy Analysis
Exec. Manager, Dr. S.S. Grimley
Management Services
Gen. Manager, Dr. M.D. Watson
Industrial Research Assistance Program —
Field Network
Gen. Manager, J.H. Braams
Technical Advisory Manager, Dr. C.D. Cox
Field Advisory Services
Manager, Dr. R.J. Paquin
Industrial Research Assistance Program —
Laboratory Network

Gen. Manager, J.D. Robar
Canadian Institute of Industrial Technology
Director, Alex Mayman

CANADA INSTITUTE FOR SCIENTIFIC AND
TECHNICAL INFORMATION
Montreal Rd., Ottawa, K1A 0S2
Inquiries: (613) 993-1600
Director, E.V. Smith
National Services
Asst. Director, M. Walshe
Resource Development
Asst. Director, B. Dumouchel
Administrative Services Chief, M. Bergevin
Policy, Planning and Systems
Chief, M. Brandreth
Acquisitions Head, J. Parkkari
Health Sciences Resource Centre
and MEDLARS
Head, M. Wong
Branch Services Head, S. Suart
Publicity and Communications
Head, Elizabeth Katz
Numeric Databases Manager, Dr. G. Wood
Document Delivery and Lending
A/Head, C. MacKeigan
Cataloguing Head, S. Burvill
NRC Research Journals
Editor-in-Chief, Dr. C.T. Bishop

Natural Sciences and Engineering Research Council of Canada

200 Kent St., Ottawa, K1A 1H5
General Inquiries: (613) 995-6295

The Natural Sciences and Engineering Research Council (NSERC) is a federal Crown corporation that was established on May 1, 1978. The functions of NSERC are to promote and assist research in the natural sciences and engineering, other than the health sciences, and to advise the Minister of State for Science and Technology. NSERC carries out its functions through the program of scholarships and grants in aid of research.

The general objectives of the program are to promote and support the development and maintenance of research in the natural sciences and engineering and ensure the provision of highly qualified manpower in these areas. Accordingly, NSERC supports excellence in research for the creation of new knowledge in the natural sciences and engineering, promotes and supports the development of research in selected fields of regional and national importance, and assists in the provision and development of highly qualified manpower. NSERC grants and scholarships are intended primarily for university researchers and students.

President, Arthur W. May
Exec. Vice-President, Gilles Julien
Secretary-Gen., Mireille Brochu
Communications Head, Pierre Normand

Policy and Planning Director, Steve Shugar
Scholarships and International Programs
Director Gen., R.J. Kavanagh
Director, Teresa Brychey
International Relations Officer
Alfred A. Kugler
Targeted Research
Director Gen., Leo Derikx
Strategic Grants
A/Director, Janet Walden
University-Industry Program
Director, Paul Latour
Research Grants
Director Gen., Janet E. Halliwell
Engineering and Computing Sciences
Asst. Director, Nigel Lloyd
Life and Earth Sciences
Asst. Director, Marilyn Taylor
Physical and Mathematical Sciences
Director, Vacant
Cross-Disciplinary Activities
Chief, Carmen Charette
Corporate Systems and Services
Director Gen., André Molino
Comptroller, Fred Turner
Administration Chief, Elaine Salmon
Personnel Chief, Christopher Klus
Information Systems
Director, Roger W. Ellerton
Inter-Council Program Directorate/ Networks of Centres of Excellence
Director, Elaine Isabelle

Northern Pipeline Agency

Centennial Towers, Ste. 210
200 Kent St., Ottawa, K1A 0E6
Inquiries: (613) 993-7466

The Northern Pipeline Agency was established by the *Northern Pipeline Act* in April 1978, to oversee the planning and construction of the Canadian segments of the Alaska Highway Gas Pipeline Project.

Under the Act, the Agency has two main responsibilities. It is required to regulate the project and to facilitate its expeditious planning and construction in Canada by the Foothills Group of Companies. The Agency is also required to ensure that the project maximizes the social, economic and industrial benefits for Canada and minimizes the potential adverse social and environmental impacts.

The Northern Pipeline Agency was created to provide a "single window" for virtually all of the dealings at the federal level with the Foothills Group of Companies which was authorized under the Act to undertake the project in Canada. The principal exception involves the responsibilities reserved exclusively to the National Energy Board or shared between the Board and the Agency.

The Agency is also responsible for co-ordinating activities that bear on the project with other federal departments, other levels of government in Canada, and U.S. departments and agencies.

The Agency comes under the authority of a minister designated by the Governor in Council. A Commissioner appointed by Order-in-Council serves under the minister as his deputy and is located at the Agency's head office in Ottawa.

Minister responsible,
The Hon. Don Mazankowski, P.C.

Commissioner, G.E. Shannon

Pension Appeals Board

Box 8567, Postal Terminal
Ottawa, K1G 3H9

The Pension Appeals Board is a tribunal which was constituted in 1965 by an Act of Parliament pursuant to an agreement with the Government of Quebec through the Canada Pension Plan.

Its membership is appointed by the Governor in Council on recommendation of the Minister of Justice, and consists of a chairman, a vice-chairman and 10 members. Three members constitute a quorum.

The Board is responsible for the hearing of appeals which arise from decisions of the Minister of National Revenue and the Minister of National Health and Welfare under the *Canada Pension Plan Act;* from decisions of the Minister of Revenue of Quebec; and, in some circumstances, from decisions of La Commission des Affaires sociales under the *Quebec Pension Plan Act.*

Appeals heard by the Board are by way of trial de novo. Its sittings take place in every province of Canada as the need arises. Written reasons for decision are given on every appeal heard by the board and copies are forwarded by the registrar to the parties to the appeal.

Minister responsible, The Hon. Jake Epp

Chairman, Hon. Mr. Justice A.J. Cormier
A/Registrar, Colette E. Poitras
A/Dep. Registrar, Mina McNamee

Public Service Staff Relations Board

C.D. Howe Bldg., W. Twr., 6th Flr.
Box 1525, Stn. B, Ottawa, K1P 5V2
General Information: (613) 990-1800

The Public Service Staff Relations Board is the quasi-judicial statutory tribunal responsible for the administration of the systems of collective bargaining and grievance adjudication established under the *Public Service Staff Relations Act,* the *Parliamentary Employment and Staff Relations Act,* the *Yukon Public Service Staff Relations Act,* and the *Yukon School Act.* In addition it is responsible for the administration of certain provisions of Part IV of the *Canada Labour Code* concerning occupational health and safety applicable to employees in the Public Service. The Board consists of a chairperson, vice-chairperson, not less than three deputy chairpersons, and such other full-time and part-time members as the Governor in Council considers necessary.

Proceedings before the Board include applications for certification, revocation of certification, complaints of unfair labour relations practices, designation of persons employed in a managerial capacity or confidential capacity, designation of employees whose duties are required to be performed in the interest of the safety or security of the public, and reference of safety officers' decisions and complaints under the health and safety provisions of Part IV of the *Canada Labour Code.* By far the heaviest volume of cases are grievances referred to adjudication concerning the interpretation or application of provisions of collective agreements or major disciplinary action.

The Pay Research Bureau, a branch of the Board, conducts research and carries out surveys on rates of pay, benefits and conditions of employment primarily as they relate to those units of employees in the Public Service to which the system of collective bargaining established by the *Public Service Staff Relations Act* applies. The Bureau also engages in similar activities in respect of groups that are excluded from that process. The Bureau receives advice in the planning of its survey activities from the Advisory Committee on Pay Research, a body composed of representatives of employers and bargaining agents coming within the purview of this Act.

The Board reports to Parliament through a designated minister, the President of the Privy Council.

Minister responsible,
The Hon. Don Mazankowski

Chairperson, Ian Deans
Vice-Chairman, J.M. Cantin, Q.C.
Dep. Chairmen: G. D'Avignon,
M. Korngold Wexler, P. Chodos
Board members (full-time):
J. Galipeault, T.W. Brown, R. Young,
D. Kwavnick, T.O. Lowden, M.M.L. Galipeau
Sec.-Registrar, G.E. Plant
Mediation Services Director, A.K. Strike
Gen. Counsel, J.E. McCormick
Director of Administration, L. Labrecque
Pay Research Bureau
Exec. Director, J.T. Cunningham
National Joint Council
Gen. Secretary, D. Davidge

Science Council of Canada

100 Metcalfe St., 17th Flr.
Ottawa, K1P 5M1
General Inquiries: (613) 996-1729

The Science Council of Canada is Canada's national advisory agency on science and technology policy. Created in 1966, its primary functions are to:

• analyze science and technology policy issues;
• recommend policy directions to government;
• alert Canadians to the impact of science and technology on their lives; and

- stimulate discussion of science and technology policy among governments, industry and academic institutions.

Reporting to Parliament through the Minister of State (Science and Technology), the Science Council operates at arm's length from the government, designing its own programs of research and publishing its findings at its own discretion.

The Science Council has published over 300 titles and produces a variety of publications including research reports, background studies, occasional papers on important topics in Canadian science policy issues, annual reports, newsletters and brochures.

Chairman, Dr. Geraldine Kenney-Wallace
Vice-Chairman, Dr. V. Vikis-Freibergs
Director of Policy Analysis
Dr. J.M. Gilmour
A/Director of Programs, Dr. G. Steed
Corporate Secretary, E.V. Nyberg
Science Advisors: K. Arkay, Dr. C. Davis, Dr. P. Enros, Dr. W. Smith, Ruth Wherry
Librarian, F.R. Bonney

Standards Council of Canada

350 Sparks St., Ste. 1200
Ottawa, K1P 6N7

The Standards Council of Canada, created by Act of Parliament in October 1970, is the national co-ordinating agency for voluntary standardization in Canada. It manages the National Standards System, a federation made up of independent Canadian organizations accredited to carry out standards-writing, certification, and testing activities. The Council is also responsible for Canadian participation in the technical work of international non-governmental standard-writing organizations.

The Council is an autonomous public corporation, consisting of a maximum of 57 members, 41 of whom represent primary and secondary industries, trade associations, labour unions, consumer associations and the academic community. Ten other members represent the provinces, while six are representatives of the federal government.

A Standards Information Service was established by the Council in 1977 to help standards users identify and locate the national, foreign and international standards they need. The Service — which is also the Canadian GATT Enquiry Point — can be reached toll-free from anywhere in Canada at 1-800-267-8220.

In addition, the Council provides the sales outlet for standards and publications of the International Organization for Standardization (ISO) and the International Electrotechnical Commission (IEC). National standards of Canada's major trading partners are also available from the Standards Sales Division. The division can be reached at 1-800-267-8220.

President, Georges Archer

Exec. Director, John R. Woods
Secretary of Council, Lloyd Duhaime

ADMINISTRATION AND FINANCE BRANCH
Treasurer of the Council and
Director of Administration, Richard Parsons
Administration Manager, Rod MacDonald

STANDARDIZATION BRANCH
Director, Dr. Jack Perrow
Standards Division Manager, Bill Pullen
Certification Manager, Frank Brewer
Testing Manager, Marc Archambault
International Manager, Charles Ender
Education Officer, Dennis Coffey

PUBLIC RELATIONS BRANCH
Director, Jacques Robitaille
Communications Manager, Pierre Normand
Publications Manager, Steven Brasier

INFORMATION AND SALES BRANCH
Director, Mary Crainey
Standards Information
Manager, Diane Thompson
Standards Sales Manager, Kathy Kilfeather
Toll-free: 1-800-267-8220
GATT Notifications Service
(TELEGATT)
English: (613) 238-1501
French: (613) 238-1450

Hazardous Materials Information

Review Commission
Twr. B, 355 River Rd., Vanier, K1A 0C9
Manager, John Armstrong

Patented Medicines Prices Review Board
Legion House, 359 Kent St., Ottawa, K1A 0C9

Chairman, Harry Eastman
Vice-Chairman, Robert Goyer
Exec. Director, Roy Atkinson
Compliance and Liaison
Director, Tom Brogan

Statistics Canada

R.H. Coats Bldg., Tunney's Pasture
Ottawa, K1A 0T6

As Canada's central statistical agency, Statistics Canada has a mandate to collect, compile, analyze, abstract and publish statistical information relating to the commercial, industrial, financial, social, economic and general activities and condition of the people of Canada.

The agency, which is subject to the budgetary control of Parliament, is committed to meeting the statistical needs of all levels of government and the private sector for research, policy formulation, decision-making and general information purposes.

Census operations, household and business surveys are conducted across Canada from eight regional offices. The agency's nine regional Advisory Services reference centres and its

Central Inquiries service in Ottawa offer reference and consultative services, answering about 300,000 inquiries per year.

Statistics Canada prepares and produces more than 400 publications annually. These include survey results as well as such compendia as the *Canada Year Book*, the *Canada Handbook*, the *Canadian Economic Observer, Human Activity and the Environment*, and the *Market Research Handbook*. In addition, the agency maintains an extensive on-line computerized data base called CANSIM. Statistics Canada is also a focal point for the co-ordination of activities with its federal and provincial partners in the national statistical system to avoid duplication of effort and to promote the consistency of statistical information.

The Agency fosters relations not only within Canada but also throughout the world. By participating in a number of international meetings and professional exchanges, Statistics Canada enhances Canada's reputation with international organizations and foreign countries. Through such activities, Statistics Canada is contributing to the continuing development of internationally comparable statistics, as well as improving the Canadian statistical system. These contacts also assist in achieving the wider goals of the government in fields such as foreign relations, foreign trade and development co-operation.

Minister responsible, The Hon. Otto Jelinek

Chief Statistician of Canada, Ivan P. Fellegi

Communications and Operations Field

Asst. Chief Statistician, Y. Fortin

MARKETING AND INFORMATION SERVICES BRANCH
Director Gen., D. Desjardins
Communications Division
Director, Douglas Newson
Electronic Data Dissemination Division
Director, E. Boyko
Library Services Division
Director, G. Ellis
Publications Division Director, H. Nightingale

OPERATIONS BRANCH
Director Gen., B.J. Lynch
Headquarters Operations Division
Director, T. Thompson
Regionalization Planning Division
Director, M. Lefebvre
Operations Automation Division
Director, A.R. Grenier

REGIONAL OPERATIONS BRANCH
Assoc. Director Gen., J. Riddle
Survey Operations Division
Director, M.R. Coutts
User Advisory Services Director, G. Graser
Statistical Reference Centre
(National Capital Region): (613) 951-8116
National toll-free order line: 1-800-267-6677

REGIONAL OFFICES:
Atlantic Region
1770 Market St., Halifax, B3J 1Y6
Director, J. Hughes
Operations
Asst. Director, D. Condy
Advisory Services
Asst. Director, B.W. Ruth
Regional Reference Centre: (902) 426-5331
Toll-free: 1-800-565-7192
Newfoundland and Labrador
3rd Flr., Viking Bldg., Crosbie Rd.
St. John's, A1B 3P2
Assoc. Director, B. Underhay
Advisory Services
Asst. Director, D. Courtney
Regional Reference Centre: (709) 772-4073
Toll-free: 1-800-563-4255
Quebec
Place Guy Favreau, bur. 412
200, boul. René-Lévesque ouest
Montréal, H2Z 1X4
Director, N. Montreuil
Operations
Asst. Director, M. Maillette
Advisory Services
Asst. Director, Y. Deslauriers
Regional Reference Centre: (514) 283-5725
Toll-free: 1-800-361-2831
Ontario
Arthur Meighen Bldg., 10th Flr.
25 St. Clair Ave. E., Toronto, M4T 1M4
Director, V. Glickman
Operations
Asst. Director, A.G. Connolly
Advisory Services
Asst. Director, P. Bassett
Regional Reference Centre: (416) 973-6586
Toll-free: 1-800-268-1151
Eastern and Northern Ontario
Civic Administration Ctr.
225 Holditch St.
Sturgeon Falls, ON P0H 2G0
Assoc. Director, R.L. Potvin
Operations
Asst. Director, R. Proulx
Reference Centre: (705) 753-3200
Toll-free: 1-800-268-1151
Prairie Region
HYS Ctr., Ste. 215, 11010-101st St.
Edmonton, T5H 4C5
Director, C.J. Page
Operations
Asst. Director, G. Demers
Advisory Services
Asst. Director, B. Meyers
Reference Centre: (403) 495-3027
Toll-free: 1-800-282-3907
N.W.T. call collect: (403) 495-3028
Pacific Region
757 W. Hastings St., Ste. 440F
Vancouver, V6C 3C9
Director, D.I. Rushton
Advisory Services
Asst. Director, R. Green

Operations
Asst. Director, G. Fentimen
Regional Reference Centre: (604) 666-3691
Toll Free:
(South and Central BC): 1-800-663-1551
(Yukon and Northern BC): Zenith 08913

Business and Trade Statistics Field

Asst. Chief Statistician, J. Ryten

RESOURCES, TECHNOLOGY AND SERVICES
STATISTICS BRANCH
Director Gen., Y. Goulet
Services Division Director, A. Ansmits
Agriculture Division Director, G. Andrusiak
Industrial Organization and Finance Division
Director, R.W. Collins
Science, Technology and
Capital Stock Division
Director, P. Koumanakos
Small Business and Special Surveys
Director, J. Gagnon

INDUSTRY, TRADE AND PRICES STATISTICS
BRANCH
Director Gen., J.P. Trudel
Industry Division Director, D. Triandafillou
International Trade Division
Director, J.M. Léger
Prices Division Director, B. Slater
Transportation Division Director, R.E. Drover
Business Survey Redesign Project
Project Manager, J. Ryten
Geocartographics Division
Director, S. Witiuk

Informatics and Methodology

Asst. Chief Statistician, G.J. Brackstone
International and Professional
Relations Division
Director, B. Prigly

INFORMATICS BRANCH
Director Gen., E. Outrata
Sr. Advisor, D. Venables
Main Computer Centre Division
Director, J.P. Moore
Informatics Services and Development Division
Director, W.M. Podehl
Client Services Division
Director, D. Croot

CLASSIFICATION SYSTEMS BRANCH
Director Gen., Vacant
Business Register Division
Director, A. Monty
Standards Division Director, S. Nijhowne
Geography Division Director, D.R. Bradley

METHODOLOGY BRANCH
A/Director Gen., G.J. Brackstone
Small Area and Administrative

Data Division Director, J. Leyes
Social Survey Methods Division
Director, G.J. Hole
Business Survey Methods Division
Director, N. Chinnappa
Time Series Research and Analysis Division
Director, E.B. Dagum

National Accounts and Analytical Services Field

Asst. Chief Statistician, J.S. Wells
Sr. Research Advisor, T. Gigantes
Sr. Social Scientist, P. Reed

ANALYTICAL STUDIES BRANCH
A/Director Gen., J.S. Wells
Social and Economic Studies Division
Director, M. Wolfson
Population Studies Division
Director, L.O. Stone
Language Studies
Research Director, R. Lachapelle
Environment and Natural Resources
Manager, K. Hamilton
Business and Labour Market Analysis
Manager, Vacant

SYSTEM OF NATIONAL ACCOUNTS BRANCH
Director Gen., K. Lal
Integration and Development Division
Director, B. Clift
Income and Expenditure Accounts Division
Director, P. Smith
Input-Output Division
Director, C. Simard
Industry Measures and Analysis Division
Director, D. Rhoades
International and Financial Economics Division
Director, A. Meguerditchian

Social, Institutions and Labour Statistics Field

Asst. Chief Statistician, D.B. Petrie

CANADIAN CENTRE FOR JUSTICE
STATISTICS
A/Exec. Director, D.B. Petrie

CENSUS AND DEMOGRAPHIC STATISTICS
BRANCH
Director Gen., E.T. Pryor
Census Operations Division
Director, B. Laroche
Demography Division Director, A. Romaniuc
Housing, Family and Social Statistics Division
Director, G.E. Priest
1986 Census Project Manager, E.T. Pryor
1991 Census
Content and Planning
Manager, G.J. Goldmann

INSTITUTIONS AND SOCIAL STATISTICS
BRANCH
Director Gen., J.W. Coombs
Health Division Director, D. Bray
Education, Culture and Tourism Division
Director, K.K. Campbell
Public Institutions Division
Director, Tim Davis

LABOUR AND HOUSEHOLD SURVEYS
BRANCH
Director Gen., R. Ryan
Household Surveys Division
A/Director, R.T. Ryan
Labour and Household Surveys Analysis
Director, I. Macredie
Labour Division Director, J. Selley

Management Services Field
Asst. *Chief Statistician*, G.R. Labossière
Corporate Assignments Division
Director, M. Blauer
Data Access and Control Services Division
Director, L. Desramaux
Departmental Security Officer, J. Thibodeau

MANAGEMENT PRACTICES BRANCH
Director Gen., M. Levine
Corporate Planning and
Management Systems Division
Director, R. Barnabé
Program Evaluation Division
Director, M. Hubbard
Internal Audit Division
Director, A. Martin

OPERATIONAL PLANNING AND FINANCE
BRANCH
Director Gen., W.J.L. Hill
Operational Planning and
Programming Division
Director, R. Gross
Financial Policies and Systems Division
Director, A.F. Scullion
Financial Operations Division
Director, A. Bastian

PERSONNEL BRANCH
Director Gen., J.P. McLaughlin
Personnel Policies and
Affirmative Action Division
Director, E.W.L. Reid
Personnel Operations Division
Director, M.A. Cuerrier
Official Languages Division
Director, R. Campbell
Employee Assistance Program
Co-ordinator, I. Roberts

Status of Women Canada
151 Sparks St., Ottawa, K1A 1C3
General Inquiries: (613) 995-7835

Status of Women Canada is the central co-or-dinating agency which reports to the Minister responsible for the Status of Women. Its mandate is to ensure that federal legislation, policies and programs take into consideration the concerns of women. It recommends policy changes to other federal bodies and provides liaison with other federal departments, with provincial govern-ments, advisory councils, and with national women's organizations.

Status of Women Canada started in 1971 with the establishment of a Status of Women Co-ordi-nator position within the Privy Council Office. The co-ordinator and the Minister responsible for the Status of Women do not have legislative power to make or enforce policies and directives on the status of women. However, they recommend constructive changes to policy proposals brought forward by other federal bodies and initiate proposals to meet unfilled needs.

Status of Women Canada maintains liaison with other federal departments and agencies at the ministerial and deputy head levels and with departmental officers, ensuring that women's concerns are reflected in policy and program development and that departments consult with other concerned departments, with provincial bodies and with experts in pertinent fields.
Minister responsible,
The Hon. Barbara McDougall

OFFICE OF THE CO-ORDINATOR
Co-ordinator, Kay Stanley
Dep. Co-ordinator,
Louise Bergeron-de Villiers
FINANCE, PERSONNEL AND
ADMINISTRATION
Director, John Conroy

POLICY ANALYSIS AND DEVELOPMENT UNIT
Director, Vacant
Sr. Policy Analysts:
Hélène Dwyer-Renaud, E. Hornby
Policy Analysts: Joan Bercovitch,
Anne Rachlis, Kay Rogers
Sr. Economist, Lorraine Garneau

INTER-GOVERNMENTAL AND
NON-GOVERNMENTAL RELATIONS
Director, Rhonda Ferderber
V. Collins, M.L. Levisky, S. Regehr

COMMUNICATIONS
Director, Jacques Taky
M. Latrémouille, L. Lavoie, A. McLaughlin

FEDERAL JUDICIARY AND JUDICIAL OFFICERS

THE SUPREME COURT OF CANADA

Supreme Court Bldg.
Wellington St., Ottawa, ON K1A 0J1

Chief Justice of Canada:
The Rt. Hon. Mr. Justice R.G.B. Dickson, P.C.

Puisne Judges:
The Hon. Mr. Justice W.R. McIntyre
The Hon. Mr. Justice Antonio Lamer
The Hon. Madame Justice Bertha Wilson
The Hon. Mr. Justice Gérard La Forest
The Hon. Madame Justice Claire
  L'Heureux-Dubé
The Hon. Mr. Justice John Sopinka
The Hon. Mr. Justice Charles Gonthier
The Hon. Mr. Justice Peter Cory
The Hon. Madame Justice Beverley
  McLachlin

Officers:
Registrar, Guy Y. Goulard, Q.C.
Deputy Registrar, Anne Roland
Director of Operations, Michael E. Doherty
Asst. Registrar (Process), E.J. Bisson
Chief Law Editor, Vacant
Revisor, R.D. Berberi
Law Editors, A. McDonald, C. Marquis
Chief Librarian, Diane Teeple
Assistant Librarians:
  Civil Law, Adèle Berthiaume
  Common Law, Mary Jane Sinclair
  Technical Services and Systems,
    Rosemary Murray-Lachapelle

THE FEDERAL COURT OF CANADA

Supreme Court Bldg.
Wellington St., Ottawa, ON K1A 0H9

Chief Justice:
The Hon. Frank Iacobucci

Associate Chief Justice:
The Hon. Mr. Justice James A. Jerome

Court of Appeal Judges:
The Hon. Mr. Justice Louis Pratte
The Hon. Mr. Justice Darrel V. Heald
The Hon. Mr. Justice John J. Urie
The Hon. Mr. Justice Patrick M. Mahoney, P.C.
The Hon. Mr. Justice Louis Marceau
The Hon. Mr. Justice James K. Hugessen
The Hon. Mr. Justice Arthur J. Stone
The Hon. Mr. Justice Mark R. MacGuigan
The Hon. Mr. Justice Bertrand Lacombe
The Hon. Madame Justice Alice Desjardins

Trial Division Judges:
The Hon. Mr. Justice Frank U. Collier
The Hon. Mr. Justice George A. Addy
The Hon. Mr. Justice J.E. Dubé, P.C.

The Hon. Mr. Justice Paul U.C. Rouleau
The Hon. Mr. Justice Francis C. Muldoon
The Hon. Mr. Justice Barry L. Strayer
The Hon. Mr. Justice John C. McNair
The Hon. Madame Justice Barbara J. Reed
The Hon. Mr. Justice Pierre Denault
The Hon. Mr. Justice Yvon Pinard
The Hon. Mr. Justice L. Marcel Joyal
The Hon. Mr. Justice J.S.G. Bud Cullen
The Hon. Mr. Justice Leonard A. Martin
The Hon. Mr. Justice Max M. Teitelbaum
The Hon. Mr. Justice William A. MacKay

PROTHONOTARIES
Sr. Prothonotary, Jacques Lefebvre
Assoc. Sr. Prothonotary, Peter A.K. Giles

REGISTRY OF THE COURT
Administrator of the Court, Robert Biljan
Judicial Administrators:
  Appeal Division, Huguette R. Narum
  Trial Division, Pauline C. Bratt
Deputy Administrators:
  Appeal Division, Gerald E. Parlee
  Trial Division, Raymond P. Guenette
  Judicial Information Services,
  William F. Wendt
  Administration, Pierre R. Gaudet
Assistant Administrators:
  Local Offices, Charles E. Stinson
  Personnel, Gordon Wilkins
Clerks of Process, A. Gratton, G. McNulty,
  D. Cousineau, J.A.L. Lamothe, P. Scott,
  G. Bureau

DISTRICT ADMINISTRATORS

Calgary, Dan J. Buell
Charlottetown, George E. MacMillan
Edmonton, R.O.J. Splane
Fredericton, A.M. DiGiacinto
Halifax, François Pilon
Montreal, Monique Giroux
Quebec City, Mireille Bonin
Regina, F.C. Newis
Saint John, Vacant
St. John's, Henry J. Thorne
Saskatoon, Dennis Berezowski
Toronto, John E. Clegg
Vancouver, Vacant
Whitehorse, William R. Williamson
Winnipeg, Gregory M. Smith
Yellowknife, James R. Posynick

COURT MARTIAL APPEAL COURT OF CANADA

Supreme Court Bldg.
Wellington St., Ottawa, ON K1A 0H9

Chief Justice:
The Hon. Mr. Justice Patrick M. Mahoney, P.C.
  Federal Court of Canada (Court of Appeal)

Judges:

The Hon. Louis Pratte
   Federal Court of Canada (Court of Appeal)
The Hon. Darrel V. Heald
   Federal Court of Canada (Court of Appeal)
The Hon. Frank U. Collier
   Federal Court of Canada (Trial Division)
The Hon. David M. Dickson
   Supreme Court of New Brunswick
   (Queen's Bench Division)
The Hon. Gordon C. Hall
   Manitoba Court of Appeal
The Hon. Gordon L.S. Hart
   Supreme Court of Nova Scotia
   (Appeal Division)
The Hon. William R. Sinclair
   Supreme Court of Alberta (Trial Division)
The Hon. John J. Urie
   Federal Court of Canada (Court of Appeal)
The Hon. George A. Addy
   Federal Court of Canada (Trial Division)
The Hon. Alphonse Barbeau
   Superior Court of Quebec (Montreal District)
The Hon. James K. Hugessen
   Federal Court of Canada (Court of Appeal)
The Hon. Yves Forest
   Superior Court of Quebec (Montreal District)
The Hon. Jean-Eudes Dubé, P.C.
   Federal Court of Canada (Trial Division)
The Hon. Louis Marceau
   Federal Court of Canada (Court of Appeal)
The Hon. Benjamin Hewak
   Court of Queen's Bench for Manitoba
The Hon. Alexander M. MacIntosh
   Supreme Court of Nova Scotia
   (Trial Division)
The Hon. William J. Trainor
   Supreme Court of B.C. (Trial Division)
The Hon. Robert C. Rutherford
   Supreme Court of Ontario
   (High Court of Justice)
The Hon. Charles C. Locke
   Court of Appeal for B.C.
The Hon. Lloyd G. McKenzie
   Supreme Court of B.C. (Trial Division)
The Hon. Hugh P. Legg
   Supreme Court of B.C. (Trial Division)
The Hon. James A. Jerome, P.C.
   Assoc. Chief Justice,
   Federal Court of Canada
The Hon. Lawrence A. Poitras
   Superior Court of Quebec (Montreal District)
The Hon. John Watson Brooke
   Supreme Court of Ontario (Court of Appeal)
The Hon. James Creighton Cavanagh
   Court of Queen's Bench of Alberta
The Hon. N.H.A. Goodridge
   Supreme Court of Newfoundland
   (Trial Division)
The Hon. Jacques Vaillancourt
   Superior Court of Quebec
The Hon. D. Gordon Blair
   Supreme Court of Ontario (Court of Appeal)
The Hon. François Chevalier
   Superior Court of Quebec (Montreal District)
The Hon. Mary J. Batten

Court of Queen's Bench for Saskatchewan
The Hon. Frederick A. Large
   Supreme Court of Prince Edward Island
The Hon. Louis-Philippe Landry
   Superior Court of Quebec (Montreal District)
The Hon. Paul U.C. Rouleau
   Federal Court of Canada (Trial Division)
The Hon. John C. McNair
   Federal Court of Canada (Trial Division)
The Hon. Francis C. Muldoon
   Federal Court of Canada (Trial Division)
The Hon. Edward C. Malone
   Court of Queen's Bench for Saskatchewan
The Hon. Arthur J. Stone
   Federal Court of Canada (Court of Appeal)
The Hon. Barry L. Strayer
   Federal Court of Canada (Trial Division)
The Hon. Barbara J. Reed
   Federal Court of Canada (Trial Division)
The Hon. Yvon Pinard, P.C.
   Federal Court of Canada (Trial Division)
The Hon. Joseph H. Potts
   Supreme Court of Ontario (Court of Appeal)
The Hon. J.S.G. Bud Cullen, P.C.
   Federal Court of Canada (Trial Division)
The Hon. L. Marcel Joyal
   Federal Court of Canada (Trial Division)
The Hon. Pierre Denault
   Federal Court of Canada (Trial Division)
The Hon. Mark R. MacGuigan
   Federal Court of Canada (Court of Appeal)
The Hon. Allyre Louis Sirois
   Court of Queen's Bench for Saskatchewan
The Hon. Bertrand Lacombe
   Federal Court of Canada (Court of Appeal)
The Hon. Leonard A. Martin
   Federal Court of Canada (Trial Divison)
The Hon. Max M. Teitelbaum
   Federal Court of Canada (Trial Division)
The Hon. Frank Iacobucci
   Chief Justice, Federal Court of Canada
The Hon. William Andrew MacKay
   Federal Court of Canada (Trial Division)
The Hon. Alice Desjardins
   Federal Court of Canada (Appeal Division)

REGISTRY OF THE COURT
Judicial Administrator, Joan Bond
Administrator of the Court, Robert Biljan
Assistant Administrator, Gerald E. Parlee
Clerk of Process, G. Bureau

TAX COURT OF CANADA

Centennial Towers, 200 Kent St.
Ottawa, ON K1A 0M1

Chief Judge:
The Hon. J.-C. Couture

Associate Chief Judge:
The Hon. D.H. Christie

Judges:
The Hon. Roland St-Onge
The Hon. Guy Tremblay

The Hon. Delmer E. Taylor
The Hon. M.J. Bonner
The Hon. J.B. Goetz
The Hon. A.A. Sarchuk
The Hon. G.J. Rip
The Hon. J.A. Brulé
The Hon. W. Kempo
The Hon. A. Garon

The Hon. G. Teskey
The Hon. M.A. Morgan
The Hon. L. Lamarre Proulx

Officers:
Registrar, Eric M. Germain
Deputy Registrars:
    M.L. Artelle, J.D.C. Létang

CANADIAN DIPLOMATIC AND TRADE REPRESENTATIVES ABROAD

Country	Representative	Address
Albania	Ambassador: Terence C. Bacon First Secretary (Commercial): C.R. Larabie	c/o The Canadian Embassy Kneza Milosa 75 11000 Belgrade, Yugoslavia
Algeria	Ambassador: Gilles Mathieu Counsellor (Commercial): R. Turcotte	27 Bis, rue d'Anjou, Hydra *Postal address:* Box 225 Gare Alger, Algiers
Angola	Ambassador: Roger A. Bull Counsellor (Development): D.A. McMaster	c/o The Canadian High Commission Box 1430, Harare, Zimbabwe
Antigua and Barbuda	High Commissioner: Arthur Wright Counsellor (Commercial): K.G. Whiting	c/o The Canadian High Commission Box 404, Bridgetown, Barbados
Argentina	Ambassador: Clayton G. Bullis Counsellor (Commercial and Economic): D. Thibault	Suipacha 1111, Brunetta Bldg., 25th Flr. Suipacha and Santa Fé, Buenos Aires *Postal address:* Casilla de Correo 1598 Buenos Aires
Australia	High Commissioner: R. Allen Kilpatrick Counsellor (Commercial): B.E. Baker Consul General: G.B. Rush Consul General: Roger B. Blake Honorary Consul: J. Lyall	Commonwealth Ave. Canberra A.C.T. 2600 1 Collins St., 6th Flr. Melbourne, Victoria 3000 A.M.P. Centre, 8th Flr., 50 Bridge St. Sydney N.S.W. 2000 St. Martin's Tower, 19th Flr. 44 St. George Terrace, Perth Western Australia 6000
Austria	Ambassador: Michael Shenstone Counsellor (Commercial): A. Sulzenko	Dr. Karl Lueger Ring 10 A-1010 Vienna
Bahamas, The	High Commissioner: Kathryn E. McCallion Counsellor: M.P. Whalen	c/o The Canadian High Commission Box 1500, Kingston 10, Jamaica
Bahrain	Ambassador: Lawrence T. Dickenson Counsellor (Commercial): R.P.W. Mason	c/o The Canadian Embassy Box 25281, 13113 (Safat), Kuwait City, Kuwait
Bangladesh	High Commissioner: Emile Gauvreau	House CWN 16/A, Road 48, Gulshan, Dhaka *Postal address:* G.P.O. Box 569, Dhaka
Barbados	High Commissioner: Arthur Wright Counsellor (Commercial): K.G. Whiting	The Canadian High Commission Bishops Court Hill, St. Michael *Postal address:* Box 404, Bridgetown
Belgium	Ambassador: Jacques Asselin Counsellor (Economic and Commercial): J.D. Welsh	2, av. de Tervuren, 1040 Brussels

Country	Representative	Address
Belize	High Commissioner: Kathryn E. McCallion Honorary Consul: G. David	c/o The Canadian High Commission Box 1500, Kingston 10, Jamaica 5325 A St., Belize City
Benin, People's Republic of	Ambassador: Sandelle D. Scrimshaw First Secretary (Commercial): S. Cartwright	c/o The Canadian High Commission Box 1639, Accra, Ghana
Bermuda	Commissioner: Vacant Counsellor: R.A. Nauman	c/o Canadian Consulate General 1251 Ave. of the Americas New York, NY 10020, U.S.A.
Bolivia	Ambassador: M. Anna Charles Counsellor (Commercial) and Consul: G.W. Wood Honorary Consul: Barbara Canedo Patino	c/o The Canadian Embassy Casilla 1212, Lima, Peru 2342 Av. Arce, La Paz
Botswana	High Commissioner: Roger A. Bull Counsellor (Commercial): R.D.P. Lee	c/o The Canadian High Commission Box 1430, Harare, Zimbabwe
Brazil	Ambassador: John P. Bell Counsellor (Commercial/Economic): J.M. Roy	Av. das Nacoes, Number 16 Setor das Embaixadas Sul., Brasilia Postal address: Caixa Postal 07-0961 70.410 Brasilia D.F.
	Consul General: N.J.L. Villeneuve	Edificio Top Centre, 5th Flr. Av. Paulista 854, Sao Paolo Postal address: Caixa Postal 22002 Sao Paulo
	Honorary Consul: F.C. Williams	Rua Dom Gerardo 35, Terceiro Andar Centro CEP 20.090, Rio de Janeiro
Britain	High Commissioner: The Hon. Donald Macdonald Minister (Commercial/Economic): R.J.L. Berlet Honorary Consul: D.J. McKichan	Macdonald House 1 Grosvenor Square London, W1X 0AB, England c/o MacLay, Murray and Spens, Solicitors 151 St. Vincent St. Glasgow, G2 5NJ, Scotland
Brunei	High Commissioner: Manfred G. von Nostitz Counsellor (Commercial): D. Comeau	c/o The Canadian High Commission Box 845, Singapore 9016, Rep. of Singapore
Bulgaria	Ambassador: Terence C. Bacon First Secretary (Commercial): C.R. Larabie	c/o The Canadian Embassy Kneza Milosa 75 11000 Belgrade, Yugoslavia
Burkina Faso	Ambassador: Jean-Guy Saint-Martin First Secretary (Commercial): L.R. Ledoux Honorary Consul: M. Leblanc	c/o The Canadian Embassy 01 Box 4104, Abidjan 01, Ivory Coast Box 548, Ouagadougou
Burma	Ambassador: Emile Gauvreau Counsellor (Commercial): R. Vanderloo	c/o The Canadian High Commission G.P.O. Box 569, Dhaka, Bangladesh
Burundi	Ambassador: Colleen L. Cupples Counsellor (Development): D.B. Marantz Honorary Consul: Jacques M.A. Persoons	c/o The Canadian Embassy Box 8341, Kinshasa, Zaire Siruco S.A.R.L., Box 5, Bujumbura
Cameroon	Ambassador: André S. Simard First Secretary (Commercial): J.Y. Dionne Honorary Consul: Georges E. Mareine	Immeuble Stamatiades Place de l'Hôtel de Ville, Yaoundé Postal address: Box 572, Yaoundé Bata S.A. Camerounaise, Box 1348, Douala
Cape Verde	Ambassador: Jean-Paul Hubert	c/o The Canadian Embassy Box 3373, Dakar, Senegal

Country	Representative	Address
Central African Republic	Ambassador: André S. Simard First Secretary (Commercial): J.Y. Dionne	c/o The Canadian Embassy Box 572, Yaoundé, Cameroon
Chad	Ambassador: André S. Simard First Secretary (Commercial): J.Y. Dionne	c/o The Canadian Embassy Box 572, Yaoundé, Cameroon
Chile	Ambassador: Michel de Goumois Counsellor (Commercial): R. Goulet	Ahumada 11, 10th Flr., Santiago *Postal address:* Casilla 427, Santiago
China, People's Republic of	Ambassador: Earl G. Drake Minister (Commercial): M.J. Hladik Consul General: Norman H. Mailhot	10 San Li Tun Rd. Chao Yang District, Beijing Union Bldg., 4th Flr. 100, Yan'an Rd. (East), Shanghai
Colombia	Ambassador: Gaétan Lavertu Counsellor (Commercial): J.E. Graham	Calle 76, No. 11-52, Bogota *Postal address:* Apartado Aereo 53531 Bogota 2
Comoros	Ambassador: A. Raynell Andreychuk Counsellor (Commercial): A.L. Lyons	c/o The Canadian High Commission Box 30481, Nairobi, Kenya
Congo	Ambassador: Colleen L. Cupples Counsellor (Development): D.B. Marantz	c/o The Canadian Embassy Box 8341, Kinshasa, Zaire
Costa Rica	Ambassador: Stanley E. Gooch Counsellor (Commercial) and Consul: H.H. McNairnay	Cronos Bldg., 6th Flr. Calle 3 y Av. Central, San José *Postal address:* Apartado Postal 10303 San José
Cuba	Ambassador: Michael F. Kergin Counsellor (Commercial) and Consul: J.M.B. White	Calle 30 No. 518 Esquina a7a Miramar, Havana
Cyprus	High Commissioner: James K. Bartleman Counsellor (Commercial): J.H. Lang Honorary Consul: Michael G. Ioannides	c/o The Canadian Embassy Box 6410, Tel Aviv 61063, Israel Margarita House, Ste. 403 15 Themistocles Dervis St., Nicosia *Postal Address:* Box 2125, Nicosia
Czechoslovakia	Ambassador: Barry M. Mawhinney Counsellor (Commercial): R.B. Johnson	Mickiewiczova 6 Prague 6
Denmark	Ambassador: Dorothy J. Armstrong Counsellor (Commercial): K.A. Hewlett-Jobes Honorary Consul: Polv Brandt	Kr. Bernikowsgade 1 1105 Copenhagen K 427 Aqqusinersuaq, Nuuk *Postal address:* Magasinet APS Box 22, 3900 Nuuk
Djibouti	Ambassador: Vacant	c/o The Canadian Embassy Box 1130, Addis Ababa, Ethiopia
Dominica	High Commissioner: Arthur Wright Counsellor (Commercial): K.G. Whiting	c/o The Canadian High Commission Box 404, Bridgetown, Barbados
Dominican Republic	Ambassador: John W. Graham Counsellor (Commercial) and Consul: D.G. Adam Honorary Consul: José A. Brache	c/o The Canadian Embassy Apartado 62302, Caracas 1060A, Venezuela Mahatma Gandhi 200 Corner Juan Sanchez Ramirez Santo Domingo 1
Egypt	Ambassador: Marc A. Brault Counsellor (Commercial) and Consul: G.L. Shannon	6 Mohamed Fahmi El Sayed St. Garden City, Cairo *Postal address:* Box 2646, Cairo

Country	Representative	Address
El Salvador	Ambassador: Stanley E. Gooch Counsellor (Commercial) and Consul: H.H. McNairnay	c/o The Canadian Embassy Apartado Postal 10303 San José, Costa Rica
Ecuador	Ambassador: Gaétan Lavertu Counsellor (Commercial): J.E. Graham Honorary Consul: F.J. Costa Echeverria Honorary Consul: G. Vorbeck	c/o The Canadian Embassy Apartado Aereo 53531 Bogota 2, Columbia Edificio Torres de la Merced Oficina 11—Piso 4, General Cordova 800 y Victor Manuel Redon, Guayaquil Edifice Josueth Gonzalez, Av. Diciembre 2816 y James Orton, Quito
Equatorial Guinea	Ambassador: Jean Nadeau	c/o The Canadian Embassy Box 4037, Libreville, Gabon
Ethiopia	Ambassador: Vacant	African Solidarity Insurance Bldg., 6th Flr. Churchill Ave., Addis Ababa *Postal address:* Box 1130, Addis Ababa
European Communities	Head of Mission, Ambassador: Daniel Molgat Minister-Counsellor: T.A. MacDonald	c/o The Canadian Embassy 2, av. de Tervuren, 1040 Brussels Belgium
Fiji	High Commissioner: A. Douglas Small Counsellor (Commercial): J.R. Brocklebank Honorary Consul: M. Waters	c/o The Canadian High Commission Box 12-049, Thorndon Wellington, New Zealand Canadian Airlines International 50 Thompson St., Suva
Finland	Ambassador: Mary Vandenhoff Counsellor (Commercial) and Consul: C.C. Charland	P. Esplanadi 25B, 00100 Helsinki 10 *Postal Address:* Box 779, 00101 Helsinki 10
France	Ambassador: Claude T. Charland Minister-Counsellor (Commercial): R. Frenette Consul: B. Desjardins Honorary Consul: J.-P. Andrieux Honorary Consul: Jean-Jacques Hetzel	35, av. Montaigne, 75008 Paris VIIIe Édifice Bonnel, Par-Dieu 74, rue de Bonnet, 3e étage 69003 Lyon Place du Général de Gaulle Box 297, Saint-Pierre Saint-Pierre-et-Miquelon c/o Polysar France, rue du Ried F-67610, La Wantzenau, Strasbourg
Gabon	Ambassador: Jean Nadeau	Box 4037, Libreville
Gambia, The	High Commissioner: Jean-Paul Hubert	c/o The Canadian Embassy Box 3373, Dakar, Senegal
German Democratic Republic	Ambassador: Eric Bergbusch Counsellor (Commercial) and Consul: D.H. Leavitt	c/o The Canadian Embassy Ulica Matejki 1/5, Warsaw 00-481, Poland
Germany, Federal Republic of	Ambassador: W.T. Delworth Minister-Counsellor (Commercial/ Economic): D. Vanbeselaere Head of Mission: W.T. Delworth Consul General: Denis S.M. Baker Honorary Consul: W. Woitas Consul General: George E.B. Blackstock	Friedrich Wilhelm Strasse 18 5300 Bonn 1 Canadian Military Mission and Consulate Europa-Center, 1000 Berlin 30 Immermann HOF, Immermannstrasse 65D *Postal address:* Box 4729, 4000 Dusseldorf 1 Europa Carton AG, Spitalerstrasse II 2000 Hamburg Maximiliansplatz 9 8000 Munich 2
Ghana	High Commissioner: Sandelle D. Scrimshaw Counsellor: H.P.G. Fraser	42 Independence Ave., Accra *Postal address:* Box 1639, Accra
Greece	Ambassador: André Couvrette Counsellor (Commercial): S.B. McDowall	4 Ioannou Gennadiou St. Athens 115 21
Grenada	High Commissioner: Arthur Wright Counsellor (Commercial): K.G. Whiting	c/o The Canadian High Commission Box 404, Bridgetown, Barbados

Country	Representative	Address
Guatemala	Ambassador: Vacant Chargé d'Affaires a.i. and Consul: Dilys Buckley-Jones	Galerias Espana, 6th Flr. 7 Av. 11-59, Zona 9, Guatemala City Postal address: Box 400, Guatemala, C.A.
Guinea	Ambassador: Jean-Paul Hubert Chargé d'Affaires, a.i. and Consul: Vacant	Box 99, Conakry
Guinea-Bissau	Ambassador: Jean-Paul Hubert	c/o The Canadian Embassy, Box 3373 Dakar, Senegal
Guyana	High Commissioner: Frank T. Jackman Counsellor (Commercial): J.B.W. Motta	High and Young Streets, Georgetown Postal address: Box 10880, Georgetown
Haiti	Ambassador: Pierre Giguère Counsellor (Commercial): C.A. Carruthers	Édifice Banque Nova Scotia Route de Delmas, Port-au-Prince Postal address: C.P. 826, Port-au-Prince
Holy See	Ambassador: E. Pattyson Black	Via della Conciliazione 4/D 00193 Rome, Italy
Honduras	Ambassador: Stanley E. Gooch Counsellor (Commercial) and Consul: H.H. McNairnay	c/o The Canadian Embassy Apartado Postal 10303 San José, Costa Rica
Hong Kong	Commissioner: Anne Marie Doyle Counsellor (Commercial): H.W.R. Guy	Office of the Commission for Canada 11th-14th Flrs, One Exchange Square 8 Connaught Place Postal address: G.P.O. Box 11142
Hungary	Ambassador: Derek R.T. Fraser Counsellor (Commercial) and Consul: H.J. Himmelsbach	Budakeszi, ut. 32, 1021 Budapest
Iceland	Ambassador: R.H. Graham Mitchell Counsellor (Commercial) and Consul: M.L. MacDonald Honorary Consul General: Jon H. Bergs	c/o The Canadian Embassy Oscar's Gate 20, 0352 Oslo 3, Norway Sudurlandsbraut 10, 108 Reykjavik Postal address: Box 8094, 128 Reykjavik
India	High Commissioner: James G. Harris Counsellor (Commercial): R.R.M. Logie Consul: J.P. MacArthur	7/8 Shantipath, Chanakyapuri New Delhi 110021 Postal address: Box 5207, New Delhi Hotel Oberoi Towers, Ste. 2401 Nariman Point, Bombay 400 021
Indonesia	Ambassador: Jack A. Whittleton Counsellor (Commercial) and Consul: D.I. Campbell	5th Floor WISMA Metropolitan Jalan Jendral Sudirman, Jakarta Postal address: Box 52/JKT, Jakarta
Iran	Chargé d'Affaires, a.i.: S. Mullin	57 Shahid-Sarafraz St. Ostad-Motahari Ave., Teheran Postal address: Box 11365-4647, Teheran
Iraq	Ambassador: David Karsgaard Counsellor (Commercial) and Consul: T.D. Greenwood	Hay Al-Mansour, Mahalla 609 Street 1, House 33, Baghdad Postal address: Box 323 Central Post Office, Baghdad
Ireland	Ambassador: Dennis McDermott Counsellor (Commercial): G. Morin	65 St. Stephen's Green Dublin 2
Israel	Ambassador: James K. Bartleman Counsellor (Commercial): J.H. Lang	220, Rehov Hayarkon, Tel Aviv 63405 Postal address: Box 6410 Tel Aviv 61063
Italy	Ambassador: Alan Sullivan Minister-Counsellor (Economic/ Commercial): A.D. McArthur Consul General: M.-A. Beauchemin	Via G.B. de Rossi 27 00161 Rome Via Vittor Pisani 19, 20124 Milan
Ivory Coast	Ambassador: Jean-Guy Saint-Martin Counsellor and Consul: S. Marcoux	Immeuble Trade Center 23, av. Nogues, Le Plateau Postal address: 01 C.P. 4104 Abidjan 01
Jamaica	High Commissioner: Kathryn E. McCallion Counsellor (Development): R. Beadle	Royal Bank Bldg. 30-36 Knutsford Blvd., Kingston 5 Postal address: Box 1500, Kingston 10

Country	Representative	Address
Japan	Ambassador: Barry C. Steers Minister (Economic/Commercial): D.J.S. Winfield Consul General: Michael C. Spencer	3-38 Akasaka 7-chome Minato-ku, Tokyo 107 Box 150, Osaka, Minami 542-91
Jordan	Ambassador: Michael D. Bell First Secretary (Commercial) and Consul: G.E. Rishchynski	Pearl of Shmeisani Bldg. SH Shmeisani, Amman
Kenya	High Commissioner: A. Raynell Andreychuk Counsellor (Commercial): A.L. Lyons	Comcraft House Hailé Sélassie Ave., Nairobi Postal address: Box 30481, Nairobi
Kiribati, Republic of	High Commissioner: A. Douglas Small	c/o The Canadian High Commission Box 12-049, Thorndon, Wellington, New Zealand
Korea	Ambassador: Brian W. Schumacher Minister-Counsellor (Commercial) and Consul: R.C. Mann	Kolon Bldg., 10th Flr. 45 Mugyo-Dong, Jung-Ku, Seoul 100-170 Postal address: Box 6299, Seoul 100-662
Kuwait	Ambassador: Lawrence T. Dickenson Counsellor (Commercial) and Consul: R.P.W. Mason	28 Quaraish St., Nuzha District, Kuwait City Postal address: Box 25281 13113 (Safat) Kuwait City
Laos	Ambassador: Lawrence A.H. Smith Counsellor (Commercial) and Consul: R. Vanderloo	c/o The Canadian Embassy Box 2090, Bangkok 10500, Thailand
Lebanon	Ambassador: Vacant Chargé d'Affaires, a.i.: H.E. Sarafian	c/o The Canadian Embassy Box 3394, Damascus, Syria
Lesotho	High Commissioner: Ronald S. MacLean	c/o The Canadian Embassy, Box 26006 Arcadia, Pretoria 0007, South Africa
Liberia	Ambassador: Sandelle D. Scrimshaw Counsellor (Commercial): L.R. Ledoux	c/o The Canadian High Commission Box 1639, Accra, Ghana
Libya	Ambassador: Alan Sullivan Minister-Counsellor (Commercial): A.D. McArthur	c/o The Canadian Embassy Via G.B. de Rossi 27, 00161 Rome, Italy
Luxembourg	Ambassador: Jacques Asselin Counsellor (Commercial/ Economic): J.D. Welsh Honorary Consul: William J. Bannerman	c/o The Canadian Embassy 2, av. de Tervuren, 1040 Brussels, Belgium c/o Price Waterhouse, 20, av. Pasteur 2310 Luxembourg
Macao	Consul General: Anne Marie Doyle Consul (Commercial): H.R.W. Guy	c/o Office of the Commission for Canada Box 20264 Hennessy Road P.O., Hong Kong
Madagascar	Ambassador: J. David L. Rose Counsellor (Commercial): A.L. Lyons	c/o The Canadian High Commission Box 1022, Dar-es-Salaam, Tanzania
Malawi	High Commissioner: David C. Reese Counsellor (Commercial): R.D.P. Lee	c/o The Canadian High Commission Box 31313, Lusaka, Zambia
Malaysia	High Commissioner: Garrett Lambert Counsellor (Commercial): M. Romoff	7th Floor, Plaza MBF, 172 Jalan Ampang 50540 Kuala Lumpur Postal address: Box 10990 50732 Kuala Lumpur
Maldives	Ambassador: Carolyn McAskie Counsellor (Commercial): C.S. Russel	c/o The Canadian High Commission Box 1006, Colombo, Sri Lanka
Mali	Ambassador: J.-G. Saint-Martin Counsellor (Commercial): L.R. Ledoux	Box 198, Bamako
Malta	High Commissioner: Alan Sullivan Minister-Counsellor (Economic/ Commercial): A.D. McArthur Honorary Consul: J.M. Demajo	c/o The Canadian Embassy Via G.B. de Rossi 27, 00161 Rome, Italy Demajo House, 103 Archbishop St., Valleta
Mauritania	Ambassador: Jean-Paul Hubert Counsellor (Development): R. Couture	c/o The Canadian Embassy Box 3373, Dakar, Senegal

Country	Representative	Address
Mauritius	High Commissioner: J. David L. Rose Counsellor (Commercial): A.L. Lyons Honorary Commercial Representative: I. Birger	c/o The Canadian High Commission Box 1022, Dar-es-Salaam, Tanzania Port Louis
Mexico	Ambassador: Vacant Minister-Counsellor (Commercial/Economic): J.D. Leach Honorary Consul: Diane McLean de Huerta	Calle Schiller no. 529, (Rincon del Bosque) Colonia Polanco, 11560 Mexico, D.F. *Postal address:* Apartado Postal 105-05 11580 Mexico, D.F. Hotel Club Del Sol, Mezzanine Flr. Costera Miguel Aleman, Acapulco *Postal address:* Apartado Postal 691 Acapulco, Gro.
	Honorary Consul: Allan C. Rose, Q.C. Honorary Consul: Norbert J. Gibson	Hotel Fiesta Americana, Local 30 Aurelio Aceves 225, Guadalajara, Jalisco Av. Albatros 52(705), Mazatlan *Postal address:* Apartado Postal 614 82110 Mazatlan, Sin.
	Honorary Consul: Margaret Loggie de Fernandez	Calle 62, No. 309 Dx, Av. Colon, Depto 9 97070 Merida, Yucatan *Postal address:* Apartado Postal 101-D 97100 Merida, Yucatan
	Honorary Consul: Roberto Encinas	German Gedovius 5-201, Condominio del Parque Desarrollo Urbano Rio Tijuana 22320 Tijuana, Baja California Norte
Monaco	Honorary Consul: N. Caralopoulos	Le Continental, Bloc C, Place des Moulins 98000 Monte Carlo
Mongolia	Ambassador: Vernon G. Turner Minister-Counsellor (Commercial): D.E.F. Taylor	c/o The Canadian Embassy 23 Starokonyushenny Pereulok Moscow, U.S.S.R.
Morocco	Ambassador: Wilfrid-Guy Licari Counsellor (Commercial): J. Broadbent	13, Bis, Rue Jaafar As-Sadik, Rabat-Agdal *Postal address:* C.P. 709, Rabat-Agdal
Mozambique	Ambassador: Roger A. Bull Counsellor (Commercial) and Consul: R.D.P. Lee	c/o The Canadian High Commission Box 1430, Harare, Zimbabwe
Nepal	Ambassador: James G. Harris Counsellor (Commercial): R.R.M. Logie	c/o The Canadian High Commission Box 5207, New Delhi, India
Netherlands	Ambassador: Jacques Gignac Minister-Counsellor (Commercial): C.W. Ross Honorary Consul: Allan G. Blake	Sophialaan 7 EG The Hague c/o Maduro and Curiels Bank, N.V. Plaza JoJo Correa 2-4, Willemstad Curaçao, Netherlands Antilles
New Zealand	High Commissioner: A. Douglas Small Counsellor (Commercial): J.R. Brocklebank Consul: D.R. Pennick	I.C.I. Bldg., Molesworth St., Wellington *Postal address:* Box 12-049, Thorndon Wellington Box 6186, Wellesley St. P.O., Auckland
Nicaragua	Ambassador: Stanley E. Gooch Counsellor (Commercial) and Consul: H.H. McNairnay	c/o The Canadian Embassy Apartado Postal 10303 San José, Costa Rica
Niger	Ambassador: J.-G. Saint-Martin Counsellor (Commercial): L.R. Ledoux	Sonara II Bldg Av. du Premier Pont, Niamey *Postal address:* Box 362, Niamey
Nigeria	High Commissioner: Robert L. Elliot First Secretary (Commercial): S. Cartwright	Committee of Vice-Chancellors Bldg. Plot 8A, 4 Idowu-Taylor St., Victoria Island, Lagos *Postal address:* Box 54506, Ikoyi Station, Lagos
Norway	Ambassador: R.H. Graham Mitchell Counsellor (Commercial) and Consul: M.L. MacDonald	Oscar's Gate 20, Oslo 3 *Postal address:* Oscar's Gate 20 0352 Oslo
Oman	Ambassador: Lawrence T. Dickenson Counsellor (Commercial) and Consul: R.P.W. Mason Honorary Consul: Housang Dan Danesh	c/o The Canadian Embassy Box 25281, 13113 (Safat) Kuwait City, Kuwait Box 443, Muscat

Country	Representative	Address
Pakistan	Ambassador: Manfred von Nostitz Counsellor: J.A. Junke Honorary Consul: Byram Avari	Diplomatic Enclave, Sector G-5, Islamabad *Postal address:* G.P.O. Box 1042, Islamabad c/o Beach Luxury Hotel Tamizuddin Khan Rd., Ste. 336, Karachi 0227
Panama	Ambassador: Stanley E. Gooch Counsellor (Commercial) and Consul: H.H. McNairnay Honorary Consul: Ruth L. de Denton	c/o The Canadian Embassy Apartado Postal 10303, San José, Costa Rica Apartado Postal 3658, Balboa, Panama City
Papua New Guinea	High Commissioner: R. Allen Kilpatrick Counsellor (Commercial): M. Vujnovich Honorary Commercial Representative: J. Cruikshank	c/o The Canadian High Commission Commonwealth Ave., Canberra A.C.T. 2600 Australia c/o Piacc, Box 1621, Port Moresby
Paraguay	Ambassador: Michel de Goumois Counsellor (Commercial): R. Goulet Honorary Consul: B. Wiebe	c/o The Canadian Embassy Casilla 27, Santiago, Chile Sociedad Cooperative, Colonizadora Chortitzer Komitee, Casilla de Correo 883, Asuncion
Peru	Ambassador: M. Anne Charles Counsellor (Commercial) and Consul: G.W. Wood	Federico Gerdes 130 (Antes Calle Libertad), Miraflores, Lima *Postal address:* Casilla 1212, Lima
Philippines	Ambassador: Russell H. Davidson Counsellor (Commercial): D.K. McNamara	Allied Bank Centre, 9th Flr. 6754 Ayala Ave., Makati, Metro Manila *Postal address:* Box 971 Commercial Centre, Makati, Rizal, Manila
Poland	Ambassador: Eric Bergbusch Counsellor (Commercial) and Consul: D.H. Leavitt	Ulica, Matejki 1/5 Warsaw, 00-481
Portugal	Ambassador: Geoffrey F. Bruce Counsellor (Commercial) and Consul: L.A. Bustos	Av. Liberdade 144/56, 4th Flr. 1200 Lisbon
Qatar	Ambassador: Lawrence T. Dickenson Counsellor (Commercial) and Consul: R.P.W. Mason	c/o The Canadian Embassy Box 25281, 13113 (Safat) Kuwait City Kuwait
Romania	Ambassador: Saul Grey Counsellor (Commercial) and Consul: J.N. Grantham	36 Nicolae Iorga, 71118 Bucharest *Postal address:* Box 2966 Post Office No. 22, Bucharest
Rwanda	Ambassador: Colleen L. Cupples First Secretary and Consul: P. Abols	c/o The Canadian Embassy Box 8341, Kinshasa, Zaire
St. Kitts and Nevis	High Commissioner: Arthur Wright Counsellor (Commercial): K.G. Whiting	c/o The Canadian High Commission Box 404, Bridgetown, Barbados
St. Lucia	High Commissioner: Arthur Wright Counsellor (Commercial): K.G. Whiting	c/o The Canadian High Commission Box 404, Bridgetown, Barbados
St. Vincent and the Grenadines	High Commissioner: Arthur Wright Counsellor (Commercial): K.G. Whiting	c/o The Canadian High Commission Box 404, Bridgetown, Barbados
San Marino	Consul: H.S. Sterling	c/o The Canadian Embassy Via G.B. de Rossi 27, 00161 Rome, Italy
Sao Tomé and Principe	Ambassador: Jean Nadeau	c/o The Canadian Embassy Box 4037, Libreville, Gabon
Saudi Arabia	Ambassador: G. Douglas Valentine Minister-Counsellor (Commercial): P.H. Sutherland Honorary Consul: T.Y. Zahid	Diplomatic Quarter, Riyadh *Postal address:* Box 94321, Riyadh 11693 Box 8928, Jeddah
Senegal	Ambassador: Jean-Paul Hubert	45, av. de la République, Dakar *Postal address:* Box 3373, Dakar
Seychelles	High Commissioner: J. David L. Rose Counsellor (Commercial): A.L. Lyons	c/o The Canadian High Commission Box 1022, Dar-es-Salaam, Tanzania
Sierra Leone	High Commissioner: Robert L. Elliot Counsellor (Commercial): L.R. Ledoux	c/o The Canadian High Commission Box 54506, Ikoyi Station, Lagos, Nigeria

Country	Representative	Address
Singapore	High Commissioner: Sean Brady Counsellor (Commercial): D. Comeau	80 Anson Rd., 14th and 15th Flrs IBM Towers, Singapore 0207 *Postal address:* Maxwell Rd. P.O. Box 845, Singapore 9016
Solomon Islands	High Commissioner: R. Allen Kilpatrick	c/o The Canadian High Commission Commonwealth Ave., Canberra, A.C.T. 2600 Australia
Somalia	Ambassador: A. Raynell Andreychuk Counsellor (Commercial): A.L. Lyons	c/o The Canadian High Commission Box 30481, Nairobi, Kenya
South Africa, Republic of	Ambassador: Ronald S. MacLean Counsellor and Consul: J.R. Schram	Nedbank Plaza, 5th Flr., Arcadia, Pretoria, 0083 *Postal address:* Box 26006 Arcadia, Pretoria, 0007
Spain	Ambassador: Julie Loranger Counsellor (Commercial): D.T. Wismer Honorary Consul: P.S. Baugh Honorary Consul: John Schwarzmann Honorary Consul: Julian Garcia Hidalgo	Edificio Goya, Calle Nunez de Balboa 35, Madrid *Postal address:* Apartado 587, 28080 Madrid Via Augusta 125, Atico 3A, Barcelona 08006 Plaza de la Malagueta 3, 29016 Malaga *Postal Address:* Box 99, 29080 Malaga Av. de la Constitucion, 30, 2nd Flr. Seville 41001
Sri Lanka	High Commissioner: Carolyn McAskie Counsellor: M. Temple	6 Gregory's Rd. Cinnamon Gardens, Colombo 7 *Postal address:* Box 1006, Colombo
Sudan	Ambassador: Vacant Counsellor (Commercial) and Consul: G.J. Shannon	c/o The Canadian Embassy Box 1130, Addis Ababa, Ethiopia
Suriname	Ambassador: Frank T. Jackman Counsellor (Commercial): J.B.W. Motta	c/o The Canadian High Commission Box 10880, Georgetown, Guyana
Swaziland	High Commissioner: Ronald S. MacLean Counsellor: J.R. Schram	c/o The Canadian Embassy Box 26006, Arcadia, Pretoria 0007 South Africa
Sweden	Ambassador: Dennis B. Browne Counsellor (Commercial): W.J. Roberts	Tegelbacken 4 (7th Flr.), Stockholm *Postal address:* Box 16129 S-10323 Stockholm 16
Switzerland	Ambassador: Jacques Dupuis Counsellor (Commercial) and Consul: A.G. Virtue	Kirchenfeldstrasse 88, 3005 Berne *Postal address:* Box 3000, Berne 6
Syria	Ambassador: Gary R. Harman Counsellor and Consul: H.E. Sarafian	c/o Sheraton Hotel, Damascus *Postal address:* Box 3394, Damascus
Tanzania	High Commissioner: J. David L. Rose Counsellor (Commercial): A.L. Lyons	Pan Africa Insurance Bldg. Samora Machel Ave., Dar-es-Salaam *Postal address:* Box 1022, Dar-es-Salaam
Thailand	Ambassador: Lawrence A.H. Smith Counsellor (Commercial) and Consul: R. Vanderloo	Boonmitr Bldg., 11th Flr. 138 Silom Rd., Bangkok 10500 *Postal address:* Box 2090, Bangkok 10500
Togo	Ambassador: Sandelle D. Scrimshaw First Secretary (Commercial): S. Cartwright	c/o The Canadian High Commission Box 1639, Accra, Ghana
Tonga	High Commissioner: A. Douglas Small Counsellor (Commercial): J.R. Brocklebank	c/o The Canadian High Commission Box 12-049, Thorndon, Wellington New Zealand
Trinidad and Tobago	High Commissioner: Rodney Irwin Counsellor (Commercial): J.B.W. Motta	Huggins Bldg., 72 South Quay, Port of Spain *Postal address:* Box 1246, Port of Spain
Tunisia	Ambassador: Timothy A. Williams Counsellor (Commercial) and Consul: P. Furesz	3, rue du Sénégal, Place Palestine, Tunis *Postal address:* C.P. 31 Belvédère, Tunis

Country	Representative	Address
Turkey	Ambassador: Terrence B. Sheehan First Secretary (Commercial): R.G. Farrell Honorary Consul: Y. Kireç	Nenehatun Caddesi No. 75 Gaziosmanpasa, Ankara Buyukdere Cad. 107/3 Bengun Han, Gayrettepe, Istanbul
Tuvalu	High Commissioner: A. Douglas Small	c/o The Canadian High Commission Box 12-049, Thorndon, Wellington New Zealand
Uganda	High Commissioner: A. Raynell Andreychuk Counsellor (Commercial): A.L. Lyons	c/o The Canadian High Commission Box 30481, Nairobi, Kenya
Union of Soviet Socialist Republics	Ambassador: Vernon G. Turner Minister-Counsellor (Commercial): D.E.F. Taylor	23 Starokonyushenny Pereulok Moscow
United Arab Emirates	Ambassador: Lawrence T. Dickenson Counsellor (Commercial) and Consul: R.P.W. Mason	c/o The Canadian Embassy, Box 25281 13113 (Safat), Kuwait City, Kuwait
United States of America	Ambassador: Derek H. Burney Minister-Counsellor (Commercial): W.A. Dymond Consul General: Geoffrey Elliot Consul General: Vacant Consul General: G.H. Musgrove Consul General: A.L. Halliday Consul: L.D. Lederman Consul General: Carl E. Rufelds Consul General: Marc Lemieux Consul General: Joan P. Winser Consul General: John D. Blackwood Consul General: Anthony Eyton Consul General: Vacant Consul General: Ian Wood	1746 Massachusetts Ave. N.W. Washington, DC 20036-1985 One CNN Center, South Tower, Ste. 400 Atlanta, GA 30303-2705 3 Copley St., Ste. 400, Boston, MA 02116 1 Marine Midland Centre, Ste. 3550 Buffalo, NY 14203-2884 310 South Michigan Ave., Ste. 1200 Chicago, IL 60604-4295 Illuminating Bldg., 55 Public Square Cleveland, OH 44113-1983 St. Paul Place, Ste. 1700 750 N. St. Paul St., Dallas, TX 75201 660 Renaissance Center, Ste. 1100 Detroit, MI 48243-1704 300 S. Grand Ave., 10th Flr. Los Angeles, CA 90071 Chamber of Commerce Bldg., 701-4th Ave. S. Minneapolis, MN 55415 1251 Avenue of the Americas New York, NY 10020-1175 50 Fremont St., Ste. 200 San Francisco, CA 94105 412 Plaza 600, Seattle, WA 98101-1286
Uruguay	Ambassador: Clayton G. Bullis Counsellor (Commercial and Economic): D. Thibault Honorary Consul: R. Lannes Clinton	c/o The Canadian Embassy Casilla de Correo 1598, Buenos Aires Argentina Juan Carlos Gomez 1348-1, Montevideo
Vanuatu	High Commissioner: R. Allen Kilpatrick Counsellor (Commercial): M. Vujnovich	c/o The Canadian High Commission Commonwealth Ave., Canberra A.C.T. 2600 Australia
Venezuela	Ambassador: John W. Graham Counsellor (Commercial) and Consul: D.G. Adam	Edificio Torre Europa, 7th Flr. Av. Francisco de Miranda Campo Alegre, Caracas *Postal address:* Apartado 62302 Caracas 1060A
Viet Nam	Ambassador: Lawrence A.M. Smith Counsellor (Commercial) and Consul: R. Vanderloo	c/o The Canadian Embassy Box 2090, Bangkok 10500, Thailand
West Indies Associated States and Montserrat	Commissioner: Arthur Wright	c/o The Canadian High Commission Box 404, Bridgetown, Barbados
Western Samoa	High Commissioner: A. Douglas Small Counsellor (Commercial): J.R. Brocklebank	c/o The Canadian High Commission Box 12-049, Thorndon, Wellington New Zealand

Country	Representative	Address
Yemen Arab Republic	Ambassador: G. Douglas Valentine Minister-Counsellor (Commercial): P.H. Sutherland	c/o The Canadian Embassy Box 94321, Riyadh 11693 Saudi Arabia
Yemen, People's Democratic Republic of	Ambassador: G. Douglas Valentine Minister-Counsellor (Commercial): P.H. Sutherland	c/o The Canadian Embassy Box 94321, Riyadh 11693 Saudi Arabia
Yugoslavia	Ambassador: Terence C. Bacon First Secretary (Commercial): C.R. Larabie	Kneza Milosa 75, 11000 Belgrade
Zaire	Ambassador: Colleen L. Cupples First Secretary and Consul: P. Abols	17 Pumbu Ave., Kinshasa *Postal address:* Box 8341, Kinshasa
Zambia	High Commissioner: David C. Reese Counsellor (Commercial): R.D.P. Lee	Barclays Bank, North End Branch Cairo Rd., Lusaka *Postal address:* Box 31313, Lusaka
Zimbabwe	High Commissioner: Roger A. Bull Counsellor (Commercial): R.D.P. Lee	45 Baines Ave., Harare *Postal address:* Box 1430, Harare

FOREIGN AMBASSADORS AND HIGH COMMISSIONERS TO CANADA

(H.E. = His/Her Excellency)

Country	Representative	Embassy Address
Algeria	Ambassador: H.E. Mohammed Ghoualmi	435 Daly Ave., Ottawa, ON K1N 6H3
Antigua and Barbuda	High Commissioner: H.E. Conrad F. Richards	112 Kent St., Ste. 205, Ottawa, ON K1P 5P2
Argentina	Ambassador: H.E. Francisco José Pulit	Royal Bank Center, Ste. 620 90 Sparks St., Ottawa, ON K1P 5B4
Australia	High Commissioner: H.E. Robert Stephen Laurie	50 O'Connor St. Ste. 710 Ottawa, ON K1P 6L2
Austria	Ambassador: H.E. Dr. Hedwig Wolfram	445 Wilbrod St., Ottawa, ON K1N 6M7
Bahamas, The	High Commissioner: H.E. Idris Reid	360 Albert St., Ste. 625, Ottawa, ON K1R 7X7
Bahrain	Ambassador: H.E. Ghazi Mohamed Algosaibi	3502 International Dr. N.W. Washington, DC 20008 U.S.A.
Bangladesh	High Commissioner: H.E. Brig. A.N.M. Nuruzzaman	85 Range Rd., Ste. 402, Ottawa, ON K1N 8J6
Barbados	High Commissioner: H.E. Peter G. Morgan	151 Slater St., Ste. 210, Ottawa, ON K1P 5H3
Belgium	Ambassador: H.E. Jean-François de Liedekerke	85 Range Rd., Ste. 601-604 Ottawa, ON K1N 8J6
Belize	High Commissioner: H.E. Edward Arthur Laing	3400 International Dr. N.W., Ste 2-J Washington, DC 20008 U.S.A.
Benin	Ambassador: H.E. Bernardine do Rego	58 Glebe Ave., Ottawa, ON K1S 2C3
Bolivia	Ambassador: H.E. Luis Pelaez Rioja	77 Metcalfe St., Ste. 608, Ottawa, ON K1P 5L6
Botswana	High Commissioner: H.E. Serara T. Ketlogetswe	Van Ness Centre, Ste. 404 4301 Connecticut Ave. N.W. Washington, DC 20008 U.S.A.
Brazil	Ambassador: H.E. M.A. de Salvo Coimbra	255 Albert St., Ste. 900, Ottawa, ON K1P 6A9
Britain	High Commissioner: H.E. Sir Alan B. Urwick	80 Elgin St., Ottawa, ON K1P 5K7

Country	Representative	Embassy Address
Brunei Darussalam	High Commissioner: H.E. Haji Abdul Latif	866 U.N. Plaza, Ste. 248 New York, NY 10017 U.S.A.
Bulgaria	Ambassador: H.E. Boyko Milkov Tarabanov	325 Stewart St., Ottawa, ON K1N 6K5
Burkina Faso	Ambassador: H.E. Léandre B. Bassolé	48 Range Rd., Ottawa, ON K1N 8J4
Burma	Ambassador: H.E. Thein Aung	The Sandringham Apts., Ste. 902 85 Range Rd., Ottawa, ON K1N 8J6
Burundi	Ambassador: H.E. Julien Nahayo	151 Slater St., Ste. 800, Ottawa, ON K1P 5H3
Cameroon	Ambassador: H.E. Philémon Yunji Yang	170 Clemow Ave., Ottawa, ON K1S 2B4
Cape Verde	Ambassador: H.E. José Luis Fernandes Lopes	3415 Massachusetts Ave. N.W. Washington, DC 20007 U.S.A.
Central African Republic	Ambassador: H.E. Christian Lingama-Toleque	1618-22nd St. N.W. Washington, DC 20008 U.S.A.
Chad	Ambassador: H.E. Mahamat Ali Adoum	2002 R Street N.W. Washington, DC 20006 U.S.A.
Chile	Ambassador: H.E. Jorge Berguno Barnes	151 Slater St., Ste. 605 Ottawa, ON K1P 5H3
China, People's Republic of	Ambassador: H.E. Zhang Wenpu	515 St. Patrick St., Ottawa, ON K1N 5H3
Colombia	Ambassador: H.E. Jaime Vidal Perdomo	150 Kent St., Ste. 404, Ottawa, ON K1P 5P4
Commission of the European Communities	Head of Delegation: H.E. Jacques Lecomte	350 Sparks St., Ste. 1110 Ottawa, ON K1R 7S8
Comoros	Ambassador: H.E. Amini Ali Moumin	336 East 45th St., 2nd Flr. New York, NY 10017 U.S.A.
Congo, The	Ambassador: H.E. Benjamin Bounkoulou	4891 Colorado Ave. N.W. Washington, DC 20011 U.S.A.
Costa Rica	Ambassador: H.E. Dr. Marco Aurelio Guillén	150 Argyle St., Ste. 115 Ottawa, ON K2P 1B7
Côte d'Ivoire	Ambassador: H.E. Gen. Issouf Koné	9 Marlborough Ave., Ottawa, ON K1N 8E6
Cuba	Ambassador: H.E. Bienvenido Garcia Negrin	388 Main St., Ottawa, ON K1S 1E3
Cyprus	High Commissioner: H.E. Andreus J. Jacovides	2211 R Street N.W. Washington, DC 20008 U.S.A.
Czechoslovakia	Ambassador: H.E. Jan Janovic	50 Rideau Terrace, Ottawa, ON K1M 2A1
Denmark	Ambassador: H.E. Bjorn Olsen	85 Range Rd., Ste. 702 Ottawa, ON K1N 8J6
Dominica	(See Organization of Eastern Caribbean States)	
Ecuador	Chargé d'Affaires, a.i.: Dr. Emilio Izquierdo	2535 15th St. S.W. Washington, DC 20009 U.S.A.
Egypt, Arab Republic of	Ambassador: H.E. Mahmoud Kassem	454 Laurier Ave. E. Ottawa, ON K1N 6R3
El Salvador	Ambassador: H.E. Ernesto Rivas-Gallont	150 Kent St., Ste. 302 Ottawa, ON K1P 5P4
Ethiopia	Ambassador: H.E. Tesfaye Tadesse	866 U.N. Plaza, Ste. 560 New York, NY 10017 U.S.A.
Fiji	Ambassador: H.E. Winston Thompson	One U.N. Plaza, 26th Flr. New York, NY 10017 U.S.A.
Finland	Ambassador: H.E. Erkki Maentakanen	55 Metcalfe St., Ste. 850 Ottawa, ON K1P 6L5
France	Ambassador: H.E. Philippe Husson	42 Sussex Dr., Ottawa, ON K1M 2C9
Gabon	Ambassador: H.E. Simon Ombegue	4 Range Rd., Ottawa, ON K1N 8J5

Country	Representative	Embassy Address
Gambia, The	High Commissioner: H.E. Ousman A. Sallah	1030 15th St. N.W., Ste. 720 Washington, DC 20005 U.S.A.
German Democratic Republic	Ambassador: H.E. Heinz Birch	150 Kent St., Ste. 710 Ottawa, ON K1P 5P4
Germany, Federal Republic of	Ambassador: H.E. Wolfgang Behrends	1 Waverley St., Ottawa, ON K2P 0T8
Ghana	High Commissioner: H.E. D.O. Agyekum	85 Range Rd., Ste. 810, Ottawa, ON K1N 8J6
Greece	Ambassador: H.E. Leonidas Mavromichalis	76-80 MacLaren St., Ottawa, ON K2P 0K6
Grenada	(See Organization of Eastern Caribbean States)	
Guatemala	Ambassador: H.E. Federico Adolfo Urruela-Prado	294 Albert St., Ste. 500 Ottawa, ON K1P 6E6
Guinea	Ambassador: H.E. Thomas Curtis	Place de Ville, Tower B, Ste. 208 112 Kent St., Ottawa, ON K1P 5P2
Guinea-Bissau	Ambassador: H.E. Alfredo Lopes Cabral	211 East 43rd St., Ste. 604 New York, NY 10017 U.S.A.
Guyana	High Commissioner: H.E. Gavin Bunston Kennard	151 Slater St., Ste. 309 Ottawa, ON K1P 5H3
Haiti	Ambassador: H.E. Livinston Jean-François	Place de Ville, Tower B, Ste. 1308 112 Kent St., Ottawa, ON K1P 5P2
Holy See	Pro Nuncio: H.E. The Most Reverend Angelo Palmas	724 Manor Ave. Rockcliffe Park, ON K1M 0E3
Honduras	Ambassador: H.E. Juan Ramon Molina Cisneros	151 Slater St., Ste. 300-A Ottawa, ON K1P 5H3
Hungary	Ambassador: H.E. Rezso Banyasz	7 Delaware Ave., Ottawa, ON K2P 0Z2
Iceland	Ambassador: H.E. Ingvi Ingvarsson	2022 Connecticut Ave. N.W. Washington, DC 20008 U.S.A.
India	High Commissioner: H.E. Surbir Jit Singh Chhatwal	10 Springfield Rd., Ottawa, ON K1M 1C9
Indonesia	Ambassador: H.E. Adiwoso Abubakar	287 MacLaren St., Ottawa, ON K2P 0L9
Iran	Chargé d'Affaires, a.i.: Mr. Mohammad Ali Mousavi	411 Roosevelt Ave., 4th Flr. Ottawa, ON K2A 3X9
Iraq	Ambassador: H.E. Hisham Ibrahim Al-Shawi	215 McLeod St., Ottawa, ON K2P 0Z8
Ireland	Chargé d'Affaires, a.i.: Mr. Declan Kelly	170 Metcalfe St., Ottawa, ON K2P 1P3
Israel	Ambassador: H.E. Israël Gur-Arieh	410 Laurier Ave. W., Ste. 601 Ottawa, ON K1R 7T3
Italy	Ambassador: H.E. Valerio B.C. Angelini	275 Slater St., 11th Flr. Ottawa, ON K1P 5H9
Jamaica	High Commissioner: H.E. Herschel Dale Anderson	275 Slater St., Ste. 402 Ottawa, ON K1P 5H9
Japan	Ambassador: H.E. Hiroshi Kitamura	255 Sussex Dr., Ottawa, ON K1N 9E6
Jordan	Ambassador: H.E. Hani Khalifeh	100 Bronson Ave., Ste. 701 Ottawa, ON K1R 6G8
Kenya	High Commissioner: H.E. Peter M. Nyamweya	415 Laurier Ave. E., Ste. 600 Ottawa, ON K1N 6R4
Korea	Ambassador: H.E. Soo Gil Park	151 Slater St., 5th Flr., Ottawa, ON K1P 5H3
Kuwait	Ambassador: H.E. Saud Nasir Al-Sabah	2940 Tilden St. N.W. Washington, DC 20008 U.S.A.
Laos	Chargé d'Affaires, a.i.: Mr. Done Somvorachit	2222 S St. N.W. Washington, DC 20008 U.S.A.
Lebanon	Ambassador: H.E. Makram Abdel Halim Ouaidat	640 Lyon St., Ottawa, ON K1S 3Z5

Country	Representative	Embassy Address
Lesotho	High Commissioner: H.E. Raphael Ramaliehe Kali	202 Clemow Ave., Ottawa, ON K1S 2B4
Liberia	Ambassador: H.E. M. Fonie Delano Fred Sherman	Royal Trust Bldg., Ste. 805 116 Albert St., Ottawa, ON K1P 5G3
Libya	Ambassador: H.E. Dr. Ali A. Treiki	309-315 East 48th St. New York, NY 10017 U.S.A.
Luxembourg	Ambassador: H.E. André Philippe	2200 Massachusetts Ave. N.W. Washington, DC 20008 U.S.A.
Madagascar	Ambassador: H.E. Blaise Rabetafika	801 Second Ave., Ste. 404 New York, NY 10017 U.S.A.
Malawi	High Commissioner: H.E. M.W. Machinjili	7 Clemow Ave., Ottawa, ON K1S 2A9
Malaysia	High Commissioner: H.E. Tan S.D. Thomas Jayasuriya	60 Boteler St., Ottawa, ON K1N 8Y7
Mali	Ambassador: H.E. Sadibou Koné	50 Goulburn Ave., Ottawa, ON K1N 8C8
Malta	High Commissioner: H.E. Salv J. Stellini	2017 Connecticut Ave. N.W. Washington, DC 20008 U.S.A.
Mauritania	Ambassador: H.E. Mohamed Mahjoub Ould Boye	9 East 77th St. New York, NY 10021 U.S.A.
Mauritius	High Commissioner: H.E. Chitamansing Jesseramsing	Van Ness Centre, Ste. 134 4301 Connecticut Ave. N.W. Washington, DC 20008 U.S.A.
Mexico	Ambassador: H.E. Emilio Carrillo-Bamboa	130 Albert St., Ste. 206 Ottawa, ON K1P 5G4
Mongolia	Ambassador: H.E. Gendengiin Nyamdo	6 East 77th St. New York, NY 10021 U.S.A.
Montserrat	(See Organization of Eastern Caribbean States)	
Morocco	Ambassador: H.E. Maati Jorio	38 Range Rd., Ottawa, ON K1N 8J4
Mozambique	Ambassador: H.E. Valeriano Ferrao	1990 M St. N.W., Ste. 570 Washington, DC 20036 U.S.A.
Nepal	Chargé d'Affaires, a.i.: Mr. Singha Bahadur Basnyat	2131 Leroy Place N.W. Washington, DC 20008 U.S.A.
Netherlands, The	Ambassador: H.E. Jan Frederick Evert Breman	275 Slater St., 3rd Flr. Ottawa, ON K1P 5H9
New Zealand	High Commissioner: H.E. Bruce Brown	Metropolitan House, Ste. 727 99 Bank St., Ottawa, ON K1P 6G3
Nicaragua	Ambassador: H.E. Sergio Lacayo	170 Laurier Ave. W., Ste. 908 Ottawa, ON K1P 5V5
Niger	Ambassador: H.E. Aboubacar Abdou	38 Blackburn Ave., Ottawa, ON K1N 8A3
Nigeria	High Commissioner: H.E. G.O. George	295 Metcalfe St., Ottawa, ON K2P 1R9
Norway	Ambassador: H.E. Jan E. Nyheim	90 Sparks St., Ste. 532, Ottawa, ON K1P 5B4
Oman	Ambassador: H.E. Adwah Bader Al-Shanfari	2342 Massachusetts Ave. N.W. Washington, DC 20008 U.S.A.
Organization of Eastern Caribbean States	High Commissioner: H.E. Dr. J. Bernard Yankey	Place de Ville, Tower B, Ste. 1701 112 Kent St., Ottawa, ON K1P 5P2
Pakistan	Ambassador: H.E. Najmuddin A. Shaikh	Burnside Bldg., Ste. 608 151 Slater St., Ottawa, ON K1P 5H3
Panama	Chargé d'Affaires, a.i.: Mr. Leonard Kam	866 U.N. Plaza, Ste. 544-545 New York, NY 10017 U.S.A.
Papua New Guinea	High Commissioner: H.E. Rengai Renagi Lohia	1330 Connecticut Ave. N.W., Ste. 350 Washington, DC 20036 U.S.A.
Paraguay	Ambassador: H.E. Dr. Marcos Martinez-Mendieta	2400 Massachusetts Ave. N.W. Washington, DC 20008 U.S.A.
Peru	Ambassador: H.E. Dr. Oscar Maurtua	170 Laurier Ave. W., Ste. 1007 Ottawa, ON K1P 5V5

Country	Representative	Embassy Address
Philippines	Chargé d'Affaires, a.i.: Mr. Eloy R. Bello III	130 Albert St. Ste. 606, Ottawa, ON K1P 5G4
Poland	Ambassador: H.E. Alojzy Bartoszek	443 Daly Ave., Ottawa, ON K1N 6H3
Portugal	Ambassador: H.E. Joao Uvade Matos Proenca	645 Island Park Dr., Ottawa, ON K1Y 0B8
Qatar	Ambassador: H.E. Hamed Abdelaziz Al-Kawari	747 Third Ave., 22nd Flr. New York, NY 10017 U.S.A.
Romania	Ambassador: H.E. Dr. Emilian Rodean	655 Rideau St., Ottawa, ON K1N 6A3
Rwanda	Ambassador: H.E. Joseph Nsengiyumva	121 Sherwood Dr., Ottawa, ON K1Y 3V1
St. Christopher/ Nevis	(See Organization of Eastern Caribbean States)	
St. Lucia	(See Organization of Eastern Caribbean States)	
St. Vincent & the Grenadines	(See Organization of Eastern Caribbean States)	
Sao Tomé and Principe	Ambassador: H.E. Joaquin Rafael Branco	801 Second Ave., Room 1504 New York, NY 10017 U.S.A.
Saudi Arabia	Ambassador: H.E. Ziad Shawwaf	99 Bank St., Ste. 901, Ottawa, ON K1P 6B9
Senegal	Ambassador: H.E. Abd'el Kader Fall	57 Marlborough Ave., Ottawa, ON K1N 8E8
Seychelles	High Commissioner: Vacant	53 Bis, rue François 1er, 75008, Paris, France
Sierra Leone	Chargé d'Affaires, a.i.: Mr. William B. Wright	1701-19th St. N.W. Washington, DC 20009 U.S.A.
Singapore	High Commissioner: H.E. Kishore Mahbubani	Two United Nations Plaza, 26th Flr. New York, NY 10017 U.S.A.
Solomon Islands	Ambassador: H.E. Francis Joseph Saemala	820 Second Ave., Ste. 800A New York, NY 10017 U.S.A.
Somaia	Ambassador: H.E. Abdikamir Ali Omar	130 Slater St., Ste. 1000 Ottawa, ON K1P 6P2
South Africa	Ambassador: H.E. Johannes Hendrik de Klerk	15 Sussex Dr., Ottawa, ON K1M 1M8
Spain	Ambassador: H.E. Antonio José Fournier	350 Sparks St., Ste. 802 Ottawa, ON K1R 7S8
Sri Lanka	High Commissioner: H.E. Gen. Tissa Weeratunga	85 Range Rd., Ste. 102-104, 201 Ottawa, ON K1N 8J6
Sudan, The	Ambassador: H.E. Nuri Khalil Siddig	457 Laurier Ave. E., Ottawa, ON K1N 6R4
Suriname	Ambassador: H.E. Arnold T. Halfhide	Van Ness Center, Ste. 108 4301 Connecticut Ave. N.W. Washington, DC 20008 U.S.A.
Swaziland	A/High Commissioner: Mr. Carlton M. Dlamini	Van Ness Centre, Ste. 441 4301 Connecticut Ave. N.W. Washington, DC 20008 U.S.A.
Sweden	Ambassador: H.E. Ola Ullsten	441 MacLaren St., 4th Flr. Ottawa, ON K2P 2H3
Switzerland	Ambassador: H.E. Erik R. Lang	5 Marlborough Ave., Ottawa, ON K1N 8E6
Syria	Chargé d'Affaires, a.i.: Miss Bushra Kanafani	2215 Wyoming Ave. N.W. Washington, DC 20008 U.S.A.
Tanzania	High Commissioner: H.E. Ferdinand K. Ruhinda	50 Range Rd., Ottawa, ON K1N 8J4
Thailand	Ambassador: H.E. Manaspas Xuto	180 Island Park Dr., Ottawa, ON K1Y 0A2
Togo	Ambassador: H.E. Kossivi Osseyi	12 Range Rd., Ottawa, ON K1N 8J3
Trinidad and Tobago	High Commissioner: H.E. Gerald Yetming	75 Albert St., Ste. 508, Ottawa, ON K1P 5E7

Country	Representative	Embassy Address
Tunisia	Ambassador: H.E. Mohamed Salah Lejri	515 O'Connor St., Ottawa, ON K1S 3P8
Turkey	Ambassador: H.E. Kaya G. Toperi	197 Wurtemburg St., Ottawa, ON K1N 8L9
Uganda	High Commissioner: H.E. Joseph Tomusange	231 Cobourg St., Ottawa, ON K1N 8J2
Union of Soviet Socialist Republics	Ambassador: H.E. Alexei A. Rodionov	285 Charlotte St., Ottawa, ON K1N 8L5
United Arab Emirates	Ambassador: H.E. Mohammad Hussain Al-Shaali	747 Third Ave. New York, NY 10017 U.S.A.
United States of America	Ambassador: H.E. Thomas M.T. Niles	100 Wellington St., Ottawa, ON K1P 5T1
Uruguay	Chargé d'Affaires, a.i.: Mrs. Zulma Guelman	130 Albert St., Ste. 1905 Ottawa, ON K1P 5G4
Venezuela	Ambassador: H.E. Gilberto Carrasquero	294 Albert St., Ste. 602 Ottawa, ON K1P 6E6
Viet Nam	Ambassador: H.E. Tran Van Hung	12-14 Victoria Rd. London, England, W85RD U.K.
Western Samoa	High Commissioner: H.E. Maiava Iulai Toma	820 Second Ave., Ste. 800-D New York, NY 10017 U.S.A.
Yemen Arab Republic	Ambassador: H.E. Moshin Ahmed Alaini	Watergate Six Hundred, Ste. 840 600 New Hampshire Ave. N.W. Washington, DC 20037 U.S.A.
Yemen, People's Democratic Republic of	Ambassador: H.E. Abdalla Saleh Al-Ashtal	413 East 51st St. New York, NY 10022 U.S.A.
Yugoslavia	Ambassador: H.E. Dr. Vladimir Pavicevic	17 Blackburn Ave. Ottawa, ON K1N 8A2
Zaire	Ambassador: H.E. Mbeka Makosso	18 Range Rd., Ottawa, ON K1N 8J3
Zambia	High Commissioner: H.E. Humphrey Mulemba	130 Albert St., Ste. 1610 Ottawa, ON K1P 5G4
Zimbabwe	High Commissioner: H.E. Stanislaus G. Chigwedere	332 Somerset St. W. Ottawa, ON K2P 0J9

CONSULATES & TRADE COMMISSIONS IN CANADA

Country	Representative	Address
Antigua and Barbuda	Hon. Consul: Mr. Castor H.F. Williams	6156 Quinpool Rd., Halifax, NS B3L 1A3
	Consul: Miss Constance Blackman	60 St. Clair Ave. E., Ste. 205 Toronto, ON M4T 1N5
Argentina	Consul General: Mr. José Isaac Garcia Ghirelli	1010, rue Ste-Catherine ouest, bur. 737 Montréal (Québec) H3B 1G7
Australia	Consul General: Mr. Graham H. Scott	Commerce Court N., Ste. 2200 25 King St. W., Toronto, ON M5L 1B9
	Consul General: Mr. H. David M. Combe	Oceanic Plaza, Ste. 800, 1066 W. Hastings St. Box 12519, Vancouver, BC V6E 3X1
Austria	Hon. Consul General: Mr. H. Ockermueller	1131 Kensington Rd. N.W., Calgary, AB T2N 3P4
	Hon. Consul: Mr. M. Novac	1716 Argyle St., Ste. 710, Halifax, NS B3J 3N6
	Hon. Consul General: Mr. Nandor F. Loewenheim	1350, rue Sherbrooke ouest, bur. 1030 Montréal (Québec) H3G 1J1
	Hon. Consul General: Dr. Hans Abromeit	390 Bay St., Ste. 2018 Toronto, ON M5H 2Y2
	Hon. Vice-Consul: Mr. Michael Kent Norville	525 Seymour St., Vancouver, BC V6B 3H9

Country	Representative	Address
Bahrain	Consul: Mr. Ahmed M. Al-Haddad	1869, boul. René-Lévesque ouest Montréal (Québec) H3H 1R4
Barbados	Hon. Consul: Mr. Mayer Lawee	800, boul. René-Lévesque ouest, bur. 2535 Montréal (Québec) H3B 1X9
	Consul General: Miss Lolita Applewaite	20 Queen St. W., Ste. 1508 Box 18, Toronto, ON M5H 3R3
	Hon. Consul: Mrs. Annette Goodridge	2020 Haro St., Ste. 401, Vancouver, BC V6G 1J3
Belgium	Hon. Consul: Mr. Bernard Callebout	907-17th Ave. S.W., Calgary, AB T2T 0A4
	Hon. Consul: Mr. W.J. Henning	1800 Standard Life Centre 10405 Jasper Ave., Edmonton, AB T5Y 3N4
	Hon. Consul: Mr. Joz De Belie	Box 1590, Stn. M, Halifax, NS B3J 2Y3
	Hon. Consul: Mr. Frank Edward Swinnen	376 Richmond St., Ste. B London, ON N6A 3C7
	Consul General: Mr. Xavier Dumoulin	1001, boul. de Maisonneuve ouest Bur. 1250, Montréal (Québec) H3A 3C8
	Hon. Consul: Mr. John Hudson	1048 Fleury St., Regina, SK S4N 4W8
	Hon. Consul: Mr. Anthony G. Ayre, O.B.E.	Box 1506, St. John's, NF A1C 5N8
	Consul General: Mrs. Ingeborg Kristoffersen	8 King St. E., Ste. 1901, Toronto, ON M5C 1B5
	Consul General: Mr. Michel Delfosse	Pacific Centre, Ste. 1250, 701 W. Georgia St. Box 10119, Vancouver, BC V7Y 1C6
	Hon. Consul: Mr. Paul Deprez	15 Acadia Bay, Winnipeg, MB R3T 3J1
Belize	Hon. Consul: Mr. Harry J.F. Bloomfield	1080, côte du Beaver Hall, bur. 1720 Montréal (Québec) H2Z 1S8
Bénin	Hon. Consul: Mrs. Marie B. Archambault	429, av. Viger est, Montréal (Québec) H2L 2N9
Bolivia	Hon. Consul: Mr. Carlos Pechtel	11231 Jasper Ave., Edmonton, AB T5K 0L5
	Hon. Consul: Mrs. Pilar Arto	18, av. Severn, Westmount (Québec) H3Y 2C7
	Hon. Consul: Mr. Alan Stewart Andree	Ste. 505, 470 Granville St. Vancouver, BC V6B 1V5
Brazil	Hon. Consul: Mr. Ernest Zieter	10120-118th St., Ste. 210 Edmonton, AB T5K 0N7
	Hon. Consul: Mr. Raymond W. Ferguson	3600 Kempt Rd., Halifax, NS B3X 5M5
	Consul General: Mr. José Mauricio de Figueiredo Bustani	200, rue Mansfield, bur. 1700 Montréal (Québec) H3A 3A5
	Hon. Consul: Mr. John Stanislaus Fowler	Box 4246, St. John's, NF A1B 3N9
	Consul General: Mr. Odilon de Camargo Penteado	77 Bloor St. W., Ste. 1109 Toronto, ON M5S 1N2
	Deputy Consul General: Mr. Guilherme Parreiras-Horta	Royal Center, Ste. 1700, 1055 W. Georgia St. Vancouver, BC V6E 3P3
Britain	Consul General: Mr. J.F. Doble	Three McCauley Plaza, Ste. 1404 10025 Jasper Ave., Edmonton, AB T5J 1S6
	Hon. Consul: Mr. L. Strachan	Purdy's Wharf, Ste. 1501, 1959 Upper Water St. Box 310, Halifax, NS B3J 2X1
	Consul General: Mr. P.M. Newton	1155, rue University, Montréal (Québec) H3B 1R6
	Hon. Consul: Mr. F.D. Smith	34 Glencoe Dr., Box 8833, St. John's, NF A1B 3T2
	Consul General: Mr. B. Sparrow	College Park, Ste. 1910 777 Bay St., Toronto, ON M5G 2G2
	Consul General: Mr. B. Watkins	1111 Melville St., Ste. 800 Vancouver, BC V6E 3V6
	Hon. Consul: Mr. Jack R. Hignell	c/o Hignell Printing Ltd. 488 Burnell St., Winnipeg, MB R3G 2B4
Bulgaria	Consul General: Mr. Yordan Velichkov	100 Adelaide St. W., Ste. 1410 Toronto, ON M5H 1S3
Burkina Faso	Hon. Consul: Mr. Frederick Stinson	200 Adelaide St. W., Toronto, ON M5H 1W4

Country	Representative	Address
	Hon. Consul: Mr. Pierre Bastien	1055, boul. René-Lévesque est, 10e ét. Québec (Québec) H2L 4S5
Burundi	Hon. Consul: Mr. Jean-Guy Larendeau	4017, av. Lacombe Montréal (Québec) H3T 1M7
Central African Republic	Hon. Consul General: Mr. Jean-François Boisvert	225, rue St-Jacques, 3e ét. Montréal (Québec) H2Y 1M6
	Hon. Consul: Mr. Marc Dorion	112, rue Dalhousie, bur. 201 Québec (Québec) G1K 4C1
Chile	Consul General: Mr. César Ravazzano	1010, rue Ste-Catherine ouest, bur. 731 Montréal (Québec) H3B 3R3
	Consul General: Mr. Umberto Alvarez	1240 Bay St., Ste. 700, Toronto, ON M5R 3L9
	Hon. Consul: Mr. Joaquin Grubner	1130 W. Pender St., Ste. 530 Vancouver, BC V6E 4A4
China, People's Republic of	Consul General: Mr. Xia Zhongcheng	240 St. George St., Toronto, ON M5R 2P4
	Consul General: Mr. Duan Jin	3338 Granville St., Vancouver, BC V6H 3K3
Colombia	Consul General: Vacant	1010, rue Sherbrooke ouest, bur. 420 Montréal (Québec) H3A 2R7
	Consul General: Mr. Edouardo Osorio-Munoz	1 Dundas St. W., Ste. 2108 Toronto, ON M5G 1Z3
	Hon. Consul: Mrs. Beatriz De Horry	5389 Oak St., Vancouver, BC V6M 2V5
Congo	Hon. Consul: Mr. Marcel P. Rigny	2, rue Cedar, Pointe Claire (Québec) H9S 4Y1
Costa Rica	Consul: Mr. Bernal Mesen	933, rue Antonine-Maillet Outremont (Québec) H2V 2Y8
	Hon. Consul General: Mr. Peter A. Kircher	164 Avenue Rd., Toronto, ON M5R 2H9
	Hon. Consul: Mr. William Andrew Dow	1550 Alberni St., Ste. 804 Vancouver, BC V6G 1A5
Côte d'Ivoire	Hon. Consul: Mr. André Vannerum	2525, av. Hâvre-des-Iles, bur. 402-B Laval (Québec) H7W 4C5
	Hon. Consul: Mr. J.T.A. Wilson	260 Adelaide St. E., Box 90 Toronto, ON M5A 1N0
Cuba	Consul General: Mrs. Lourdes Urutia	1415, av. des Pins ouest Montréal (Québec) H3G 2B2
	Consul General: Mr. Rolando Rivero Perellano	372 Bay St., Ste. 406, Toronto, ON M5H 2W9
Cyprus	Hon. Consul: Mr. M.P. Paidoussis	2930, boul. Edouard-Montpetit, bur. PH2 Montréal (Québec) H3T 1J7
Czechoslovakia	Consul and Trade Commissioner: Mr. Viktor Horak	128, rue St-Marc, bur. 202 Montréal (Québec) H3H 2G1
Denmark	Hon. Consul: Mr. Kai Mortensen	1235-11th Ave. S.W., Calgary, AB T3C 0M5
	Hon. Consul: Mr. Donn Larsen	10235-101st St., Ste. 908 Edmonton, AB T5J 3G1
	Hon. Consul: Mr. H.I. Mathers Jr.	1525 Birmingham St., Box 3550 S. Halifax, NS B3J 3J3
	Consul General: Mr. Jens Henryk Jensen	1245, rue Sherbrooke ouest, bur. 1525 Montréal (Québec) H3G 1G2
	Hon. Consul: Mr. Jacques Ewart Fortier	880, ch. Ste-Foy, bur. 860 Québec (Québec) G1S 2L2
	Hon. Consul: Mr. Gordon Allen Rasmussen	22 Millar Rd., Regina, SK S4S 1N2
	Hon. Consul: Mr. Eric Lawrence Teed	Harbour Bldg., Ste. 306, 133 Prince William St. Box 6639, Stn. A, Saint John, NB E2L 4S1
	Hon. Consul: Mr. Peter Norman Outerbridge	55 Duckworth St., Box 6150 St. John's, NF A1C 5X8
	Consul General: Mr. Erling Harild Nielsen	151 Bloor St. W., Ste. 310 Toronto, ON M5S 1S4
	Hon. Consul: Mr. Finn Karlo Petersen	475 Howe St., Ste. 1102 Vancouver, BC V6C 2B3

Country	Representative	Address
	Hon. Consul: Mr. Anders Bruun	50 Morley Ave., Winnipeg, MB R3L 0X4
Dominican Republic	Consul General: Mrs. Esmeralda Villanueva	1464, rue Crescent, Montréal (Québec) H3G 2B6
	Hon. Vice-Consul: Dr. André Joffre Gravel	1155, av. Turnbull, bur. 503 Québec (Québec) G1R 5G3
	Hon. Consul: Mr. John Driscoll	59 Broad St., Saint John, NB E2L 1Y3
	Hon. Consul: Mr. Harry T. Renouf	10 Forest Ave., St. John's, NF A1C 3J9
	Hon. Consul: Mr. Cyrus H. McLean	1445 Marpole Ave., Ste. 808 Vancouver, BC V6H 1S5
Ecuador	Consul General: Mr. Luis Moreno Guerrar	1010, rue Ste-Catherine ouest, bur. 625 Montréal (Québec) H3B 3R3
	Consul: Mr. José Munez-Tamayo	151 Bloor St. W., Ste. 670 Toronto, ON M5S 1S4
	Hon. Consul: Mr. John Joseph Fedyk	1155 W. Georgia St., Ste. 420 Vancouver, BC V6E 3H4
Egypt, Arab Republic of	Consul General: Mr. Mohamed Mounir Gohar	3754, ch. de la Côte-des-Neiges Montréal (Québec) H3H 1V6
Fiji	Hon. Consul: Dr. D. Elaine Pressman	130 Slater St., Ste. 750 Ottawa, ON K1P 6E2
	Hon. Consul: Mr. Raj Gopal Pillai	1437 West 64th Ave. Vancouver, BC V6P 2N5
Finland	Hon. Consul: Miss Judith Romanchuk	350-7th Ave. S.W., Ste. 3500 Calgary, AB T2P 3N9
	Hon. Consul: Mr. Christian Graefe	Westin Hotel, 10135-100th St. Edmonton, AB T5J 0N7
	Hon. Consul: Mr. John B. Claxton	1, place Ville-Marie, bur. 3725 Montréal (Québec) H3B 3P4
	Hon. Consul: Mr. Henry Grondin	1, parc Samuel-Holland, bur. 2340 Québec (Québec) G1S 4P2
	Hon. Consul: Mr. Thomas L. McGloan	Box 7174, Stn. A, Saint John, NB E2L 4S6
	Hon. Consul: Mr. Teuvo Eloranta	219 Pine St., Sudbury, ON P3C 1X4
	Hon. Consul: Mr. Aatto Arthur Kajander, Q.C.	76 Algoma St. N., Box 2870 Thunder Bay, ON P7B 5G3
	Hon. Vice-Consul: Mr. Gerard Evans, Q.C.	101 Mall, Pine St. N., Ste. 131 Timmins, ON P4N 6K6
	Consul: Mr. Markku Knappila	1200 Bay St., Ste. 604, Toronto, ON M5R 2A5
	Hon. Consul General: Mr. Keijo Seppala	Ste. 1120, 1176 W. Georgia St. Vancouver, BC V6E 4A2
	Hon. Consul: Mr. Robert Purves	167 Lombard Ave., Ste. 704 Winnipeg, MB R3B 0V3
France	Consul and Trade Commissioner: Mr. Jean-Yves Conte	Bow Valley Sq. IV, Ste. 2920 250-6th Ave. S.W., Calgary, AB T2P 3H7
	Hon. Consul: M. François Brochet	1596, av. Bejin, Chicoutimi (Québec) G7H 5T6
	Consul General: Mr. Serge Pinot	Highfield Place, Ste. 300 10010-106th St., Edmonton, AB T5J 3L8
	Hon. Vice-Consul: Mr. Pierre Gérin	35 Bayview Rd., Halifax, NS B3M 1N8
	Consul General: Mr. Michel Couthures	250 Lutz St., Box 1109 Moncton, NB E1C 8P6
	Consul General: Mr. Jean-Pierre Beauchataud	2 Elysée, Place Bonaventure C.P. 177, Montréal (Québec) H5A 1A7
	Consul General: Mr. Daniel Jouanneau	1110, av. des Laurentides Québec (Québec) G1S 3C3
	Hon. Vice-Consul: Mr. René Rottiers	Box 3663, Regina, SK S4P 3N8
	Consular Agent: Mr. Charles Frédéric Whelly, Q.C.	122 Carleton St., Saint John, NB E2L 2Z7

Country	Representative	Address
	Hon. Vice-Consul: Mr. Pierre Morin	19 Diefenbaker St., St. John's, NF A1A 2N2
	Hon. Vice-Consul: Mr. Bernard M. Michel	920 Saskatchewan Cr. E. Saskatoon, SK S7N 0L5
	Hon. Consul: Mr. Onésime Tremblay	1101 Lake Ramsey Rd., Ste. 3 Sudbury, ON P3C 5J2
	Consul General: Mr. Jacques Royet	130 Bloor St. W., Ste. 400, Toronto, ON M5S 1N5
	Consul and Trade Commissioner: Mr. Louis Morris	210 Dundas St. W., Ste. 800 Toronto, ON M5G 2E8
	Consul General: Mr. René Delille	736 Granville St., Ste. 1201 Vancouver, BC V6Z 1H9
	Consul and Trade Commissioner: Mr. Thierry Rosset	736 Granville St., Ste. 320 Vancouver, BC V6Z 1J1
	Hon. Consul: Mr. David Albert Griffiths	3946 Emerald Place, Victoria, BC V8P 4T6
	Hon. Consul: Mr. Rolf Hougen	305 Main St., Whitehorse, YT Y1A 2B4
Gabon	Hon. Consul: Mr. Luc Benoît	85, rue Ste-Catherine ouest Montréal (Québec) H2X 3P4
	Hon. Consul: Dr. Ian Efford	1909 Broadmoor Ave., Ottawa, ON K1H 5B3
Gambia, The	Hon. Consul General: Mr. Jochem Carton, O.C.	363, rue St-François-Xavier, bur. 300 Montréal (Québec) H2Y 3P9
	Hon. Consul General: Mr. Irving Gould	102 Bloor St. W., Ste. 510, Toronto, ON M5S 1M8
Germany, Federal Republic of	Hon. Consul: Mr. Osmar Beltzner	840-6th Ave. S.W., Ste. 337-338 Calgary, AB T2P 3E5
	Consul General: Dr. Gerhard Braumueller	2500 CN Tower, 10004-104th Ave. Edmonton, AB T5J 0K1
	Hon. Consul: Dr. Edgar Gold	Bank of Commerce Bldg., Ste. 708 1809 Barrington St., Halifax, NS B3J 3K8
	Hon. Consul: Mr. Peter Dietrich Kruse	370 Frederick St., Kitchener, ON N2H 2P3
	Consul General: Dr. Hermann Hillger	3455, rue de la Montagne Montréal (Québec) H3G 2A3
	Hon. Consul: Dr. Guenter Kocks	3534 Argyle Rd., Regina, SK S4S 2B8
	Hon. Consul: Mr. Gunter Sann	22 Poplar Ave., St. John's, NF A1B 1C8
	Consul General: Dr. Henning Leopold von Hassel	77 Admiral Rd., Toronto, ON M5R 2L4
	Consul General: Mr. Siegfried Haller	325 Howe St., Ste. 501 Vancouver, BC V6C 2A2
	Hon. Consul: Mr. Gerhard Spindler	310 Donald St., Ste. 208 Winnipeg, MB R3B 2H4
Greece	Consul General: Mr. Elias Dimitrakopoulos	2015, rue Peel, bur. 750 Montréal (Québec) H3A 1T8
	Consul General: Mr. Vassilios Moutsoglou	100 University Ave., Ste. 902 Toronto, ON M5G 1V6
	Consul: Mr. Jean (Yannis) Lacatzis	1200 Burrard St., Ste. 501 Vancouver, BC V6Z 2C7
Grenada	Consul General: Mr. Mark Isaac	439 University Ave., Ste. 820 Toronto, ON M5G 1Y8
Guatemala	Consul General: Vacant	1140, boul. de Maisonneuve ouest Bur. 1040, Montréal (Québec) H3A 1M8
	Hon. Consul: Mr. Paul Bouchard	50, rue Aberdeen, Québec (Québec) G1R 2C7
	Hon. Consul: Dr. Bernard W. Hoeter	736 Granville St., Ste. 1400 Vancouver, BC V6Z 1G7
Guinea-Bissau	Hon. Consul: Mr. Nicolas M. Matte	433, rue Chabanel, tour A, bur. 1204 Montréal (Québec) H2N 2J8
Guyana	Vice-Consul: Mr. David D. Dharampal Karran	505 Consumers Rd., Ste. 206 Willowdale, ON M2J 4V8
Haiti	Consul General: Mr. Auguste G.P. d'Méza	Place Bonaventure, 44 Fundy, ét. F C.P. 187, Montréal (Québec) H5A 1A9

Country	Representative	Address
Honduras	Consul General: Miss Ileana Ulloa de Thuin	1500, rue Stanley, bur. 330 Montréal (Québec) H3A 1R3
	Hon. Consul: Mrs. Thérèse Lacroix	1334, rue Maréchal-Foch Québec (Québec) G1S 2C4
	Hon. Consul General: Mrs. Mercedes Bourqui	R.R. 3, Newmarket, ON L3Y 4W1
	Hon. Consul: Mr. Enrique Gonzalez-Calvo	535 West Georgia St., Ste. 104 Vancouver, BC V6B 1Z6
Hungary	Consul General and Trade Commissioner: Mr. Lajos Szuhay	3400, boul. de Maisonneuve ouest, bur. 1250 Montréal (Québec) H3Z 3B8
	Consul and Trade Commissioner: Mr. Pal Egervari	102 Bloor St. W., Ste. 450 Toronto, ON M5S 1M8
Iceland	Hon. Vice-Consul: Mr. Clifford A. Marteinson	158 Cornwallis Dr., Calgary, AB T2K 1V1
	Hon. Consul: Mr. Gudmundur A. Arnason	14434 McQueen Rd., Edmonton, AB T5N 3L6
	Hon. Consul: Mr. Lawrence John Cooke	c/o Dover Mills Ltd., Terminal Rd. Box 2185, Halifax, NS B3J 3C4
	Hon. Consul General: Mr. Jean-Guy Gauvreau	5005, rue Jean-Talon ouest Montréal (Québec) H4P 1W7
	Hon. Consul General: Mrs. E.T. Lahey	116 Lisgar St., Ste. 700, Ottawa, ON K2P 0C2
	Hon. Consul: Mr. Avalon M. Goodridge	57 Military Rd., St. John's, NF A1C 2C5
	Hon. Consul: Mr. J. Ragnar Johnson, Q.C.	20 Queen St. W., Ste. 3000 Toronto, ON M5H 1V5
	Hon. Consul: Mr. Harold S. Sigurdsson	Four Bentall Centre, Ste. 1804, 1055 Dunsmuir St. Box 49272, Vancouver, BC V7X 1C5
	Hon. Consul: Mr. Birgir Brynjolfsson	200 Augusta Dr., Winnipeg, MB R3T 4G5
India	Consul General: Mr. Virendra Pal Singh	2 Bloor St. W., Ste. 500, Toronto, ON M4W 3E2
	Consul General: Mr. J.C. Sharma	325 Howe St., 1st Flr., Vancouver, BC V6C 1Z7
Indonesia	Consul: Mr. E.M. Ruru	425 University Ave., 9th Flr. Toronto, ON M5G 1T6
	Consul: Mr. Eddy Sumantri	1455 West Georgia St., 2nd Flr. Vancouver, BC V6G 2T3
Israel	Consul General: Mr. Chalom Schirman	1155, boul. René-Lévesque ouest, bur. 2620 Montréal (Québec) H3B 4S5
	Consul General: Mr. Benjamin Abileah	180 Bloor St. W., Ste. 700 Toronto, ON M5S 2V6
Italy	Hon. Vice-Consul: Mr. Arcangelo Martino	288 Murray St., Brantford, ON N3S 5T1
	Hon. Vice-Consul: Mrs. Gloria Vinci	Ste. 630, 840-6th Ave. S.W., Calgary, AB T2P 3E5
	A/Vice-Consul: Mr. Giovanni Bincoletto	1240 Standard Life Center, Ste. 1020 10404 Jasper Ave., Edmonton, AB T5J 3N4
	Hon. Vice-Consul: Mrs. Imelda Porce Mato	120 Chadwick St., 2nd Flr. Guelph, ON N1H 3V3
	Hon. Vice-Consul: Mr. Rodolfo Meloni	9 Downview Dr., Dartmouth, NS B2W 4C7
	Vice-Consul: Vacant	100 Main St. E., Hamilton, ON L8N 3W4
	Hon. Vice-Consul: Mr. Diego Bastianutti	221 King St. E., Kingston, ON K7L 3A6
	Hon. Vice-Consul: Mr. Luigi Rossetti	344 Richmond St., London, ON N6A 3C3
	Consul General: Mr. Alberto Candilio	3489, rue Drummond Montréal (Québec) H3G 1X6
	Hon. Vice-Consul: Mr. Domenico Morabito	4904 Victoria Ave., Niagara Falls, ON L2E 4C6
	Hon. Consular Agent: Mr. Mario Giovanni Marogna	222-3rd Ave. W., Ste. 2 Prince Rupert, BC V8J 1L1

Country	Representative	Address
	Hon. Consul: Mr. Antonio Servello	367, 82ième rue ouest Québec (Québec) G1G 5L9
	Hon. Vice-Consul: Mrs. Lucia Papini	82 Lowry Place, Regina, SK S4S 4P5
	Hon. Consular Agent: Mr. Simon Lono	437 Portugal Cove Rd., St. John's, NF A1A 2X3
	Hon. Vice-Consul: Mr. Antonio Dominichini	785 Exmouth St., Sarnia, ON N7T 5P7
	Hon. Vice-Consul: Mr. Rudolph C. Peres	Professional Place, Ste. 104 212 Queen St. E., Sault Ste. Marie, ON P6A 5X8
	Hon. Vice-Consul: Dr. Roberto Grosso	96 Larch St., Sudbury, ON P3E 1C1
	Hon. Consular Agent: Mr. Lino Regato	2 Kennedy Dr., Sydney, NS B0A 1E2
	Hon. Vice-Consul: Mrs. Giovanna Pirotta Zovatto	419 Victoria Ave. E. Thunder Bay, ON P7C 1A6
	Hon. Vice-Consul: Mr. Rino Charles Bragagnolo	38 Pine St. S., Ste. 131, Timmins, ON P4N 6K6
	Consul General: Mr. Giovanni Lajolo	136 Beverley St., Toronto, ON M5T 1Y5
	Hon. Consular Agent: Mrs. Emily Tenisci	1190-2nd Ave., Trail, BC V1R 1L4
	Consul General: Mr. Gianfranco Alfonso Manigrassi	1200 Burrard St., Ste. 505 Vancouver, BC V6Z 2C7
	Hon. Vice-Consul: Mrs. Yolanda Pagnotta McKimmie	1050 Park Blvd., Ste. 207 Victoria, BC V8V 2T4
	Hon. Vice-Consul: Mr. Francesco De Angelis	1291 Erie St. E., Windsor, ON N9A 3Z6
	Hon. Vice-Consul: Mr. Domenico Povoledo	283 Portage Ave., Ste. 381 Winnipeg, MB R3B 2B5
Jamaica	Hon. Consul: Mrs. Dolli Booth	36 Windermere Cres., St. Albert, AB T8N 3S5
	Consul General: Mrs Kay A. Baxter	214 King St. W., Ste. 216, Toronto, ON M5H 1K4
	Hon. Consul: Mr. Donald Keith Gordon	11 Wadham Bay, Winnipeg, MB R3T 3K2
Japan	Consul General: Mr. Tetsuo Nonogaki	Manulife Place, Ste. 2480 10180-101st St., Edmonton, AB T5J 3S4
	Hon. Consul General: Mr. Bruce S.C. Oland	c/o Lindwood Holdings Ltd. Keith Hall, 1475 Hollis St., Halifax, NS B3J 1V1
	Consul General: Mr. Tsukasa Abe	600, rue de la Gauchetière ouest Bur. 1785, Montréal (Québec) H3B 4L8
	Hon. Consul General: Dr. Morris C. Shumiatcher	Haldane House, 2100 Scarth St. Regina, SK S4P 2H6
	Consul General: Mr. Yasuo Naguchi	Toronto-Dominion Centre, Ste. 2702 Box 10, Toronto, ON M5K 1A1
	Consul General: Mr. Shunji Maruyama	1177 W. Hastings St., Ste. 900 Vancouver, BC V6E 2K9
	Consul General: Mr. Yuzuki Kaku	Credit Union Central Plaza 215 Garry St., Ste. 730 Winnipeg, MB R3C 3P3
Korea	Consul General: Mr. Won Chan Rah	1000, rue Sherbrooke ouest, bur. 1710 Montréal (Québec) H3A 3G4
	Consul General: Mr. Song Tack Park	439 University Ave., Ste. 700 Toronto, ON M5G 1Y8
	Consul General: Mr. Kie Ok Chung	1066 W. Hastings St., Ste. 830 Vancouver, BC V6E 3X1
Kuwait	Hon. Consul: Mr. Ernest W. Assaly	1510 Walkley Rd., Ottawa, ON K1V 6P5
Lebanon	Consul General: Mr. Youssef Arsanios	40, ch. Côte Ste-Catherine Montréal (Québec) H2V 2A2
Liberia	Hon. Consul: Mr. Stuart E. Hendin	101 Princess St., Kingston, ON K7L 1A0
	Hon. Consul General: Mr. Harry J.F. Bloomfield	1080, côte du Beaver Hall, bur. 1720 Montréal (Québec) H2Z 1S8

Country	Representative	Address
	Hon. Consul General: Mr. Gordon Fripp Henderson	160 Elgin St., Box 466, Stn. A Ottawa, ON K1N 8S3
	Hon. Consul: Mr. Gilles Varin	76, rue Dalhousie, bur. 751 Québec (Québec) G1K 8W6
	Hon. Consul: Mr. Ralph Devine	52 Clarksville Dr., Toronto, ON M9W 5T9
	Hon. Consul General: Mr. H.A.D. Oliver	Ste. 1920, 777 Hornby St. Vancouver, BC V6Z 2L1
Lithuania	A/Hon. Consul General: Dr. Jonas Zmuidzinas	1 Trillium Terrace, Toronto, ON M8Y 1V9
Luxembourg	Hon. Consul: Mr. Z.G. Havlena	Palliser Sq. 1, Ste. 700 125-9th Ave. S.E., Calgary, AB T2G 0P6
	Hon. Consul General: Mrs. Marie-Claire Lefort	3877, av. Draper, Montréal (Québec) H4A 2N9
Madagascar	Hon. Consul: Mr. Z.G. Havlena	Palliser Sq. 1, Ste 700 125-9th Ave. S.W., Calgary, AB T2G 0P6
	Hon. Consul: Mr. Léopold Bernier	451, rue St-Sulpice, Montréal (Québec) H2Y 2V9
	Hon. Vice-Consul: Mr. Julien Randrianarivony	8530, rue Saguenay, Brossard (Québec) J4X 1M6
	Hon. Consul: Mr. James Morten Goodfellow	396 Claremont Ave., Oakville, ON L6J 6K1
Malawi	Hon. Consul: Mr. Yvon Maloney	5437, cres. Plamondon St-Lambert (Québec) J4S 1W2
	Hon. Consul: Mr. Robert A. Elek	155 Crescent Rd., Toronto, ON M4W 1V1
Malaysia	Consul and Trade Commissioner: Mr. Md. Nor bin Md. Said	34 King St. E., Ste. 1201, Toronto, ON M5C 1E5
	Hon. Consul: Mr. David McClary Johnston	2800 Park Place, 666 Burrard St. Vancouver, BC V6C 2Z7
Mali	Hon. Consul: Mr. Paul Fortin	1420, rue Sherbrooke ouest, bur. 900 Montréal (Québec) H3G 1K5
Malta	Hon. Consul: Mr. Henry J. Calleja	465, rue St-Jean, bur. 501 Montréal (Québec) H2Y 2R6
	Hon. Consul General and Trade Commissioner: Mr. Lou Alfred Bondi	3323 Dundas St. W., Toronto, ON M6P 2A6
	Hon Consul General: Mr. Charles E. Puglisevich	Crosbie Bldg., Crosbie Rd. Box 186, Stn. C, St. John's, NF A1C 5J2
Mexico	Hon. Consul: Mr. Angus G. MacDonald	1350 Scotia Place, 10060 Jasper Ave. Edmonton, AB T5J 3R8
	Consul General: Mrs Zoila Arroiyo de Rodriguez	1000, rue Sherbrooke ouest, bur. 2215 Montréal (Québec) H3A 3G4
	Hon. Consul: Mrs. Madeleine Charland Therrien	380, ch. St-Louis, bur. 1407 Sillery (Québec) G1S 4M1
	Consul General: Mr. Juan Miralles-Ostos	60 Bloor St. W., Ste. 203, Toronto, ON M4W 3B8
	Consul General: Vacant	625 Howe St., Ste. 310, Vancouver, BC V6C 2T6
Monaco	Hon. Consul General: Mr. Michel Pasquin	1, place Ville-Marie, bur. 1200 Montréal (Québec) H3B 4A8
	Hon. Consul General: Mr. Fritz Alfred Wilhelm Ziegler	736 Granville St., Ste. 1400 Vancouver, BC V6Z 1G7
Morocco	Consul General: Mr. Abdeslam Benjelloun	1010, rue Sherbrooke ouest, bur. 1510 Montréal (Québec) H3A 2R7
Nepal	Hon. Consul General: Mr. William H. Baxter	310 Dupont St., Toronto, ON M5R 1V9
Netherlands, The	Hon. Consul: Mr. G.A. Van Wielingen	Calgary Place 1, Ste. 2628 300-5th Ave. S.W., Calgary, AB T2P 0L4
	Consul: Mr. J.J. Koster	Phipps McKinnon Bldg., Ste. 930 10020-101A Ave., Edmonton, AB T5J 3G2
	Hon. Consul: Mr. D.W. Salsman	Box 1571, Halifax, NS B3J 2Y3
	Hon. Vice-Consul: Dr. H. Westenberg	115 Lower Union St., Kingston, ON K7L 2N9

Country	Representative	Address
	Hon. Vice-Consul: Dr. R.D. Ver-Trugt	650 Colborne St., London, ON N5A 5A1
	Consul General: Vacant	Edifice Standard Life, bur. 1500 1245, rue Sherbrooke ouest Montréal (Québec) H3G 1G2
	Hon. Consul: Mr. E.A. Price	10, rue Ste-Anne, Québec (Québec) G1R 4S7
	Hon. Consul: Mr. E.H. Grolle	4114-18th Ave., Regina, SK S4S 0C4
	Hon. Consul: Mr. C.D. Whelly	167 Prince William St., Box 6337, Stn. A Saint John, NB E2L 2B4
	Hon. Consul: Dr. A.A. Bruneau	55 Kenmount Rd., Box 8910 St. John's, NF A1B 3P6
	Hon. Vice-Consul: Mr. R.P. Welter	179 South Algoma St. Thunder Bay, ON P7B 3C1
	Consul General: Mr. J.W. Jansen	1 Dundas St. W., Ste. 2106 Toronto, ON M5G 1Z3
	Consul General: Mr. D.J.J. van Lottum	Crown Trust Bldg., Ste. 821, 475 Howe St. Vancouver, BC V6C 2B3
	Hon. Consul: Mr. B.A. van Ruiten	3119 Assiniboine Ave., Winnipeg, MB R3K 0A2
New Zealand	Consul and Trade Commissioner: Mr. Anthony J. Pervan	Box 10071, Pacific Centre, IBM Tower Vancouver, BC V7Y 1B6
Niger	Hon. Consul: Mr. Pierre Thomas	245, rue St-Jacques ouest, bur. 420 Montréal (Québec) H2Y 1M6
Norway	Hon. Consul: Mr. Jan-Erik Hagen	10201 Southport Rd. S.W., Ste. 1110 Calgary, AB T2W 4X9
	Hon. Consul: Mr. Arne J. Johannessen	6003-102A Ave. N.W., Edmonton, AB T6A 0R5
	Hon. Consul: Mr. Karl Karlsen	2089 Upper Water St., Halifax, NS B3K 2X1
	Hon. Consul General: Mr. Trygve Husebye	2600 South Sheridan Way Mississauga, ON L5J 2M4
	Hon. Consul General: Mr. Ivar Traa	407, rue McGill, bur. 802 Montréal (Québec) H2Y 2G3
	Hon. Vice-Consul: Mr. John A. Ellis	5026 Argyle St., Port Alberni, BC V9Y 7M9
	Hon. Consul: Mr. Gaétan Thivierge	2, rue Nouvelle-France C.P. 40, succ. B, Québec (Québec) G1K 7A2
	Hon. Consul: Mr. Donald F. MacGowan	40 Wellington Row, Box 6850, Stn. A Saint John, NB E2L 4S3
	Hon. Consul: Mr. Henry Collingwood	Baine Johnstone Centre, Ste. 800 10 Fort William Place, Box 5367 St. John's, NF A1C 5W2
	Hon. Consul: Mrs. Randi Elizabeth Anstensen	846 University Dr., Saskatoon, SK S7N 0J7
	Hon. Vice-Consul: Mrs. Joan E. Harriss	5 Kings Rd., Box 1925, Sydney, NS B1P 6W4
	Vice-Consul and Trade Commissioner: Mr. Jan Aagenaes	1200 Bay St., Ste. 702, Toronto, ON M5R 2A5
	Consul General: Mr. Odvar Mesnesset	Marine Bldg., Ste. 540 355 Burrard St., Vancouver, BC V6C 2G8
	Hon. Consul: Mr. Cecil Paul Ridout	401 Hartwig Court, 1208 Wharf St. Box 577, Victoria, BC V8W 2P5
	Hon. Consul: Mr. J.C. Tremblay	1522, Sixième av. Ville-de-la-Baie (Québec) G7B 1R6
	Hon. Consul: Mr. Martin Edwin Benum	39 Brookhaven Bay, Winnipeg, MB R2J 2S4
Pakistan	Consul General: Mr. Ejaz Ahmad Qureshi	3421, rue Peel, Montréal (Québec) H3A 1W7
	Consul General: Mr. Afzal Akbar Khan	8 King St. E., Ste. 505, Toronto, ON M5C 1B5
Panama	Hon. Consul: Mrs. Lynette Anderson De Kew	62 Bedford Hwy., Halifax, NS B3M 2J2

Country	Representative	Address
	Consul: Mrs Olga de Alba	2315 Bromsgrove Rd., Ste 130 Mississauga, ON L5G 4A6
	Hon. Consul: Mrs. Elena Eunices Herrera	1222, rue McKay, bur. 101 Montréal (Québec) H3G 2H4
Paraguay	Hon. Consul: Mr. Claude J.Y. Le Gris	1110, rue Sherbrooke ouest, bur. 1611 Montréal (Québec) H3A 1G8
Peru	Consul General: Mr. Jorge Perez-Garreaud	2250, rue Guy, bur. 304 Montréal (Québec) H3H 2M3
	Consul: Mr. Oscar Barrenechea	1200 Bay St., Ste. 503, Toronto, ON M5H 2X6
	Consul: Mr. Jaime A. Pomareda	505 Burrard St., Ste. 1770 Vancouver, BC V7X 1M6
	Hon. Consul: Mr. Kenneth Wong	201 Alexander Ave., Winnipeg, MB R3B 3C1
Philippines	Hon. Consul General: Mr. Larry Belgica	Edifice Dominion Square, bur. 337 1010, rue Ste-Catherine ouest Montréal (Québec) H3B 1G1
	Consul General: Mr. Juan A. Ona	151 Bloor St. W., Ste. 365 Toronto, ON M5S 1T5
	Consul General: Mr. Rufino Martinez	470 Granville St., Ste. 301-308 Vancouver, BC V6C 1V5
	Hon. Consul: Mr. Rolando D. Guzman	708 Medical Arts Bldg. 233 Kennedy St., Winnipeg, MB R3C 3J5
Poland	Consul General: Mr. Janusz Karski	1500, av. des Pins ouest Montréal (Québec) H3G 1B4
	Consul & Trade Commissioner: Mr. Marian Kalinowski	3501, av. du Musée, Montréal (Québec) H3G 2C8
	Consul General: Mr. Jerzy Palasz	2603 Lake Shore Blvd. W. Toronto, ON M8V 1G5
Portugal	Hon. Consul: Mr. Arthur R. Moreira	1646 Barrington St., Box 355 Halifax, NS B3J 2N7
	Consul General: Mr. Carlos Maria de Barros e Sa David Calder	1010, rue Ste-Catherine ouest, bur. 937 Montréal (Québec) H3B 3R7
	Vice-Consul & Trade Commissioner: Mr. Armando Dias Godinho	500, rue Sherbrooke ouest, bur. 940 Montréal (Québec) H3A 3C6
	Hon. Consul: Mr. Fernao Mendonça Perestrelo	775, av. Murray, bur. 710 Québec (Québec) G1S 4T2
	Hon. Vice-Consul: Mr. Hernani Eurico da Silva Martins	40 Mansfield Cres., St. John's, NF A1E 5A8
	Consul General: Mr. Antonio Tanger Correa	121 Richmond St. W., 7th Flr. Toronto, ON M5H 2K1
	Vice-Consul: Vacant	Pender Place, Ste 904 700 W. Pender St., Vancouver, BC V6B 3S3
	Hon. Consul: Mr. Gustavo Uriel da Rosa Junior	228 Notre Dame Ave., Room 902 Winnipeg, MB R3B 1N7
Romania	Consul General & Trade Commissioner: Mr. Nicolae Dragoiu	1111, rue St-Urbain Montréal (Québec) H2Z 1X6
Rwanda	Hon. Consul General: Mr. Pierre Valcour	1600, av. de Lorimier Montréal (Québec) H2K 3W5
	Hon. Consul: Mr. Ronald Heynneman	200 Consumers Rd., Ste. 500 Willowdale, ON M2J 4R4
Saint Christopher and Nevis	Hon. Consul: Mr. E. Anthony Ross	6 Armada Dr., Halifax, NS B3M 1R7
Saint Lucia	Consul: Mr. Dunstan Fontenelle	151 Bloor St. W., Ste. 425 Toronto, ON M5S 1S4
Saint Vincent and the Grenadines	Hon. Consul: Mr. Ceford E. Providence	16 Denmar Rd., Ste. 1945 Pickering, ON L1V 3E2
San Marino	Hon. Consul General: Mr. Raymond Lette	27, av. McNider, Montréal (Québec) H2V 3X4
	Hon. Consul: Mr. Germano Valle	15 McMurrich St., Ste 104 Toronto, ON M5R 3M6

Country	Representative	Address
Sao Tomé and Principe	Hon. Consul: Mr. Alain Berranger	85, rue Ste-Catherine ouest, bur. 1400 Montréal (Québec) H2X 3P4
Senegal	Hon. Consul: Dr. Gerard Bastien	2472 Bayview Ave., Toronto, ON M2A 2A7
	Hon. Consul: Mr. Louis Philippe Lavoie	2155, rue Guy, bur. 1200 Montréal (Québec) H3H 2L9
	Hon. Consul: Mr. Kenneth John Bodnarchuk	320 Industrial Ave., Vancouver, BC V6A 2P5
South Africa	Consul: Mr. Klaus W. Praekelt	1, place Ville-Marie, bur. 2615 Montréal (Québec) H3B 4S3
	Consul (Trade): Mr. Albertus J. van Zyl	Stock Exchange Tower, Ste. 2515 2 First Canadian Place, Toronto, ON M5X 1E3
Spain	Hon. Vice-Consul: Mr. Louis Holmes	1525 Birmingham St., Box 3550 S. Halifax, NS B3J 3J3
	Hon. Vice-Consul: Mr. Rafael Rodriguez-Candela	123 Portledge Ave., Moncton, NB E1C 5S8
	Consul General: Mr. Mariano Uriarte Y Llodra	1, Westmount Square, bur. 1456 Montréal (Québec) H3Z 2P9
	Hon. Vice-Consul: Mr. Pierre Villa	250, rue Lachance, Québec (Québec) G1P 2H3
	Hon. Vice-Consul: Mr. Nathaniel Cooper	10 Topsail Rd., Box W 2097 St. John's, NF A1C 5R6
	Consul General: Mr. Guillermo Cebrian	1200 Bay St., Ste. 400, Toronto, ON M4R 2A5
	Hon. Vice-Consul: Mr. F.P. Bernard	Pacific Centre, Ste. 1100 700 Georgia St. W., Box 10025 Vancouver, BC V7Y 1A1
Swaziland	Hon. Consul: Mr. William J. Campbell	111 Echo Dr., Ste. 603, Ottawa ON K1S 5K8
Sweden	Hon. Consul: Mrs. Armilda Zoumer	420-47th Ave. S.W., Calgary, AB T2S 1C4
	Hon. Consul: Mr. Lars Goran Fahlstrom	11523-100th Ave., Ste. 305 Edmonton, AB T5K 0J8
	Hon. Consul: Mr. Gunnar K.G. Jennegren	Bayers Lake Industrial Park 15 Chain Lake Dr., Box 2027 Halifax, NS B3J 2Z1
	Consul General: Mr. Bengt Rosio	1155, boul. René-Lévesque ouest, bur. 800 Montréal (Québec) H3B 2H7
	Hon. Consul: Mr. Georges de Lery Demers, Q.C.	995, ch. St-Louis, C.P. 337, succ. H-V Québec (Québec) G1R 4P8
	Hon. Consul: Mr. Larry Alvan Kyle	Ste. 720, 2103-11th Ave., Regina, SK S4P 4G1
	Hon. Consul: Mr. Gerard McGillivray	c/o Furncan Marine, Hillyard Place Bldg. 560 Main St., Box 6340, Saint John, NB E2L 3Z5
	Hon. Consul: Mr. Peter Norman Outerbridge	55 Duckworth St., Box 6150 St. John's, NF A1C 5X8
	Hon. Consul: Mr. Larry Alvan Kyle	410-22nd St. E., Ste. 850 Saskatoon, SK S7K 5T6
	Hon. Consul General: Mr. Staffan Englund	150 Bloor St. W., Ste. 835 Toronto, ON M5S 2X9
	Consul General: Mr. Karl Bertil Eriksson	1177 W. Hastings St., Ste. 1109 Vancouver, BC V6E 2K3
	Hon. Consul: Mr. Neil Edwin Carlson	1035 Mission St., Winnipeg, MB R2J 0A4
Switzerland	Hon. Consul: Mr. Klaus D. Zahnd	2836-42nd St. S.W., Calgary, AB T3E 3M1
	Hon. Consul: Mr. Erwin W. Baumann	11207-103rd Ave., Edmonton, AB T5K 2V9
	Consul General: Mr. Théodore E. Portier	1572, av. Dr. Penfield Montréal (Québec) H3G 1C4
	Hon. Consul: Mr. Jean-Pierre Beltrami	3293, Première av., Québec (Québec) G1L 3R2
	Consul General: Mr. Ernst Keller Egger	100 University Ave., Ste. 1000 Toronto, ON M5J 1V6

Country	Representative	Address
	Consul General: Mr. Max Inhelder	World Trade Centre, Ste. 790 999 Canada Place, Vancouver, BC V6C 0T6
Syria	Hon. Consul General: Mr. Muhammad Fayez Al-Rifai	324, cr. Arlington Beaconsfield (Québec) H9W 2K3
Thailand	Hon. Consul: Mr. Kurt A. Beier	11204-127th St., Edmonton, AB T5M 0T6
	Hon. Consul General: Mr. Marc J. Besso	3766, ch. de la Côte-des-Neiges Montréal (Québec) H3H 1V6
	Hon. Consul General: Mr. Richard C. Meech, Q.C.	Bank of Canada Bldg., 8th Flr. 250 University Ave., Toronto, ON M5H 3E5
	Hon. Consul General: Mr. Horst Gergen Paul Koehler	736 Granville St., Ste. 106 Vancouver, BC V6Z 1G3
Togo	Hon. Consul: Mr. Garry Tarrant	Ste. 500, 111-11th Ave. S.W. Calgary, AB T2R 0G5
	Hon. Consul: Mr. Gérard Shanks	484, Sixième av., Verdun (Québec) H4G 2K1
Trinidad and Tobago	Consul General: Mr. Trevor Carlton Spencer	365 Bloor St. E., Ste. 1700 Toronto, ON M4W 3L4
Tunisia	Hon. Consul: Mr. Emile Colas	511, place d'Armes, bur. 603 Montréal (Québec) H2Y 2W7
Turkey	Hon. Consul General: Prof. Ozdemir Erginsav	99A Wilmot Place, Winnipeg, MB R3L 2J9
Union of Soviet Socialist Republics	Consul General: Mr. Evgueni N. Kotchetkov	3685, av. du Musée, Montréal (Québec) H3G 2E1
United States of America	Consul General: Mr. Robert J. Kott	615 Macleod Trail S.E., Rm. 1050 Calgary, AB T2G 4T8
	Consul General: Mr. James D. Walsh	Cogswell Tower, Scotia Sq., Ste. 910 Halifax, NS B3J 3K1
	Consul General: Mr. Robert William Maule	1, place Desjardins, Tour sud, bur. 1122 C.P. 65, succ. Desjardins Montréal (Québec) H5B 1G1
	Consul General: Mr. Robert M. Maxim	2, place Terrasse-Dufferin C.P. 939, succ. H-V, Québec (Québec) G1R 4T9
	Consul General: Mr. John E. Hall	360 University Ave., Toronto, ON M5G 1S4
	Consul General: Mr. Samuel C. Fromovitz	1075 West Georgia St., Vancouver, BC V6E 4E9
Uruguay	Hon. Consul: Mr. Charles Villiers	1889, rue Workman, Montréal (Québec) H3J 2P1
	Hon. Consul: Mr. Mario Campomar Mira	Ste. 1250, 650 W. Georgia St. Box 11526, Vancouver, BC V6B 4N7
Venezuela	Consul General: Mr. Jose Ramon Dovale	1410, rue Stanley, bur. 600 Montréal (Québec) H3A 1P8
	Consul General: Mr. Carlos Alberto Taylhardat	2 Carlton St., Ste. 703 Toronto, ON M5B 1J3
Yemen Arab Republic	Hon. Consul: Mr. Taha A. Qirbi	56 Sparks St., Ste. 500, Ottawa, ON K1P 5A9
Yugoslavia	Hon. Consul: Mr. Kalman Samuels	1, place Ville-Marie, bur. 3424 Montréal (Québec) H3B 3N6
	Consul General: Mr. Mihajlo Dika	377 Spadina Rd., Toronto, ON M5P 2V7
	Vice-Consul: Mr. Nenad Ugrina	1237 Burrard St., Box 48359 Vancouver, BC V7X 1A1
Zaire	Hon. Consul General: Mr. Luc Jacques Pirard	407, rue McGill, bur. 705 Montréal (Québec) H2Y 2G3

INFORMATION FOR CANADIANS TRAVELLING ABROAD

CANADIAN PASSPORTS

Canadian passports are issued only to Canadian citizens. The total life of a Canadian passport is five years. The passport is a valuable document, the loss of which must be reported to the local police and either to the Passport Bureau, Ottawa, one of the regional offices *(See Passport Bureau in the Department of External Affairs listing earlier in this chapter),* or to the nearest Canadian Embassy, High Commission, or consular office abroad.

A passport does not necessarily confer the right to enter any country. *(See "Visa and Entry Requirements" below.)*

Passport Requirements

All applicants (including children whose names will appear in a parent's passport) must submit documentary proof of Canadian citizenship:

(a) applicants born in Canada
—Certificate of Birth;
OR
—Certificate of Canadian Citizenship*

(b) applicants not born in Canada
—Certificate of Canadian Citizenship*
OR
—Certificate of Naturalization in Canada;
OR
—Certificate of Registration of Birth Abroad;
OR
—Certificate of Retention of Canadian Citizenship

* Includes miniature certificate. Large certificates issued after Feb. 14, 1977 are not acceptable.

Applicants not born in Canada who do not hold one of the certificates mentioned above must confirm their citizenship status with the nearest Citizenship Court Office or the Registrar of Canadian Citizenship, Ottawa, and submit, with the passport application, a Certificate of Canadian Citizenship.

Fee Schedule:

Canadian passport $25.00
Businessperson's Canadian passport $27.00
Addition of a married name to a
   maiden name passport. $5.00

Application for Passport

Application for a passport should be mailed to reach the Passport Bureau, Department of External Affairs, Ottawa, ON K1A 0G3, at least two weeks plus mailing time before the passport is required. Alternatively, applications may be presented in person at any of the regional passport offices of the Department of External Affairs. Regional offices do not accept mailed-in applications. However, a passport may be obtained from a regional office in a shorter period of time. Canadian citizens residing abroad should apply to the Canadian mission in their country of residence.

Regulations and instructions for persons applying for Canadian passports in Canada are contained in "Passport Application Form A" for applicants 16 and over, and "Passport Application Form B" for a child under 16. These can be obtained from any main branch post office in Canada (but not from a sub-post office), the Passport Office in Ottawa, the regional offices or travel agencies.

Every application for a passport must be signed by a guarantor from one of the eligible categories listed on the form, who must also certify (sign the back of) one of the applicant's photographs. In addition to being a member of one of the groups listed, the guarantor must be a Canadian citizen who has known the applicant personally for at least two years. If there is no person available within the group of eligible guarantors who has known the applicant for the required two years, appropriate instructions will be found in the application form.

Passport fraud by applicants or guarantors is covered by section 58(2) of the *Criminal Code* whereby: "Everyone who, while in or out of Canada, for the purpose of procuring a passport for himself or any other person, makes a written or oral statement that he knows is false or misleading is guilty of an indictable offence and is liable to imprisonment for two years."

Children. Separate passports for children under 16 years may be obtained by submitting application Form B. The name of a child under 16 years of age may be included in the passport of either parent but may not be included in the passports of both parents at the same time. If a child's name is to be added to an existing passport or transferred from one parent's passport to the passport of the other parent, Form B-1 must be submitted.

TRAVEL REGULATIONS ABROAD

Visa and entry requirements. Although Canadians planning to travel abroad should hold valid Canadian passports, they may not require visas, entry permits or tourist cards for short visits to many countries; however, before leaving Canada, travellers are urged to check with the embassy or consulate of the country concerned to determine visa and entry/exit requirements, current regulations concerning residence and work permits, health certificates, customs, currency, etc., all of which are subject to change without notice.

Addresses of foreign representatives *(see listings earlier in this section)* are contained in the book *Diplomatic, Consular, and Other Representatives in Canada, which is available from Canadian Government Publishing Centre, Supply and Services Canada, Ottawa, ON K1A 0S9.*

Foreign authorities will expect visitors to have sufficient funds for their stay, to possess either return or onward transportation tickets, and to be in good health.

Work permits. Most countries will not allow non-residents to accept gainful employment unless they have applied for and been granted work permits prior to their entry.

Vaccination requirements. Before leaving Canada, travellers are advised to consult their doctor, their municipal or provincial Department of Health, or an office of Health and Welfare Canada about vaccination requirements or recommendations for each of the countries that are to be visited. Because health regulations are subject to change with little notice, it is recommended that the vaccination requirements be confirmed just before departure and en route if the itinerary is lengthy. Travellers are no longer required to present International Certificates of Vaccination upon return to Canada.

Travel in remote or dangerous areas. Canadians planning to travel in areas where their personal safety might be at risk are encouraged to contact the Department of External Affairs for information on the latest developments and on the risks involved. To do so, either:

a) write or call the Department in Ottawa (613) 992-3705;
b) call the nearest passport office; or
c) if outside Canada, contact a Canadian mission.

Before travelling in remote areas or proceeding on mountain climbing expeditions, Canadians should consult the Canadian mission in or accredited to the country concerned and *obtain special insurance to cover medical evacuation.* Furthermore, they are urged to leave detailed itineraries with responsible persons before departure to facilitate the task of search and rescue parties in case of mishap.

Consular assistance. International law provides the right of consular authorities to have access to their nationals if they have been detained or imprisoned in a foreign country. Canadian citizens arrested or detained for any reason in a foreign country should be aware of this right and insist that the nearest Canadian consul be notified if they wish assistance.

NOTE: Canada does not have diplomatic or consular relations with, and therefore cannot provide normal consular services or assistance to Canadians travelling in these countries: Cambodia (Kampuchea), North Korea, Taiwan, Namibia, and the so-called independent homelands in the Republic of South Africa.

Foreign laws and regulations. Canadian travellers are considered subject to the laws, both criminal and civil, of the country they are visiting. Behaviour, dress and general appearance, an open expression of political opinions or religious beliefs, the active or even symbolic participation in local political, liberation or revolutionary movements, even the taking of pictures may be considered crimes under local laws and regulations.

Illegal drugs and narcotics. Severe penalties are being imposed in most countries on persons convicted of possessing, smuggling or trafficking in drugs. As part of a major international effort to curtail the use and transportation of drugs, heavy fines and/or long prison sentences are now the rule, notwithstanding the fact that in many countries drugs are readily available, inexpensive and openly used. In late 1987, over 200 Canadians of all ages were being held in foreign jails for drug-related offences, either awaiting trial or serving lengthy sentences including life imprisonment. In some countries, possession of even small amounts carries the death penalty.

Registration Abroad

Canadian citizens visiting a country for an extended period or residing therein are advised to register at the nearest Canadian diplomatic or consular post. In those countries where Canada is not represented, Canadians may register with the nearest British representative. Failure to register may, in an emergency, result in difficulty or delay in obtaining assistance and protection.

Prompt notification of departures or changes of address should be given. Canadians visiting a country which maintains exit controls whereby travellers are required to have or obtain exit visas or similar documentation before they are free to leave that country may wish, in their own interests, to notify, in person if possible, the nearest Canadian mission, or mission of a friendly country, if there is no Canadian office, both on their arrival in the country and on their departure.

Should it not be possible to appear personally, the following particulars may be provided by telephone or mail: full name, permanent Canadian address, serial number, date and place of issue of passport, details of itinerary, expected date of departure, and next destination. If, as in the nations mentioned above, there is no resident Canadian or British representation, notification may be given to the Canadian mission in the country from which the traveller is proceeding.

Dual Nationality

Canadian citizens born abroad, or whose parents were born abroad, may be considered by the governments of the countries of their birth or descent to be nationals of these countries, although by Canadian law they are citizens of Canada. Similarly, Canadians married to aliens may be considered by the foreign governments concerned to have automatically acquired their spouse's citizenship. When such persons visit those countries, they are subject to their laws and regulations on the basis of citizenship, and are not exempt from any obligations imposed by the foreign law, including military service, taxation, etc. It is extremely difficult for them to be accorded the consular protection of the Canadian Government available otherwise.

Persons desiring further information concerning their status should consult the representative in Canada of the country concerned. *(For addresses, see listings of Canadian Diplomatic Representatives earlier in this section.)*

CUSTOMS INFORMATION FOR CANADIAN RESIDENTS

NOTE: All dollar figures quoted below are in Canadian dollars.)

Gifts. You may send gifts from abroad to friends or relatives in Canada under certain conditions. Firstly, each gift must be valued at no more than $40 and, secondly, the gifts must *not* consist of alcoholic beverages, tobacco products or advertising matter. If any gift is valued at more than $40, your friend or relative will be required to pay regular duty and taxes on the excess amount. Gifts sent from abroad do *not* count against your personal exemption. A gift card should be enclosed to avoid misunderstanding. Gifts that you bring back with you DO count against your personal exemption.

Personal exemptions. Any resident of Canada returning from a trip abroad may qualify for a personal exemption and therefore be able to bring into Canada goods up to a certain value — free of duty and taxes. This also applies to temporary residents of Canada and to former residents who are returning to resume residence in Canada. Even an infant may qualify and in that case the parent or guardian may make a Customs declaration on behalf of the infant. The goods purchased in the child's name must be for his or her exclusive use.

The "personal exemption" entitlement has certain limitations — the frequency of its use, the length of stay abroad and, in the case of alcoholic beverages and tobacco products, the age of the individual. In general, the goods brought in under a personal exemption must be for personal or household use, as souvenirs of your trip or as gifts for friends or relatives. Goods acquired for *commercial* use, or on behalf of another person, do not qualify and will be subject to full duty and taxes.

The exemption is a *personal* thing, for which each individual does — or does not — qualify at any given time. Your exemption cannot be pooled with, or transferred to, other individuals. You cannot, for example, combine your 48-hour ($100) and yearly ($300) exemptions and claim a "special" exemption of $400. Nor can you use half of your yearly exemption now and "save" the other $150 for another trip six months from now.

After 24 hours' absence or more: (any number of times per year) you may bring in goods to the value of $20 (excluding tobacco products and alcoholic beverages). Only an oral declaration is required. Note that if the total value of all goods imported exceeds $20, this exemption may not be claimed.

After 48 hours' absence or more: (any number of times a year) you may bring in goods to the value of $100. A written declaration may be required.

After seven days' absence or more (by calendar days, including date of return but not date of departure, once every calendar year) you may bring in goods to the value of $300. A written declaration will be required.

Alcohol and tobacco allowances. Subject to the conditions below, you may bring in alcoholic beverages and tobacco products free of duty and taxes if you are eligible for the 48-hour ($100) or yearly ($300) exemption. The dollar value of these items will of course form part of your personal exemption. Note that these items may *not* be claimed under a $20 exemption.

Any person aged 16 or over may bring in 200 cigarettes *and* 50 cigars (or cigarillos) *and* 1 kg (2.2 lbs) of tobacco. Additional quantities may be brought in, if you are willing to pay duty and taxes on the excess amount.

If you meet the age requirements set by the province or territory *through which you re-enter Canada,* you may bring in 1.1 litres of wine or liquor, or twenty-four 355 ml cans or bottles of beer or ale (or its equivalent — 8.5 litres). All provinces except the Northwest Territories allow you to exceed the normal allowance by up to nine extra litres, though the cost is high. On your return, Customs can assist you with the special documentation required. For further information, check with the appropriate liquor control authority before you leave Canada.

All tobacco products and alcoholic beverages must accompany you in your hand or checked luggage.

Customs declarations. When you re-enter Canada, you must declare to Customs *everything* you have acquired abroad, whether as purchases, gifts, prizes or awards. This must include goods still in your possession that you bought at a Canadian or foreign duty-free store. These goods should be easily accessible for inspection, and it is a good idea to have with you receipts for goods purchased, for accommodation while you were away and for repairs done (or parts added) to articles you had in your possession when you left Canada, including your motor vehicle, outboard motor, camera, etc. Such repairs and parts may be subject to duty and taxes. When repairs or replacement parts for your motor vehicle, cruiser, yacht or aircraft were *essential* to your safe return to Canada, a remission of duty and taxes may be granted.

Goods you bring in under the $20 or $100 exemption must accompany you in hand or checked luggage in all situations. Goods you bring in under the $300 (yearly) exemption may follow you by mail or other means of transport. List with Customs, on your declaration form, all the goods that are "to follow". Also fill out form E-24 and obtain a receipt copy.

When you are advised that your goods have arrived, you have 40 days in which to clear them through Customs, by presenting your copy of Form E-24.

If any of the goods you bought abroad have to be repaired or replaced, you have 60 days from the date of your return to Canada in which to contact Customs and arrange documentation to cover the exchange.

Excluding of course those items that are restricted, there is nothing to stop you from bringing back any quantity of goods (even if you cannot qualify for *any* kind of personal exemption), provided you are willing to pay the full rate of duty and taxes.

Special tax rate. After any trip abroad for 48 hours or more, you are entitled to a special 20 per cent tax rate on:

(a) goods valued up to $300 *over and above* your $100 or $300 personal exemption;
(b) goods valued up to $300, if no personal exemption is being claimed.

The special tax rate applies only to goods which accompany you and may not include alcohol or tobacco products. Regular duty and taxes apply to all importations in excess of (a) or (b) above.

If you are bringing in a lot of goods, the Customs officer can advise you which goods to charge to your personal exemption — to give you maximum duty and tax advantages.

If you are bringing in far *less* than your personal exemption allows, the Customs officer can let you know if it would pay to clear the goods under the 20 per cent special rate — and save your personal exemption for another trip.

To clear your goods through Customs, payment can be in cash, by travellers' cheques or by certified cheque. If duty and taxes do not exceed $75, a personal cheque (with proper identification) will be accepted. VISA and Mastercard are accepted at a number of Customs locations.

The Customs officer is required to protect Canada's safety, economic life and environment, and your co-operation is requested. The officer is legally entitled to examine your luggage, while you are responsible for opening, unpacking and repacking it. You may occasionally find yourself going through a very detailed Customs inspection. The unexpectedness of the search is intended to upset the careful planning of the professional smuggler, while for the law-abiding traveller it means only a minor delay.

Customs penalties. Goods not declared — or falsely declared — may be subject to seizure and forfeiture and the traveller may face severe penalties. Penalties are imposed according to the law and the circumstances. If, for example, you were caught smuggling an item, it could be seized and forfeited outright, or you might have to pay much more than its actual value to have it released. In addition, the car (or boat, or aircraft) that transported the item could be seized and forfeited, or you or the owner might have to pay to get it back. You might also face prosecution for smuggling and the possibility of a fine or imprisonment.

Customs offices. To learn the rate of duty and taxes on any given item, contact the nearest Customs office before you leave Canada. A list of the regional Customs offices can be found in the departmental listings for Revenue Canada under Customs and Excise (*see earlier in this section*). There are also offices in some of the smaller cities: look in your local telephone book under "Government of Canada, Customs and Excise."

THE CANADIAN ARMED FORCES

The Department of National Defence

The Department of National Defence was created by the *National Defence Act, 1922*, R.S.C. 1970, Chapter N-4, which established one department of government in place of the previous departments of Militia and Defence, Naval Service and the Air Board.

The Minister of National Defence, and the Associate Minister of National Defence, appointed in 1985, are charged with the control and management of the Canadian Forces and all matters relating to national defence establishments and works for the defence of Canada. They are also responsible for Emergency Preparedness Canada.

In December 1976, the Minister of National Defence was further designated the minister responsible for all aspects of air search and rescue in the areas of Canadian SAR responsibility, and for the overall co-ordination of marine search and rescue, including provision of air resources for marine SAR.

(For senior officials of the Department of National Defence, see the departmental listing earlier in this chapter.)

The Command Structure of the Canadian Forces

The Canadian Armed Forces are organized on a functional basis to reflect the major commitments assigned by the government. All forces devoted to a primary mission are grouped under a single commander who is assigned sufficient resources to discharge his responsibilities. Specifically, the Canadian Forces are formed into a Headquarters and the major Commands reporting to the Chief of the Defence Staff; these Commands are described below.

Maritime Command. The Commander, Maritime Command, headquartered in Halifax, has responsibility over all Canadian maritime forces. In addition, he exercises operational control of aircraft assigned to him either by the Commander of Maritime Air Group for maritime operations, or by the Commander of Air Transport Group for search and rescue in the Atlantic region.

The role of Maritime Command is the surveillance and control of the sea approaches of the three oceans bordering Canada, and the provision of combat-ready ships in support of Canada's commitment to NATO and continental defence. The Commander, Maritime Command, is also the Commander of the Canadian Atlantic Sub-Area of the Western Atlantic Command, under the Supreme Allied Commander Atlantic. Additional responsibilities are the support of Canadian military operations as required, and search and rescue operations within the Halifax and Victoria regions.

Since Canada declared her 200-nautical mile exclusive economic zone effective Jan. 1, 1977, increased maritime surface and air resources have been devoted to the surveillance and control of Canadian waters. A multitude of ships is identified each year and many are boarded by fisheries officers of the Department of Fisheries and Oceans, assisted by Canadian military personnel.

The following vessels are in service in Maritime Command: 20 Destroyer Escorts/Destroyer Escorts Helicopter Equipped; three Underway Replenishment Ships; three Oberon Class Submarines; six Bay Class Coastal Patrol Vessels (employed as training ships); five Trawler-type ships and one Patrol Cutter for Reserve training; a Diving Support Vessel; plus three Destroyer Escorts in operational reserve.

Construction contracts have been let for several new frigates and a plan to add nuclear-powered submarines to the Canadian fleet is also in the works.

Naval Reserve. The Naval Reserve is an essential component of Maritime Command. Its primary function during emergencies is naval control of shipping and maritime coastal defence. Another function is the provision of reinforcements to Maritime Command. The Naval Reserve Division's headquarters is located in Quebec City, and there are 21 naval reserve units located in major Canadian cities, of which the three from Chicoutimi, Rimouski and Trois Rivières are the most recent, and a Naval Reserve Training Centre on the west coast. They are as follows:

HMCS *Tecumseh*, Calgary, Alta.
HMCS *Nonsuch*, Edmonton, Alta.
Naval Reserve Training Centre, Esquimalt, B.C.
HMCS *Discovery*, Vancouver, B.C.
HMCS *Malahat*, Victoria, B.C.
HMCS *Chippawa*, Winnipeg, Man.
HMCS *Brunswicker*, Saint John, N.B.
HMCS *Cabot*, St. John's, Nfld.
HMCS *Scotian*, Halifax, N.S.
HMCS *Star*, Hamilton, Ont.
HMCS *Cataraqui*, Kingston, Ont.
HMCS *Carleton*, Ottawa, Ont.
HMCS *Griffon*, Thunder Bay, Ont.
HMCS *York*, Toronto, Ont.
HMCS *Hunter*, Windsor, Ont.
HMCS *Champlain*, Chicoutimi, Que.
HMCS *Donnacona*, Montreal, Que.
HMCS *Montcalm*, Quebec City, Que.
HMCS *D'Iberville*, Rimouski, Que.
HMCS *Radisson*, Trois Rivières, Que.
HMCS *Queen*, Regina, Sask.
HMCS *Unicorn*, Saskatoon, Sask.

Mobile Command. The role of Mobile Command is to provide military units, suitably trained and equipped, for the protection of Canadian territory; to maintain combat-ready formations in Canada required for overseas commitments; and to support United Nations or other peace-keeping operations.

The forces assigned include a brigade-group in the West, with headquarters at Calgary; a brigade-group in the East, with headquarters at Valcartier, Que.; and an air-transportable brigade and group-sized formation, the Special Service Force, with headquarters at Petawawa, Ont. In addition, the Command provides troops (at present approximately battalion size) to the United Nations Forces in Cyprus.

Militia. Mobile Command exercises command and control of 131 units through 5 Militia area Headquarters and 22 Militia Districts. The Militia is charged with: providing trained individuals for reinforcement of the Regular Force; providing trained sub-units to support the field force for the defence of Canada and the maintenance of internal security; providing aid for the civil emergency operations organization; and forming the base on which the Regular Force could be expanded in the event of an emergency.

Air Command. The Command's principal function is to provide operationally ready regular and reserve air forces to meet Canada's national, continental and international commitments, and to carry out regional commitments within the Prairie region, comprising Saskatchewan, Alberta, Manitoba and the northwest part of Ontario.

Air Command, with headquarters at Winnipeg, consists of the following functional elements:

The **Fighter Group,** with headquarters at North Bay, Ont., is charged with maintaining the sovereignty of Canada's air space, supporting Mobile Command and Maritime Command training, and providing combat aircrew to meet Canada's North American Aerospace Defence (NORAD) and North Atlantic Treaty Organization (NATO) commitments. It has command of all fighter aircraft resources in Canada. This includes one fighter/ground attack operational training squadron equipped with CF-5s, two ground attack squadrons and two air defence squadrons both equipped with CF-18s, and one CF-18 operational training squadron, one electronic warfare training squadron that includes EC-144 (Challenger) and CT-133 aircraft. As the CF-18 aircraft phase-in continues, the CF-5s committed to NATO will be phased out and replaced by CF-18s. The Fighter Group also has command of the North Warning System and former Pinetree Line sites, a space sensor unit and an electronic warfare squadron, which will be equipped with Electronic System Training Challengers.

The **Air Transport Group,** with headquarters at Trenton, Ont., provides airlift resources for the Canadian Forces and undertakes other national and international tasks as directed by the government. The group provides search and rescue service for downed aircraft and marine search and rescue operations.

Its heavy transport resources consist of 28 C-130 Hercules aircraft and five Boeing 707 aircraft. Four of the Hercules are equipped for navigation training and are located at Winnipeg, while a squadron at Ottawa provides medium-range passenger transport with Cosmopolitan and Challenger aircraft. In addition, two Dash 8 aircraft are located in Lahr, West Germany for passenger transport in Europe.

Transport and Rescue squadrons located at Comox, B.C., Edmonton, Trenton, Ont. and Summerside, P.E.I., are equipped with a combination of fixed-wing aircraft and helicopters. Either Buffalo or Twin Otter aircraft together with Twin Huey or Labrador helicopters are utilized. Squadrons at Edmonton operate Twin Otters and Hercules. Three helicopters are now based at Gander, Nfld., as 103 Rescue Unit, to enable a quicker response to emergency situations in Newfoundland, Labrador and surrounding waters.

The **Maritime Air Group** (MAG), with headquarters at Halifax, is responsible for management of all air resources engaged in maritime patrol, maritime surveillance and anti-submarine warfare.

The commander of Maritime Air Group is responsible to the Commander Air Command but provides aircraft and crews to the Commander Maritime Command for the conduct of maritime surveillance patrols and anti-submarine operations. A close working relationship between Maritime Command and Maritime Air Group enables them to utilize a common operations centre.

Mobile Command has operational control over Air Command's **10 Tactical Air Group** (10 TAG); both have headquarters in St-Hubert, Que. The group operates all rotary wing air resources engaged in the close support of land forces. This involves helicopter fire-support, reconnaissance and tactical transport over the battle area.

14 Training Group, formed in 1981, is responsible to the Commander of Air Command for aircrew selection, aircrew training to wings standard, junior leadership and survival training, and meteorological training. The Group, located in Winnipeg, develops all training policy and monitors and evaluates all Air Command training.

The **Air Reserve Group** was formed on April 1, 1976. Commanded by a reserve officer of brigadier general rank, Air Reserve Group headquarters are co-located with Air Command headquarters at Winnipeg.

The Air Reserve comprises two wings, each having two squadrons located in Montreal and Toronto and three other squadrons located in Winnipeg, Edmonton and Summerside, P.E.I. In addition, Air Reserve Augmentation flights at nine different bases in Canada have been formed to provide a cadre of trained personnel available for war establishment augmentation and for base expansion.

The Canadian Forces Communication Command. The Canadian Forces Communication Command, with headquarters in Ottawa, manages, operates and maintains strategic communications for the Canadian Forces and, in emergencies, for the federal and provincial governments. As well, the Command provides points for interconnecting strategic and tactical networks. Through the Supplementary Radio System, the Command provides a signal intelligence service in support of Canada's foreign and defence policies, operates high-frequency direction-finding facilities to assist search and rescue operations and collects data to support research in long distance arctic communications.

The Communication Reserve, which is assigned to the Canadian Forces Communication Command, is responsible for augmenting and supporting Communication Command forces in peace and war. It is composed of 21 units which are located all across Canada.

Canadian Forces Europe. The Canadian forces allocated to NATO and stationed in Europe consist of land and air elements located in the southwest of the Federal Republic of Germany. The land element, 4th Canadian Mechanized Brigade Group, is operationally responsible to NATO's Central Army Group. The air element, 1 Canadian Air Division, consists of three CF-18 squadrons and two rapid-reinforcement CF-18 squadrons (which belong to Fighter Group and are normally stationed in Canada, but in the event of hostilities are assigned to CFE), operationally assigned to Fourth Allied Tactical Air Force. These elements are located in the Schwarzwald area of the Federal Republic of Germany and are supported administratively by CFB Baden-Soellingen and CFB Lahr.

Functional Regional Organization. Functional Commanders have been assigned a regional as well as a functional responsibility for such actions as representation to provincial governments, aid of the civil power, emergency and survival operations, and administration of cadets, as well as regional support services for all units in the region.

Canada has been divided into six geographical regions. Five are assigned to functional Commands as follows: Atlantic Region (Newfoundland, Nova Scotia, P.E.I., New Brunswick) — Maritime Command; Eastern Region (Quebec) — Mobile Command; Central Region (Ontario) — Canadian Forces Training System; Prairie Region (Manitoba, Saskatchewan and Alberta) — Air Command; Pacific Region (B.C.) — Maritime Forces Pacific. One region, comprising Yukon and the Northwest Territories, has been assigned to Commander Northern Region, with headquarters in Yellowknife, N.W.T.

Liaison in Other Countries

The **Canadian Military Representative to NATO** is the representative of the Chief of the Defence Staff and acts as military adviser to Canadian NATO delegations.

Canadian Defence Liaison Staff, London, represents the Canadian Armed Forces in Britain, and the Commander is responsible for the provision of military advice and appropriate support and assistance to the Canadian High Commissioner in London.

Canadian Defence Liaison Staff, Washington, represents the Canadian Armed Forces in the U.S. and the Commander is responsible for the provision of military advice and appropriate support and assistance to the Canadian Ambassador.

In addition, representatives are provided to SACLANT headquarters, the Canadian Permanent Representative to the North Atlantic Council, to SHAPE, and to other levels of NATO headquarters. Canadian Forces attachés are also attached to a number of embassies and high commissions throughout the world.

The Permanent Joint Board on Defence was formed as a result of a meeting between Prime Minister King and President Roosevelt at Ogdensburg, New York, on Aug. 18, 1940. The Board (which has two co-chairmen) reports through the chairmen directly to the President and to the Prime Minister on matters involving the defence of the north half of the Western Hemisphere. The board meets three times a year: February in the U.S., June in Canada, and in October, alternately in the national capitals. The agenda has included almost all of the important joint defence measures — the North Warning System, which has replaced the Distant Early Warning (DEW) Line, and NORAD, for example — taken by the two governments.

Operations. Maritime, air, surface and sub-surface forces participate in NATO exercises in North Atlantic areas and in combined exercises with forces from New Zealand, Australia, Britain and the United States in Pacific waters. In conjunction with such exercises, naval ships often visit other nations. In addition, deployments are occasionally made to the Arctic to assess capabilities in northern waters, to assist other government departments engaged in technical and environmental research, and to visit northern settlements.

In fulfilment of obligations under NATO, Canada provides land and air forces for the defence of Western Europe. Every fall, a series of exercises is conducted in which troops of 4th Canadian Mechanized Brigade Group, Lahr, West Germany train alongside those of the Federal Republic of Germany, The Netherlands, Belgium, the United States and the United Kingdom. CF-18s of 1 Canadian Air Division often fly close support during this training. Usually once a year, CF-5s from Canada utilizing air-to-air refuelling from

Boeing 707s are deployed to northern Norway to train for wartime contingencies there. About every second year, Canadian forces of the Allied Command Europe Mobile Force Land and Air components also carry out a deployment to northern Norway to exercise northern flank defensive commitments.

To exercise Canadian sovereignty and to familiarize troops with the problems of living, moving and fighting in the North, Exercise Sovereign Viking is Mobile Command's most important northern exercise. The operation takes place at various locations throughout the Arctic archipelago.

The Canadian Forces continues support for UN peacekeeping operations. Canada's 515-man contribution to the United Nations Force in Cyprus is based on a combat arms unit and includes a contingent headquarters as well as Canadian elements at Force Headquarters.

In the Middle East, Canada is involved in the United Nations Disengagement Observer Force (UNDOF) in the Golan Heights and the United Nations Truce Supervision Organization (UNTSO) which operates in Egypt, Israel, Syria, Lebanon and Jordan. The Canadian contingent in UNDOF, totalling 220 persons, is primarily responsible for providing communications, logistic and technical support. There are also 20 Canadian officers assigned to UNTSO for employment as military observers or as staff. Canada also contributes a Rotary Wing Aviation Unit of 140 personnel to the Multinational Force and Observers (MFO) in the Sinai.

As of May 2, 1988, five Canadian Armed Forces officers are participating in the United Nations Good Offices Mission in Afghanistan and Pakistan (UNGOMAP) for a period of one year to facilitate the implementation of the Geneva agreements of April 14, 1988.

Training

All recruit and most basic and advanced trades training in support of the Canadian Armed Forces takes place at various schools under the supervision of the Canadian Forces Training System, headquartered in Trenton, Ont. Maritime Command, Mobile Command and Air Command maintain functional control of trades and operational training for their personnel.

The Combat Training Centre, Gagetown, N.B., conducts training for officers and men of the armour, artillery and infantry units of the Regular and Reserve Forces, ranging from basic trades to advanced courses. Similar courses for French-speaking personnel are given at the Combat Training Centre Detachment, Valcartier, Que. Training for field engineers and construction trades is given at Chilliwack, B.C.

Recruit training takes place at Cornwallis, N.S., for anglophone recruits and at St-Jean-sur-Richelieu, Que., for francophone recruits. Basic technical training in French is also given at CFB St-Jean, and an expanding trades-training program in French is given at most bases and schools.

St-Jean is also the site of the English-French Language School, although the official languages are also taught on a limited scale at selected Canadian Forces bases and in civilian centres. Training in other languages is given at the Canadian Forces Foreign Language School in Ottawa.

Support trades training is conducted at the School of Administration and Logistics at CFB Borden near Barrie, Ont. Communications, electronics operations and maintenance training is conducted at the School of Communications and Electronic Engineering at CFB Kingston, aerospace training at the School of Aerospace, and Ordnance Engineering at CFB Borden. Training for various other technical specialties is conducted at a number of bases across Canada. Two Fleet Schools, one at CFB Esquimalt, and the other at CFB Halifax, provide basic and advanced maritime trades training and have training facilities for the operational warships on the east and west coasts.

Flying training to "wings" standard is based in the Prairie provinces: primary flying training, pilot selection and basic helicopter flying training at Portage la Prairie, Man.; and flying training to wings standard at Moose Jaw, Sask. Air Navigator and Airborne Electronic Sensor Operator training is conducted at the Air Navigation School at CFB Winnipeg. The operational Groups maintain operational flying training units and technical training units to train tradesmen and specialist officers on the handling of equipment.

The cadet movement in Canada. Three civilian agencies co-sponsor with the Canadian Forces the operation of the Canadian Cadets organizations. The Air Cadet League of Canada, the Army Cadet League and the Navy League of Canada promote the Royal Canadian Air Cadets, the Royal Canadian Army Cadets and the Royal Canadian Sea Cadet Corps for boys and girls between the ages of 13 and 19. In addition, the Navy League has two other organizations, the Navy League Cadets for boys aged 11 to 13 and the Wrenette Corps for girls aged 11 to 13. The Department provides a number of summer camps across the country, and sponsors exchange programs between provinces, and with the United States, Britain and several European countries.

Military Assistance Programs. Bilateral agreements covering legal, financial and administrative arrangements for the provision of military training assistance exist or are under negotiation with 25 countries. These are: Antigua and Barbuda, Bangladesh, Barbados, Belize, Botswana, Cameroon, Ghana, Guyana, Ivory Coast, Jamaica, Kenya, Kuwait, Malawi, Malaysia, Nepal, Nigeria, Oman, Sierra Leone, Sudan, Tanzania, Thailand, Trinidad and Tobago, Uganda, Zambia and Zimbabwe.

Canada provides training facilities for some NATO countries on a cost-recovery basis according to the provisions of the *Visiting Forces Act* and the NATO Status of Forces Agreement. Under the terms of such agreements, military forces from Great Britain and Germany have trained in Canada.

Pilots from NATO countries have trained at Canadian defence establishments for many years. Over the years, pilots from Denmark, Italy, Germany, Norway and the Netherlands have benefited from the program.

Canadian Military Colleges

The three Canadian Military Colleges are the Royal Military College of Canada, founded at Kingston, Ont., in 1876; Royal Roads Military College, established in 1941 near Victoria, B.C.; and Collège militaire royal de St-Jean, established at St-Jean-sur-Richelieu, Que., in 1952. The role of the colleges is to educate and train officer cadets and commissioned officers for a career in the Canadian Forces. *(For more information, see the listings in the Education chapter of Volume 1.)*

The Canadian Forces Bases

BADEN-SOELLINGEN
CFB Baden-Soellingen
CFPO 5056, Belleville, ON K0K 3R0

BAGOTVILLE
BFC Bagotville, Alouette (Québec) G0V 1A0

BORDEN
CFB Borden, Borden, ON L0M 1C0

CALGARY
CFB Calgary, Calgary, AB T3E 1T8

CHATHAM
CFB Chatham, Curtis Park, NB E0C 2E0

CHILLIWACK
CFB Chilliwack, Chilliwack, BC V0X 2E0

COLD LAKE
CFB Cold Lake, Medley, AB T0A 2M0

COMOX
CFB Comox, Lazo, BC V0R 2K0

CORNWALLIS
CFB Cornwallis, Cornwallis, NS B0S 1H0

EDMONTON
CFB Edmonton
Lancaster Park, AB T0A 2H0

ESQUIMALT
CFB Esquimalt, FMO Victoria, BC V0S 1B0

EUROPE
Canadian Forces Headquarters Europe
CFPO 5000, Belleville, ON K0K 3R0

GAGETOWN
CFB Gagetown, Oromocto, NB E0G 2P0

GANDER
CFB Gander, Box 600, Gander, NF A1X 2X1

GREENWOOD
CFB Greenwood, Greenwood, NS B0P 1N0

HALIFAX
CFB Halifax, FMO Halifax, NS B3K 2X0

KINGSTON
CFB Kingston, Kingston, ON K7L 2Z2

LAHR
CFB Lahr, CFPO 5000
Belleville, ON K0K 3R0

LONDON
CFB London, London, ON N5Y 4T7

MONCTON
CFB Moncton, Moncton, NB E1C 8K4

MONTREAL
BFC Montréal, St-Hubert (Québec) J3Y 5T4

MOOSE JAW
CFB Moose Jaw
Bushell Park, SK S0H 0N0

NORTH BAY
CFB North Bay
Hornell Heights, ON P0H 1P0

OTTAWA
CFB Ottawa, Ottawa, ON K1A 0K5

PENHOLD
CFB Penhold, Mynarski Park, AB T0M 1N0

PETAWAWA
CFB Petawawa, Petawawa, ON K8H 2X3

PORTAGE LA PRAIRIE
CFB Portage la Prairie
Southport, MB R0H 1N0

SHEARWATER
CFB Shearwater, Shearwater, NS B0J 3A0

SHILO
CFB Shilo, Shilo, MB R0K 2A0

ST-JEAN
BFC St-Jean, Richelain (Québec) J0J 1R0

SUFFIELD
CFB Suffield, Ralston, AB T0J 2N0

SUMMERSIDE
CFB Summerside
Slemon Park, PE C0B 2A0

TORONTO
CFB Toronto, Downsview, ON M3K 1Y6

TRENTON
CFB Trenton, Astra, ON K0K 1B0

VALCARTIER
BFC Valcartier
Courcelette (Québec) G0A 1R0

WINNIPEG
CFB Winnipeg, Westwin, MB R2R 0T0

MAJOR WORLD ORGANIZATIONS
TO WHICH CANADA BELONGS

NORTH ATLANTIC TREATY ORGANIZATION (NATO)

The North Atlantic Treaty was concluded in 1949 for an initial period of 20 years. It was renewed for a further, indefinite period in 1969.

The Treaty provides for the collective security and defence of the 16 signatory nations and NATO was established to promote this objective. The Treaty also promises to promote political, economic, social/scientific and cultural co-operation between the member nations. The main pillars of NATO's policy are defence, deterrence and détente. Defence and deterrence are achieved through a strategy of flexible response or the use of a well balanced mixture of conventional, intermediate range and strategic nuclear weapons to permit a flexible response to aggression by direct defence at an appropriate level, should deterrence fail.

The 16 member countries of NATO are: Belgium, Canada, Denmark, France, the Federal Republic of Germany, Greece, Iceland, Italy Luxembourg, the Netherlands, Norway, Portugal Spain, Turkey, the United Kingdom and the United States of America.

The North Atlantic Council is the supreme body of NATO. In 1952, a council in Permanent Session was created in which each member government is represented by a Permanent Representative and Ambassador, or his deputy. The permanent representatives meet as frequently as necessary for consultation and decision-making and also develop the analysis of major policy issues for the twice-yearly meetings of the Council, Defence Planning Committee and Nuclear Planning Group at ministerial levels. The secretary-general of NATO, or his deputy, presides over these meetings and also directs the activities of the international staff in light of the council's decisions and guidance.

North Atlantic Council

Delegation of Canada to the North Atlantic Council
Léopold III Blvd., 1110 Brussels, Belgium

Permanent Representative and Ambassador 8 Domaine du Fuji, 1970 Wezembeek, Brussels Belgium (Tel.: 731-6927)	Mr. Gordon S. Smith
Minister-Counsellor and Deputy Permanent Representative	Mr. J.A. Malone
Counsellor	Mr. H. Leduc
Counsellor	Mr. P. Meyer
Counsellor (Defence Production)	Mr. J.A. Holt
Counsellor (Defence Planning and Policy)	Col. G. Brown
Counsellor	Col. B.A. Goetze
Counsellor (Finance)	Mr. D. Gray
Counsellor (Armaments)	Lt.-Col. P.A. Vlossak
Counsellor (Finance)	Mr. H.A. Dagilis
Attaché (Emergency Measures)	Mr. B. Klotz
First Secretary	Mr. M. Grinius
First Secretary (Finance)	Mr. R.W. Adams
First Secretary	Maj. A.B. Bowles
Second Secretary (Defence Production)	Mr. P.C. McGovern
Second Secretary (Administration)	Mr. J.P. Laframboise

OTHER INTERNATIONAL ORGANIZATIONS

Canada-United States

International Boundary Commission
(Canada-United States Boundary)
615 Booth St., Rm. 130, Ottawa, ON K1A 0E9

International Joint Commission
Berger Bldg., 18th Flr.
100 Metcalfe St., Ottawa, ON K1P 5M1

Colombo Plan

Colombo Plan for Co-operative Economic and Social Development in Asia and the Pacific
Colombo Plan Bureau, 12 Melbourne Ave.
Box 596, Colombo 4, Sri Lanka

Conservation

International Commission for the Conservation of Atlantic Tuna (ICCAT)
Calle Principe de Uerogara 17, 28001
Madrid, Spain

International Council for the Exploration of the Sea
Palaegade 2-4
DK-1261 København K., Denmark

International Pacific Salmon Fisheries Commission (IPSFC)
Box 30, Dominion Building
New Westminster, BC V3L 4X9

North Pacific Fur Seal Commission (NPFSC)
c/o National Marine Fisheries Service
Washington, DC 20235, U.S.A.

Northwest Atlantic Fisheries Organization (NAFO)
Box 638, Dartmouth, NS B2Y 3Y9

Energy

International Atomic Energy Agency
Canadian Office: 365 Bloor St. E., Ste. 1702
Toronto, ON M4W 3L4

Inter-American

Centre for Latin American Monetary Studies
Durango No. 54, Col. Roma
Delegacion Cuauhtémoc
06700, Mexico 7, D.F., Mexico

Inter-American Development Bank
1300 New York Ave. N.W.
Washington, DC 20577, U.S.A.

Inter-American Institute for Co-operation on Agriculture (IICA)
Canadian Office:
130 Albert St., Ste. 1002
Ottawa, ON K1P 5G4

Inter-American Statistical Institute
c/o General Secretariat, OAS
Pan American Union Bldg., 1889 F St. NW
Washington, DC 20006, U.S.A.

Pan American Health Organization
525-23rd St. NW
Washington, DC 20037, U.S.A.

Pan American Institute of Geography and History
Ex-Arzobispado 29, Col Observatorio 11860
Mexico 18, D.F., Mexico

Postal Union of the Americas and Spain
Calle Buenos Aires 495, Calle Cebollati 1468/70
Casilla de Correos 20.042
Montevideo, Uruguay

Labour

International Labour Organization
Canadian Office: 75 Albert St., Ste. 202
Ottawa, ON K1P 5E7

Europe

Canadian Delegation to the Mutual and Balanced Force Reduction Talks
Dr. Karl Lueger Ring 10
A-1010 Vienna, Austria
Head of Delegation: Michael Shenstone

Canadian Delegation to the Vienna Follow-Up Meeting of the Conference on Security and Co-operation in Europe
Dr. Karl Lueger Ring 10
A-1010 Vienna, Austria
Head of Delegation: William E. Bauer

Mission of Canada to the European Communities
(The European Economic Community
The European Atomic Energy Community
The European Coal and Steel Community)
2, av. de Tervuren
1040 Brussels, Belgium
Head of Mission: Daniel Molgat

Organization for Economic Co-operation and Development

The Permanent Delegation of Canada to the Organization for Economic Co-operation and Development
15 bis, rue de Franqueville
75116 Paris, France
Ambassador and Permanent
    Representative: L. Michael Berry

Organization of American States

Permanent Observer Mission of Canada to the Organization of American States
2450 Massachusetts Ave. N.W.
Washington, DC 20008, U.S.A.
Ambassador and Permanent Observer:
Richard V. Gorham

United Nations

Permanent Mission of Canada to the United Nations
866 United Nations Plaza, Ste. 250
New York, NY 10017, U.S.A.
Permanent Representative and
    Ambassador: L. Yves Fortier

Permanent Delegation of Canada to the United Nations Educational, Scientific and Cultural Organization (UNESCO)
1, rue Miollis, 75015 Paris, France
Postal Address: C.P. 3.07, Paris VIIe, France
Ambassador and Permanent Delegate:
    Mr. Jean Drapeau

Permanent Mission of Canada to the International Civil Aviation Organization (ICAO)
1000, rue Sherbrooke ouest, bur. 876
Montréal (Québec) H3A 3G4
Representative: Mr. D.M. Fiorita

Permanent Mission of Canada to the Office of the United Nations at Geneva and to the Conference on Disarmament
(also accredited to: International Labour Organization (ILO); International Telecommunications Union (ITU); World Health Organization (WHO); World Meteorological Organization (WMO); and World Intellectual Property Organization (WIPO))
10A, av. de Budé
1202 Geneva, Switzerland
Permanent Representative and
    Ambassador: Mr. de Montigny Marchand

Permanent Mission of Canada to the Secretariat of the General Agreement on Tariffs and Trade (GATT)
1, rue du Pré-de-la-Pichette, 1er ét.
1202 Geneva, Switzerland
Permanent Representative and Ambassador:
    John M. Weekes

Permanent Mission of Canada to the United Nations Centre for Human Settlements (HABITAT)
Comcraft House, Hailé Sélassie Ave.
Box 30481, Nairobi, Kenya
Permanent Representative:
A. Raynell Andreychuk

Permanent Mission of Canada to the United Nations Environment Program (UNEP)
Comcraft House, Hailé Sélassie Ave.
Box 30481, Nairobi, Kenya
Permanent Representative:
A. Raynell Andreychuk

Permanent Mission of Canada to the Food and Agriculture Organization (FAO)
Via Zara 30, 00198 Rome, Italy
Permanent Representative:
Mr. E. Weybrecht

Permanent Mission of Canada to the International Organizations at Vienna
Dr. Karl Lueger Ring 10
A-1010 Vienna, Austria
Permanent Representative and
    Ambassador: Michael Shenstone

COMMONWEALTH OF NATIONS

Canada is one of 48 freely associated sovereign nations which form the Commonwealth. The Statute of Westminster of 1931 gave legal expression to the independence of Canada, Australia, South Africa, and New Zealand and to their equal status with Britain. (South Africa left the Commonwealth in 1961.) When India became independent in 1947 and chose to retain the Commonwealth link, the formation of the "new" Commonwealth was launched. Other members of the Commonwealth are, in order of entry, Sri Lanka, Ghana, Malaysia, Nigeria, Cyprus, Sierra Leone, Tanzania, Jamaica, Trinidad and Tobago, Uganda, Kenya, Malawi, Malta, Zambia, The Gambia, Singapore, Guyana, Botswana, Lesotho, Barbados, Nauru, Mauritius, Swaziland, Tonga, Western Samoa, Bangladesh, The Bahamas, Grenada, Papua New Guinea, Seychelles, Solomon Islands, Tuvalu, Dominica, St. Lucia, Kiribati, St. Vincent, Zimbabwe, Vanuatu, Belize, Antigua and Barbuda, Maldives, St. Christopher and Nevis, and Brunei.

In its widest sense, the Commonwealth is understood to include: the 48 member countries; self-governing states associated with a Commonwealth member for the purpose of foreign policy and defence; protected states; trust territories administered by a member on behalf of the United Nations; and territories still dependent on a member. Including dependencies, the Commonwealth covers one fifth of the world's land surface and embraces roughly one quarter of its population.

Of the 48 member countries of the Commonwealth, 23 have retained a monarchical form of government. Queen Elizabeth II is head of state of Canada and 16 other members. Malaysia has a monarch as Head of State who is elected for a five-year term from among themselves by the nine hereditary Malay rulers of West Malaysia. On attaining independence, two members of the Commonwealth, Lesotho and Swaziland, declared their paramount chiefs king and head of state. The Kingdom of Tonga and Brunei remained monarchies after Britain relinquished responsibility for the external affairs of these countries. All members of the Commonwealth recognize Queen Elizabeth as the symbol of their free association and, as such, the Head of the Commonwealth.

As the territories within the British Empire became self-governing and independent, similarities of language, habits, institutional traditions and working methods convinced many national leaders of the value of maintaining some form of association. The outcome of this belief is the modern Commonwealth. The Commonwealth is a voluntary association of 48 independent countries. The two most recent members are St. Christopher and Nevis (1983), and Brunei (1984). Two of the 48 Commonwealth countries (Nauru and Tuvalu) are special members which may take part in functional meetings and activities but do not participate at the Commonwealth Heads of Government Meetings. On Oct. 15, 1987, Fiji was declared to no longer be a member of the Commonwealth in the wake of the coup that took place in that country. The new rulers dismissed the Governor General and appointed a president to replace the Queen as Head of State.

The Commonwealth, in its beginnings, was still modelled on the Empire. However, in the international arena of the day, the self-governing members, and especially Canada, sought to enlarge their independent role. Since the end of the Second World War, with the emergence of super-power politics, Britain's joining the European Communities, and the third-world nationalist movement, the Commonwealth has evolved into the organization we know today in which Britain is no longer seen to be the only leader.

While Britain still plays a role in the defence of some of the smaller members, this aspect of the Commonwealth is diminishing. Long gone, as well, is the Stirling Area in the face of new trade agreements on the parts of both the older and newer members of the Commonwealth. The falling away of these former ties centred on Britain has, however, allowed other forms of multilateral co-operation to flower.

The most important of these areas is development. The Commonwealth is active both in training and education and in finance and trade. The major thrust is in education and training. Through primary and secondary education programs, general literacy and numeracy rates are being raised. Through scholarships at Commonwealth colleges and universities, professionally and technically trained personnel are being supplied to assist in the social and economic growth of the less-developed nations of the Commonwealth.

On the training side, the Commonwealth Fund for Technical Co-operation (CFTC) assists in the training of managers, engineers, agriculturalists, nurses, etc. Importance is given to sharing the expertise of nations on the road to development with those beginning the process. This expertise is often more applicable and more easily learned than that of developed countries.

The second avenue in development assistance is on the macro-economic level. The Commonwealth is working with the governments of the poorer members to help them deal with their debt problems. This includes lobbying before international lending institutions on behalf of Commonwealth debtor nations. Britain and Canada, in particular, have both eased the repayment of their own development loans.

On the trade side, many smaller Commonwealth nations rely on a few commodities (coffee, tea, sugar, cocoa, spices, ores, petroleum, fibres) for a large portion of their economic output. These exports generate foreign currency for investment and for the purchase of technology. Commodity prices, however, are notoriously unstable. The Commonwealth has encouraged the producers of these commodities to plan production and supply more carefully and to market their products more agressively. It is hoped that this will help to stabilize prices and even out the boom/bust cycles commodities so often suffer.

Because so many of the member nations of the Commonwealth are in black Africa, the problem of apartheid has always been prominent. In 1987, the report of the Commonwealth Eminent Persons' Group was instrumental in heightening the level of sanctions against Pretoria and in increasing aid to the nations bordering South Africa and bearing the military and economic brunt of her power. The leadership role that the Commonwealth has taken in diplomatic actions and in sanctions against South Africa is indicative of the special nature of the modern Commonwealth: it shows that there is still a place for multilateralism.

Commonwealth Consultation and Co-operation

The Commonwealth is known for its tradition of regular meetings of Heads of Government to discuss world problems and works of the association. The meetings occur every two years. They have taken place in: Singapore in 1971; Ottawa, in

1973; Kingston, Jamaica, in 1975; London, England, in 1977; Lusaka, Zambia, in 1979; Melbourne, Australia, 1981; New Delhi, in 1983; Nassau, Bahamas, 1985; and Vancouver, in 1987.

Ministers of Finance meet every year, and ministers of Education, Health and Law every three years; other ministers meet as the need arises. Secretaries to the cabinets and permanent heads of foreign ministries meet together every two years. There are also meetings of other officials and specialists in many fields of work. At these meetings, Commonwealth experiences are pooled, ideas exchanged, and decisions taken for joint action.

The *Commonwealth Secretariat*, located in London, is the focal point for consultations, the exchange of information, and for many joint activities.

Many organizations have been assisted by the *Commonwealth Foundation,* set up by governments to support the growth of professional skills, links and exchanges.

Commonwealth Secretariat

Marlborough House, Pall Mall
London, England SW1Y 5HX

Senior Officials:

Commonwealth Sec.-General,
  H.E. Shridath S. Ramphal
Deputy Sec.-General (Political),
  Chief Emeka C. Anyaoku
Deputy Sec.-General (Economic),
  Sir Peter Marshall
Asst. Sec.-General and Managing Director, Commonwealth Fund for Technical Co-operation,
  Mr. W.H. Montgomery
Asst. Sec.-General, Mr. M. Malhoutra

In 1965, Commonwealth heads of government decided to establish the Commonwealth Secretariat to facilitate communication between member governments and to administer programs of co-operation. The first Secretary-General of the Commonwealth was Arnold Smith, a Canadian diplomat who relinquished this post in July 1975 after ten years' service. His successor is Shridath S. Ramphal, who was formerly Foreign Minister and Justice Minister of Guyana.

The total staff of the Secretariat, including the Commonwealth Fund for Technical Co-operation (CFTC), is now over 400 people, drawn from many member countries. With a view to increasing the number of member countries represented in the staff complement, vacancies continue to be widely advertised in member countries.

The Secretary-General has about 400 staff members from some 30 countries. Their work reflects the major interests of member nations. They deal with international affairs, both political and economic, and service co-operation in such fields as economic development, exports, indus-

try, food production, public management, education, health, science, legal matters, women and development, and youth affairs. Through the Commonwealth Fund for Technical Co-operation, financed by all governments, the Secretariat assists development in the poorer countries.

The Commonwealth Secretariat's approved budget is borne in agreed shares by all Commonwealth governments, whose contributions are related to their capacity to pay and are based on their population and national income, with the UN contribution scales being used as a guide.

Canada's Role in the Commonwealth

Canada and Canadians have played a major role in supporting and developing the "new Commonwealth" since World War II.

Canada's international role as peace-maker, a proportionately large foreign aid budget and the belief among many third-world governments that Canada is more disinterested and less ideologically aligned than most western nations has heightened her leadership role in the Commonwealth. On the question of South Africa especially, Prime Minister Thatcher's unwillingness to support strong sanctions has prompted some to suggest Canada as a replacement for Britain in her traditional role.

Speculation aside, the Commonwealth, along with La Francophonie, will continue to be an important avenue for Canadian foreign aid as well as a vital forum for Canadian foreign policy initiatives.

Canada contributes approximately $30 million annually to Commonwealth institutions and programs designed to assist the smaller, developing member countries. The largest contributions were to the Commonwealth Fund for Technical Co-operation (approximately $17.5 million in 1987-88, or well over a third of its total resources) and the Commonwealth Scholarship and Fellowship Plan ($7.4 million). Additionally, in 1986, Canada directed $438.8 million of bilateral development assistance to Commonwealth countries.

Inter-governmental Commonwealth institutions and programs in which Canadian Government representatives participate and to which a financial contribution is made include the following:

Commonwealth Advisory Aeronautical Research Council. The Council promotes co-operation among those Commonwealth countries which undertake aeronautical research.

Commonwealth Air Transport Council. The Council, which includes members from 36 Commonwealth countries, is to keep members up-to-date on developments in civil aviation and to serve as a medium for the exchange of views and information. Thirty members of the Commonwealth contribute.

Commonwealth Assn. of Tax Administrators. Founded in 1978, the Association is concerned with techniques of government tax assessment.

Commonwealth Forestry Institute. Funded by grants from Commonwealth countries, the Commonwealth Forestry Institute provides a comprehensive information service and organizes courses on forest research and planning for foresters from the Commonwealth. Contributions are voluntary.

Commonwealth Foundation. Established in 1965 to foster the development of professional organizations and societies in Commonwealth countries, the Commonwealth Foundation is financed by contributions from member countries.

Commonwealth Fund for Technical Co-operation. The CFTC is the principal multilateral mechanism for development assistance within the Commonwealth. It is financed by voluntary contributions from all Commonwealth countries, both developed and developing.

Commonwealth Legal Advisory Service. The British Institute of International and Comparative Law on behalf of the Commonwealth governments operates this service which provides advice, information and surveys on legal topics of Commonwealth concern. Contributions are voluntary.

Commonwealth of Learning Agency. At their 1987 meeting, the Commonwealth Heads of Government agreed in principle to the establishment of an institution to promote and facilitate Commonwealth co-operation in distance education. It is expected that a central agency to assist teaching institutions in Commonwealth countries will also have been established by the end of 1988 with headquarters in Vancouver.

Commonwealth Scholarship and Fellowship Plan. Awards are granted on a voluntary basis by 15 Commonwealth countries. For the fiscal year 1986-87, Canada contributed approximately $7.4 million (approximately 500 scholarships). The program in Canada is administered on behalf of the Commonwealth Scholarship and Fellowship Plan by the Assn. of Universities and Colleges of Canada (CIDA funds).

Commonwealth Science Council. The Council's aim is to promote collaboration between member countries to increase the capabilities of individual nations to use science and technology for their economic, social and environmental development. Contributions are voluntary and are made by 27 Commonwealth countries.

Commonwealth Telecommunications Organization. This organization was established in 1966 to replace an earlier body for collaborative arrangements, consultation and mutual assistance in respect of the external communications services of the Commonwealth countries. It comprises a Conference, Council and Bureau and the Organization provides, among other things, for the financial settlement of communications traffic problems and for technical co-operation.

Commonwealth War Graves Commission. This Commission was established to mark and maintain the graves of all members of the Commonwealth forces in the two world wars, and as a result, its membership includes both Pakistan and South Africa.

Commonwealth Youth Program. Inaugurated in 1973 at the Ottawa Heads of Government Meeting, the Commonwealth Youth Program is aimed at encouraging and facilitating the exchange of ideas and experiences between people involved in youth programs at all levels. Voluntary contributions to this program are made by all Commonwealth countries.

CANADA AND THE DEVELOPING WORLD

Since the early 1950s and the enactment of the Colombo Plan to assist nations in southeast Asia, Canada's relations with developing countries have evolved to reflect the complex interdependence of aid, trade and foreign policy objectives.

Relations between Canada and the Third World span a number of departments and agencies, with the major contribution being in the form of Official Development Assistance (ODA). Program contributions have increased from some $100 million over a five year span in the early 1950s to $2.7 billion in 1987-88, 0.5 per cent of GNP.

Canadian aid is delivered through various mechanisms. Overall foreign policy priorities are determined by the Department of External Affairs. The Canadian International Development Agency (CIDA), established in 1968, acts as the administrative body for three-quarters of the aid. The

Minister for External Relations, Monique Landry, is the minister responsible for CIDA. While giving policy direction to the agency, External Affairs also provides assistance to multilateral institutions such as the World Health Organization and the Food and Agriculture Organization.

A large amount of money is allocated by the Department of Finance for developing nations through multilateral development banks such as the International Bank For Reconstruction and Development (IBRD), better known as the World Bank. Canada contributed $342 million in 1987-88, with much of the money channelled through the IBRD's "soft loan" facility, the International Development Assn.

Oil and gas exploration in developing nations is also enhanced by the use of Canadian technology. Since 1981, the Petro-Canada International Assistance Corp. has been funding technological aid, spending $61 million on developmental projects in 1987-88.

International Development Research Centre (IDRC)

Canada also makes a unique contribution to science and technology for development through the IDRC. This Crown corporation was established by Parliament in 1970, with a mandate to improve conditions in rural areas of developing countries (where three-quarters of the people of the world live), by applying new advances in science and technology.

With a head office in Ottawa and regional centres in Singapore, New Delhi, Nairobi, Cairo, Dakar, and Bogota, IDRC conducts research projects initiated and managed by researchers from developing countries, based on their own priorities. Research programs cover agriculture, food, energy, nutrition, health, social sciences, information sciences, earth and engineering sciences, training, and the implementation of results.

Specifically, research studies are being carried out to aid farmers of southern Mali to develop new cropping systems, and special water pumps have been tested and used in various parts of Africa, Asia, and Latin America. The Centre funds research on adult literacy programs, and also supports attempts to link women researchers who can pool information about the role women play in the development process.

Another major component of IDRC's operations is the dissemination of scientific information through regional and international development centres and computer networks. As well, the Centre funds collaborative efforts initiated by scientific research groups in developing countries who wish to work with their counterparts in Canada.

Canadian International Development Agency (CIDA)

CIDA's main objective is to help the poorest countries and people in the world to help themselves. To encourage self-reliance rather than dependence, human resource development is the lens through which all programs and projects are viewed. In response to current development problems, CIDA has placed special priority on poverty alleviation, structural adjustment, increased participation of women, environmentally sound development, food security, and energy availability. To achieve its objective and cover these key sectors, CIDA's assistance (which amounted to $2.2 billion in 1988-89) is now divided into two main components — the National Initiatives Program, in which CIDA works directly with recipient country governments, and the

Partnership Program, in which CIDA works with its partners, such as Canadian non-governmental organizations and institutions, private sector businesses, or international institutions. Each program constitutes 50 per cent of Canadian ODA allocations.

National Initiatives Program. While over one hundred countries benefited from more than 1,000 CIDA projects in 1987-88, three-quarters of the bilateral assistance is concentrated in approximately 30 countries. In Asia, the main programs are in Bangladesh, China, India, Indonesia, Nepal Pakistan, Philippines, Sri Lanka and Thailand. The famine in Africa has concentrated efforts in the area of agricultural productivity, and CIDA's activities are focused on 14 countries and groupings on the continent. They are: Cameroon Egypt, Ghana, Guinea, Côte d'Ivoire, Kenya Rwanda, Sahel (Burkina Faso, Mali, Niger) Senegal, Tanzania, Zaire, Zambia and Zimbabwe Special efforts are also being made, through the Southern African Development Co-ordination Conference (SADCC), to help countries bordering South Africa overcome their dependence on that regime. In the Americas, the bilateral program concentrates on Colombia, Guyana, Haiti, Honduras, Jamaica, The Leeward and Windward Islands, and Peru.

In order to improve program delivery, CIDA is decentralizing the administration of the bilateral aid component of the National Initiatives Program. Over 100 person-years will be transferred to regional and field offices, greater project approval authority will be delegated to the field, and increased local procurement will occur. In addition, a Canadian Fund for Local Initiatives will expand on the Mission-Administered Fund, which supports local grass-roots development projects.

Also included in the National Initiatives Program are the International Humanitarian Assistance Program, bilateral food aid, the Scholarships Program and Petro-Canada International Assistance Corporation.

Partnership Program. The Partnership Program provides support for more than 400 non-governmental organizations (NGOs) involved in international development. Thousands of grass roots projects are implemented each year by voluntary organizations ranging from large groups like CUSO to much smaller organizations such as Help The Aged. The Partnership Program matches donations from the public to NGOs, thereby multiplying the impact of work done by these organizations. Funding of $10.2 million in 1987-88 ($150 million over five years) was administered through the African 2000 program as well, which funds programs specifically for Africa. Since 1981, NGOs have implemented sections of CIDA's own bilateral programs under the "country focus" strategy. In addition, Canadian institutions such as universities, co-operatives, unions, and others carry out over 3,500 co-operation projects with their counterparts in the developing countries.

The business co-operation program, which partners CIDA with the Canadian private sector, is designed to help exporters penetrate new markets, establish joint ventures, and transfer technology to developing countries. Over $38.5 million was provided for this effort in 1987-88.

CIDA also supports global and regional multilateral organizations. The agency contributes to the regional development bank in each of the four major regions. Most of the funds placed in the Asian, African, Inter-American and Caribbean development banks are reserved for lending to the poorest nations. CIDA's participation in these banks helps stimulate private investment in these developing countries and fosters the sale of Canadian goods and services.

Multilateral organizations distribute 40 per cent of Canada's food aid, mainly through the United Nations' World Food Program (WFP). CIDA's international initiatives involve a range of co-operative efforts in the technical area. General funds are provided for organizations such as UNICEF which serve the basic health needs of mothers and children. Assistance is also provided to specialized bodies conducting research in population, and the health and natural resources areas.

Rapid reaction to disasters and relief for refugees is channelled through multilateral organizations such as the International Committee of the Red Cross (ICRC), and the United Nations High Commissioner for Refugees (UNHCR). CIDA also provides support for a wide range of other international non-governmental aid programs.

New Policy on Tied Aid

Tied aid — the practice of requiring that aid funds provided to a developing country are used to procure goods and services in that country — has been part of Canada's development strategy for many years. Since 1970, 80 per cent of Canada's bilateral aid allocations, which are roughly one third of Canada's aid, were used to purchase Canadian goods and services. Cana-

da's new policy substantially relaxes these provisions. For partnership programs, all cash transactions are untied. In the National Initiatives Program, all sub-Saharan African and least-developed country programs will be untied up to a level of 50 per cent, and all other country programs will be untied up to a level of 33 per cent. Only food aid will be excluded from these levels.

New Initiatives

Among the programs implemented this year is a project for child immunization in developing countries of the Commonwealth and La Francophonie. The program received $50 million in funding and was administered by the Canadian Public Health Assn., UNICEF, Laval University and the Rotary Club.

In response to recent research that has suggested that many aid projects in the Third World are not environmentally sound, special emphasis is being placed on ensuring that environmental concerns are taken into consideration in the planning and execution of projects sponsored by CIDA.

A moratorium has also been placed on the repayment of ODA loans by countries of sub-Saharan Africa, and, since April 1986, all new bilateral development assistance has been in grant form to all countries. Further, in the fall of 1987, Canada indicated its intention to forgive the ODA debt of a number of Francophonie and Commonwealth African countries eligible for the ODA debt moratorium.

A new framework for eligibility for aid has also been put in place. The old categories have been abolished and all developing countries are eligible for Canadian ODA funds channeled through multilateral institutions and organizations. All independent developing countries will be eligible for all forms of Canadian development assistance, including food aid. Exclusions to eligibility will be made for political, human rights or economic reasons, except in the case of disaster relief, to which all developing countries are eligible.

For a listing of the address and senior officials of CIDA and IDRC, see the references under "Independent Agencies" earlier in this chapter.

The Premier of New Brunswick, Frank McKenna, whose Liberals swept all 58 seats in the provincial legislature in the 1987 general election.
Canapress Photo Service.

PROVINCIAL AND TERRITORIAL GOVERNMENTS

(Listings of government personnel found below are taken from the *Corpus Administrative Index*. This directory is updated four times a year, and is an accurate source for names and titles of provincial and territorial government officials. Subscription rate: $367/year, 4 issues. Available from: Southam Business Information and Communications Group Inc., 1450 Don Mills Rd., Don Mills, ON M3B 2X7.)

Government of Alberta
Provincial profile 17-11
Executive Council 17-13
Legislative Assembly 17-13

Advanced Education, Department of 17-15
Agriculture, Department of 17-17
Attorney General, Department of the 17-21
Career Development and Employment, Department of 17-24
Consumer and Corporate Affairs, Department of 17-25
Culture and Multiculturalism, Department of 17-26
Economic Development and Trade, Department of 17-28
Education, Department of 17-30
Energy, Department of 17-31
Environment, Department of the 17-34
Federal and Intergovernmental Affairs, Department of 17-35
Forestry, Lands and Wildlife, Department of 17-36
Health, Department of 17-37
Labour, Department of 17-39
Municipal Affairs, Department of 17-40
Occupational Health and Safety, Department of 17-43
Public Works, Supply and Services, Department of 17-44
Recreation and Parks, Department of 17-45
Social Services, Department of 17-46
Solicitor General, Department of the 17-47
Technology, Research and Telecommunications, Department of 17-48
Tourism, Department of 17-48
Transportation and Utilities, Department of 17-49
Treasury Department 17-51

Independent Agencies, Boards and Commissions
Alberta Alcohol and Drug Abuse Commission 17-52
Alberta Educational Communications Corp. (ACCESS) 17-52
Alberta Public Safety Services 17-53
Alberta Research Council 17-53
Alberta Women's Secretariat 17-54
Personnel Administration Office 17-54
Public Affairs Bureau 17-54
Workers' Compensation Board 17-55

Judiciary and Judicial Officers
Court of Appeal of Alberta 17-56
Court of Queen's Bench 17-56
Provincial Courts 17-57
Court Officials 17-58
Family and Youth Courts 17-59
Small Claims Courts 17-59
Property Registration 17-59
Mineral Rights 17-59

Government of British Columbia
Provincial profile 17-61
Executive Council 17-63
Legislative Assembly 17-63

17

Advanced Education and Job Training, Ministry of 17-65
Agriculture and Fisheries, Ministry of 17-68
Attorney General, Ministry of the 17-71
Crown Lands, Ministry of 17-73
Education, Ministry of 17-73
Energy, Mines and Petroleum Resources, Ministry of 17-74
Environment, Ministry of 17-75
Finance and Corporate Relations, Ministry of 17-75
Forests, Ministry of 17-79
Government Management Services, Ministry of 17-79
Health, Ministry of 17-81
International Business and Immigration, Ministry of 17-83
Labour and Consumer Services, Ministry of 17-84
Municipal Affairs, Recreation and Culture, Ministry of 17-87
Parks, Ministry of 17-89
Regional Development, Ministry of 17-90
Social Services and Housing, Ministry of 17-90
Solicitor General, Ministry of the 17-91
Tourism and Provincial Secretary, Ministry of 17-94
Transportation and Highways, Ministry of 17-94

Independent Agencies, Boards, Commissions and Crown Corporations
   B.C. Rail 17-95
   Native Affairs Secretariat 17-96

Judiciary and Judicial Officers
   Court of Appeal for British Columbia 17-97
   Supreme Court of British Columbia 17-97
   County Court Judges 17-97
   Supreme Court and County Court Registrars 17-98
   Provincial Court of British Columbia 17-99
   Registrars in Bankruptcy 17-101

Government of Manitoba
   Provincial profile 17-103
   Executive Council 17-105
   Legislative Assembly 17-105

Agriculture, Department of 17-107
Attorney General, Department of the 17-112
Community Services, Department of 17-114
Co-operative, Consumer and Corporate Affairs, Department of 17-115
Culture, Heritage and Recreation, Department of 17-116
Education, Department of 17-118
Employment Services and Economic Security, Department of 17-120
Energy and Mines, Department of 17-122
Environment and Workplace Safety and Health, Department of 17-123
Finance, Department of 17-125
Government Services, Department of 17-125
Health, Department of 17-126
Highways and Transportation, Department of 17-129
Housing, Department of 17-130
Industry, Trade and Tourism, Department of 17-131
Labour, Department of 17-133
Municipal Affairs, Department of 17-135
Natural Resources, Department of 17-136
Northern Affairs, Department of 17-137
Urban Affairs, Department of 17-138

Independent Agencies, Boards, Commissions and Crown Corporations
   Civil Service Superannuation Board 17-138
   Communities Economic Development Fund 17-138
   Liquor Control Commission 17-138
   Manfor Ltd. 17-139
   Manitoba Civil Service Commission 17-139
   Manitoba Hydro 17-139
   Manitoba Lotteries Foundation 17-140

Manitoba Public Insurance Corp. 17-140
Manitoba Telephone System 17-140
Public Investments Corp. 17-141
Sanatorium Board of Manitoba 17-141

Judiciary and Judicial Officers
Court of Appeal 17-142
Court of Queen's Bench 17-142
Provincial Court 17-142
Judicial Centres 17-143

Government of New Brunswick
Provincial profile 17-145
Executive Council 17-147
Legislative Assembly 17-147

Advanced Education and Training, Department of 17-149
Agriculture, Department of 17-150
Auditor General, Office of the 17-151
Board of Management 17-151
Commerce and Technology, Department of 17-151
Education, Department of 17-153
Finance, Department of 17-153
Fisheries and Aquaculture, Department of 17-154
Health and Community Services, Department of 17-154
Income Assistance, Department of 17-154
Intergovernmental Affairs, Department of 17-155
Justice, Department of 17-155
Labour, Department of 17-155
Municipal Affairs and Environment, Department of 17-158
Natural Resources and Energy, Department of 17-159
Solicitor General, Department of the 17-160
Supply and Services, Department of 17-160
Tourism, Recreation and Heritage, Department of 17-160
Transportation, Department of 17-162

Independent Agencies, Boards, Commissions and Crown Corporations
Alcoholism and Drug Dependency Commission 17-163
Civil Service Commission 17-164
Comptroller, Office of the 17-164
Liquor Licensing Board 17-164
New Brunswick Coal Ltd. 17-164
New Brunswick Forest Products Commission 17-165
New Brunswick Housing Corp. 17-165
New Brunswick Liquor Corp. 17-165
New Brunswick Police Commission 17-165
New Brunswick Power 17-166
New Brunswick Well Drilling Advisory Board 17-166
Occupational Health and Safety Commission 17-166
Public Service Labour Relations Board 17-166
Regional Development Corp. 17-167

Judiciary and Judicial Officers
Court of Appeal 17-168
Court of Queen's Bench of New Brunswick 17-168
Judges of the Provincial Court 17-168
Judicial Officers 17-169

Government of Newfoundland
Provincial profile 17-171
Executive Council 17-173
House of Assembly 17-174

Career Development and Advanced Studies, Department of 17-175
Consumer Affairs and Communications, Department of 17-176
Culture, Recreation and Youth, Department of 17-177

Development and Tourism, Department of 17-178
Education, Department of 17-180
Energy, Department of 17-181
Environment and Lands, Department of 17-181
Finance, Department of 17-181
Fisheries, Department of 17-182
Forestry, Department of 17-183
Health, Department of 17-183
Justice, Department of 17-184
Labour, Department of 17-185
Labrador Affairs, Department of 17-186
Mines, Department of 17-186
Municipal Affairs, Department of 17-187
Public Works and Services, Department of 17-187
Rural, Agricultural and Northern Development, Department of 17-188
Social Services, Department of 17-190
Transportation, Department of 17-191

Independent Agencies, Boards, Commissions and Crown Corporations
    Alcohol and Drug Dependency Commn. of Newfoundland and Labrador 17-191
    Churchill Falls (Labrador) Corp. Ltd. 17-192
    Lower Churchill Development Corp. 17-192
    Newfoundland and Labrador Computer Services Ltd. 17-192
    Newfoundland and Labrador Hydro 17-192
    Newfoundland Commission of Public Utilities 17-193
    Newfoundland Liquor Corp. 17-193
    Newfoundland Liquor Licensing Board 17-193
    Newfoundland Medical Care Commission 17-193
    St. John's Metropolitan Area Board 17-193
    Twin Falls Power Corp. Ltd. 17-194
    Workers' Compensation Commission 17-194

Judiciary and Judicial Officers
    Supreme Court of Newfoundland 17-194
    Provincial Court, St. John's 17-195
    Unified Family Court 17-195
    Court Officials 17-195

Government of the Northwest Territories
    Territorial profile 17-197
    Executive Council 17-199
    Legislative Assembly 17-201

Culture and Communications, Department of 17-201
Economic Development and Tourism, Department of 17-202
Education, Department of 17-202
Equal Employment Directorate 17-202
Finance, Department of 17-202
Financial Management Secretariat 17-202
Government Services, Department of 17-202
Health, Department of 17-203
Justice, Department of 17-203
Municipal and Community Affairs, Department of 17-203
Personnel, Department of 17-203
Public Works and Highways, Department of 17-203
Renewable Resources, Department of 17-203
Safety and Public Services, Department of 17-204
Social Services, Department of 17-204
Transportation, Department of 17-204

Independent Agencies, Boards and Councils 17-204

Federal Government Directory 17-210

Judiciary and Judicial Officers
    Court of Appeal and Court Officials 17-211

Supreme Court and Court Officials 17-211
Territorial Court and Court Officials 17-211

Government of Nova Scotia
Provincial profile 17-213
Executive Council 17-215
Legislative Assembly 17-216

Advanced Education and Job Training, Department of 17-217
Agriculture and Marketing, Department of 17-218
Attorney General, Department of the 17-219
Auditor General's Office 17-220
Community Services, Department of 17-220
Consumer Affairs, Department of 17-222
Education, Department of 17-222
Environment, Department of the 17-223
Finance, Department of 17-223
Fisheries, Department of 17-224
Government Services, Department of 17-225
Health and Fitness, Department of 17-225
Housing, Department of 17-226
Industry, Trade and Technology, Department of 17-227
Labour, Department of 17-227
Lands and Forests, Department of 17-229
Mines and Energy, Department of 17-230
Municipal Affairs, Department of 17-230
Small Business Development, Department of 17-230
Solicitor General, Department of the 17-231
Tourism and Culture, Department of 17-232
Transportation and Communications, Department of 17-232
Independent Agencies, Boards, Commissions and Crown Corporations
Advisory Council on Status of Women 17-233
Board of Commissioners of Public Utilities 17-233
Civil Service Commission 17-234
Council of Applied Science and Technology 17-234
Emergency Measures Organization 17-234
Halifax Infirmary 17-234
Human Rights Commission 17-234
Metropolitan Authority/Metropolitan Area Planning Commission 17-235
Nova Scotia Boxing Authority 17-235
Nova Scotia Business Capital Corp. 17-235
Nova Scotia Commission on Drug Dependency 17-235
Nova Scotia Government Employees Union 17-236
Nova Scotia Government Purchasing Agency 17-236
Nova Scotia Hospital 17-236
Nova Scotia Information Service 17-236
Nova Scotia Liquor Commission 17-237
Nova Scotia Liquor License Board 17-237
Nova Scotia Lottery Commission 17-237
Nova Scotia Municipal Board 17-237
Nova Scotia Municipal Finance Corp. 17-237
Nova Scotia Power Corp. 17-238
Nova Scotia Research Foundation Corp. 17-238
Nova Scotia Resources Ltd. 17-238
Nova Scotia Sport and Recreation Commission 17-239
Novaco Ltd. 17-239
Province House Credit Union Ltd. 17-239
Public Archives of Nova Scotia 17-240
Sydney Steel Corp. (SYSCO) 17-240
Technology Transfer Corp. 17-240
Tidal Power Corp. 17-240
Victoria General Hospital 17-241
Waterfront Development Corp. Ltd. 17-241
World Trade and Convention Centre 17-241

Judiciary and Court Officials
   Supreme Court 17-242
   County Court 17-242
   Provincial Court 17-242
   Family Court 17-243
   County Court Officials 17-244
   Registrars and Receivers in Bankruptcy 17-245

Government of Ontario
   Provincial profile 17-247
   Executive Council 17-249
   Legislative Assembly 17-250

   Agriculture and Food, Ministry of 17-254
   Attorney General, Ministry of the 17-258
   Citizenship, Ministry of 17-261
   Colleges and Universities, Ministry of 17-262
   Community and Social Services, Ministry of 17-263
   Consumer and Commercial Relations, Ministry of 17-265
   Correctional Services, Ministry of 17-268
   Culture and Communications, Ministry of 17-269
   Education, Ministry of 17-273
   Energy, Ministry of 17-275
   Environment, Ministry of the 17-276
   Financial Institutions, Ministry of 17-279
   Government Services, Ministry of 17-280
   Health, Ministry of 17-282
   Housing, Ministry of 17-284
   Industry, Trade and Technology, Ministry of 17-285
   Intergovernmental Affairs, Ministry of 17-288
   Labour, Ministry of 17-288
   Management Board of Cabinet 17-291
   Municipal Affairs, Ministry of 17-292
   Natural Resources, Ministry of 17-292
   Northern Development and Mines, Ministry of 17-294
   Provincial Auditor, Office of the 17-295
   Revenue, Ministry of 17-295
   Skills Development, Ministry of 17-296
   Solicitor General, Ministry of the 17-296
   Tourism and Recreation, Ministry of 17-297
   Transportation, Ministry of 17-300
   Treasury and Economics, Ministry of 17-302

   Independent Agencies, Boards and Commissions
      Ontario Advisory Council on Women's Issues 17-303
      Ontario Native Affairs Directorate 17-303
      Ontario Women's Directorate 17-303

   Judiciary and Judicial Officers
      Supreme Court of Ontario 17-304
      District Court of Ontario 17-305
      Provincial Judges and Provincial Courts 17-307
      Bankruptcy Administrators 17-311
      Mining Recorders 17-311

Government of Prince Edward Island
   Provincial profile 17-313
   Executive Council 17-315
   Legislative Assembly 17-315

   Agriculture, Department of 17-316
   Community and Cultural Affairs, Department of 17-318
   Education, Department of 17-318
   Energy and Forestry, Department of 17-318
   Finance, Department of 17-318
   Fisheries, Department of 17-319

Health and Social Services, Department of 17-319
Industry, Department of 17-319
Justice, Department of 17-320
Labour, Department of 17-320
Tourism and Parks, Department of 17-321
Transportation and Public Works, Department of 17-321

Independent Agencies, Boards, Commissions and Crown Corporations
   Charlottetown Area Development Corp. 17-322
   Civil Service Commission 17-322
   Energy Corp. 17-322
   Georgetown Shipyard Inc. 17-322
   Horse Racing and Sports Commission 17-323
   Hospital and Health Services Commission 17-323
   Human Rights Commission 17-323
   Island Information Service 17-323
   Land Use Commission 17-323
   Liquor Control Commission 17-323
   Office of the Auditor General 17-324
   P.E.I. Advisory Council on the Status of Women 17-324
   P.E.I. Crop Insurance Agency 17-324
   P.E.I. Development Agency 17-324
   P.E.I. Grain Elevators Corp. 17-325
   P.E.I. Housing Corp. 17-325
   P.E.I. Land Development Corp. 17-325
   P.E.I. Lending Authority 17-325
   P.E.I. Lotteries Commission 17-325
   P.E.I. Museum and Heritage Foundation 17-325
   Public Utilities Commission 17-326
   Queen's Printer 17-326
   Summerside Waterfront Development Corp. 17-326
   Workers' Compensation Board 17-326

Judiciary and Judicial Officers
   Supreme Court 17-327
   Provincial Court 17-327

Government of Quebec

Provincial profile 17-329
Conseil des ministres 17-331
L'Assemblée nationale 17-331

Affaires culturelles, Ministère des 17-335
Affaires internationales, Ministère des 17-341
Affaires municipales, Ministère des 17-341
Agriculture, des Pêcheries et de l'Alimentation, Ministère de l' 17-344
Approvisionnements et Services, Ministère des 17-347
Commerce extérieur et du Développement technologique, Ministère du 17-348
Communautés culturelles et de l'Immigration, Ministère des 17-349
Communications, Ministère des 17-350
Conseil du Trésor 17-351
Éducation, Ministère de l' 17-352
Énergie et des Ressources, Ministère de l' 17-353
Enseignement supérieur et de la Science, Ministère de l' 17-358
Environnement, Ministère de l' 17-359
Finances, Ministère des 17-361
Industrie, du Commerce et de la Technologie, Ministère de l' 17-363
Inspecteur général des Institutions financières 17-366
Justice, Ministère de la 17-366
Loisir, de la Chasse et de la Pêche, Ministère du 17-369
Main-d'oeuvre et de la Sécurité du revenu, Ministère de la 17-371
Revenu, Ministère du 17-373
Santé et des Services sociaux, Ministère de la 17-374
Sécurité publique, Ministère de la 17-376
Tourisme, Ministère du 17-377
Transports, Ministère des 17-378

Travail, Ministère du 17-380

Independent Agencies
  Commission administrative du régime de retraite et d'assurances 17-383
  Commission des valeurs mobilières du Québec 17-383
  Office de planification et de développement du Québec 17-383
  Régie de l'Assurance-maladie du Québec 17-384

Judiciary and Judicial Officers
  La Cour supérieure 17-385
  La Cour d'appel 17-386
  La Cour du Québec 17-387
  District Court Officers 17-389
  Registrars in Bankruptcy 17-391

Government of Saskatchewan
  Provincial profile 17-393
  Executive Council 17-395
  Legislative Assembly 17-395

  Agriculture, Department of 17-397
  Consumer and Commercial Affairs, Department of 17-401
  Economic Development and Trade, Department of 17-401
  Education, Department of 17-402
  Energy and Mines, Department of 17-403
  Environment and Public Safety, Department of the 17-403
  Finance, Department of 17-404
  Health, Department of 17-405
  Highways and Transportation, Department of 17-406
  Human Resources, Labour and Employment, Department of 17-407
  Justice, Department of 17-409
  Northern Affairs Secretariat 17-412
  Parks, Recreation and Culture, Department of 17-413
  Property Management Corp. 17-415
  Provincial Auditor 17-416
  Provincial Secretary, Department of the 17-416
  Public Participation, Department of 17-418
  Rural Development, Department of 17-418
  Science and Technology, Department of 17-418
  Social Services, Department of 17-418
  Trade and Investment, Department of 17-419
  Urban Affairs, Department of 17-419

Independent Agencies, Boards and Commissions
  CAMECO 17-419
  Indian and Native Affairs Secretariat 17-420
  Potash Corp. of Saskatchewan 17-420
  Saskatchewan Alcohol and Drug Abuse Commission (SADAC) 17-420
  Saskatchewan Archives Board 17-421
  Saskatchewan Assessment Management Agency 17-421
  Saskatchewan Computer Utility Corp. (SaskComp) 17-421
  Saskatchewan Development Fund Corp. 17-421
  Saskatchewan Economic Development Corp. (SEDCO) 17-422
  Saskatchewan Forest Products Corp. 17-422
  Saskatchewan Government Insurance (SGI) 17-422
  Saskatchewan Government Printing Company 17-423
  Saskatchewan Housing Corp. 17-423
  Saskatchewan Liquor Board 17-423
  Saskatchewan Municipal Board 17-423
  Saskatchewan Public Service Commission 17-424
  Saskatchewan Research Council 17-424
  Saskatchewan Telecommunications (SASK TEL) 17-424
  Saskatchewan Transportation Co. 17-425
  Saskatchewan Water Corp. 17-425

Judiciary and Judicial Officers
  Court of Appeal 17-425

Court of Queen's Bench 17-425
Unified Family Court 17-426
Judicial Offices 17-426
Registrar in Bankruptcy 17-427
Judges of Provincial Court 17-427
Land Registration Officials 17-427

Government of the Yukon Territory
Territorial profile 17-429
Executive Council 17-431
Legislative Assembly 17-432

Community and Transportation Services, Department of 17-432
Economic Development: Mines and Small Business, Department of 17-433
Education, Department of 17-434
Finance, Department of 17-434
Government Services, Department of 17-434
Health and Human Resources, Department of 17-435
Justice, Department of 17-435
Public Service Commission 17-436
Renewable Resources, Department of 17-436
Tourism, Department of 17-437

Independent Agencies, Boards and Commissions 17-437

Federal Government Directory 17-438

Judiciary and Judicial Officers
Court of Appeal 17-440
Supreme Court and Court Officials 17-440
Territorial Court and Court Officials 17-440
Yukon Land Registry 17-440

This map is based on information taken from map MCR 4032. © Her Majesty in Right of Canada with permission of Energy, Mines and Resources.

PROVINCE OF ALBERTA

Wild Rose
(Rosa acicularis)

Entered Confederation: Sept. 1, 1905
Capital: Edmonton
Motto: Fortis et Liber (Strong and free)
Flower: Wild rose
Area: 661,185 km²
  percentage of Canada's total area: 6.6
  LAND: 644,389 km²
  FRESHWATER: 16,796 km²
Elevation:
  HIGHEST POINT: Mount Columbia (3,747 m)
  LOWEST POINT: Lake Athabasca and
    Slave River shores
Population (April 1988): 2,391,700

  five-year change: +2.4%
  per square kilometre: 3.6
percentage of Canada's total population: 9.3
  URBAN: 79%
  RURAL: 21%
Gross domestic product, 1987: $59.0 billion
Government Finance:
  REVENUE, 1986/87 est.: $11.5 billion
  EXPENDITURE, 1986/87 est.: $14.3 billion
  DEPT PER CAPITA (March 1987): $4,775
Personal income per capita, 1986: $17,776
Unemployment rate, 1988
(annual average): 8.0%

HISTORY

Dinosaurs once roamed the land which is now Alberta. Spectacular evidence of their existence remains in fossil form in various areas of the province. Plains Indians were the original human inhabitants until the arrival of European explorers — largely fur traders and missionaries — in the 1700s. However, it was not until the latter half of the 19th century that European immigrants began to build a permanent base. The arrival of the North West Mounted Police in 1874 and the building of the Canadian Pacific Railway in the 1880s brought transportation and security to the new settlements.

Alberta was established as a province of Canada in 1905, and was named after Princess Louise Caroline Alberta, fourth daughter of Queen Victoria.

The province has attracted immigrants in a continuous flow, with major influxes occurring between 1896 and 1913, and following the two world wars. Alberta's history has been stable, although some very difficult periods were experienced in the early years. It was one of the most harshly affected areas during the Great Depression of the 1930s. The year 1947, when a major oil discovery was made near Leduc, was a landmark for the province. Since then, Alberta has grown at a dramatic rate and now has a strong economy.

THE LAND

Alberta has one of the most varied geographies in Canada with the rugged Rocky Mountains rising from flat prairies along the western border. The sparsely populated north is a vast wilderness of forest and muskeg. Central Alberta and the Peace River country to the northwest of Edmonton are rich agricultural regions which include undeveloped plains and forested tracts of parkland.

The unique badlands in the Red Deer River Valley contrast sharply with the undulating prairies stretching north from the 49th parallel (the international boundary between Canada and the

U.S.). In southern Alberta, irrigation helps farmers and ranchers produce bountiful crops and feed for livestock. The Rocky Mountains and foothills of the southwestern quarter can only be described as spectacular.

The province sprawls over 661,185 km². About 97.5 per cent of the surface is land, laced by rushing rivers, sparkling streams, and many lakes.

THE PEOPLE

The Alberta Bureau of Statistics indicated the population of Alberta to be 2,391,700 as of April 1, 1988, up 0.6 per cent from the same date in 1987. Alberta had a small net migration of 120 in the first three months of 1988, the first quarterly gain in almost nine months. The turnaround was attributable to a lower net interprovincial outflow of 1,240 compared to 5,550 in the previous quarter. The net inflow of international migrants, at 1,360, more than offset the interprovincial outflow.

Alberta has the fourth highest population in Canada behind Ontario, Quebec, and B.C. The province's population has almost tripled since 1947, the year of the first major oil discovery at Leduc.

Alberta's two major urban centres, Calgary and Edmonton, are close in population size. Calgary, the biggest city in the province, has 647,285 people, which represents a 32.1 per cent jump in the ten-year period between 1977 and 1987. Edmonton, the provincial capital, has a population of 576,249, a 22.2 per cent increase for the same ten-year period. Other major centres in the province are Lethbridge (60,610), Red Deer (54,309), Medicine Hat (41,804), St. Albert (37,008), Fort McMurray (34,949), and Grande Prairie (26,471). Approximately 79 per cent of Alberta's population is urban residents.

THE ECONOMY

Indicators of Alberta's economic position are:

- Gas well completions decreased by a substantial amount. In 1987, there were 462 gas well completions, down 79.3 per cent from 2,232 completions in 1986. Over the same time period, oil well activity fell by 7.9 per cent.

- The preliminary value of construction work purchased in Alberta in 1987 totalled $10.4 million, up 0.9 per cent from 1986. Anticipated expenditures for 1988 indicate an increase in activity with work purchased expected to be up by 14.4 per cent from 1987.

- 1987 annual per capita retail sales were the second highest in Canada at $6,242. Ontario was first at $6,368, and Nova Scotia third at $5,944; the national figure was $5,999.

- From June 1987 to June 1988, Alberta's employed labour force (seasonally unadjusted) increased by 5.0 per cent to total 1.2 million. The unemployment rate (seasonally unadjusted) decreased by 2.6 percentage points to 7.2 per cent over the same period. This figure is slightly higher than the national rate of 7.1 per cent. In June 1988, Alberta's unemployment rate was the fourth lowest in Canada, following Ontario (4.6 per cent), Saskatchewan (6.2 per cent), and Manitoba (6.7 per cent).

- Wages and salaries continued to show modest real growth of 1.8 per cent. Corporation profits, on the other hand, fell by 47.1 per cent.

- Albertans have the lowest overall tax rates in Canada. The Major Provincial Tax Rates (Personal Income Tax, Basic Rates) for Alberta is 46.5 per cent, which is the lowest of all the provinces. Other rates range from 50 per cent for Saskatchewan and Ontario (the second lowest rate) to 60 per cent for Newfoundland (the highest rate excluding Quebec's whose taxes are calculated on a different base). As of Jan. 1, 1988, the flat rate tax on personal income was cut by one half.

- Albertans enjoy an inflation rate substantially lower than the Canadian average. The percentage of change in the CPI from June 1987 to June 1988 showed a national increase of 3.9 per cent. The CPI in Calgary and Edmonton increased approximately 2.1 and 2.2 per cent respectively. (The highest rates of increase were recorded in Regina, Saskatoon, and Toronto, all at 5.3 per cent. The lowest rate was in Halifax at 3.1 per cent.)

- According to revised estimates published by the Alberta Bureau of Statistics, Alberta's current Gross Domestic Product (GDP) fell by 9.6 per cent to an estimated $56.4 billion during 1986. In real terms, after discounting the effects of inflation, GDP grew by 1.6 per cent for an estimated $54.0 billion.

- Provincial per capita GDP for 1986 stood at $23,764, which was down 10.6 per cent from 1985. By way of comparison, the per capita figure for Canada was $20,112.

- Alberta's trade surplus increased from $7.4 million in 1986 to $8.8 million in 1987. Domestic exports rose from $10.5 billion to $11.8 billion — a 12.4 per cent increase. Total imports decreased from $3.1 million to $3.0 million.

Text is based on information provided by the Alberta Public Affairs Bureau.

GOVERNMENT OF ALBERTA

Seat of Government:
Legislature Bldg., Edmonton, T5K 2B6

Lieutenant-Governor,
The Hon. W. Helen Hunley
Legislature Bldg., 3rd Flr.
Edmonton, AB T5K 2B6

EXECUTIVE COUNCIL

NOTE: Some of the ministers listed did not stand for re-election on March 20; others were defeated. While election results are reflected in the list of Members of the Legislative Assembly, the new Cabinet was not named in time for inclusion in this edition.
(In order of precedence, as of Jan. 1, 1989)

Premier, President of Executive Council,
The Hon. Donald Getty
Deputy Premier, Minister of Advanced Education,
The Hon. David Russell
Minister of Special Projects,
The Hon. Neil Crawford
Minister of Federal and Intergovernmental Affairs,
The Hon. James D. Horsman
Minister of Economic Development and Trade,
The Hon. Larry R. Shaben
Provincial Treasurer,
The Hon. Dick Johnston
Minister of Energy,
The Hon. Dr. P. Neil Webber
Minister of Technology, Research and Telecommunications, Government House Leader,
The Hon. Leslie G. Young
Minister of Transportation and Utilities,
The Hon. J. Allen Adair
Solicitor General,
The Hon. Marvin Moore
Minister of Forestry, Lands and Wildlife,
The Hon. LeRoy Fjordbotten
Minister of Labour,
The Hon. Rick Orman
Minister of Social Services,
The Hon. Connie Osterman
Minister of Tourism,
The Hon. Donald Sparrow
Minister of Environment,
The Hon. Dr. Ian Reid
Minister of Public Works, Supply and Services,
The Hon. Ernie Isley

Minister of Agriculture,
The Hon. Peter Elzinga
Assoc. Minister of Agriculture,
The Hon. Shirley Cripps
Minister of Municipal Affairs,
The Hon. Dennis Anderson
Minister of Recreation and Parks,
The Hon. Norm A. Weiss
Minister of Career Development and Employment,
The Hon. Ken Kowalski
Minister of Education,
The Hon. Jim Dinning
Attorney General, Minister responsible for Native Affairs,
The Hon. Ken Rostad
Minister of Consumer and Corporate Affairs,
The Hon. Elaine McCoy
Minister of Health,
The Hon. Nancy Betkowski
Minister of Culture and Multiculturalism,
The Hon. Greg Stevens

STANDING POLICY COMMITTEES OF CABINET

Priorities, Finance and Co-ordination
Chairman, The Hon. Donald Getty
Treasury Board
Chairman, The Hon. Dick Johnston
Economic Planning
Chairman, The Hon. Dr. P. Neil Webber
Metropolitan Affairs
Chairman, The Hon. Dennis Anderson
Agriculture and Rural Economy
Chairman, The Hon. Donald Getty
Social Planning
Chairman, The Hon. David Russell
Energy
Chairman, The Hon. Donald Getty

LEGISLATIVE ASSEMBLY

22nd Legislature, 1st Session
Last election: March 20, 1989
(Maximum legal duration 5 years)
Majority party: Progressive Conservative
Total number of seats: 83
Party standings:
Conservatives: 59
New Democrats: 16
Liberals: 8

For further information regarding any aspect of the Government of Alberta, contact:
Public Affairs Bureau (RITE)
Beaver House, 4th Flr., 10158-103rd St., Edmonton, T5K 2G6
(403) 427-2711

Salaries, Indemnities and Allowances

MEMBERS: $29,548 Sessional Indemnity, plus $7,883 expense allowance (tax free), and up to $75 per day during sessions when necessarily away from home.

MINISTERS WITH PORTFOLIO: $40,841 salary, plus Sessional Indemnity and expenses.

MINISTERS WITHOUT PORTFOLIO: $28,972 salary, plus Sessional Indemnity and expenses.

PREMIER: $50,157 salary, plus Sessional Indemnity and expenses.

SPEAKER: $40,841 salary, plus Sessional Indemnity and expenses.

DEPUTY SPEAKER: $20,420 salary, plus Sessional Indemnity and expenses.

DEPUTY CHAIRMAN OF COMMITTEES: $10,210 salary, plus Sessional Indemnity and expenses.

LEADER OF THE OPPOSITION: $40,841 salary, plus Sessional Indemnity and allowance.

LEADER OF A RECOGNIZED OPPOSITION PARTY: $7,243 salary, plus Sessional Indemnity and allowance.

Members

Constituency	Member and Affiliation
Athabasca/Lac La Biche	Mike Cardinal (PC)
Banff/Cochrane	Brian Evans (PC)
Barrhead	The Hon. Ken Kowalski (PC)
Bonnyville	The Hon. Ernie Isley (PC)
Bow Valley	Tom Musgrove (PC)
Calgary Bow	Bonnie Laing (PC)
Calgary Buffalo	Sheldon Chumir (Lib)
Calgary Currie	The Hon. Dennis Anderson (PC)
Calgary Egmont	The Hon Dr. David Carter (PC)
Calgary Elbow	Ralph Klein (PC)
Calgary Fish Creek	William Payne (PC)
Calgary Foothills	Pat Black (PC)
Calgary Forest Lawn	Barry Pashak (NDP)
Calgary Glenmore	Dianne Mirosh (PC)
Calgary McCall	Stan Nelson (PC)
Calgary McKnight	Yolande Gagnon (Lib)
Calgary Millican	Gordon Shrake (PC)
Calgary Montrose	The Hon. Rick Orman (PC)
Calgary Mountain View	Bob Hawkesworth (NDP)
Calgary North Hill	Fred Stewart (PC)
Calgary North West	Frank Bruseker (Lib)
Calgary Shaw	The Hon. Jim Dinning (PC)
Calgary West	The Hon. Elaine McCoy (PC)
Camrose	The Hon. Ken Rostad (PC)
Cardston	Jack Ady (PC)
Chinook	Shirley McClellan (PC)
Clover Bar	Kurt Gesell (PC)
Cypress Redcliff	Alan Hyland (PC)
Drayton Valley	Tom Thurber (PC)
Drumheller	Stan Schumacher (PC)
Dunvegan	Glen Clegg (PC)
Edmonton Avonmore	Marie Laing (NDP)
Edmonton Belmont	Tom Sigurdson (NDP)
Edmonton Beverly	Ed Ewasiuk (NDP)
Edmonton Calder	Christie Mjolsness (NDP)
Edmonton Centre	William Roberts (NDP)

Constituency	Member and Affiliation
Edmonton Glengarry	Laurence Decore (Lib)
Edmonton Glenora	The Hon. Nancy Betkowski (PC)
Edmonton Gold Bar	Bettie Hewes (Lib)
Edmonton Highlands	Pam Barrett (NDP)
Edmonton Jasper Place	John McInnis (NDP)
Edmonton Kingsway	Alex McEachern (NDP)
Edmonton Meadowlark	Grant Mitchell (Lib)
Edmonton Mill Woods	Gerry Gibeault (NDP)
Edmonton Norwood	Ray Martin (NDP)
Edmonton Parkallen	Doug Main (PC)
Edmonton Strathcona	Gordon Wright (NDP)
Edmonton Whitemud	Percy Wickman (Lib)
Fort McMurray	The Hon. Norm Weiss (PC)
Grande Prairie	Dr. Bob Elliott (PC)
Highwood	Don Tannas (PC)
Innisfail	Gary Severtson (PC)
Lacombe	Ron Moore (PC)
Lesser Slave Lake	Pearl M. Calahasen (PC)
Lethbridge East	The Hon. Dick Johnston (PC)
Lethbridge West	John Gogo (PC)
Little Bow	Raymond A. Speaker (PC)
Lloydminster	Doug Cherry (PC)
Macleod	The Hon. LeRoy Fjordbotten (PC)
Medicine Hat	The Hon. James D. Horsman (PC)
Olds/Didsbury	Roy Brassard (PC)
Peace River	The Hon. J. Allen Adair (PC)
Pincher Creek/Crowsnest	Fred D. Bradley (PC)
Ponoka/Rimbey	Halvar Jonson (PC)
Red Deer North	Stockwell Day (PC)
Red Deer South	John Oldring (PC)
Redwater/Andrew	Steve Zarusky (PC)
Rocky Mountain House	Ty Lund (PC)
St. Albert	Dick Fowler (PC)
St. Paul	John Drobot (PC)
Sherwood Park	The Hon. Peter Elzinga (PC)
Smoky River	Walter Paszkowski (PC)
Stettler	Brian Downey (PC)
Stony Plain	Stan Woloshyn (NDP)
Taber/Warner	Bob Bogle (PC)
Three Hills	The Hon. Connie Osterman (PC)
Vegreville	Derek Fox (NDP)
Vermilion/Viking	Dr. Steve West (PC)
Wainwright	Robert Fischer (PC)
West Yellowhead	Jerry Doyle (NDP)
Westlock/Sturgeon	Nick Taylor (Lib)
Wetaskiwin/Leduc	The Hon. Donald Sparrow (PC)
Whitecourt	Peter Trynchy (PC)

Lib — Liberal
NDP — New Democrat
PC — Progressive Conservative

Officers

Speaker, The Hon. David Carter
Clerk, Dr. David McNeil
Clerk Assistant, Karen South
Parliamentary Counsels: Michael Clegg, Michael Ritter

Sergeant-at-Arms, Oscar J. Lacombe
Auditor General, D.D. Salmon
Chief Electoral Officer,
  Patrick D. Ledgerwood

Head of Information and Reference Services,
  Lorne R. Buhr
Co-ordinator of Co-operative Government
  Library Services, Karen L. Powell

Office of the Premier

307 Legislature Bldg., Edmonton, T5K 2B7

Premier, The Hon. Donald Getty
Exec. Director, R.D. (Bob) Giffin
Exec. Assistant to the Premier,
  Gordon M. Young
Press Secretary, Geoff Davey

Premier's Office (Calgary):
McDougall Centre, Level 2
455-6th St. S.W., Calgary, T2P 4E8
Director, Tom Wood

EXECUTIVE COUNCIL
Deputy Minister, Dr. Barry Mellon
Deputy Secretary of Cabinet, Joyce Ingram
Director of Project Management,
  Al W. Anderson

Offices of the Official Opposition

202 Legislature Bldg., Edmonton, T5K 2B6

Leader of the Official Opposition,
  Ray Martin
Research Director, Kim Pollack
Caucus Co-ordinator
Director, Cindy Hickmore

Offices of the Liberal Party

204 Legislature Annex, Edmonton, T5K 1E4

Leader, Laurence Decore
Chief of Staff (Political), Alex Macdonald
Chief of Staff (Legislature), Bob Russell

Legislature Library

216 Legislature Bldg., Edmonton, T5K 2B6
General Inquiries: (403) 427-2473

The Legislature Library serves two basic purposes. First, it provides parliamentary library services for the Province of Alberta. Second, it provides technical counsel concerning the development of provincial government department libraries and co-ordinates some of the co-operative programs which have been established among these libraries.

Legislature Librarian, D. Blake McDougall

Office of the Provincial Ombudsman

1630 Phipps-McKinnon Bldg.
10020-101A Ave., Edmonton, T5J 3G2
General Inquiries: (403) 427-2756

The Office of the Ombudsman was established in the Province of Alberta in 1967, the first such office in North America. The Ombudsman is appointed by, and reports to, the Legislative Assembly.

The Ombudsman investigates complaints against the departments and agencies of the government of the Province of Alberta. Any person may complain in writing to this office and if the complaint can be supported after full investigation, the Ombudsman may make a recommendation to the department asking that the matter of the complaint be rectified.

Provincial Ombudsman, Aleck Trawick

Branch Office:
1080 McFarlane Tower
700-4th Ave. S.W., Calgary, T2P 3J4
Inquiries: (403) 297-1685

DEPARTMENT OF ADVANCED EDUCATION

Devonian Bldg., East Tower
11160 Jasper Ave., Edmonton, T5K 0L3
Information: (403) 427-2781

MINISTER'S OFFICE
323 Legislature Bldg., Edmonton, T5K 2B6
Minister, The Hon. David Russell
Note: The Hon. David Russell did not run in the recent general election. A replacement had not yet been named as of date of publication.

DEPUTY MINISTER'S OFFICE
Dep. Minister, G. Lynne Duncan
PAI Management Support
Director, E. Cunningham

Operations Division
Asst. Dep. Minister, Neil Henry
Operating and Endowment Support
Director, P.G. Gougeon
Campus Development Services
Director, L. Pastuszenko
Special Programs
Director, Dr. B.W. Pickard
Community Programs
Director, J.F. Fisher

Private Vocational Schools
Director, Dr. A.M. Hendry
Pakistan Project
Director, K. Oliver

Policy and Planning Division
Asst. Dep. Minister, Dr. W. Workman
System Development
Director, Dr. G.R. Babcock
Program Co-ordination
Director, W.E. Novasky
Research and Information Support
Director, P. Hill

DEPARTMENT SERVICES
Exec. Director, P.E. Schmidt
Communications Branch
Director, J.M. Simmons
Librarian, L.E. Harris
Information Services
A/Director, S. Rajwani
Personnel Services
Director, D.R. Sheppard
Legislative Services
Director, L.J. Richardson
Finance Director, G. Waisman
Internal Review
Director, L.N. Robbins

PROVINCIALLY ADMINISTERED
INSTITUTIONS
Alberta Vocational Centre—Calgary
President, Dr. F.J. Speckeen
Alberta Vocational Centre—Edmonton
President, M. Andrews
Alberta Vocational Centre—Lesser Slave Lake
President, D. Vandermuelen
Alberta Vocational Centre—Lac La Biche
President, D.E. Langford

AGENCIES, BOARDS AND COMMISSIONS

Alberta Council on Admissions and Transfer
430, 108th St. Bldg.
9942-108th St., Edmonton, T5K 2J5

The Alberta Council on Admissions and Transfer, established in 1974 as an independent body which reports annually to the Minister of Advanced Education, is responsible for developing policies, guidelines, and procedures designed to facilitate transfer arrangements among post-secondary institutions. The 14-member Council plays an active role in the implementation of these policies through monitoring, mediation, and research. It has a continuing responsibility for facilitating improvement in communications and working relationships among institutions regarding the admission of transfer students and the awarding of transfer credit. Each year in its *Alberta Transfer Guide,* it publishes a compilation of all existing admissions policies and transfer arrangements duly negotiated and approved within the Alberta system of post-secondary education. The publication, which is the official statement of such transfer arrangements, is considered indispensable for transfer operations within the province and is used by other jurisdictions in support of Alberta students transferring there.

The Council includes the chairman and representatives from the public, students, universities, public colleges and technical institutes, provincially administered institutions, hospital schools of nursing, and private colleges.

Chairman, T. Moore

Alberta Foundation for Nursing Research
3125 Manulife Place
10180-101st St., Edmonton, T5J 3S4

The Alberta Foundation for Nursing Research was established by the government of Alberta in October 1982 with the aim of enhancing the quality and quantity of nursing research in Alberta for the purpose of improving nursing practice. In 1988, the Foundation was given an additional one million dollars to administer over a five-year period to nurses wishing to conduct nursing research. Grants are available in research categories which include: Conferences/Workshops, Demonstration/Evaluation Projects, Facilitation Grants, Research Projects, Research Support Services Grants, and Student Research Bursaries.

Chairman, J. Calkin
Professor and Dean, Faculty of Nursing
University of Calgary
2500 University Dr., Calgary, T2N 1N4

Policy Advisory Committee

The Advanced Education Policy Advisory Committee was established by ministerial order in October 1987 in accordance with section 5 of the *Department of Advanced Education Act.* It was created by the Minister of Advanced Education to receive public input regarding the Alberta post-secondary education system as well as to inquire into issues referred to it by the minister, to recommend studies to assist long-term planning, and to provide access to knowledge and expertise respecting post-secondary education and its relationship to Alberta's economic, scientific, social, and cultural objectives. The Advisory Committee consists of 12 members drawn from the private, student, and institutional sectors.

Chairman, W. Gould
Box 688, Mayerthorpe, T0E 1N0

Private Colleges Accreditation Board
Devonian Bldg., East Twr., 6th Flr.
11160 Jasper Ave., Edmonton, T5K 0L3

The Private Colleges Accreditation Board was established by an amendment to Alberta's *Universities Act* in May 1984. The Board is responsible for receiving and reviewing applications from private colleges that are interested in obtaining the authority to grant their own baccalaureate degrees. The Board may inquire into any matter that relates to the approval of programs of study, other than programs in divinity, leading to a baccalaureate that may be granted by a private college. If the Board determines that a private college has met the prescribed conditions, it approves the program of study and recommends to the Minister of Advanced Education that the private college be granted the power to grant a baccalaureate in respect of that approved program of study. On the recommendation of the minister, the Lieutenant-Governor in Council may by order designate a private college as an institution that may grant such a degree. The Board also is responsible for establishing procedures for the periodic review of approved programs of study and for recommending to the minister that programs of study should no longer be designated.

The Board consists of 12 members and a chairman, all appointed by the Minister of Advanced Education. The chairman reports to the minister. The 12 members are made up of four academic staff members of Alberta's universities, nominated by the Universities Co-ordinating Council; four members nominated by the chief executive officers of Alberta's private colleges; and four members of the public.

As of November 1987, the Board has received applications from four private colleges. On the recommendation of the Board, the Government has granted three of these colleges the authority to grant specific degrees: Camrose Lutheran College in Camrose, and The King's and Concordia Colleges in Edmonton. The Board is still considering the fourth application.

Chairman, Dr. W. Worth
Exec. Secretary, Dr. L.J. Orton

Students' Finance Board
Baker Ctr., 10th Flr., 10025-106th St.
Edmonton, T5J 1G7
General Inquiries: (403) 427-2740

The eleven-member Students' Finance Board, which includes two student representatives, consists of members of the public appointed by the Minister of Advanced Education. The Board administers a wide variety of programs designed to offer educational assistance, predominantly at the post-secondary level, but also at the junior high and high school levels. These programs consist of loans, grants, bursaries, scholarships, and prizes, including the Alberta Heritage Scholarship Fund, which rewards achievement at all levels of institutional study, in the work place, and in the fields of athletics and recreation.

Chairman, Mark Tims
CEO, F.T. Hemingway

DEPARTMENT OF AGRICULTURE
Agriculture Bldg., 7000-113th St.
Edmonton, T6H 5T6
Information: (403) 427-2727

MINISTER'S OFFICE
324 Legislature Bldg., Edmonton, T5K 2B6
Minister, The Hon. Peter Elzinga

ASSOCIATE MINISTER'S OFFICE
319 Legislature Bldg., Edmonton, T5K 2B6
Assoc. Minister, The Hon. Shirley Cripps
Note: The Hon. Shirley Cripps did not run in the recent general election. A replacement had not yet been named as of date of publication.

DEPUTY MINISTER'S OFFICE
Dep. Minister, H.B. McEwen
Financial and Administrative Services
Director, D. Yakabuski
Personnel Services
Director, C. Davidson
Research Division
Director, R. Christian

Field Services
Asst. Dep. Minister, W.J. Dent
RURAL SERVICES DIVISION
Director, I. Leavitt
Home Economics Branch
Head, S. Myers
4-H Branch
Head, R.T. Youck
Agricultural Engineering Branch
Head, R.S. Forrest
Agricultural and Community Services Branch
Head, Reg Kontz
Agriculture Education Branch
Head, W. Wismer

INFORMATION SERVICES DIVISION
Director, J. Armet
Broadcast Media
Branch Head, Vacant
Print Media
Branch Head, S. Reid
Librarian, Robert Bateman

REGIONAL OFFICES:
Southern Region
Agriculture Centre, Jail Rd.
Lethbridge, T1J 4C7
Director, R.R. Young
South Central Region
Agriculture Centre, Bag Service 1
Airdrie, T0M 0B0
Director, G.W. Werner
Central Region
Provincial Bldg., 3rd Flr.
4920-41st St., Red Deer, T4N 6K8
Director, W.A. Hall
Northeast Region
Provincial Bldg., Box 330, Vermilion, T0B 4M0
Director, R.F. Berkan
Northwest Region
Provincial Bldg., Box 1540, Barrhead, T0G 0E0
Director, J.B. Tackaberry
Peace Region
Provincial Bldg., Box 7777, Fairview, T0H 0L0
Director, J.A. Knapp

Marketing
Asst. Dep. Minister, B.D. Mehr
MARKET DEVELOPMENT
Exec. Director, Cliff Wulff
International Trade
(Europe, Middle East and Africa)
Director, D. Hill
International Trade (Pacific, Asia)
Sr. Director, D. Wong
Trade (Americas)
Sr. Director, Arnold de Leeuw
Marketing Services
Director, D. Glover
Food Processing Development Centre
Branch Head, D.J. Schroder
Food Laboratory Services
Branch Head, V.W. Kadis
Agriculture Processing and Agri-Food
Development
Branch Head, L. Norman
Business Analysis
Branch Head, S.G. Hanna
Rural Development
Exec. Director, Dr. J.E. Wiebe
Trade Policy Secretariat
Director, Dr. J.A. Rosario

Planning and Development
Asst. Dep. Minister, C.D. Radke
Irrigation Secretariat
Provincial Bldg., Lethbridge, T1J 4C7
Manager, G.P. Hartman
Irrigation and Resource Management Division
7000-113th St., Edmonton, T6H 5T6
Director, B. Colgan
Irrigation Branch
Agriculture Centre, Lethbridge, T1J 4C7
Head, A. Pungor
Land Evaluation and Reclamation Branch
Agriculture Centre, Lethbridge, T1J 4C7
Head, B. Paterson
Conservation and Development Branch
7000-113th St., Edmonton, T6H 5T6
Head, P. Barlott
Economic Services Division
7000-113th St., Edmonton, T6H 5T6
Director, L. Lyster
Production Economics
Head, Carlyle Ross
Statistics Branch
Head, C. Sterling
Market Analysis Branch
Head, D. Walker
Farm Business Management Branch
Provincial Bldg., Olds, T0M 1P0
Head, W. Loree
Planning Secretariat
Chairman, S. Schellenberger
Resource Planning
Systems Development
Director, D. Daviduk

Production
Asst. Dep. Minister, J. Harold Hanna
Centralized Program Support, Alberta Farm

Credit Stability Program, Alberta Red Meat
Stabilization Program
Administrator, Ken Moholitny

ANIMAL INDUSTRY DIVISION
204, 7000-113th St., Edmonton, T6H 5T6
Director, Ken J. Spiller
Beef Cattle and Sheep Branch
Head, Ron D. Weisenburger
Pork Industry Branch
Head, Fred W. Schuld
Poultry Branch
Head, T. Sydness
Regulatory Services Branch
Head, C.W. (Bill) Herbert
Horse Industry Branch
205, 2003 McKnight Blvd. N.E.
Calgary, T2E 6L2
Head, J. Doug Milligan
Dairy Branch
5201-50th Ave., Wetaskiwin, T9A 0S7
Head, Ed Bristow
Dairy Processing Branch
5201-50th Ave., Wetaskiwin, T9A 0S7
Head, K. Waldon

PLANT INDUSTRY DIVISION
Director, D. Macyk
Alberta Special Crops and Horticulture
Research Ctr., Brooks, T0J 0J0
Director, Thomas Krahn
Soil and Animal Nutrition Laboratory
O.S. Longman Bldg.
6909-116th St., Edmonton, T6H 4P2
Director, E. Redshaw
ANIMAL HEALTH DIVISION
A/Director, T.L. Church

AGENCIES, BOARDS, COMMISSIONS AND CROWN CORPORATIONS

MARKETING BOARDS

Marketing boards for agricultural products in Canada are created by a number of different pieces of legislation. National wheat and dairy products plans flow from the *Canadian Wheat Board Act* and the *Canadian Dairy Commission Act* respectively. Egg and poultry boards derive their authority from the *Farm Products Marketing Agencies Act.* As well, many have their own provincial statutes and are normally within the jurisdiction of an umbrella provincial agency. The individual boards are, however, non-governmental and made up largely of elected farmer representatives.

There is also a variety of types. The Economic Council of Canada's study on marketing boards identified five: promotional and developmental boards with little power; selling-desk boards that handle marketing but do not set prices; boards that negotiate prices; boards that set prices; and full-fledged boards that establish quotas. These last are known as supply-management marketing boards. Currently, there are more than 100 active boards in Canada.

AGRICULTURAL PRODUCTS MARKETING COUNCIL
305, 7000-113th St., Edmonton, T6H 5T6

The Agricultural Products Marketing Council was formed in 1965 to administer the *Marketing of Agricultural Products Act* (Alberta). It facilitates the establishment of marketing boards and commissions and supervises their operation. At present, there are eight boards and three commissions which cover such commodities as eggs, broiler chickens, turkeys, hogs, cattle, fresh vegetables, processed vegetables, potatoes, sheep and wool, hatching eggs, and sugar beets.

The Council currently consists of a chairman and nine members who are appointed by the Lieutenant-Governor in Council.

Chairman, H. Buckley
Gen. Manager, K. Smith
Secretary, C. Foster

ALBERTA CATTLE COMMISSION
241, 2116-27th Ave. N.E., Calgary, T2E 7A6

The Alberta Cattle Commission was established by cattle producers in 1969. The Commission helps maintain a viable and competitive cattle industry in Alberta by representing the views of cattle producers to governments, by promoting beef sales, and by fostering communication among all facets of the beef industry.

All cattle producers are required to pay a per-head-sold fee to the Commission. Consequently, they are considered members and have access to work done by the Commission. Ninety delegates meet twice a year to determine policy and elect a board of directors for a one-year term.

Chairman, George Schoepp
Manager, Dennis Laycraft

ALBERTA CHICKEN PRODUCERS' MARKETING BOARD
101, 11826-100th Ave., Edmonton, T5K 0K3
Chairman, D. Falkenberg
Sec.-Manager, Roger King

ALBERTA DAIRY CONTROL BOARD
5201-50th Ave., Wetaskiwin, T9A 0S7

The Board is appointed by the Lieutenant-Governor in Council under provisions of the *Dairy Board Act* to control and regulate the sale of milk in Alberta.

The Board may make such regulations and orders as it considers necessary in governing and controlling the production, processing, supply, transportation, distribution, or sale of milk within Alberta.

Specific functions in the fluid sector include the licensing of producers and processors and the administration of quotas and prices. In the industrial sector, the Board is the signatory agency to the National Milk Marketing Plan and administers the program in Alberta for milk that is used for butter, milk powder, and cheese.

Chairman, M. Dordevic
Sec.-Manager, L. Johnston

ALBERTA EGG AND FOWL MARKETING BOARD
15, 1915-32nd Ave. N.E., Calgary, T2E 7C8
Chairman, Charles Van Arnam
R.R. 2, Carstairs, T0M 0N0
Gen. Manager, Warren P. Chorney

ALBERTA FRESH VEGETABLE MARKETING BOARD
220E N. 12th St., Lethbridge, T1H 2J1

The general purpose of the Board is, to the extent of its mandate, to provide for the promotion, control, and regulation of fresh vegetable marketing within Alberta. Its related responsibilities include establishing a base price for producers, issuing licences, establishing and maintaining a system of marketing, establishing a system of grading, and organizing promotional and research activities.

Chairman, Reuben Huber
Sec.-Manager, Sharon Chmielewski

ALBERTA HATCHING EGG MARKETING BOARD
14815-119th Ave., Edmonton, T5L 2N9
Chairman, G. Wickersham
Sec.-Manager, Leo Douziech

ALBERTA PORK PRODUCERS' MARKETING BOARD
10319 Princess Elizabeth Ave.
Edmonton, T5G 0Y5

The Alberta Pork Producers' Marketing Board was formed in 1969 as the sole selling agency for market hogs in the province.

The Board is a producer-elected, nine-member body which meets regularly to formulate policy with respect to the sale of market hogs, the development of new markets, the promotion of pork and pork products, and the general well-being of the Alberta pork industry.

Chairman, Bill Devereux
Gen. Manager, Ed Schultz

ALBERTA POTATO MARKETING BOARD
244, 2116-27th Ave. N.E., Calgary, T2E 7A6

The purpose of the Alberta Potato Marketing Board is to establish and maintain a minimum price at which any class of potatoes, except potatoes for processing, may be sold in Alberta. Registered producers growing over five acres of potatoes are licensed by the Board, as are dealers, packers, and processors.

The responsibilities of the Board encompass study and research in potato production, processing, and marketing. This information reaches producers through extension services provided by the Board's office. Advertising and sales promotion are activities that increase awareness of an Alberta-grown product.

The Commission consists of seven members, of which four are elected from districts and three persons are elected at large.

Chairman, Jim Visser
Visser Farms (1984) Ltd., R.R. 6
Box 171, Edmonton, T5B 4K3
Manager, Jan Brown

ALBERTA SHEEP AND WOOL COMMISSION
231, 2116-27th Ave. N.E., Calgary, T2E 7A6

The Alberta Sheep and Wool Commission was established in 1972. The Commission is controlled by the sheep producers of Alberta through a board of directors elected at the annual zone meetings held in March.

The mandate of the Commission is to assist in the development of the sheep and wool industry in Alberta and the promotion of lamb consumption. The Commission also serves as the voice of the Alberta sheep producer to provincial and federal governments. In recent years, the Commission has, on behalf of the Canada Sheep Council, become involved in trade issues involving lamb importation from Oceania. The Commission publishes a magazine entitled *The Western Sheep and Wool Producer,* which serves as a communication tool to sheep producers and provides timely news on sheep industry issues.

Chairman, Geoff DeBoer
Sec.-Manager, Will Verboven

ALBERTA SUGAR BEET GROWERS' MARKETING BOARD
3514 N. 6th Ave., Lethbridge, T1H 5C3

An association of sugar beet growers originally formed in Alberta in 1925. It has evolved through several name changes to its current status as the Alberta Sugar Beet Growers' Marketing Board, formed in August 1985.

The Board's primary objective is to bring growers together as a unit for the continued progress of the sugar beet industry. Annual negotiations with the processor, the Alberta Sugar Company (a subsidiary of the B.C. Sugar Company), to establish a master contract are followed by individual contracting between growers and the processor. The Board, along with the processors, monitors the growing of the crop to ensure the continued high quality of the product.

A joint company-grower research committee endeavours to have only top quality seed used. Testing of seed from various suppliers is carried out annually. Also, information is gathered on purity, sugar content, beet storability, and other topics that are helpful to growers and to the industry.

The Alberta Sugar Beet Growers' Marketing Board and the Manitoba sugar beet growers elect members to the Canadian Sugar Beet Producers Assn., a body that deals with matters of national interest such as the establishment of a Canadian sugar policy.

Chairman, Paul Thibodeau
Sec.-Treasurer, Rita McEwen

ALBERTA TURKEY GROWERS' MARKETING BOARD
11826-100th Ave., Edmonton, T5K 0K3
Chairman, Henry Zolkewski
Sec.-Manager, Don Potter

ALBERTA VEGETABLE GROWERS' MARKETING BOARD
Box 2273, Taber, T0K 2G0

The Alberta Vegetable Growers' Marketing Board, established in 1958, was the first marketing board in Alberta.

Its policy objectives are as follows:
- to negotiate fair returns to producers;
- to ensure fair grades and weights;
- to promote better grower-processor relations; and
- to promote the industry.

An Industry Advisory Committee advises the Board regarding (a) prices payable to growers for the regulated product; (b) prices of seed, harvesting costs, etc.; (c) problems in the industry such as grades, dockage, seed, harvesting, and contracts. It is composed of an equal number of growers and processors with an independent chairman agreed upon by both parties.

The Board has the power to license producers and processors and to set the terms of sale and prices. The minimum prices are set after negotiation with processors. Growers pay a levy of one and one quarter per cent of the total sale price of the product delivered to the processor.

Chairman, Jim Tanner
Sec.-Manager, A. Anderson

Agricultural Development Corp.
Bag 5000, Camrose, T4V 4E8

The Agricultural Development Corporation (ADC) was established in 1972 as a provincial agency of the Crown responsible to the Minister of Agriculture. ADC provides financial assistance to primary producers of agricultural products, the owners of associated businesses, and to agricultural processing and service industries in Alberta through its various direct and guaranteed lending programs.

The Corporation functions as a supplementary lender to help meet the legitimate credit needs of Albertans involved in the agricultural industry who are unable to borrow from other sources at reasonable terms and conditions. Other sources of credit should be investigated before applying to ADC, except for beginning farmers who may apply to ADC without first approaching other lenders.

Chairman of the Board, Harold P. Thorton
President and Man. Director, Robert A. Splane

Alberta Agriculture Research Institute
7000-113th St., 2nd Flr., Edmonton, T6H 5T6
Chairman, Bob Bogle
Exec. Director, R. Christian

Alberta Grain Commission

J.G. O'Donoghue Bldg.
7000-113th St., Edmonton, T6H 5T6

The Alberta Grain Commission was established in March 1972. The Commission continuously reviews all aspects of the grain industry in Alberta in order to make policy recommendations to the minister. Its aim is to increase net farm income in Alberta.

Chairman, Ken Beswick

Alberta Hail and Crop Insurance Corp.

Alberta Agriculture Bldg., 2nd Flr.
5718-56th Ave., Bag 16, Lacombe, T0C 1S0

The Alberta Hail and Crop Insurance Corporation is a Crown corporation of the province of Alberta established under authority of the *Hail and Crop Insurance Act* (1969). The Corporation administers two separate insurance programs: hail insurance and "all-risk" crop insurance. It also administers the Wildlife Damage Fund for the Fish and Wildlife Division of the Department of Forestry, Lands and Wildlife.

The Corporation offers farmers the opportunity to insure their grain crops against losses caused by natural hazards, and by so doing to help stabilize the farm economy.

Chairman, Peter Trynchy
Gen. Manager, Glenn M. Gorrell
Office Manager, L.H. Nelson
Comptroller, L.G. Bannerman
Director of Country Operations,
Dwayne Campbell

Farmers' Advocate

7000-113th St., Edmonton, T6H 5T6

The Office of the Farmers' Advocate was created by the Government of Alberta to assist farmers with their individual and collective problems and to mediate between farmers and ranchers and other industrial groups, notably manufacturers and energy companies.

The Farmers' Advocate represents the farming community as a whole in its dealings with the various levels of government and with other industries on larger questions. As well, the Advocate will assist or mediate in disputes between individual farmers in cases such as machinery warranty, trespass or damage by seismic or drilling contractors, predator damage, or mineral rights. The Advocate cannot become involved in cases where a legal resolution has been sought.
C. Downey

Irrigation Council

Provincial Bldg., Lethbridge, T1J 4C7

The Irrigation Council, which operates under the legislative authority of the *Irrigation Act* of Alberta, is composed of eight members: two civil servant members and six non-civil-servant members, who are appointed by the Lieutenant-Governor in Council on the recommendation of the Minister of Agriculture.

The objectives of the Irrigation Council are to implement a sound irrigation policy for the province, to administer the *Irrigation Act,* and to administer any cost-sharing agreements entered into between the province and the irrigation districts for the rehabilitation and expansion of district works.

The Irrigation Council acts as an advisory body to the Minister of Agriculture on matters pertaining to irrigation policies, and to the irrigation district boards on the conduct of the affairs of their district, and carries out the duties and exercises the powers as specifically laid out in the *Irrigation Act.* Some of these specific powers and duties include: the approval of irrigation district money by-laws, rates, and budgets; the approval of petitions to add or delete lands to or from a district; and the preparation of land classification standards.

Chairman, Ed Shimbashi
Manager, G.P. Hartman

Surface Rights Board

Phipps-McKinnon Bldg., 18th Flr.
10020-101A Ave., Edmonton, T5J 3G2

The Surface Rights Board is a quasi-judicial board established under *The Surface Rights Act.* It grants operators the right to enter on and use the surface of land for mineral recovery operations and for the construction and operation of power transmission lines, pipelines, and telephone lines, where the operator has been unable to acquire the necessary right by consent of the owner or occupant of that land. It also holds hearings, in those cases where a private agreement can not be reached, to determine the compensation payable by the operator and the person entitled to receive the compensation.

The Board holds hearings with respect to damage disputes and requests for review of annual compensation under Board compensation orders and surface leases.

The Board issues written decisions to the parties concerned as required by *The Administrative Procedure Act* in all cases where a hearing is held and a decision required. The Board issues orders granting right of entry, terminating right of entry, fixing compensation, amending or varying compensation on review, and various incidental orders, and assists in the recovery of money owed by an operator to any person under Board orders or surface leases.

Chairman, C.J. (Cec) Purves
Exec. Director and Secretary,
T. Alan Champion

DEPARTMENT OF THE ATTORNEY GENERAL

The Bowker Bldg.
9833-109th St., Edmonton, T5K 2E8
(except where otherwise indicated)
Information: (403) 427-2745

ATTORNEY GENERAL'S OFFICE
127 Legislature Bldg., Edmonton, T5K 2B6
Attorney General, The Hon. Ken Rostad, Q.C.

DEPUTY ATTORNEY GENERAL'S OFFICE
Dep. Attorney General and Dep.
Provincial Secretary, D.W. Perras, Q.C.

ADMINISTRATION
Exec. Director, D. Medwid
Executive Support Services
Manager, R. Petruk
Administrative Services
Director, H.A. Brinton
Materials and Facilities
Manager, R. Remmer
Records and Micrographics
Manager, W. Joyce
Communications/Public Affairs
Director, L. Gronow
Financial Services
Director, I. Hope
Internal Audit
Director, E. Berg
Personnel Services
Director, D. Dawson
Systems and Information Services
J.E. Brownlee Bldg., 6th Flr.
10365-97th St., Edmonton, T5J 3W7
Director, J. Sorenson
Planning and Policy Co-ordination Branch
J.E. Brownlee Bldg., 3rd Flr.
10365-97th St., Edmonton, T5J 3W7
Director, J. Wilson

Civil
General Inquiries: (403) 427-5114
Asst. Dep. Minister, D.G. Rae, Q.C.
Civil Law
Exec. Director, R.N. Dunne
Legal Research and Analysis
General Inquiries: (403) 427-5293
Director, C. Dalton
Constitutional and Energy Law
Director, N. Steed

Court and Property Services
Asst. Dep. Minister, J.E. Klinck
PUBLIC TRUSTEE
J.E. Brownlee Bldg., 4th Flr.
10365-97th St., Edmonton, T5J 3Z8
General Inquiries: (403) 427-2744
Public Trustee, William A. deNance

PROPERTY REGISTRATION
10365-97th St., Mezz., Edmonton, T5J 3W7
Director, K. Payne
10365-97th St., 5th Flr., Edmonton, T5J 3W7
Asst. Director, G. Ho
Land Titles
10365-97th St., 3rd Flr., Edmonton, T5J 3W7
General Inquiries: (403) 427-2742
Dep. Registrar, (Technical), W.E. Campion
J.J. Bowlen Bldg.
620-7th Ave. S.W., Calgary, T2P 0Y8

General Inquiries: (403) 297-6511
Registrar, P. Hartman
Personal Property
10365-97th St., 5th Flr., Edmonton, T5J 3W7
A/Registrar, R. Shariff
Rm. 304, J.J. Bowlen Bldg.
620-7th Ave. S.W., Calgary, T2P 0Y8
Manager, J. Bleviss

COURT SERVICES
Exec. Director, B. Dunster
REGIONAL DIRECTORS:
Rural
John Bachinski
Court House, 3 St. Anne St.
St. Albert, T8N 2E8
Edmonton
D.S. Huff
Law Courts Bldg., Mezz.
1-A Sir Winston Churchill Sq.
Edmonton, T5J 0R2
Calgary
J. McLaughlin
Court House, 611-4th St. S.W.
Calgary, T2P 1T5
Masters in Chambers
Law Courts Bldg.
1-A Sir Winston Churchill Sq.
Edmonton, T5J 0R2
W.A. Breitkreuz, M.B. Funduk, W.J. Quinn
Court House, 611-4th St. S.W.
Calgary, T2P 1T5
W.H. Dalgleish, Q.C., R.M. Cairns,
L. Alberstat, J.P. Floyd

Libraries
Law Courts Bldg.
1-A Sir Winston Churchill Sq.
Edmonton, T5J 0R2
Chief Provincial Law Librarian, Shih-Sheng Hu
Law Society Librarian (Northern Region)
Ahlam Balazs
The Bowker Bldg.
9833-109th St., Edmonton, T5K 2E8
Departmental Librarian, Andrew Balazs
Court House, 611-4th St. S.W.
Calgary, T2P 1T5
Law Society Librarian (Southern Region),
Melody Hainsworth
Law Courts Bldg.
1-A Sir Winston Churchill Sq.
Edmonton, T5J 0R2
Chief Provincial Court Librarian,
Neil A. Campbell
Provincial Court Libraries (South)
Provincial Court Bldg.
323-6th Ave. S.E., Calgary, T2G 4V1
Regional Librarian, Penelope Hamilton
J.E. Brownlee Bldg., 10365-97th St.
Edmonton, T5J 3W7
Crown Counsel Librarian (North),
Dani Pahulje
Court House, 320 S. 4th St.
Lethbridge, T1J 3W6
Law Society Librarian, Grant Janzen

Sheriff's Operations
Law Courts Bldg.
1-A Sir Winston Churchill Sq.
Edmonton, T5J 0R2
Asst. Sheriff/Manager, J.D. Blower
Court House Annex, 603-6th Ave. S.W.
Box 1830, Stn. M, Calgary, T2P 0Y3
Asst. Sheriff/Manager, G. Fofonoff

Criminal
General Inquiries: (403) 427-5050
Asst. Dep. Minister, N. McCrank
Gen. Counsel, J.S. Koval, Q.C.
General Prosecutions Branch
Director, R.H. Davie, Q.C.
Asst. Director, P.V. Teasdale
Law Branch
A/Director, R. Wacowich
Appeals, Research and Special Projects Branch
Director, P. Bourque
Special Prosecutions
Standard Life Bldg., 4th Flr.
639-5th Ave. S.W., Calgary, T2P 0M9
Director, B.R. Fraser, Q.C.
Gaming Control
J.E. Brownlee Bldg., 5th Flr.
10365-97th St., Edmonton, T5J 3W7
Director, W.W. McCall

LEGISLATIVE COUNSEL
The Bowker Bldg.
9833-109th St., Edmonton, T5K 2E8
Chief Legislative Counsel, P. Pagano

MEDICAL EXAMINER/FATALITY INQUIRIES
4070 Browness Rd. N.W., Calgary, T3B 3R7
Chief Medical Examiner, Dr. J.C. Butt
7007-116th St., Edmonton, T6H 5R8
Dep. Chief Medical Examiner,
Dr. G.P. Dowling

AGENCIES, BOARDS AND COMMISSIONS

Crimes Compensation Board
J.E. Brownlee Bldg., 7th Flr.
10365-97th St., Edmonton, T5J 3W7
General Inquiries: (403) 427-7217

The Crimes Compensation Board, established in 1969 by the *Criminal Injuries Compensation Act*, is responsible for the investigation and assessment of claims for compensation made by victims of violent crimes.

Compensation for damage to property can be claimed in only two cases: (a) for loss of or damage to clothing and eyeglasses worn at the time; (b) for damage caused by a peace officer while he is preventing a criminal offence or arresting a criminal or suspect. There is a $10,000 limit to the damage that can be claimed.

Compensation for pain and suffering (maximum amount: $10,000) can only be awarded if the victim was making an arrest, or helping a peace officer in the performance of his duties. If the victim is killed, funeral expenses and support for any dependent relative may be claimed. There is no limit to an award for pecuniary loss.

The Board investigates the claim and must hold a hearing. The applicant may be represented by counsel and the Board may order payment of a counsel's fee. There is no appeal from a decision of the Board except on a question of law or of jurisdiction; in that case, an appeal is made to the Appellate Division of the Supreme Court of Alberta. The crime must have been committed in Alberta but anyone suffering injury and damage, whether a resident or not, may make a claim.

The three members of the Board are appointed by the Lieutenant-Governor in Council; one must be a lawyer.

Chairman, B.A. Nahornick
Vice-Chairman, T.J. Nugent
Member, Elva Rowland
Secretary, L. Unger

Fatality Review Board
4070 Bowness Rd. N.W., Calgary, T3B 3R7
Chairman, Dr. K. Vic

Gaming Commission
J.E. Brownlee Bldg., 5th Flr.
10365-97th St., Edmonton, T5J 3W7

The Commission was established in 1981 by Order-in-Council, in accordance with section 190 of the *Criminal Code*. Its role is to license and oversee gaming activities by charitable and religious groups in the province. This includes receiving and approving applications for licences, providing information to the public on the management of gaming events, and auditing the financial records of organizations operating bingos, raffles, casinos, etc. Only charitable or religious organizations may be licensed to conduct these activities.

Chairman, K. Joshee, C.M.
Exec. Director, I. Taylor

Land Compensation Board
Canada Trust Twr., 20th Flr.
10140-103rd Ave., Edmonton, T5J 0H8

The Land Compensation Board of Alberta was established pursuant to the province's *Expropriation Act* (1974). The Board deals with expropriations initiated by the Crown through its ministers, departments and agencies or municipal bodies. The Board's primary function is quasi-judicial: to hear and decide disputes as to compensation arising out of expropriations. The Board also has responsibility for a variety of other matters relating to expropriation procedure and rights, proceedings, and other ancillary matters under the Act.

The Board is comprised of a chairman, one full-time and three part-time members.

Chairman, L.L. Wood
Members: W.A. Anderson, C.E. Rusnell,
E. DeArmond, D. Scragg
Secretary to the Board, A. Looye

Legal Aid Society
Sunlife Bldg., 16th Flr.
10123-99th St., Edmonton, T5J 3H1
Exec. Director, N. Nichols

Public Utilities Board
10055-106th St., 11th Flr., Edmonton, T5J 2Y2

The Public Utilities Board is an independent quasi-judicial tribunal which was established in 1915 to regulate public utilities in Alberta. Accordingly, most telecommunications, electric, water, and gas utilities in the province are within the Board's jurisdiction. The primary purpose of the Board is to ensure that customers of these regulated utilities receive service at the lowest rates which are consistent with continuing safe and adequate service. The Board also performs other regulatory functions, including the establishment of the minimum wholesale and retail prices of fluid milk, and the approval of franchise agreements and supply contracts between municipal councils and public utilities. A public hearing is held in connection with all these matters, which enables the Board to consider the views of all interested parties in arriving at its decision.

At present the Board is comprised of seven full-time members.

Chairman, Ammon Ackroyd, Q.C.
Members: A. Jah, A.C. Barfett,
N.W. MacDonald, R.D.S. Ward
Secretary and Exec. Director, W. Paterson
Directors:
Technical Services,
H. Jainarine, R.L. Bruggeman
Regulatory Administration, B. Torrance
Finance and Administration, G. Poston
Systems, D.C. Mackie
Legal Counsel, A.V. Lapko
Regulatory Managers:
A.P. Merani, C. Retnanardan
CALGARY OFFICE:
Energy Resources Bldg., 10th Flr.
640-5th Ave. S.W., Calgary, T2P 0M6
Member, T.D. Hetherington
Supervisor, Mrs. N. Andrews
LETHBRIDGE OFFICE:
Courthouse, Rm. 1-10, 320 S. 4th St.
Lethbridge, T1J 1Z8
Member, J.R. Dunstan

DEPARTMENT OF CAREER DEVELOPMENT AND EMPLOYMENT
Park Sq., 10001 Bellamy Hill
Edmonton, T5J 3W5

MINISTER'S OFFICE
132 Legislature Bldg., Edmonton, T5K 2B6
Minister, The Hon. Ken Kowalski

DEPUTY MINISTER'S OFFICE
Dep. Minister, Al Craig

FINANCE AND ADMINISTRATIVE SERVICES DIVISION
Exec. Director, Reid Zittlau
A/Finance Director, Schubert Kwan
Administrative Services
Director, Dennis Hill
Personnel Director, Jeff Thompson
Communications
A/Director, Mary Layman
LABOUR MARKET RESEARCH DIVISION
Exec. Director, Jim A. Corneil
Labour Markets Statistics Branch
Director, Bob Nicoll
Labour Market Program Evaluation
Director, Dr. Bill Wong
Labour Market Industry Analysis Branch
and Training Information Branch
Director, Dr. Bev MacKeen

Policy and Program Development Division
Asst. Dep. Minister, Dr. Earl Mansfield
Career Programs and Resources
Director, Bill Brandon

TRAINING AND EMPLOYMENT PROGRAMS
Exec. Director, Geoff Anderson
Industry-based Training
Director, Lyn Tait
Employment Programs
Director, Judy Carss
Vocational Training Services
Director, Syl Villett
Alberta Immigration and Settlement
Director, Dave Corbett
Immigration Programs
Manager, Pat Shanahan
Settlement Programs
Manager, Michael Phair
English as a Second Language Secretariat
Manager, Norm Kinsella

APPRENTICESHIP AND TRADE CERTIFICATION
Exec. Director, Don Bell
Program Planning
Director, Don Ogaranko
Programs Support and Registrar
Director, Wayne Nixon
Program Development and Standards
Director, Bob Spencer
Equity Initiatives
Manager, Anne Smith

Field Services Division
Asst. Dep. Minister, Dave Chabillon

REGIONS:
North Region
Box 41, Bag 900, Peace River, T0H 2X0
Reg. Director, John Van Eden
Central Region
Rm. 420, 9942-108th St., Edmonton, T5K 2J5
Reg. Director, Jim Geekie

South Region
Rm. 308, 1015 Centre St. N.W.
Calgary, T2E 2P8
Reg. Director, Ivan Cancik

DEPARTMENT OF CONSUMER AND CORPORATE AFFAIRS

10025 Jasper Ave., 19-22nd Flr.
Edmonton, T5J 3Z5
(except where otherwise indicated)
Information: (403) 427-5782

MINISTER'S OFFICE
104 Legislature Bldg., Edmonton, T5K 2B6
Minister, The Hon. Elaine McCoy

DEPUTY MINISTER'S OFFICE
Dep. Minister, R.J.C. Ford
Corporate Planning
Director, Dave Thompson
Communications
Director, Brian Miller

Community Services
Asst. Dep. Minister, Dave Hudson
Personnel Director, Shirley Howe
Finance Director, Don Woytowich
Consumer Education and Information
Director, Ken Shields
Resource Centre
Supervisor, Heather Gordon

REGIONAL SERVICES
Exec. Director, Pat Brennan

REGIONAL OFFICES:
Calgary
301 Centre 70, 7015 S. Macleod Tr.
Box 5880, Calgary, T2H 2M9
Reg. Director, Francis Smith
Edmonton
Capilano Ctr., 3rd Flr.
9945-50th St., Edmonton, T6A 3X5
Reg. Director, Rick Solkowski
Southern
300 Professional Bldg.
740 S. 4th Ave., Lethbridge, T1J 4C7
Director, Alf Kazuba
Red Deer
4920-51st St., Red Deer, T4N 6K8
Reg. Director, Dale McLaren
Northern
9621-96th Ave., Bag 900, Box 9
Peace River, T0H 2X0
Reg. Director, Shirley Dul

Professional Standards and Services
Asst. Dep. Minister, D.E.L. Keown
Standards Development
Director, Rob Turner
Sup't of Real Estate, Rudy Palovcik
Licensing Director, Harold Baker

Consumer Credit
Director, Don Bence
Co-operatives
A/Director, Burt Eldridge
A/Sup't of Insurance, Bernie Rodrigues
CORPORATE REGISTRY
10365-97th St., 8th Flr., Edmonton, T5J 3W7
Registrar of Corporations, W.W. Proskiw
Public Information: (403) 427-2311

AGENCIES, BOARDS AND COMMISSIONS

Alberta Securities Commission
10025 Jasper Ave., 21st Flr.
Edmonton, T5J 3Z5

The Alberta Securities Commission is an independent agency operating under the umbrella of the Department of Consumer and Corporate Affairs. The main purpose of the Alberta Securities Commission is to protect investing members of the public by regulating both the sale of investments and the sales people. The Commission has legislative authority to protect investors under the *Securities Act,* the *Franchises Act,* and the *Deposit Regulation Act.*

The Alberta Securities Commission is made up of two bodies: the Board and the Agency. The Board a) hears appeals from decisions taken by the Agency, b) receives delegated authority under the above Acts to grant and revoke exemptions, and c) creates policy relating to the securities and deposit regulation legislation. The Agency registers, licenses, and monitors companies and sales persons under the three above Acts. It also enforces the provisions of those Acts and their Regulations.

The Alberta Securities Commission Board consists of a chairman and nine members.

Chairman, Ronald J. Will
Chief of Securities Administration,
R. (Bob) Demcoe, C.A.
Exec. Director, M.A. Lemay, C.A.
Dep. Director, Securities, R. Sczinski, C.A.
Dep. Director, Franchises, M. Childs, C.A.
Dep. Director, Enforcement, Vacant
A/Registrar, M. Childs, C.A.

Automobile Insurance Board
10025 Jasper Ave., 19th Flr.
Edmonton, T5J 3Z5

The Board functions under sections 337 to 347 inclusive of the *Insurance Act,* R.S.A. 1980. It is essentially a regulating body to which insurers licensed to write insurance in Alberta make application for approval of rates for third party liability and accident benefits, which are the compulsory coverages of the automobile insurance policy. The Board also entertains complaints from the public in the area it regulates.

Chairman,
The Hon. Mr. Justice A.H. Wachowich
Administrator to the Board, Susan Steeves

DEPARTMENT OF CULTURE AND MULTICULTURALISM

CN Tower, 10004-104th Ave.
Edmonton, T5J 0K5
General Inquiry: (403) 427-6530

MINISTER'S OFFICE
103 Legislature Bldg., Edmonton, T5K 2B6
Minister, The Hon. Greg Stevens
Note: The Hon. Greg Stevens did not run in the recent general election. A replacement had not yet been named as of date of publication.

DEPUTY MINISTER'S OFFICE
Dep. Minister, J.S. O'Neill
Policy and Planning
Director, Ken MacLean
Communications Director, Jan Streader

FINANCE AND ADMINISTRATION DIVISION
Exec. Director, Rai Batra
Personnel Services
Director, Don Clevett
Financial Services
Director, Chi Loo
Financial Planning
Director, Winnie Yiu-Yeung
Information Services
Director, Vacant
Department Librarian, Paula O'Donnell
Public Records Officer, Tony Kelly

Cultural Development Division
Asst. Dep. Minister, Glen Buick
Divisional Administration
Co-ordinator, Robert Hood
Visual Arts
Beaver House, 3rd Flr., 10158-103rd St.
Edmonton, T5J 0X6
Director, Les Graff
Performing Arts
Director, Dr. Clive Padfield
Film and Literary Arts
Director, R.B. Fraser
Library Services
16214-114th Ave., Edmonton, T5M 2Z5
Director, Joe Forsyth
Northern Alberta Jubilee Auditorium
114th St. and 87th Ave., Edmonton, T5K 2C1
Manager, Ron Wigmore
Southern Alberta Jubilee Auditorium
1415-14th Ave. N.W., Calgary, T2N 1M4
Manager, Brian Burke

FIELD SERVICES
Director, Ron duFort
525-11th Ave. S.W., 3rd Flr., Calgary, T2R 0C9

REGIONAL OFFICES:
Calgary
525-11th Ave. S.W., 3rd Flr., Calgary, T2R 0C9
Southern Area Co-ordinator, Randee Louckes
Medicine Hat

218, 770-6th St. S.W., Medicine Hat, T1A 4J5
Reg. Representative, Rob Benn
Red Deer
Parkland Sq., 3rd Flr., 4901-48th St.
Red Deer, T4N 1S8
Reg. Representative, Phyllis Hall
Edmonton/West
CN Tower, 12th Flr., Edmonton, T5J 0K5
Northern Area Co-ordinator, Jim Singbeil
St. Paul
316-5025-49th Ave., St. Paul, T0A 3A0
Reg. Representative, J. Boulet
Grande Prairie
2501 Provincial Bldg., 10320-99th St.
Grande Prairie, T8V 2H4
Reg. Representative, D. Laing

Cultural Heritage Division
12431 Stony Plain Rd., 2nd Flr.
Edmonton, T5N 3N3
A/Asst. Dep. Minister, Terry Keyko
Northern Alberta
Director, Terry Keyko
Southern Alberta
Director, Susan Coombes
525-11th Ave. S.W., Calgary, T2R 0C9

Historical Resources Division
Old St. Stephen's College
8820-112th St., Edmonton, T6G 2P8
Asst. Dep. Minister, Dr. W.J. Byrne
Divisional Operations
Manager, Mark Rasmussen
Provincial Museum
12845-102nd Ave., Edmonton, T5N 0M6
Director, John Fortier
Provincial Archives
12845-102nd Ave., Edmonton, T5N 0M6
Provincial Archivist, Brian Speirs
Historic Sites Service
Old St. Stephen's College
8820-112th St., Edmonton, T6G 2P8
Director, Dr. Frits Pannekoek
Archaeological Survey of Alberta
Old St. Stephen's College
8820-112th St., Edmonton, T6G 2P8
Director, Dr. Jack Ives
Tyrrell Museum of Palaeontology
Midland Provincial Park, Dinosaur Trail
Box 7500, Drumheller, T0J 0Y0
Director, Dr. Emlyn Koster
Reynolds-Alberta Museum
Old Courthouse, 4705-50th Ave.
Wetaskiwin, T9A 0R8

AGENCIES, BOARDS, COMMISSIONS AND CROWN CORPORATIONS

Alberta Art Foundation
Beaver House, 4th Flr.
10158-103rd St., Edmonton, T5J 0X6

The Alberta Art Foundation was created in 1972 under the *Alberta Art Foundation Act.* The AAF's mandate is to encourage and promote Alberta art and artists, and to support public art galleries in the province. Acquiring art, exhibiting and conserving it, and providing grants to galleries as well as to some visual arts organizations for special arts projects, are the principal methods of fulfilling its mandate. Nine directors serve on the AAF Board. They represent the interests of the artistic community and the general public. The Board is set up on a revolving basis, whereby two or three members are appointed each year. Funding to the AAF comes primarily from the Western Canada Lottery (Alberta Division). The Department of Culture and Multiculturalism, directed by the minister, provides the AAF with administrative support and assistance in maintaining the art collection. The Foundation is recognized by the Taxation Division of Revenue Canada as an agent of Her Majesty in right of Alberta and is qualified to receive gifts pursuant to the provision of paragraph 110(1)(b) of the *Income Tax Act*. It is also designated by the Secretary of State as an institute to receive Canadian cultural properties.

Chairman, R.C. Jarvis
Exec. Director, W. Tin Ng

Alberta Cultural Heritage Council
12431 Stony Plain Rd., 2nd Flr.
Edmonton, T5N 3N3

The Alberta Cultural Heritage Council advises the government of Alberta, through the Minister of Culture and Multiculturalism, on all matters relating to the following objectives of the *Alberta Cultural Heritage Act:*

• to encourage respect for the cultural heritage of Alberta;
• to promote tolerance and understanding of others through appreciation of the ethno-cultures that make up the cultural heritage of Alberta;
• to recognize that the presence of ethno-cultural groups in Alberta provides Albertans with an opportunity to develop relationships with other countries;
• to foster an environment in which volunteer groups and individuals can contribute to the cultural heritage of Alberta; and
• to enhance the cultural heritage of Alberta so that present and future Albertans can benefit from its richness and diversity.

The Alberta Cultural Heritage Council is made up of a Provincial Co-ordinating Committee and the following eight Regional Councils: Fort McMurray and District, Lakeland, Southeastern Alberta, Southwestern Alberta, Calgary and District, Central Alberta, Edmonton and District, and Peace River.

Membership on Council is for a two-year term and will include: a) one representative elected by each ethno-cultural group in the region; b) representatives elected by volunteer organizations working in the cultural heritage area; c) ministerial appointees; and d) one staff member from the Cultural Heritage Division (ex officio).

Chairman, Orest M. Olineck

Alberta Cultural Heritage Foundation
12431 Stony Plain Rd., 3rd Flr.
Edmonton, T5N 3N3

The Alberta Cultural Heritage Foundation was established through the *Cultural Foundations Act* in 1978. Its objectives are as follows:
a) to preserve the cultural wealth of Alberta's past, including the language, arts, music, and rites of ethno-cultural groups;
b) to support and contribute to the development of an understanding of the ethno-cultural background of Alberta; and
c) to provide to persons and organizations the opportunity to participate in the preservation and promotion of the culture of Alberta.

Funds for the operation and work of the Foundation come from revenues of the Western Canada Lottery Foundation (Alberta Division). The Alberta Cultural Heritage Foundation is one of a number of foundations and organizations receiving funds from the lottery.

The Foundation is governed by an appointed 14-member board of directors. The board reports to the Legislature through the Minister of Culture and Multiculturalism.

The Foundation provides financial assistance to groups or individuals undertaking projects which relate to the objects stated above, meet guidelines established by the Foundation's board of directors, and whose applications are approved by the board. The amount of assistance provided depends upon such factors as the amount of funds currently at the Foundation's disposal, the financial need of the applicant, the amount of money raised through the applicant's own resources, and availability of funds from other sources.

Chairman, Craig Curtis
Exec. Director, Gene Zwozdesky

Alberta Foundation for the Literary Arts
303, 1204 Kensington Rd. N.W.
Calgary, T2N 3P5

The Alberta Foundation for the Literary Arts was established by the Government of Alberta in 1984 and receives funding from the Western Canada Lottery Foundation (Alberta Division) up to a maximum of $1 million.

As an agency of the Crown, the Foundation uses most of its annual income for grant purposes and invests the remainder to provide for funding for its long-term grant program.

The Foundation funds projects submitted by individual writers and writer organizations; individual book and periodical publishers and publisher organizations; libraries and library organizations in Alberta; and related institutions that carry out programs for the development of the literary arts.

The Foundation is composed of a board whose members are appointed by the Lieutenant-Governor in Council. The members represent a wide range of professions and reside in various areas of the province.

Chairman, Dr. Howard Platt

Alberta Foundation for the Performing Arts
9722-110th St., Edmonton, T5K 1H8

The Foundation was established in 1978 under the *Cultural Development Amendment Act* to promote the performing arts in Alberta, to provide persons and organizations with the opportunity to participate in the performing arts, and to support and contribute to the development of the performing arts in Alberta through discretionary support of special projects.

To date, the sole source of funding is the Western Canada Lottery (Alberta Division).

Chairman, Jack Goth
Exec. Director, Julie Kehler

Alberta Historical Resources Foundation
102-8th Ave. S.E., Calgary, T2G 0K6

The Alberta Historical Resources Foundation is a provincial Crown agency established to assist in the preservation of Alberta's historic sites, buildings, and objects and to encourage and promote public awareness of the province's past. Among the programs of the Foundation are:

- *The Cornerstone:* a quarterly newsletter containing information about the Foundation's activities and heritage news from around the province;
- Funding: grants are awarded February 1st and September 1st annually to projects which are within the mandates of the Foundation; and
- Heritage Awards: presented annually to individuals or groups who make significant contributions to the preservation of Alberta's history.

The Alberta Historical Resources Foundation is funded through the Western Canada Lottery (Alberta Division), private and corporate donations, and an active membership program.

Chairman, Hugh Craig, C.M.

Alberta Library Board
16214-114th Ave., Edmonton, T5M 2Z5

The Alberta Library Board is appointed to advise the Minister of Culture and Multiculturalism on matters relating to the expansion, development, co-ordination, and encouragement of libraries in the province.

The Board may, with the minister's approval, carry out surveys, encourage community activities, call public meetings, promote publicity campaigns, and carry on its activities in co-operation with or through an established organization or agency.

Chairman, Robert Maskell

Alberta Motion Picture Censor Board
CN Tower, Main Flr.
10004-104th Ave., Edmonton, T5J 0K5

The Censor Board, under the authority of the Department of Culture and Multiculturalism, reviews all films to be shown publicly in Alberta. The films are classified under four designations: General, Parental Guidance, Mature, and Restricted Adult.

Chairman, Sharon McCann

Alberta Multicultural Commission
12431 Stony Plain Rd., 3rd Flr.
Edmonton, T5N 3N3
Chairman, John Oldring, M.L.A.

Historic Sites Board
Old St. Stephen's College
8820-112th St., Edmonton, T6G 2P8

The Alberta Historic Sites Board was established in 1973 by the *Alberta Historical Resources Act*. Its principal function is to advise the Minister of Culture and Multiculturalism on heritage issues within the province and on the naming of geographical features.

The Board is currently made up of 12 members appointed for a specific period of time by the Lieutenant-Governor in Council. The Board meets six to eight times per year in various Alberta communities. Members of the public may bring heritage issues to the attention of the Board by contacting its secretary.
Chair, Darlene Comfort
Secretary, Dr. Frits Pannekoek

DEPARTMENT OF ECONOMIC DEVELOPMENT AND TRADE
Sterling Place Bldg., 9940-106th St.
Edmonton, T5K 2P6
(except where otherwise indicated)
Departmental Information: (403) 422-9494
The Business Line: 1-800-272-9675
Fax: (403) 427-0610; Telex: 037-42815

MINISTER'S OFFICE
407 Legislature Bldg., Edmonton, T5K 2B6
Minister, The Hon. Larry R. Shaben
Note: The Hon. Larry R. Shaben did not run in the recent general election. A replacement had not yet been named as of date of publication.

DEPUTY MINISTERS' OFFICES
Chief Dep. Minister, Economic Development and Trade, George de Rappard
Dep. Minister, Policy and Planning, Clarence J. Roth

FINANCE AND ADMINISTRATION
Director, Terry Eliuk
Central Services
Administrator, Linda Gogal
Financial Planning
Manager, Brian Huygen
Financial Services
Manager, Wilson Ng
Librarian, Donna Gordon
Records Officer, Rookie Sobhraj
Systems Head, Richard Snyder

COMMUNICATIONS AND INFORMATION
Director, D'Arcy Levesque
HUMAN RESOURCES
Director, Vacant

Small Business and Industry Division

Asst. Dep. Minister, Ronald H. Blake
Research and Analysis Services
Director, Mel Wong
BUSINESS COUNSELLING AND
DEVELOPMENT BRANCH
Exec. Director, Roger Jackson
Business Counselling
Director, Norm Greenwood
Northern Regions
Director, Francie Harle
Southern Regions
Director, David Morgan
999-8th St. S.W., 5th Flr., Calgary, T5R 1J5

CALGARY OFFICE
999-8th St. S.W., 5th Flr., Calgary, T5R 1J5
Gen. Manager, Doug Neil
Manager, Brent Harding
Business Counselling
Director, Michael Meraw
BUSINESS FINANCE DEVELOPMENT BRANCH
Exec. Director, Brian Williams
Sr. Director, Keith Wiggins
Investment Financial Section
Manager, Joanne Miller
Small Business Term Assistance Plan
Administrator, Carolyn LePage
Small Business Equity Corporation
A/Director, Jim Jobb

INDUSTRY DEVELOPMENT BRANCH
Exec. Director, Frank McMillan
Advanced Manufacturing
Sr. Director, Kai Lynge
Aerospace Industries and Offsets
Director, Ronald Robinson
Business Locations
Manager, Lori MacQueen
Engineering and Construction
Director, Roly Ferris
Film Industry
Director, Bill Marsden
Food and Consumer Products Section
Director, Doug Gerrard
Housing and Wood Manufacturing
Director, Bill Jones
Industrial Products and Services Section
Sr. Director, Doug Does
Process Industries
Sr. Director, Chrys Dmytruk
Plastics
Director, Denny Ross-Smith

Trade and Investment Division
Asst. Dep. Minister, Murray Rasmusson

INTERNATIONAL TRADE BRANCH
Man. Director, E.R.W. Lack

Program Development/Korea
Trade Director, Ed Ilnicki
A.S.E.A.N./Australasia
Trade Director, Larry Lang
East Europe
Trade Director, Hans Bergman
West Europe
Trade Director, Greg Whyte
Trade and Investment
Director, Julius Nemeth
China
Trade Director, Simon Wan
Japan
Trade Director, Gerry Royer
Middle East/Africa
Director, Abbas Al Saigh
Hong Kong
Rm. 1003/4, 10th Flr., Tower 2, Admiralty Ctr.
18 Harcourt Rd., Central, Hong Kong
Asia Pacific Operations
Trade Director, Henry Armstrong
Korea
Ste. 400, Leema Bldg., Exec. Business Centre
146-1 Soo Song-Dong
Chongro-Ku, Seoul 110-140, Korea
Trade Director, Neil Simpson
London
Alberta House, 1 Mount St.
London, W1Y 5AA, England
European Operations
Trade Director, Paul W. King

CANADA AND THE AMERICAS BRANCH
Man. Director, Bryan Edmundson
U.S. Sector
Chicago & Midwest
Trade Director, Bob Hunter
South Central U.S.
Trade Director, Paul Moreau
West Coast U.S.
Trade Director, Brian Westlund
Upper Midwest U.S.
Trade Director, Cam MacMillan
Southwest U.S.
Trade Director, Bill Jaschke
Canada Sector
Canada East
Trade Director, Jerry Keller
Canada West
Trade Director, Vacant
Latin America and Caribbean
Trade Director, Michael Milroy
Houston
Ste. 1425, 5444 Westheimer Rd.
Houston, TX 77056 U.S.A.
Southwestern U.S. Operations
Trade Director, Bryce I. Nimmo
Los Angeles
Ste. 3535, 333 South Grand Ave.
Los Angeles, CA 90071 U.S.A.
Western U.S. Operations
Trade Director, Ron Liepert

INVESTMENT PROMOTION BRANCH
Man. Director, George Adorjany

Investment Promotion
Director, Rabin Mendis
Investment Promotion
Director, Sam Chow
Investment Promotion
Director, Dean Sanduga
East U.S.
Director, Tren Cole
West U.S.
Director, Tandy McGibbon

TRADE SHOW PROMOTION SERVICES
Director, Behrooz Sadrehashemi
Assoc. Directors: Norm Morrison, Don Chinski
MARKET RESEARCH AND INTERNATIONAL
FINANCIAL SERVICES
Director, Aki Nawata
Manager, Roy MacMillan
FUTURES COMPENDIUM
Chairman, Dr. Brian E. Sullivan
Sr. Policy Advisor, Takashi Ohki

POLICY DEVELOPMENT AND
CO-ORDINATION BRANCH
Exec. Director, Dave Walker
Trade and Investment Policy
Sr. Director, Bob Fox
Economic and Diversification Policy
Director, Bernie MacDonald
Domestic Policy and Investment Policy
Director, Kailas Patel
Industrial, Policy and Evaluation
Director, Walter Hordowick

TRANSPORTATION SERVICES BRANCH
A/Exec. Director, Ray Bassett
Agricultural Transportation
Director, Cliff Weber
Freight Transportation Services
Sr. Director, Jack Soulsby
Rail/Highway Freight Services
Director, James Morrison
Physical Distribution Program
Director, Glen Johnston
International Distribution/Ports
Director, Stein Jahnsen
Transportation Economics and Analysis
Sr. Director, Rod D. Thompson
Transportation Analysis
Director, G. Goyeau
Pricing Analysis
Director, Garry Rosko
Passenger Transportation Services
Sr. Director, Victor Hamm
Air Passenger
Director, Andy Shanks
Surface Passenger
Director, Peter Dawes
POLICY AND PLANNING SPECIAL PROJECTS
Exec. Director, Ed Shaske

AGENCIES, BOARDS AND COMMISSIONS

Agency for International Development (A.I.D.)
Sterling Place, 9940-106th St.
Edmonton, T5K 2P6

The Agency provides financial assistance to those Canadian Non-Governmental Organizations (NGOs), to which the people of Alberta contribute, to assist in the implementation of their projects and programs in the less developed countries.

Director, Ray Verge

Alberta Opportunity Company
Box 1860, Ponoka, T0C 2H0

The Alberta Opportunity Company is a Crown corporation which provides financing and management assistance to small and medium-size businesses in Alberta which are unable to obtain financing from the private sector on reasonable terms and conditions. The Company has a number of branch offices throughout the province in order to service existing accounts and to provide prompt decisions for new applicants.

As of March 31, 1988, the Company had in excess of 1,500 loans on its books and approximately $147 million in loans outstanding. A further $39 million in new loans will be made in 1988-89. AOC also provided venture funding of approximately $4 million to 9 applicants in 1987-88, and expects to provide $15 million in venture investments in 1988-89. Funding for AOC is provided by the Alberta Heritage and Savings Trust Fund. The Company reports to the Legislature of Alberta through the Minister of Economic Development and Trade.

President, Roy W. Parker
Loans
Vice-President, Jim R. Anderson
Administration
Vice-President, Brian W. Parsk
Support Services
Vice-President, Don E. Trenerry
Venture Funding
1530 Royal Trust Twr., Edmonton, T5J 2Z2
Vice-President, John D. Kennedy
Legal and Disbursement
Manager, Neil Macaulay
Finance and Comptroller
Asst. Vice-President, Jim D. Gill

Commissioner General for Trade and Tourism
1800 Royal Trust Tower, Edmonton, T5J 2Z2
Commissioner General, Dr. Horst A. Schmid

DEPARTMENT OF EDUCATION

West Tower, Devonian Bldg.
11160 Jasper Ave., Edmonton, T5K 0L2
(except where otherwise noted)
Information: (403) 427-7219

MINISTER'S OFFICE
130 Legislature Bldg., Edmonton, T5K 2B6
Minister, The Hon. Jim Dinning

DEPUTY MINISTER'S OFFICE
Dep. Minister, Dr. R.A. Bosetti
Communications
Director, Mark Gregory
Planning, Policy and Research Secretariat
Director, G. Zatko

Finance and Administration
Asst. Dep. Minister, Carl Daneliuk
School Buildings Services Branch
Director, Dr. Marian Weleschuk
Financial and Administrative Services Branch
Director, Dr. B. Fennell
School Business Administration
Services Branch
Director, S. Cymbol
Learning Resources Distributing Centre
Director, Dr. J. Myroon
Human Resources Services Branch
Director, D. Pinckston
Legislative Services Branch
Director, A. Dean
Information Services Branch
A/Director, D. Laing

Student Programs and Evaluation
Asst. Dep. Minister, Roger Palmer
Curriculum Design Branch
Director, Dr. L. Symyrozum
Curriculum Support Branch
Director, Keith Wagner
Language Services Branch
Director, Adrien Bussiere
Student Evaluation and Records
Director, F. Horvath
Alberta Correspondence School
Box 4000, Barrhead, T0G 2P0
Director, Gary Popowich

Program Delivery
Asst. Dep. Minister, W. Duke
Teacher Certification and Development Branch
Director, Dr. L. Rappel
Special Education Response Centre
6420-113th St., Edmonton, T6H 3L2
Exec. Director, W. Lockhart

REGIONAL OFFICES OF EDUCATION:
Edmonton
Harley Crt., 8th Flr., 10045-111th St.
Edmonton, T5K 2M5
Director, Russ Wiebe
Grande Prairie
Nordic Court, 5th Flr.
10014-99th St., Grande Prairie, T8V 3N4
Director, F. Reinholt
Red Deer
Provincial Bldg., 3rd Flr. W.
4920-51st St., Red Deer, T4N 5Y5
Director, C. Allan
Calgary

Rm. 1200, Rocky Mountain Plaza
615 MacLeod Tr. S.E., Calgary, T2G 4T8
Director, G. Wilson
Lethbridge
Provincial Bldg., 200 S. 5th Ave.
Bag Service 3014, Lethbridge, T1J 4C7
Director, C. McLean

DEPARTMENT OF ENERGY
Petroleum Plaza Twr.
9915-108th St., Edmonton, T5K 2C9
Information Centre: (403) 427-3590
Fax: (403) 427-2548; Telex: 037-3676

MINISTER'S OFFICE
407 Legislature Bldg., Edmonton, T5K 2B6
Minister, The Hon. Dr. P. Neil Webber
Note: The Hon. Dr. P. Neil Webber did not run
in the recent general election. A replacement
had not yet been named as of date of
publication.

DEPUTY MINISTER'S OFFICE
9945-108th St., Edmonton, T5K 2C9
Dep. Minister, M.F. Kanik

Finance and Administration
Sr. Asst. Dep. Minister, E.K. Barry
Internal Audit
Director, G.A. Ford

HUMAN RESOURCE DIVISION
Exec. Director, G.R. Shopland
Personnel Services
Director, M. Koshuta
Human Resource Consulting
Manager, M. Mun
Asst. Director, M. Koshuta
Training and Organizational Development
Manager, Vacant
Employee Relations
Manager, N.J. Dickenson
Forest Technology School
Head, B.F. Simpson
Occupational Health and Safety
Co-ordinator, R.H. Brown

FINANCIAL SERVICES DIVISION
Exec. Director, K. Borch
Financial Accounting
Director, Vacant
Financial Planning and Control
Director, B. Giffen

AUTOMATED INFORMATION SYSTEMS
Exec. Director, Vacant
Computer Systems
Director, R.A. Askin
Data Base Administrator, Dr. P.S. Ravindra
Production Systems
Director, J. Finlaison

LEGAL SERVICES DIVISION
Exec. Director, M. Kaga
Energy Resources
Solicitor, W.E. McKeown
Renewable Resources
Solicitors: T.S. Freedman, K. Galloway

SCIENTIFIC AND ENGINEERING SERVICES
AND RESEARCH DIVISION
Exec. Director, R.D. McDonald
Sr. Advisor, Coal, Vacant
Energy Conservation and Renewable
Energy Research
Director, J. Kleta

Policy Analysis and Planning Division
9945-108th St., Edmonton, T5K 2C9
Asst. Dep. Minister, N.E. MacMurchy
Markets and Regulations
Exec. Director, R. Hyndman
Forecasting and Financial Assessment
Exec. Director, D. Philips
Energy Conservation
Director, I. Burn

Projects and Supply Development Division
Asst. Dep. Minister, G.J. Protti
Oil Sands and Upgrading
Exec. Director, P. Precht
Conventional Oil, Gas and Coal
Exec. Director, G. Durrani

Mineral Resources Division
9945-108th St., Edmonton, T5K 2C9
Asst. Dep. Minister, M.J. Day
Oil and Gas Agreements
Exec. Director, W.C. Harlan
Oil and Gas Agreement Sales
Manager, B. Goltz
Oil and Gas Lease Continuation
Director, A.J. Lauder
Oil and Gas Agreements Administration
Director, D. Luff
Mineral Agreements
Director, Vacant
Mineral Resource Planning
Manager, B. Hudson
Minerals Support
Director, D. Coombes

Mineral Revenues Division
A/Asst. Dep. Minister, T.M. Collins
Revenue Operations
Exec. Director, T. Collins
Petroleum Royalties
Director, C.E. Manz
Gas Royalty Director, S.F. Pugh
Audit
Exec. Director, H. Cormick
Field Audit (Edmonton)
Director, A. Remtulla
Field Audit (Calgary)
Director, J. Clarke
Mineral Tax Sup't, L. Corse

AGENCIES, BOARDS AND COMMISSIONS

Alberta Oil Sands Equity
9945-108th St., 11th Flr., Edmonton, T5K 2G6

Alberta Oil Sands Equity was established in 1975 as a separate organization under the Minister of Energy with a mandate to manage the Alberta government's equity investment in the Syncrude Project. Currently, it is involved with several industry participants in an exploration and development program on six oil sand leases in northeastern Alberta in addition to managing their interest in the Syncrude Project.

Chairman, T.R. Vant
Administration
Exec. Director, D.H. Sheppard
Finance and Accounting
Exec. Director, R.H. LeMasurier
Engineering
Exec. Director, R.W.E. Jansen
Engineering Associate, A.A. Pradhan
Project Analysis
Director, C.C. Calvert

Alberta Oil Sands Technology and Research Authority (AOSTRA)
500 Highfield Place, 10010-106th St.
Edmonton, T5J 3L8

The Alberta Oil Sands Technology and Research Authority is a provincial Crown corporation established in 1974 by the *Oil Sands Technology and Research Authority Act.* Its purpose is to provide the means to assist, promote, and encourage the research necessary to develop new oil sands technology; to compile, assess, and disseminate technological information relative to oil sands deposits and products; to promote co-operation among the government of Alberta, universities, industry, and other institutions and agencies in respect of matters under the Act; and to solve the problems impeding the production capacity to meet the demand for synthetic crude oil, crude oil, and products derived therefrom. The Act has been amended to include recovery of heavy oils and enhanced recovery from conventional petroleum reservoirs.

The Authority is made up of not less than three nor more than nine members, all of whom are appointed by Order-in-Council. One member is designated as chairman and another as vice-chairman.

Chairman, W.J. Yurko
A/Vice-Chairman, E.J. Wiggins
Registrar, G.A. Villett
Gen. Counsel, E.K. Spady
Mining, Extraction, Upgrading
Director, L.R. Turner
Technical Programs and International Activities
Director, D.A. Redford
CFO, W.G. Kowaluk
Exec. Asst. and Public Relations Manager,
L.G. Benzer

CALGARY OFFICE:
700-4th Ave. S.W., 18th Flr., Calgary, T2P 0J2
In-Situ Operations
Director, R.W. Luhning

Alberta Petroleum Marketing Commission
1900, 250-6th Ave. S.W., Calgary, T2P 3H7

The Alberta Petroleum Marketing Commission operates under authority of the *Petroleum Marketing Act*, under which it sells the royalty share of crude oil production from Crown leases and the province's share of production from the Syncrude Canada Ltd. project. The Commission also provides marketing services to producers on a contractual basis. In addition, the Commission administers several responsibilities under the province's *Natural Gas Marketing Act* and represents the Government of Alberta at regulatory hearings in Canada and the U.S. that affect the value of the province's crude oil and natural gas production.

In administering its crude oil responsibilities, the Commission actively markets crude oil of all qualities in both domestic and export markets and is a shipper on all major domestic pipelines. The Commission is the largest seller of Canadian crude oil.

Its functions and responsibilities under the *Natural Gas Marketing Act* are as follows:

- The determination that the required level of producer support, as the resale price or pricing terms, is obtained where producers and buyers have agreed to a netback pricing clause in their natural gas purchase contract.
- The collection of the field purchase, consumption, and market data relative to the purchase and sale of Alberta natural gas as required to meet the province's internal information needs.
- The provision of contract services to shippers and their producers relative to confirmation of price components under the terms of netback pricing agreements.

Chairman, D.A. Lucas
Vice-Chairman, D.L. Willis
Commissioner, J.E. Mackenzie
Gen. Counsel and Secretary, S.F. McAllister
Finance and Administration
Man. Director, G.K. Palmer
Crude Oil
Man. Director, G.R. Scott
Natural Gas and Market Analysis
Man. Director, R.H. Cook
Natural Gas
Gen. Manager, V.M. Thomas
Commission Auditor, E.K. Adams
Information Services
Man. Director, R.W. Tovell

Energy Resources Conservation Board
640-5th Ave. S.W., Calgary, T2P 3G4

The Energy Resources Conservation Board (ERCB) was established by the Alberta Government to regulate the responsible, safe, efficient development of Alberta's energy resources. These resources include oil, natural gas, coal, oil sands, electrical energy, and the pipelines and transmission lines to move resources to markets.

The ERCB's functions fall into three main categories:

- evaluating and deciding on applications for new or expanded energy projects, including related work in the area of public involvement and public hearings;
- regulating existing energy facilities to ensure they operate efficiently, avoiding waste and controlling pollution; and
- providing advice, information, and statistics to the public, the government, and the energy industry about Alberta's energy resources (i.e. reserves, production, sales, exploration and development activity, markets, investments and revenues, and end-use requirements).

In its environmental management role, the ERCB works closely with Alberta's departments of Environment and of Forestry, Lands and Wildlife to ensure appropriate safeguards for provincial lands, water, and air.

The ERCB reports directly to the Executive Council of Alberta, but makes its formal decisions in accordance with the eight statutes it administers. The Board consists of up to seven members appointed by the Alberta Cabinet, supported by approximately 700 employees. Headquartered in Calgary, the ERCB also has eight field offices located in areas of high energy activity throughout Alberta. The ERCB also operates a core research centre, a chemical laboratory, and a public visitor centre, the Energeum, all located in Calgary.

Half the ERCB's budget is paid by the energy industry, through an administration levy on each producing oil or gas well in the province; the other half, by the Alberta government.

Chairman, G.J. DeSorcy
Vice-Chairman, N.A. Strom
Board Members:
F.J. Mink, E.J. Morin, Dr. P. Prince
Accounting Manager, R.T. Bording
Administrative Services
Manager, K.G. Sharp
Coal Manager, R.G. Paterson
Communications Advisor, J. Bales
Data Processing
Manager, H. Antonio
Drilling and Production
Manager, J. Nichol
Economics Manager, J.W. Newton
Employee Relations
Manager, R.F. Braun
Environment Protection
Manager, E. Brushett
Field Operations Manager, W. Remmer
Gas Manager, J.D. Dilay
Geology Manager, Cynthia Langlo
Hydro and Electric Energy
Manager, F. Homeniuk
Legal Manager, M.J. Bruni

Oil Manager, N. Guy Berndtsson
Oil Sands Manager, R.G. Evans
Pipeline Manager, E. Fox

Office of Coal Research and Technology
Petroleum Plaza, S. Twr.
9915-108th St., Edmonton, T5K 2C9

The Office of Coal Research and Technology was created in 1983 with the adoption of the Alberta Coal Research Strategy by the Alberta government. It furthers the aims of that strategy through the funding of research projects to: 1) enhance the competitiveness of Alberta coal; 2) minimize the environmental damage caused by the mining and use of coal; and 3) create new uses for Alberta coal. Projects in recent years have been in areas such as exploration, upgrading, liquefaction and gasification, and marketing. A total of $5.1 million was budgeted for coal research projects in fiscal 1987-88.

Chairman, R.D. McDonald
Registrar, Vacant
Member, G. Page

DEPARTMENT OF THE ENVIRONMENT

Oxbridge Place
9820-106th St., Edmonton, T5K 2J6
(except where otherwise indicated)
Information: (403) 427-2739

MINISTER'S OFFICE
420 Legislature Bldg., Edmonton, T5K 2B6
Minister, The Hon. Ian Reid
Note: The Hon. Ian Reid was defeated in the recent general election. A replacement had not yet been named as of date of publication.

DEPUTY MINISTER'S OFFICE
Dep. Minister, Vance MacNichol
Personnel and Organization Development
Director, M. Wartenbe
Training and Development
Co-ordinator, J. Wilson
Occupational Health and Safety
Co-ordinator, B. Dompe
Corporate and Strategic Management Division
Exec. Director, R.N. Briggs
Alberta Environmental Centre—Vegreville
Postal Bag 4000, Vegreville, T0B 4L0
Director, Dr. R.S. Weaver
Asst. Director, Vacant

Finance Administration and Land Reclamation Services
Asst. Dep. Minister, William (Bill) Simon
Financial Planning Division
Director, Ray Duffy
Financial Operations Division
Director, E. Luczak
Systems and Computing Division

Director, D. Lougheed
Land Reclamation Division
Director, John M. King
Administrative Support
Director, Jerry Kolar

Water Resources Management Services
Asst. Dep. Minister, P.G. Melnychuk
Development and Operations Division
A/Director, John Campbell
Planning Division
A/Director, R.B. MacLock
Technical Services Division
Director, R. Deeprose
Water Resources Administration Division
Director, A. Strome
Controller, V. Carlson
Oldman River Dam Project
Jake Thiessen

Environmental Protection Services
Asst. Dep. Minister, K.R. Smith
Pollution Control Division
Director, A. Schulz
Wastes and Chemicals Division
Director, Dr. Bruce Taylor
Standards and Approvals Division
Director, J. Lack
Environment Assessment Division
Director, F. Schulte

AGENCIES, BOARDS AND COMMISSIONS

Alberta Environmental Research Trust
J.J. Bowlen Bldg., 3rd Flr.
620-7th Ave. S.W., Calgary, T2P 0Y8
Chairman, H.V. Page, P.Eng.
Board of Trustees: A. Gaskell, W. Cary, V. MacNichol, R. Brassard, G. Lambert, T. Maine, B. Duckett

Alberta Special Waste Management Corp.
Pacific Plaza, 9th Flr.
10909 Jasper Ave., Edmonton, T5J 3L9

The Alberta Special Waste Management Corporation, created in April 1984, is responsible for the establishment and operation of facilities to handle hazardous wastes in the province. Under the *Special Waste Management Corporation Act* and the *Hazardous Chemicals Act,* the Corporation is implementing a system of special waste collection, treatment, and disposal. Construction has been completed on an integrated treatment facility, under a joint venture agreement with Bow Valley Resources Services Ltd., Calgary, on a site near Swan Hills, Alberta, 190 km northwest of Edmonton. Appropriate technologies will be installed to reduce organic and inorganic wastes to safer residues for deposit in a secure landfill for dry materials, and deepwell injection for treated liquids. The system is planned to protect health and the environment, and to enhance industrial operations. The Corporation also manages a special waste storage operation in Nisku, south of Edmonton.

The board of the Corporation is composed of the chairman and five citizens at large from Calgary, Edmonton, Slave Lake, and Swan Hills.

Chairman of the Board, R. Clark
President and CEO, R.L. Mick
Sr. Vice-President, K. Simpson
Communications
Vice-President, B. Paddon

Environment Council of Alberta
Weber Ctr., 8th Flr.
5555 Calgary Tr. Southbound N.W.
Edmonton, T6H 5P9
Information: (403) 427-5792

The Environment Council of Alberta is a Crown corporation operating under authority of the *Environment Council Act.* The Council consists of persons appointed from time to time by the Lieutenant-Governor in Council and the chief executive officer, supported by 19 full time staff members divided into three operating groups: Research, Liaison, and Administration.

The objectives and functions of the Council include encouraging public participation in the examination and analysis of environmental issues by: a) conducting a continuing review of government policies and programs and government agencies in relation to environment conservation; b) investigating any matter pertaining to environment conservation when requested by the Minister of the Environment; c) holding, when requested by an order of the Lieutenant-Governor in Council, public hearings for the purpose of receiving briefs and submissions on matters pertaining to environment conservation; and d) reporting on these activities to the Lieutenant-Governor in Council or the Minister of the Environment.

CEO, Vacant
Liaison Director, A. Landals
Research Director, D. Buchwald
Admin. Director, A. Giacomazzi
Communications Officer, K. Nelson

Land Conservation and Reclamation Council
Oxbridge Pl., 3rd Flr.
9820-106th St., Edmonton, T5K 2J6

The Land Conservation and Reclamation Council is a branch of the Department of the Environment established in 1963 under the *Surface Reclamation Act.* This Act was repealed in 1973 and replaced by the *Land Surface Conservation and Reclamation Act,* S.A. 1973, Chapter 34. The Council has the responsibility to ensure that the construction, operation, and abandonment of well sites, pipelines, batteries, transmission lines, coal and oil sands exploration and development, waste disposal sites, and landfill sites are performed in such a manner as to return the land to the same productive capability as existed prior to disturbance.

Proper reclamation is achieved by field inspec-

tions carried out by a Reclamation Officer from the Department of the Environment and/or the Department of Forestry, Lands and Wildlife, accompanied by a Reclamation Officer appointed by the local municipality. These Reclamation Officers inspect projects to ensure that reclamation standards such as the saving of topsoil are being followed.

When operators are not following reclamation standards, Reclamation Officers can, in writing, order specified work to be done. Failure to comply with a Reclamation Order would result in the issuance of a Stop Order or the government doing the reclamation work and billing the operator and/or deducting the cost from the security deposit or any combination of the above. Before an operator can abandon an operation or surrender the surface lease, he must apply for and receive a Reclamation Certificate.

Chairman, John M. King
Sr. Council Member, B. Onciul

Natural Resources Co-ordinating Council
Oxbridge Place
9820-106th St., Edmonton, T5K 2J6
General Inquiries: (403) 427-6247

The Natural Resources Co-ordinating Council was established on March 31, 1971 under the provisions of section 11 of *The Department of the Environment Act.* It may inquire into any matter pertaining to the environment or review any policies, programs, services, or administrative procedures of departments of the government or of government agencies in matters pertaining to the environment. The Council makes its recommendations to the Minister of the Environment.

The Council is chaired and administered by the Deputy Minister of the Department of the Environment. Its members include the deputy ministers of the departments of Agriculture; Economic Development and Trade; Energy; Forestry, Lands and Wildlife; Municipal Affairs; Occupational Health and Safety; Recreation and Parks; and Transportation and Utilities, and the chairman of the Energy Resources Conservation Board.

Chairman, Vance MacNichol
Secretary, K.R. Smith

DEPARTMENT OF FEDERAL AND INTERGOVERNMENTAL AFFAIRS
2200, 10025 Jasper Ave., Edmonton, T5J 1S6
Information: (403) 427-2611; Telex: 037-3300

MINISTER'S OFFICE
320 Legislature Bldg., Edmonton, T5K 2B6
Minister, The Hon. James D. Horsman, Q.C.
Director, Randy A. Fischer

DEPUTY MINISTER'S OFFICE
Dep. Minister, A.G. McDonald
Communications
A/Manager, Judith Parr

ADMINISTRATION
Director, Rob Simmons
Department Accountant, Marion J. Johnston
Personnel, Sylvia Getschel
Departmental Librarian, Anita Duncan
Records Manager, Joanne Yu
Translation Bureau
Manager, Heidi Seeholzer

Social and Constitutional Division
Exec. Director, Oryssia J. Lennie
Constitutional Affairs/Co-ordination
Director, Garry Pocock
Native Intergovernmental Matters
Director, John Kristensen
Social and Fiscal Policy
Director, Nancy Stewart
Sr. Intergovernmental Officers:
Dr. Peter Blaikie, Paul Whittaker,
Lorelei Campbell
Intergovernmental Officers:
Phillip Burke, David Liles, Don Kwas
Special Intergovernmental Advisor,
Joe Forsyth

Economics and Resources Division
Exec. Director, A. Ron Thumlert
Development Policy
Director, D.A. Keith
Assoc. Director, Neil Kirkpatrick
Economic and Regional Development
Agreement
Canada/Alberta
Manager, D.A. Keith
Economic Policy
Director, Lyn Tait
Assoc. Director, Jaymore Bell
Natural Resource Policy
Director, W.A. Oppen
Assoc. Director, R.A. Bowcott
Intergovernmental Officer, Debbie Lamash

International Division
Exec. Director, Wayne Clifford
International Relations
Director, Rory Campbell
International Economic Relations
Director, Helmut Mach
Assoc. Director, U.S.A., Susan Cribbs
Visits and Cultural/Educational Affairs,
Melanie Stephens
Assoc. Director, Marvin Schneider
International Economist, Derrick Wilkinson
Asia-Pacific
Director, Morris Maduro
Assoc. Director, Amy Gerlock
Asia-Alberta Exchange
Co-ordinator, Markus Lemke
Research Officer, Barbara Belzerowski

OUT-OF-PROVINCE OFFICES:
Ottawa
Alberta Government Office
Royal Bank Ctr., Ste. 1110
90 Sparks St., Ottawa, K1P 5B4

Intergovernmental Relations
Exec. Director, Terry Roberts
New York
Alberta Government Office
General Motors Bldg., 27th Flr.
767 Fifth Ave., New York, NY 10153 U.S.A.
Agent General—United States,
James J. Seymour
Sr. International Trade Counsel
David Manning
Economic/Commercial Officer, Ken Lang
Houston
Alberta Government Office
Ste. 1425, 5444 Westheimer Rd.
Houston, TX 77056 U.S.A.
Southwestern U.S. Operations—
Alberta Economic Development and Trade
Director, Bryce I. Nimmo
Los Angeles
Alberta Government Office
Ste. 3535, 333 S. Grand Ave.
Los Angeles, CA 90071 U.S.A.
Western U.S. Operations—
Alberta Economic Development and Trade
Director, Ron Liepert
Alberta Tourism
Director, Gordon Coombs
London
Alberta House, 1 Mount St.
London W1Y 5AA, England
Agent General, United Kingdom and Europe,
Mary J. LeMessurier
European Operations—
Alberta Economic Development and Trade
Director, Paul W. King
European Operations—
Alberta Tourism
Manager, Lori Dowling
Hong Kong
Alberta Government Office
Rms. 1003-4, Admiralty Centre, Tower Two,
Harcourt Rd., Central, Hong Kong
Agent General, China, Hong Kong, Southeast
Asia, Australia and New Zealand,
Jack W. Kennedy
Economic Development and Trade
Sr. Director, Henry Armstrong
Asia-Pacific Business Immigration
Director, Jack Li
Asst. Trade Director, K.M. Christopher
Tokyo
Alberta Government Office
17th Flr., New Aoyama Bldg. W.
1-1, 1-Chome, Minamiaoyama
Minato-Ku, Tokyo 107, Japan
Agent General, Japan/Korea, Ivan Bumstead
Sr. Director, John Cotton
Sr. Commercial Officer, Charles Hachiya
Trade Director, Korea, Neil Simpson

DEPARTMENT OF FORESTRY, LANDS AND WILDLIFE

Petroleum Plaza, South Twr.
9915-108th St., Edmonton, T5K 2C9

MINISTER'S OFFICE
403 Legislature Bldg., Edmonton, T5K 2B6
Minister, The Hon. LeRoy Fjordbotten

DEPUTY MINISTER'S OFFICE
Dep. Minister, F.W. McDougall

Alberta Forest Service
Asst. Dep. Minister, C.B. Smith
Program Support Director, C.H. Geale
Timber Management
Director, C.A. Dermott
Reforestation and Reclamation
Director, Vacant
Forest Land Use Director, D.H. Fregren
Forest Protection Director, J.E. Benson
Forest Research Director, K. Higginbotham

FORESTRY INDUSTRY DEVELOPMENT
DIVISION
Exec. Officer, J.A. Brennan
Forestry Industry
Director, Rod Simpson
Economic and Financial Analysis
Director, Nicholas Gartaganis
Renewable Resources
Director, Paul Short
Forest Resource Development Analyst,
Kelvin Mak
Forest Products Research
Manager, T. Szabo
Forest Products Advisor, B. Karaim

Public Lands Division
Asst. Dep. Minister, M.G. Turnbull
Office Manager, Jennifer Bertram
Program Support Director, M. Mohan
Land Management Director, R.T. Marvin
Land Administration
Director, R.F. Raitz
Resource Planning Director, E. Wyldman

Fish and Wildlife Division
Asst. Dep. Minister, L.J. Cooke
Co-ordinator/Liaison Officer, L. Ramstead
Operations
Exec. Co-ordinator, E. Psikla
Director, J. Nichols
Regulations Development
Director, D. Empson
Enforcement Services
Director, R. Adams
Program Support Director, T. Smith
Fisheries Management Director, T. Mill
Wildlife Management Director, R. Andrews
Habitat Services
Director, K. Ambrock
Co-ordination Services
Director, Andrew B. Masiuk
Regional Co-ordination Services
Northeast Region, St. Paul
Morley Christie
Peace River Region, Peace River
Ron Davis

Eastern Slopes Region, Rocky Mountain House
Cameron McGregor
Southern Region, Lethbridge
Ian Dyson

POLICY SECRETARIAT
Director, P. Andersen
Sr. Policy Analysts: D. Belyea, J. Rivait,
S. Brown, M. Anielski, K. Ainsley, B. Bullock

Land Information Services Division
Asst. Dep. Minister, M.A.G. Toomey
Survey and Mapping
A/Sr. Director, E. Tessari
Land Survey Director, R. Baker
Program Support
Director, P. Merrick
Land Related Information Services
Director, I. Crain
Resource Information
Sr. Director, J.R. Harrower

DEPARTMENT OF HEALTH

Seventh Street Plaza, 3rd Flr.
10030-107th St., Edmonton, T5J 3E4
(except where otherwise indicated)

MINISTER'S OFFICE
130 Legislature Bldg., Edmonton, T5K 2B6
Minister, The Hon. Nancy Betkowski

COMMUNITY HEALTH

DEPUTY MINISTER'S OFFICE
Dep. Minister, Jan Skirrow
Director, Phyllis Kohut
Communications
A/Director, Gillian Garner

Public Health Division
A/Asst. Dep. Minister, Dennis Barr
Environmental Health Services
Director, Carl Primus
Health Program Development
Director, Vacant
Local Health Services
Director, Gordon Thomas
Aids to Daily Living/Extended Health Benefits
Manager, Vacant
Homecare Manager, Sheila Weatherill
Dental Health Services
Director, Dr. Tom Curry
Community Health Nursing
Manager, Vacant
Early Intervention Program
Consultant, Billye Kay
Speech Pathology and Audiology
A/Manager, Margaret Wanke

COMMUNICABLE DISEASE AND
EPIDEMIOLOGY
Director, Dr. John Waters

Sexually Transmitted Disease (STD) Control
Executive Bldg., 4th Flr.
10105-109th St., Edmonton, T5J 1M8
Director, Dr. Barbara Romanowski
Provincial AIDS Program
Director, Dr. Bryce Larke
Tuberculosis Control
c/o Aberhart Hospital
11402 University Ave., Edmonton, T6G 2J3
Director, Dr. E.A. Fanning

Mental Health Division
Asst. Dep. Minister, Dr. Roger Bland
A/Exec. Director, Frank Langer
Extended Care Services
Exec. Director, Dennis Ostercamp
Claresholm Care Centre
Box 490, Claresholm, T0L 0T0
Exec. Director, John Grant
Raymond Home
Raymond, T0K 2S0
Exec. Director, Diane Abel
Rosehaven Care Centre
4612-53rd St., Camrose, T4V 1Y6
Exec. Director, William Marshall

REGIONS:
Northwest Region
Nordic Court, 6th Flr., 10014-99th St.
Grande Prairie, T8V 3N4
Reg. Director, Dave Moncrieff
Northeast Region
Provincial Bldg., 9th Flr.
9915 Franklin Ave., Fort McMurray, T9H 2K4
Reg. Director, Leslie Larson
Edmonton Region
108th St. Bldg., 5th Flr.
9942-108th St., Edmonton, T5K 2J5
Reg. Director, B.E. Krewski
Central Region
204, 4920-51st St., Red Deer, T4N 6K8
Reg. Director, Don Ehman
Calgary Region
206 Hillhurst Professional Bldg.
301-14th St. N.W., Calgary, T2N 2A4
Reg. Director, Barnabas Walther
South Region
2105-20th Ave., Box 60, Coaldale, T0K 0L0
Reg. Director, Adin Stafford

FAMILY AND COMMUNITY SUPPORT
SERVICES
Exec. Director, Gordon Thomas
MANAGEMENT SUPPORT SERVICES DIVISION
Exec. Director, Sharon Matthias
Planning Director, Dr. Habib Fatoo
Evaluation and Management Audit
Director, Ray LaFleur
Legislative Affairs
A/Manager, Janice Trylinski

PROGRAM SUPPORT SERVICES
Exec. Director, Vacant
Administrative Services
Director, Roger Mariner

Financial Services
Director, Joseph Sadovia
Library Services
Director, Keith McLaughlin
Information Systems and Services
Director, Ron Chilibeck
Vital Statistics
Texaco Bldg., 10130-112th St.
Edmonton, T5K 2P2
Director, Bill Gilroy

HUMAN RESOURCES DIVISION
Exec. Director, Terry Chugg

HOSPITALS AND MEDICAL CARE
Hys Centre Bldg., 7th Flr., 11010-101st St.
Box 2222, Edmonton, T5J 2P4

DEPUTY MINISTER'S OFFICE
Dep. Minister, Rhéal J. LeBlanc
Sr. Medical Consultant, G.H. Platt, M.D.

CORPORATE DEVELOPMENT DIVISION
Exec. Director, T.T. Buck
Management Services Branch
Director, P.R. Kennett
Training and Development Branch
Director, R.P. Schnell
Personnel Branch
Director, D.A. Owram

INFORMATION RESOURCE MANAGEMENT
DIVISION
Exec. Director, R.C. Alvarez
Information Planning Branch
A/Director, G. Chaney
Systems Consulting Services Branch
Director, M. Steele
Systems Development Branch
Director, F. Poppe

Hospital Services Division
Asst. Dep. Minister, Dr. Donald J. Philippon
Institutional Operations Branch
Director, M.H. Lamb
Hospital Systems Branch
Director, J.A. Borody
Planning and Construction Branch
Director, G. Flynn
Provincial Programs Branch
A/Director, G. Ward
Standards, Evaluation and Ambulance
Services Branch
Director, W.J. Tudge

Policy Development Division
Asst. Dep. Minister, D.J. Junk
Health Economics and Statistics Branch
Director, Y.M. Cheung
Research and Strategic Planning Branch
Director, Vacant

Finance and Administration Division
Asst. Dep. Minister, G.R. Beck

Accounting Branch
A/Director, J. Thygesen
Administrative Services Branch
Director, R.W. Cooper
Financial Planning and Control Branch
Sr. Financial Advisor, A. Bhatti
Legislative Research Planning Branch
Director, B.W. Jones
Internal Audit Branch
Director, Vacant
Public Communications Branch
Director, L.W. McLennan

Health Care Insurance Division
10025 Jasper Ave., Box 1360
Edmonton, T2P 1E5
Asst. Dep. Minister, C.A. MacKenzie
Registration Branch
Director, M. MacGregor
Claims Branch Director, D.J. Duncan
Health Care Systems Branch
A/Director, G. Sundquist

AGENCIES, BOARDS AND COMMISSIONS

Occupational Health and Safety Council
Seventh Street Plaza, 3rd Flr.
10030-107th St., Edmonton, T5J 3E4
Chairman, Maureen Shaw

Provincial Advisory Committee on Suicide Prevention
Seventh Street Plaza, 3rd Flr.
10030-107th St., Edmonton, T5J 3E4
Chairman, Dr. Ron Dyck

Provincial Mental Health Advisory Council
Seventh Street Plaza, 3rd Flr.
10030-107th St., Edmonton, T5J 3E4
Chairman, Al Maiani

Public Health Advisory and Appeal Board
Seventh Street Plaza, 3rd Flr.
10030-107th St., Edmonton, T5J 3E4

The Public Health Advisory and Appeal Board was created by section 2 of the *Public Health Act,* R.S.A. 1980, Chapter P-27.1 on July 31, 1985. It replaced the former Provincial Board of Health, created in 1909.

The Board has a dual mandate as an appeal and advisory body. As an appeal tribunal, the Board is available to any person who is adversely affected by a decision made by a local health unit board and who feels unjustly treated. The decision can be appealed to the Board, which can confirm, reverse, or vary it.

The Board's other role is to advise the minister on matters regarding the public health by making investigations or inquiries, collecting information, or conducting research. On the request of the Lieutenant-Governor in Council, the Board may be empowered to hold public hearings to receive submissions on public health matters.

The Board is made up of 10 members with varied professional backgrounds who represent all sections of the province.

Chairman, Dr. John Walker

DEPARTMENT OF LABOUR

10808-99th Ave., Edmonton, T5K 0G5
Information: (403) 427-2723

MINISTER'S OFFICE
126 Legislature Bldg., Edmonton, T5K 2B6
Minister, The Hon. Rick Orman

DEPUTY MINISTER'S OFFICE
Dep. Minister, C.S. Mellors

Support Services Division
Asst. Dep. Minister, Wendy Kinsella
Finance and Administration Branch
Director, C. Broemling
Financial Advisory Services
Sr. Financial Advisor, J. Fleming
Systems Branch Director, J. Stocco
Communication Branch
Director, G. Bourdeau
Planning and Research Branch
Director, J. Howell
Library Services Branch
Director, M. Dworaczek
Personnel Branch
A/Director, Dianne Dunn

Labour Relations Division
Asst. Dep. Minister, John Mason
Mediation Services Branch
Director, W. Pangrass
Employment Standards Branch
Director, M. Kolmatycki
Employment Pension Branch
Sup't, E. Groch

General Safety Services Devision
Asst. Dep. Minister, A.E. Kennedy
Boilers and Pressure Vessels Branch
Chief Inspector, J.L. Smith
Building Standards Branch
Director, D. Monsen
Electrical Protection Branch
A/Chief Inspector, Cliff White
Elevator and Fixed Conveyances Branch
Director, J.L. Smith
Fire Prevention Branch
Fire Commissioner, T. Makey
Plumbing and Gas Branch
Director, Denis St. Arnaud

AGENCIES, BOARDS AND COMMISSIONS

Alberta Human Rights Commission
Ste. 902, 10808-99th Ave., Edmonton, T5K 0G5

The Alberta Human Rights Commission is

responsible to the Minister of Labour for the administration of the *Individual's Rights Protection Act,* Alberta's anti-discrimination legislation. The seven members of the Commission are concerned citizens appointed by the Lieutenant-Governor in Council.

The Commission has a two-fold responsibility: first, to develop and implement public education programs to forward the principle that all persons are equal in dignity and rights without regard to race, colour, religious beliefs, sex, physical disability, age (18 and over), ancestry, or place of origin; and second, to investigate and endeavour to settle alleged contraventions of the Act.

The *Individual's Rights Protection Act* has jurisdiction over all provincial government departments, Crown corporations, and agencies, as well as all provincially licensed businesses and industries. Any person who has reasonable grounds for believing that there has been a contravention of the Act may file a complaint with the Commission.

Chairman, Stanley Scudder
Exec. Director, J. Lynch
Northern Region Office
Ste. 801, 10011-109th St., Edmonton, T5J 3S8
Reg. Director, Carol Wodak
Southern Region Office
1333-8th St. S.W., Calgary, T2R 1M6
Reg. Director, L. Paron
Commissioners: Suzanne Mah, William Leslie, Edna Short, Enrico Lazo, Pearl Calahasen

Labour Relations Board
10808-99th Ave., Edmonton, T5K 0G5

The Labour Relations Board is a quasi-judicial tribunal that administers the *Labour Relations Code,* assented to July 6, 1988. The effective date of implementation was the fall of 1988. The Board, through the application of the provisions of this Act, administers and controls labour relations between employers and trade unions in the private sector. The Act provides the legislative framework in matters such as the following: applications for certification and revocation of trade unions acting as bargaining agents; the procedure by which an employee may proceed to a lawful strike; the procedure by which an employer may proceed to a lawful lockout; and unfair labour practices.

Significant changes in the new legislation emphasize the importance of communications between labour and management, while reinforcing government's role in providing advisory support. This occurs through multi-sector advisory councils and the convening of round-table conferences to help facilitate a general understanding of mutually significant aspects of the economy.

Less formality and more flexibility in the Labour Relations Board's approach to disputes, along with an emphasis on settlement is also found in the new *Code.* This occurs through a number of formal and informal options to resolve differences through the Board's involvement.

Certifications and revocations of trade unions

will now all require a secret ballot vote. As well, the new *Code* includes permanent long-term construction legislation initiatives in the form of Regulations.

The Board is comprised of a chairman, two full-time vice-chairmen, one part-time vice-chairman and 20 part-time board members. The chairman, as chief executive officer, is responsible for the Board's day-to-day administrative activities. The chairman, vice-chairmen, board members, and officers of the Board have special expertise in labour relations matters. The board members participate on a part-time basis, maintaining other professions or employment, and are appointed for terms of one to three years.

Chairman, A. Sims
Vice-Chairmen: W. Canning, K. Aldridge
Director of Administration, V. Paniak
Registrars: J. Jung, D. Bykowski
Solicitors: R. Albert, L. Wallace

DEPARTMENT OF MUNICIPAL AFFAIRS

Jarvis Bldg., 9925-107th St.
Edmonton, T5K 2H9
Information: (403) 427-2732

MINISTER'S OFFICE
229 Legislature Bldg., Edmonton, T5K 2B6
Minister, The Hon. Dennis Anderson

NATIVE AFFAIRS
127 Legislature Bldg., Edmonton, T5K 2B6
Minister responsible for Native Affairs,
The Hon. Ken Rostad

DEPUTY MINISTER'S OFFICE
Dep. Minister, A.R. Grover
Solicitor, W.J. Nugent
Internal Auditor, Ram Rajendra
Communications Director, Tony Gronow
Personnel Administration
Director, S. Juniper

Municipal Administrative Services Division
Asst. Dep. Minister, T.D. Forgrave
Municipal Inspection and Advisory Services
Director, John McGowan
Tax Recovery and Property Administration
Director, K.W. Metcalfe
Grants and Subsidies
Director, D.W. Gingara

Finance and Administration Division
Asst. Dep. Minister, R.S. Leitch
Financial Services Branch
Director, Phil Birch
Internal Auditor, Ram Rajendra
Information Systems Branch
Director, Lloyd Livingstone
Administrative Services Branch
Director, Gary Durie

Planning Services Division
Asst. Dep. Minister, Jack Thomas
Planning Research and Development Branch
Director, Dr. G. Power
Support Services Branch
Director, V. Fraser
Planning Branch Director, Rae Runge

Assessment Services Division
Sterling Pl., 9940-106th St.
Edmonton, T5K 2H9
Asst. Dep. Minister, R.G. Gagne
Assessment Inspection
Director, A. Fenton
Assessment Operations
Director, A.C. Bell
Assessment Standards and Training
Director, A. Mackay

Improvement Districts and Native Services Division
Asst. Dep. Minister, Dennis Surrendi
Northern Region (Peace River)
Director, Chuck Curr
Central/Eastern Region
Director, Pieter de Bos
Land Programs Branch
Director, Murray McKnight
Native Services Unit
Exec. Director, Cliff Supernault
Métis Settlements Branch
Director, Rick McDonald
Métis Services Branch
Director, Ron Harrison
Policy Unit
Manager, Cameron Henry
Special Services Branch
Director, John Shannon
Support Services
Director, Siona Monaghan

Housing Division
Asst. Dep. Minister, W.K. Mann
PLANNING SECRETARIAT
A/Exec. Director, L. Allan
FINANCIAL ASSISTANCE AND RESEARCH
BRANCH
Exec. Director, B. Quickfall
Research and Development
Director, Linden Holmen
Grants Administration
Director, Steve Thompson
Home Improvement
Devonian Bldg., Main Flr.
11156 Jasper Ave., Edmonton, T5K 0L1
Director, P. Monteith

RURAL HOUSING BRANCH
Exec. Director, R. Beaupré
Rural and Native Housing Program
Director, R. Wright
Rural Home Assistance Program
Slave Lake Development Bldg., 2nd Flr.
Box 1250, Slave Lake, T0G 2A0

Director, R. McCullough
Rural Emergency Home Program
Postal Bag 2, High Prairie, T0G 1E0
Director, R. Martin

AGENCIES, BOARDS AND COMMISSIONS

Alberta Mortgage and Housing Corp.
9405-50th St., Edmonton, T6B 2T4

Alberta Mortgage and Housing Corporation is a provincial Crown corporation, created on Aug. 1, 1984, to provide mortgage lending, development and property management services, and loan insurance to its clients. The Corporation's main client groups include: mortgagors, volunteer management agencies, municipalities and northern/isolated families. Where possible, the Corporation facilitates the provision of housing services through the private sector and volunteer management boards. The Corporation is also directly involved in housing in smaller centres and resource towns where needs are not being met by the private sector.

The Corporation's current emphasis is on the management of land and housing projects and loan portfolios put in place by its predecessors: the Alberta Housing Corp. and the Alberta Home Mortgage Corp. These holdings include housing units for low- to moderate-income Albertans, senior citizens, and northern/isolated families.

The Corporation has over 7,000 hectares of land holdings which are intended to provide long-term residential and industrial land banks for Alberta municipalities. The Corporation's fully serviced lots are available at affordable prices in several communities.

As a mortgage lender, the Corporation's loans portfolio represents more than $2.5 billion on some 60,000 housing units. These include direct mortgage loans to families, loans to builders and developers, and financing for the servicing of subdivisions in growing municipalities. The Corporation also facilitates the provision of loans through the private sector by means of its loan insurance program for mobile home purchasers.

President, J.M. Engelman
Vice-Presidents:
Property Management, D. Earl
Marketing and Loans, T. Fikowski
Finance and Administration, S. Kent
Loans Administration
Exec. Director, E. Kinsman
Program Support/Marketing and Loans
Exec. Director, T. Edwards
Realty Administration
Exec. Director, D. Kassian
Program Support/Property Management
Exec. Director, Dr. D. Orn
Controller, S. Kent
Systems Director, L. Dahl
Corporate Services, H. Pederson
Edmonton Regional Office
100, 8657-51st Ave., Edmonton, T6E 6A8

Northern Region, Land and Housing
Exec. Director, E. Hodder
Northern Region, Marketing and Loans
Exec. Director, D. Kassian
Calgary Regional Office
2924-11th St. N.E., Calgary, T2E 8C4
Southern Region, Property Management
Exec. Director, G. Teply
Southern Region, Marketing and Loans
Exec. Director, J. Martin
Grande Prairie District Office
9909-102nd St., Grande Prairie, T8V 2V4
Dist. Manager, M. Fushtey
Red Deer District Office
5913 Gaetz Ave., Red Deer, T4N 4C4
Dist. Manager, S. Menzies
Lethbridge Regional Office
220-4th St. S., Lethbridge, T1J 4J7
Dist. Manager, B. McGlashan
Fort McMurray District Office
194 Grenfell Cres., Fort McMurray, T9H 2M6
Sr. Property Administrator, C. Slade
St. Paul Regional Office
5238-50th Ave., Box 3189, St. Paul, T0A 3A0
Dist. Manager, E. Hoeft
Peace River Sub-Office
9710-94th St., Peace River, T0H 2X0
High Prairie Sub-Office
4801-52nd Ave., Boyt Bldg.
High Prairie, T0G 1E0

Alberta Planning Board

9925-107th St., 9th Flr., Edmonton, T5K 2H9
General Inquiries: (403) 427-4864

The Alberta Planning Board is established by the *Planning Act* of the Province of Alberta and is the senior land use planning authority in the province. Its purpose is to co-ordinate the land use planning activities of the various departments of government as well as the operation of the ten regional planning commissions.

The Board administers the Subdivision Regulation, the *Planning Act*, and the *New Towns Act*, and its conduct and operation are governed by these Acts together with other related Acts and Regulations. It approves regional plans, amendments to regional plans and plan cancellations; it may grant exemption from various requirements of the Act and the Regulation, as applied for by the subdivision-approving authorities.

The Board also hears appeals on the decisions of the subdivision-approving authorities as well as on amendments to regional plans and hears inter-municipal disputes and disputes with the regional planning commissions. It recommends the formation or designation of New Towns and approves all land use planning matters for such towns. Furthermore, the Board administers the Alberta Planning Fund and approves special planning projects and studies.

Chairman, A.R. Grover
Vice-Chairmen:
L.A. Kluthe, J.G. Thomas, D.H. Cole
Director of Administration, A.J. Suelzle

Finance and Administration
Manager, Helen E. Engels
Planning and Appeals
Manager, K.J. Sawchuk
Members: R.N. Briggs, R.W. Clement,
D.H. Cole, B.L. Colgan, A.R. Grover,
L.A. Kluthe, D. Morgan, J.K. Maitland,
D.C. McKay, K. Newman, P. Polischuk,
B. Quickfall, B.M. Stecyk, A.J. Suelzle,
J.G. Thomas, E.C. Wyldman

Assessment Appeal Board

Ste. 201, Energy Sq.
10109-106th St., Edmonton, T5J 1H3

The Alberta Assessment Appeal Board was created in 1957 by an Act of the provincial legislature. The Board is an independent, autonomous, quasi-judicial body which hears appeals and renders decisions with respect to assessments in Alberta.

The main functions of the Board are the hearing and determining of appeals from:

- decisions of Courts of Revision throughout the province of Alberta in respect of: a) real property, business, and local improvements assessments made under authority of *The Municipal Taxation Act* and the *Municipal and Provincial Properties Valuation Act;* and b) Mobile Home Licensing Valuations made under the authority of *The Municipal Government Act;*
- assessments made by the Alberta Assessment Commissioner under authority of *The Municipalities Assessment and Equalization Act;*
- assessments made by the Chief Provincial Assessor under authority of *The Electric Power and Pipe Line Assessment Act;*
- decisions of Courts of Revision of Irrigation District in respect of all assessment roll entries;
- orders of the Alberta Assessment Equalization Board made under authority of *The Municipalities Assessment and Equalization Act.*

Under the existing legislation, the Board is permitted to operate as a Board or as divisions of the Board with two members forming a quorum of a division. Numerous Board decisions are handed down orally and confirmed in writing, while other decisions are handed down in writing, setting forth the grounds of appeal, the relevant facts, the arguments, the relevant statutory provisions, and the resultant findings of the Board.

Chairman, Wallace Daley
Sec.-Member, J.M. Swelin
Members:
J.W. Chaney, R.N. McGregor, J.M. Schmidt

Assessment Equalization Board

Sterling Pl., 3rd Flr.
9940-106th St., Edmonton, T5K 2N2

Municipalities in the province are involved in a number of cost-shared programs by which each municipality, based on an equalized assessment, contributes an equitable amount of funding for operational programs, such as schools, hospitals, community recreation, and land planning. The Board is appointed by the Lieutenant-Governor in Council and is responsible to the Minister of Municipal Affairs. The five-member board consists of a member from the Alberta Urban Municipalities Assn., a member from the Alberta Assn. of Municipal Districts and Counties, a member from the Department of Education, and a chairman and vice-chairman from the Department of Municipal Affairs.

Property assessments in the province are tied to a base year and established from the market value of non-farm lands, the depreciated replacement cost of improvements, and the productive capabilities of farm land. Property assessments in municipalities are not all generated on the same base year; therefore, levels of value may vary due to the economic conditions in a specific base year. This variation in assessment would create a disparity between municipalities in the amount contributed to various cost-shared programs, if contributions were based on actual property assessments. Equalized assessment is a procedure established by the Alberta government that measures the property wealth of each Alberta municipality. This is accomplished by converting each municipality's overall property tax assessment base to a common provincial level.

Chairman, R.G. Gagne
Vice-Chairman, A. Waters
Members: D. Bryan, J. Smith, S. Bemount
Board Secretary, R. Kozack

Local Authorities Board
Pacific Plaza, 6th Flr.
10909 Jasper Ave., Edmonton, T5J 3L9

The Local Authorities Board of Alberta considers and decides upon:

a) petitions for annexation of lands to municipalities, including the fixing of terms and conditions;

b) applications by local authorities for authorization of debenture borrowings;

c) applications for inquiry into affairs of local authorities where financial difficulties are involved;

d) authorization of financial programs for controlled local authorities and New Towns;

e) applications by non-profit organizations for exemption from assessment and taxation of properties;

f) referrals by the Irrigation Council to form, change, or dissolve a district; and

g) petitions to separate lands from urban municipalities and revert same to rural ones.

A/Chairman, B.T. Clark
Member, Henry Thiessen

Special Areas Board
Box 820, Hanna, T0J 1P0

The Special Areas Board was established in 1938 to rehabilitate 2.1 million hectares of public land. A special form of municipal government, the Special Areas Board provides all municipal services on behalf of the Minister of Municipal Affairs. Land use is controlled under a leasing system that includes grazing, cultivation, and mineral surface leases.

The Special Areas are divided into 13 subdivisions, located in southeast central Alberta. Each subdivision is represented by an elected advisory council member whose function is to confer with and advise the minister and the Board on matters affecting the Special Areas.

The administration of the Board itself is set out in the *Special Areas Act,* R.S.A. 1980, Chapter S-20: "(1) There is hereby established a corporation with the name "Special Areas Board" composed of the members appointed under this section; (2) The Board is an agent of the Crown in the right of Alberta; (3) The Board shall consist of not more than 3 members appointed by the Lieutenant-Governor in Council."

Chairman, A.G. Grover
Members: J.D. Sumner, T. Osadczuk
Finance and Administration
Director, B.E. Davies
Properties Administration
Director, Jay Slemp
Municipal Services
Director, D.J. Hungle

DEPARTMENT OF OCCUPATIONAL HEALTH AND SAFETY

10030-107th St., Edmonton, T5J 3E4
(except where otherwise indicated)

MINISTER'S OFFICE
420 Legislature Bldg., Edmonton, T5K 2B6
Minister responsible, The Hon. Dr. Ian Reid
Note: The Hon. Dr. Ian Reid was defeated in the recent general election. A replacement had not yet been named as of date of publication.
A/Man. Director, Dr. G. Gibbs
Industry and Technical Services
A/Exec. Director, Dave Gibson
Education and Liaison
Director, Dave Gibson
Research and Epidemiology
Director, Dr. Lynn Hewitt
Technical Services
Director, Atanu Das
Occupational Health
Director, Dr. Ray Copes
Work Site Services
Exec. Director, William Rozel
Work Site Services North
9321-48th St., Edmonton, T6B 2R4
Director, John Johnston
Work Site Services South
1021-10th Ave. S.W., Calgary, T2R 0B7
Director, Keith Smith

DEPARTMENT OF PUBLIC WORKS, SUPPLY AND SERVICES

6950-113th St., Edmonton, T6H 5V7
(except where otherwise indicated)

MINISTER'S OFFICE
131 Legislature Bldg., Edmonton, T5K 2B6
Minister, The Hon. Ernie Isley

DEPUTY MINISTER'S OFFICE
Dep. Minister, Edward R. McLellan
Personnel Division
Director, M. Clifford
Public Relations Director, Bill Rees

ACCOMMODATION SERVICES
8215-112th St., Edmonton, T6G 5A9
Exec. Director, Herman Lucas
ACCOMMODATION PLANNING DIVISION
Exec. Director, Ray Reshke
Project Administration Branch
Director, D. Berry
REALTY DIVISION
Exec. Director, Dave Hudson
Leasing Branch
Director, Bob Smith
Land Acquisition Branch
Director, Gary Summers
Land Planning and Management Branch
Director, Alex Jacob

Capital Development
8215-112th St., Edmonton, T6G 5A9
Asst. Dep. Minister, A. (Tony) Hargreaves
Sr. Admin. Manager, Lillian Brooks
CONSTRUCTION DIVISION
Exec. Director, Larry James
Reg. Director, Central, Russ Andruko
Reg. Director, Northern, Richard Knutton
Reg. Director, Southern, Derek Etherington
J.J. Bowlen Bldg., 10th Flr.
620-7th Ave. S.W., Calgary, T2P 0Y8
Cost Control and Analysis Division
Director, John Pettie

PROJECT MANAGEMENT DIVISION
Exec. Director, George Gerencser
Commissioning Branch
Director, Bill Kotylak
Project Management—Calgary
J.J. Bowlen Bldg., 10th Flr.
620-7th Ave. S.W., Calgary, T2P 0Y8
Reg. Director, Conrad Loban
Specifications and Standards Branch
Director, John Walker
Site Development Division
Director, Tom Bahniuk

Finance and Administration
6950-113th St., Edmonton, T6H 5V7
Asst. Dep. Minister, Gordon H. Hill
Financial Systems Branch
Director, George Sharp

Financial Planning Branch
College Plaza, 11th Flr.
8215-112th St., Edmonton, T6G 5A9
Director, Gary Boddez
Financial Services Branch
Director, Harold Brown
Management Services Branch
Director, David Bass

Information Services
6950-113th St., Edmonton, T6H 5V7
Asst. Dep. Minister, Bob Gehmlich
COMPUTER PROCESSING DIVISION
Exec. Director, Stan Petrica
Terrace Computing Centre
Director, Joyce Majnarich
Central Computing Centre
Director, Roger Roberts
Calgary Computing Centre
Director, Roy Hauer
Tax Administration Computing Centre
Director, Jim Thrower
Technical Support Branch
Director, Al Schut
Production Processing Branch
Director, Vacant

COMPUTER SYSTEMS DIVISION
Exec. Director, Ron Lippa
Systems Maintenance and
Co-ordination Branch
Director, Peter Broadbent
Planning and Policy
Director, Doug Sigler
Application Maintenance and Support Branch
Director, Wayne Halibisky

TELECOMMUNICATIONS DIVISION
Exec. Director, Stu MacPherson
Telecommunications Operations Branch
Director, Leon Mevel
Telecommunications Network
Management Branch
Director, Kwan Wong

Property Management
8215-112th St., Edmonton, T6G 5A9
Asst. Dep. Minister, Dan Bader
Southern Region
Director, Peter Kruselnicki
Central Region
Director, Andy Boys
Northern Region
Director, R.W. Polowaniuk
Operational Support Branch
Director, Charles Hitschfeld

PROPERTY TECHNICAL PLANNING DIVISION
Exec. Director, Malcolm Johnson
Technical Services
Director, Harold Butchart
Mechanical Engineering
Director, John Kovacs
Electrical Engineering
Director, Dave Robinson

Building Services
Director, John O'Connor
Maintenance Planning and Evaluation
Director, Casey Skakun
CONTRACT MANAGEMENT DIVISION
8215-112th St., Edmonton, T6G 5A9
Exec. Director, Bruce Smith
Property Contracts—Central
Director, John Enns
Property Contracts Branch—North
Director, Garry Russ
Property Contracts Branch—South
Director, Gregg Hook

Supply Management
6950-113th St., Edmonton, T6H 5V7
Asst. Dep. Minister, S.A. Pepper
Air Transportation Services Branch
Director, John Tenzer
PROCUREMENT DIVISION
12360-142nd St, Edmonton, T5L 2H1
Exec. Director, Bob Peyton
Purchasing Branch
Director, Michael Long
Warehousing and Distribution Branch
Director, Reg Williamson
Contracted Services Branch
Director, Ron Caruk
SUPPLY OPERATIONS DIVISION
Exec. Director, Murray Tyreman
Printing Services Branch
Director, Vacant
Equipment, Courier and Surplus Branch
Director, Ray Nugent
Records Management Branch
12360-142nd St., Edmonton, T5L 2H1
Director, Marcel Roy

DEPARTMENT OF RECREATION AND PARKS

Standard Life Ctr.
10405 Jasper Ave., Edmonton, T5J 3N4
(except where otherwise indicated)
Recreation Information: (403) 427-6549
Parks Information: (403) 427-9429

MINISTER'S OFFICE
107 Legislature Bldg., Edmonton, T5K 2B6
Minister, The Hon. Norm A. Weiss

DEPUTY MINISTER'S OFFICE
Dep. Minister, Julien J. Nowicki
Public Communications
Manager, Tony Myers

KANANASKIS COUNTRY
412, 1011 Glenmore Tr. S.W.
Calgary, T2V 4R6
Man. Director, Ed S. Marshall
Construction and Maintenance
Director, Fred G. Wilmot
Operations Director, R.H. Reynolds
Box 280, Canmore, T0L 0M0

Planning and Design
Director, Robert K. Jenkins
Finance and Administration
Director, Rod Burkard
Public Affairs
Director, Margaret W. Qually

Corporate Services Division
Asst. Dep. Minister, David H. Rehill
Corporate Planning Services
Manager, Sherri Thorsen
Human Resource Services
Manager, Mike Boyd
Financial Services
Director, Terry Knull
Information Services
Director, Robbert Jasperse
Internal Audit
Director, Vacant

Parks Division
Asst. Dep. Minister, Donn E. Cline
Divisional Support Branch
A/Director, Vern H. Wiebe
Field Support Branch
Director, Bruce M. Duffin
Visitor Services Branch
A/Director, Will C. Pearce
Program Development Branch
Director, Paul E. Skydt
Professional and Technical Services Branch
Director, W.J. (Bill) Porter
Project Management Branch
Director, Fred W. Moffatt

REGIONAL OFFICES:
West Central Region
Box 920, Rimbey, T0C 2J0
Director, W.Y. (Bill) Cadre
East Central Region
Box 1019, Lac La Biche, T0A 2C0
Director, Keith H. McDonald
Northern Region
Box 570, Valleyview, T0H 3N0
Director, Gerry F. Tranter
Southern Region
Drawer 930, Vulcan, T0L 2B0
Director, Terry C. Hall

Recreation Development Division
Asst. Dep. Minister, Vacant
Planning Support Branch
Director, J.H. Ross
Administrative Support Branch
Director, Doug Thompson
Community Recreation Services Branch
Director, Ken Wilson
Provincial Recreation and
Sport Services Branch
Director, Dwight Ganske
Blue Lake Centre
Box 850, Hinton, T0E 1B0

AGENCIES, BOARDS AND COMMISSIONS

Alberta Sport Council
Hanover Place, 4th Flr.
101-6th Ave. S.W., Calgary, T2P 3P4
Man. Director, Max Gibb

Recreation, Parks and Wildlife Foundation
Harley Court, 7th Flr.
10045-111th St., Edmonton, T5K 1K4

The Recreation, Parks and Wildlife Foundation was erected by an Act of the Alberta Legislature in 1976. The purpose of the Foundation is to provide Albertans with the opportunity to donate cash or items of value toward worthwhile projects within the province dealing with the areas of recreation, parks and/or wildlife. The Foundation is also a recipient of a portion of the profits generated by Alberta Lotteries. With these donations and lottery funds, the Foundation then entertains applications for funding assistance from associations, clubs, and individuals to enrich their projects.

During the period between June 1980 and June 1987, the Foundation awarded more than 1,500 grants totalling more than $16 million. Projects include recreation programs and facility enrichment; park, campground, and golf course development; and wildlife research, and habitat restoration and conservation.

Funding decisions are made by 12 volunteer board members who meet four times a year to discuss applications submitted in the previous quarter. The office of the Foundation is situated in Edmonton, and is staffed by four permanent employees.

Exec. Director, Chuck Moser

DEPARTMENT OF SOCIAL SERVICES

Seventh St. Plaza
10030-107th St., Edmonton, T5J 3E4
(except where otherwise indicated)
Information: (403) 427-2734

MINISTER'S OFFICE
424 Legislature Bldg., Edmonton, T5K 2B6
Minister, The Hon. Connie Osterman
Director, Tom Burns
Appeal and Advisory Secretariat
Director, Mickey Casavant
Senior Citizens Secretariat
Director, Mary Engelmann
Sr. Communications Advisor, Hugh Tadman

OFFICE OF THE DEPUTY MINISTER
Dep. Minister, Stan Remple
Director, Lorraine Kureluk
Public Communications
Director, Patricia Derrick
Office of the Children's Guardian
A/Children's Guardian, John Mould
Correspondence Manager, Linda Hall

Resource Management
Asst. Dep. Minister, Barry J. Burgess
Financial Operations and Budgets
Director, Brian Elliott
Financial Standards and Systems
Director, Frank Wilson
Administrative Services
Director, Jack McKendry
Federal/Provincial Co-ordination
Director, Ralph Pruden
Management Audit
Director, Bernie Leins
HUMAN RESOURCES
Exec. Director, Ken Wickenberg
Employee Resources
A/Director, Dave Banick
Organizational Resources
Director, Dave Banick
Staff Development
Director, Sally Huemmert
INFORMATION RESOURCE MANAGEMENT
Exec. Director, Al Schut
Information Systems Services
Director, Vacant
Management Information Services
Director, Ron Sohnle
EDP Planning
Director, Dave Huet

Policy Development and Service Design
Asst. Dep. Minister, David Kelly
Planning Support
Director, Valerie Richmond
LEGISLATIVE PLANNING
Exec. Director, Bernd Walter
CHILD PROTECTION SERVICES
Exec. Director, Matt Hanrahan
Adoptions Director, Dean Melsness
Native Issues Director, Bonnie McMillan
Quality Assurance and Evaluation
Director, John McDermott
Services to Children
Director, Val Kinjerski

FAMILY SUPPORT SERVICES
Exec. Director, Diane McAmmond
Child Care Programs
Director, Pauline Peters
Office for the Prevention of Family Violence
Director, Katrine McKenzie
Special Support Programs
Director, Dennis Maier
Evaluation Services
Director, Jon Brehaut
INCOME SUPPORT
Exec. Director, Tina MacDonald
Income Security Initiatives
A/Director, Norma Harder
Income Security Programs
Director, Andrew Law
Quantitative Support
Manager, Rudy Hoehn

Pensions Programs
Director, Yolanda Stojak
L1SA/DDP Implementation Project
Director, Dani Beet
SERVICES TO THE HANDICAPPED
A/Exec. Director, Robert Pritchard
Employment Support Services
Director, Allan Douglas
Residential Services
A/Director, Norm McLeod
OFFICE OF THE PUBLIC GUARDIAN
Public Guardian, Melane Hotz

Service Delivery
Asst. Dep. Minister, John LaFrance

REGIONAL OFFICES:
Edmonton Region
11748 Kingsway Ave., Edmonton, T5G 0X5
Reg. Director, Denis Bell
Calgary Region
Main Flr., Deerfoot Junction, Twr. 3
1212-31st Ave. N.E., Calgary, T2E 7S8
Reg. Director, Dr. David Paley
Northwest Region
Box 326, McLennan, T0H 2L0
Reg. Director, Ann Ward Neville
Northeast Region
Lakeview Bldg., 15 Nipewan Rd.
Lac La Biche, T0A 2C0
Reg. Director, Don Fleming
Central Region
4415-49th St., Box 1680, Innisfail, T0M 1A0
Reg. Director, Gordon Stangier
South Region
2105-20th Ave., Box 60, Coaldale, T0K 0L0
Reg. Director, Lorene M. Harrison
Michener Centre
Box 5002, Red Deer, T4N 5Y5
Exec. Director, Wayne Wright

DEPARTMENT OF THE SOLICITOR GENERAL

10365-97th St., Edmonton, T5J 3W7
(except where otherwise indicated)
Information: (403) 427-7178

MINISTER'S OFFICE
127 Legislature Bldg., Edmonton, T5K 2B6
Minister, The Hon. Marvin E. Moore
Note: The Hon. Marvin E. Moore did not run in
the recent general election. A replacement had
not yet been named as of date of publication.

DEPUTY SOLICITOR GENERAL'S OFFICE
Dep. Solicitor General, R.J. King
Asst. Dep. Minister, Administration,
D.A. McGeachy

FINANCE SERVICES
Exec. Director, Vacant
Finance Operations
Director, John Gerle

Finance Planning and Advisory Services
Director, D. Essensa
Supply and Support Services
Director, J. Fedun
Internal Audit
Director, G. O'Donnell
Personnel Services
Director, H. Geddes
Systems and Information Services
Director, Chris Bowdler
Asst. Directors: S. Watson, Dan Sheplowy

Motor Vehicle Division
Asst. Dep. Minister, C. Procuik
Management Services
Director, Hans Helder
Program Services
Director, E. Hagen
Driver Management Branch
Director, J. Farmer
Finance Services Branch
Director, D. Essensa
Motor Vehicle Accident Claims
John E. Brownlee Bldg., 10th Flr.
10365-97th St., Edmonton, T5J 3W7
Administrator, E. Hagen

Correctional Services Division
Asst. Dep. Minister, Jack Davis
Planning and Operations Support Unit
Director, J. Pascoe
CORPORATE SERVICES
A/Exec. Director, R. Bricker
Communications
Director, C. Zorica
Planning and Project Management Branch
Director, P. Gick

AUDIT AND STANDARDS INVESTIGATION
BRANCH
Exec. Director, H.A. O'Handley
South Region
Natural Resources Bldg., 7th Flr.
205-9th Ave. S.E., Calgary, T2G 0R3
Reg. Director, D. Dixon
North Region
Reg. Director, A. Galet
Young Offender Program
Exec. Director, B. Mason
Law Enforcement
Director, Ed Hahn

AGENCIES, BOARDS AND COMMISSIONS

Alberta Liquor Control Board
50 Corriveau Ave., St. Albert, T8N 3T5

The Alberta Liquor Control Board is a corporation created by and operating pursuant to the
Liquor Control Act. The Liquor Board was first
created in 1924 after Prohibition was lifted. The
Board has two basic and separate functions:
liquor sale and distribution; and the licensing of
outlets and enforcement of the Regulations in

these outlets.

Respecting liquor sale and distribution, the Board, by legislation, has control of the importation and sale of all liquor in the province. This is done through its more than 200 (liquor and beer) retail outlets in various locations throughout the province.

There are currently 23 classes of premises which may obtain a liquor licence. These range from dining lounges and theatres to stadiums and racetracks. For each class of premises, there is a set of detailed Regulations governing its operation. The Board is responsible for issuing licences and ensuring that licensees comply with these Regulations.

A/Chairman and CEO, J.T. Strain
Board Member, W. Mack
Financial Services
Director, D. Dart
Information Systems
Director, K. Williams
Licensing and Permits
Director, Donald Watkins
Property and General Services
Director, D. McCallum
Personnel Services
Director, J. Isakson
Stocks Director, D. Orton
Internal Audit
Director, B. Nicholson
Stores and Warehousing
Director, I. Fraser

Alberta Racing Commission
507 Sloane Sq., 5920-1A St. S.W.
Box 5684, Stn. A, Calgary, T2H 1Y2

The Racing Commission reports to the Alberta Solicitor General and is responsible for governing all forms of horse racing on which pari mutuel betting takes place.

The seven-member Commission under its chairman allocates racing dates, licenses racetrack employees, appoints stewards, hears appeals, and disburses grants as purse supplements and breeder support.

The Commission was established in 1962 under the *Racing Commission Act,* R.S.A. 1980, Chapter R-1.

Chairman, Roy A. Farran
Vice-Chairman, D.J. Buchanan
Members: W.G. Pritchett, K.C. Amthor, J. Sheckter, I.W. Parsons, Dr. B. Gunn
Thoroughbred Racing
Supervisor, M.H. Heggie
Harness Racing
Supervisor, Don C. Stewart, Jr.

Driver Control Board
Edmonton Office:
9644-103A Ave., Edmonton, T5H 4H5
Calgary Office:
Sloane Sq., Rm. 300A
5920-1A St. S.W., Calgary, T2H 0G3
General Inquiries: (403) 427-7178

The Driver Control Board is a quasi-judicial authority operating under the authority of the *Motor Vehicle Administration Act.* Persons whose driving records are of concern are referred to the Board by the Solicitor General, a judge, or the Registrar of Motor Vehicles. The Board conducts an inquiry, at which the person appears, and, in the interest of public safety, the Board may suspend an operator's licence, prescribe any measure of remedial action, or prescribe conditions for the possession of a licence.

Chairman, G. Pedersen
Vice-Chairman, R. Sales
Members: B. Smith, J. Farmer, G. Macdonald

DEPARTMENT OF TECHNOLOGY, RESEARCH AND TELECOMMUNICATIONS

Pacific Plaza, 12th Flr., 10909 Jasper Ave.
Edmonton, T5J 3M8

MINISTER'S OFFICE
404 Legislature Bldg., Edmonton, T5K 2B6
Minister, The Hon. Leslie G. Young
Note: The Hon. Leslie G. Young was defeated in the recent general election. A replacement had not yet been named as of date of publication.

DEPUTY MINISTER'S OFFICE
Dep. Minister, Ken H.G. Broadfoot

DEPARTMENT OF TOURISM

10025 Jasper Ave., Edmonton, T5J 3Z3
(except where otherwise indicated)
General Information: (403) 427-2280

MINISTER'S OFFICE
418 Legislature Bldg., Edmonton, T5K 2B6
Minister, The Hon. Donald Sparrow

DEPUTY MINISTER'S OFFICE
Dep. Minister, Bernard F. Campbell
Sr. Advisor, Barbara Spencer

CORPORATE DEVELOPMENT DIVISION
Exec. Director, Peter C. Crerar
Finance and Administration
Director, R.H. Turner
Systems and Computing
Director, Colin Sparrow-Clarke
Financial Services
Director, Gerald Lamoureux
Human Resources
Director, Neil Murray
Corporate Communications
Director, Vacant
Strategic Planning
Director, E. Neil Taylor

TRAVEL ALBERTA
General Information: (403) 427-4321
1-800-222-6501 (Alberta)
1-800-661-8888 (Canada and U.S.A.)

MARKETING DIVISION
Exec. Director, John Zylstra
Sales Branch
Director, D. Smithson
Meetings/International Liaison Branch
Director, D. Lane
London
Alberta House, 1 Mount St., Berkeley Sq.
London, England W1Y 5AA
Los Angeles
Alberta Government Office
333 South Grand Ave., Ste. 3535
Los Angeles, CA 90071 U.S.A.
Director, Gordon Coombs
Marketing Planning Branch
Director, B. Salter
Vacation Planning Branch
Director, G. Halbersma
Calgary
McDougall Ctr., 455-64th St. S.W.
Calgary, T2P 4E8
Opportunity Marketing Branch
Director, K.C. Sears

PLANNING DIVISION
Exec. Director, W.W. Warren
Destination Planning Branch
Director, L. McGillivray
Canada/Alberta Tourism Agreement Program
Director, M. Slater
Community Services Branch
Director, D. Syrnyk

MINISTRY AND BUSINESS DEVELOPMENT
DIVISION
Exec. Director, J. Engel
Business Development Branch
Director, B. Wilson
Industry Relations and Training Branch
A/Director, D. Squires
Alberta Tourism Education Council
Chairman, S. Day
Exec. Director, S. Dowler

DEPARTMENT OF
TRANSPORTATION AND UTILITIES

Twin Atria Bldg.
4999-98th Ave., Edmonton, T6B 2X3
(except where otherwise indicated)
Information: (403) 427-2731

MINISTER'S OFFICE
208 Legislature Bldg., Edmonton, T5K 2B6
Minister, The Hon. J. Allen Adair

DEPUTY MINISTER'S OFFICE
Dep. Minister, H.M. Alton

Engineering Operations
Sr. Asst. Dep. Minister, M.A. Kehr
ENGINEERING SERVICES
Exec. Director, G.A. Berdahl
Design Engineering Branch
Director, P. Tajcnar
Contracts Engineering
Director, T. Horne
Materials Engineering
Director, L. Nichols
Property Services
Director, P. Roche
OPERATIONAL PLANNING
Exec. Director, K. Howery
Roadway Planning
Director, R. Sawchuk
Special Projects
Director, John Freeman-Marsh
Referral Services
Director, M. Gerard

BRIDGE ENGINEERING
Exec. Director, N. Boyd
Bridge Planning
Director, R. Walters
Bridge Design
Director, R. Kornelsen
Bridge Materials
Director, W. Hamilton
Bridge Construction
Director, A. Rogers
Bridge Services
Director, T. Belke
EQUIPMENT, SUPPLY AND SERVICES
Exec. Director, H. Wilson
Equipment Management
Director, R. Pasichnuk
Shop Operations
Director, W. Wuchterl
Material and Support Services
Director, I. Pregitzer

Regional Operations
Asst. Dep. Minister, L. Root
Exec. Director, J. Glowach
Department Solicitor, J.A. McFadzen
Public Communications
Director, D. Nicol
Operations
Director, G. Vincent
Construction Programming
Director, C.D. Burton
Aviation
Director, L. Nelson

REGIONAL DIRECTORS:
Region 1
Administration Bldg., 3rd Flr.
Lethbridge, T1H 0H5
B. Comchi
Region 2
Box 3550, Airdrie, T0M 0B0
Bernie Kathol
Region 3
4920-51st St., Red Deer, T4N 6K8
Jim Bussard

Region 4
Box 38, St. Paul, T0A 3A0
Henri Hetu
Region 5
Box 1810, Barrhead, T0G 0E0
Charles Lendzion
Region 6
Provincial Bldg., Postal Bag 900, Box 25
Peace River, T0H 2X0
P.J. Sawchuk

Administration
Asst. Dep. Minister, D.J. Porter
FINANCE
Exec. Director, R. James
Accounting Operations
Director, D. Tworowski
Systems and Methods
Director, K. Chrisp
Financial Planning and Control
Director, L. Hempsey
PERSONNEL
Exec. Director, Stan Hayter
General Services
Director, E. Tywoniuk

Planning and Development
Asst. Dep. Minister, June Zatko
Strategic Planning
Exec. Director, M. Duncan
Transportation Policy
Director, D. Szarko
Systems Planning
Director, A. Werner
Special Planning Projects
Director, S. Quiring
Information Services
Director, D. McTavish
Utilities Policy
Director, L. Charach
Research and Development
Director, J. Konarzewski

Support Programs
Asst. Dep. Minister, D. Shillabeer
Urban Transportation
Exec. Director, G. Halls
Urban Engineering
A/Director, B. Marcotte
Gas Utilities
Exec. Director, T. Brown
Municipal Services
Director, M. Znak
Utility Services
Exec. Director, W. Brown
Rural Electric
Director, J. Mann
Rebates Director, G. Breckenridge

Motor Transport Services
Asst. Dep. Minister, C. Procuik
Highway Safety and N.S.C.
Director, R. Hogg
Planning and Statistics
Director, L. Keown

Red Deer Office:
Provincial Bldg., 4th Flr.
4920-51st St., Red Deer, T4N 6K8
Support Services Director, R. Clarke
Transport Field Operations
Director, R. Pagnucco
Motor Transport Engineering
Director, R. Houston

AGENCIES, BOARDS AND COMMISSIONS

Alberta Resources Railway Corp.
501, Royal LePage Bldg.
10130-103rd St., Edmonton, T5J 3N9

The Lieutenant-Governor in Council, pursuant to the *Alberta Resources Railway Corporation Act,* designated a Resource Area and authorized the Corporation to construct a railway from Swan Landing north to Grande Prairie (a distance of 388 km).

The Alberta Resources Railway was leased to Canadian National Railways for operation for a period of 20 years, effective Jan. 1, 1970. It is shown in tariffs as the Grande Cache Subdivision of the CN.

The board of directors of the Corporation is appointed by the Lieutenant-Governor in Council. The Act also provides for a chairman, vice-chairman, secretary-treasurer, and managing director.

Chairman, The Hon. J. Allen Adair
Man. Director, Charles Anderson

Electric Energy Marketing Agency
Woodward Twr., Ste. 711
400 S. 4th Ave., Lethbridge, T1J 4E1

The Electric Energy Marketing Agency, the largest single purchaser of electrical energy in Canada, began operations on Sept. 1, 1982. Responsible for administering the *Electric Energy Marketing Act,* the Agency was formed to alleviate the problems arising from the large electric energy cost differential between consumers in northern and southern Alberta. It essentially buys and resells all the power generated in Alberta, with total purchases of approximately $900 million per year.

Chairman, Fred J. Dumont
Exec. Director, Eileen Fedor

Motor Transport Board
Provincial Bldg., 4th Flr.
4920-51st St., Red Deer, T4N 6K8

The Motor Transport Board governs, in the public interest, highway transportation in and for the Province of Alberta. The Board is a body corporate whose chairman and board members are appointed by the Lieutenant-Governor in Council.

The Board allots and exercises powers under the *Motor Vehicle Transport Act* (Canada) and the *Motor Transport Act* (Alberta). Its power under the *Highway Traffic Act* (Alberta) is delegated by the Minister of Transportation and Utilities. The Board may prescribe rules regarding the conduct of business, procedures for hearings, and the conduct of inquiries.

Chairman, G. Bellingham
Board Secretary, A.C. Smythe

TREASURY DEPARTMENT

9515-107th St., Edmonton, T5K 2C3
(except where otherwise indicated)
Information: (403) 427-3035
Treasury Branches Information: (403) 427-2721

PROVINCIAL TREASURER'S OFFICE
224 Legislature Bldg., Edmonton, T5K 2B6
Treasurer, The Hon. Dick Johnston

DEPUTY PROVINCIAL TREASURERS' OFFICE
Dep. Provincial Treasurer, Management and Control, A.D. O'Brien
Dep. Provincial Treasurer, Finance and Revenue, A.J. McPherson
Controller, J.D. Peters
Asst. Dep. Provincial Treasurers:
Revenue, A.H. Kalke
Finance Programs, J.M. Drinkwater
Budget and Fiscal Policy, L.G. Morrison
Accounting Director, Richard Lowen
Admin. Director, M.D. Faulkner
Banking and Cash Management
Director, D.R. Bishop
Budget Bureau Director, G.G. Trogen
Budget Planning and Economics
Director, G.K. Robertson
Bureau of Statistics
Sir Frederick W. Haultain Bldg., 7th Flr.
9811-109th St., Edmonton, T5K 2L5
Director, H.W. Ford
CORPORATE MANAGEMENT SERVICES
8 S.E. Sir Frederick W. Haultain Bldg.
9811-109th St., Edmonton, T5K 2L5
Exec. Director, H.H. Strohbach

CORPORATE TAX ADMINISTRATION
Sir Frederick W. Haultain Bldg., 2nd Flr.
9811-109th St., Edmonton, T5K 2L5
Exec. Director, L.H. Landry
Tax Operations
Director, L.M.L. Rokosh
Audits Director, C. Calarco
Interpretations and Appeals
Director, E. Ramsay
Systems Director, J.W.K. Parton
Calgary Office
Eighth and Eighth Bldg., 4th Flr.
Calgary S.W., T2P 3P1
Disbursement Control
Director, T.W. Burns
Financial Institutions
Credit Unions Director, G. Malcolm
Trust Companies Director, R. Pointe
Finance Planning and Analysis
Director, R.A. Bhatia

Financial Services
Manager, L.J. Hellweg
Financial Systems
Director, F. Scarfone
Investment Management
Chief Investment Officer, S.J. Susinski
Director, R.C. Kamp
Payroll and Pensions
Park Plaza, 3rd Flr.
10611-98th Ave., Edmonton, T5K 2P7
Director, E.J. Wilcox

PENSION BOARDS
Legislature Annex, 12th Flr.
9718-107th St., Edmonton, T5K 1E4
Chairman, J.E. Faries
Personnel Services Manager, J. Groves
Policies and Procedures
Director, M.H. Mylod
Revenue Administration
Sir Frederick W. Haultain Bldg., 6th Flr.
9811-109th St., Edmonton, T5K 2L5
Director, L. Huisman
Risk Management and Insurance
Sir Frederick W. Haultain Bldg., 8th Flr.
9811-109th St., Edmonton, T5K 2L5
Director, D. Murray
Tax Policy Director, Vacant

ALBERTA TREASURY BRANCHES
(See also listing in Banking chapter, Volume 1)
9925-109th St., Edmonton, T5K 2C3
Sup't, A.O. Bray
Sr. Asst. Sup'ts:
Administration, E.S. Leahy
Head Office - Credit, R.B. Douglas
Edmonton General Office, L.R. Bellan
Calgary General Office, W.C. Tough

AGENCIES, BOARDS AND COMMISSIONS

Alberta Municipal Financing Corp.
Sir Frederick W. Haultain Bldg., 8th Flr.
9811-109th St., Edmonton, T5K 0C8

The Alberta Municipal Financing Corporation is a non-profit corporation. It assists municipal jurisdictions within the province to obtain capital funds at the lowest possible cost through access to capital markets which would not be available to them on an independent basis.

Funds are made available to borrowers in exchange for debentures. Loans to municipal and hospital authorities, and loans for school purposes are secured by debentures repayable in equal annual instalments of principal and interest.

The business of the Corporation is administered by a board of directors.

President, A.F. Collins
Vice-President, R.L. Ardiel
Gen. Manager, H.H. Strohbach
Secretary and Asst. Treasurer, E.J. Peacock

INDEPENDENT AGENCIES, BOARDS AND COMMISSIONS

Alberta Alcohol and Drug Abuse Commission

10909 Jasper Ave., 6th Flr.
Edmonton, T5J 3M9
General Inquiries: (403) 427-7301

The Alberta Alcohol and Drug Abuse Commission (AADAC) is responsible for providing the citizens of Alberta with treatment and education services related to the use of alcohol and other drugs. Information, education, counselling, detoxification, and treatment programs are delivered through a network of offices and institutions located throughout the province.

The Commission also provides funding to community-sponsored programs such as detox centres, halfway houses, in-patient treatment, counselling services, and educational programs.

The agency is directed by a citizen's board and a chairman from within the legislature who is appointed by the government.

Minister responsible,
The Hon. Nancy J. Betkowski
Chairman, S. Nelson
CEO, L. Blumenthal
Program Services
Exec. Director, Brian Kearns
Policy and Program Analysis
Director, Dr. David Hewitt
Policy Analysis
Manager, Edward Sawka
Program Analysis Manager, Art Dyer
Institutions and Funded Agencies Division
Director, Wayne Bazant
Human Resources Division
Director, George Milne
Training and Professional Development
Manager, Tom Wispinski
Finance and Administration Division
Director, Howard Faulkner
Facilities Officer, Maas Van de Vliert
Provincial Programs Division
Director, George Claxton
Communications Manager, Louise Morose
Inter-Agency Programs
Manager, Martin Parsons
Librarian, Bette Reimer
Program Resources Manager, Keith Walls
Production and Distribution
Manager, Bill Bissett
Northern Services Division
2204-10320-99th St., Grande Prairie, T8V 6J4
Director, Bob Hubbard
Central Services Division
10109-106th St., 8th Flr., Edmonton, T5J 3L7
Director, Carolyn Nutter
Southern Services Division
1177-11th Ave. S.W., 3rd Flr., Calgary, T2R 0G5
Director, Dennis Jones

The Alberta Educational Communications Corp. (ACCESS NETWORK)

16930-114th Ave., Edmonton, T5M 3S2
General Inquiries: (403) 451-7272
Fax: (403) 452-7233; Telex: 037-3948

ACCESS NETWORK is the registered trade name of The Alberta Educational Communications Corporation. The Corporation was established Oct. 17, 1973 to consolidate and upgrade a variety of educational media services developing at that time within the province.

Although a large portion of its funds is provided by the Government of Alberta, ACCESS NETWORK is an independent statutory corporation responsible to the Alberta Minister of Technology, Research and Telecommunications.

ACCESS NETWORK acquires, develops, produces, and distributes television and radio programs, microcomputer courseware, multi-media kits, and related printed support materials for educational purposes. ACCESS NETWORK CKUA AM-FM broadcasts through a province-wide AM and FM network. ACCESS NETWORK productions, intended primarily for use in Alberta, are now available for national and international distribution.

ACCESS NETWORK operates from its headquarters in Edmonton as well as program production and distribution centres in Edmonton and Calgary. It is one of the largest employers of writers, performers, musicians, and other freelance creative artists in Alberta.

Minister responsible,
The Hon. Leslie G. Young
Note: The Hon. Leslie G. Young was defeated in the recent general election. A replacement had not yet been named as of date of publication.
Chairman, Jim Woronuik
President and CEO, Peter L. Senchuk
Gen. Manager, Television, Malcolm Knox
Gen. Manager, Educational Technology and Administration, Dr. J. Kawashima
Corporate Affairs and Legal Services
Director, Linda Sherwood
Planning, Marketing and Program Research
Director, Dr. M. Plumb
Adult Formal Learning
Director, Dr. C. Shobe
Informal Learning
Director, Jean Campbell
Corporate Controller, David Muylle
ACCESS NETWORK—Calgary
295 Midpark Way S.E., Calgary, T2X 2A8
General Inquiries: (403) 256-1100
Fax: (403) 256-6837; Telex: 03-824867
Media Resources/Dubbing Centre and Calgary Administration
Director, G. Smith
Revenue Development
Director, Pamela Shanks

ACCESS NETWORK—CKUA AM/FM
General Inquiries: (403) 428-7595
Fax: (403) 428-7628
10526 Jasper Ave., Edmonton, T5J 1Z7
Gen. Manager, Don Thomas
News Manager, Ian Gray

Alberta Public Safety Services

10320-146th St., Edmonton, T5N 3A2
General Inquiry: (403) 427-2772

Alberta Public Safety Services is an agency that promotes public safety in Alberta and is responsible for two provincial programs. It prepares for, and responds to, emergencies and disasters, and controls the transportation of dangerous goods in the province.

The agency guides and assists municipalities in developing local emergency plans; and provides training courses, seminars, and exercises on subjects of emergency preparedness and operations. It disseminates information on matters of civil emergencies and public safety. During the course of an emergency, it responds to the situation by directing and co-ordinating all activities needed to deal with the event. And, it administers provincial disaster assistance programs.

APSS guides and assists industries and municipalities in the interpretation and application of dangerous goods control legislation and regulations. It develops and delivers dangerous goods training programs and administers an inspection and enforcement program that applies to the transportation and the handling of dangerous goods on Alberta roads.

Minister responsible,
The Hon. Marvin E. Moore
Note: The Hon. Marvin E. Moore did not run in the recent general election. A replacement had not yet been named as of date of publication.
Man. Director, I.D.M. Egener
Administration Division
Director, M. Kennedy
Personnel Division Director, R. Skwarek
Finance Division Director, G. Rezansoff
Public Affairs Group
Communications Director, G. Blundell

DISASTER SERVICES DIVISION
Exec. Director, S.R. Langman
Plans and Operations Branch
Director, K. Morris
Field Services Branch
Director, R.A. Willhauk
Disaster Social Services Branch
Branch Head, R. van Goethem
Disaster Health Services Branch
Director, J. Robinson
Disaster Assistance Branch
Director, T.A. Shephard
DANGEROUS GOODS CONTROL DIVISION
Exec. Director, R. Wolsey

Program Operations Director, S. Hammond
Facilities
Chief Inspector, R. Henderson
On-Highways
Chief Inspector, W.W. Smith
Compliance Centre Director, J. Harpin
Regulatory Standards and Approvals
Director, I. Zaharko
Training Division
10420-157th St., Edmonton, T5P 2V5
Director, S.K. Bricker

Alberta Research Council

250 Karl Clark Rd.
Box 8330, Stn. F, Edmonton, T6H 5X2
Digital Bldg., 3rd Flr.
6815-8th St. N.E., Calgary, T2E 1H1

The Alberta Research Council is a Crown corporation dedicated to actively promoting responsible economic development in the province of Alberta through a broad range of research in science and technology. Over 500 employees, including professional scientists and engineers, work in Edmonton, Calgary, Red Deer, Nisku, Devon, and Lethbridge. The annual budget is approximately $40 million.

The Alberta Research Council, founded in 1921, is the oldest and largest provincial research organization in Canada, and is an international leader in energy resources research. The major research programs include fundamental and engineering research of the in-situ recovery of bitumen from oil sands deposits; conversion of coal to liquid fuels; industrial technologies; natural resources research in geology, terrain sciences, and resource technologies; and biotechnology.

President, Dr. C.W. Bowman
Corporate Secretary and Director of
Public Relations, D.M. Hollands

DEVELOPMENT AND PLANNING
Vice-President, Dr. D.J. Currie
ENERGY AND BIOTECHNOLOGY
Vice-President, Dr. B.L. Barge
Coal and Hydrocarbon Processing
Head, Dr. A. Hardin
Oil Sands and Hydrocarbon Recovery
Head, Dr. M.P. du Plessis
Biotechnology Head, Dr. D. Cox

NATURAL RESOURCES
Vice-President, Dr. R.J. Fessenden
Geological Survey Head, Dr. J. Boon
Terrain Sciences Head, Dr. S.R. Moran
Resource Technologies Department
Head, Dr. Marianne English
Forestry Research
Head, P.C. Williams
INDUSTRIAL TECHNOLOGIES DIVISION
Vice-President, Dr. J.G. Douglas

Advanced Technologies
Head, Dr. E.J. Chang
Electronics Test Centre
Gen. Manager, Brian Young
Joint Research Ventures
Manager, R. Hipkin
Materials and Testing
Head, Dr. T. Heidrick

OPERATIONS
Vice-President, Dr. R. Green
Information Services
Director, Mrs. S.M. Gee
Administrative Services
Director, C. Cameron
Computing Director, W.J. Neilson
Financial Services Director, M. Legg
Human Resources Director, D.M. Peckham

Alberta Women's Secretariat

Kensington Place, 8th Flr.
10011-109th St., Edmonton, T5J 3S8

The Alberta Women's Secretariat is a central co-ordinating structure of the government of Alberta which provides a focal point for identifying government policies, programs, and legislation which have an impact on women.

Minister responsible for Women's Issues,
The Hon. Elaine McCoy
104 Legislature Bldg., Edmonton, T5K 2B6
Exec. Director, Pat DeZutter

Personnel Administration Office

Kensington Place, 7th Flr.
10011-109th St., Edmonton, T5J 3S8
Information: (403) 427-2750

The Personnel Administration Office was established in 1959 under the *Public Service Act*. The central personnel agency of the Alberta government, it is responsible for the development and administration of a comprehensive, Service-wide personnel program which is implemented through the six divisions of PAO — Administrative Services, Departmental Services, Employee Relations, Management Services, Organization Development, and Special Projects.

Principal functions include negotiation and administration of collective agreements; recruitment and position classification systems for bargaining unit employees and managerial personnel; design and conducting of career development programs for employees; and administration of a comprehensive employee benefits program.

Responsibility for the implementation and management of all personnel policies and programs rests with the Public Service Commissioner. Reporting to the Minister responsible for Personnel Administration, the Public Service Commissioner provides advice to the government on personnel policy and legislation and provides advice and assistance to departmental officials on personnel matters.

Minister responsible, The Hon. Rick Orman
420 Legislature Bldg., Edmonton, T5K 2B6
Public Service Commissioner, J.E. Dixon
Employee Relations Division
Exec. Director, L.A. Giffin
Classification and Staffing
Policy and Consulting Division
Exec. Director, R.A. Elliott
Staff Development and Occupational
Health Division
Exec. Director, J. Jossa
Management Programs Division
Exec. Director, R. Symons
Personnel Management Improvement Service
Exec. Director, B. Black
Systems and Planning Support Division
Director, R.C. Carson
Southern Alberta Region
Calgary Regional Office, Rm. 1101
620-7th Ave. S.W., Calgary, T2P 0Y8
Director, V.L. Tweed

Public Affairs Bureau

44 Capital Blvd., 2nd Flr.
10044-108th St., Edmonton, T5J 3S7

The Public Affairs Bureau works with the Communications Branch in all departments of the Alberta government, providing a wide range of public relations and communications services. These include:

- a media training program for departmental personnel;
- assistance in the preparation of advertising materials, print materials, audio-visual presentations, and displays through the provision of staff, equipment, and expertise;
- the maintenance of a list of freelance communications specialists;
- R.I.T.E., a telephone service providing information from the government to provincial employees and to Alberta residents;
- a wire service — Alberta Communications Network — which sends news releases province-wide; and
- a newspaper clipping service.

In addition, the Bureau indexes and catalogues all Alberta Government publications and operates two bookstores for their sale. For visitors to the province, the Bureau offers hospitality grants to charitable organizations hosting delegates at an international, national, or regional event in Alberta; and it provides scheduling and other assistance to visiting journalists and to those missions which are not already served by another department.

Minister responsible, The Hon. David Russell
Note: The Hon. David Russell did not run in the recent general election. A replacement had not yet been named as of date of publication.

323 Legislature Bldg., Edmonton, T5K 2B6
Man. Director, M. Bateman
Administration Director, R. DeGagne
Human Resources Director, J. McDonald

PUBLIC AFFAIRS
Exec. Director, B. Deters
Advertising Director, J. Edmunds
Visits and Hospitality
Director, L. Salloum

COMMUNICATIONS SERVICES
Exec. Director, D. Steiner
A/V and Exhibit Services
Director, M. Spak
Creative Services Director, A. Re
Print Graphic Services
Director, R. Grant
Regional Information Telephone Enquiries
Director, J. MacTavish
Visitor Services Manager, M. Gibson
Publication Services
Manager, A. Daniel

Workers' Compensation Board

9912-107th St., Box 2415, Edmonton, T5J 2S5
General Inquiries: (403) 427-1100

The Workers' Compensation Board was established by the Alberta government in 1918 as a Crown board to administer the *Workmen's Compensation Act,* subsequently changed in 1974 to the *Workers' Compensation Act.* The Board is responsible to the Minister responsible for Occupational Health and Safety who recommends appointments to the Board to the Lieutenant-Governor in Council.

The Board's primary function is to establish liability for compensation to workers injured while working in an industry coming under the terms of the Act.

Medical and vocational rehabilitation services are also provided under comprehensive programs, and a system of pensions and other benefits is administered in cases of permanent disability or, in the case of a fatality, for the support of dependants.

Minister responsible, The Hon. Dr. Ian Reid
Note: The Hon. Dr. Ian Reid was defeated in the recent general election. A replacement had not yet been named as of date of publication.
Chairman, Kenneth C. Pals
Vice-Chairman, Morris E. Bahry
Secretary to the Board, John E. Hillary

REGIONAL OFFICES:
Calgary Office
132-16th Ave. N.E., Calgary, T2E 1J5
Grande Prairie Office
10022-102nd Ave., Grande Prairie, T8V 0Z7
Lethbridge Office
212 S. 13th St., Lethbridge, T1J 2V4
Medicine Hat Office
204 Chinook Place, 623-4th St. S.E.
Medicine Hat, T1A 0L1
Red Deer Office
208 Centre 5010 Bldg.
5010-43rd St., Red Deer, T4N 6H2

JUDICIARY AND JUDICIAL OFFICERS

Court of Appeal of Alberta

Court House, 530-7th Ave. S.W.
Calgary, T2P 0Y3
General Inquiries: (403) 297-2206

Chief Justice: The Hon. J.H. Laycraft

Justices:
The Hon. Mr. Justice J.D. Bracco
The Hon. Mr. Justice A.M. Harradence
The Hon. Madam Justice M. Hetherington
The Hon. Mr. Justice R.P. Kerans
The Hon. Mr. Justice D.C. Prowse

Law Courts Bldg.
1A Sir Winston Churchill Sq.
Edmonton, T5J 0R2
General Inquiries: (403) 422-2416

The Hon. Mr. Justice R.P. Belzil*
The Hon. Mr. Justice J.E. Coté
The Hon. Mr. Justice R.P. Foisy
The Hon. Mr. Justice W.J. Haddad*
The Hon. Mr. Justice H.L. Irving
The Hon. Mr. Justice S.S. Lieberman*
The Hon. Mr. Justice J.W. McClung
The Hon. Mr. Justice W.A. Stevenson
The Hon. Mr. Justice J.J. Stratton

Court of Queen's Bench

Court House, 611-4th St. S.W.
Calgary, T2P 1T5
General Inquiries: (403) 297-7211

Chief Justice: The Hon. Wm. K. Moore

Justices:
The Hon. Mr. Justice W.R. Brennan
The Hon. Mr. Justice P. Chrumka
The Hon. Madam Justice C.M. Conrad
The Hon. Mr. Justice R.V. Deyell
The Hon. Mr. Justice R.A. Dixon
The Hon. Mr. Justice W.G.N. Egbert
The Hon. Mr. Justice G.R. Forsyth
The Hon. Mr. Justice E.A. Hutchinson
The Hon. Mr. Justice J.J. Kryczka
The Hon. Mr. Justice M.E. Lomas
The Hon. Mr. Justice A.M. Lutz
The Hon. Mr. Justice J.L. MacPherson
The Hon. Mr. Justice D.B. Mason
The Hon. Mr. Justice R.T.G. McBain
The Hon. Mr. Justice D.H. Medhurst
The Hon. Mr. Justice R.A.F. Montgomery
The Hon. Mr. Justice V.P. Moshansky

The Hon. Mr. Justice W.E. O'Leary
The Hon. Mr. Justice H.S. Patterson*
The Hon. Mr. Justice P.C.G. Power
The Hon. Mr. Justice H.S. Prowse
The Hon. Mr. Justice F.H. Quigley
The Hon. Mr. Justice H.S. Rowbotham*
The Hon. Mr. Justice M.E. Shannon
The Hon. Mr. Justice A.B. Sulatycky
The Hon. Mr. Justice C.G. Virtue
The Hon. Mr. Justice J.H. Waite

Law Courts Bldg.
1A Sir Winston Churchill Sq.
Edmonton, T5J 0R2
General Inquiries: (403) 422-2437

Associate Chief Justice: The Hon. T.H. Miller

Justices:
The Hon. Mr. Justice J.A. Agrios
The Hon. Mr. Justice A. Andrekson
The Hon. Mr. Justice R.L. Berger
The Hon. Mr. Justice J.C. Cavanagh*
The Hon. Mr. Justice R.A. Cawsey
The Hon. Mr. Justice A.T. Cooke
The Hon. Mr. Justice A.W. Crossley
The Hon. Mr. Justice J.B. Dea
The Hon. Mr. Justice J.B. Feehan
The Hon. Madam Justice N.L. Foster
The Hon. Mr. Justice T.W. Gallant
The Hon. Mr. Justice W.J. Girgulis
The Hon. Mr. Justice J.M. Hope
The Hon. Mr. Justice S.V. Legg*
The Hon. Mr. Justice E.P. MacCallum
The Hon. Mr. Justice E.A. Marshall
The Hon. Mr. Justice D.R. Matheson
The Hon. Mr. Justice D.C. McDonald
The Hon. Madam Justice E.A. McFadyen
The Hon. Mr. Justice A.T. Murray
The Hon. Mr. Justice M.B. O'Byrne
The Hon. Madam Justice E.I. Picard
The Hon. Mr. Justice Y. Roslak
The Hon. Mr. Justice W.R. Sinclair*
The Hon. Mr. Justice V.W.M. Smith
The Hon. Madam Justice M.J. Trussler
The Hon. Madam Justice J. Veit
The Hon. Mr. Justice A.H.J. Wachowich

Court House, 320 S. 4th St.
Lethbridge, T1J 1Z8
The Hon. Mr. Justice L.D. MacLean
The Hon. Mr. Justice C.G. Yanosik

Court House, 4909-48th St.
Red Deer, T4N 3T5
The Hon. Mr. Justice J.K. Holmes
The Hon. Mr. Justice J.H. MacKenzie

* Supernumerary

Provincial Courts

Law Courts Bldg., 6th Flr.
1A Sir Winston Churchill Sq.
Edmonton, T5J 0R2
General Inquiries: (403) 422-2200

Chief Judge: The Hon. C.A. Kosowan
F.T. Byrne*, J.C. Gorman*

CALGARY
Provincial Courts Bldg.
323-6th Ave. S.E., T2G 4V1
Asst. Chief Judge: H.G. Oliver
Judges: E.P. Adolphe, G.G. Cioni, E.L. Collins,
A.P. Demong, R.S. Dinkel, W.J. Harvie,
B.N. Laven, A.W. Ludwig, D.M. McDonald,
T.B. McMeekin, J.J. O'Connor, W.R. Pepler,
J.D. Reilly, G.R. Rennie, J.M. Robbins,
B.C. Stevenson, W.A. Troughton

CAMROSE
Courthouse, 5210-49th Ave., T4V 3Y2
Judge: J.A. Murray

CANMORE
Provincial Bldg., 500 Access Rd., T0L 0M0
Judge: A.W. Aunger

DRUMHELLER
Court House, T0J 0Y0
Judge: G.W. Clozza

EDMONTON
Law Courts Bldg.
1A Sir Winston Churchill Sq., T5J 0R2

Asst. Chief Judge, Edmonton Region: C.H. Rolf
Judges: D.C. Abbott, G.E. Beaudry,
A.P. Blakey, P.R. Broda, J. Campbell,
H.R. Chisholm, A.G. Chrumka, K.L. Crockett,
J.H. Day, J. Dimos, S.A. Friedman, R.E. Hyde,
L.L. Jones, P.G.C. Ketchum, J.Z. Koshuta,
P.C.C. Marshall, W.F. McLean, K.J. Plomp,
J.B. Ritchie, D. Saks, E.D. Stack,
E.R. Wachowich, D.R. Wong

Asst. Chief Judge, Edmonton Rural: C.L. Liden
Judges: P.P. Ayotte, R.W. Bradley, K.A. Cush,
R.L. Dzenick, J.E. Enright, B.H. Fraser,
M.W. Hopkins, N.A.F. Mackie, J. Maher,
M.F. McInerney, M.H. Porter, A. Shamchuk,
R.B. Spevakow, R.L. Tibbitt, M.G. Tomyn

FORT MACLEOD
Court House, Box 1360, T0L 0Z0
Judge: L.B. Levine

FORT McMURRAY
Court House, 9700 Franklin Ave., T9H 2K5
Judges: M. Horrocks, J.C. Spence

FORT SASKATCHEWAN
Court House, 10504-100th Ave., T8L 3S9
Judges: K.A. Cush, N.A.F. Mackie

GRANDE PRAIRIE
Court House, 10260-99th St., T8V 6J4
Asst. Chief Judge, Northern Region:
D.E. Patterson
Judges: J.N.G. Mitchell, K.S. Staples

HIGH PRAIRIE
Provincial Bldg., T0G 1E0
Judge: R.P. Smith

HINTON
Court House, Box 878, T0E 1B0
Judge: M.H. Porter

LEDUC
Leduc Court, 4612-50th St., T9E 2Y2
Judge: M.G. Tomyn

LETHBRIDGE
Court House, 320 S. 4th St., T1J 1Z8
Asst. Chief Judge, Southern Region:
A.G. Lynch-Staunton
Judges: F.W. Coward, G.R. DeBow,
L.B. Hogan, M. Hoyt, R.A. Jacobson,
J.A. Wood

MEDICINE HAT
1119 Kingsway S.E., T1A 2Y1
Judges: D. Brand, J.P. Wambolt

PEACE RIVER
Court House, T0H 2X0
Judges: P.M. Dube, E.D. Riemer

RED DEER
Court House, 4909-48th Ave., T4N 3T5
Asst. Chief Judge, Central Region: D.L. Crowe
Judges: P.L. Adilman, H.B. Casson,
N.P. Lawrence, D.P. MacNaughton,
T.G. Schollie

ST. ALBERT
3 St. Anne St., T8N 2E8
Judges: R.W. Bradley, R.B. Spevakow

ST. PAUL
Provincial Bldg., Box 1900, T0A 3A0
Judge: B.H. Fraser, M.W. Hopkins

SHERWOOD PARK
190 Chippewa Rd., T8A 4H5
Judge: J. Maher, A. Shamchuk

STONY PLAIN
Court House, 4711-44th Ave., T0E 2G0
Judges: P.P. Ayotte, J.E. Enright,
M.F. McInerney

VERMILION
Provincial Bldg., Box 149, T0B 4M0
Judge: R.L. Tibbitt

WETASKIWIN
Law Courts Bldg., 4605-51st St., T9A 1K7
Judge: N.A. Rolf

Court Officials

REGIONAL MANAGERS
Court House
611-4th St. S.W., Calgary, T2P 1T5
James McLaughlin (Calgary Region)

Law Courts Bldg., 1A Sir Winston Churchill Sq.
Edmonton, T5J 0R2
David Huff (Edmonton Region)

Court House, 3 St. Anne St.
St. Albert, T8N 2E8
John Bachinski (Rural Region)

CALGARY
Court House, 611-4th St. S.W., T2P 1T5
Court of Queen's Bench Manager: E. Kisel

Court of Appeal Bldg.
530-7th Ave. S.W., T2P 0Y3
Court of Appeal Administrator: J. Ford

Court House Annex, 603-6th Ave. S.W.
Box 1830, Stn. M, T2P 2L8
Small Claims Crt. Administrator: N. Philip

Provincial Court Bldg.
323-6th Ave. S.E., T2G 4V1
Provincial Crt. Manager (Criminal): L. Miles

Rocky Mountain Plaza, Rm. 1402
230-7th Ave. S.E., T2G 0H9
Provincial Crt. Manager (Civil): D.L. Paul

J.J. Bowlen Bldg.
620-7th Ave. S.W., T2P 0Y8
Family and Youth Crt. Manager: L. Olson

CAMROSE
Court House, 5210-49th Ave., T4V 3Y2
Provincial Crt. Administrator: D. Kirwer

CANMORE
Provincial Bldg., 800 Access Rd.
Box 17000, T0L 0M0
Provincial Crt. Administrator: E. Campbell

DRUMHELLER
Court House, 511 W. 3rd Ave., T0J 0Y0
Court of Queen's Bench Administrator:
  D. Blake
Provincial Crt. Administrator: D. Rogers

EDMONTON
Law Courts Bldg.
1A Sir Winston Churchill Sq., T5J 0R2
Court of Queen's Bench Manager:
  E.W. Klatchuk
Court of Appeal Administrator: P. Sydorka
Provincial Crt. Manager (Criminal): R. Babyn
Provincial Crt. Manager (Civil): E. Stoik
Small Claims Crt. Administrator: L.H. Obnoski
Family and Youth Crt. Manager: B.W. Thomson

FORT MACLEOD
Court House, Box 1360, T0L 0Z0
District Manager: R. Aoki
Court of Queen's Bench Administrator:
  C. Baker
Provincial Crt. Administrator: C. Dash

FORT McMURRAY
Court House, 9700 Franklin Ave., T9H 4W3
District Manager: J. Easton
Court of Queen's Bench Administrator:
  B. Patterson
Provincial Crt. Administrator: L. Magas

FORT SASKATCHEWAN
Court House, 10504-100th Ave., T8L 3S9
Provincial Crt. Administrator: W. Komarnisky

GRANDE PRAIRIE
Court House, 10260-99th St., T8V 6J4
A/District Manager: I. Callioux
Court of Queen's Bench Administrator:
  P. Webber
Provincial Crt. Administrator: J. Palmu
Family and Youth Crt. Administrator:
  D. Sorensen

HIGH LEVEL
Provincial Court House, 9812-101st St.
Box 1560, T0H 1Z0
Provincial Crt. Administration: M.I. Weir

HIGH PRAIRIE
Court House, 4911-53rd Ave., Box 1470
Provincial Crt. Administrator: W. Smith

HINTON
Court House, 237 Jasper St.
West & Pembina Ave., Box 878, T0E 1B0
Provincial Crt. Administrator: L. Rusk

LEDUC
Court House, 4612-50th St.
Box 430, T9E 2Y2
Provincial Crt. Administrator: U. Owre

LETHBRIDGE
Court House, 320 S. 4th St., T1J 1Z8
District Manager: R. Aoki
Court of Queen's Bench Administrator:
  C. Robertson
Provincial Crt. Administrator: R. Aoki
Family & Youth Crt. Administrator: M. Harvie

MEDICINE HAT
Court House, 460-1st St. S.E.
Box 220, T1A 0A8
District Manager: C. Finan
Court of Queen's Bench Administrator: J. Hay
Provincial Crt. Administrator: M.F. Girling
Family & Youth Crt. Administrator: T. Jackie

PEACE RIVER
Court House, Bag 900-34, T0H 2X0
A/District Manager: I. Callioux
Court of Queen's Bench Administrator:
  W. Martz
Provincial Crt. Administrator: I. Callioux

RED DEER
Court House, 4909-48th Ave., T4N 3T5
District Manager: O.D. Lowe
Court of Queen's Bench Administrator:
  J. Doyle

Provincial Crt. Administrator: J. Moger
Family & Youth Crt. Administrator: L. Varty

ST. ALBERT
Court House, 3 St. Anne St., T8N 2E8
Provincial Crt. Administrator: S. Boisvert

ST. PAUL
Provincial Bldg., Box 1900, T0A 3A0
Provincial Crt. Administrator: P. Laramee

SHERWOOD PARK
Court House, 190 Chippewa Rd., T8A 4H5
Provincial Crt. Administrator: P. Grabowski

STONY PLAIN
Court House, 4711-44th Ave., T0E 2G0
Provincial Crt. Administrator: M. McCulloch

VEGREVILLE
Court House, 4904-50th St., T0B 4L0
District Manager: K. Kereliuk
Court of Queen's Bench Administrator:
  W. Brazeau

Provincial Bldg., 4809-50th St.
Box 1812, T0B 4L0
Provincial Crt. Administrator: A. Soldan

VERMILION
Provincial Bldg., 4701-52nd St.
Box 149, T0B 4M0
Provincial Crt. Administrator: A.I. Stone

WETASKIWIN
Law Courts Bldg., 4605-51st St., T9A 1K7
District Manager: E.G. Towers
Court of Queen's Bench Administrator:
  Vacant
Provincial Crt. Administrator: F. Beatty

Family and Youth Courts

CALGARY
J.J. Bowlen Bldg.
620-7th Ave. S.W., T2P 0Y8
Senior Judge: H.A. Allard
Judges: W.J. Anderson, J. Brownlee,
  L.T.L. Cooke-Stanhope, D.F. Fitch,
  K.E. Helmer, H.F. Landerkin, N.P. Leveque

EDMONTON
Law Courts Bldg., 6th Flr.
1A Sir Winston Churchill Sq., T5J 0R2
Asst. Chief Judge: W.G.W. White
Judges: J.G. Bradburn, A.P. Catonio,
  E.H. Gerhart, D.M.M. Hansen,
  J.P. Jorgensen, A.H. Russell, L.S. Witten

GRANDE PRAIRIE
Court House, 10260-99th St., T8V 6J4
Judges: D.E. Patterson, K.S. Staples

MEDICINE HAT
Court House, Box 729, T1A 7G6
Judge: D. Brand

RED DEER
306 Professional Bldg., Box 5002, T4N 1X5
Judge: N.P. Lawrence

Small Claims Courts

CALGARY
Court House, 603-6th Ave. S.W.
Box 1830, Stn. M, T2P 0T3
Asst. Chief Judge: J.S. Woods
Judges: I.A. Blackstone, W.C. Kerr,
  D.J. Tompkins

EDMONTON
Law Courts Bldg.
1A Sir Winston Churchill Sq., T5J 0R2
Judges: J. Allford, M.M. Donnelly,
  E.G. Hughson, H.F. Wilson

Property Registration Branch

(includes Land Titles Offices and Personal
Property Registry)

10365-97th St., Edmonton, T5J 3W7
Land Titles Offices: (403) 427-2742
Personal Property Registry: (403) 427-2069

Director of Property Registration
  (Inspector of Land Titles): K.B. Payne
Asst. Director of Property Registration
  (Asst. Inspector of Land Titles): G.B.N. Ho
LAND REGISTRATION DISTRICTS
North Alberta L.R.D.
10365-97th St., Edmonton, T5J 3W7
Deputy Registrar: W.E. Campion

South Alberta L.R.D.
620-7th Ave. S.W., Calgary, T2P 0Y8
Registrar: P. Hartman

PERSONAL PROPERTY REGISTRY
(includes Central and Vehicle Registries)
5th Flr., 10365-97th St., Edmonton, T5J 3W7
A/Registrar: R. Shariff
Deputy Registrar, Searches: D.L. Pruden
Deputy Registrar, Registrations: M.L. Alano

Calgary Office:
620-7th Ave. S.W., Calgary, T2P 0Y8
Deputy Registrar: J. Bleviss

Coal, Metallic Minerals/Quarriable Minerals/Placer Mineral Rights/Salt Rights

Contact:
Eugene Saldanha, Manager
Mineral Agreements
Alberta Dept. of Energy
South Tower, 11th Flr., Petroleum Plaza
9915-108th St., Edmonton, T5K 2C9
General Inquiries: (403) 427-8167

This map is based on information taken from map MCR 4032. © Her Majesty in Right of Canada with permission of Energy, Mines and Resources.

PROVINCE OF BRITISH COLUMBIA

Pacific Dogwood
(Cornuus nuttallii)

Entered Confederation: July 20, 1871
Capital: Victoria
Motto: Splendor Sine Occasu
(Splendour without diminishment)
Flower: Pacific dogwood
Area: 947,800 km^2
  percentage of Canada's total area: 9.5
  LAND: 929,730 km^2
  FRESHWATER: 18,070 km^2
Elevation:
  HIGHEST POINT: Fairweather Mt. (4,663 m)
  LOWEST POINT: coastal area at sea level
Population (1986 Census): 2,889,207

five-year change: +5.1%
per square kilometre: 3.2
percentage of Canada's total population: 11.4
  URBAN: 79%
  RURAL: 21%
Gross domestic product, 1987: $61.6 billion
Government Finance:
  REVENUE, 1988/89 est.: $11.4 billion
  EXPENDITURE, 1988/89 est.: $11.8 billion
  DEBT PER CAPITA (March 1987): $3,446
Personal income per capita, 1986: $16,896
Unemployment rate, 1988
(annual average): 10.3%

THE LAND

Most of the province contains mountains and plateaux. The Rockies in the east and the Coast Mountains in the west traverse the province from south to north. In the south are a number of elongated and relatively narrow valleys, such as the Okanagan Valley, in which agriculture thrives.

British Columbia can be divided into three major climatic regions: the Coast, Interior, and Northeast. This reflects basic landform patterns and emphasizes the importance of topographic features such as the Coast and Rocky Mountains as climatic divides.

The Coast region, on the windward side of the Coast Mountains, is influenced by maritime conditions ensuring plentiful precipitation and moderate temperatures. The Interior, between the Coast and Rocky Mountains, is affected by continental and modified maritime conditions resulting in mixtures of climatic characteristics, greater extremes of temperature and generally lower rainfall. The Northeast, on the lee side of the Rocky Mountains, is dominated by continental influences and has a climate similar to that of northern Alberta.

THE PEOPLE

On June 3, 1986, British Columbia's population was estimated to be 2,889,207. It is heavily concentrated in the metropolitan areas of Vancouver and Victoria. Together they comprise 56.6 per cent of the province's total population. The population of Metropolitan Vancouver rose from 1,207,600 in 1979 to 1,380,725 in 1986, an increase of 14.3 per cent. The Victoria metropolitan area population increased from 223,500 in 1979 to 255,545 in 1986, an increase of 14.3 per cent. Major cities outside the metropolitan areas — with the 1986 Census population figure in brackets — include: Prince George (67,621); Kamloops (61,773); Kelowna (61,213); and Nanaimo (49,029).

A large part of the population is made up of young persons, with an estimated 35.7 per cent under age 25 in 1986.

THE ECONOMY

Forestry. British Columbia has 43.3 million hectares of forest land, which covers 46 per cent of its land area. Of this forest cover, 8,241 million m^3 have mature forest with a possible allowable annual cut of over 75 million m^3.

The province is preeminent in softwood timber resources, holding 50 per cent of the total amount in Canada. It also produces almost 70 per cent of Canada's sawtimber. British Columbia's standing timber represents approximately 20 per cent of the North American inventory.

The forest lands in B.C. support 8 billion m^3 of mature timber, 95 per cent of which is softwood. The principal species, in descending order by volume, are: hemlock, spruce, balsam, lodgepole pine, red cedar, and Douglas fir.

The total cut from British Columbia's forests during 1987 was 90.6 million m^3. The province produced 61 per cent of all softwood lumber manufactured in Canada, 82 per cent of the softwood plywood, 29 per cent of the pulp, and 17 per cent of the paper.

Mining and Minerals. A considerable part of British Columbia lies within the Canadian Cordillera, a region known for the discovery of a wide variety of minerals. In 1987, mineral and petroleum production value was estimated at $3.4 billion.

Copper, with an estimated value of $744.7 million, was the most important metal by value in 1987, followed by gold at $231.6 million, zinc at $98.1 million, and silver at $125.7 million.

Metallurgical coal is currently being mined and exported, primarily to Japan, from four major properties in the East Kootenay-Crowsnest coalfield and two properties in the Peace River coalfield. Thermal coal is also mined in these regions.

Tourism and recreation. Tourist expenditure in British Columbia is estimated at approximately $3.2 billion for 1986.

More than 15 million persons visited or toured B.C. in 1986. Non-resident tourists spent $1.9 billion in B.C. and this "export" of services represents a significant contribution to gross provincial product. Sixty-five per cent of the trips in B.C. are by Canadians or B.C. residents. American travellers in 1986 accounted for 4.7 million trips. Offshore residents touring in B.C. have a larger economic impact in relation to their numbers, with expenditures per trip well above average.

Agriculture. British Columbia has limited acreage for tillage because of its mountains. Even so, agriculture ranks fourth in value of production, after forestry, mining, and tourism.

The greatest single livestock industry is dairying. The bulk of milk production comes from the Lower Fraser Valley where the climate is mild and where nearby Greater Vancouver provides the largest market. Dairy farming is also practised on Vancouver Island and in the Okanagan and Creston valleys, but elsewhere, the industry is small, limited by the size of local markets.

Egg production and chicken raising is the next largest source of farm cash income.

Tree-fruit crops are chiefly grown in the Okanagan Valley, the leading apple-producing area of Canada. In addition, quality pears, cherries, peaches, prunes, grapes, and apricots are produced in abundance.

Fishing. Fishing has been important throughout the province's history. Salmon canning began in 1870 on the Fraser River and spread quickly northward. Canning made possible the marketing of the fish harvest in distant places.

The fishing industry has benefited from expenditures on fish hatcheries, spawning channels, fish ladders to facilitate the upstream passage of salmon, and programs to rationalize fish catching effort with the capacity of the resource. Historically, the province's fishing industry has been the most valuable in Canada.

More than 20 species of fish and marine animals indigenous to provincial waters are valued for commercial utilization. Salmon is the single most valuable species, accounting for roughly two thirds of the landed and wholesale values of fisheries products. Principal species are spring (chinook), sockeye, coho, pink, and chum.

Manufacturing. British Columbia's manufacturing industry has been developed largely on a resource base — namely forest products, refined non-ferrous metals, fish products, and processed agricultural products.

Manufactured wood products and the pulp and paper industry accounted for approximately 45.7 per cent of the value of provincial factory shipments in 1986. This domination is expected to continue in the near future, although increased processing of resource products and an expansion in higher technology products is anticipated.

Transportation. Deep-sea international shipping lanes reach out from B.C. to the major ports of the world. Coastal shipping, including specialized freight and passenger steamers, and log-towing vessels comprise an important segment of the transportation picture.

Electric power. Rapid growth of both industry and population within British Columbia has been accompanied by a steady increase in demand for electric power. In the ten-year period from 1974 to 1984, consumption increased by 34 per cent.

Owing to the combination of a wet climate and mountainous terrain, B.C. has an abundance of fresh water. The total hydroelectric power potential is difficult to assess precisely. Current capacity of approximately 11,100 megawatts could be increased over three times by tapping unused water power.

Text provided by B.C. Government Information Services.

GOVERNMENT OF BRITISH COLUMBIA

Seat of Government:
  Parliament Buildings, Victoria, V8V 1X4
Lieutenant-Governor,
  The Hon. David C. Lam
  Government House
  1401 Rockland Ave., Victoria, V8S 1V9

EXECUTIVE COUNCIL

(As of Jan. 1, 1989)
Premier, President of the Executive Council,
  The Hon. William N. Vander Zalm
Minister of Education,
  The Hon. Anthony J. Brummet
Minister of Finance and Corporate Relations,
  The Hon. Melville B. Couvelier
Minister of Energy, Mines and Petroleum Resources,
  The Hon. John Davis
Minister responsible for Crown Lands, Minister of State for Thompson-Okanagan and Kootenay,
  The Hon. Howard Dirks
Minister of Health, Responsible for Seniors,
  The Hon. Peter A. Dueck
Minister of Advanced Education and Job Training, Responsible for Science and Technology,
  The Hon. Stanley Hagen
Minister of Labour and Consumer Services,
  The Hon. Lyall Hanson
Minister responsible for Parks, Minister of State for Vancouver Island-Coast-North Coast,
  The Hon. Dr. Terry Huberts
Minister of International Business and Immigration,
  The Hon. John Jansen
Minister of Municipal Affairs, Recreation and Culture,
  The Hon. Rita M. Johnston
Minister of Government Management Services,
  The Hon. Clifford Michael
Minister of Forests,
  The Hon. David Parker
Solicitor-General,
  The Hon. Angus Ree
Minister of Tourism, Provincial Secretary,
  The Hon. William E. Reid
Minister of Social Services and Housing,
  The Hon. Claude H. Richmond

Minister of Agriculture and Fisheries,
  The Hon. John Savage
Attorney-General,
  The Hon. Stuart (Bud) Smith, Q.C.
Minister responsible for Environment, Minister of State for Cariboo,
  The Hon. W. Bruce Strachan
Minister of Transportation and Highways,
  The Hon. Neil Vant
Minister of Regional Development, Minister of State for Mainland-Southwest,
  The Hon. Elwood Veitch
Minister responsible for Native Affairs, Minister of State for Nechako and Northeast,
  The Hon. Jack Weisgerber

CABINET MANAGEMENT AND CO-ORDINATING COMMITTEES
Planning & Priorities
Chairman, The Hon. William N. Vander Zalm
Treasury Board
Chairman, The Hon. Mel Couvelier
Legislation and Regulations
Chairman, The Hon. Stuart (Bud) Smith

CABINET STANDING POLICY COMMITTEES
Regional Development
Chairman, The Hon. Elwood Veitch
Environment and Land Use
Chairman, The Hon. Bruce Strachan
Social Policy
Chairman, The Hon. Claude Richmond
Native Affairs
Chairman, The Hon. Jack Weisgerber

CABINET SPECIAL COMMITTEES
Cultural Heritage
Chairman, The Hon. William Reid
B.C. Transit
Chairman, The Hon. Rita Johnston

LEGISLATIVE ASSEMBLY

34th Legislative Assembly, 2nd Session
Last election: Oct. 22, 1986
  (Maximum legal duration 5 years)

For further information regarding any aspect of the Government of British Columbia, contact:
Public Affairs Bureau
Ministry of Tourism & Provincial Secretary
Parliament Bldgs., Victoria, V8V 1X4
(604) 387-1337

Total number of seats: 69
Party standings (as of Jan. 1, 1989):
Social Credits: 45
New Democrats: 23
Independent: 1

Salaries, Indemnities and Allowances

MEMBERS: $28,324 Member's annual allowance, plus $14,161 for expenses.
MINISTERS WITH PORTFOLIO: $39,000 salary, plus Member's annual allowance and expenses.
PREMIER: $45,000 salary, plus Member's annual allowance and expenses.
LEADER OF THE OPPOSITION AND SPEAKER OF THE HOUSE: Member's annual allowance and expenses, plus $39,000 special allowance.
DEPUTY SPEAKER: Member's annual allowance and expenses, plus $19,500 special allowance.

Officers

Speaker, The Hon. John Reynolds
Deputy Speaker, F.C. Austin Pelton
Clerk of the Assembly, Ian M. Horne, Q.C.
Sergeant-at-Arms, R.A. Nicol

Members

Constituency	Member and Affiliation
Alberni	Gerard Janssen (NDP)
Atlin	Larry Guno (NDP)
Boundary/ Similkameen*	Bill Barlee (NDP) Ivan Messmer (SC)
Burnaby North	James Barry Jones (NDP)
Burnaby/Edmonds	Dave Mercier (SC)
Burnaby/Willingdon	The Hon. Elwood Veitch (SC)
Cariboo*	Alexander V. Fraser (SC) The Hon. T. Neil Vant (SC)
Central Fraser Valley*	Harry De Jong (SC) The Hon. Peter A. Dueck (SC)
Chilliwack	The Hon. John Jansen (SC)
Columbia River	Duane D. Crandall (SC)
Comox	The Hon. Stanley Hagen (SC)
Coquitlam/Moody	Mark W. Rose (NDP)
Cowichan/Malahat	Graham Bruce (SC)
Delta*	K. Walter Davidson (SC) The Hon. John Savage (SC)
Dewdney*	Austin Pelton (SC) Norman Jacobsen (SC)
Esquimalt/Port Renfrew	Munmohan S. Sihota (NDP)
Kamloops*	The Hon. Claude Richmond (SC) The Hon. Stuart (Bud) Smith (SC)
Kootenay	Kathleen Anne Edwards (NDP)
Langley*	Dan Peterson (SC) Caroline Mary Gran (SC)

Constituency	Member and Affiliation
Mackenzie	Harold Long (SC)
Maillardville/ Coquitlam	John Massey Cashore (NDP)
Nanaimo*	David D. Stupich (NDP) Laurence D. Lovick (NDP)
Nelson/Creston	The Hon. Howard Dirks (SC)
New Westminster	Anita M.J. Hagen (NDP)
North Island	Colin Stuart Gabelmann (NDP)
North Peace River	The Hon. Anthony J. Brummet (SC)
North Vancouver/ Capilano	The Hon. Angus Ree (SC)
North Vancouver/ Seymour	The Hon. Jack Davis (SC)
Oak Bay/Gordon Head	Brian R.D. Smith (SC)
Okanagan North	The Hon. Lyall Hanson (SC)
Okanagan South*	Clifford J. Serwa (SC) Larry Chalmers (SC)
Omineca	Jack J. Kempf (Ind)
Prince George North	Lois Ruth Boone (NDP)
Prince George South	The Hon. Bruce Strachan (SC)
Prince Rupert	Dan Miller (NDP)
Richmond*	Nick Loenen (SC) The Hon. William Vander Zalm (SC)
Rossland/Trail	Christopher D'Arcy (NDP)
Saanich and the Islands*	The Hon. Mel Couvelier (SC) The Hon. Dr. Terry Huberts (SC)
Shuswap/ Revelstoke	The Hon. Cliff Michael (SC)
Skeena	The Hon. Dave Parker (SC)
South Peace River	The Hon. Jack Weisgerber (SC)
Surrey*	The Hon. Rita Johnston (SC) The Hon. William Reid (SC)
Surrey/Guildford/ Whalley	Joan K. Smallwood (NDP)
Vancouver Centre*	Emery O. Barnes (NDP) Michael F. Harcourt (NDP)
Vancouver East*	Glen David Clark (NDP) Robert A. Williams (NDP)
Vancouver South*	C. Stephen Rogers (SC) Russell G. Fraser (SC)
Vancouver/Little Mountain*	Grace McCarthy (SC) Douglas L. Mowat (SC)
Vancouver/Point Grey*	Darlene R. Marzari (NDP) Kim Campbell (SC)
Victoria*	Gordon W. Hanson (NDP) Robin Blencoe (NDP)
West Vancouver/ Howe Sound	John Reynolds (SC)
Yale-Lillooet	James Rabbitt (SC)

Ind — Independent
NDP — New Democrat
SC — Social Credit

* Denotes two-member constituency

Office of the Premier

Parliament Bldgs., Victoria, V8V 1X4

Premier, The Hon. William N. Vander Zalm
Principal Secretary, Vacant
Press Secretary, Ian Jessop

Offices of the Official Opposition

Parliament Bldgs., Victoria, V8V 1X4

Leader of the Official Opposition,
   Michael F. Harcourt, MLA
Exec. Director, Linda Baker

B.C. Legislative Library

Parliament Bldgs., Victoria, V8V 1X4
General Inquiries: (604) 387-6510
Fax: (604) 387-2813

The Legislative Library provides reference services for the Members of the Legislative Assembly, their researchers, the Executive Council, the Officers of the House, Legislative support staffs, and the Press Gallery. Provided there is no conflict with services to these core users, it assists research staffs of the public service and makes its resources available to other individuals who have need of the Library's special collections.

The Legislative Library provides a general reference service based on a collection of approximately 150,000 volumes and extensive government publications and periodical files, including all B.C. newspapers. It maintains an index of the Vancouver and Victoria daily newspapers.

The Legislative Library gives inter-library loan service and provides Cataloguing in Publication (CIP) for B.C. government publications.

Legislative Librarian, Joan A. Barton
Reference Services, Head, Maureen Lawson
Technical Services, Head, Sheila Gann
Government Publications, Head,
   John MacEachern

Office of the Ombudsman

8 Bastion Square, Victoria, V8V 1X4
General Inquiries: (604) 387-5855

On July 1, 1979, the Province of British Columbia appointed its first Ombudsman. It is the ninth province in Canada to have passed Ombudsman legislation.

The *Ombudsman Act* empowers the Ombudsman to receive citizens' complaints about certain provincial government authorities (including ministries of the province) and boards, corporations, and commissions appointed by or responsible to the provincial government. When a complaint is received, the Ombudsman's office will contact the authority and seek an informal resolution. If a resolution is not possible, the Ombudsman's office will investigate the complaint with the aim of uncovering pertinent laws, regulations, policies, facts, and perceptions of all parties involved in the

dispute. The office then makes the results of the investigation known to the authority and to the complainant. If the investigation shows that an authority's action, decision, procedure, or practice was essentially correct, fair, and appropriate, the office explains that finding to both the complainant and the authority, and closes the matter. If the investigation shows fault on the agency's part, or shortcomings in existing procedures or practices, the Ombudsman recommends corrective action to the agency. It is then up to the agency to implement the Ombudsman's recommendations. If the Ombudsman is not satisfied with an authority's response to his recommendations, he may refer the matter to the Cabinet and the Legislative Assembly.

On a daily basis, the Ombudsman's office seeks to rectify injustices or to resolve complaints informally. In the long range, the Ombudsman's task is to question and to seek change to those bureaucratic procedures and practices that repeatedly lead to errors and injustices.

Ombudsman, Stephen Owen
Exec. Director, Brent Parfitt

MINISTRY OF ADVANCED EDUCATION AND JOB TRAINING

Parliament Bldgs., Victoria, V8V 1X4
(except where otherwise indicated)
General Inquiries: (604) 387-3165
Telex: 0497109; FAX: 387-2100

MINISTER'S OFFICE
337 Parliament Bldgs., Victoria V8V 1X4

Minister, The Hon. Stanley B. Hagen

DEPUTY MINISTER'S OFFICE
818 Broughton St., Victoria, V8W 1E4

Dep. Minister, Gary Mullins

PUBLIC AFFAIRS
3rd Flr., 818 Broughton St.
Victoria, V8V 1X4
A/Director, David Reilley
Information Officer, Dawna Desrosier

Universities, Colleges and Institutions

Asst. Dep. Minister, John Watson
POLICY, PLANNING AND LEGISLATION
Director, Dr. Grant Fisher
Legislation Manager, Lisa Harney
Planning Manager, Jim Soles
FUNDING AND ANALYSIS
Director, Shell Harvey
Senior Financial Analyst, Alex Blackwood
Facilities Manager, Jim Parker
Allocations and Data Development
Manager, Vacant
Research and Analysis
Manager, Scott MacInnis

PROGRAMS
Director, Dr. Jack Newberry
Health and Business Manager, Vacant
Arts and Science Program Manager, Vacant
Trades and Technical
Manager, Duncan MacRae
Program Development Manager, Vacant
Distance Education Manager, Vacant
International Education
Manager, Nick Rubidge

Science and Technology
Asst. Dep. Minister, Ron Woodward
Director, Deborah George
TRIUMF/KAON Project
Director, Dr. Craig Greenhill

**Job Training, Apprenticeship and Labour
Market Policy**
Asst. Dep. Minister, Joyce E. Ganong
Job Training Branch
Director, Calvin Shantz
Field Services
Asst. Director, Stan Killeen
Program Service
Manager, Ingrid Fischer

STUDENT SERVICES SECTION
823 Broughton St., Victoria, V8W 1E4
Manager, Mary Browning
Program Manager, Heather Martin
Private Training Institutions
220, 4946 Canada Way, Burnaby, V5G 4J6
Director, Ossie Sylvester
Certification and Standards
Manager, Gregg Biggs
Field Services
A/Manager, Michael Hardman
MINISTRY AREA OFFICES
Vancouver
5th Flr., 805 West Broadway
Vancouver, V5Z 1K1
Supervisor, Gwen Upton
Burnaby
200, 4946 Canada Way, Burnaby, V5G 4J6
Supervisor, Richard Kurcherka
Chilliwack
45904 Victoria Ave., Chilliwack, V2P 2T1
Training Counsellor, Dick Martin
Surrey
104, 96480-128th St., Surrey, V3T 2X9
Supervisor, Gail Wilson
Port Coquitlam
510-2755 Lougheed Hwy.
Port Coquitlam, V3B 5Y9
Supervisor, Rolf Fagerlund
Victoria
838 Fort St., Victoria, V8V 1X4
Supervisor, Bob Enwright
Nanaimo
190 Wallace St., Nanaimo, V9R 5B1
Supervisor, Al Hooson
Campbell River
101, 1180 Ironwood Rd.
Campbell River, V9W 5P7
Training Counsellor, Frank Pavan

Cranbrook
101, 117-10th Ave. S., Cranbrook, V1C 2N1
Supervisor, John Anderson
Kelowna
200-1626 Richter St., Kelowna, V1Y 2M3
A/Supervisor, Ray Smith
Prince George
500 Victoria St., Prince George, V2L 2J9
Supervisor, Richard Little
Vernon
3407-31st Ave., Vernon, V1T 2H6
Training Counsellor, Ed Devlin
Nelson
310 Ward St., Nelson, V1L 5S4
Training Counsellor, Dave Chiz
Kamloops
240, 546 St. Paul St., Kamloops, V2C 5T1
Supervisor, Keith Carson
Williams Lake
540 Borland St., Williams Lake, V2G 1R8
Training Counsellor, Ken Kelly
Dawson Creek
1201-103rd Ave., Dawson Creek, V1G 4J2
Supervisor, Bev Verboven
Terrace
4548 Lakelse Ave., Terrace, V8G 1P8
Supervisor, Patrick Roy

Administration and Support Services Division
3rd Flr., 818 Broughton St., Victoria V8V 1X4
Exec. Director, Jim Crone
Financial Services Branch
Director, Susan Reynolds
Financial Operations and Policy
Senior Manager, Neil Matheson
Financial Analysis and Budgets
Manager, Ian Walpole
Cost-Sharing Programs Manager, Al Hill
Administrative Services Manager, Steve Green
Personnel Services Director, Randy McEwen
Information Systems
Director, Dorothy Drislane
Student Services
823 Broughton St., Victoria, V8W 1E4
Director, Mary Browing
Program Administrator, Linda Dallin

AGENCIES, BOARDS AND COMMISSIONS

Advanced Systems Foundation
302, 3700 Gilmore Way, Burnaby, V5G 4M1
    Canada and B.C. must foster technological
advances in order to enhance economic competitiveness. In response to this need, the B.C.
Advanced Systems Foundation has been established under the Canada/British Columbia
Science and Technology Subagreement. The
Foundation is charged with providing leadership
in promoting basic and applied research through
co-operative efforts among B.C. universities and
industry; in facilitating transfer and exploitation of
the resultant technology; and in enhancing
educational opportunities in the advanced systems fields of computing science, microelectron-

ics, artificial intelligence and robotics.

The Foundation's board of trustees and the executive director, in consultation with the International Scientific Advisory Board, are responsible for establishing and maintaining the Advanced Systems Institute, the operating arm of the Foundation, to ensure the effective participation of the universities and industry and the effective use of available resources. The Institute will ensure that its work reflects both national and provincial priorities relating to advanced systems. Affiliation agreements among the universities and contract agreements between the Institute and government are in place to aid the Institute in meeting its objectives.

Exec. Director, Mike Volker

B.C. Research Council
3650 Wesbrook Mall, Vancouver, V6S 2L2

The British Columbia Research Council is a non-profit, independent society incorporated in 1944 under the *B.C. Societies Act*. B.C. Research is the technical operation of the Council and it conducts cost-accountable research, development and other technical work in the fields of biology, chemistry, engineering, physics, management and related disciplines under contract to sponsors in industry and government, both in Canada and internationally.

B.C. Research offers services through staff in operating divisions of Applied Biology, Industrial Chemistry, Applied Physics and Engineering, Forest Biotechnology, and the Industry Development Group. General areas of capability can be described as product development, process development, systems and operational analysis, research studies, testing and analysis, and industrial development and technology transfer. B.C. Research operates a 16,740 m^2 fully equipped research facility complete with laboratories, office and workshops, an Ocean Engineering Centre, and a substantial pilot plant area.

Exec. Director, Dr. Terry Howard

B.C. Youth Advisory Council
5th Flr., 1483 Douglas St.
Victoria, V8W 3X4

The British Columbia Youth Advisory Council was created in October 1985, to establish a direct link between the government of British Columbia and young people. The mandate of the Council is to represent the views of young people on a range of issues; to organize regional discussions with youth in order to identify common ideas, goals and opportunities; and to provide input into the development of government programs for youth.

Council members are young people, 15 to 24 years of age. The Council, as a group, is representative of young people from various regions, age groups, career interests and ethnic backgrounds in the province. There is a chairperson, vice-chairperson and 10 to 16 members.

Administrator, Rick Pepper

Discovery Foundation/Enterprises
3700 Gilmore Way, Burnaby, V5G 4M1

The Discovery Foundation, initially funded by the Government of British Columbia, is a registered non-profit society in the province, and was established to pursue the advancement of scientific, technological, and industrial research and skills in British Columbia. The Foundation works towards broadening and strengthening the economic base of the province by enhancing the establishment and growth of scientific and technological industries, skills and expertise with local and world markets.

The Foundation has a wholly-owned subsidiary, Discovery Parks Inc., which was designed to create world technology research parks adjacent to the principal education centres in the province — Simon Fraser University, the University of British Columbia, the University of Victoria and the British Columbia Institute of Technology.

Chairman and CEO, Don Hamilton

Premier's Advisory Council on Science and Technology
5th Flr., 14183 Douglas St.
Victoria, V8W 3K4

The Council was established by Order-in-Council in 1987 to provide advice on matters of science and technology as they impact on the economic and social fabric of British Columbia.

The Council currently has 14 members, including representatives from the academic, business and public sectors, and is chaired by Robert F. Alexander, president of Microtel Ltd.

The Council, besides providing advice in direct response to requests from the government, is developing a science and technology policy for consideration and implementation by the province. It is preparing a strategy for developing a strong scientific base in the province, and for obtaining the maximum benefit from the integration of technology throughout all sectors of the economy, while creating the least possible disruption in the lives of B.C.'s citizens. The Council will be considering a public awareness program to ensure that the average British Columbian understands and is comfortable with the greater integration of science and technology into their daily life.

Administrator, Rick Pepper

Provincial Apprenticeship Board
818 Broughton St., Victoria, V8V 1X4

The Provincial Apprenticeship Board, established under the *Apprenticeship Act,* is comprised of 13 members. It has specific responsibilities under sections 11 and 12 of the Act, reviews various apprenticeship matters and recommends actions that will improve administration and policy.

In addition to its responsibilities under the Act, the Board receives additional assignments from the Minister of Advanced Education and Job Training. One such assignment is to assist the minister in the development of new long-term apprenticeship training policies to meet B.C.'s trade skills needs.

Director, Danny O'Neill

Science Council of B.C.
100, 3700 Gilmore Way, Burnaby, V5G 4M1

The Science Council of British Columbia was established in 1978 by the provincial Legislature to advise the government on science policy; to award grants to researchers in B.C. industry, universities and other institutions; to encourage and participate in exhibits and programs that will help explain science and scientific research to students and the general public; and to keep in contact with other scientific organizations in the rest of Canada.

Since 1980, the Council has awarded grants to over 600 projects in applied scientific research for a total investment of over $30 million. The Council looks with greatest favour upon projects that promise to deliver to the marketplace new or improved systems or products for the economic and social benefit of the people of B.C. Additionally, the Council has a program of post-graduate scholarships and post-doctoral fellowships designed to encourage closer co-operation between the private sector of the economy and the universities. Each autumn, it also awards the B.C. Science and Engineering Gold Medals to individuals and research groups who have made outstanding achievements in these areas.

The Council is composed of a chairman and 15 volunteer members from the academic, business and industrial communities. It is served by a permanent staff including a president, a director, and a number of program officers and support staff.

President, Dr. James McEwen
Director, Dr. Max Cairns

University Advisory Council
818 Broughton St., Victoria, V8V 1X4

The University Advisory Council was established in April 1987 to provide the Minister of Advanced Education and Job Training advice on the major system-wide issues which face the public university system of British Columbia. Generally, the minister is the originator of the issues to which the Council lends its expertise and advice. From time to time, the Council pursues issues of its own identification.

Membership on the Council consists of individuals who, collectively, encompass a broad range of backgrounds in post-secondary education. Each of the three public universities has nominated a member to the Council. In addition, individuals with experience in community colleges, distance education, small business, as well as a university student representative are included in the Council membership. The minister selects and appoints each of the members.

Chairman, Rendina Hamilton

Women's Secretariat
3rd Flr., 838 Fort St., Victoria, V8V 1X4

The Women's Secretariat is an agency, within the provincial government, that co-ordinates efforts to improve the standing of women in British Columbia. The Secretariat conducts research into issues affecting women, assists government to develop policies of benefit to women, and produces and distributes a range of publications on topics of interest to women. The Women's Grants Program of the Secretariat provides financial support for the development of innovative employment and training projects for women of all ages. The Secretariat's Vancouver Resource Centre provides information and resources to women throughout B.C. Both it and the main office carry information on equal employment opportunities, training and education programs, women in non-traditional occupations, women in business, effective job-search strategies, and a range of other issues.

Exec. Director, Chris Bullen
Resource Centre
325-800 Hornby St., Vancouver, V6Z 2C5
Supervisor, June Love

MINISTRY OF AGRICULTURE AND FISHERIES
Parliament Bldgs., Victoria V8W 2Z7
(except where otherwise indicated)
General Inquiries: (604) 387-5121
Telex: 049-7443; Fax: (604) 387-5130

MINISTER'S OFFICE
342 Parliment Bldgs., Victoria V8W 2Z7
Minister, The Hon. John Savage

DEPUTY MINISTER'S OFFICE
Dep. Minister, Dr. Lorne Greenaway
Asst. Dep. Minister, W. Hatch
Sr. Marketing Advisor, Dr. H.V. Walker

POLICY DEVELOPMENT AND ECONOMICS
Exec. Director, D.M. Matviw
Policy Analysis and Co-ordination Branch
Director, L.E. Bomford
Management Services
A/Exec. Financial Officer, D.G. Davies
Personnel Division
Director, J.D. Cherrington

Field Operations
Asst. Dep. Minister, J.T.R. Husdon
Specialist Services
Exec. Director, R.J. Miller

Financial Assistance Programs
Asst. Dep. Minister, B.A. Hackett
Agriculture and Rural Development (ARDA)
Director, R. Kohlert
Crop Protection Branch
Director, W. Wiebe

Farm Management Extension Branch
Manager, T.N. Peterson
4607-23rd St., Vernon V1T 4K7
Soils and Engineering Branch
33832 S. Fraser Way, Abbotsford, V2S 2C5
Director, R. Bertrand
Agricultural Finance Branch
Director, Al Sakalauskas
Farm Income Insurance
and Crop Insurance Branch
Director, R. Jarvin
Farmland Resources
Director, J.D. Anderson
Aquaculture and Commercial Fisheries Branch
A/Director, J.D. Anderson
Information Services Branch
Director, R.A. Sera
Chief Veterinarian, Dr. P. Hewitt
Veterinary Laboratory
Box 100, Abbotsford, V2S 4N8
A/Supervisor, R.J. Lewis
Brands Recorder, L.D. Reay
Marketing Branch
Director, D.A. Rugg
Rural Organizations and Services Branch
Director, D.E. Freed

REGIONAL EXTENSION SERVICE

North Central/River Region
Experimental Farm, R.R. 8, RMD 7
Prince George, V2N 4M6
Reg. Director, T. Dever

Okanagan-Kootenay Region
1873 Spall Rd., Kelowna, V1Y 4R2
Reg. Director, B.E. Baehr

South Coastal Region
205, 33780 Laurel St., Abbotsford, V2S 1X4
Reg. Director, W.E.A. Wickens

AGENCIES, BOARDS AND COMMISSIONS

MARKETING BOARDS

Marketing boards for agricultural products in Canada are created by a number of different pieces of legislation. National wheat and dairy products plans flow from the *Canadian Wheat Board Act* and the *Canadian Dairy Commission Act* respectively. Egg and poultry boards derive their authority from the *Farm Products Marketing Agencies Act.* As well, many have their own provincial statutes and are normally within the jurisdiction of an umbrella provincial agency. The individual boards are, however, non-governmental and made up largely of elected farmer representatives.

There is also a variety of types. The Economic Council of Canada's study on marketing boards identified five: promotional and developmental boards with little power; selling-desk boards that handle marketing but do not set prices; boards that negotiate prices; boards that set prices; and full-fledged boards that establish quotas. These last are known as supply-management marketing boards. Currently, there are more than 100 active boards in Canada.

B.C. MARKETING BOARD
c/o Ministry of Agriculture and Fisheries
Parliament Bldgs., Victoria, V8W 2Z7

The British Columbia Marketing Board is a supervisory board appointed by the Lieutenant-Governor in Council, as provided for in the *Natural Products Marketing (British Columbia) Act,* to oversee the operation of the various marketing boards and commissions of the province. The provincial board also serves as a quasi-judicial appeal board to which a person who is aggrieved or dissatisfied by an order, decision or determination of a marketing board or commission may appeal.

Chairman, C.E. Emery
Box 1207, Osoyoos, V0H 1V0
Secretary, Dr. H.V. Walker
Vice-Chairman, Mrs. E.M. Brun
Members: G. Aylard, A. Austring, J. Reger

COUNCIL OF MARKETING BOARDS OF B.C.
846 Broughton St., Victoria, V8W 1E4

The Council of Marketing Boards of British Columbia, established in 1965, is a voluntary association of the 11 marketing boards and commissions incorporated under the *Natural Products Marketing (British Columbia) Act.*
The objectives of the Council are:
• to publicize and defend the principles of the marketing boards and commissions;
• to facilitate, by exchange of information, the solutions of problems of mutual concern; and
• to advise producer organizations on the formation of new boards or commissions.

Chairman, Terry Wells
Secretary, Steve Thomson

B.C. CHICKEN MARKETING BOARD
Ste. 203, Dale Bldg.
5752-176th St., Surrey, V3S 4C8

Chairman, R. Sendall
Manager, R.A. Stafford

B.C. CRANBERRY MARKETING BOARD
c/o Bell Farms, 2851 No. 8 Rd.
Richmond, V6V 1S2

Chairman, Bruce May
Sec.-Manager, H. Knoedler

B.C. EGG MARKETING BOARD
Box 310, Abbotsford, V2S 4P2

The British Columbia Egg Marketing Board was created on July 13, 1967 and is governed by the British Columbia Egg Marketing Scheme, 1967.

Board policy is set by a four-member elected board. The chairman is appointed by the provincial government. Each board member is elected for a two-year term by the registered egg producers of the area in which he operates.

The BCEMB selects one of its members to represent British Columbia egg producers on the Canadian Egg Marketing Agency (CEMA).

The main purposes of the BCEMB are to manage egg production with regard to anticipated consumer demand and to relate producer prices for eggs to production costs so that egg farming returns a reasonable income to the farmer.

Chairman, Alfred Giesbrecht
Gen. Manager, Neall Carey

B.C. GRAPE MARKETING BOARD
Ste. 5, 864 Spall Rd., Kelowna, V1Y 4R1

Chairman, Alan Brock
Secretary, Connie Bielert

B.C. HOG MARKETING COMMISSION
202, 34314 Marshall Rd.
Abbotsford, V2S 1L9

The B.C. Hog Marketing Commission was established in 1980 to initiate, support or conduct programs for promoting, stimulating, increasing and improving the economic well-being of persons engaged in the production, processing and marketing of pork and pork products.

Funding is derived from the collection of a levy for each hog produced in the province. Packers, processors and producers obtain a licence annually to produce, pack, market or transport the regulated product.

The Commission is operated by a board of directors, elected from the membership.

Chairman, David Craven
Gen. Manager, David Van der Flier

B.C. MILK BOARD
800 S. Cassiar St., Vancouver, V5K 4N6

The Milk Board is constituted under Part III of the *British Columbia Milk Industry Act* and is responsible for its administration.

The Milk Board consists of three members appointed by the Lieutenant-Governor in Council. The Board must ensure there is an adequate but not excessive supply of milk for the fluid market. It determines classes of milk according to use and establishes accounting values for these classes. The Class 1 or fluid value is established by means of an economic formula. Manufacturing values are established on the basis of current market yields taking into consideration target support prices announced by the federal government. The Board fixes producer quotas and minimum producer prices for deliveries of milk within quota and for deliveries of milk in excess of quota.

The Board is also responsible for the administration of controls on the production of manufactured milk. The British Columbia Milk Board is a regulatory board, not a marketing board, in that it does not take physical possession of the milk.

Chairman, G.G. Thorpe
Administrator, P. Knight

B.C. MUSHROOM MARKETING BOARD
Box 1203, Stn. A, Surrey, V3S 2B3

Chairman, G. Krulitski
Recording Secretary, Marcia Dube

B.C. OYSTER MARKETING BOARD
Box 970, Ladysmith, V0R 2E0

The British Columbia Oyster Marketing Board was constituted on Dec. 17, 1964 to promote, regulate and control the transportation, packing, storing and marketing of oysters.

The Board consists of five registered oyster growers who are elected annually by the membership of the B.C. Oyster Growers' Assn. for a term of three years.

The Board requires that all growers, grower-packers and wholesalers register with and be licensed by the Board. Grower-packers and growers are required to report monthly sales to the Board and pay a licensing fee thereon. Wholesalers may also be required to make reports to the Board. There are no sales quotas set by the Board.

The Board, in consultation with the membership of the B.C. Oyster Growers' Assn., establishes a minimum price for all oysters grown and marketed in B.C. and specifies the size and type of container in which they may be sold.

Chairman, Peter McLellan
Sec.-Treasurer, Pat Irvine

B.C. SHEEP AND WOOL COMMISSION
c/o B.C. Federation of Agriculture
846 Broughton St., Victoria, V8W 1E4

The British Columbia Sheep and Wool Commission is the recognized producer-elected organization representing all sheep producers in British Columbia. Empowered under the *Natural Products Marketing Act,* its stated purpose is to initiate, support or conduct programs for promoting, stimulating, increasing or improving the economic well-being of persons engaged in the production, processing and marketing of the regulated product: sheep and wool.

Although it is not exercising its entire mandate at this time, the Commission has the power to regulate the production of sheep, including rams, ewes and lambs, and the raw wool shorn from these animals.

At present, the B.C. Sheep and Wool Commission is concentrating on the promotion of sheep production through support of local organizations, participating in educational programs for both the experienced and inexperienced producer, co-ordinating grazing projects on forestry lands, administering the Farm Income Insurance Program for sheep, and taking an active role in the national organization to protect the interests of producers from adverse influence from foreign lamb producers.

Chairman, B. Currie

B.C. TREE FRUIT MARKETING BOARD
Box 1619, Stn. A, Kelowna, V1Y 8M3

The British Columbia Tree Fruit Marketing Board is a three-member agency elected from the members of the British Columbia Fruit Growers' Assn. In 1934 it became the first marketing board in the province sanctioned by the *Natural Prod-*

ucts Marketing (B.C.) Act. The Board has the authority "to promote, control, and regulate the transportation, packing, storage, and marketing of British Columbia tree fruits." The Board does not currently exercise its full authority in all these areas, but takes its direction from the grower body from time to time as conditions within the industry change. In 1974 the Board allowed growers not wishing to sell through the central sales agency, B.C. Tree Fruits Ltd., to market their fruit independently.

Chairman, D. Claridge
Sec.-Treasurer, D. Taylor

B.C. TURKEY MARKETING BOARD

17704-56th Ave., Ste. 218, Surrey, V3S 1C7

Chairman, J. Pennington
Sec.-Manager, Colyn Welsh

B.C. VEGETABLE MARKETING COMMISSION

212, 17704-56th Ave., Surrey, V3S 1C7

On July 1, 1980, the Coast and Interior Vegetable Marketing Boards were amalgamated to form the B.C. Vegetable Marketing Commission (BCVMC). Seven Commission members, elected by the commercial producers within their districts, regulate products from three districts: Vancouver Island and the Gulf Islands, Lower Mainland-Fraser Valley, and the Southern Interior Region. However, the Commission does not regulate products unless a request is made by at least 60 to 70 per cent of the producers.

The Commission also promotes the production, transportation, packing, storage and marketing of the regulated products. Producers must advise the Commission of the volume and variety of crops grown so the quantity of each product that will reach market can be predicted.

Apart from maintaining a registry, and licensing industry producers, wholesalers and processors, the Commission supervises a quota system which comes into effect when the supply of a particular vegetable exceeds its demand. The Vegetable Marketing Commission has seven designated sales agencies located throughout British Columbia where producers must sell regulated products. At present, 13 vegetables in the fresh market and 11 in the processing market are under Commission control.

Chairman, Jim Harris
Gen. Manager, Charles Amor

B.C. Agricultural Land Commission

4940 Canada Way, Burnaby, V5G 4K6

The Agricultural Land Commission develops and administers the farmland preservation program, which is based on the establishment in 1973 of Agricultural Land Reserves totalling approximately 4.7 million hectares.

The Commission consists of five or more members appointed by the Lieutenant-Governor in Council. Legislation administered and enforced includes the *Agricultural Land Commission Act,* R.S.B.C. 1980, Chapter 9 and the *Soil Conserva-*

tion Act, R.S.B.C. 1980, Chapter 81.

The prime objective of the Commission is to preserve lands capable of food production for present and future agricultural use. This is achieved by interacting with local government authorities, by reviewing major Agricultural Land Reserve boundaries, and by reviewing Community and Settlement Plans with the co-operation of municipalities and regional districts.

While most of the Commission's work relates to ALR applications from individual land owners, local government, and Crown agencies, there is recognition that a strong farm community is essential in farmland preservation.

Chairman, I.D. Paton
Gen. Manager, Robert P. Murdoch
Planning, Processing and Technical Division
Director, Jim Plotnikoff
Property and Soils Management
Director, Kirk Miller

MINISTRY OF THE ATTORNEY GENERAL

Parliament Bldgs., Victoria, V8V 1X4
General Inquiries: (604) 387-4574

MINISTER'S OFFICE
232 Parliament Bldg., Victoria, V8V 1X4
Attorney General,
The Hon. Stuart (Bud) Smith, Q.C.

DEPUTY ATTORNEY GENERAL'S OFFICE
Dep. Attorney General,
The Hon. Edward N. Hughes, Q.C.

Management Services and Regulatory Programs
Asst. Dep. Minister, Krysia Strawczynski
Exec. Counsel, Bob Simson
Public Affairs Division
Director, Mary K. Beeching
Policy and Program Services Division
Director, Gary Martin
Community Programs
Director, Sandra Edelman
Family Maintenance Enforcement
Director, Sandra Edelman
Personnel Services Division
Director, Patti Stockton
Finance and Administration Division
Exec. Director, Ian Smith
Internal Audit
Exec. Director, Gary F. Hepburn
Public Trustee, Steven Rumsey

Legal Services Branch
Asst. Dep. Attorney General,
E. Robert A. Edwards, Q.C.
Exec. Counsel, Norman J. Prelypchan
Chief Solicitor, Donald Clancy, Q.C.
Chief Legislative Counsel, Clifford S. Watt
Library Services Director, Jane Taylor

Criminal Justice Branch

Asst. Dep. Attorney General,
William F. Stewart
Director of Policy and Support Services,
Hal N. Yacowar
Director of Operations, Ernie Quantz

Court Services Branch

Asst. Dep. Minister, A.K.B. Sheridan
Management Resources
Director, Donald J. Rose
Inspections Director, Bill Austin

AGENCIES, BOARDS AND COMMISSIONS

B.C. International Commercial Arbitration Centre
670, 999 Canada Place
Vancouver, V6C 2E2
Exec. Director, Bonita Thompson

Expropriation Compensation Board
514 Government St., Victoria, V8V 2L7

Chairman, Jack Heinrich, Q.C.

Land Title Office
4th Flr., 910 Government St.
Victoria, V8V 1X4

The Land Title Office is part of the provincial Ministry of the Attorney General. It administers the *Land Title Act* which establishes the land title registration system in British Columbia. It is based on the "Torrens Principles", and its major objectives are certainty of title and facility of transfer.

There are seven land title districts in British Columbia with offices located in: Kamloops, Nelson, New Westminster, Prince George, Prince Rupert, Vancouver and Victoria. Each of these offices is administered by a registrar of titles. Director, J.P. Malcolm McAvity

Law Foundation (Board of Governors)
410-1190 Hornby St., Vancouver, V6Z 2K5
Exec. Director, Michael Jacobson
Chairman of Governors, Kenneth Antifaev
Ste. 221, 3030 Lincoln Ave.
Coquitlam, V3B 6B4

Law Reform Commission
Ste. 601, Chancery Pl.
865 Hornby St., Vancouver, V6Z 2H4

The Law Reform Commission of British Columbia was constituted by the *Law Reform Commission Act,* which became law on July 1, 1969. The Commission's mandate is set out in section 2 of the Act which states:

"The Commission is to take and keep under review all the law of the Province, including statute law, common law and judicial decisions, with a view to its systematic development and reform, including the codification, elimination of anomalies, repeal of obsolete and unnecessary enactments, reduction in the number of separate enactments and generally the simplification and modernization of the law, and for that purpose to:

a) receive and consider any proposals for the reform of the law that may be made to the Commission;

b) prepare and submit to the Attorney General programs for the examination of different branches of the law with a view to reform, and to recommend an agency, whether the Commission, or a committee or other body, to carry out the examination;

c) undertake, at the request of the Attorney General, or under a recommendation of the Commission approved by the Attorney General, the examination of particular branches of the law, and the formulation, by means of draft bills or otherwise, of proposals for reform; and

d) provide advice and information to government ministries and, at the request of the Attorney General, to other authorities or bodies concerned with proposals for the reform or amendment of any branch of the law."

Chairman, Arthur L. Close
Counsel to the Commission,
Thomas G. Anderson
Legal Research Officers:
J. Bruce McKinnon, Linda Reid

Legal Services Society
Box 3, Ste. 300, 1140 W. Pender St.
Vancouver, V6E 4G1

The Legal Services Society of British Columbia is responsible for the delivery of legal services in the province. The Society aims to ensure that:

a) services ordinarily provided by a lawyer are afforded to individuals who would not otherwise receive them because of financial or other reasons; and

b) education, advice and information about the law are provided for the people of B.C.

The Legal Services Society provides legal aid services to individuals who cannot otherwise afford them. Eligible clients are referred to lawyers in private practice who receive a fee on a tariff basis. Services are also provided through Legal Services Society branch offices located in 15 communities throughout the province and through community law offices located in 13 communities. The Society provides legal information services through its Public Legal Education Program, its Schools Program, and its Library Services Program.

The Society also provides special legal services to native people through three of its community law offices that specialize in native problems and through the funding of native legal information counsellors in four Native Indian Friendship Centres.

Exec. Director, Jack Olsen
Chairman, Ace Henderson
Ste. 280, 666 Burrard St., Vancouver, V6Z 2Z7
Vice-Chairman, Hon. Bruce Cohen
800 Smithe St., Vancouver, V6Z 2E1

MINISTRY OF CROWN LANDS

Parliament Bldgs., Victoria, V8V 1X4
MINISTER'S OFFICE
104 Parliament Bldgs., Victoria, V8V 1X4
Minister, The Hon. Howard Dirks

ASSOCIATE DEPUTY MINISTER'S OFFICE
6th Flr., 712 Yates St., Victoria, V8V 1X4
Assoc. Dep. Minister, Ed Macgregor
Asst. Dep. Minister, Frank Edgell
Exec. Director, Jack Hall
Communications Division
Director, Shawn Robins

LANDS SERVICES DIVISION
Real Estate Services Branch
3rd Flr., 4000 Seymour Place
Victoria, V8V 1X5
Director, Wes Umphrey
Land Policy Branch
3rd Flr., 4000 Seymour Place
Victoria, V8V 1X5
Director, Greg Roberts
Surveyor General Branch
3400 Davidson St., Victoria, V8V 1X5
Surveyor-Gen. and Director, Don Duffy
Surveys and Resource Mapping Branch
553 Superior St., Victoria, V8V 1X5
Director, Gary Sawayama

LANDS OPERATIONS
Cariboo Region
201, 172 N. 2nd Ave.
Williams Lake, V2G 1Z6
Reg. Director, Steve Mazur
Kootenay Region
828A Baker St., Cranbrook V1C 1A2
Reg. Director, Dick Roberts
Lower Mainland Region
210, 4240 Manor St., Burnaby, V5G 1B2
Reg. Director, Vacant
Omineca Region
1011-4th Ave., Prince George, V2L 3H9
Reg. Director, Al Sanderson
Peace Region
220, 9900-100th Ave.
Fort St. John, V1J 5S7
Reg. Director, Egon Weger
Skeena Region
3726 Alfred Ave., Smithers, V0J 2N0
Reg. Director, Jim Yardley
Thompson-Okanagan Region
478 St. Paul St., Kamloops, V2C 2J6
Reg. Director, John Thompson
Vancouver Island Region
851 Yates St., Victoria, V8V 1X5
Reg. Director, Doug McColl

MINISTRY OF EDUCATION

Parliament Bldgs., Victoria, V8V 2M4

MINISTER'S OFFICE
103 Parliament Bldgs., Victoria, V8V 1X4
Minister, The Hon. Anthony J. Brummet

DEPUTY MINISTER'S OFFICE
Dep. Minister, A.L. (Sandy) Peel
Exec. Co-ordinator, Dr. Sam Lim
Information Services Branch
Director, Vacant

Finance and Administration Department

Asst. Dep. Minister, Wayne Desharnais
Financial Planning and Operations
Director, Vacant
School Finance Branch
Director, Doug Hibbins
Schools Facilities Branch
Director, Tom Austin
Legislative Services Branch
Director, Peter Owen
Comptroller's and Administration Branch
Comptroller and Director, Steve Woodward
Accounting Services
Manager, Richard Riopel
Budget Development Manager, John Fuller
Systems Services Manager, Ian Chisholm
Librarian, Norma Lofthouse
Support Services
A/Manager, Ron Schneider
Personnel Services
Manager, Roy Empringham

Educational Programs Department

Asst. Dep. Minister, J.R. Fleming
Educational Liaison Director, Gib Lind
Professional Relations Branch
Director, Earl Cherrington

PROGRAM DEVELOPMENT DIVISION
Exec. Director, Oscar Bedard
Curriculum Development Branch
Director, Dr. Brian Frankcombe
Educational Program Implementation Branch
Director, Becky Matthews
Modern Languages and
Multicultural Programs Branch
2840 Nanaimo St., Victoria, V8V 1X4
Director, Dr. Geoff Mills
Special Education Branch
Director, Shirley McBride
Special Education Programs
Manager, Rick Connolly
Child Abuse Programs
Co-ordinator, Bonnie Spence-Vinge
Special Education Services
4196 W. 4th Ave., Vancouver, V6R 4J5
Manager, Henry Minto

Jericho Hill School for the Deaf
4125 W. 8th Ave., Vancouver, V6R 1Z7
Principal, John Anderson

Provincial Educational Media Centre (PEMC)
12140 Horseshoe Way, Richmond, V7A 4V5
Manager, Kenneth Van Apeldoorn
Publication Services
878 Viewfield Rd., Victoria, V8V 1X4
Director, Gordon Howard

PROGRAM EFFECTIVENESS DIVISION
Exec. Director, Dr. Barry Anderson
Student Assessment Branch
Director, Dr. Barry Carbol
Program Evaluation and Research Branch
Director, Vacant
Data Systems Administration Branch
Director, Bill Moncur

Policy, Planning and Independent Education Department
Asst. Dep. Minister, Glenn Wall
Policy and Planning Branch
Director, Dr. Jerry Mussio
Independent Schools Branch
Director, Tom Ellwood
National and International Education Branch
Director, Peter Northover
Correspondence and
Distance Learning Branch
A/Director, Emily Walker

MINISTRY OF ENERGY, MINES AND PETROLEUM RESOURCES

133 Parliament Bldgs., Victoria, V8V 1X4
General Inquiries: (604) 387-5178

MINISTER'S OFFICE
Minister, The Hon. Jack Davis

DEPUTY MINISTER'S OFFICE
Dep. Minister, D. Horswill
Director of Communications,
Irwin Henderson

REVENUE AND OPERATIONAL SERVICES DIVISION
Exec. Director, Vacant
Data Services Branch
A/Director, Mike Baker
Personnel Branch Director, Barry Turner
Financial Services Branch
Comptroller, Jennifer Smith
Administration Branch
Director, Tim Chatton
Librarian, Sharon Ferris
Resource Revenue Branch
Manager, Bruce Garrison

Mineral Resources Division
Asst. Dep. Minister, B. McRae
Mineral Policy Branch
A/Director, K. Koncohrada
Geological Branch
Chief Geologist, R. Smyth

Analytical Laboratory
A/Chief Analyst, Paul Matysek
Engineering and Inspection Branch
525 Superior St., Victoria, V8V 1X4
Chief Inspector, R. McGinn
Mineral Titles Branch
Chief Gold Commissioner, J. Clancy

Energy Resources Division
Asst. Dep. Minister, John Allan
Engineering and Operations Branch
Director, Bruce Hanwell
Geological Branch
A/Director, J. MacRae
Petroleum Titles Branch
A/Commissioner, G. German
Forecasts and Special Projects Branch
A/Director, W. Bell
Energy Policy Branch
A/Directors, G. Douglas

AGENCIES, BOARDS, COMMISSIONS AND CROWN CORPORATIONS

B.C. Utilities Commission
800 Smithe St., 4th Flr., Vancouver, V6Z 2E1

The British Columbia Utilities Commission is an independent provincial government agency established under the the terms of the *Utilities Commission Act.* The two main areas of responsibility for the Commission are Utility Regulation and Major Energy Project Review. It has exclusive jurisdiction for the purpose of ensuring that all regulated utilities operate in the public interest, and reviewing proposed major energy projects, upon referral jointly by the ministers of Energy, Mines and Petroleum Resources and of the Environment.

The Commission performs a regulatory role with respect to public utilities operating in the province and providing light, heat, power and certain communication services. It also has a mandate to conduct public hearings and to serve as an impartial forum for the review of submissions from all segments of the communities served, whether industry, government or the public.

New provisions in the *Utilities Commission Act* relate to procedures for reviewing proposed major energy-producing and consuming projects and the requirement for Energy Project Certificates and Energy Operation Certificates.

Chairman, Vacant
Dep. Chairman, J.D.V. Newlands
Commission Secretary, A.C. Michelson
Commissioners:
D.B. Kilpatrick, N. Martin, W. Wolfe

Mediation and Arbitration Board (Petroleum and Natural Gas Act and Mineral Tenure Act)
10142-101st Ave., Fort St. John, V1J 2B3

The Mediation and Arbitration Board is established under Part III of the *Petroleum and Natural Gas Act.* This authority empowers the board:

1) to grant Right of Entry to oil and gas companies over alienated lands where such Right of Entry has been refused by the land owner;
2) to determine conditions for Right of Entry and set compensation to be paid therefor;
3) to appoint a member of the Board to act as a mediator between a petroleum company and a land owner when an impasse develops respecting Right of Entry;
4) if mediation proves unsuccessful, to arbitrate the matter and set compensation for Right of Entry respecting wellsites, campsites, roadways and/or pipeline installations;
5) to conduct arbitration hearings to review and set annual rental on leases and previous Board Orders of more than five years duration;
6) to terminate Rights of Entry when an operator ceases to occupy land;
7) to perform the same duties with respect to geothermal exploration as outlined respecting gas and oil exploration; and
8) to provide a mediation and arbitration function under the *Mineral Tenure Act* respecting disputes between landowners and mineral rights holders.

Chairman, D. Ed Smith
Vice-Chairman, C.A. Ruddell
Members: John Strain, Viggo Pedersen

MINISTRY OF ENVIRONMENT
Parliament Bldgs., Victoria, V8V 1X5
(except where otherwise indicated)

MINISTER'S OFFICE
Minister, The Hon. Bruce Strachan

DEPUTY MINISTER'S OFFICE
Dep. Minister, Richard Dalon

Environment
A/Asst. Dep. Minister, J. O'Riordan
Conservation Officer Service
Chief Conservation Officer, R. Aldrich
Information Services Branch
Director, R. Kawalilak
Wildlife Branch Director, J. Walker
Fisheries Branch Director, D. Narver
Waste Management Branch
Director, R.H. Ferguson
Pesticide Control Branch
Director, R. Kobylnyk
Water Management Branch
Director, D. Kasianchuk
Planning and Assessment Branch
A/Director, R. Wilson

REGIONAL OPERATIONS

Vancouver Island Region
2569 Kenworth Rd., Nanaimo, V9T 4P7
Reg. Director, Donald R. Hehn

Southern Interior Region
1259 Dalhousie Dr., Kamloops, V2C 2T6
Reg. Director, Bill A. Kastelen

Kootenay Region
310 Ward St., Nelson, V1L 5R4
Reg. Director, Dennis McDonald

Northern Region
1011-4th Ave., Prince George, V2L 3H9
Reg. Director, Earl Warnock

OPERATIONS DIVISION
Exec. Director, J.R. Marshall
Officer, Heather Hawrys

AGENCIES, BOARDS AND COMMISSIONS

B.C.-Yukon-N.W.T. Boundary Commission
533 Superior St., Victoria, V8V 1X4
Commissioner, Kenneth Bridge

B.C.-Alberta Boundary Commission
533 Superior St., Victoria, V8V 1X4
Commissioner, Kenneth Bridge

Environmental Appeal Board
Parliament Bldgs., Victoria, V8V 1X5

The Environmental Appeal Board was established under the provisions of the *Environment Management Act,* on Jan. 1, 1982. Its purpose is to hear appeals to decisions made under environmental legislation, and in so doing, it replaces the Pollution Control Board and the Pesticide Control Appeal Board. It also assumes the responsibility of hearing appeals that were previously made directly to cabinet under the *Water Act* and *Wildlife Act.*

The Environmental Appeal Board is appointed by cabinet, and at present consists of 24 members of specialized expertise and regional representation. A sitting board consists of a chairman plus two members, or if the issue under appeal is time-consuming and contentious, a chairman plus four members. A panel of the Board may sit in place of the Board.

The decisions of the Board, in the form of judgments, are presented to the Minister of Environment and to all parties to the appeal. The judgment is considered a public document after all parties to the appeal have received their copies. Procedural regulations have been established as operating procedures by the Environmental Appeal Board.

Chairman, F.A. Hillier, P.Eng.

MINISTRY OF FINANCE AND CORPORATE RELATIONS
Parliament Bldgs., Victoria, V8V 1X4

MINISTER'S OFFICE
152 Parliament Bldgs., Victoria, V8V 1X4
Minister, The Hon. Mel Couvelier

DEPUTY MINISTER'S OFFICE
109, 617 Government St.
Victoria, V8V 1X4

Dep. Minister, Philip G. Halkett
Communications Branch Director, Vacant

ADMINISTRATION AND SUPPORT SERVICES
DIVISION
Exec. Director, W.H. Bell
Information Systems Branch
Gen. Manager, A. Carr
Financial Services and Administration Branch
A/Director, J. Powell
Personnel Branch Director, Grant Price

CENTRAL STATISTICS BUREAU
Provincial Statistician, W. McReynolds
Statistics Branch Director, Tom Benyon
Data Dissemination Chief, Gary Weir
Quantitative Analysis
A/Director, Tom Benyon

Provincial Treasury Division

Asst. Dep. Minister, Michael Costello
Investment Branch Director, D.G. Pearce
Banking/Cash Management and Administration
Director, A. van Iersel
Debt Management Branch
Director, Brenda J. Eaton
Securities Registrar, T. Lim

Office of the Comptroller General

Comptroller-Gen., D.B. Marson
Dep. Comptroller-Gen., Al Barnard
Internal Audit, Director, F.G. Hepburn
Government Payroll Office
Director, A.C. Pickering
System Support Branch
Director, A.R. Horner
Administrative Services
Manager, F.G. Hammond
Financial Disbursement Operations
Director, M.A. Petrie
Financial Management
Director, H. Maltby
Accounting and Reporting
Director, V. Skaarup

Revenue Division

Asst. Dep. Minister, E. Lloyd Munro
Revenue Administration Branch
Director, Vacant
Consumer Taxation Branch
Exec. Director, E.J. Turner
Appeals Director, G.A. Reimer
Real Property Taxation Branch
Surveyor of Taxes, D. Sandell
Income Taxation Branch
Director, A.B. Carver

Vancouver Office:
Robson Sq., Vancouver, V6Z 2C5
Director, Vancouver Operations
E.S. Tucker

Treasury Board Staff

A/Asst. Dep. Minister and Dep. Secretary,

Treasury Board, Dennis M. Anholt
Taxation and Intergovernmental Relations
Director, A. Eastwood
Social Policy Director, Thea Vakil
Economic Development Policy
Director, Chris Trumpy
Financial and Economic Analysis
Director, Bob Hobart
Government Estimates and
Administrative Policy
A/Director, Lois McNabb
Risk Management Director, Phil Grewar

Corporate Relations

Asst. Dep. Minister, Gerry Armstrong
Corporate, Central and
Mobile Home Registry
940 Blanshard St., 2nd Flr.
Victoria, V8W 3E6
Registrar, David Boyd
Dep. Registrar of Companies,
Roberta Lowdon
Dep. Registrar General, Deanna Koskie

Financial Institutions
865 Hornby St., Vancouver, V6Z 2H4
Sup't, Allan Mulholland

Policy and Legislation
Rm. 105, 617 Government St.
Victoria V8V 1X4
Director, Dan Perrin

AGENCIES, BOARDS, COMMISSIONS AND CROWN CORPORATIONS

Assessment Appeal Board
Ste. 101, 22356 McIntosh Ave.
Maple Ridge, V2X 3C1
Fax: 467-3892
General Inquiries: (604) 463-9300

The Assessment Appeal Board is appointed by the Lieutenant-Governor in Council under provisions contained within the *Assessment Act* to hear complaints arising from the Courts of Revision on matters concerning property tax assessments. In appointing members, regard is had to persons trained in law or experienced in real property appraisal.

The Board has a chairman, two vice-chairmen, and a pool of members from which panels of the Board are formed.

Hearings are held in each of the 23 assessment areas throughout the province, and the Board is the final adjudicator of fact, with further appeal procedures being available to the Supreme Court of British Columbia on questions of law only.
Chairman, C. Chilton
Vice-Chairmen: D.L. Brothers, L.A. King

Auditor Certification Board
2nd Flr., 940 Blanshard St.
Victoria, V8W 3E6
General Inquiries: (604) 356-8658

The Auditor Certification Board is authorized pursuant to section 205 of the B.C. *Company Act.* Its purpose is to set standards for audits required by British Columbia statutes that are conducted by accountants other than chartered accountants and certified general accountants. It also licenses those persons who are able to meet these standards.

Members are appointed by Order-in-Council for up to a three-year period.

Chairman, B. Adams
Secretary, David Boyd

B.C. Assessment Authority
1537 Hillside Ave., Victoria, V8T 4Y2
General Inquiries: (604) 595-6211

The British Columbia Assessment Authority was established under the *Assessment Authority of British Columbia Act* (1974) as an independent corporation with responsibility for real property assessment in both municipal and non-municipal areas. Prior to the creation of this centralized authority, municipal assessors were responsible for assessments in cities, towns and districts, while provincial assessors valued property in unorganized areas and village municipalities. The Assessment Authority is governed by a six-member Board from which two members retire each year to be replaced or reappointed for three-year terms.

The Authority is responsible for determining the actual value of all land and improvements in the province. The number of parcels is approximately 1.25 million with an actual value of over $140 billion.

Originally, the Authority established 27 area offices throughout the province, but the merging of certain offices has now reduced the number to 23, each with an assessor and appropriate appraisal and clerical staff. With the assistance of support staff in the Authority's head office and an on-line data processing system, all properties are valued, assessment rolls and assessment notices are prepared and delivered to the taxing authorities and taxpayers respectively, and appeals against assessments are defended before the courts established for this purpose.

Chairman, John P. Taylor
Members: Robert Ostler, Jacob Dick, Stan Hamilton, Walter Siemens, Gary Grelish

B.C. Educational Institutions Capital Financing Authority
Parliament Bldgs., Victoria, V8V 1X4

The British Columbia Educational Institutions Capital Financing Authority is the marketing agency for the capital funding requirements of universities, colleges and provincial institutes. Long-term borrowings of $7 million were undertaken in the fiscal year ended March 31, 1988. The gross outstanding guaranteed debt as at March 31, 1988 was $436.5 million and the net guaranteed debt was $76.9 million.

Chairman, The Hon. Mel Couvelier
Members: The Hon. A.J. Brummet,
The Hon. S. Hagen
Secretary, Philip G. Halkett
Registrar, T. Lim

B.C. Housing and Employment Development Financing Authority
Parliament Bldgs., Victoria, V8V 1X4

Chairman, The Hon. Mel Couvelier
Member, The Hon. C. Richmond
Secretary, Philip G. Halkett
Registrar, T. Lim

B.C. Regional Hospital Districts Financing Authority
Parliament Bldgs., Victoria, V8V 1X4

The British Columbia Regional Hospital Districts Financing Authority is the marketing agency for the capital funding requirements of regional hospital districts. The Authority provided $83 million in the fiscal year ending March 31, 1988. The gross outstanding debt as of March 31, 1988 was $1,135.7 million and the net guaranteed debt was $368.0 million.

Chairman, The Hon. Mel Couvelier
Members: The Hon. Peter Dueck,
The Hon. Rita Johnston
Secretary, Philip G. Halkett
Registrar, T. Lim

B.C. School Districts Capital Financing Authority
Parliament Bldgs., Victoria, V8V 1X4

The British Columbia School Districts Capital Financing Authority is the marketing agency for capital funding requirements of school districts. The Authority raised $45 million in the fiscal year ending March 31, 1988. The gross outstanding debt as at March 31, 1988 was $1,547.0 million and the net guaranteed debt was $667.7 million.

Chairman, The Hon. Mel Couvelier
Member, The Hon. A.J. Brummet
Secretary, Philip G. Halkett
Registrar, T. Lim

B.C. Securities Commission
1100, 865 Hornby St., Vancouver, V6Z 2H4
General Inquiries: (604) 660-4800
Fax: 660-2688

The British Columbia Securities Commission was created under the authority of a new provincial *Securities Act* which took effect in February 1987. The new *Securities Act* amalgamated the Office of the Superintendent of Brokers with the Commission.

The Securities Commission administers the *Securities Act,* and the *Commodity Contract Act* and is responsible for:
• promoting the growth and development of B.C.'s securities industry consistent with the government's economic objectives;
• participating with other provincial securities

administrators in the development of uniform national securities policies;

- protecting investors from fraud, misconduct or manipulation in the securities market;
- ensuring, in conjunction with self-regulatory organizations, that registered participants in the securities industry meet standards of honesty and competence;
- ensuring that investors have timely and reliable information to help them make informed investment decisions;
- ensuring that the policies and operations of the Vancouver Stock Exchange are consistent with the goals of the Commission; and
- providing an open and sufficient public market for listed shares.

Chairman, Doug Hyndman
Commissioner, Jeremy McCall
Secretary to the Commission,
Sandy MacDonald
Gen. Counsel, David Thompson
Sup't of Brokers, Neil de Gelder

Dep. Sup'ts:
Compliance and Enforcement, Wade Nesmith
Corporate Finance, Wayne Redwick
Exemptions and Orders, Margaret Sheehy
Finance and Administration, Gordon Mulligan
Policy and Legislation, Adrienne Wanstall
Registration and Statutory Filings,
Jerry Matier
Central Services
Manager, Joanne Caldwell
Financial Services
Manager, Sharon Pickthorne
Information and Records
Manager, Irma Mueller
Information Officer, Shandie Hertslet

Courts of Revision
152 Parliament Bldg., Victoria, V8V 1X4

The Courts of Revision are the first step in appealing assessed values of properties in the province of British Columbia, as set by the B.C. Assessment Authority.

Courts of Revision, consisting of a chairman and two other members, are appointed annually by the Lieutenant-Governor in Council to hear appeals on assessments of land and improvements in all municipalities and rural areas throughout the province. In 1987, 92 courts heard appeals in 76 separate areas of the province.

The courts are required to hear appeals delivered to the assessor under the *Assessment Act,* and investigate and adjudicate upon the assessments in a fair and equitable manner. Decisions of the courts may be appealed to the B.C. Assessment Appeal Board.

Contact, Maureen Trottier

Credit Union Deposit Insurance Corp. of B.C.
7th Flr., 1380 Burrard St.
Vancouver, V6Z 2B7

The Credit Union Deposit Insurance Corporation of British Columbia was established under the *Credit Union Act* of B.C. in 1958. Members of the Board are appointed by the Lieutenant-Governor in Council.

The Corporation administers an insurance fund that provides deposit insurance on non-equity shares and deposits in credit unions in the province of British Columbia.

President, G.R. Wallace

Insurance Council of B.C.
Ste. 225-701 W. Georgia St.
Box 10135, Vancouver, V7Y 1C6
Fax: 662-7767
General Inquiries: (604) 688-0321

Chairman, Walter Siemens
Sec.-Manager, Gary M. Harper
Asst. Secretary, Arlene R. Chow
Staff Investigator, Wayne Popp
Complaints Administrator, Mark McConchie

Real Estate Council of B.C.
5th Flr., 626 West Pender St.
Vancouver, V6B 1V9

The Real Estate Council of British Columbia was established under the *Real Estate Act* of 1958.

Among the Council's specific responsibilities are providing pre-licensing education programs, generally supervising the conduct of real estate licensees, inquiring into real estate transactions or practices in order to protect the interests of the public, as well as issuing real estate licences and maintaining licence records.

Members of the Council are experienced licensees elected on a proportional basis to ensure representation to all regions of the province.

Chairman, Edward Collinson
Secretary, P. Dermot Murphy

Treasury Board
Parliament Bldgs., Victoria, V8V 1X4

The Treasury Board is a committee of the Executive Council and consists of the Minister of Finance and Corporate Relations as chairman and other members of the cabinet appointed by order-in-council. The role of the Board is to manage and allocate provincial government resources.

Chairman, The Hon. Mel Couvelier
Secretary, Philip G. Halkett
Members: The Hon. Jack Davis,
The Hon. Peter Dueck, The Hon. Lyall Hanson,
The Hon. Elwood N. Veitch,
The Hon. Stanley Hagen,
The Hon. Cliff Michael,
The Hon. Bud Smith, The Hon. John Jansen

Vancouver Stock Exchange
Box 10333, 609 Granville St.
Vancouver, V7Y 1H1
General Inquiries: (604) 689-3334

Chairman, John Mathers
Public Governors:
Tom Cantell, Joan A. Harrison,
Peter Lusztig, James L. McPherson

MINISTRY OF FORESTS
1450 Government St., Victoria, V8W 3E7
(except where otherwise indicated)
Information: (604) 387-5255

MINISTER'S OFFICE
346 Parliament Bldgs., Victoria, V8V 1X4
Minister, The Hon. Dave Parker

EXECUTIVE
Dep. Minister, Ben Marr
Sr. Operations Asst., Blanche Congdon
Public Affairs Branch
Director, Laura Stringer
Industry Development and Marketing Branch
A/Director, Hartley Lewis
Valuation Branch
Director, Hartley Lewis

Management Services Division
Asst. Dep. Minister, Doug Ausman
Exec. Co-ordinator, Nick Krischanowsky
Audit Services Branch
Director, Ian Birch
Financial Services Branch
Director, Bob Battles
Human Resources Branch
Director, Laurie Geddes
Information Systems Branch
Director, John Ellis
Legal Services Branch
Director, Jack Ebbels
Technical and Administrative
Services Branch Director, Les Underwood

Forestry Division
Chief Forester, John Cuthbert
Integrated Resource Branch
Director, Jack Bickert
Integrated Resource Planning Section
Manager, Dennis O'Gorman
Range Section Manager, Ray Addison
Recreation Section Manager, Tom Hall
Inventory Branch Director, Frank Hegyi
Protection Branch Director, Jim Dunlop
Research Branch Director, Ted Baker
Silviculture Branch
Director, Peter Ackhurst

Forest Operations Division
Asst. Dep. Minister, Wes Cheston
Timber Harvesting Branch
Director, Julius Juhasz
Engineering Section
Manager, Younas Mirza

FOREST OPERATIONS
Exec. Director, Mike Wilkins

Cariboo Forest Region
540 Borland St.
Williams Lake, V2G 1R8
Reg. Manager, Mike Carlson

Prince George Forest Region
1011-4th Ave., Prince George, V2L 3H9
Reg. Manager, Fred Baxter

Prince Rupert Forest Region
3726 Alfred St., Smithers, V0J 2N0
Reg. Manager, Bob Friesen

Kamloops Forest Region
515 Columbia St., Kamloops, V2C 2T7
Reg. Manager, Peter Levy

Nelson Forest Region
518 Lake St., Nelson, V1L 4C6
Reg. Manager, Ross Tozer

Vancouver Forest Region
4595 Canada Way, Burnaby, V5G 4L9
Reg. Manager, Ken Ingram

MINISTRY OF GOVERNMENT MANAGEMENT SERVICES
468 Belleville St., Victoria, V8V 1W9
General Inquiry: (604) 387-7933

MINISTER'S OFFICE
Minister, The Hon. Clifford Michael

DEPUTY MINISTER'S OFFICE
Dep. Minister, Allen Brent

Privatization and Communications Division
Asst. Dep. Minister, Peter Clark
Privatization Director, Heather Dickson
Communications Director, John Glaab

Government Services Division
Asst. Dep. Minister, Jerry Woytack
Supply Operations
Exec. Director, Vern Burkhardt
Air Services Branch
Director, John M. Taylor
Postal Services Director, Bob Goy
Vehicle Management Branch
Director, Lorrie Adam
Computer Systems Branch
Director, Byron Barnard
Financial Services Branch
Comptroller, Ian G. Fraser
Personnel Management Branch
Director, Vacant

Government Personnel Services Division
Asst. Dep. Minister, Gary Moser
Policy, Benefits and Program Review
Director, Wayne Scale
Labour Relations
Director, Ron McEachern

AGENCIES, BOARDS AND COMMISSIONS

B.C. Buildings Corp.
3350 Douglas St., Box 1112
Victoria, V8W 2T4
President and C.E.O., Dennis Truss

B.C. Enterprise Centre
750 Pacific Boulevard S.
Vancouver, V6B 5E7
Director, Brian Dolsen
Event Services
Division Manager, Kathie Moseley

B.C. Pavilion Corp.
3rd Flr., 770 Pacific Blvd. S.
Vancouver, V6B 5E6
President, Michael Horsey
Marketing
Vice-President, Warren Buckley
Convention Sales
Director, Ernie Pshebnisky
Event Sales Director, Phil Heard
Manager, Brenda Sandes
Conferences Sales Manager, Bill Ellwyn

B.C. Systems Corp.
4000 Seymour Pl., Victoria, V8X 4S8
Chairman, Geoffrey J. Hook
Members:
Donald Buchanan, Hon. M.B. Couvelier,
William E. Evans, Michael J. Falkins,
Robert J. Gayton, J. Roger Webber

Pacific National Exhibition
Box 69020, Exhibition Park
Vancouver, V5K 4W3

The Pacific National Exhibition, a provincially chartered public institution, celebrated its 75th birthday in 1982. Located near the geographical centre of the Greater Vancouver area, the PNE's 15 buildings on approximately 69.6 hectares annually accommodate over six million people for events such as trade and consumer shows, conventions, meetings, rallies, and horse shows. The Exhibition provides facilities for all major sports, including professional and amateur hockey, soccer, football and basketball; and the B.C. Sports Hall of Fame. Pari mutuel thoroughbred racing is a popular event between April and October, while the 17-day annual fair held in late August/early September usually draws over 1.25 million people. An amusement park, Playland, is open from March through Labour Day.

The 18.2 hectares of parking lots can accommodate more than 7,000 vehicles, and can be used for heavy equipment shows and demonstrations.

President, Erwin Swangard
Gen. Manager, Russ W. Smith
Fair Planning
Division Manager, Brian Ratcliffe
Operations
Division Manager, Jim Barr
Marketing and Sales
Division Manager, Neil Story
Communications and Public Relations
Manager, Roger Young

Purchasing Commission
2nd Flr., 4000 Seymour Pl.
Victoria, V8X 4Y3

The Purchasing Commission is the central procurement agency for the Government of British Columbia, responsible to the Legislative Assembly under the *Purchasing Commission Act.* The Commission membership includes a full-time chairman and two part-time members appointed by the Lieutenant-Governor in Council.

For administrative purposes, the Commission reports to the Minister of Government Management Services.

The Commission exists to ensure that the procurement, management and disposal of public goods is undertaken in a manner that guarantees probity, professional service, best overall value, and economic benefit to the people of B.C. Purchases are valued at $500 million annually.

The Purchasing Commission is organized into four operating branches: Executive Services, Supplier Development, Purchasing, and Supply Management Services.

Chairman, Vacant
CEO, C.S. Hutchings
Exec. Co-ordinator, C. Laforest
Exec. Secretary, S.M. Robertson
Supplier Development Branch
Director, F.A. Leonard
Purchasing Branch Director, P. Sloan
Supply Management Services
Director, L. Lee

Superannuation Commission
Parliament Bldgs., Victoria, V8V 4R5

The Superannuation Commission, through its commissioner, provides policy direction as well as all administrative and support services for the operation of eight pension plans and employee health and welfare benefits for employees of the public service only. These services include receipt of contributions, calculation and payment of pensions and refunds, short-term and long-term investment of available funds, maintenance of accounting and statistical records, and counselling of contributors and employers.

Superannuation Commissioner, John W. Cook
Benefits and Policy Director, M.A. Marriott
Finance Director, V. Barwin
Information Management
Director, J.L. Arduini
Accounts Manager, L.A. Jacobi
Contributor Services Manager, Vacant
Counselling Services
Manager, R.K. Hesketh
Systems Manager, P. Seward
Employee Benefits Manager, C. Browne
Pensioner Services Manager, D. Noga
Special Services Manager, S. Quan
Financial Systems Analyst, B. Pollard
Financial Systems Officer, Vacant

Vancouver Trade and Convention Centre
Ste. 200-999 Canada Pl.
Vancouver, V6C 3C1
Convention and Incentive Sales
Manager, David Freestone
Convention Sales Manager, Ken Evans
Corporate Sales Manager, Chris McBeath

Whistler Conference Centre
4010 Whistler Way, Box 1700
Whistler, V0N 1B0
Gen. Manager, Debbie Smythe

MINISTRY OF HEALTH
Rm. 109, Parliament Bldgs.
Victoria, V8V 1X4
(except where otherwise indicated)

MINISTER'S OFFICE
Minister, The Hon. Peter A. Dueck

DEPUTY MINISTER'S OFFICE
1515 Blanshard St., Victoria, V8V 3C8
Dep. Minister, Stan Dubas
Sr. Medical Consultant, Dr. C.B. Henderson
Information Services Branch
Director, Andrew Hume
Operational Review Branch
Director, Glen Nuttall

Management Operations
Asst. Dep. Minister, Leslie T. Foster

FINANCIAL SERVICES DIVISION
Exec. Director, Rod A. Munro
Accounting Operations Branch
Director, W. Boomer
Financial Analysis, Planning and Budgets
Branch
Director, Rod MacDonald
Financial Policy and Internal
Monitoring Branch
Director, Ken MacKay

HUMAN RESOURCES DIVISION
Exec. Director, David Colussi
Sr. Personnel Officer, Carol Pinhey
Labour Management Services Branch
Director, David Torrison
Organization and Classification Branch
Director, Cliff Brown
Staff Development and Safety Programs Branch
Director, Vel Clark

SYSTEMS DIVISION
Exec. Director, Barry Gray
Administration
A/Manager, Lesley Ewing
Ministry of Health Systems
A/Director, Ken Buss
Medical Services Plan and
Management Operations Systems
A/Director, Tim Suttie
System Facilities Director, J. Ross McLaren
Data Management Director, Dave Rees
Legal Services
Director, Gerrit W. Clements

POLICY, PLANNING AND LEGISLATION
DIVISION
Exec. Director, Garry Curtis

Policy Branch Director, Bob de Faye
Associate Director, Jim Redford
Research and Evaluation Branch
Director, Bill Lawrence
Health Economics and Planning Branch
Director, Vicki Farrally

MINISTRY SUPPORT SERVICES DIVISION
Exec. Director, Vacant
Space Planning and Facilities Management
Director, Paddy Langran
Management Services Branch
Director, Roy Natsuhara
VITAL STATISTICS DIVISION
Director, Ron Danderfer
Asst. Director, Judy Dyrland

MEDICAL SERVICES PLAN
A/Exec. Director, John Mullin
Plan Operations
Director, Dan Cunningham
Asst. Director, Vacant
Medical Service Plan Systems
Director, J. Suttie
Medical Consultation Branch
Sr. Medical Consultant,
Doug Schneider, M.D.
Salaried and Sessional Branch
Director, John Greschner
Claims Branch Manager, Janet McGregor
Registration and Premium Billing Branch
Manager, Jack Whittaker
PHARMACARE
Exec. Director, John Herbert

Community and Family Health
Asst. Dep. Minister, Brian Copley
Program Support
A/Exec. Director, A. Campbell

MENTAL HEALTH SERVICES DIVISION
Exec. Director, Bill Fletcher
Consultant in Psychiatry and
Clinical Director, Dr. Walter Goresky
Children's Services Branch
Director, Dr. T. Russell
Acute Care and Adult Services
A/Director, Paul Charron
Alternate Care, A/Director, Vacant
Services to Elderly Branch
Director, Dr. John Gray
Program Support Services Branch
A/Director, Bill Douglas
Regional Operations
A/Director, Dr. Barry Morrison
Regional Managers:
Burnaby, Dr. William Holt
Fraser Valley/North Shore,
Christine Kline
North, Ron Benson
Okanagan/Kootenay, Gary Olsen
Vancouver Island, Dennis Suwala

SERVICES TO THE HANDICAPPED
Exec. Director, Peter Van Rheenen

Clinical Services Director,
Dr. Andre Blanclet
Special Care Services Director, Brad Gee
Support Services Director, David Weicker
Program Planning and Operations
Director, Peter Melhuish
Community Service Development
A/Manager, Derek Underwood

FORENSIC PSYCHIATRIC SERVICES
Exec. Director, Dr. Derek Eaves
Forensic Psychiatric Institute
Director, Adult Services, J.A. Richardson
The Maples Adolescent Treatment Centre
3405 Willingdon Ave., Burnaby, V5G 3H4
Director, F. Bannon
Juvenile Services to Courts
Director, F. Bannon

HEALTH PREVENTION AND PROMOTION
DIVISION
Exec. Director, Rick FitzZaland
Field Operations Director, Dave Sargent
Provincial Health Officer,
Dr. Hugh M. Richards
Fitness Branch Director, Tony Casey
Nutrition Branch
A/Director, Anne Carrow
Speech and Hearing Branch
A/Director, Marilyn Shinto
Public Health Nursing Branch
Director, June Wick
Public Health Inspection Branch
Director, Andrew Hazelwood
Dental Health Services Branch
A/Director, Malcolm Williamson
Epidemiology Consultant, Dr. R. Fish
Community Care Facilities Licensing
Director, Glen Timbers

Institutional Services
Asst. Dep. Minister, Dr. J.C. Lovelace
INSTITUTIONAL MANAGEMENT
RESOURCES DIVISION
Exec. Director, N. Haazen
CONTINUING CARE DIVISION
A/Exec. Director, Andrew Butler

HOSPITAL PROGRAMS DIVISION
Exec. Director, Steve Kenny
Sr. Medical Consultant, Dr. A.R. Hutchinson
Equipment Grants Secretariat
Manager, Danny Dare
Regional Team #1
A/Reg. Team Director, John Cheung
Regional Team #2
Reg. Team Director, Ronald Anderson
Regional Team #3
Reg. Team Director, Ken Fairburn
Regional Team #4
A/Reg. Team Director, Linda Farmer
Regional Team #5
Reg. Team Director, Fred Jessup
Planning and Construction Branch
Director, Walter MacLean

EMERGENCY HEALTH SERVICES
Exec. Director, Fred Bates
Operations Branch Director, Neil Leard
GOVERNMENT INSTITUTIONS
Riverview Hospital
500 Lougheed Hwy.
Port Coquitlam, V3C 1J0
CEO, John Yanske

AGENCIES, BOARDS AND COMMISSIONS

B.C. Centre for Disease Control
828 W. 10th Ave., Vancouver, V5Z 1L8

The British Columbia Centre for Disease Control is a component of the public health service of the province. At the core of its operations is the Provincial Public Health Laboratories, Sexually Transmitted Disease Control and Tuberculosis Control. These services provide referral, reference, and consultation for the investigation, diagnosis, treatment and control of communicable disease. All activities are conducted in accordance with the *Health Act* and the Regulations for the Control of Communicable Disease.

Associated services at the Centre include the Medical Supply Services Branch, which supports the medical needs of patients receiving specialized home maintenance care with the primary service being kidney dialysis. The Radiation Protection Service provides consultation concerning radiation hazards, conducts inspections, and performs laboratory analysis of radiation in the environment. Government Employees Health Services provides occupational health services to all government employees, as well as those of Crown corporations. The dual focus of this service is the promotion of healthy and safe working practices and the assistance of ill or injured workers through assessment, rehabilitation, and monitoring.
Exec. Director, Ron Zapp
Program Support Director, Tom Cox
Pharmacist, John Collinson
Epidemiologist, Dr. John Farley
Government Employee Health Services
Director, Dr. L. Kornder
Radiation Protection Services
Director, Brian Phillips
Provincial Laboratory
Director, Dr. J.A. Smith
Tuberculosis and Willow Chest Clinic
Director, Dr. E.A. Allen
S.T.D. Clinic Director, Dr. Michael Rekart
Kidney Dialysis Service
Director, Margaret Ann Irwin

Dental Technicians' Board
828 West 10th Ave., Vancouver, V5Z 1L8

The Dental Technicians' Board is a government-appointed board under the Minister of Health.

The purpose of the Board is to license and register dental technicians/mechanics and to administer the *Dental Technicians' Act* where work is performed directly with the public.

The Board is responsible for the education and technical training of apprentices, and administers provincial examinations for certification in the trade.

The Dental Technicians' Board is composed of five members, including a chairman, all of whom are appointed for a period of one year, by the Lieutenant-Governor in Council.

Registrar, June Lepinski

Emergency Health Services Commission
1515 Blanshard St., Victoria, V8W 3C8

The Emergency Health Services Commission was established under the *Emergency Health Services Act,* in May 1974. (The name of this Act was changed to *Health Emergency Act* in 1979.)

The primary concern of the Commission has been to provide ambulance service throughout the province. It also has the power and authority to: provide emergency health services; establish, equip and operate emergency health centres and stations; assist hospitals, other health institutions and agencies, municipalities, and other organizations and persons to provide emergency health services, and to train personnel to provide such services; establish and/or improve communications systems for emergency health services; make available the services of medically trained persons on a continuous, continual, or temporary basis to those residents of the province who are not, in the opinion of the Commission, adequately served with existing health services; recruit, examine, train, register and license emergency medical assistants; perform any other function related to emergency health services as the Lieutenant-Governor in Council may order.

Chairman, Stan Dubas

Forensic Psychiatric Services Commission
3405 Willingdon Ave., Burnaby, V5G 3H4

The Forensic Psychiatric Services Commission was established in 1974. Its mandate is granted under the *Forensic Psychiatry Act* (1982). The Commission provides psychiatric and psychological assessments, diagnosis and treatment of individuals with mental disorders who are in conflict with the law.

The Commission operates a number of institutions designed to meet specific areas of need and is staffed by multi-disciplinary teams. Adult Services offers a secured hospital, two adult outpatient clinics and a travelling clinic. Juvenile Services to Courts provides services for Youth Courts and young persons who are in conflict with the law under the *Young Offenders Act.* The Maples is a designated provincial mental health facility under the British Columbia *Mental Health Act.* It is mandated to provide treatment for the most seriously psychiatrically disturbed adolescents, some of whose admissions may be court-related.

The Support Services mandate is to develop and maintain a cross-program human, financial and information resource base, and planning capability responsive to the needs of the Commission.

Chairman, Dr. M. Vallance

Medical Services Commission
1515 Blanshard St., Victoria, V8W 3C8

The *Medical Service Act* of 1967 constituted a Commission appointed by the Lieutenant-Governor to be the public authority responsible to the Minister of Health for administering the Medical Services Plan for all residents of British Columbia.

The Medical Services Plan provides for payment of the costs of required medical, surgical, obstetric and diagnostic services of medical practitioners and certain other limited additional benefits. These services are provided to all eligible British Columbia residents regardless of age, state of health or financial circumstances provided the premiums fixed by the Commission are paid. Premium assistance and temporary premium assistance are available for people with low income or financial hardships. Payment for these insured services is made according to a tariff of fees approved by the Commission.

Chairman, Dr. C.B. Henderson
Secretary, J. Nicholson

MINISTRY OF INTERNATIONAL BUSINESS AND IMMIGRATION
Parliament Bldgs., Victoria, V8V 1X4

MINISTER'S OFFICE
310 Parliament Bldgs., Victoria, V8V 1X4
Minister, The Hon. John Jansen

DEPUTY MINISTER'S OFFICE
Dep. Minister, R. Lorne Seitz

MANAGEMENT OPERATIONS
Exec. Director, Brian Warburton
Financial Services Director, Cathy Bryce
Personnel Services Director, Ben Cator

Investment and Immigration Division
Asst. Dep. Minister, Doug Allen
Business Immigration Director, John Gray
Immigration Policy Director, Stuart Clark
Investment Development Director, Vacant
Institutional Infrastructure
Associate Director, Glen Scobie
Trade Policy Director, Stuart Culbertson

International Marketing Division
Asst. Dep. Minister, J. Chris Poole
Asia Pacific Branch
Director, Harold Middleton
Canada/U.S. Branch
Director, Michael Clark
Europe and Other Markets
Director, Tom Santosham

Asia Pacific Advisory Committee Secretariat
Exec. Director, Robert Merner
Communications Advisor, Norman Stowe
FOREIGN OFFICES:
London
B.C. House London, 1 Regent St.
London SW1Y 4NS, England
Agent General, Garde Gardom, Q.C.
Ottawa
B.C. House Ottawa, Royal Bank Centre
90 Sparks St., Ste. 506, Ottawa, K1P 5B4
Exec. Director, Gordon Edwards
Dusseldorf
Immermannstrasse 65D, D-4000 Dusseldorf
Federal Republic of Germany
Manager, Reinie Koschiuw
Hong Kong
Box 11142, General P.O., Twr. 1, Exchange Sq.
8 Connaught Pl., Hong Kong
Investment and Trade Commissioner,
Dickson Hall
Japan
3F, No. 8 Yoshida Bldg.
27-26, Minami Aoyama 2-chome
Minato-ku, Tokyo 107, Japan
Sr. Representative, Russell Mark
Korea
Box 6299, Kolon Bldg.
45 Mugyo-Dong, Jung-Ku
Seoul 100, Republic of Korea
B.C. Manager, Ray Holland
San Francisco
100 Bush St., San Francisco, CA 94104
Seattle
930-720 Olive Way
Seattle, Washington 98101
Los Angeles
34-3400 Wilshire Blvd.
Los Angeles, CA 90010
Trade and Investment Office
2600 Michelson Dr., Ste. 1050
Irvine, CA 92715

AGENCIES, BOARDS AND COMMISSIONS
B.C. Film Commission
Commissioner, Dianne Neufeld

MINISTRY OF LABOUR AND CONSUMER SERVICES

Parliament Bldgs., Victoria, V8V 1X4
VICTORIA OFFICE:
1019 Wharf St., Victoria, V8V 1X4
BURNABY OFFICE:
4946 Canada Way, Burnaby, V5G 4J6
VANCOUVER OFFICE:
815 Hornby St., Vancouver, V6Z 2E6
(except where otherwise indicated)

MINISTER'S OFFICE
306 Parliament Bldgs., Victoria, V8V 1X4
Minister, The Hon. Lyall Hanson

DEPUTY MINISTER'S OFFICE
Dep. Minister, Lee Doney
Public Services Director, Rick Stevens
Policy and Legislation
Director, Bruce McCulloch

Administration and Consumer Services
Asst. Dep. Minister, Jacqueline Rice
Legal Officer, Gordon Houston

ADMINISTRATION
Finance and Administration
Director, Heinz Schwarz
Personnel Services
Director, Patrick Mulcahy
Information Systems Director, Doug Stuart
CONSUMER SERVICES
Debtor Assistance
Director, Harry Atkinson
Consumer Services and Trade Practices
Registrar, Mike Poulton
Credit Reporting
Registrar, Michael Poulton
Residential Tenancy Branch
Director, Tara McDiarmid
503, 815 Hornby St., Vancouver, V6Z 2E6
Travel Services Registrar, Frank Basiren
503, 815 Hornby St., Vancouver, V6Z 2E6

Labour Relations
Asst. Dep. Minister, Claude Heywood
Employment Standards
Director, Gary Barnes
Compensation Advisory Services
Workers' Advisor, Blake Williams
8171 Ackroyd Rd., Richmond, V6X 3K1
Employers' Advisor, Lynn Joli
8171 Ackroyd Rd., Richmond, V6X 3K1

LIQUOR CONTROL AND LICENSING
A/Gen. Manager, Tom Venner
LIQUOR DISTRIBUTION BRANCH
3200 E. Broadway, Vancouver, V5M 1Z6
Gen. Manager, David A. Anderson
Internal Audit Director, Dennis W. Chung
Systems and Data Processing
A/Director, Phil Bulled
Merchandising and Communications
Director, Maurice Walford
Finance Director, Laurie N. Dyer
Store Operations Director, Bill Cross
Purchasing Director, Peter W. Choate
Distribution Director, Bruce D. Wilkinson
Security Services
Director, Jordan R. Bowcott
Personnel Services
Director, Patrick Malcahy

ALCOHOL AND DRUG PROGRAMS
1019 Wharf St., Victoria, V8V 1X4
Exec. Director, David Gilbert
Medical Advisor, Dr. Doug Graham
Program Support Services
A/Director, Valerie Lannon

Program Development and Prevention
Manager, Vacant

REGIONAL MANAGERS:

Greater Vancouver
1202-601 W. Broadway, Vancouver, V5Z 4C2
Dr. Carl Stroh

Fraser Valley
201, 10090-152nd St., Surrey, V3R 8X8
Pat Gilchrist

Okanagan-Kootenays
532 Leon St., Kelowna, V1Y 6J6
Larry Barter

Vancouver Island
20-5th St., Nanaimo, V9R 1M7
Joe Leins

AGENCIES, BOARDS AND COMMISSIONS

B.C. Council of Human Rights
1019 Wharf St., Victoria, V8V 1X4

The mandate of the B.C. Council of Human Rights is to administer and enforce the *Human Rights Act* as well as to foster an awareness of the principles of human rights and individual rights and responsibilities under the Act.

The five-member Council is appointed under the *Human Rights Act* and is authorized to receive, investigate and adjudicate complaints alleging discrimination on the basis of sex, colour, ancestry, place of origin, religion, marital status, physical or mental disability, or sex and, in certain cases, age, political belief, and unrelated criminal or summary convictions.

Chairman, John Joe
A/Manager, Alan Andsion

Industrial Relations Council
1125 Howe St., Vancouver, V6Z 2K8

The Industrial Relations Council of British Columbia was brought into existence by the *Industrial Relations Reform Act,* which amended the *Labour Relations Act.* The Council was formerly called the Labour Relations Board.

The Council is a quasi-judicial agency which administers the *Industrial Relations Act* and the *Public Service Labour Relations Act.* As well, the Council has limited authority under certain related legislation. Its major functions include the regulation of the acquisition and termination of bargaining rights by trade unions, councils of trade unions and employers' associations; the determination of unfair labour practices; the regulation of strikes, lockouts, and picketing; and the review of decisions of arbitration boards. The Council has broad authority to make declarations and determinations concerning matters which arise under the *Industrial Relations Act* and related legislation.

The Council is divided into a Disputes Resolution Division and an Industrial Relations Adjudication Division to deal with contract negotiations and arbitration respectively. The divisions deal with many applications on the basis of the submissions of the parties and the reports of the investigating officers. However, they also hold formal hearings where it proves necessary to do so. All final decisions of the Council are issued in writing.

In addition to the above powers, which were mostly held by the previous Labour Relations Board, a number of new powers were created in the *Industrial Relations Reform Act.* The Council has greater authority to decertify or take into trusteeship local unions; it has the authority to act in the "public interest" to end strikes or lockouts; and it may ensure the provision of "essential services".

The Council currently consists of a commissioner, several vice-chairmen (who are appointed as chairmen or registrars of the divisions as needed) and members who are representative of both employers and employees. The commissioner and vice-chairmen are assisted by a staff of lawyers and the Disputes Resolution Division employs a cadre of mediators. The Council also employs investigating officers, who investigate matters before the Council and assist the parties in achieving informal resolution of disputes.

Commissioner, Edward R. Peck
Disputes Resolution Division

Chairman, Darwin Benson
Adjudication Division

Chairman, Bud Gallagher
Registrar, Ken Albertini
Finance and Administration
Manager, Andy Danyliu

Insurance Corp. of B.C.
151 W. Esplanade St.
North Vancouver, V7M 3H9

The Insurance Corporation of British Columbia is a self-supporting provincial Crown corporation which employs about 2,600 people. Its primary function is to administer Autoplan, a compulsory automobile insurance program introduced in British Columbia on March 1, 1974. The Corporation is the exclusive supplier of compulsory basic liability coverage and accident benefits to all licensed motor vehicles in the province. In competition with other insurance companies doing business in B.C., it also offers a comprehensive range of optional auto coverages.

Chairman, Raymond J. Addington
President and CEO, Thomas E. Holmes

Office of the Fire Commissioner
2780 E. Broadway St., Vancouver, V5M 1Y8

The Fire Commissioner administers the *Fire Services Act,* which covers requirements for fire prevention in the province. The *Municipal Act* provides for municipalities, if they so wish, to form fire departments to carry out fire suppression in their areas.

The primary responsibilities of the Fire Commissioner are as follows:

a) to collect and disseminate information about fires in the province;

b) to conduct investigations and inquiries into fires;

c) to investigate conditions under which fires are likely to occur;

d) to study methods of fire prevention; and

e) to establish minimum standards for selection and training of fire services personnel.

Forest fire protection, because of its special nature, is the responsibility of the Protection Branch, Ministry of Forests and Lands.

To assist in the administration of the *Fire Services Act,* there is a Division of Fire Safety and regional offices in Nanaimo, Kamloops, Cranbrook, Prince George, and Vancouver. There are also over 700 local assistants to the Fire Commissioner who enforce the Act and Regulations. A local assistant may be the local fire chief, fire prevention officer, or in unorganized areas, a Royal Canadian Mounted Police officer.

There are about 3,000 full-time career fire fighters, 5,000 volunteers and 300 industrial fire fighters in approximately 300 fire departments within British Columbia.

A/Fire Commissioner, Richard Dumala
A/Dep. Fire Commissioner, Robert Hickey

Travel Assurance Board
503, 815 Hornby St., Vancouver, V6Z 2E6

The Travel Assurance Board is an independent body of members appointed by the Minister of Labour and Consumer Services to determine the eligibility of claims and to administer the travel assurance fund.

Chairman, Gustav Kroll
Secretary, Frank Basiren

University Endowment Lands
5495 Chancellor Blvd., Vancouver, V6T 1E2

The University Endowment Lands are an unincorporated territory, owned and administered by the provincial government, under the provisions of the *University Endowment Land Act.*

The U.E.L. consists of 1,018 hectares of Crown land and privately held residential and commercial properties. Its administration has been a provincial responsibility since 1920, and the current program is one of providing the delivery of local government services such as zoning, building permits, public works maintenance and fire protection.

Manager, Bruce Stenning

Workers' Compensation Board
6951 Westminster Hwy., Richmond, V7C 1C6

The Workers' Compensation Board (WCB) of B.C. is a provincial agency established by the *Workers' Compensation Act* of 1917.

The WCB has three primary objectives:

1) the prevention of industrial injury and disease;

2) the payment of compensation benefits to workers who are injured or diseased as a result of their employment or to the dependents of fatally injured or diseased workers; and

3) the collection of assessments from employers to fund the operations of the Workers' Compensation Board.

Chairman, Jim Nielsen
Commissioners: Bev Korman, Joan Nutter, Erik Wood
Board Secretary, Ed Bates
Human Resources
Director, George Balfour

COMPENSATION AND MEDICAL SERVICES DIVISION
Gen. Manager, R.W. Taylor
Medical Counsel, Dr. F. Norm Rigby
Claims and Rehabilitation
Director, Art Quinn
Medical Services
Exec. Director, Dr. Tony Nichini
Physical Rehabilitation
Director, Dr. J.R. Naismith
Clinic Director, Thomas Wharton

FINANCIAL SERVICES DIVISION
Gen. Manager, Robert Gunn
Chief Revenue Officer, Vacant
Assessment Director, H.S. DuGas
Statistical Services
Co-ordinator, Keith Mason
Actuary, Keith Younie
Treasurer, William Evans
Controller, Doug Smith
Chief Information Officer, W. Kurz
Development Services Director, Don Calder
Computer Services Director, M. Marriott
Internal Audit Manager, Tom Hum

ADMINISTRATIVE SERVICES DIVISION
Gen. Manager, Grant McMillan
Community Relations
Director, Alastair Gordon
Technical Services Director, Roy Holloway
OCCUPATIONAL HEALTH AND SAFETY DIVISION
Gen. Manager, F.W. Greer
Research and Standards
Director, A.L. Riegert
Field Services Director, H. Carruthers
Occupational Health
Director, Dr. W. Whitehead

Workers' Compensation Review Board
3000-8171 Ackroyd Rd.
Richmond, V6X 3K1

The Review Board is a quasi-judicial administrative agency responsible for determining appeals under the *Workers' Compensation Act* of British Columbia. Vice-chairmen and members are appointed by the Lieutenant-Governor in Council. The agency is independent of the Workers' Compensation Board. It deals with approximately 5,000 appeal cases per year.

Members appointed to the boards of review

have a background in labour or management, while the chairmen are lawyers or former members. Each panel consists of a labour and a management member and a vice-chairman. A decision of the majority is the decision of the panel.

The jurisdiction of the Review Board is confined to decisions of an officer of the Workers' Compensation Board made with respect to a worker. Therefore, a decision of an officer of the Board with respect to an employer cannot be appealed to this agency.

All findings of the boards of review are rendered in writing. At the discretion of the Board, an oral hearing may be held before the decision is made. Further appeals are available under the *Workers' Compensation Act* to a Medical Review Panel or to the Commissioners of the Workers' Compensation Board.

Chairman, Jack D. Bibby
Sr. Vice-chairman, G.D. Strongitharm
Registrar and Vice-Chairman, Judith Williamson
Dep. Registrar, Walter Peain
Administration Manager, Bev Greenlaw
VICE-CHAIRMEN: Wally Auerbach, Michelle Gelfand, Tom Kennedy, Iain Macdonald, Isabel Otter, Brian Prentice, Peter Steele, Clinton Foote, Mike Karton, Robin Kimpton, Mike O'Brien, Tom Petras, Jim Renwick, Bill Beeby

MINISTRY OF MUNICIPAL AFFAIRS, RECREATION AND CULTURE
747 Fort St., Victoria, V8W 3E1
(except where otherwise indicated)
General Inquiries: (604) 387-7912

MINISTER'S OFFICE
301 Parliament Bldgs., Victoria, V8V 1X4
Minister, The Hon. Rita Johnston

DEPUTY MINISTER'S OFFICE
Dep. Minister, Ken MacLeod
Asst. Dep. Minister, Gary Harkness
Inspector of Municipalities, Ken MacLeod

Culture, Recreation and Historic Resources
Asst. Dep. Minister, Barry Kelsey
Provincial Museum Director, W. Barkley
Cultural Services Branch
Director, Richard Brownsey
Recreation and Sport Branch
Director, Russell Irvine
Library Services Branch
A/Director, Barbara Greenhiaus
Heritage Conservation Branch
Director, Colin K. Campbell

Policy and Services Division
Asst. Dep. Minister, Vacant

Finance, Administration and Systems
Director, Larry Seminiuk
Facilities and Services Manager, Allan Goldade
Financial Operations Manager, Dave Smith
Financial Planning and Analysis
Manager, Harold Hilton
Information Systems
A/Director, Mike Chadwick
Personnel Services Director, Lorne Bulmer
Public Affairs Director, Philip Newton
Municipal Engineering Services
Director, Andrew MacTaggart
Municipal Administration Services
Director, Norman McCrimmon
Improvement District Section
Manager, Robert Rounds

DEVELOPMENT SERVICES BRANCH
Exec. Director, Erik Karlsen
Islands Trust and Projects Section
Manager, Cynthia Hawksworth
Programs Section Manager, Elizabeth Cull
Organizational Policy Branch
Director, Gary Paget
Policy and Research Branch
Director, Brian Walisser
Engineering Services
Director, Andrew MacTaggart
Municipal Administrative Services
Director, Norman McCrimmon
Municipal Financial Services
Exec. Director, Al Tamblin
Group I Manager, Neil Goldie
Group II Manager, John H. MacDonald
Improvement District Section
Manager, Robert Rounds

Safety and Standards Division
Asst. Dep. Minister, Gary Harkness
Building Standards Branch
633 Courtney St., Victoria, V8V 1X4
Director, Jack Robertson
Downtown Revitalization Program
747 Fort St., Victoria V8W 3E1
Administrator, Martin Thomas
Safety Engineering Services
Director, George McAffer
Boiler and Pressure Vessel Safety Branch
Director, Ray Mullaney
Field Operations Manager, Alf Miller
Electrical Safety Branch
Director, Dr. James Hill
Field Operations Manager, Joe Laminski
Elevating Devices Safety Branch
Director, Roy Broderick
Field Operations Manager, Nick Keogh
Gas Safety Branch
Director, Gordon Cherry
Field Operations Manager, Graham Turnbull

AGENCIES, BOARDS AND COMMISSIONS
Board of Examiners
c/o Ministry of Municipal Affairs
747 Fort St., Victoria, V8W 3E1

The Board of Examiners is established under section 879 of the *Municipal Act* of the Province of British Columbia. It is comprised of three members appointed by the Lieutenant-Governor in Council on the recommendation of the minister.

The main function of the Board is the granting of certificates of proficiency in the areas of administration and finance to persons in municipal employment. Requirements for certification are the attainment of a recognized level of academic qualification, together with the appropriate amount of work experience in the local government field.

The Board also administers a provincially funded scholarship program established to commemorate the 75th anniversary of the Union of British Columbia Municipalities. This program provides financial assistance to persons working in local government in the province who wish to upgrade their professional skills through enrolment in post-secondary courses of study and/or attendance at workshops or seminars relating to local government administration.

The Municipal Officers' Assn. has established an Education Council which acts in the capacity of an advisory council to assist the Board in the performance of its various duties.

Chairman, Christopher L. Woodward
Members: W.S. Fleming, R. Taylor

B.C. Arts Board
Parliament Bldgs., Victoria, V8V 1X4

The British Columbia Arts Board is an advisory body to the Minister of Municipal Affairs, Recreation and Culture. The Board was established in 1974 and consists of 15 members. These people are appointed by the minister and represent all regions of the province and the various cultural disciplines.

The B.C. Arts Board is involved in the determination of policies and grants in the professional and community arts. It is supported in its work by advisory committees in each artistic discipline and by the professional staff of the Cultural Services Branch.

The Board recommends policies and financial programs in the arts to the minister. However, the minister has the right to approve such programs submitted to and reviewed by the ministry without referral to the Board.

Chairman, Philip Keatley

B.C. Heritage Trust
Parliament Bldgs., Victoria, V8V 1X4

The B.C. Heritage Trust receives its mandate from the *Heritage Conservation Act* of 1977. Its purpose is to "encourage and facilitate the conservation, maintenance, and restoration of heritage property in the Province". This mandate is carried out primarily through its grant programs, which consist of the following:

- the Publications Assistance Program, which provides assistance for the publication of materials dealing with the province's urban and rural heritage, or technical aspects of the conservation field;
- Planning and Inventory, which assists municipalities, villages, and regional districts with inventory surveys of heritage buildings, sites, heritage resources, or planning studies;
- the Scholarship Program, under which the Trust awards three scholarships per year to graduate students in the fields of B.C. history/archival studies, B.C. architecture or B.C. archaeology;
- the Building Restoration Program, which assists with the exterior restoration of religious and other heritage buildings (but not usually private buildings or dwellings);
- the Heritage Area Revitalization Program, which is intended to rehabilitate well-defined networks of streets that are accessible to the public;
- the Historical Archaeology Program, which provides financial assistance for historical archaeology projects;
- the Commemorative Monuments Program, which supports the erection of monuments commemorating people, places or events of provincial or national significance in B.C.;
- the Religious Building Restoration Program, which assists with exterior restoration of designated heritage buildings of a religious nature;
- the Student Employment Program, which provides B.C. university students with opportunities to develop skills in the area of heritage conservation;
- the Conference Program, which assists organizations hosting conferences, seminars, lectures or workshops that will examine aspects of B.C.'s heritage; and
- additional activities funds projects that do not meet the criteria of the existing programs.

Apart from being a granting agency which offers financial assistance to local government bodies, heritage societies, and other organizations, it also initiates B.C. heritage conferences and provides funds to local groups to employ university students in heritage-related projects.

Chairman, Vacant

BC Transit
1200 W. 73rd Ave., Ste. 1500
Vancouver, V6P 6G5

BC Transit is a Crown corporation that serves over 2.1 million people throughout British Columbia. The Corporation's 27 conventional transit systems in Greater Vancouver, Greater Victoria and 25 communities across the province carry 115 million people annually.

The provincial fleet consists of 1,094 conventional buses and trolleys, 139 handyDART vehicles, 12 paratransit vehicles, two SeaBus ferries, and 114 rapid transit cars. BC Transit operates with a total budget of $352.4 million. Costs are shared by the province, local government, and transit riders. The running of the Corporation is a co-operative partnership combining centralized planning, marketing, and financial services with a strong component of local decision-making.

In Greater Vancouver and Greater Victoria, for instance, transit commissions comprising locally elected representatives from member municipalities decide on local matters, including: setting fares, determining new routes and levels of service, and raising the local share of transit costs through taxation. In smaller communities, municipal councils and regional district boards provide similar direction. Opportunities for private sector participation are extensive.

Chairman and CEO, Stuart M. Hodgson
Directors: Gordon Campbell, Frank Carson, Eric Clarke, Jackie Drysdale, Don Lanskail, Don Ross, Jim Stuart, William Vogel
Corporate Secretary, Victor Irving
Regional Vice-President (Vancouver), Vacant
Corporate Services
Exec. Vice-President, John M. Cawood
Finance
Exec. Vice-President, R. Krowchuk
Planning and Scheduling
Vice-President, J. Mills
Vancouver (Lower Mainland) Operations
Vice-President, Brian Beattie
Communications and Marketing Services
Director, George Stroppa
Victoria and the Small Communities
Reg. Vice-President and Gen. Manager, Robert G. Lingwood

Islands Trust
747 Fort St., Victoria
MAILING ADDRESS:
Parliament Bldgs., Victoria, V8W 3E1
General Inquiry: (604) 387-5219

The Islands Trust is an agency established in 1974 by an Act of the British Columbia Legislature. The *Islands Trust Act* gives the Trust the responsibility of preserving and protecting the unique amenities and environment of the trust area for the benefit of the people of the islands and the province generally.

In 1977, the British Columbia Legislature amended the *Islands Trust Act* to transfer authority for all land planning matters on the islands to the Islands Trust from the regional districts.

Chairman, Nick Gilbert
Vice-Chairman, Carol Martin
Vice-Chairman, John Dunfield

Provincial Capital Commission
835 Humboldt St., Victoria V8V 4W8

The British Columbia Provincial Capital Commission (PCC) is a corporate entity with the Minister of Municipal Affairs, Recreation and Culture being responsible for reporting to the Legislature on its behalf. Although the legislation creating the PCC only goes back to 1977, its origins date from the first meeting of the Capital Improvement District Commission held on June 5, 1956. The PCC, a semi-autonomous corporate body, is established by the *Capital Commission Act.* The Act calls for a Commission of 14 persons. Eight of the appointments are made by Order-in-Council, including those of the chairman and vice-chairman. The four core municipalities of Greater Victoria appoint, by by-law, the remaining six commissioners from among their members or the citizenry at large.

The PCC has jurisdiction over 45 properties within the Capital Improvement District, an area of approximately 40,065 hectares. The PCC's mandate is to enhance and beautify the environment of the Capital Region.

The majority of the PCC's beautification work has taken place in co-operation with, and often at the initiation of area municipalities. Since 1956, the PCC has expended or committed some $8 million on almost 100 different beautification projects in the Capital Region in association with Greater Victoria municipalities.

Chairman, Kenneth Hill
Exec. Director, Larry R. Beres
Projects Manager, G. Ken Patton

MINISTRY OF PARKS
810 Blanshard St., Victoria, V8V 1X5

MINISTER'S OFFICE
323 Parliament Bldgs., Victoria, V8V 1X4

Minister, The Hon. Terry Huberts

Assoc. Dep. Minister,
Stephen R. Stackhouse

Asst. Dep. Minister, J. Masselink
Communications Manager, Ed Wall

PARK PROGRAMS
4000 Seymour Pl., Victoria, V8V 1X5
A/Director, Bob Dalziel
Finance and Administration
Manager, Jennifer Pite
Planning and Ecological Reserves
Manager, Derek Thompson
Visitor Services
A/Manager, John Block
Resource Services Manager, Denis Moffatt

REGIONAL DIRECTORS:

South Coast Region
1610 Indian River Dr.
North Vancouver, V7G 1L3
G. Trachuk

Southern Interior Region
101, 1050 W. Columbia St.
Kamloops, V2C 1L4
Tom Moore

Northern B.C. Region
1011-4th Ave., Prince George, V2L 3H9
Struan Robertson

MINISTRY OF REGIONAL DEVELOPMENT

Parliament Bldgs., Victoria, V8V 1X4

MINISTER'S OFFICE
Minister, The Hon. Elwood Veitch

DEPUTY MINISTER'S OFFICE
Dep. Minister, Bob Plecas

Business Development Division
Asst. Dep. Minister, C.D. Nelson
Business Development Branch
A/Director, G. Beatty
Regional Development Branch
Director, C. Dary
Business Finance Branch
Director, M. Lofthouse
Equity Programs Director, G. Blair
Info. Business Centre
750 Pacific Blvd. S., Vancouver, V6B 5E7
A/Director, B. Dolsen

Economic Development Division
Asst. Dep. Minister, S.R. Hollett
Economic Analysis and Strategy Branch
Director, Bill Freeman
Resources and Infrastructure
Director, F. Blasetti
Trade Policy Director, S. Culbertson
Government Agents
Director, W.D. Mitchell
Communications Programs Branch
Director, Elaine Kozak
Manager, P.M. Templeman

TOURISM DEVELOPMENT DIVISION
Project Director, Peter Maundrell
Personnel Services Director, R.C. Webber
Financial Services Director, W. Edwards
Computing Services
Director, Flemming Anderson
Central Services Manager, P. Gardener
Surveys and Resource Mapping Branch
Director, G. Sawayama
Environmental Laboratory
3650 Westbrook Cres., Vancouver, V6S 2L2
Director, R. Swingle

MINISTRY OF SOCIAL SERVICES AND HOUSING

Parliament Bldgs., Victoria, V8V 1X4

MINISTER'S OFFICE
128 Parliament Bldgs., Victoria, V8V 1X4
Minister, The Hon. Claude Richmond

DEPUTY MINISTER'S OFFICE
Dep. Minister, R.K. Butler
Asst. Dep. Ministers: S.G. Travers,
R.F. Cronin, T.J. Pyper

SUPERINTENDENT'S OFFICE
Sup't of Family and
Child Service, Leslie Arnold
Dep. Sup't, B. Talbot

DIVISIONS
Finance Division
Comptroller, Stew Churlish
Administrative Services Division
Director, Morris Wadds
Corporate Services Division
A/Director, Ron Willems
Family and Children's Services Division
Director, P. Buchanan
Income Assistance Division
A/Director, G. Tadsen
Information Services
Director, Sharon Russell
Personnel Administration/Staff Training
Director, Russell Dean
Rehabilitation and Support
Services Division
Director, Ms. Paula Grant
Services to Seniors
Supervisor, Lynda Clark
Health Services Section
916 Johnson St., Victoria, V5V 3N4
A/Manager, S. Doyle

REGIONAL OFFICES:

Vancouver/Richmond- Region A
270-1200 W. 73rd Ave.
Vancouver, V6P 6G5
Reg. Director, Joyce Preston

Vancouver/Howe Sound- Region B
411 Dunsmuir St., 4th Flr.
Vancouver, V6B 1X4
Reg. Director, Fred Milowsky

Fraser North- Region C
105-504 Cottonwood Ave.
Coquitlam, V3J 2R5
Reg. Director, Elaine Murray

Fraser South- Region D
202, 17618-58th Ave., Surrey, V3S 1L3
Reg. Director, Jean Macdonald

Okanagan/Kootenay- Region F
204, 1433 St. Paul St., Kelowna, V1Y 2E4
Reg. Director, Larry Ohlmann

South Central Interior- Region G
201-180 Seymour St., Kamloops, V2C 2E2
Reg. Director, Geoff Eggleton

Prince George/Cariboo- Region H
409, 280 Victoria St.
Prince George, V2L 4X3
Reg. Director, Chris Haynes

North- Region J
208, 1011-4th Ave., Prince George, V2L 3H9
Reg. Director, Suzanne Veit

North Island- Region K
Ste. 10, 2480 Kenworth Rd., Nanaimo, V9T 3Y3
Reg. Director, Terry Prysiazniuk

South Island- Region L
4573 Blenkinsop Rd., Victoria, V8X 2C7
Reg. Director, Bill MacBeth

RESIDENTIAL RESOURCES FOR THE MENTALLY HANDICAPPED

Woodlands
9 East Columbia St.
New Westminster, V3L 3V5
Exec. Director, Susan Poulos

AGENCIES, BOARDS COMMISSIONS AND CROWN CORPORATIONS

B.C. Housing Management Commission
Ste. 1701, 4330 Kingsway
Burnaby, V5H 4G7

The British Columbia Housing Management Commission, established as an agency of the Province of British Columbia in 1967, is governed by Order-in-Council No. 2388 dated Sept. 7, 1978. In addition to its role in managing rental housing developed and financed under provincial and federal-provincial agreements, the Commission also administers federal-provincial rent supplement programs. The Commission, in all its programs and activities, is accountable to the Minister of Social Services and Housing.

The Commission now provides direct property management services for approximately 8,000 units of housing in 118 developments. More than 15,000 people in 46 municipalities throughout the province are accommodated.

The Board of Commissioners is appointed by the Lieutenant-Governor in Council.

Chairman, Vacant
Gen. Manager, J.C. Leman
Corporate Secretary, Erica Westley
Field Operations Branch
Director, Peter Robinson
Development Technical Services Branch
Director, Richard Staehli
Social Housing Branch
Director, Enid Buchanan
Financial and Administrative
Services Branch Director, R.L. Matthews
Personnel and Labour Relations Services
Manager, Sylvia Porter

REGIONAL OFFICES:

Burrard Regional Office
203, 1661 W. 8th Ave.
Vancouver, V6J 1V1
Reg. Manager, Chris Teply

Central Regional Office
135 E. 8th Ave., Vancouver, V5T 1R8
Reg. Manager, Sandra Sharkey

Fraser Regional Office
200, 10252-135 St., Surrey, V3T 4C2
Reg. Manager, Dorothy Wilson

Interior Regional Office-Northern
305 Scotia Bank Bldg.
1488-4th Ave., Prince George, V2L 4Y2
Reg. Manager, Tom Proudlock

Interior Regional Office-Southern
290 Nanaimo Ave. W., Penticton, V2A 1N5
Reg. Manager, Tom Proudlock

Coastal Regional Office
Coastal Region
201, 3440 Douglas St., Victoria, V8Z 3L5
Reg. Manager, George Lawrie
Coastal Region-Prince Rupert
1400 Kootenay Ave., Prince Rupert, V8J 3X5
Manager, Linda Movold

MINISTRY OF SOLICITOR GENERAL
Parliament Bldg., Victoria, V8V 1X4
General Inquiries: (604) 387-4574

MINISTER'S OFFICE
124 Parliament Bldg., Victoria, V8V 1X4
Solicitor General, The Hon. Angus Ree

DEPUTY SOLICITOR GENERAL'S OFFICE
Dep. Solicitor General,
Dennis T.R. Murray, Q.C.
A/Commissioner of Corrections, Jim Graham
Asst. to the Commissioner, Tim Stiles

Police Services Branch
Asst. Dep. Minister, Robin Bourne
Police Services Policy Division
Director, Vacant
Policing Programs Division
Director, Vacant
Security Program Division
Director, Lorne M. Newson
Co-ordinated Law Enforcement Unit (CLEU)
Director, Peter Engstad
Provincial Emergency Program
Director, Murray C. Stewart

MOTOR VEHICLE DEPARTMENT
Licenses
2631 Douglas St., Victoria, V8T 5A3
Sup't, Keith P. Jackman
Dep. Sup't, Grant Tyndall
Internal Review (Audit) Unit
Manager, Ian Walpole
Drivers Licence Branch
Manager, June Byers
Vehicle Licences Branch
Manager, Geoff R. Amy
Prorate, Reciprocal and Financial Responsibility
A/Manager, Jackie Franklin
Administration and Roads Safety Branch
Director, John F. Phillips
Commercial Transport Branch
Manager, John McDicken
Motor Carrier Branch
Inspector, Vacant
Standards and Compliance Branch
Director, Phillip Toogood
Vehicle Inspection Branch
Manager, Gerry W. Brown

SUPPORT AND REGULATORY BRANCH
Film Classification Division
Director, Mary-Louise McCausland

Public Gaming Branch
Director, Cary R. Crobeil

AGENCIES, BOARDS AND COMMISSIONS

B.C. Board of Parole
301, 10090-152nd St., Surrey, V3R 8X8

The Board of Parole is the decision-making authority which determines whether or not parole will be granted to inmates incarcerated in provincial correctional centres in B.C. This authority is based on the provisions of the *Parole Act* (Canada) and was assumed on behalf of the Province of British Columbia in February 1980.

The Board is constituted by Order-in-Council of the Lieutenant-Governor and is currently comprised of a full-time chairman and 23 community members. Terms of appointment are time-limited. The Board reflects a strong community orientation in that its membership consists of citizens drawn from many walks of life and from communities throughout the province.

The Office of the Chairman consists of administrative, clerical and support staff and is under the general management of the executive director of the Board.

Chairman, Lynn Stevenson
Exec. Director, Michael E. Redding
MEMBERS:

Interior Region:
Norma Kenoras, Ian Urquhart, Daniel Kilburn

Northern Region:
William Young, Ann McCaffray, A.D. McMillan

Fraser Region:
Rev. Ronald Dowbush, Kathleen Marshall, Magdalene Isaak, Jim Lee, Arthur Thornhill

Vancouver Island Region:
Mary Ann Waldmann, Gerard Edwards, Lloyd Sproule, Virginia Giles, Lyn Greenhill, Susan Knott, Virginia Marshall-Lang, Gerry Turner, Ted Woodyard

B.C. Coroners Service
Imperial Square, 2nd Flr.
4595 Canada Way, Burnaby, V5G 4L9

The British Columbia Coroners Service, headed by the Chief Coroner, is a fact-finding service charged with the investigation and reporting of violent, sudden or unusual deaths. The office of coroner has its roots in the oldest of common law institutions. Modern coroners in British Columbia have been granted extremely powerful judicial authority in connection with their casework, and have access to expert opinion in the forensic fields of pathology, toxicology, odontology, radiology, anthropology and other scientific fields to supplement normal investigations by government agencies. Every province in Canada has some form of modified coroner's system or medical examiner's service.

The Coroners Service has a mandate to investigate and report factually and publicly and, like other court systems, is responsible directly to the public it serves. This mandate may be met adequately by simple investigation of circumstances, or through the more formal judicial procedures of inquiry or inquest. A role in prevention of fatalities is inferred from the ability to propose recommendations when concluding a report or when accepting the verdict of a jury.

Since proclamation of the current legislation (in 1979), the Coroners Service has become decentralized, with regional offices in Nanaimo and Kamloops. A metro network serves the lower mainland.

Chief Coroner, Vincent Cain

B.C. Gaming Commission
848 Courtney St., Victoria, V8V 1X4

The B.C. Gaming Commission was established April 1, 1987 to determine policy with regard to the licensing, conduct, management and operation of gaming activities such as bingos, ticket lotteries and casinos. The Commission is also responsible for issuing licences to charities that use gaming activities to raise funds; licensing casino management companies and commercial bingo halls, and hearing appeals of licence denials, suspensions and revocations. The Commission provides information to the public; sets the terms and conditions respecting the licensing of lottery events in B.C. in consultation with service and charitable organizations and the province's Public Gaming Branch; and responds to written inquiries from the public. The Commission recently completed a report entitled *Report on the Status of Gaming in British Columbia* which was released to the public on March 11, 1988. The Commission is made up of seven members and meets once a month.

Chairman, Richard MacIntosh
Exec. Officer, Gary Hoskins

B.C. Police Commission
405, 815 Hornby St., Vancouver, V6Z 2E6

The Police Commission was established under the *Police Act, 1974,* to insure an adequate standard of police service in the province, and of accountability of the police to the public. The major responsibilities of the Commission are:

(a) to assist in the establishment of minimum standards of police staff selection and training, staff strength, equipment, and facilities;
(b) to ensure compliance with minimum standards of police staff selection and training, staff strength, equipment, and facilities;
(c) to assist municipal forces in the province in the development of higher levels of service;
(d) to promote co-operation, understanding, and positive attitudes towards the police and encourage assistance to citizens by the police;
(e) to ensure compliance with procedures for holding the police accountable to the public;
(f) to ensure, on appeal, fair and impartial disposition of the Private Investigator and Security Agency Licensing applications;

(g) to ensure the Commission's own efficiency, impartiality, and accountability to the minister;

(h) to assist municipal forces in improving the operational efficiency and effectiveness of their organizations; and

(i) to perform such other functions and duties as may be given to it under the *Police Act* or the Regulations.

The B.C. Police Commission consists of not fewer than three members who are appointed by Order-in-Council for a maximum term of five years.

Chairman, David J. Edgar
Members: Mary E. Saunders,
David D. Wilson, Audrey L. Moore
Director, William F. Beamish
Exec. Officer, Insp. Jack Crich
Exec. Officer, Insp. Harry Wallace

B.C. Racing Commission
Ste. 200, 4595 Canada Way
Burnaby, V5G 4L9

Chairman, R. Bruce Harvey, Q.C.
Commissioner-Secretary, Robert E. Collis
Commissioners:
Jack Short, Dr. Gordon L. Davis
Chief Investigator, Wilfred E. Denty

Commercial Appeals Commission
1304, 865 Hornby St., Vancouver, V6Z 2H4

The Commercial Appeals Commission was constituted on Oct. 1, 1982 under the *Commercial Appeals Commission Act*. The Commission hears appeals from decisions rendered under a number of statutes, which currently includes the *Company Act*, the *Credit Reporting Act*, the *Credit Union Act*, the *Insurance Act*, the *Liquor Control and Licensing Act*, the *Liquor Distribution Act*, the *Mortgage Brokers Act*, the *Motor Dealers Act*, the *Real Estate Act*, the *Societies Act*, and the *Travel Agents Act*.

Chairman, Arthur M. Roberts
Vice-Chairman, P.D. Meyers

Criminal Injury Section
6951 Westminster Hwy., Richmond, V7C 1C6

The *Criminal Injury Compensation Act* has been in effect since July 1, 1972. The Act is administered by the Workers' Compensation Board and enables compensation to be provided where a person is injured or killed in B.C. as a result of:

a) the commission of any one of 51 criminal offences set out in the schedule of the Act; or

b) the lawful arrest or attempt to arrest an offender or suspected offender, or assisting a peace officer in making or attempting to make an arrest; or

c) the lawful prevention or attempt to prevent the commission of a criminal offence or suspected offence or assisting a peace officer in preventing or attempting to prevent the commission of such offence or suspected offence.

The funds for the Criminal Injury Program come from the consolidated revenue fund of British Columbia. The province is partly reimbursed by the federal government.

Solicitor, L.C. Timoffee

Justice Institute of B.C.
4180 W. 4th Ave., Vancouver, V6R 4J5

Chairman, Robert J. Stewart
Principal, Lawrence E. Goble

Motion Pictures Appeal Board
2nd Flr., 93-6th St.
New Westminster, V3L 2Z4

Chairman, Neil A. McDiarmid, Q.C.
Admin. Officer, Debra Twerdun

Motor Carrier Commission
108, 4240 Manor St, Burnaby, V5G 3X5

The transportation of goods or persons by motor vehicle for compensation is regulated under licence by the Motor Carrier Commission. The authority of the Commission is derived from a provincial statute, the *Motor Carrier Act*, and from a federal statute, the *Motor Vehicle Transport Act*.

It is the duty of the Commission to regulate motor vehicles with the objects of promoting adequate and efficient service and reasonable and just charges, promoting safety on the public highways, and fostering sound economic conditions in the province's transportation business.

Approximately 3,000 applications are filed each year with the Commission, either for new licences, amendments to existing licence authorities, or transfers of licences.

The Motor Carrier Commission maintains a Motor Carrier Branch in Burnaby, B.C., which is responsible for accepting, investigating and reporting on applications, as well as seven other field offices strategically located throughout the province.

A/Chairman, Gerald M. Morris
Commissioners:
Ian W. Craig, William H. Preston

Order-in-Council Review Board
2nd Flr., 93-6th St.
New Westminster, V3L 2Z4

The Order-in-Council Review Board is comprised of a lawyer, as chairman; a judge; and two psychiatrists.

The Board meets weekly on an informal basis, to review medical records and interview patients held in custody in the Forensic Psychiatric Institute, following a finding by the court of "Not guilty by reason of insanity", or "Unfit to stand trial". In addition, the Board reviews those persons who have been discharged from the Institute and are currently living in the community subject to the conditions of a modified Order-in-Council.

Patients may be represented by legal counsel or

other interested parties at these meetings. Following review, recommendations are made regarding the legal status of these patients and submitted to the Lieutenant-Governor in Council.

Chairman, Neil A. McDiarmid, Q.C.
Admin. Officer, Debra Twerdun

MINISTRY OF TOURISM AND PROVINCIAL SECRETARY
Parliament Bldgs., Victoria, V8V 1X4
(except where otherwise indicated)

MINISTER'S OFFICE
248 Parliament Bldg., Victoria, V8V 1X4
Minister, The Hon. Bill Reid

DEPUTY MINISTER'S OFFICE
247 Parliament Bldg., Victoria, V8V 1X4
Dep. Minister of Tourism and Dep.
Provincial Secretary, Melvin H. Smith, Q.C.
Order-in-Council Administration,
Manager, Bruce deBeck
Public Relations Branch
1117 Wharf St., Victoria, V8W 2Z2
A/Director, Mike Hughes

Support Services
Asst. Dep. Minister, John Mochrie
Financial Services
Director, Marr Henderson
Central Services Director, Gary Loat
Computer Systems Director, Ramsay Millar

Tourism Product and Services
1117 Wharf St., Victoria, V8W 2Z2
Asst. Dep. Minister, Jim Doswell
Tourism Services Director, Rick Lemon
Tourism Product and Planning
Director, Stuart Gale

Tourism Marketing
802, 865 Hornby St., Vancouver, V6Z 2G3
Asst. Dep. Minister, Ad van Haaften
Marketing Director, Don Foxgord
International Marketing
Manager, Donna Dornik
Marketing Services Director, Vacant
Los Angeles Office
34-3400 Wilshire Blvd.
Los Angeles, CA 90010
Sales Manager, John Bateman
San Francisco Office
100 Bush St., San Francisco, CA 94104
Sales Manager, Jean Ohman
Seattle Office
930-720 Olive Way, Seattle, WA 98101
Sales Manager, Karyl Pagel
London Office
1 Regent St., London
England SW1Y 4NS
Sales Manager, Julie Preedy

RESEARCH SERVICES BRANCH
1st Flr., 1117 Wharf St., Victoria V8W 2Z2
Research Services
Director, Jim Lee

Provincial Secretary Programs
3rd Flr., 1117 Wharf St.
Victoria, V8W 2Z2
Asst. Dep. Minister, John Mochrie
Public Programs
Exec. Director, Peter Martin
Lottery Grants
1117 Wharf St., Victoria, V8V 1X4
Director, Vacant
Protocol and Special Services Branch
028 Parliament Bldgs., Victoria, V8V 1X4
Chief of Protocol, David Harris
Elections Branch
421 Menzies St., Victoria, V8V 1X4
Chief Electoral Officer and Registrar-Gen.
of Voters, Harry M. Goldberg
Dep. Chief Electoral Officer
and Dep. Registrar-Gen. of Voters,
Robert A. Patterson

PROVINCIAL ARCHIVES
655 Belleville St., Victoria, V8V 1X4
Provincial Archivist, John A. Bovey
Records Management Branch
865 Yates St., Victoria, V8V 1X4
Director, Reuben Ware

AGENCIES, BOARDS, COMMISSIONS AND CROWN CORPORATIONS

Public Service Commission
633 Courtney St., Victoria, V8V 1X4

The Commission was established as an independent agency to review and conduct hearings of the application of the merit principle in the public service.

Chairman, Graeme C. Roberts
Registrar, Brian McNally

Public Affairs Bureau
612 Government St., Victoria, V8V 1X4
Assoc. Dep. Minister, Eli Sopow
Exec. Director, John Usher

MINISTRY OF TRANSPORTATION AND HIGHWAYS
Parliament Bldgs., Victoria, V8V 1X4

MINISTER'S OFFICE
Minister, The Hon. Neil Vant

DEPUTY MINISTER'S OFFICE
940 Blanshard St., Victoria, V8W 3E6
Dep. Minister, R.D. Flitton

Administrative Services

Asst. Dep. Minister, G.S. Hogg
Financial Services
Director, R.W. Buckingham
Information Systems Director, D. Rhodes
Management Support Services
Director, Vacant
Personnel Programs Director, B. Wilton
Policy And Public Affairs
A/Director, I.S. Watson

Highway Division

Asst. Dep. Minister, M.V. Collins, P.Eng.

HIGHWAY CONSTRUCTION DIVISION
Exec. Director, W.S. Bedford
Director of Construction,
R.L. Chapman, P. Eng.
Director of Paving, O.R. Tisot, P.Eng.
Property and Program Services
A/Director, D. MacSween
HIGHWAY ENGINEERING DIVISION
Exec. Director, B. McKuen
Bridge Engineering
Director, P.H. Brett, P.Eng.
Geotechnical and Materials Engineering
Director, L. deBoer, P.Eng.
Highway Safety Engineer, J. Lisman, P.Eng.
Highway Traffic and Design
A/Director, P. Bonser

OPERATIONS AND EQUIPMENT SERVICES
Exec. Director, E.A. Lund, P.Eng.
Communications Engineer,
C.G. Shearing, P.Eng.
Equipment Services Manager, L. Thornton
Marine Manager, Ian Smart
Maintenance Services
Director, J.L.S. Buckle, P.Eng.

HIGHWAYS REGIONAL OFFICES

Burnaby
7818-6th St., Burnaby, V3N 4N8
Reg. Director, D. Doyle, P.Eng.

Kamloops
523 Columbia St., Kamloops, V2C 2T9
Reg. Director, K.E. Bespflug, P. Eng.

Nanaimo
3260 Norwell Dr., Nanaimo, V9T 1X5
Reg. Director, J. Jensen

Nelson
310 Ward St., Nelson, V1L 5S4
Reg. Director, G. Sutherland

Prince George
1011-4th Ave., Prince George, V2L 3H9
Reg. Director, M. Webster, P. Eng.

Terrace
400, 4546 Park Ave., Terrace, V8G 1V4
Reg. Director, N. Hope, P.Eng.

AGENCIES, BOARDS, COMMISSIONS AND CROWN CORPORATIONS

B.C. Ferry Corp.
1112 Fort St., Victoria, V8V 4V2

In 1960 the history of B.C. Ferries began with two ships on one route and has since expanded to cover 26 coastal routes with 38 modern ships. The service operates year-round through some of the most scenic coastal areas in North America. This includes services connecting Prince Rupert, on B.C.'s north coast, to the Queen Charlotte Islands and to northern Vancouver Island. Bus services between major centres are integrated with the main ferry routes.

Over the past 27 years, 233 million passengers have been carried and, since 1960, in excess of 85 million vehicles have been driven on and off the many vessels.

Many innovations have been carried out during this quarter century. Ships have been stretched and lifted and extra deck space added to increase lift-off capacities.

Minister responsible, The Hon. Neil Vant

Chairman of the Board, R.W. Long
Corporate Secretary, P. Morris
CEO, R.W. Long
Gen. Manager, R.J. Morrison
Finance
Asst. Gen. Manager, G. Brown
Engineering (Fleet)
Asst. Gen. Manager, J. Watson
Human Resources and Administration
Asst. Gen. Manager, A.G. Harbidge
Operations
Asst. Gen. Manager, Capt. C.H. Partridge
Engineering (Terminal Construction)
Asst. Gen. Manager, E. Meads, P.Eng.

INDEPENDENT AGENCIES, BOARDS, COMMISSIONS AND CROWN CORPORATIONS

B.C. Rail Ltd.

221 West Esplanade, North Vancouver
MAILING ADDRESS:
Box 8770, Vancouver, V6B 4X6

B.C. Rail Ltd., originally the Pacific Great Eastern Railway, was incorporated by a private Act in 1912, when it was owned by private investors.

In 1918, the railway passed into provincial government ownership and in 1972, an Act was introduced renaming it the British Columbia Railway. On June 19, 1984, the railway incorporated under its current name, B.C. Rail Ltd.

Originally conceived as a development railway, its role was defined by statute in 1912 as "for the purpose of securing to the people of British Columbia reasonable passenger and freight rates and to assist in the opening-up and development of the province."

The railway's present role is to provide an efficient and reliable commercial transportation service to all communities and industries along its

2,017 km route extending from North Vancouver to Fort Nelson and to earn a commercial return on the shareholders' investment to ensure the company's long-term existence as a profit-oriented business enterprise responsible to provincial needs.

President and CEO, M.C. Norris
Chairman of the Board, Gerry Strongman
Directors: Victor F. Bowman, James Inkster, Winton Derby, Beverly Ellis, E.A. Moffatt, M.C. Norris, Jim T. Rabbitt, Eddie John
Finance and Administration
Vice-President, R. Clarke
Operations and Maintenance,
Marketing and Sales
Sr. Vice-President, A.C. Sturgeon
Industrial Relations and Information Systems
Vice-President, Brian Foley
Materials Management
Manager, D. Anstee
Controller, A.T. Owen
Treasurer, S. Luton
Information Services Manager, W. McNicol
Operations and Maintenance
Manager, J.C. Trainor
Corporate Information Manager, Barrie Wall

Real Estate Development and Corporate Secretary
Gen. Manager, Walter Young
Properties Development
Manager, B. Cooper
Chief Engineer, V.W. Shtenko
Chief Mechanical Officer, G.L. Kelly
Chief of Transportation, Barry McIntosh

Native Affairs Secretariat
468 Belleville St., Victoria, V8V 1X4
Minister responsible,
The Hon. Jack Weisgerber

Asst. Dep. Minister, Eric Denhoff
Policy Development
Director, Ruth Montgomery
Programs Officer, Nicholas May

FIRST CITIZENS' FUND
33 Quebec St., Victoria
Director, Claire Eraut
Project Officer, Rhonda Wilson
Project Clerk, Deanna Daniels

JUDICIARY AND JUDICIAL OFFICERS

Court of Appeal for British Columbia

The Law Courts, 800 Smithe St.
Vancouver, V6Z 2E1
General Inquiries: (604) 660-2710

Chief Justice of British Columbia:
The Hon. Allan McEachern

Justices of Appeal:
The Hon. John David Taggart
The Hon. Peter Donald Seaton
The Hon. A. Brian B. Carrothers
The Hon. Ernest Edward Hinkson
The Hon. William Alastair Craig
The Hon. John Somerset Aikins*
The Hon. John Douglas Lambert
The Hon. James Allen Macdonald*
The Hon. Richard Philip Anderson*
The Hon. Henry Ernest Hutcheon*
The Hon. Alan Brock Macfarlane
The Hon. William Arthur Esson
The Hon. Beverley M. McLachlin
The Hon. Wilfred John Wallace
The Hon. Charles Conrad Locke
The Hon. Mary Frances Southin
The Hon. Samuel Martin Toy

Registrar: Jennifer L. Jordan

Supreme Court of British Columbia

The Law Courts, 800 Smithe St.
Vancouver, V6Z 2E1
General Inquiries: (604) 660-2760

Chief Justice of the Supreme Court:
The Hon. Beverley M. McLachlin

Justices:
The Hon. Kenneth Elliott Meredith
The Hon. Albert Abraham Mackoff*
The Hon. Samuel Martin Toy
The Hon. John Charles Bouck
The Hon. Lloyd G. McKenzie*
The Hon. George L. Murray*
The Hon. Hugh P. Legg
The Hon. William J. Trainor
The Hon. Patricia M. Proudfoot
The Hon. Howard A. Callaghan
The Hon. A. Gordon MacKinnon
The Hon. Martin R. Taylor
The Hon. Patrick D. Dohm
The Hon. Raymond M.P. Paris
The Hon. David B. Hinds

The Hon. Alan A.W. Macdonell
The Hon. John E. Spencer
The Hon. William H. Davies
The Hon. C. Ross Lander
The Hon. Bruce D. Macdonald
The Hon. Kenneth M. Lysyk
The Hon. Lance S.G. Finch
The Hon. Josiah Wood
The Hon. Reginald John Gibbs
The Hon. Mary F. Southin
The Hon. George S. Cumming
The Hon. Douglas B. MacKinnon
The Hon. Wallace T. Oppal
The Hon. Mildred A. Rowles
The Hon. Bruce I. Cohen
The Hon. Carol M. Huddart
The Hon. James J. Gow
The Hon. Duncan W. Shaw
The Hon. Gerald R.B. Coultas
The Hon. Harold A. Hollinrake
The Hon. John Caldwell Cowan
The Hon. Jo-Ann E. Prowse
The Hon. Allan M. Stewart
The Hon. Frank Maczko

Master/Registrar: T.J. Halbert, Victoria

County Court Judges

Chief Judge of County Courts:
David H. Campbell

CRANBROOK
Court House, 102 S. 11th Ave., V1C 2P3
Judges: Michelangelo Provenzano,
Thomas J. Melnick

DAWSON CREEK
Court House, 1201-103rd Ave., V1G 2G9
Judge: Bruce Preston

KAMLOOPS
Court House, 455 Columbia St., V2C 6K4
Judges: Donald M. MacDonald,
Kenneth D. Houghton, Robert Robinson,
George W. Lamperson

KELOWNA
Court House, 1420 Water St., V1Y 1J2
Judges: Howard J. Hamilton,
Nicholas A. Drossos

NANAIMO
Court House, 35 Front St., V9R 5J1
Judges: Leslie F. Cashman*,
Ralph M.J. Hutchinson

* Supernumerary

NELSON
Court House, 320 Ward St., V1L 1S6
Judge: Raymond McLean Cooper

NEW WESTMINSTER
Court House, Begbie Sq., V3M 1C9
Judges: Donald E. McTaggart,
Allen S. McMorran, Charles M. Hyde,
Thomas K. Fisher, William S. Selbie,
Douglas A. Hogarth, Jane E. Godfrey,
Ronald A. McKinnon, Thimersingh M. Singh,
John T. Steeves, John Rowan

PRINCE GEORGE
Court House, 1600-3rd Ave., V2L 3G6
Judges: Frank S. Perry, Richard T.A. Low,
Victor R. Curtis

PRINCE RUPERT
Court House, 100 Market Place, V8J 1B8
Judge: Robert Thomas Errico

VANCOUVER
The Law Courts, 800 Smithe St., V6Z 2E1
Judges: Herbert L. Skipp, Michael I. Catliff,
Douglas T. Wetmore, John J. Anderson,
John C. Cowan, John P. van der Hoop,
Stephen J. Hardinge, Dennis R. Sheppard,
Randall J. Wong, Harry D. Boyle,
Stuart M. Leggatt, Ian L. Drost,
Mary Ellen Boyd, Jo-Ann E. Prowse,
Catherine A. Ryan, William B. Scarth,
Marion J. Allan, H.A.D. Oliver

VERNON
Court House, 3001-27th St., V1T 4W5
Judge: Kenneth Frederick Arkell

VICTORIA
Court House, 850 Burdett Ave., V8W 1B4
Judges: Montague L. Tyrwhitt-Drak,
Peter J. Millward, Frederick A. Melvin,
Kenneth C. Murphy, Robert B. McDiarmid
Hutchison, Dermod Dimitri Owen-Flood

SUPREME AND COUNTY COURT REGISTRARS

CARIBOO COUNTY
Ashcroft
308 Brink St., Box 639, V0K 1A0
Registrar: S. Henswold

Dawson Creek
1201-103rd Ave., V1G 4J2
Registrar: G. Schmidt

Fort Nelson
Box 190, V0C 1R0
Registrar: L. Boran

Fort St. John
10600-100th St., V1J 4L6
Registrar: Muriel Lythall

Lillooet
Bag 700, V0K 1V0
Registrar: Lori Smith

100 Mile House
272-5th Ave., Box 1060, V0K 2E0
Registrar: Maureen Menzies

Prince George
1600-3rd Ave., V2L 3G6
Registrar: G. Goddard

Quesnel
350 Barlow St., V2J 2C1
Registrar: S. Wilson

Vanderhoof
Box 1220, V0J 3A0
Registrar: Olga Smith

Williams Lake
540 Borland St., V2G 1R8
Registrar: R. Girvan

KOOTENAY COUNTY
Cranbrook
102 S. 11th Ave., V1C 2P2
Registrar: K. Burton

Creston
Box 1790, V0B 1G0
Registrar: R. Grout

Fernie
401-4th Ave., Box 1800, V0B 1M0
Registrar: Marva Black

Golden
Box 1500, V0A 1H0
Registrar: Bonnie Carter

Grand Forks
524 Central Ave., Box 1059, V0H 1H0
Registrar: G. Redding

Nelson
320 Ward St., V1L 1S6
Registrar: Elaine Beaulac

Rossland
2288 Columbia Ave., Box 639, V0G 1Y0
Registrar: H. Bondaroff

PRINCE RUPERT COUNTY
Atlin
3rd St., Box 100, V0W 1R0
Registrar: P.S. Welock

Kitimat
603 City Centre, V8C 2N1
Registrar: W. Kallies

Prince Rupert
100 Market Place, V8J 1B7
Registrar: D. D'Altroy

Smithers
Postal Bag 5000, V0J 2N0
Registrar: L. Macgillivray

Terrace
3408 Kalum St., V8G 2N6
Registrar: D. Bell

VANCOUVER COUNTY
Powell River
Ste. 103, 6953 Alberni St., V8A 2B8
Registrar: M. Hammell

Vancouver
800 Smithe St., V6Z 2E1
Registrars: K. Doolan, Elizabeth Huddart,
   R. Tweedale, A. Patterson

VANCOUVER ISLAND COUNTY
Campbell River
500-13th Ave., V9W 6P1
Registrar: K.H. Scott

Courtenay
420 Cumberland Rd., V9N 5M6
Registrar: R. Krayenhoff

Duncan
238 Government St., V9L 1A5
Registrar: Elizabeth Rustulka

Nanaimo
35 Front St., V9R 5J1
Registrar: V. Gardner

Port Alberni
2999-4th Ave., V9Y 8A5
Registrar: P. Whitton

Victoria
850 Burdett Ave., V8W 1B4
Registrar: W.C. McCallum

WESTMINSTER COUNTY
Chilliwack
9391 College St., V2P 4L7
Registrar: M. Bakker

New Westminster
Begbie Sq., Carnarvon St., V3M 1C9
Registrar: N. Bolton

YALE COUNTY
Kamloops
455 Columbia St., V2C 6K4
Registrar: R. Powers

Kelowna
#232, 1420 Water St., V1Y 1J2
Registrar: K.G. Grahame

Merritt
Box 880, V0K 2B0
Registrar: Elaine O'Hata

Penticton
100 Main St., V2A 5A5
Registrar: T. Knight

Princeton
Box 1210, V0X 1W0
Registrar: Agnes Marshall

Revelstoke
Box 2130, V0E 2S0
Registrar: W.D. Macrae

Salmon Arm
Box 1990, V0E 2T0
Registrar: Margaret Mann

Vernon
3001-27th St., V1T 4W5
Registrar: S.R. Smith

Provincial Court of British Columbia

Judiciary Headquarters:
Pacific Centre, Ste. 501, 700 W. Georgia St.
Box 10287, Vancouver, V7Y 1E8
General Inquiries: (604) 660-2864

Chief of the Provincial Court:
   His Honour I. Bruce Josephson
Judges: William J. Diebolt, Dorothy E. Field††,
   John L. McCarthy, T. D'Arcy McGee†,
   Anthony J. Spence

BURNABY
6263 Deer Lake Ave., Burnaby, V5G 3Z8
Assoc. Chief Judge: Kenneth D. Page†
Judges: Jane Auxier, Delores R. Holmes,
   Leo A.T. Nimsick, Selwyn R. Romilly

CAMPBELL RIVER
500-13th Ave., V9W 6P1
Judges: Anthony Sarich, E. Dennis Schmidt

CASTLEGAR
Courthouse, 555 Columbia Ave., V1N 1G8
Assoc. Chief Judge: I.B. Josephson

CHILLIWACK
9391 College St., V2P 4L7
Judges: Thomas W. Meagher,
   Darragh M. Vamplew

COQUITLAM
2165 Kelly St., V3C 4W6
Judges: Kimball J. Husband, Alfred J. Scow

COURTENAY
420 Cumberland Rd., V9N 5M6
Judge: Edward O'Donnell

CRANBROOK
102 S. 11th Ave., V1C 2P2
Judges: David J. Lunn†,
   Donald M. Waurynchuk

DAWSON CREEK
1201-103rd St., V1G 4J2
Judge: David M. Levis†

DELTA
4465 Clarence Taylor Cres., V4K 3W4
Judges: Ralph E. Hudson, G. Ross Sutherland

DUNCAN
238 Government St., V9L 1A5
Judges: Frederick S. Green, Darrall S. Collins

FORT ST. JOHN
10600-100th St., V1J 4L6
Judge: Robert G. Skelhorne

KAMLOOPS
455 Columbia St., V2C 6K4
Judges: William A. Blair†, James P. Gordon,
    Terry W. Shupe, Donald R. Simpson,
    Harry F. Thomas

KELOWNA
1456 St. Paul St., V1Y 2E6
Judge: Gordon H. Gilmour, Hugh M. Ellis††

LANGLEY
20389 Fraser Hwy., V3A 4E9
Judge: Eugene A. Sather

MAPLE RIDGE
22460 Dewdney Trunk Rd., V2X 3J6
Judge: John B. Varcoe

MATSQUI
32203 S. Fraser Way, V2T 1W6
Judges: Nick Friesen, M. Ian MacAlpine

NANAIMO
Courthouse, 35 Front St., V9R 5J1
Judges: Douglas M. Greer†, Stanley H. Wardill,
    Eric W. Winch††

NELSON
320 Ward St., Nelson, V1L 1S6
Judge: Stewart W. Enderton

NEW WESTMINSTER
Law Courts, Begbie Sq., V3M 1C9
Judge: Lorne P. Clare

NORTH VANCOUVER
200 E. 23rd St., V7L 4R4
Judges: Charles E. Bakony, John D. Layton†,
    Jerome B. Paradis, James K. Shaw

PENTICTON
Courthouse, 100 Main St., V2A 5A5
Judge: Wilfred W. Klinger†, Gale G. Sinclair

PORT ALBERNI
2999-4th Ave., V9Y 8A5
Judge: William E. MacLeod

POWELL RIVER
6953 Alberni St., V8A 2B8
Judge: Shirley E. Giroday

PRINCE GEORGE
1033-4th Ave., V2L 5H9
Judges: J. Harold Kenney,
    Clifford B. MacArthur, Ronald S. Munro*,
    George O. Stewart†

PRINCE RUPERT
Courthouse, 100 Market Place, V8J 1B7
Judge: Robert C.S. Graham

QUESNEL
Ste. 115, 350 Barlow Ave., V2J 2C1
Judge: Robert B. Macfarlane

RICHMOND
Criminal Division
6900 Minoru Blvd., V6Y 1Y1
Judges: William E. Campbell*,
    John A.W. Drysdale, Lawrence S. Goulet*,
    Joel R. Groberman

Family & Small Claims Division
6931 Granville Ave., V7C 4M9
Judge: Bryan K. Davis

ROSSLAND
Courthouse, Box 639, V0G 1V0
Judge: Ronald G. Fabbro

SALMON ARM
Courthouse, Box 1990, V0E 2T0
Judge: Marvin A. Lundeen

SMITHERS
#40, Postal Bag 5000, V0J 2N0
Judge: David I. Smyth

SQUAMISH
Box 1580, V0N 3G0
Judge: Carl I. Walker

SURREY
Criminal Division
17850-56th Ave., V3S 1C7
Judges: Norman C.M. Collingwood,
    Philip R. Govan, Patrick A. Hyde,
    William G. MacDonald, Roy S. McQueen,
    Douglas C. Reed†, Edward D. Scarlett,
    Cyril J. Woodliffe

Family & Small Claims Division
10475-138th St., V3T 4K4
Judges: Glenson J.F. Baker,
    Anne E. Rounthwaite

TERRACE
3408 Kalum St., V8G 2N6
Judges: E. Lloyd Iverson†, Paul R. Lawrence

VANCOUVER
Criminal Division
222 Main St., V6A 2S8
Judges: Brian E. Bastin, Erik H. Bendrodt,
    Ross D. Collver, Wallace G. Craig,
    Edmond J. Cronin, John L. Davies,
    Gordon H. Johnson†, Robert J. Lemiski,
    Keith I. Libby, John L. Macintyre,
    Pauline L. Maughan, Hugh J. McGivern,
    David Moffett, Kenneth J. Scherling,
    Kerry A.P.D. Smith, L. Wayne Smith

Small Claims Division
814 Richards St., V6B 3A7
Judges: Ian G. Henley†, M.F. Puhach,
    Valerie Taggart, Harry A. White

---

* Supernumerary   † Administrative Judge   †† Ad Hoc

Family Division
2625 Yale St., V5K 1C2
Judges: B. Patricia M. Byrne,
  Douglas R. Campbell†, Phillip d'A. Collings,
  G. Derek Gillis, William J. Kitchen,
  David R. Pendleton, Reginald Poole

VERNON
Courthouse, 3001-27th St., V1T 4W5
Judges: Jurgen P.W. Behncke,
  Dennis B. Overend

VICTORIA
Criminal & Small Claims Division
850 Burdett Ave., V8W 1B4
Judges: Lawrence C. Brahan,
  Darrall S. Collins, G. Stephen Denroche,
  Alan E. Filmer, Robert W. Greig†,
  J. Michael Hubbard, Duncan K. McAdam*,
  Robert W. Metzger

Family Division
1119 Pembroke St., V8V 1J3
Judge: Loretta F.E. Chaperon

WEST VANCOUVER
1310 Marine Dr., V7T 1B5
Judge: Reginald D. Grandison

WILLIAMS LAKE
540 Borland St., V2G 1R8
Judges: C. Cunliffe Barnett, Thomas C. Smith†

REGISTRARS IN BANKRUPTCY

NELSON
The Law Courts, 320 Ward St., V1L 1S6
Registrar: Elaine Beaulac

PRINCE GEORGE
The Law Courts, 1600-3rd Ave., V2L 3G6
Registrar: G. Goddard

PRINCE RUPERT
The Law Courts, 100 Market Place, V8J 1B7
Registrar: W.R. Williamson

VANCOUVER
The Law Courts, 800 Smithe St., V6Z 2E1
Registrars: K. Doolan, E. Huddart,
  R. Tweedale, A. Patterson

VERNON
The Law Courts, 3001-27th St., V1T 4W5
Registrar: Stan Smith

VICTORIA
The Law Courts, 850 Burdett Ave., V8W 1B4
Registrar: T.J. Halbert, W.C. McCallum

---

* Supernumerary   † Administrative Judge   †† Ad Hoc

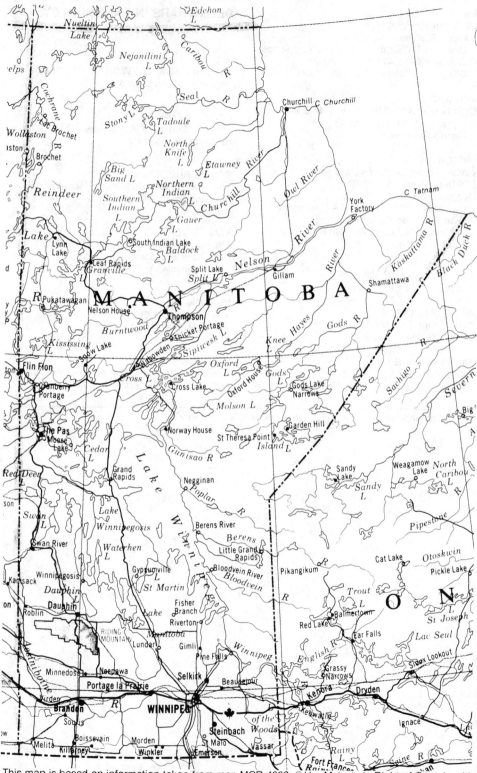

This map is based on information taken from map MCR 4032. © Her Majesty in Right of Canada with permission of Energy, Mines and Resources.

PROVINCE OF MANITOBA

Prairie Crocus
(Anemone patens)

Entered Confederation: July 15, 1870
Capital: Winnipeg
Motto: None
Flower: Prairie crocus
Area: 649,947 km²
   percentage of Canada's total area: 6.5
   LAND: 548,355 km²
   FRESHWATER: 101,592 km²
Elevation:
   HIGHEST POINT: Baldy Mountain (831 m)
   LOWEST POINT: Hudson Bay shore
Population (April 1988): 1,083,600
   five-year change: +3.9%

per square kilometre: 1.7
percentage of Canada's total
   population: 4.2
   URBAN: 72%
   RURAL: 28%
Gross domestic product, 1987: $20.1 billion
Government Finance:
   REVENUE, 1988/89 est. $4.4 billion
   EXPENDITURE, 1988/89 est. $4.6 billion
   DEBT PER CAPITA (March 1987): $1,386
Personal income per capita, 1986: $15,807
Unemployment rate, 1988
   (annual average): 7.8%

HISTORY

In 1869, the Hudson's Bay Company agreed to relinquish control of its land in western Canada upon payment of 300,000 pounds sterling by the Canadian government. However, no clear terms were spelled out for the people of the Red River area and, during negotiations on their status, resistance developed in the colony. The Métis, a mostly French-speaking people of white and Indian blood, opposed the Canadian proposals under the leadership of Louis Riel. Riel succeeded in uniting both the French- and English-speaking groups and established a locally elected provisional government in December 1869.

Delegates of this provincial government negotiated terms with the federal government that led to Parliament's passing the *Manitoba Act* (May 12, 1870), under which Manitoba joined the other provinces in Confederation. The Act was proclaimed, making Manitoba a province of Canada, on July 15, 1870.

The years 1889-90 saw the development of one of the most vexing problems in the province's history — the "Manitoba School Question" — and a related one concerning official languages. In 1890, the legislature passed the *Public Schools Act,* which abolished the dual school system and

teaching in the French language. The issue was whether it had the power to do away with the denominational schools established in 1871 under the *Manitoba Act*. The legislature in 1890 also abolished the use of French in debates, proceedings, and in the courts.

The Manitoba School Question was a major constitutional, legal, and political controversy for Canada during the next six years. In 1897, a compromise was worked out, providing for religious exercises under certain conditions and the use of languages other than English for teaching. The number of languages used multiplied until 1916 when the legislature abolished the use of all languages except English in the schools.

In 1970, changes in provincial legislation again made French a language of instruction in Manitoba public schools. In 1979, the Supreme Court of Canada ruled invalid Manitoba's *Official Language Act* of 1890.

In May 1983, agreement was reached to amend the *Manitoba Act, 1870*. The Manitoba legislature and Parliament were to adopt constitutional resolutions authorizing an amendment by Dec. 31, 1983. This agreement would also have ended a challenge to the validity of Manitoba legislation since 1890, which appellants were about to take to the Supreme Court of Canada. However, passage of the constitutional resolution by the Manitoba legislature was delayed by a long and heated debate which continued into early 1984, when the issue was referred to the Supreme Court. In June 1985, the Court ruled Manitoba laws passed since 1890 invalid because they had not been passed and printed in both English and French, but allowed them to stand temporarily to enable the province to prepare proposals to validate the legislation.

move from farm to city that has influenced other Canadian provinces. Today, about 70 per cent of the population lives in large urban centres and the rest on farms or in small communities.

More than half the population now lives in the metropolitan area of Winnipeg, Manitoba's main manufacturing and distribution centre. Other important Manitoba population centres include Brandon, Flin Flon, Portage la Prairie, and Thompson.

THE LAND

Manitoba's area is 649,947 km^2. The province extends 1,225 km from north to south, from the 60th to the 49th parallels. Its width at the southern end is 449 km, at the widest point 793 km, and at the northern boundary 418 km. The province has a coastline of more than 645 km on Hudson Bay and through the bay has access to ocean shipping routes part of the year.

Manitoba is comparatively level, with land elevations rising gradually south and west from sea level at Hudson Bay. Most of the province has an elevation between 150 and 300 metres.

Manitoba's climate is characterized by warm, sunny summers and cold, but bright winter days. Afternoon temperatures in July and August average 25°C, but mid-winter daytime readings almost always remain well below freezing.

THE PEOPLE

Manitoba's first great influx of settlers was largely English-speaking and from Ontario. In 1875, some French-Canadians who had left Quebec to settle in New England were joined in Manitoba by others from Quebec and a few immigrants from France. The year 1874 saw the arrival of the first Mennonites from Russia, and 1875, the vanguard of the Icelanders. By 1881, many British immigrants had settled in the province and Manitoba's population was more than 62,000 — most of whom had arrived in the previous five years. In 1891, the cosmopolitan aspect was further broadened with the arrival of the first of substantial numbers of Ukrainians.

Today, Manitoba can genuinely claim a multi-cultural heritage with citizens from many ethnic backgrounds — British, French, German, Ukrainian, Native Indian, Métis, Polish, Dutch, Scandinavian, Jewish, Italian, Hungarian, Filipino, Portuguese, Chinese, and others.

In its early years, Manitoba was an agricultural province. The bulk of the population lived on farms or in small rural centres. A shift to urban living was noticeable as early as the turn of the century. Manitoba has been affected by the same

THE ECONOMY

The earliest economic activity in Manitoba was the exchange of furs by Indians for French and British trade goods. Furs were exported to Europe by the companies that traded into what is now western Canada.

Agriculture. Agriculture on a commercial scale began to develop as the Red River Settlement grew. Wheat was first exported from the West in 1876 (a Manitoba shipment sent to Toronto) and quickly became a major export crop.

Wheat is still the most important crop, accounting for more than one third of production. Other grains are also grown in abundance, especially canola (rapeseed) and barley. Hay, flax, and oats are also important, as are livestock, special grains, and vegetables. In 1987, agricultural production in Manitoba was valued at $1.9 billion.

Forestry. The influx of settlers into Manitoba after 1870 created a demand for lumber for farmsteads, barns, and commercial buildings, which started Manitoba's forest industry. After 1886, timber was shipped to eastern Canada on the Canadian Pacific Railway.

Mining. The first mining activity occurred in the Flin Flon area, where copper, zinc, and other minerals were discovered in 1915. All the province's mines are in the Precambrian Shield, which arches across Manitoba from the southeast to the northwest. The first major oil discoveries in the province were made in the 1950s, in the southwest near Virden. The value of mineral production in 1987 was $1 billion.

Manufacturing. Railways and Winnipeg's strategic location established the city as a major distributing centre and, later, as a manufacturing centre. Manitoba has developed a diversified economy, with manufacturing being the largest industry in the goods-producing sector in terms of employment, wages paid, and value of production.

Information provided by Information Services Branch, Government of Manitoba.

GOVERNMENT OF MANITOBA

Seat of Government:
  Legislative Bldg., Winnipeg, R3C 0V8
Lieutenant-Governor,
  The Hon. George Johnson
  Legislative Bldg., Rm. 235
  Winnipeg, R3C 0V8

EXECUTIVE COUNCIL

(In order of precedence, as of Jan. 1, 1989)
Premier, President of the Executive Council,
Minister of Federal-Provincial Relations,
  The Hon. Gary Filmon
Minister of Northern Affairs, Minister
responsible for Native Affairs,
  The Hon. James Downey
Minister of Health,
  The Hon. Donald Orchard
Minister of Highways and Transportation,
Minister of Government Services,
  The Hon. Albert Driedger
Minister of Finance,
  The Hon. Clayton Manness
Minister of Community Services, Minister of
Employment Services and Economic Security,
Minister responsible for the Status of Women,
  The Hon. Charles Oleson
Deputy Premier, Minister of Municipal Affairs,
  The Hon. James Cummings
Attorney General, Minister of Co-operative,
Consumer and Corporate Affairs, Minister
responsible for the Liquor Control Board,
  The Hon. James McCrae
Minister of Labour, Minister of Environment and
Workplace Safety and Health, Minister
responsible for the Workers Compensation
Board,
  The Hon. Edward Connery
Ministry of Industry, Trade and Tourism,
  The Hon. James Ernst
Ministry of Agriculture, Minister responsible for
Manitoba Telephone,
  The Hon. Glen Findlay
Minister of Education,
  The Hon. Leonard Derkach
Minister of Urban Affairs, Minister of Housing,
  The Hon. Gerald Ducharme
Minister of Culture, Heritage and Recreation,
Minister responsible for the Manitoba Lotteries,
  The Hon. Bonnie Mitchelson

Minister of Natural Resources,
  The Hon. John Penner
Minister of Energy and Mines, Minister
responsible for Manitoba Hydro and Seniors,
  The Hon. Harold Neufeld

CABINET COMMITTEES
c/o Legislative Bldg., Winnipeg, R3C 0V8

Treasury Board
Chairperson, The Hon. Gary Filmon
Secretary, Michael Mendelson

Provincial Land Use Committee
Chairperson, The Hon. J. Glen Cummings

Urban Affairs Committee
Chairperson, The Hon. Gerald Ducharme

THE OFFICE OF THE PROVINCIAL AUDITOR
Ste. 905, 386 Broadway, Winnipeg, R3C 3R6

Provincial Auditor, Fred Jackson
Asst. Provincial Auditor, John W. Singleton
Public Accounts Audit
Director, J.W. Bothe
Audit Administration
Director, W. Johnson
Special Audits
Director, R.B. Mayer

LEGISLATIVE ASSEMBLY

34th Legislature, 1st Session
Last election: April 26, 1988
  (Maximum duration 5 years and 10 days)
Majority party: Progressive Conservative Party
Total number of seats: 57
Party standings (as of Jan. 1, 1989):
  Conservatives: 24
  Liberals: 21
  New Democrats: 12

Salaries, Indemnities and Allowances

MEMBERS: Indexed to cost of living, amounts
  change each year. In 1988-89: Annual Indemnity, $25,904.35; annual expense allowance,
  $12,952.17 (tax free); total: $38,856.52. (See

For further information regarding any aspect of the
Government of Manitoba, contact:
Citizens' Inquiry Service
Rm. 511, 401 York Ave., Winnipeg, R3C 0P8
(204) 945-3744

Section 59(6) of the *Legislative Assembly Act* for Indexing Formula.)

PREMIER: $26,600 salary, plus Member's Annual Indemnity and expense allowance.

MINISTERS WITH PORTFOLIO: $20,600 salary, plus Member's Annual Indemnity and expense allowance.

MINISTERS WITHOUT PORTFOLIO: $15,600 salary, plus Member's Annual Indemnity and expense allowance.

LEADER OF THE OFFICIAL OPPOSITION: $20,600 salary, plus Member's Annual Indemnity and expense allowance.

SPEAKER OF THE LEGISLATURE: Member's Annual Indemnity and expense allowance; additional Annual Indemnity, $12,000.00; additional annual allowance, $3,500.00.

DEPUTY SPEAKER: Member's Annual Indemnity and expense allowance; additional Annual Indemnity, $3,500.

Officers

Speaker, The Hon. Denis Rocan
Clerk of the Assembly, W.H. (Binx) Remnant
Deputy Clerk, Beverley I. Bosiak

Members

Constituency	Member and Affiliation
Arthur	The Hon. James E. Downey (PC)
Assiniboia	Edward Mandrake (Lib)
Brandon East	Leonard S. Evans (NDP)
Brandon West	The Hon. Jim McCrae (PC)
Burrows	William Chornopyski (Lib)
Charleswood	The Hon. Jim Ernst (PC)
Churchill	Jay M. Cowan (NDP)
Concordia	Gary Doer (NDP)
Dauphin	John S. Plohman (NDP)
Ellice	Avis Gray (Lib)
Elmwood	Jim Maloway (NDP)
Emerson	The Hon. Albert Driedger (PC)
Flin Flon	Jerry Storie (NDP)
Fort Garry	Laurie E. Evans (Lib)
Fort Rouge	Jim Carr (Lib)
Gimli	Ed Helwer (PC)
Gladstone	The Hon. Charlotte Oleson (PC)
Inkster	Kevin Lamoureux (Lib)
Interlake	Bill Uruski (NDP)
Kildonan	Gulzar Cheema (Lib)
Kirkfield Park	Gerrie Hammond (PC)
La Verendrye	Helmut Pankratz (PC)
Lac du Bonnet	Darren Praznik (PC)
Lakeside	Harry J. Enns (PC)
Logan	Maureen L. Hemphill (NDP)
Minnedosa	Harold Gilleshammer (PC)
Morris	The Hon. Clayton Manness (PC)
Niakwa	Herold Driedger (Lib)
Osborne	Reg Alcock (Lib)
Pembina	The Hon. Donald W. Orchard (PC)
Portage la Prairie	The Hon. Edward Connery (PC)
Radisson	Allan Patterson (Lib)
Rhineland	The Hon. Jack Penner (PC)

Constituency	Member and Affiliation
Riel	The Hon. Gerry Ducharme (PC)
River East	The Hon. Bonnie Mitchelson (PC)
River Heights	Sharon Carstairs (Lib)
Roblin/Russell	The Hon. Len Derkach (PC)
Rossmere	The Hon. Harold Neufeld (PC)
Rupertsland	Elijah Harper (NDP)
St. Boniface	Neil Gaudry (Lib)
St. James	Paul Edwards (Lib)
St. Johns	Judy Wasylycia-Leis (NDP)
St. Norbert	John Angus (Lib)
Ste. Rose	The Hon. James Cummings (PC)
St. Vital	Bob Rose (Lib)
Selkirk	Gwen Charles (Lib)
Seven Oaks	Mark Minenko (Lib)
Springfield	Gilles Roch (Lib)
Sturgeon Creek	Iva J. Yeo (Lib)
Swan River	Parker Burrell (PC)
The Pas	Harry Harapiak (NDP)
Thompson	Steve Ashton (NDP)
Transcona	Richard Kozak (Lib)
Turtle Mountain	Denis Rocan (PC)
Tuxedo	The Hon. Gary Filmon (PC)
Virden	The Hon. Glen M. Findlay (PC)
Wolseley	Harold Taylor (Lib)

Lib — Liberal
NDP — New Democrat
PC — Progressive Conservative

Office of the Premier

204 Legislative Bldg., Winnipeg, R3C 0V8

Premier, The Hon. Gary Filmon
Principal Secretary to the Premier, Greg Lyle
Clerk of the Executive Council, Don Leitch
Communication Secretary, Robert Parkins
Media Secretary, Garth Cramer
Policy Management Secretariat
Secretary, Mike Bessey

French Language Services Secretariat
Sr. Advisor, Roger Turenne

Intergovernmental Relations
Minister of Federal/Provincial Relations,
    The Hon. Gary Filmon

Offices of the Official Opposition

172 Legislative Bldg., Winnipeg, R3C 0V8

Leader of the Official Opposition,
    Sharon Carstairs

Offices of the New Democratic Party

Legislative Bldg., Rm. 141, Winnipeg, R3C 0V8

Leader of the Manitoba NDP, Gary Doer

Legislative Library

200 Vaughan St., Winnipeg, R3C 0V8
General Inquiries: (204) 945-4330

The Legislative Library is the main source of information for the Government of Manitoba and serves as a depository for the publications of all departments of the government. A checklist of these materials is published monthly with annual cumulations. The Library serves the members of the Legislative Assembly on a priority basis, and all other government personnel. It also acts as a major research collection for the academic community and the general public, and provides an interlibrary loan service to extend borrowing privileges to researchers outside the provincial civil service.

Files and scrapbooks of clippings from the local newspapers on Manitoba and Winnipeg politics, history, and biography, provide an unparalleled source of Manitoba information dating back to before 1900. The Rare Book Collection includes some of the oldest published material on the Canadian West.

A/Legislative Librarian, S. Bishop

Office of the Ombudsman

Ste. 750, 500 Portage Ave., Winnipeg, R3C 3X1
General Inquiries: (204) 786-6483

The Ombudsman is appointed by the Lieutenant-Governor in Council on the recommendation of a Special Committee of the Legislative Assembly. He is an officer of the Legislature.

The Ombudsman investigates complaints against departments and agencies of the provincial government related to matters of administration. After investigation, if the complaint is deemed to be valid, the Ombudsman may make a recommendation to the appropriate department or agency of the provincial government to bring about redress of the grievance. The Ombudsman is accountable to the Legislature and submits his annual report to the Legislature through the Speaker.

Ombudsman, Gordon S. Earle
Asst. Ombudsman, Barry E. Tuckett

DEPARTMENT OF AGRICULTURE

165 Legislative Bldg., Winnipeg, R3C 0V8
General Inquiries: (204) 945-3722

MINISTER'S OFFICE
Minister, The Hon. Glen Findlay

DEPUTY MINISTER'S OFFICE
159 Legislative Bldg., Winnipeg, R3C 0V8
A/Dep. Minister, G.J. Lacomy

COMMUNICATIONS BRANCH
307, 255 Memorial Blvd., Winnipeg, R3C 4G7
Director, V.E. McNair

Management and Operations Division
Woodsworth Bldg., 8th Flr., Winnipeg, R3C 3L6

A/Asst. Dep. Minister, R.L. Baseraba
Federal-Provincial Co-ordinator, A. Chorney
Internal Auditor and Systems Specialist, J.M. Vielgut
Administrative and Accounting Services
A/Director, D.H. Burch
Financial Administration
A/Financial Administrator, Marvin H. Richter
Computer Services Unit
Unit Manager, J.V. Epp
Personnel Services
Director, D.H. Burch
Program Analysis
Program Officer, G.A. Fearn

Agricultural Development and Marketing Division
Woodsworth Bldg., 8th Flr., Winnipeg, R3C 3L6

Asst. Dep. Minister, T.L. Pringle

ANIMAL INDUSTRY BRANCH
Agricultural Services Complex
University of Manitoba, Winnipeg, R3T 2N2
Director, Dr. F. Baker
MARKETING BRANCH
Director, A.E. Gascoigne
SOILS AND CROPS BRANCH
Director, G.D. Webster

TECHNICAL SERVICES AND TRAINING BRANCH
Director and Sup't of Agricultural Societies, R.M. Deveson
Agricultural Extension Ctr.
1129 Queens Ave., Brandon, R7A 1L9
A/Principal, Ken Young
VETERINARY SERVICES BRANCH
Agricultural Services Complex
University of Manitoba
Winnipeg, R3T 2N2
Director, Dr. J.A. McPhedran
Semen Distribution Centre
Manitoba Veterinary Drug Centre

Policy and Economics Division
Woodsworth Bldg., 8th Flr., Winnipeg, R3C 3L6

Asst. Dep. Minister, C. Lee
Programs and Policies
Co-ordinator, B. Dryburgh
Economics Branch
Director, H. Gregory
FARM AND RURAL DEVELOPMENT DIVISION
Agricultural Crown Lands Branch
1495 St. James St., Winnipeg, R3H 0W9
Director, J.L. Neabel

REGIONAL OFFICES:

Central Region
Reg. Director, B. Manning
25 N. Tupper St., Portage la Prairie, R1N 1W9

Eastern Region
Reg. Director, D. Donaghy
20-1st St., Box 50, Beausejour, R0E 0C0

Interlake Region
Reg. Director, A.T. Dickson
W. River Rd., Arborg, R0C 0A0

Northwest Region
Reg. Director, R. Chychota
27-2nd Ave. S.W., Dauphin, R7N 3E5

Southwest Region
Reg. Director, W. Digby
1129 Queens Ave., Brandon, R7A 1L9

AGENCIES, BOARDS AND COMMISSIONS

MARKETING BOARDS

Marketing boards for agricultural products in Canada are created by a number of different pieces of legislation. National wheat and dairy products plans flow from the Canadian Wheat Board Act and the Canadian Dairy Commission Act respectively. Egg and poultry boards derive their authority from the Farm Products Marketing Agencies Act. As well, many have their own provincial statutes and are normally within the jurisdiction of an umbrella provincial agency. The individual boards are, however, non-governmental and made up largely of elected farmer representatives.

There is also a variety of types. The Economic Council of Canada's study on marketing boards identified five: promotional and developmental boards with little power; selling-desk boards that handle marketing but do not set prices; boards that negotiate prices; boards that set prices; and full-fledged boards that establish quotas. These last are known as supply-management marketing boards. Currently, there are more than 100 active boards in Canada.

MANITOBA NATURAL PRODUCTS
MARKETING COUNCIL
901 Norquay Bldg., Winnipeg, R3C 0P8

The Manitoba Natural Products Marketing Council administers the Manitoba Natural Products Marketing Act.

The Act enables the institution of commodity marketing plans, which may be governed either by producer boards or by marketing commissions. There are seven marketing boards and three commissions in Manitoba with varying degrees of authority.

The main duties and functions of the Council are prescribed under the Act as follows:

1) to provide advice to the minister on all matters relating to the establishment, operation, and control of producer boards and marketing commissions;

2) to supervise the operation of producer boards and marketing commissions;
3) to enforce the Regulations and supervise the work of inspectors; and
4) to conduct votes, elections, and referendums.

The Act also prescribes that any person affected by a decision, directive, or order made by a producer board or marketing commission may appeal to the Council.

Chairman, Howard Motheral
Secretary, G.H. MacKenzie

HONEY PRODUCERS' MARKETING BOARD
Box 24, Sinclair, R0M 2A0

Currently involved in the administration of the federal government's Advance Payment for Crops Program for honey producers, the Board is not involved in supply management, honey marketing, or honey promotion.

Chairman, Herb Isaac

MANITOBA BEEF COMMISSION
1135, 444 St. Mary Ave., Winnipeg, R3C 3T1

The Manitoba Beef Commission, administered by a seven-member, all-producer board of directors, came into being on Sept. 1, 1982. Its mandate is the administration of a Beef Stabilization and Marketing Plan.

Producers are guaranteed a stabilized price for calves, feeders, and finished animals. The Plan is considered an ongoing arrangement with no specific start-up or termination date, allowing for long-term planning. The realistic and guaranteed support prices are adjusted on January 1 and July 1 of each year in relation to a prescribed formula. The Commission regularly monitors 12 well-known input cost items to maintain the support level in tune with changing input costs. When market prices fall below the support price, a deficiency payment is paid by the Commission to bring returns up to the support level.

Administration costs are covered by a marketing fee (one half of one percent of market value) and a government grant. The stabilization fund is made up of producer and provincial contributions.

There are also subsidiary plans to provide financial and technical assistance to those changing from marketing calves to marketing finished animals.

Chairman, Dave Fulton
Gen. Manager, Joe Dunsmore
Marketing Manager, John Kruzenga
Administration Manager, Vacant

MANITOBA BROILER HATCHING EGG
COMMISSION
204, 666 St. James St., Winnipeg, R3G 3J6

The Manitoba Broiler Hatching Egg Commission was established April 19, 1985. A chairman and four members were appointed by order of the Lieutenant-Governor in Council.

The Manitoba Broiler Hatching Egg Marketing Plan was filed April 19, 1985, as Man. Reg. 93/85, Regulation Respecting a Plan to Provide for the Control and the Regulation of the Marketing of Broiler-type Hatching Eggs in Manitoba under *The Natural Products Marketing Act.*

Section 3 of the Plan outlines its "Purposes" to be as follows:

1) The general purpose and intention of this Plan is to provide for effective control, regulation, and promotion in any and all respects by the Commission, of the marketing of the regulated product within the province.
2) The specific purposes of this Plan are: a) to maintain fair and equitable prices for broiler hatching eggs; b) to develop and maintain the orderly marketing of the product; c) to provide a consistently high quality of broiler hatching eggs for market; d) to maintain an adequate supply for hatcheries; and e) to gather, compile, and distribute statistical information related to the production and marketing of broiler hatching eggs, chicks, and broiler breeder pullets.

Chairman, R.W. Scott

MANITOBA CHICKEN BROILER PRODUCERS' MARKETING BOARD
1200 King Edward St., Winnipeg, R3H 0R5

The Manitoba Chicken Broiler Producers' Marketing Board was established on Jan. 15, 1969, by Man. Reg. 164/68, at the request of the chicken producers of Manitoba.

The objective of the Board is to provide for the effective control, regulation, and promotion, in any and all respects, of the marketing of the regulated product within the province.

Specific purposes are: to maintain fair and equitable prices with, as a minimum, return on input costs, including a minimum return on investment; to maintain an adequate but not burdensome supply of product for all requirements; to provide a uniform high quality of product; and to provide statistical information related to the marketing of the product.

This Board co-operates with other producer boards in the operation of the Canadian Chicken Marketing Agency, which has objectives similar to the above, but for the total Canadian market.

Chairman, Waldie Klassen
Gen. Manager, B.F. Waters

MANITOBA EGG PRODUCERS' MARKETING BOARD
1200 King Edward St., Winnipeg, R3H 0R5

The Manitoba Egg Producers' Marketing Board was established in 1971 by Man. Reg. N20-R9 pursuant to the *Natural Products Marketing Act.* The general purpose of the Board is to provide effective control, regulation, and promotion of the regulated product.

The specific purposes are as follows:

1) to maintain fair and equitable prices;
2) to develop and maintain orderly marketing;
3) to provide a uniform high quality for the market;
4) to maintain adequate advertising and promotion;
5) to encourage a continuous supply for the trade; and
6) to gather, compile, and distribute statistical information related to the production and marketing of eggs and pullets.

Funds to operate all programs are obtained by a levy assessed to producers based on dozens of eggs marketed.

Chairman, Harold Froese
Gen.-Manager, Ms. P. Kelly

MANITOBA HOG PRODUCERS' MARKETING BOARD
750 Marion St., Winnipeg, R2J 0K4

The Manitoba Hog Producers' Marketing Board was established under the Manitoba Hog Producers' Marketing Plan, Man. Reg. N20-R4, filed Dec. 8, 1971.

The Board was formed in 1972, succeeding the Manitoba Hog Marketing Commission, which had been established in 1964. The Marketing Plan provides for a board of directors of eight registered hog producers to be elected by district delegates for a three-year term.

The Board is responsible for operating a hog sales agency for approximately 3,000 commercial hog producers in the province. The Board operates a daily "Dutch Clock" auction for the sale of dressed hogs and conducts an extensive market information and pork promotion program.

Chairman, W. Vaags
Gen. Manager, R.L. Sedgwick

MANITOBA MILK PRODUCERS' MARKETING BOARD
104, 1580 Dublin St., Winnipeg, R3E 0L4

The Manitoba Milk Producers' Marketing Board was established April 9, 1974 by Man. Reg. 72/74. The Regulation stipulates that the Board shall consist of not more than nine members, all of whom shall be registered milk producers.

The Manitoba Milk Producers' Marketing Plan, Man. Reg. 242/74, defines the general purpose of the Plan: "to provide for the effective control, regulation, and promotion, in any and all respects, by the producer board of the marketing of the regulated product within Manitoba."

Chairman, Louis Balcaen
Gen. Manager, W.J.S. Wade

MANITOBA TURKEY PRODUCERS' MARKETING BOARD
1200 King Edward St., Winnipeg, R3H 0R5

The Manitoba Turkey Producers' Marketing Board was established Jan. 15, 1969 by Man. Reg. 165/68, at the request of the turkey producers of

Manitoba.

The objective of the Board is to provide for the effective control and promotion of the marketing of the regulated product within the province.

Specific purposes are: to maintain fair and equitable prices with at least a return on input costs, including a minimum return on investment; to maintain an adequate but not burdensome supply of product for all requirements; to provide a uniform high quality of product; and to provide statistical information related to the marketing of the product.

This Board co-operates with other producer boards in the operation of the Canadian Turkey Marketing Agency which has objectives similar to the above, but for the total Canadian market.

Chairman, Bob Byle
Gen. Manager, B.F. Waters

MANITOBA VEGETABLE PRODUCERS' MARKETING BOARD
1200 King Edward St., Winnipeg, R3H 0R5

The Manitoba Vegetable Producers' Marketing Board was created in 1972. In 1982, the Manitoba Root Crop Producers' Marketing Board amalgamated with the Vegetable Board.

The Board was established by growers to better serve the growers of Manitoba and to provide for the effective control, regulation, and promotion of the regulated products (potatoes, onions, rutabagas, parsnips, and carrots). Through regulation, the Board strives to maintain fair prices to producers, to develop and maintain orderly marketing of uniformly high quality product, to maintain adequate advertising and promotion, to encourage a continuous supply of product for the trade and consumers, and to gather, compile, and distribute statistical information related to the production and marketing of vegetables. Out-of-province sales are also handled by the Board.

The Board is financed entirely by deductions from payments to growers and receives no ongoing financing from either the federal or provincial governments.

Chairman, John Kuhl
Gen. Manager, Ken McLean

Agricultural Societies Advisory Board
810, 401 York Ave., Winnipeg, R3C 0P8

The Agricultural Societies Advisory Board is established under the authority of the *Agricultural Societies Act* which governs the activities of agricultural societies in Manitoba. The Superintendent of Agricultural Societies for the province of Manitoba is assisted in the general direction and supervision of societies by the Advisory Board, which is composed of 11 directors, representing various districts of the province. The primary function of the Advisory Board is to advise the superintendent and government on policy and programs related to agricultural society activities.

Chairman, Ron Church
Sup't, R.M. Deveson

Farm Machinery Board
914 Norquay Bldg.
401 York Ave., Winnipeg, R3C 0P8

The Manitoba Farm Machinery Board administers the *Manitoba Farm Machinery and Equipment Act.* This includes the bonding and licensing of dealers and the processing of complaints about such things as delivery delays or shortages of repair parts. A lender who seeks to repossess farm machinery must submit a "Lien Note" to the Board. Either party has the right to apply for a court order to revoke the board's decision. Farm machinery can also be released to the lender with the execution of a "Voluntary Surrender".

The Board is composed of five farmer members including a chairman, a secretary-manager, two dealer representatives and one member representing manufacturers or suppliers.

Chairman, Lyall W. Stone
Box 58, MacGregor, R0H 0R0
Sec.-Manager, B. Grapentine

Manitoba Agricultural Credit Corp.
125 Garry St., 7th Flr., Winnipeg, R3C 3P2

This Corporation was established under the *Agricultural Credit Corporation Act,* C.C.S.M., Chapter A10. Its objectives are "to provide credit facilities for farmers, to assist farmers in obtaining credit and to assist in development of farms in the Province."

Under its current Regulation, Man. Reg. 81/79 and amendments thereto, the Corporation may assist individual farmers, farming co-operatives, corporations (including producer boards) and partnerships to purchase land, livestock and equipment, construct new buildings or renovate old buildings, improve land, or consolidate outstanding debts. In so doing, the Corporation may make direct loans and guarantee loans advanced by other approved lending institutions to assist in the development of economic farm units.

Under the *Fisheries Act,* C.C.S.M., Chapter F90 and Man. Reg. F90-R1 thereto, the Corporation may make direct loans to individual fishermen, groups of fishermen, fisheries co-operatives and incorporated fishing companies for the purchase of fishing equipment, consolidation of outstanding debt and for other purposes related to the establishment and development of economic commercial fishing operations.

Chairman, Robert Manns
Vice-Chairperson, Grant Fotheringham
Gen. Manager, N.A. Potter
Credit Administration
Director, D.A. Parnell
Finance and Administration
Director, J.D. Bilsland
Field Operations
Director, A.W. Todosichuk
Fishermen's Loans
Director, O.P. Josephson
Program Planning, Development
and Evaluation
Director, E.R. Poore

Manitoba Crop Insurance Corp.
25 N. Tupper St., Portage la Prairie, R1N 3K1

The Manitoba Crop Insurance Corporation is incorporated under the *Crop Insurance Act*, C.C.S.M., Chapter C-310. The statute provides authority for the appointment of a five-member board of directors whose duty it is to set policy for the Canada-Manitoba Crop Insurance program in accordance with the conditions set out in the *Crop Insurance Act* (Manitoba) and the Regulations thereunder.

The Canada-Manitoba Crop Insurance Program, through the Manitoba Crop Insurance Corporation, makes available a comprehensive all-risk crop insurance program to all farmers in the province on a voluntary basis, in an effort to reduce the instability of farm income due to crop disasters resulting from uncontrollable natural hazards. The Manitoba Crop Insurance Corporation also provides additional hail insurance coverage to those farmers insured under the all-risk program on a voluntary basis under Part II of the *Crop Insurance Act* (Manitoba).

Chairman, Dr. J. Clay Gilson
A/Gen. Manager, D.E. Forsberg
Research and Planning
Director, Henry Nelson
Finance and Administration
Director, Michael J. Gagne

Manitoba Dairy Board
Agricultural Services Complex
University of Manitoba, Winnipeg, R3T 2N2

The Manitoba Dairy Board examines requests for approval to establish or alter dairy processing plants in the province and recommends to the Minister of Agriculture the approval or rejection of such requests based upon the effect that such establishment or alteration could have on the dairy industry in Manitoba.

Chairman, T.L. Pringle
Secretary, Dr. F. Baker

Manitoba Farm Lands Ownership Board
805, 401 York Ave., Winnipeg, R3C 0P8

The Farm Lands Ownership Board was created to administer and enforce the provisions of the *Manitoba Farm Lands Ownership Act* (1983). The purpose of this Act is to preserve the province's farm land resources for use by present and future generations of Manitoba residents. The Board's responsibilities involve investigations, hearings, and the issuance of exemption and divestiture orders. The Board has the authority to exempt individuals or corporations, farm land, or interests in farm land from any provision of the legislation.
A/Exec. Director, Dale Osborne

Manitoba Fluid Milk Commission
Norquay Bldg., Ste. 903, 401 York Ave.
Winnipeg, R3C 0P8
Chairman, Darryl Kraft
Exec. Secretary, A. Strutinsky

Manitoba Horticultural Assn.
908 Norquay Bldg., Winnipeg, R3C 0P8

The Manitoba Horticultural Association is made up of over 40 individual societies and has a membership of approximately 4,000 amateur and professional gardeners. There are nine elected and two appointed positions on the board of directors, with the secretary-treasurer being in charge of program direction and policy. An annual meeting is held to discuss educational items and to prepare resolutions.

President, Mary Ann Swierstra
Sec.-Treasurer, Reg Curle

Manitoba Mediation Board
491 Portage Ave., 6th Flr., Winnipeg, R3B 2E4

Chairman, William E. Harrison
Exec. Director, S. Westdal

Manitoba Water Services Board
2022 Currie Blvd., Box 1059
Brandon, R7A 6A3

The *Manitoba Water Services Board Act* was passed in July 1972, to supercede the *Manitoba Water Supply Board Act* of 1959. Under the Act, the Manitoba Water Services Board, a Crown corporation under the Department of Agriculture of the Province of Manitoba, has wide-ranging powers to facilitate the provision of water and sewage services to municipalities and water districts.

Services provided include project management and administration of provincial financial assistance for the installation of appropriate water and sewage facilities for municipalities. Technical and financial assistance are also provided to individual farmers while groups of rural residents, communities and/or a municipality may form a water district to qualify for project management and financial assistance on a regional water system. The Board also operates 47 water treatment plants on behalf of municipalities and water districts.

Chairman, C.C. Cranston
Vice-Chairman, T.E. Weber
Gen. Manager, W.E. Griffin

R.O.P. Swine Committee
Agricultural Services Complex
University of Manitoba, Winnipeg, R3T 2N2

The purpose of the Manitoba Swine Record of Performance Advisory Committee is to act in an advisory capacity to the federal and Manitoba departments of agriculture in matters related to swine improvement in Canada and in Manitoba.

Among its objectives are the following:
a) to develop testing and evaluation programs which provide optimum opportunity for selection;
b) to encourage and assist breeders in designing breeding programs which will permit effective within-herd genetic improvement to meet industry needs; and

c) to examine continuously the role of the R.O.P. program and its effectiveness in meeting the requirements of swine breeders.

Members are appointed by the director of the Animal Industry Branch, Manitoba Department of Agriculture.

Chairman, Clarence Froese

DEPARTMENT OF THE ATTORNEY GENERAL

405 Broadway, 9th Flr., Winnipeg, R3C 3L6 (except where otherwise indicated)
General Inquiries: (204) 945-2878

ATTORNEY GENERAL'S OFFICE
104 Legislative Bldg., Winnipeg, R3C 0V8
Minister, The Hon. James McCrae

DEPUTY MINISTER'S OFFICE
110 Legislative Bldg., Winnipeg, R3C 0V8
Dep. Minister, Tanner Elton
Asst. Dep. Minister, Justice, Ron Perozzo

ADMINISTRATION
Exec. Director, P.J. Sinnott
Financial Administration
Director, B.W. Arnason
Manager of Administration Services,
A.E. Billett
Systems Director, R. Warner
Personnel Director, A.E. Proulx
Communications Director, Linda Lee
Research, Planning and Evaluation
Director, Lyle Thompson

Criminal Prosecutions
Asst. Dep. Minister, Criminal Justice,
John P. Guy, Q.C.
Information: (204) 945-2852
Director, Stuart Whitley
Chief Medical Examiner,
Dr. P.H. Markesteyn
Gen. Counsel, J.D. Montgomery, Q.C.
LEGAL SERVICES
Director, Tom Hague
FAMILY LAW
Director, Robyn Diamond
CONSTITUTIONAL LAW
Director, Vacant

Corrections
A/Asst. Dep. Minister, J. Wolfe
ADULT CORRECTIONAL SERVICES
Exec. Director, J. Wolfe
Assoc. Director, W. Scarth
CORRECTIONAL INSTITUTIONS:
Provincial Remand Centre
151 Princess St., Winnipeg, R3B 1L1
Sup't, P. Durant

Headingley Correctional Institution
Box 891, Winnipeg, R3C 2S7
Sup't, R. Forrester
Brandon Correctional Institution
375 Smithfield Rd., Box 1, Brandon, R7A 6M9
Sup't, Brian McVicar
Dauphin Correctional Institution
Box 40, Dauphin, R7N 2T9
Sup't, D. LaFond
The Pas Correctional Institution
Box 659, The Pas, R9A 1K7
Sup't, S.G. Tavener
Portage Correctional Institute
329 Duke Ave., Portage la Prairie, R1N 0S4
A/Sup't, W. Bott

COMMUNITY AND YOUTH CORRECTIONS
Exec. Director, B. Thiessen
Assoc. Director, M. Thomson
172 Doncaster St., Winnipeg, R3N 1X9
JUVENILE CENTRES:
Manitoba Youth Centre
170 Doncaster St., Winnipeg, R3N 1X9
Sup't, J. Ross
Agassiz Youth Centre
Box 1342, Portage la Prairie, R1N 3A9
Sup't, T. Rempel

Statutes
Asst. Dep. Minister/Legislative Counsel,
Shirley Strutt
Legal Translation
Director, Michel Nantel

Court Division
Asst. Dep. Minister, Marvin Bruce

COURT OF APPEAL/COURT OF QUEEN'S BENCH/PROVINCIAL COURT
(See judiciary)

COURT SERVICES
Director, W.W. Flattery
Court Communicator Services
Chief Court Communicator, A.J.G. Chartrand
Court Reporting Services
Chief Court Reporter, H. Dent
Legal Library Resources
Manager, M.J. Hernandez
Maintenance Enforcement Program
Manager, K. McCuaig
Sheriff's Services
Chief Sheriff, A.J. Nielsen
Law Enforcement Services
Director, C.A. Hill

LAND TITLES OFFICE
Lower Level, Woodsworth Bldg.
405 Broadway, Winnipeg, R3C 3L6
Registrar-General, Vacant
Gen. Manager, B. Hall
Surveys Branch
Examiner of Surveys, Vacant

OFFICE OF THE PUBLIC TRUSTEE
Woodsworth Bldg., 7th Flr.
405 Broadway, Winnipeg, R3C 3L6
Public Trustee, J.D. Raichura, Q.C.
Dep. Public Trustee, P.O. Jachetta
PERSONAL PROPERTY REGISTRY
Woodsworth Bldg., 15th Flr.
405 Broadway, Winnipeg, R3C 3L6
Registrar, D.A. Crockatt
Information: (204) 945-3123

AGENCIES, BOARDS AND COMMISSIONS

Criminal Injuries Compensation Board
101, 696 Portage Ave., Winnipeg, R3G 0M6

Under the *Criminal Injuries Compensation Act*, effective July 16, 1970, the Criminal Injuries Compensation Board was established to assist persons who have suffered injuries or death in Manitoba either as victims of crime or in the course of assisting a police officer.

Claims for assistance are made by applying directly to the Board. Any person who is a victim of crime and who sustains an injury in the province of Manitoba may apply.

Benefits shall be determined in an amount equivalent to those available to a worker within the meaning of the *Workers Compensation Act*, except that no payment shall be made with respect to medical and hospital benefits that are payable by any public or private scheme, or for benefits of less than $150. Appropriate rehabilitation services are also available to victims.

The *Criminal Injuries Compensation Act* is a federal/provincial cost-shared program and is administered by a Board appointed by the Lieutenant-Governor in Council.

Chairperson, Brian King
Commissioners: Lissa Donner, Elaine Smith
CEO, Graham Lane
Registrar, Ann Lovell

Human Rights Commission
301, 259 Portage Ave., Winnipeg, R3B 2A9

The Manitoba Human Rights Commission administers legislation to further the principle of equality, of opportunities and in the exercise of civil and legal rights regardless of status. It receives, investigates, and attempts to resolve complaints of unlawful discriminatory practices related to ancestry, ethnic or national origin, religion or creed, age, sex (including pregnancy), gender-determined characteristics, sexual orientation, marital/family status, source of income, political belief, or physical or mental disability. Protection for individuals under *The Human Rights Code* is provided in the areas of employment, housing, accommodations, services and facilities, publications, notices and signs, and contracts. There is no charge to the public for the investigative, conciliatory and legal services provided by the Commission.

Commission staff respond to requests for speaking engagements, seminars, workshops, and other activities in an effort to disseminate knowledge and promote a better understanding of prejudice, discrimination, and human rights in Manitoba.

Chairperson, Ken Filkow
Vice-Chairperson, Molly Robinson
Exec. Director, Darlene Germscheid

Law Reform Commission/Commission de réforme du droit
521, 405 Broadway, Winnipeg, R3C 3L6

The Commission was established by the *Law Reform Commission Act* in 1970. Its mandate is to make recommendations for the improvement, modernization, and reform of law, including the removal of provisions of law that are outdated or inconsistent; the maintenance and improvement of the administration of justice; the review of judicial and quasi-judicial procedures; the development of new approaches to and new concepts of law in keeping with and responsive to the changing needs of society; and the consideration of any subject referred to it by the Attorney General.

Chairman, Tanner Elton
Members: J.C. Irvine,
Hon. Mr. Justice G.O. Jewers,
Eleanor Dawson, Hon. Pearl McGonigal
Director of Legal Research, Jeffrey A. Schnoor

Legal Aid Services Society of Manitoba
402, 294 Portage Ave., Winnipeg, R3C 0B9

The Legal Aid Services Society of Manitoba, under provincial legislation, provides legal services to individuals as well as groups and organizations who, when left to their own means, could not afford the services of a lawyer. In most instances, representation before courts and tribunals is without charge, though in some cases the recipient may be required to pay back to Legal Aid a portion of the legal costs. Legal Aid Manitoba also provides without charge legal advice and information through staff solicitors located at seven different community law centres in the province. As well, it utilizes very extensively the services of private practitioners who are enrolled on Legal Aid's panels.

Chairman of the Board, Doug Yard
Exec. Director, Allan Fineblit
Dep. Director, Sheila Rogers
Area Director (Winnipeg), William Merrett
Legal Director, William Dunn
Public Interest Law Centre
Director, Arne Peltz

Manitoba Police Commission
Woodsworth Bldg., 5th Flr.
405 Broadway, Winnipeg, R3C 3L6

The Manitoba Police Commission, established in 1972, consists of a seven-member board of commissioners who are appointed by Order-in-Council and who report to the provincial

Attorney General.

The duties of the Commission are described in the *Provincial Police Act*, which states generally that the Commission shall promote the prevention of crime, efficiency of police services, and police-community relationships in the province. Full-time staff carry out the day-to-day programs of the Commission consistent with the *Police Act*. These include crime prevention programs, information services, training seminars for municipal and native police officers, research into minimum standards for selection and training of municipal police officers, post-secondary education programs for police, and criminal-justice education.

Although the Commission meets each month, it may be directed at any time, by the Lieutenant-Governor in Council, to inquire into and report upon any matter pertaining to the control of crime or the enforcement of law. Further, it may hear an appeal on disciplinary action imposed upon a police officer or an appeal made by any person who is a party to an inquiry or investigation touching upon the conduct of any member of a police force or the operation of a police force.

The Commission also has certain appellate functions stemming from the law enforcement review commissioner's decisions concerning citizen complaints.

Chairperson, Vacant

DEPARTMENT OF COMMUNITY SERVICES

Legislative Bldg., Winnipeg, R3C 0V8
(except where otherwise indicated)
General Inquiries: (204) 945-2211

MINISTER'S OFFICE
357 Legislative Bldg., Winnipeg, R3C 0V8
Minister, The Hon. Charlotte L. Oleson

DEPUTY MINISTER'S OFFICE
310 Legislative Bldg., Winnipeg, R3C 0V8
Dep. Minister, Conrad Hnatiuk
Research and Planning
125 Garry St., 4th Flr., Winnipeg, R3C 3P2
Director, K. Maskiw
Communications
125 Garry St., 4th Flr., Winnipeg, R3C 3P2
A/Director, D. Robertson

ADMINISTRATION AND FINANCE
270 Osborne St., Winnipeg, R3C 1V7
Exec. Director, K. Gray
Internal Audit Director, Vacant
Finance and Accounting
Director, R. Dykes
Personnel Services
Director, L. MacCallum
Vital Statistics
254 Portage Ave., Winnipeg, R3C 0B6
Director, M. Kreton

Administrative Services
270 N. Osborne St., 1st Flr.
Winnipeg, R3C 1V7
Director, M. Andrews
Residential Care Licensing
Director, L. Gorski
306, 155 Carlton St., Winnipeg, R3H 3H8

Community Social Services
210 Osborne St., 3rd Flr.
Winnipeg, R3C 0V8
Asst. Dep. Minister, J. Cels
Vocational Rehabilitation, E. Hasiuk
Residential Programs, D. Brownlee
Financial Services Manager, F. Mak
REGIONAL OPERATIONS
2, 800 Portage Ave., Winnipeg, R3G 0M5
Exec. Director, J. Ross

Manitoba Developmental Centre
Box 1190, Portage la Prairie, R1N 3C6
CEO, N. Upham
Medical Director, Dr. S.S. Kang
Director of Administration, S. Zidle
REGIONAL COMMUNITY SERVICES OFFICES:
Winnipeg North
1021 Cork Ave., Winnipeg, R2P 1V7
A/Reg. Director, J. Bickford

Winnipeg West-Central
189 Evanson St., Winnipeg, R3G 0N9
Reg. Director, R. Voss

Winnipeg South
Bldg. 3, 139 Tuxedo Ave., Winnipeg, R3N 0H6
Reg. Director, P. Leveille

Family Conciliation
405 Broadway, 9th Flr., Winnipeg, R3C 3L6
Director, L. Martin

Eastman Region
Provincial Bldg., 20 S. 1st St.
Beausejour, R0E 0C0
Director, G. Suss

Interlake Region
446 Main St., Selkirk, R1A 1V7
A/Director, R. Panson

Central Region
Provincial Bldg., 25 N. Tupper St.
Portage la Prairie, R1N 1W9
Director, S. Hiltz

Westman Region
Provincial Bldg., 340-9th St.
Brandon, R7A 6C2
Director, C. Hutchinson

Parklands Region
15-1st Ave. S.W., Dauphin, R7N 1R9
Director, Y. Hrynkiw

Norman Region
Provincial Bldg., 3rd St. and Ross Ave.
Box 2550, The Pas, R9A 1M4
Director, J. Karpan

Thompson Region
Thompson General Hospital
871 S. Thompson Dr., Thompson, R8N 0C8
Director, V. Wiebe

Child and Family Services
Asst. Dep. Minister, D. Perry
114 Garry St., 2nd Flr., Winnipeg, R3C 1G1
Child and Family Support
Director, J. Bakken
Child Day Care Branch
Director, M. Humphrey
Seven Oaks Centre
290 Drury Ave., Winnipeg, R3C 2E4
Sup't, D. Michie
Family Dispute Services
Director, S. Smith
2, 210 N. Osborne St., Winnipeg, R3C 1V4
Special Children's Service
Director, B. Law

DEPARTMENT OF CO-OPERATIVE, CONSUMER AND CORPORATE AFFAIRS
800, 215 Garry St., Winnipeg, R3C 3P3
(except where otherwise indicated)

MINISTER'S OFFICE
104 Legislative Bldg., Winnipeg, R3C 0V8
Minister, The Hon. James McCrae

DEPUTY MINISTER'S OFFICE
Dep. Minister, Don Zasada
Corporate Services
Director, Marg Porcher

CO-OPERATIVE AND CREDIT UNION
DEVELOPMENT AND REGULATION
Co-operative Development Branch
Registrar and Director, V. Hryshko
Manager, Vacant
Finance and Accounting Services
Manager, Vacant
Co-operative and Credit Union
Regulation Branch
Registrar and Director, Ron Pozernick
Dep. Registrar, T. Breuer
Chief Examiner, T. Lee

CONSUMER AFFAIRS DIVISION
Research and Planning
Woodsworth Bldg., 10th Flr.
405 Broadway, Winnipeg, R3C 3L6
Chief, Ian Anderson
Consumer's Bureau
114 Garry St., Winnipeg, R3C 1G1
Director, Denis Robidoux
Dep. Director, Ed Smith
Outside of Winnipeg, toll-free: 1-800-782-0067
Consumer Communications
1023, 405 Broadway, Winnipeg, R3C 3L6
Co-ordinator, Karen Gamey

COMPANIES AND BUSINESS NAMES
REGISTRATION BRANCH
Woodsworth Bldg., 10th Flr.
405 Broadway, Winnipeg, R3C 3L6

Director, M.H. Khan
A/Director, Myron Pawlowsky
INSURANCE BRANCH
Rm. 1142, 405 Broadway, Winnipeg, R3C 3L6
Sup't, Earl McGill

AGENCIES, BOARDS AND COMMISSIONS

Board of Administration Under Embalmers and Funeral Directors Act
Legislative Bldg., Rm. 336
450 Broadway, Winnipeg, R3C 0V8

The mandate of this Board is to license and regulate funeral homes, funeral directors, and embalmers. Its main activities include the administration of the two-year Mortuary Practices School program, the licensing of individuals and funeral homes in the province, and the receiving and handling of complaints from the public.

Chairperson, Dr. Don Zasada

The Co-operative Loans and Loans Guarantee Board
800, 215 Garry St., Winnipeg, R3C 3P3
General Inquiries: (204) 945-4455

The Co-operative Loans and Loans Guarantee Board was established in 1971 to assist Manitoba co-operatives in developing and expanding viable co-operative enterprises for the social and economic benefit of their members. The Board, through the provision of direct loans and loan guarantees, provides financial assistance to new and established co-operatives for capital costs, inventory, production expenses, or operating costs.

The Board is made up of five members, with the deputy minister of the department acting as chairman, another person from the department acting as secretary, and three other persons appointed by the Lieutenant-Governor in Council.

Chairperson, Don Zasada
Secretary, V. Hryshko
Members: J. Bodnar, Y. Lafreniere

Cooperative Promotion Board
800, 215 Garry St., Winnipeg, R3C 3P3
General Inquiries: (204) 945-3748

The Cooperative Promotion Board was established in 1926 under the *Wheat Board Money Trust Act* to act as trustee for the surplus funds of the original Canadian Wheat Board. The Government of Canada apportioned $128,000 to Manitoba, which invested it under the Act.

The Board is empowered to utilize income derived from the investments to promote research into co-operative organizations, to support educational programs on co-operatives and to make grants to co-operatives or agricultural organizations for promoting the general welfare of rural Manitobans.

Chairperson, H. Rempel
Vice-Chairperson, Ms. V. Dufault
Secretary, Don Zasada

The Credit Union Stabilization Fund
1500, 215 Garry St., Winnipeg, R3C 3P3

Established in 1965 under the *The Credit Unions and Caisses Populaires Act*, the Credit Union Stabilization Fund guarantees and protects all deposits in credit unions throughout Manitoba. Since the revision of the Act in 1970, each credit union has been required to make contributions to the Fund based on the amount of money deposited by its members. In this way, total deposit protection is provided — to all members of all credit unions with no limit on the amount of a claim. All credit unions are also monitored and inspected to ensure their compliance with applicable legislation and the Fund conducts an independent audit of their financial statements.

The Fund is administered by a five-member board appointed by the Lieutenant-Governor in Council and there is a general manager and support staff.

Chairperson, Leslie Callum
Vice-Chairman, Stuart Anderson
Gen. Manager, Vacant

Le Fonds de sécurité des caisses populaires
390-D, Provencher Blvd., Box 84
Winnipeg, R2H 3B4

Le Fonds de sécurité des caisses populaires has been a Manitoba-incorporated deposit insurance corporation since 1968. Its five-member board is appointed by the Lieutenant-Governor in Council. However, everyday operations of Le Fonds are conducted by a general manager and his support staff. One of the objectives of Le Fonds de sécurité is to provide a fund and offer aid-grants to caisses populaires for the purpose of protecting the members against financial losses.

Chairperson, Gérard Rémillard
Gen. Manager, Léo Roch

The Manitoba Securities Commission
1128, 405 Broadway, Winnipeg, R3C 3L6

A regulatory agency of the Manitoba Government, the Manitoba Securities Commission is responsible for the administration of the following statutes: *The Securities Act, The Real Estate Brokers Act, The Mortgage Dealers Act,* and *The Commodity Futures Act.*

To protect the public and facilitate the legitimate raising of capital while maintaining integrity and adequate standards in the securities, real estate, and mortgage brokerage industries, the Commission performs the following activities:

- licensing securities dealers, brokers, underwriters, and investment counsel;
- requiring full, true, and plain disclosure of new issues of securities;
- attempting to ensure fair and equitable treatment of the public regarding new issues of securities;
- providing a comprehensive regulatory scheme designed to make available to shareholders and the public a full range of financial and other information;
- licensing and regulating the activities of real estate and mortgage brokers, dealers, and sales people;
- investigating alleged contraventions under four Acts; and
- overseeing the self-regulatory activities of the Winnipeg Commodity Exchange.

The Commission consists of a full-time chairman and four part-time members appointed by Order-in-Council, supported by a staff of approximately 20 professional and clerical staff.

Chairman, E.J. Robertson
Director, F.C. Tapley
Sr. Counsel, David M.R. Cheop
Sr. Auditor, R.G. McEwen
Registration Officer (Securities),
Ernest B. Gingell
Registrar (Real Estate Brokers), J.W. Storsley

Public Utilities Board
1146, 405 Broadway, Winnipeg, R3C 3L6

The Public Utilities Board is an independent quasi-judicial agency operating under the authority of the Manitoba Legislature. The Board is responsible for the regulation of public utilities as defined under *The Public Utilities Board Act.* The Board also administers:

- *The Greater Winnipeg Gas Distribution Act*
- *The Gas Pipe Line Act*
- *The Gas Storage and Allocation Act*
- *The Prearranged Funeral Services Act*
- *The Cemeteries Act*
- portions of *The Municipal Act* pertaining to water and sewer rates, utility revenue deficits, and utility reserve funds.

Further, the Board has regulatory authority under *The Manitoba Telephone Act* and adjudicatory authority under *The Manitoba Hydro Act.*

In the event of dispute(s) between the Manitoba Telephone System and a cable television operator over the terms, conditions, and rates for the use of Manitoba Telephone System hardware facilities, the Board serves as the adjudicatory body. In addition, the Board serves as an appellate tribunal under *The Highways Protection Act,* and regulates fares for some transit systems operating in the province.

Chairman, E.J. Robertson
Secretary, G. Barron

DEPARTMENT OF CULTURE, HERITAGE AND RECREATION
177 Lombard Ave., 2nd Flr.
Winnipeg, R3B 0W5
(except where otherwise indicated)
General Inquiries: (204) 945-8396
Telex: 075-875-99

MINISTER'S OFFICE
118 Legislative Bldg., Winnipeg, R3C 0V8
Minister, The Hon. Bonnie Mitchelson

DEPUTY MINISTER'S OFFICE
112 Legislative Bldg., Winnipeg, R3C 0V8

Dep. Minister, Tom Carson
Research and Planning
Director, W. Hadikin
Communication Director, L. Streich

SUPPORT SERVICES DIVISION
Exec. Director, J.K. Wilkins
Finance and Management Services
Director, D. Paton
Personnel Services
Director, R. Dick
COMMUNITY SUPPORT SERVICES DIVISION
A/Exec. Director, J.K. Wilkins
Regional Services
Director, R. de Pencier
Grants Administration
Director, P. Rosmus
Recreation Director, H. Sirett
Community Places Program
Director, W. Blackburn

Culture and Heritage Programs Division

A/Asst. Dep. Minister, S. Hardy
Cultural Resources
A/Director, P. Desaulniers
Historic Resources
Director, D. Dul
Public Library Services
A/Director, A. Davis
INFORMATION RESOURCES DIVISION
200 Vaughan St., Main Flr., Winnipeg, R3C 0V8
Provincial Archivist, P. Bower
Legislative Librarian, S. Bishop

Communication Services Division

Asst. Dep. Minister, A. Cohen
Client Support Services
Director, C. Larkin
Information Services
Director, D. MacAulay
Translation Services
Director, A. Martin
Communication Advisory Services
Director, L. Wilson

AGENCIES, BOARDS AND COMMISSIONS

Le Centre culturel franco-manitobain
340, boul. Provencher, St-Boniface, R2H 0G7

Le Centre culturel franco-manitobain is a Crown corporation that officially opened its doors in 1973. It is funded by Manitoba's Department of Culture, Heritage and Recreation and by the federal Secretary of State. The Centre's executive council is nominated by the Lieutenant-Governor in Council.

Le Centre culturel franco-manitobain has a mandate to maintain, encourage, foster, and sponsor by all means available all types of cultural activities in the French language and to make French-Canadian culture available to all residents of the province. In this spirit, the Centre has encouraged the formation of the 17 existing community cultural committees which seek to maintain and encourage French-Canadian culture in their regions.

Chairperson, Marcelle Forest
Vice-Chairperson, Hélène Bulger
Exec. Director, Maria Chaput

Manitoba Arts Council
525, 93 Lombard Ave., Winnipeg, R3B 3B1
General Inquiries: (204) 945-2237

The Manitoba Arts Council was formed in 1969 to "promote the study, enjoyment, production, and performance of works in the arts". It offers grants and services to arts organizations and individual artists in the fields of: music, opera, dance, theatre, and the visual and literary arts. The Council consists of a chairman, vice-chairman and 13 other members appointed by the government of Manitoba. It meets regularly to formulate policy, establish priorities, and consider applications for assistance. The Council employs a 16-person staff and outside advisors and jurors are regularly consulted.

The major portion of the Council's funds is awarded to professional performing arts organizations to assist them in fulfilling their programs and objectives.

Chairperson, Mr. Justice Michel Monnin
Exec. Director, Marlene Neustaedter

Manitoba Centennial Centre Corp.
555 Main St., Winnipeg, R3B 1C3

The Manitoba Centennial Centre Corporation, a Crown corporation, was established to manage and maintain the properties of the Centre, which include the Centennial Concert Hall, the Manitoba Museum of Man and Nature, and the Planetarium. The Manitoba Theatre Centre and the Playhouse Theatre are also located within the Arts Centre.

The Concert Hall and Planetarium, opened in 1968, as well as the Museum and Theatre Centre (1970), continue to provide ample and diverse cultural and educational attractions enriching the quality of life of Manitobans and visitors alike.

In addition to the featured events, tours and extensive school programming combine to ensure the daily utilization and enjoyment of the Centre's extensive facilities. Additional information and assistance may be obtained by writing to the executive director at the above address.

Chairperson, Ruby Sinha
Exec. Director, R.G. Goodman

Manitoba Film Classification Board
216, 301 Weston St., Winnipeg, R3E 3H4

The present 15-member Film Classification Board is appointed by the Executive Council under the *Manitoba Amusement Act* of 1972.

The functions of the Board are a) to screen and classify all films distributed for exhibition to the public in Manitoba, b) to ensure that all advertising of films in Manitoba indicates the classification given, c) to ensure that restrictions regarding admission of under-age persons are carried out, and d) to classify all video tapes for public exhibition.

Classifications used in Manitoba are as follows:
- General: Suitable for all ages.
- Parental Guidance: All may attend although there may be material more suited for those over 12 years of age.
- Parental Accompaniment: Parental accompaniment is required for those under 15 years; content may be considered controversial or inappropriate for those younger than 15.
- Restricted: Admission to those over 18 years of age only.

Chairperson, Barbara Cannell
Dep. Presiding Member, Ross Dobson
Administrator, J. Rooswinkel

Manitoba Heritage Council
177 Lombard Ave., 3rd Flr.
Winnipeg, R3B 0W5
General Inquiries: (204) 945-4389

Previously known as the Historic Sites Advisory Board of Manitoba (1947-1986), the Manitoba Heritage Council is an advisory body appointed by the Minister of Culture, Heritage and Recreation to make recommendations on people, places, and events in Manitoba history which should be officially commemorated or legally protected by the department. The Council's recommendations result in the protection of significant heritage buildings and sites and the establishment of provincial plaques throughout Manitoba.

The Council's role and mission statement reads: "To recognize and encourage a greater sense of community and enhanced quality of life, the Manitoba Heritage Council identifies, protects, interprets and promotes the heritage resources of this province, offering objective, candid advice and direction to the minister, and advocating a fair and balanced representation of Manitoba's cultural history and diversity."

Presiding Member, Dr. John Lehr
Historic Resources Branch
Director and Secretary, D. Dul

Manitoba Intercultural Council
500, 283 Bannatyne Ave., Winnipeg, R3B 3B2
General Inquiries: (204) 945-4576

Chairperson, Pamela Rebello
Community Resources Officer,
Maria Lonardelli
Policy Analyst, Vijay Sharma

Manitoba Museum of Man and Nature
190 Rupert Ave., Winnipeg, R3B 0N2

The Manitoba Museum of Man and Nature is a public corporation funded by the province of Manitoba, the government of Canada, and private and corporate donations. It is overseen by a 20-member board of governors.

The philosophical theme of the Museum is man in his relationship to nature, his environment, and the universe. This theme is interpreted through specimens, graphics, reconstructions, and audio-visual presentations. To date, seven major galleries have been completed: Orientation, Earth History, Grasslands, Arctic-Subarctic, Boreal Forest, Nonsuch (a re-creation of a 17th-century ketch), and Urban. Temporary and travelling exhibits are housed in Alloway Hall. The Manitoba Planetarium provides astronomy-related entertainment and education, conducting a varied program of shows and events.

President, James R. Lewis
A/Exec. Director, Joanne DiCosino
Research and Collections
Director, Vacant
Operations Director, T.W. Nickle
Community Relations Director, Vacant
Planning, Programs and Evaluation
Director, George Wirtak

DEPARTMENT OF EDUCATION
1181 Portage Ave., Winnipeg, R3G 0T3
(except where otherwise indicated)
General Inquiries: (204) 945-6185

MINISTER'S OFFICE
168 Legislative Bldg., Winnipeg, R3C 0V8
Minister, The Hon. Leonard Derkach

OFFICE OF THE DEPUTY MINISTER
162 Legislative Bldg., Winnipeg, R3C 0V8
Dep. Minister, Dr. Glenn Nicholls
Communications Branch
116, 1200 Portage Ave., Winnipeg, R3G 0T5
Director, C. Cowles
Personnel Branch
Director, W. Claydon
Planning and Research Branch
221, 1200 Portage Ave., Winnipeg, R3G 0T5
Director, L. LeTourneau
Distance Education and Technology Branch
217, 1200 Portage Ave., Winnipeg, R3G 0T5
Exec. Director, D.O. Lussier

Administration and Finance Division
Asst. Dep. Minister, Tim Sale
Administration and Professional Certification Branch
Director, A. Krawec
Teacher Certification and Records
227, 1200 Portage Ave., Winnipeg, R3G 0T5
General Inquiries: (204) 945-7943
Finance Branch Director, Helen Fast
Schools Finance Branch
Director, L. Bisson
Management Information Services
Director, G. Martens

Bureau de l'éducation française
Asst. Dep. Minister, Guy Roy

Curriculum Development and Implementation Branch
Director, Gilbert Rosset
Educational Support Services Branch
Director, Henri Grimard
Official Languages Programs and Administrative Services Branch
Director, R. Pantel
Library and Materials Production Branch
Director, A. Huberdeau

Program Development and Support Services Division

Asst. Dep. Minister, Ed Buller
Child Care and Development Branch
Director, N.J. Cenerini

Manitoba School for the Deaf
500 Shaftesbury Blvd., Winnipeg, R3P 0M1
Principal, H.W. Miller

Correspondence Branch
528 James St., Winnipeg, R3G 3J4
Director, L. Buhr
Curriculum Development and Implementation Branch
Director, G. Parasiuk
Instructional Resources Branch
Director, J. Tooth
Manitoba Textbook Bureau
277 Hutchings St., Winnipeg, R2X 2R4
Director, Bob Chapman
Native Education Branch
A/Director, D. Cooley
Regional Services Branch
116, 1200 Portage Ave., Winnipeg, R3G 0T5
Director, Heather Wood
Regional Office
59 Elizabeth Dr., Thompson, R8N 1X4
J.H. Hjalmarson
Independent Schools
Liaison Officer, F. Neufeld

Post-secondary, Adult and Continuing Education Division
185 Carlton St., 4th Flr., Winnipeg, R3C 3J1

Asst. Dep. Minister, Nancy Sullivan
Information Services
Manager, T.K. Morgan
Administration and Finance Branch
Director, J.W. Heuvel
Adult and Continuing Education Branch
410, 185 Carlton St., Winnipeg, R3C 3J1
A/Director, D. Unruh
Post-secondary Career Development Branch
407, 185 Carlton St., Winnipeg, R3C 3J1
Director, D. Unruh
President, R. Newman
Student Aid Branch
693 Taylor Ave., Winnipeg, R3M 3T9
Director, C. Sigurdson
General Student Aid Inquiries: (204) 945-6321

AGENCIES, BOARDS AND COMMISSIONS

Board of Reference
507, 1181 Portage Ave., Winnipeg, R3G 0T3
General Inquiries: (204) 945-6899

The Board of Reference for the Province of Manitoba is established under authority provided by *The Public Schools Act,* S.M. 1980, Chapter P250, and was authorized originally in 1960. Appointed by the Lieutenant-Governor in Council, the Board usually consists of five members and a secretary.

The Board's main function is to decide matters related to boundaries of school divisions and districts, at the request of resident electors, school boards, municipal councils and/or Indian Band councils. Other matters considered include school division and district wards and trustee representation. Awards of the board are subject to appeal through the Court of Queen's Bench.

Chairman, G. Schreyer
Secretary, V. Tétrault

Board of Teacher Education and Certification
227, 1200 Portage Ave., Winnipeg, R3G 0T5
General Inquiries: (204) 945-7943

The Board is established under the authority of the Minister of Education under the *Executive Government Organization Act,* sections 3 and 10.

Its membership includes the Department of Education, the Manitoba Teachers' Society, the Manitoba Assn. of School Trustees, the Manitoba Assn. of School Superintendents, the universities of Manitoba and Winnipeg, Brandon University, and St. Boniface College.

The role of the Board is to advise the minister on matters relating to teacher certification and education.

Chairman, Dr. J. Irvine

The Collective Agreement Board
162 Legislative Bldg., Winnipeg, R3C 0V8
General Inquiries: (204) 945-4176

The Collective Agreement Board is established under section 150 of *The Public Schools Act* to deal with matters referred to it concerning collective agreements between School Division Boards and Division Teachers' Associations.

The Board is composed of the Deputy Minister of Education, who acts as chairman, two members appointed by the Manitoba Teachers' Society, and two members appointed by the Manitoba Assn. of School Trustees.

Chairman, Dr. Glenn Nicholls
Vice-Chairman and Secretary, A. Krawec

Public Schools Finance Board
506, 1181 Portage Ave., Winnipeg, R3G 0T3

The Public Schools Finance Board has not more than five persons who are appointed by the Lieutenant-Governor in Council.

The purpose of the Board is to facilitate the

financing of the education support program for school divisions and to assist boards of school divisions in the economical operation of the public school system.

Chairman, A. Frechette
Recording Secretary, J. Slobodzian
Capital Facilities Section
Co-ordinator, B.H. Epp

Student Aid Appeal Board
693 Taylor Ave., Box 4, Winnipeg, R3M 3T9

Chairperson, G. Vamos

Teachers' Retirement Allowances Fund Board
115, 1200 Portage Ave., Winnipeg, R3G 0T5

The TRAF Board is appointed by the government of Manitoba in accordance with *The Teachers' Pension Act,* C.C.S.M., Chapter T20, to administer that Act and the related pension fund. The Board consists of three teachers, two school trustees, and two "citizen" members.

The Board receives contributions from all public school teachers in the province (approximately 13,000) and pays retirement benefits to about 4,000 retired plan members.

As trustee of the Fund, the Board is responsible for the investment of the Fund assets in accordance with the *Manitoba Pension Benefits Act* and Regulations, and takes its direction in this regard from an investment committee comprised of the board chairman, a "teacher" member of the board, and the Deputy Minister of Finance. The current fund size is approximately $550 million and net cash flow of over $60 million was expected in 1988.

The Board is empowered to employ such staff as is necessary to carry out its responsibilities and must appoint an actuary to carry out valuations of the Fund's liabilities and report thereon at least once every three years.

Secretary, C. DeGagné
Treasurer, W.L. Rehaluk

Universities Grants Commission
1550, 155 Carlton St., Winnipeg, R3C 3H8

The Universities Grants Commission was established by an Act of the legislature passed in 1967 and is composed of nine members appointed by the Lieutenant-Governor in Council.

The Commission advises the minister on the amount of financial assistance which should be provided to the universities by the government. The Commission is responsible for allocating to the universities the funds received from the government.

Permission must be obtained from the Commission before universities establish new facilities or programs of study, or expand existing services.

Chairman, J. Wiens
Exec. Director, Dr. B. Levin
Financial Officer, A.D. Goldstine
Secretary, R.W. Simpson

DEPARTMENT OF EMPLOYMENT SERVICES AND ECONOMIC SECURITY

MINISTER'S OFFICE
357 Legislative Bldg., Winnipeg, R3C 0V8

Minister, The Hon. Charlotte L. Oleson

DEPUTY MINISTER'S OFFICE
351 Legislative Bldg., Winnipeg, R3C 0V8

Dep. Minister, Roxy Freedman

ADMINISTRATIVE SERVICES DIVISION
615, 330 Graham Ave., Winnipeg, R3C 4A5
Exec. Director, Wes Henderson
Finance and Administration
Director, Gerben Bosma
Personnel Services Branch
Director, Myra McFarlane
Systems and Computer Support Services
Director, Karl Sproll
Communications
611, 330 Graham Ave., Winnipeg, R3C 4A5
Director, Janice Little
Research and Planning
611, 330 Graham Ave., Winnipeg, R3C 4A5
Exec. Director, Martin Billinkoff

Employment Services Division
1013, 401 York Ave., Winnipeg, R3C 0P8

Asst. Dep. Minister, Tannis Mindell
Employment Development and Youth Services Branch
114 Garry St., Winnipeg, R3C 1G1
Exec. Director, Gisela Rempel
Regional Employment and Immigration Services
1011, 401 York Ave., Winnipeg, R3C 0P8
Exec. Director, Gerry Clement
Immigration and Settlement
114 Garry St., Winnipeg, R3C 1G1
A/Director, Gail Thomson
Regional Services
1011, 401 York Ave., Winnipeg, R3C 0P8
Director, G. Schmidt
Human Resources Opportunity Program
164 Isabel St., Winnipeg, R3A 1G5
Director, M. Pedlow
Employment Training
1010, 401 York Ave., Winnipeg, R3C 0P8
Exec. Director, P. Dubienski
Labour Market Programs
Director, Claire Clement
Intergovernmental Relations
Director, C. Nordman
New Careers Program
213 Notre Dame Ave., 5th Flr.
Winnipeg, R3B 1N3
Director, Bob Knight

Economic Security Division
301, 267 Edmonton St., Winnipeg, R3C 1S2

Asst. Dep. Minister, Winston Hodgins

Income Security Services
Provincial Director, B. DePape
A/Asst. Provincial Director, Ron May
Income Supplements Program
512, 330 Portage Ave., Winnipeg, R3C 0C4
Director, Valerie Zinger
REGIONAL INCOME SECURITY OFFICES
WINNIPEG OFFICES:
North District Office
1790 Main St., Winnipeg, R2V 2A1
Director, Emma Metzlaff
South/West District Office
880 Portage Ave., Winnipeg, R3G 0P2
Director, John Petersen
Central District Office
164 Isabel St., Winnipeg, R3A 1G5
A/Director, B. Barton
Student Social Allowance
693 Taylor Ave., Winnipeg, R3M 2K2
Director, R. Golinoski
RURAL OFFICES:
Westman Region
Provincial Bldg., 340-9th St., Brandon, R7A 6C2
A/Director, John Corder
Eastman Region
Provincial Bldg., 20 S. 1st St.
Beausejour, R0E 0C0
Director, G. Liske
Central Region—Portage Office
Provincial Bldg., 25 N. Tupper St.
Portage la Prairie, R1N 1W9
Director, D. Marion
Central Region—Morden Office
63 Stephen St., Morden, R0G 1J0
Director, M. LePage
Interlake Region
446 Main St., Selkirk, R1A 1V7
Director, R. McFayden
Parklands Region—Dauphin Office
202 S. Main St., Dauphin, R7N 1C4
A/Director, R. Reid
Parklands Region—Swan River Office
Provincial Bldg., 201 S. 4th Ave.
Swan River, R0L 1Z0
Director, R. Reid
Norman Region—The Pas Office
Provincial Bldg., 3rd St. and Ross Ave.
Box 2550, The Pas, R9A 1M4
Director, B. Huycke
Norman Region—Flin Flon Office
211, 35 Main St., Flin Flon, R8A 1J7
Director, H. Gummerson
Thompson Region
Provincial Bldg., 59 Elizabeth Dr.
Thompson, R8N 1X4
Director, W. Ghostkeeper

AGENCIES, BOARDS AND COMMISSIONS

Manitoba Advisory Council on the Status of Women
450, 500 Portage Ave., Winnipeg, R3C 3X1

The Manitoba Advisory Council on the Status of Women was established in 1980 by the Govern- ment of Manitoba. Its mandate is to advise the Minister responsible for the Status of Women on matters that concern women, the objective being to advance the goal of equal participation of women in society and to promote changes in social, legal, and economic structures to that end.

Matters to be considered are initiated both from government and the Council, with laws, policies and programs under provincial jurisdiction being the Council's priority. Ongoing consultation with concerned groups and individuals assists the Council in developing its recommendations.

Twelve Council members, plus one chairper- son, have been appointed by the Government of Manitoba, representing a wide range of concerns and expertise in the field of status of women. Members and staff respond to requests for speaking engagements and other activities to promote awareness of women's concerns and participation in matters of public policy.
Exec. Director, Sheila Gordon

Chairperson, Bev Suek
Policy Analyst, D. Hudec

Manitoba Bureau of Statistics
155 Carlton St., 6th Flr., Winnipeg, R3C 3H8

The Manitoba Bureau of Statistics is the central statistical agency of the government of Manitoba and is responsible to the Minister of Employment Services and Economic Security.

The Bureau, established in 1972, operates under the terms of the *Manitoba Statistics Act*. Its objectives under section 3(1) are to plan, pro- mote, and develop integrated social and econom- ic statistics relating to the province on behalf of government departments and agencies in order to avoid duplication of effort and cost. Under an agreement with Statistics Canada, the Bureau serves as the focal point for interaction between the province and Statistics Canada.

Objectives are met through three main activities related to departmental requests. These activities are:
1) responding to requests from government departments and agencies, and from business for statistical information and maintaining a liaison with Statistics Canada, other provincial bureaus, and user departments;
2) providing statistical data common to all depart- ments of government; and
3) consulting, developing data, and ensuring data processing and the adequacy of data processing and surveys undertaken on behalf of government departments.
Director, Wilf Falk

Manitoba Training Advisory Council
329, 1200 Portage Ave., Winnipeg, R3G 3L5
General Inquiries: (204) 945-0443
Exec. Director, Paul Goyan

Manitoba Women's Directorate
440, 500 Portage Ave., Winnipeg, R3C 3X1

The role and mission of the Manitoba Women's Directorate is to co-ordinate the research, development, communication, and evaluation of government programs, policies, and legislation in order to ensure the enhancement of the status of women in Manitoba.

The Directorate accomplishes its mission by supporting the Minister responsible for the Status of Women. It also assumes a leadership role by assisting government departments and agencies, Crown corporations, the private sector, and the community to eliminate systemic discrimination, enhance services, and increase opportunities for women.

The initiatives and policy recommendations of the Women's Directorate reflect the needs of the women of Manitoba from economic, political, societal, and legal perspectives.

Exec. Director, D.M. Oulton

Social Services Advisory Committee
1001, 330 Portage Ave., Winnipeg, R3C 0C4
General Inquiries: (204) 945-3003

The Social Services Advisory Committee is established by the *The Social Services Administration Act*, and appointed by the Lieutenant-Governor in Council. The Committee consists of a chairman, vice-chairman, and 13 members.

The Committee acts as the authority for the hearing of appeals with respect to municipal and provincial income security programs, day care subsidies, family services, 55 Plus — A Manitoba Income Supplement program, and the licensing of residential care facilities, foster homes, and child day care centres. Decisions of the Committee on income security and family services can be appealed to the Court of Appeal for Manitoba on a point of law or a matter of jurisdiction. Decisions of the Committee on licensing of residential care facilities, foster homes, and child day care centres may be appealed to the Court of Queen's Bench.

The Committee also acts in an advisory capacity to the Minister of Community Services and to the Minister of Employment Services and Economic Security. As an appeal board with a quorum of three members, the Committee travels throughout the province to the communities of the appellants. Advice on options for action toward self-support or further assistance from various programs are frequently by-products of the appeal process.

Chairman, Don Tirschmann
Vice-Chairman, Gail Isaak

DEPARTMENT OF ENERGY AND MINES
555, 330 Graham Ave., Winnipeg, R3C 4E3
(except where otherwise indicated)

MINISTER'S OFFICE
301 Legislative Bldg., Winnipeg, R3C 0V8
Minister, The Hon. Harold Neufeld

DEPUTY MINISTER'S OFFICE
309 Legislative Bldg., Winnipeg, R3C 0V8

Dep. Minister, C. Kang
ADMINISTRATIVE SERVICES DIVISION
Exec. Director, Garry Barnes
COMMUNICATIONS AND COMMUNITY RELATIONS DIVISION
Exec. Director, Wayne Ferguson

Minerals Division

Asst. Dep. Minister, S. Singh
Mines Branch Director, W. Bardswich
Geological Services Branch
Director, Dr. W.D. McRitchie

Energy Division

Asst. Dep. Minister, H.C. Moster
Petroleum Branch
Director, L.R. Dubreuil
Energy Management Branch
Director, W.M. McDonald
Energy Policy Branch
Director, R. Pritchard

AGENCIES, BOARDS AND COMMISSIONS

Electrical Energy Marketing Committee
191 Lombard Ave., 12th Flr.
Winnipeg, R3B 0X1

The Electrical Energy Marketing Committee is a standing committee of the board of directors of the Manitoba Energy Authority, and has the following principal functions:
a) to investigate potential extra-provincial markets for electrical energy, and
b) to negotiate or direct negotiations for the sale or purchase of electrical energy exported from or imported to the province.

Chairman, A. Brian Ransom

Energy Allocation Committee
191 Lombard Ave., 12th Flr.
Winnipeg, R3B 0X1
General Inquiries: (204) 945-0193

The Energy Allocation Committee is a standing committee of the board of directors of the Manitoba Energy Authority, and has the following principal functions:
a) to investigate and review data respecting the supply of energy and demand for energy,
b) to develop plans for the allocation of supplies of energy,
c) to investigate and review the plans or programs of other provinces or countries for the allocation of supplies of energy, and
d) to maintain a continuing liaison with the federal government with respect to the actual or prospective implementation of the *Energy Supplies Allocation Act, 1979* (Canada).

Manitoba Energy Authority

191 Lombard Ave., 12th Flr.
Winnipeg, R3B 0X1
General Inquiries: (204) 945-0193

The Manitoba Energy Authority is a Crown corporation established pursuant to the *Manitoba Energy Act,* with its board of directors appointed by Order-in-Council as provided in the Act.

The Authority has responsibility for negotiating, directing the negotiations of, or approving all extraprovincial electrical energy transactions. Approval of extraprovincial transactions by the Authority must be evidenced before final approval is given by the Lieutenant-Governor in Council.

The Authority is also responsible for formulating and carrying out energy policies designed to promote the establishment, development, and operation within the province of industries or undertakings that are by their nature energy-dependent.

Chairperson, A.B. Ransom
Vice-Chairman, J. Arnason
CEO, C.E. Curtis

Manitoba Energy Council

555, 330 Graham Ave., Winnipeg, R3C 4E3

The Manitoba Energy Council, founded in February 1983 under the *Manitoba Energy Council Act,* is a citizen advisory group appointed by the minister. The Council consists of a chairperson, a secretary, and eight members. The Council provides the minister with assessments and recommendations concerning energy policy and conservation programs.

Chairman, Vacant
Secretary, C. Symes

Manitoba Mineral Resources Ltd.

603, 491 Portage Ave., Winnipeg, R3B 2E4

Manitoba Mineral Resources Ltd. was established in 1971 under the *Manitoba Natural Resources Development Act.* Its three principal objectives are:

1) to bring risk capital into Manitoba by initiating mineral exploration projects that will attract participation by the private sector. Conversely, the company will consider participation in exploration projects proposed by others. The company will carry out its work within the same framework of rules, regulations, and normal practice governing the private sector;
2) to manage the province's interest in mandatory participation agreements made pursuant to Man. Reg. 328/74 and previously entered into by the Department of Energy and Mines; and
3) to employ and train personnel resident in the province in all aspects of mining exploration.

Chairman, Paul Brockington
President, C.M. Wright
Secretary, Cyril Vickers
Directors: H.D.B. Wilson, C.T. Williams,
Paul Brockington, Grant R. Wilson

Mining Board

555, 330 Graham Ave., Winnipeg, R3C 4E3

The Mining Board is a quasi-judicial body appointed by Order-in-Council pursuant to the provisions of the *Mines Act.*

The primary function of the Board is the arbitration of disputes between surface rights holders and mineral rights holders with respect to the accessing of minerals other than oil and natural gas. Upon application, the Board may hold hearings, take evidence, and establish the terms and conditions under which a mineral rights holder may gain access. Such conditions may include location of workings, size of workings, compensation of the surface rights holder, and such other conditions as may be appropriate in the particular circumstances. The Board may also be requested to conduct hearings and make rulings relating to the pooling of interests and unitization agreements for mineral rights other than oil and natural gas, and to arbitrate disputes arising from the acquisition of mining claims.

Decisions of the Board are binding unless appealed to the courts.

Chairman, C. Kang
Dep. Chairman, S. Singh
Member, D.W. Crandall

Oil and Natural Gas Conservation Board

555, 330 Graham Ave., Winnipeg, R3C 4E3

The Oil and Natural Gas Conservation Board is a quasi-judicial body appointed by Order-in-Council pursuant to the provisions of the *Mines Act.* The Board is composed of three government officials and reports to the Minister of Energy and Mines.

The Board has as its primary function the issuance of orders for the optimum operation of pools and fields. These orders can concern such things as designations and delineations of fields and pools, production rates, recovery of all substances from wells, storage, water disposal, and pressure maintenance.

Disputes arising between producers with respect to the development of pooling and unitization agreements may be referred to the Board for arbitration. Decisions of the Board are final and binding unless appealed to the courts.

Chairman, C. Kang
Dep. Chairman, W.M. McDonald
Member, B. Ball

DEPARTMENT OF ENVIRONMENT AND WORKPLACE SAFETY AND HEALTH

MINISTER'S OFFICE
156 Legislative Bldg., Winnipeg, R3C 0V8

Minister, The Hon. Edward Connery

DEPUTY MINISTER'S OFFICE
156 Legislative Bldg., Winnipeg, R3C 0V8

Dep. Minister, Tanner Elton
Finance and Administration
Bldg. 2, 139 Tuxedo Ave., Winnipeg, R3C 0H6
Director, Wolf K. Boehm
Environmental Management Services
Bldg. 2, 139 Tuxedo Ave., Winnipeg, R3C 0H6
Director, Norm B. Brandson
Environmental Control Services
Bldg. 2, 139 Tuxedo Ave., Winnipeg, R3C 0H6
Director, Carl B. Orcutt
Workplace Safety and Health
1000, 330 St. Mary Ave., Winnipeg, R3C 3Z5
A/Director, Ron Glassford
Worker Advisor Office
311 Balmoral St., Winnipeg, R3L 1H9
Director, John McNevin
Community Relations
960, 330 St. Mary Ave., Winnipeg, R3C 3Z5
Director, Mark Stefanson
Planning Research and Evaluation
960, 330 St. Mary Ave., Winnipeg, R3C 3Z5
Director, Jerry Spiegel

AGENCIES, BOARDS AND COMMISSIONS

Advisory Council on Workplace Safety and Health
1000, 330 St. Mary Ave., Winnipeg, R3C 3Z5

Chairman, Prof. W.N. Fox-Decent

The Clean Environment Commission
500 Portage Ave., 5th Flr., Winnipeg, R3C 3X1

The Manitoba Clean Environment Commission is a body appointed by Order-in-Council under *The Environment Act.* It is composed of up to 10 Manitoba citizens under a full-time chairman.

The primary function of the Commission is to hold public meetings or hearings on environmental matters for the purpose of gathering evidence and reporting on such investigations to the minister.

Any person before setting into operation any development that discharges pollutants must file a proposal with the department. Such proposals are advertised and, where objections or concerns are received, the department may recommend that the minister request the Commission to hold a hearing prior to the issuance of a licence.

Chairman, O. Stanley Eagleton
Exec. Secretary, William R. Stewart
Technical Advisor, James N. Warrener

Manitoba Environmental Council
550, 500 Portage Ave., Winnipeg, R3C 3X1

The Manitoba Environmental Council is a citizens' group appointed by the Minister of Environment to advise the government of environmental problems and issues that concern Manitobans. The Council was originally established in 1972, and was named officially by the new *Environment Act* proclaimed on March 31, 1988.

The principal objective of the Council is to identify and review environmental issues and provide the findings, along with recommendations, to the minister. Topics are chosen by each of the Council's seven committees and briefs or position papers are prepared. The Council also responds to direct ministerial requests for policy, program, or legislative advice.

Another of the Council's objectives is to raise awareness and to keep the public informed of environmental issues. This is done through publications, open forums, and media releases.

The Council receives its funding through the Department of Environment, which also provides one full-time staff person as well as secretarial and administrative assistance.

Chairperson, Dr. Ian Rollo
Co-ordinator, Keri Barringer

Manitoba Hazardous Waste Management Corp.
226, 530 Century St., Winnipeg, R3H 0Y4

The Manitoba Hazardous Waste Management Corporation is a commercial Crown corporation established to develop and operate a hazardous waste management system for Manitoba. Its mandate is to provide for the handling of regulated hazardous wastes from their source through to their treatment and disposal, consistent with high standards of public health, safety, and environmental quality.

The Corporation was formed by the *Manitoba Hazardous Waste Management Corporation Act* in November 1986, and came into functional existence during 1987. It reports through its board of directors to the Minister of Environment and Workplace Safety and Health.

The Corporation is mandated to co-ordinate the elements of the system, such as transfer, storage, destruction, and disposal, in an efficient, dependable fashion that has a positive effect on the economy of Manitoba. It will give priority in its operations to waste generated in Manitoba. The Corporation proposes to develop the system on an incremental basis and starting at the waste source.

Chairman, Nick Carter
CEO, R.J. Cooke

The Workers Compensation Board of Manitoba
Box 965, Winnipeg, R3C 4J2

Workers in the majority of industries in Manitoba are protected by *The Workers Compensation Act.* This law, administered by the Workers Compensation Board, provides financial, medical, and rehabilitation assistance to workers who become disabled by industrial injury or disease.

The Act substitutes a right of legal action by the injured worker against an employer with a more positive and prompt method of compensation.

The Board, which consists of a chairperson and two full-time commissioners, is appointed by the Lieutenant-Governor in Council.

Chairperson, Brian King
Commissioners: Lissa Donner, Elaine Smith
CEO, Graham Lane
Secretary to the Board, George Davis
Information Services
Manager, James Buchok

DEPARTMENT OF FINANCE
103 Legislative Bldg., Winnipeg, R3C 0V8
General Inquiries: (204) 945-3754

MINISTER'S OFFICE
Minister, The Hon. Clayton Manness
Communications Director, Ed Reed

DEPUTY MINISTER'S OFFICE
Dep. Minister, Charles E. Curtis

ADMINISTRATION DIVISION
Director, Charles D. McKenzie
Insurance and Risk Management
Director, John K. Rislahti

Treasury Division
Asst. Dep. Minister, Neil S. Benditt
Debt Management
Director, Barry Thornson
Money Management
Director, William J. Cessford
Debt and Investment Services
Director, Gloria Kilosky

COMPTROLLER'S DIVISION
Comptroller, Eric H. Rosenhek
Disbursements and Accounting
Director, Gerry Gaudreau
Financial and Management Systems
Director, Roger Guinn
Information Systems Support
Director, Richard J. Lussier

Federal-Provincial Relations and Research Division
Asst. Dep. Minister, J. Patrick Gannon

Taxation Division
Asst. Dep. Minister, A.W. Roberts
Retail Sales Tax
Director, S.R. Moshenko
Mining and Use Taxes
Director, S.J. Puchniak
Corporation Capital Tax/Health and
Post-secondary Education Tax Levy
Director, Laurie F. Lobos
Succession Duty and Gift Tax
General Information: (204) 945-3758

TREASURY BOARD SECRETARIAT
A/Secretary, Don Potter
Office of Expenditure Review
Director, Donna Larsen

Administrative Policy Branch
Manager, Fran Gropp

AGENCIES, BOARDS AND COMMISSIONS

Manitoba Hospital Capital Financing Authority
109 Legislative Bldg., Winnipeg, R3C 0V8

The Manitoba Hospital Capital Financing Authority was created in 1972 pursuant to The Hospital Capital Financing Authority Act. It assists hospital operators to finance capital expenditures by ensuring an orderly market for the sale and purchase of their securities. Such operators may not issue securities to finance capital expenditures without the approval of the Authority. Securities of the Authority may be guaranteed by the Province of Manitoba.

The Authority has no staff of its own and is operated by the staff of the Department of Finance.

Chairman, The Hon. Clayton Manness
Secretary, Charles E. Curtis

DEPARTMENT OF GOVERNMENT SERVICES

MINISTER'S OFFICE
203 Legislative Bldg., Winnipeg, R3C 0V8
Minister, The Hon. Albert Driedger

DEPUTY MINISTER'S OFFICE
343 Legislative Bldg., Winnipeg, R3C 0V8
Dep. Minister, Eric Harbottle

ADMINISTRATION
405 Broadway, 15th Flr., Winnipeg, R3C 3L6
Exec. Director, S. Walker
Finance Director, P. Rochon
Internal Audit
Manager, S. Schroeder
Human Resource Services
390 York Ave., Winnipeg, R3C 0P3
Director, R. Stevenson
Management Support
405 Broadway, 15th Flr., Winnipeg, R3C 3L6
Director, L. Gibson
Systems
1503, 155 Carlton St., Winnipeg, R3C 3H8
Manager, K. MacIntosh

PROJECT SERVICES
1700 Portage Ave., Winnipeg, R3J 0E1
Exec. Director, G. Fejes
Corporate Accommodation Planning
Director, F. LeClair
A/Design Director, A. Lorimer
Project Management Director, †. Revak
Land Acquisition
Woodsworth Bldg., 12th Flr.
405 Broadway, Winnipeg, R3C 3L6
Director, J. deZeeuw

PROPERTY MANAGEMENT
1700 Portage Ave., Winnipeg, R3J 0E1
Exec. Director, S. Ursel
Physical Plant Director, C. Howard

Gimli Properties
Box 40, Gimli, R0C 1B0
Manager, J. Dunlop

SUPPLY AND SERVICES
530 Century St., Winnipeg, R3H 0L8
Exec. Director, G.W. Berezuk
Fleet Vehicles
626 Henry Ave., Winnipeg, R3C 1P7
Director, D. Ducharme
Telecommunications
401 York Ave., 10th Flr., Winnipeg, R3C 0P8
Director, A. Komher
Office Equipment Services
530 Century St., Winnipeg, R3H 0L8
Director, D. McNeill
Purchasing
530 Century St., Winnipeg, R3H 0L8
Director, E.F. Baranet
Materials Supply
1383 Whyte Ave., Winnipeg, R3E 1V7
Director, E. Hilditch

AGENCIES, BOARDS AND COMMISSIONS

Emergency Measures Organization
405 Broadway, 15th Flr., Winnipeg, R3C 3L6
General Inquiries (24 hours): (204) 945-5555

The Manitoba Emergency Measures Organization (EMO) was originally formed in 1954, but functions today in accordance with the *Manitoba Emergency Measures Act,* passed July 17, 1987. The organization is responsible for provincial emergency preparedness, which means readiness for emergencies and disasters, and includes planning, training, exercises, and education necessary to achieve a state of readiness for emergencies. In emergencies or disasters, EMO co-ordinates the provincial response.
Co-ordinator, F. Zeggil
Municipal Services Manager, Vacant
Planning Research
Supervisor, M. Bennett

Land Value Appraisal Commission
Imperial Broadway Twr., Ste. 1220
363 Broadway, Winnipeg, R3C 3N9

The Land Value Appraisal Commission was created in 1965; provision for the Commission is found in *The Land Acquisition Act,* C.C.S.M., Chapter L40. Its operation is governed by both *The Land Acquisition Act,* respecting government purchases, and *The Expropriation Act,* C.C.S.M., Chapter E190, respecting government expropriations.

The sole jurisdiction of the Commission is to determine and certify an amount which in the opinion of the Commission represents the due compensation payable. The Commission's primary function is adjudicative. The Commission's decision is binding on the acquiring authority but landowners are not bound by the decision and may take the matter to the Court of Queen's Bench, according to sections 12(2) and (3) and sections 15(2) and (3) of *The Land Acquisition Act* and *Expropriation Act* respectively.

Chairman, Cameron Harvey
Vice-Chairperson, Helen Unruh
Secretary, Joseph E. Krutish
Members: Stephanie Barnett, Cole Campbell, Jim Husiak, George Sawatsky

Manitoba Disaster Assistance Board
800 Portage Ave., Main Flr.
Winnipeg, R3G 0N4
Chairperson, Sydney Reimer
Vice-Chairperson, Lorne Boguski
Secretary, Joseph Masi
Member, Lois Edie

DEPARTMENT OF HEALTH
175 Hargrave St., 7th Flr., Winnipeg, R3C 0V8
(except where otherwise indicated)

MINISTER'S OFFICE
302 Legislative Bldg., Winnipeg, R3C 0V8
Minister, The Hon. Donald Orchard

DEPUTY MINISTER'S OFFICE
A/Dep. Minister, Frank A. Maynard
Provincial Gerontologist, B. Havens
Research and Planning Directorate
308, 294 Portage Ave., Winnipeg, R3C 0B9
Director, D. Pascoe
Communications Directorate
501, 294 Portage Ave., Winnipeg, R3C 0B9
Director, D. Shattuck

Administration Services Division
602, 330 Graham Ave., Winnipeg, R3C 4A5
A/Asst. Dep. Minister, L. Searcy
Administration and Financial Services
A/Director, T. Mattern
Human Resource Management Services
Director, J. Morris
Medical Supplies and Home Care Equipment
1500 Regent Ave., Winnipeg, R2C 3A8
Director, C. Jacyk

Community Health Services Division
831 Portage Ave., Winnipeg, R2C 3A8
Asst. Dep. Minister, Dr. Sharon Macdonald
REGIONAL OPERATIONS:
305, 1200 Portage Ave., Winnipeg, R3G 0T5
Exec. Director, J. Ross

Winnipeg North
1021 Court St., Winnipeg, R2P 1V7
Reg. Director, S. Hicks
Winnipeg South
139 Tuxedo Blvd., Winnipeg, R3N 0H6
Reg. Director, P. Leveille

Winnipeg West-Central
189 Evanson St., Winnipeg, R3G 0N9
Reg. Director, R. Voss
Central Region
25 N. Tupper St., Portage la Prairie, R1N 1W9
Director, S. Hiltz
Eastman Region
20-1st St., Beausejour, R0E 0C0
Reg. Director, G. Suss
Interlake Region
446 Main St., Selkirk, R1A 1V7
A/Reg. Director, R. Patson
Norman Region
Box 2550, The Pas, R9A 0K6
Director, S. Karpan
Parklands Region
15-1st Ave. S.W., Dauphin, R7N 1R9
Director, Y. Hrynkiw
Thompson Region
871 S. Thompson Dr., Thompson, R8N 0C8
Director, V. Wiebe
Westman Region
340-9th St., Brandon, R7A 6C2
PROGRAMS DIVISION
831 Portage Ave., Winnipeg, R3G 0N6
Health Promotion Services
Director, A. Wendt
Communicable Disease Control
Director, Dr. M. Fast
Hearing Conservation
Director, J. Selinger
Information Resource Centre
Director, M. Brooke
Environmental Health
Director, Vacant
Maternal and Child Health
Director, Dr. C. Becker
Continuing Care
Director, O. Zabloski
Dental Health
Exec. Director, Dr. P. Cooney
Director, P. Todman

Mental Health Services
300, 1200 Portage Ave., Winnipeg, R3G 0T5
Asst. Dep. Minister, D.F. McLean
Chief Provincial Psychiatrist, Dr. D.D. Rodgers
Mental Health Services
Director, Vacant
Child and Adolescent Mental Health Services
Director, Dr. K. Hildahl
Children's Forensic Services
Sr. Consultant Psychiatrist, Dr. C. Manswell
Adult Forensic Services
75 Emily St., Winnipeg, R3E 1V9
Director, Dr. S. Yaren
MENTAL HEALTH CENTRES:
Brandon Mental Health Centre
Box 420, Brandon, R7A 5Z5
CEO, M. Kufflick
Asst. Exec. Director, M. Balcaen
Selkirk Mental Health Centre
Box 9600, Selkirk, R1A 2B5
CEO and Medical Director, Dr. H. Andrew
Hospital Administrator, B. Surridge

AGENCIES, BOARDS AND COMMISSIONS

Alcoholism Foundation of Manitoba
1031 Portage Ave., 3rd Flr., Winnipeg, R3G 0R8
General Inquiry: (204) 944-6200

A Manitoba Crown corporation, the Alcoholism Foundation was created to assist individuals with problems related to the abuse or misuse of alcohol and other drugs and substances. It promotes the most efficient use of existing facilities and services for the treatment and rehabilitation of those with chemical dependencies.

The Foundation disseminates information concerning the recognition, prevention, and treatment of the abuse or misuse of alcohol and other drugs and substances, while informing the public about its own services and those provided by related agencies, groups, and associations. It also conducts research into the prevention and treatment of chemical dependency.

Chairperson, Judge Charles Rubin
Exec. Director, Ian J. Puchlik
Support Services Director, Tim Duprey
Program Delivery Director, J. Dragan
Planning and Research
Director, Linda DuBick

Dental Health Workers Board
800 Portage Ave., Winnipeg, R3G 0N5
General Inquiry: (204) 945-6685

The Manitoba Dental Health Workers Board is appointed by the Lieutenant-Governor in Council to administer and recommend to the Minister of Health the certification of dental health workers. Dental health workers are government employees working in the classifications of dental assistant, dental nurse, or dental hygienist.

The Board, upon receipt of complaints of unethical conduct, investigates and advises the department, which can take action against the employee.

An accreditation committee may be appointed by the Board to examine qualifications and training programs for dental workers and to recommend to the Board the inclusion of graduates for certification in a category of dental health worker.

The *Dental Health Workers Act* received Assent on June 19, 1975. The makeup and powers of the Board are outlined in Man. Reg. 122/76, filed June 3, 1976.

Chairman, Lorette Ferland
Sec.-Registrar, Karen Nikkel

Drug Standards and Therapeutics Committee
599 Empress St., Box 925, Winnipeg, R3C 2T6
General Inquiry: (204) 786-7233

The Committee supervises the periodic preparation and publication of the Manitoba Drug Standards and Therapeutics Formulary and Drug Information Bulletins. The Formulary contains a list of interchangeable drugs as a guide to pharmacists in filling prescriptions, while the Bulletins provide comment on drug therapy issues. The Committee also advises the Minister of Health on matters of a general pharmaceutical nature.

Committee members are appointed by the Lieutenant-Governor in Council under authority established in the *Manitoba Pharmaceutical Act.*

Chairman, Dr. Ian Innes
Secretary, Ken Brown

Health Sciences Centre
820 Sherbrook St., Winnipeg, R3A 1R9
General Inquiry: (204) 787-2346

The Health Sciences Centre came into being under an Act of the Manitoba legislature in 1972. As a non-profit corporation, the Centre's main purposes and objectives are defined as follows:
• the prevention and diagnosis of illness of persons and the treatment, care, and rehabilitation of sick or injured persons;
• the operation and maintenance of a hospital in Winnipeg to provide a high quality of medical and surgical care and treatment, including outpatient and other services;
• educational activities related to the promotion of health; and
• scientific research in the medical field.

Chairman, W. John A. Bulman
Vice-Chairman, Ray McQuade
Treasurer, Chris Chapman
President, A. Rodney Thorfinnson
Sr. Vice-President, Operations,
Helen A.I. Wright
Sr. Vice-President, Medical,
Dr. Douglas Craig
Sr. Vice-President, Nursing, Brenda Snider
Vice-President, Finance, Ron White
Vice-President, Planning, Mike Giffin
Asst. to the President and Corporate Secretary, James L. Rodger

The Hearing Aid Board
114 Garry St., Winnipeg, R3C 1G1
General Inquiry: (204) 956-2040

The Hearing Aid Board of Manitoba was established in 1971 and is under the control and direction of the Minister of Health. It is charged with the responsibility of administering the *Hearing Aid Act of Manitoba* and its Regulations. The Board is composed of five members. The secretary of the Board, as required by the Act, is the Director of the Consumers' Bureau, Department of Co-operative, Consumer and Corporate Affairs.

The Board regulates the activities, and promotes the education, of hearing aid dealers; certifies dealers to perform specific types of services; prescribes licence fee and standard testing procedures; and regulates the sale or servicing of hearing aids. The Board also, at its discretion, evaluates hearing aids and has the right to withdraw certification of any hearing aid dealer. The Board, through the Director of the

Consumers' Bureau, is also concerned with complaints dealing with hearing aid issues and any suspected breaches of the Act or its Regulations.

Chairperson, Joan Warrener
Secretary, Denis Robidoux

Manitoba Cancer Treatment and Research Foundation
100 Olivia St., Winnipeg, R3E 0V9
General Inquiry: (204) 787-2197

The Manitoba Cancer Treatment and Research Foundation is a government-supported institution devoted to cancer treatment, research, and education. The Foundation is closely integrated with the University of Manitoba and the primary teaching hospitals of its Faculty of Medicine.

The Foundation contains the sole radiotherapy treatment facilities for the province. It maintains a staff of radiation, medical, surgical, gynecological, and pediatric oncologists, physicists, statisticians, and epidemiologists. The staff are also the principal instructors in the University Oncology Program.

Major research laboratories in medical physics and in the basic biological sciences are an integral part of the Foundation, which also provides a Social Service and Outreach Program.

Chairman, D. McMullin
Exec. Director, Dr. L.G. Israels
Medical Advisory Board
Chairman, Dr. J. Foerster

Manitoba Health Research Council
Rm. S107, 750 Bannatyne Ave.
Winnipeg, R3E 0W3

The Manitoba Health Research Council provides support for health-related scientific research in the province of Manitoba in the form of operating grants, equipment grants, establishment grants, and personnel awards.

Chairman, Dr. K.R. Hughes
Exec. Director, F.C. Stevens, Ph.D.

Manitoba Health Services Commission
599 Empress St., Box 925, Winnipeg, R3C 2T6
General Inquiry: (204) 786-7101

The Manitoba Health Services Commission administers the Manitoba Health Services Insurance Plan, in accordance with the provisions of *The Health Services Insurance Act* and other relevant legislation. The Plan provides for the financing of hospital, medical, personal care, pharmacare, and other health services for Manitoba residents. With the approval of the Minister of Health, the Commission plans, organizes, and develops throughout the province a balanced and integrated system of hospitals and related health facilities and services.

In addition, the Commission administers the Ambulance Grant Program, which provides financial assistance to municipalities for the development and operation of ambulance services, and the Northern Patient Transportation Program, which provides financial assistance to residents of northern Manitoba for transportation to centres that can provide necessary medical and hospital services.

A/Exec. Director, F. DeCock
Facilities
A/Assoc. Exec. Director, J. McKenzie
Administration Director, F.S. Anderson
Health Information Systems
Director, G.K. Neill
FACILITIES
Rural Health Facilities
Director, J. Lock
Urban Health Facilities
Director, R.W. Siemens
Long Term Care Director, K. Thomson
Emergency Health and Ambulance Service
Director, L. Bell
Construction Programming
Director, K. Hominick

Cadham Provincial Laboratory
750 William Ave., Box 8450
Winnipeg, R3C 3Y1
Director, Dr. G. Hammond

DEPARTMENT OF HIGHWAYS AND TRANSPORTATION
203 Legislative Bldg., Winnipeg, R3C 0V8

MINISTER'S OFFICE
Minister, The Hon. Albert Driedger

DEPUTY MINISTER'S OFFICE
209 Legislative Bldg., Winnipeg, R3C 0V8
Dep. Minister, Boris Hryhorczuk

ADMINISTRATIVE SERVICES DIVISION
Director, W. Dyck
Personnel Services Director, D. McIntosh
Financial Services Director, F. Schnerch
Communications Co-ordinator, J. Heath
Budget Co-ordinator, P. Larue

Construction and Maintenance Division
Asst. Dep. Minister, S. Goodbrandson
Construction Director, D. Struthers
Construction Management
Engineer, M. Corkal
Maintenance Director, J.B. Rowley
Maintenance Management
Engineer, B. Tinkler
Bridges and Structures
Director, W. Saltzberg
DISTRICT ENGINEERS:
District 1
203, 445 Main St., Selkirk, R1A 1V7
R.C. Blackman
District 2
Box 1028, Steinbach, R0A 2A0
B. Prentice

District 3
Box 460, Carman, R0G 0J0
R. McKibbin
District 4
Box 959, Boissevain, R0K 0E0
H. Morningstar
District 5
Box 817, Brandon, R7A 5Z8
S. Kavanagh
District 6
25 N. Tupper St., Portage la Prairie, R1N 3K1
R. Scrase
District 7
Box 1140, Minnedosa, R0J 1E0
J.H. McGuirk
District 8
Box 690, Dauphin, R7N 3B3
A. Safronetz
District 9
Box 730, Swan River, R0L 1Z0
J. Gottfried
District 10
Box 2550, The Pas, R9A 1M4
A. Melnick
District 11
Box 550, Arborg, R0C 0A0
G. Stary
District 12
Unit 1, 35 Lakewood Blvd., Winnipeg, R2J 2M8
Guy Cooper
Contract Engineer, R. Gordon
Occupational Health and Safety Co-ordinator, G. Mortimer
Claims Investigation Officer, C. Hall

PLANNING, DESIGN AND LAND SURVEYS DIVISION
Director, K. Jardine
Planning Support Engineer, A. MacLeod
Sr. Planning Engineer, T. Stevens
Highway Programming Engineer, D. Lam
Sr. Design Engineer, A. Boychuk
Land Surveys Director, T. Simonson

Engineering and Technical Services Division
Asst. Dep. Minister, J. Hosang
Government Air/Radio
Director, V. Bantle
Hangar T-5, 900 Ferry Rd., Winnipeg, R3H 0Y8
Materials and Research
Director, F. Young
1181 Portage Ave. (Annex)
Winnipeg, R3G 0T3
Traffic Operations Engineer, R. Adamson
Northern Airports and Marine
Director, D. Selby

TRANSPORTATION POLICY, PROGRAMS AND RESEARCH DIVISION
Director, J. Wallace
Transportation Policy
Director, D. Schaeffer
Transportation Programs
Manager, W. Graham

Federal/Provincial Transportation
Agreements Manager, J. Wallace
Transportation Research
Manager, J. Craven

Driver and Vehicle Licensing Division
1075 Portage Ave., Winnipeg, R3G 0S1

Registrar and Asst. Dep. Minister, D. Coyle
Dep. Registrar of Safety, B. MacMartin
Director of Licencing/Dep. Registrar,
B. Hewitt
Systems Manager, A. Fulsher
Administration and Finance
Manager, D Nelson

AGENCIES, BOARDS AND COMMISSIONS

Drivers' Licence Suspension Appeal Board
1075 Portage Ave., Winnipeg, R3G 0S1

The primary function of the Drivers' Licence Suspension Appeal Board is to hear appeals by individuals who have had their drivers' licences suspended. *The Highway Traffic Act* further provides for the Board to hear appeals of suspensions, cancellations, and denials of driving school permits, driving school instructor permits, automobile dealer's permits, and salesman's permits. The Board's jurisdiction also encompasses court suspensions when authorized by that court.

The Board imposes restrictions on licences where remission is granted and full remission is authorized in special circumstances only. The Board's decisions are final. The statutory right of appeal to county court against decisions of the Appeal Board was abolished July 1, 1984.

Chairman, J. Tanner
Secretary, D. Hallson

Highway Traffic Board
Rm. 206, 301 Weston St., Winnipeg, R3E 3H4

The Highway Traffic Board was formed in 1960 and its members are appointed by the Lieutenant-Governor in Council.

The Board administers all speed limits, traffic control devices, pedestrian corridors and municipal highway weight limits, classification and bridge restrictions throughout the province. The Board's administration is for the purpose of providing motorists in every traffic jurisdiction with a province-wide consideration and uniformity in these matters, such as cannot be achieved through decisions by local jurisdictions. Prior to the Board's existence, jurisdictional anomalies in these traffic matters confused motorists, resulting in violations, accidents, complaints, and enforcement problems.

In 1962, the Traffic Board was given responsibility for new legislation to control the location of access onto and structures adjacent to major provincial highways. This legislation is for the purpose of protecting the interests of the public, promoting the safety of persons using the

highways, and generally furthering the amenities of travel on the highways.

Chairman, A. Sabeski
Secretary, A. Poltaruk

Motor Transport Board
Rm. 200, 301 Weston St., Winnipeg, R3E 3H4

The Motor Transport Board generally supervises public service vehicles and commercial trucks that use the Manitoba highways.

In its regulatory role, the Board ensures that the following Acts are carried out: the *Highway Traffic Act,* C.C.S.M., Chapter H60, the federal *Motor Vehicle Transport Act,* and the *Public Utilities Act,* C.C.S.M., Chapter P280.

The eight-member Board is appointed by the Lieutenant-Governor in Council.

Chairman, D. Norquay
Secretary, L.G. Olijnek

Taxicab Board
1075 Portage Ave., Winnipeg, R3G 0S1

The Taxicab Board is the agency responsible for the general supervision of taxicabs and limousines and their drivers within the city of Winnipeg. The Board also controls the issuance of taxicab driver's licences and tariffs, and the setting of quotas pursuant to the *Taxicab Act,* C.C.S.M., Chapter T10.

The Board is composed of (a) a member of the Council of the city of Winnipeg, nominated by the Council; (b) the chief constable of the police force of the city of Winnipeg (or his/her designate); and (c) three other persons appointed by the Lieutenant-Governor in Council, one of whom is appointed chairman.

Chairman, Don Norquay
Secretary, C. Walker

DEPARTMENT OF HOUSING
317 Legislative Bldg., Winnipeg, R3C 0V8

MINISTER'S OFFICE
Minister, The Hon. Gerald Ducharme

DEPUTY MINISTER'S OFFICE
603, 287 Broadway, Winnipeg, R3C 0R9

Dep. Minister, Saul Schubert
Communication Division
Director, Barbara Ross Czech
Planning Division
2100, 185 Smith St., Winnipeg, R3C 3G4
Director, Ken Cassin

SUPPORT SERVICES DIVISION
287 Broadway, 6th Flr., Winnipeg, R3C 0R9
Exec. Director, Gary Julius
Land Development and Mortgage Services
Director, Wayne McComb

Landlord and Tenant Affairs Branch
254 Edmonton St., 3rd Flr., Winnipeg, R3C 3Y4
Director, Hollis Singh
A/Co-ordinator of Appeals, Bob Andrews
Rentalsman, Roger Barsy

Operations Division
2100, 185 Smith St., Winnipeg, R3C 3G4

Asst. Dep. Minister, Don Ilich
Property Management Branch
Director, Ron Fallis
Program Delivery Division
287 Broadway, Winnipeg, R3C 0R9
Design Services Manager, Gae Burns
Client Services Manager, Heidi Everett

AGENCIES, BOARDS, COMMISSIONS AND CROWN CORPORATIONS

Manitoba Housing and Renewal Corp.
287 Broadway, Winnipeg, R3C 0R9

Chairman, The Hon. Gerald Ducharme
Vice-Chairman, Saul Schubert
Corporate Secretary, H.N. Dubowits

DEPARTMENT OF INDUSTRY, TRADE AND TOURISM
155 Carlton St., Winnipeg, R3C 3H8
(except where otherwise indicated)
Fax: (204) 957-1793; Telex: 07-587833

MINISTER'S OFFICE
358 Legislative Bldg., Winnipeg, R3C 0V8
Minister, The Hon. James Ernst

DEPUTY MINISTER'S OFFICE
352 Legislative Bldg., Winnipeg, R3C 0V8
Dep. Minister, Hugh Eliasson

FINANCIAL AND ADMINISTRATIVE SERVICES
Administration
Director, Harry O. Bergman
Departmental Accountant, Herb Lau
Business Library
Librarian, John W.G. Giesbrecht
Communications and Information Services
Project Officer (Exhibits), C.A. Hooey
Communication Asst., W. Sikora
CORPORATE AND COMMUNITY RELATIONS
Director, T. Lewycky

Manitoba Jobs Fund
Program Inquiries: (204) 945-8052

Health Industry Development Initiative
Asst. Dep. Minister, Ian H. Blicq
Director, HIDI, Reg Ebbeling
Sr. Marketing Development Officer, Garry Smith
Sr. Health Technology Consultant, M. Silver
Consultants: Paul Boulanger, Morris Settler

INFORMATION TECHNOLOGY BUSINESS DEVELOPMENT
1970 Ness Ave., Winnipeg, R3J 0Y9
Exec. Director, Edgardo Gonzalez
Assoc. Exec. Director, R. Sprange
Finance and Administration
Manager, T. Thompson
Educational Technology Program
Director, Duncan McCaig
Business/Public Technology Program
Manager, Consulting Services, P. Kelly
Business/Market Development Program
Director, R. Sprange

Industry and Trade Division

Asst. Dep. Minister, D. Cleve

SECTORAL DEVELOPMENT SECTION
Food and Beverage Industries
Manager, M. Wallace
Officer, Brian Walker
Electrical and Electronic Products
Manager, M.D. Clarke
Metal Fabrication Industries and Machinery
Industries, J.E. Shippam
Transportation Equipment, B. Mitchell
Transportation Industries, J. Rea
Aerospace, Bob Jack

INVESTMENT PROMOTION SECTION
U.S. Business Investments
Manager, Pat Leslie
Officer, Ted Harvey
Apparel and Textile Industries and
Entrepreneurial Immigration, Richard Allden
Entrepreneurial Immigration, Nadia Said
Hong Kong Office
Contact, Richard Allden
Rotterdam Office
Contact, Nadia Said

PROJECT MANAGEMENT SECTION
Primary Metals and Minerals, Chemicals,
Non-Metal Mineral Products and Development
Agreements Manager, Paul Brockington
Investment Analysis and Plastic Products,
Michael Wiley
Investor Identification, Len LeBrun
Health Industries, Reg Ebbeling

TRADE BRANCH
Manager, Henry Goy
Trade Development and Policy
Officer, W. Ratcliffe
Trade Development, J.C. Francey
Agricultural Components, Grain Handling
Equipment Development Officer, W. Teerhuis
Food and Beverage, Health Care, Giftware
Sr. Development Officer, S. Spiers
Trade Assistance and Export Services
Sr. Export Services Officer, R. Frey
Industrial Capabilities Manager, Vacant

Hong Kong Office
1803 China Bldg., 29 Queen's Rd. C
Hong Kong
Agent, Richard M.G. Walker

Rotterdam Office
Terbregselaan 40, 3055 RG Rotterdam
The Netherlands
Trade and Investment Representative,
Anna Maria Magnifico

Strategic Planning and Economic Development

Asst. Dep. Minister, Robert J. Adams
Program Development and Co-ordination
Director, N. Allison
Policy Analysis Manager, Stephen Watson

TECHNOLOGY DIVISION
155 Carlton St., 4th Flr., Winnipeg, R3C 3H8
Exec. Director, Dr. J.K. Reichert
Technology Commercialization Program
1329 Niakwa Rd., Winnipeg, R2J 3T4
Manager, A. Turnbull
Manitoba Aerospace Technology Program
Manager, L. Tough

REGIONAL DEVELOPMENT
Exec. Director, J. McGuire
Venture Capital Program
Manager, T.T. Dupley
Small Business Development
Manager, B.N. Docking
Manufacturing Adaptation Program
Manager, T. Gilmore
Community Development
Manager, L. Prince
Northern and Native Development
Manager, P. Rosenfeld
Marketing Network Manager, S. Webb
BUSINESS DEVELOPMENT CENTRES:
Winnipeg Business Development Centre
1329 Niakwa Rd., Winnipeg, R3C 3G5
Manager, M.B. Levy
Small Business Information
Manager, Elaine Hardinge
Dauphin Business Development Centre
40-1st Ave. N.W., Dauphin, R7N 2V4
Manager, Judi Hyde
Brandon Business Development Centre
231-10th St., Brandon, R7A 6N1
Manager, Steve Davidge

TOURISM
155 Carlton St., 7th Flr., Winnipeg, R3C 3H8
General Information: (204) 945-3796
Tourism Development
Exec. Director, J. Sigurdson
Asst. Director, Bernie Foth
Tourism Market Development
Director, Hubert Mesman
Tourism Promotion
Director, Gerry Turenne
Travel Information Services
and Industry Relations
Manager, R. Lavallee

Tourism Planning
Sr. Consultant, Neil Nixon
Cultural and Heritage Initiatives
Director, Cecil Semchyshyn
CANADA/MANITOBA TOURISM
DEVELOPMENT AGREEMENTS
General Information: (204) 945-4848
Sr. Consultant, Don Pensack

AGENCIES, BOARDS AND COMMISSIONS

Manitoba Development Corp.
1800, 155 Carlton St., Winnipeg, R3C 3H8

Chairman and Gen. Manager, H.J. Jones
Asst. Gen. Manager and Secretary,
G.M. Goodwin
Treasurer, W.E. Chiswell

Manitoba Horse Racing Commission
Box 40, Stn. A, Winnipeg, R3K 1Z9

The Manitoba Horse Racing Commission was established by 1965 legislation of the Province of Manitoba. The purpose of the Commission is to govern, direct, control, and regulate horse racing and the operation of race tracks in Manitoba. The Commission is provided with a wide range of powers which are necessary to protect the interests of the wagering public as well as owners, jockeys, trainers, and track operators.

Chairperson, Dan Williams, Q.C.
Vice-Chairman, M. Kaplan
Members: Ian MacKenzie, Jack Philpot,
Irene Bauman

Manitoba Research Council
420, 155 Carlton St., Winnipeg, R3C 3H8

The Manitoba Research Council was established in 1963 as an associated agency of the Department of Industry, Trade and Technology. The goal of the Council is to stimulate and support scientific and technological activity through which Manitoba businesses and industries can become increasingly competitive nationally and internationally.

Specific activities of the Council include providing advice and information to the minister, carrying out specific technological activity under contract, and maintaining a liaison with other research organizations and similar agencies or boards. The Council operates two centres, the Industrial Technology Centre in Winnipeg and the Canadian Food Products Development Centre in Portage la Prairie, which assist clients with a wide range of special technical skills, services, and expertise. Core funding for the operation of these centres is provided by the province.
President, Dr. E.O. Nyborg
Administration
Vice-President, W. Mialkowski

Industrial Technology Centre
1329 Niakwa Rd., Winnipeg, R2J 3T4
Vice-President, Lawrence Haberman

Canadian Food Products Development Centre
Box 1240, Portage la Prairie, R1N 3J9
Vice-President, Dr. T.J. McEwen

DEPARTMENT OF LABOUR
Norquay Bldg., 401 York Ave.
Winnipeg, R3C 0P8
(except where otherwise indicated)

MINISTER'S OFFICE
156 Legislative Bldg., Winnipeg, R3C 0V8
Minister, The Hon. Edward Connery

DEPUTY MINISTER'S OFFICE
143 Legislative Bldg., Winnipeg, R3C 0V8
Dep. Minister, Tanner Elton
Communications Director, Janet Wile
610, 401 York Ave., Winnipeg, R3C 0P8

ADMINISTRATION DIVISION
Financial and Administrative Services
Manager, J.P. Wood
Financial Officer, L. Smith
Personnel Services
Manager, Jim McFarlane
Personnel Administrator, J. Reinsch
REGIONAL OFFICES:
59 Elizabeth Dr., Thompson, R8N 1X4
340-9th St., Brandon, R7A 6C2
Research and Planning Branch
Director, Jim Nykoluk

Labour Division

Asst. Dep. Minister, Tom Bleasdale
Analyst, Phil Bonin
Special Projects Officer, Gari Whelon
Office of the Fire Commissioner
Commissioner, J. Reimer
Mechanical and Engineering Branch
Director, I. Wayne Mault, P.Eng.
Apprenticeship and Training Branch
Director, Marilyn Kenny
Employment Standards Branch
Director, R. Moggey
Conciliation and Mediation Services Branch
Director, Jim Davage
Pay Equity Bureau
609, 386 Broadway, Winnipeg, R3C 3R6
Exec. Director, Roberta Ellis-Grunfeld

AGENCIES, BOARDS AND COMMISSIONS

Apprenticeship and Trades Qualification Board
816, 401 York Ave., Winnipeg, R3C 0P8

The Apprenticeship and Trades Qualification Board has been appointed by the Minister of Labour under section 3 of *The Apprenticeship and Trades Qualifications Act.* The Board consists of three employees' representatives, three employers' representatives, one representative each from the Department of Labour and the Department of Education, and an independent chairman. Members serve a three-year term from the date of appointment.

The Board:
a) may recommend to the minister that certain regulations designed to regulate and improve the training and certification of persons in any designated trade for which a certificate of qualifications is required be made;
b) shall hear and determine all appeals made to it under the Act;
c) shall receive and review the recommendations of any trade advisory committee with respect to the training, examination, and certification of persons in the trade for which that committee was established;
d) may recommend to the minister persons that it considers suitable for appointment to any trade advisory committee; and
e) shall carry out such other duties as the minister may require it to carry out with respect to any matter within the scope and intent of this Act.

Chairman, Dr. Lionel Orlikow

Barbering Board of Examiners
816, 401 York Ave., Winnipeg, R3C 0P8

Chairperson, Mrs. I. McKibbin

Building Standards Board
510, 401 York Ave., Winnipeg, R3C 0P8

The Manitoba Building Standards Board was established in November 1974, under the *Buildings and Mobile Homes Act.* The Board's mandates include the development of a Manitoba Building Code that establishes minimum requirements for the safety of buildings with reference to public health, fire protection, and structural sufficiency, and a Manitoba Plumbing Code that establishes uniform plumbing standards that will provide water that is safe for human consumption, with venting, drainage, and the building of sewer systems that provide safe disposal of water and sewage from a building.

The fourth edition of the Manitoba Building Code consists of the 1985 National Building Code updated to June 30, 1987, and amendments made by the Building Standards Board for Manitoba.

The first edition of the Manitoba Plumbing Code, for the first time separate from the Manitoba Building Code, consists of the 1985 Canadian Plumbing Code updated to June 30, 1987, and amendments made by the Building Standards Board for Manitoba.

The Board is made up of seven members including the chairman. These members represent a wide range of expertise in the construction industry.

Chairman, P.M. Lyons
Secretary, A. Jonasson

Electricians Licensing Examining Board
500, 401 York Ave., Winnipeg, R3C 0P8
Chairman, I. Wayne Mault
Secretary, R. Kolbuch

Elevator Board
500, 401 York Ave., Winnipeg, R3C 0P8
Chairman, I. Wayne Mault

Fire Advisory Committee
510, 401 York Ave., Winnipeg, R3C 0P8

The Fire Advisory Committee, established by Order-in-Council in January 1980, was assigned the following duties:
a) to serve the Minister of Labour in an advisory capacity with respect to matters relating to fire services;
b) to advise the Minister of Labour on proposed amendments to the Manitoba Fire Code;
c) to advise the fire commissioner in respect of appeals on orders of Fire Code compliance which are subject to appeal; and
d) to serve in an advisory capacity to the fire commissioner on matters relating to Fire Code interpretation.

The Fire Advisory Committee is made up of ten members including the chairman. Its membership is such as to provide a broad representation of technical viewpoints from all aspects of the fire prevention and fire protection fields, including industry, regulatory bodies, and general interest.
Chairman, P.M. Lyons
Secretary, A. Jonasson

Hairdressing Board of Examiners
816, 401 York Ave., Winnipeg, R3C 0P8
Chairperson, I. McKibbin

Labour Management Review Committee
409, 401 York Ave., Winnipeg, R3C 0P8

The Labour Management Review Committee was established in 1964 by a unanimously approved resolution of the Manitoba legislature. Composed of labour and management representatives, the Committee is charged with reviewing labour legislation as embodied in various acts of the Manitoba legislature. A second purpose is to undertake, at the Committee's own discretion, a far-reaching examination of common problems in the hope that discussions will lead labour and management to a better understanding of each other's positions, and ultimately to tangible or intangible improvements in labour-management relations within the province.
Chairman, G. Campbell MacLean
Vice-Chairman, Prof. John Atwell
Secretary, D. Dyson

Manitoba Labour Board
404, 428 Portage Ave., Winnipeg, R3C 0E2
General Information: (204) 945-3783

The Manitoba Labour Board is responsible for furthering harmonious relations between employers and employees. In performing this function, its objectives are:
• to help develop sound union-management relations; and
• to adjudicate matters under the *Employment Standards Act*, the *Construction Industry Wages Act*, the *Vacations with Pay Act*, the *Payment of Wages Act,* and the *Workplace Safety and Health Act.*

The Board's principal responsibility, however, is to administer certain sections of the *Labour Relations Act.*

Since labour relations are not static, the Board is continually re-evaluating its functions and operations. The Board is aware that it occupies a responsible position in Manitoba's labour relations community. Consequently, the Board attempts, through its decisions, to give guidance to this community, and encourages parties to settle disputes without the need of formal Board proceedings. In this way, the Board feels it is able to promote harmonious labour relations in Manitoba.
Chairman, John Korpesho
Vice-Chairpersons: J. Cooper, D. Jones, G. Sigurdson
Registrar, Janet Duff
Board Officers: Dennis Harrison, John Rayner, Peter Sheppitt

Minimum Wage Board
600, 401 York Ave., Winnipeg, R3C 0P8

The Minimum Wage Board, made up of employers and employees (three representatives each) and an independent chairperson, meets annually to make recommendations to the Minister of Labour regarding the minimum wage level in the province.
Chairman, Prof. John Atwell
Secretary, J.P. Wood

Pension Commission
1004, 401 York Ave., Winnipeg, R3C 0V8

The Office of the Superintendent of Pensions is responsible for enforcing and administering the *Pension Benefits Act* of Manitoba, which became effective July 1, 1976.

The Act requires that all private-employer pension plans throughout the province of Manitoba be registered and monitored by the Office of the Superintendent of Pensions.

The Act also establishes a Commission — currently composed of nine members from all areas of the business community as well as public-sector representatives — which advises the government regarding current pension trends and proposes amendments to pension legislation.

One of the prime mandates under the *Pension Benefits Act* is the promotion and extension of pension plans in the province. The Superintendent's Office has produced various publications on pension legislation and pension plans which are available upon request.

As well, the Superintendent and staff members

are actively involved in pension seminars and discussion groups sponsored by the Department of Labour and various public and private organizations.

Chairperson, Vacant
Vice-Chairperson, Vacant

Power Engineers Advisory Board
500, 401 York Ave., Winnipeg, R3C 0P8

The Power Engineers Advisory Board advises the Minister of Labour on matters pertaining to *The Power Engineers Act*. It consists of five members, with representatives from both management and employees. The Board receives input from industry and people working in the power engineering field regarding updating of Regulations and instruction. These submissions and representations are used in developing recommendations for the minister to consider.

Chairman, Karel van Helden
Secretary, R. Kolbuch

Trade Advisory Committees
816, 401 York Ave., Winnipeg, R3C 0P8

All Trade Advisory Committees of the Apprenticeship Branch are appointed by the Minister of Labour under section 6 of the *Apprenticeship and Trades Qualifications Act, 1977*. One committee is appointed for each trade that has been designated for certification or for certification and training. The main function of each committee is to advise the Apprenticeship and Trades Qualification Board on any matter relating to the training of apprentices or to the certification of persons in that trade.

Each committee consists of an equal number of employers' and employees' representatives, and is chaired by the Director of Apprenticeship. The term of office for each committee is three years from the date of appointment. If a vacancy is created on a committee, the person filling that vacancy serves the remainder of the term for that position. Members are paid a per diem rate for the meetings they attend, or the equivalent amount for loss of wages suffered if loss of wages exceeds the per diem rate.

Chairman, Director of Apprenticeship or his/her appointee
(Also Chairman of the following committees: Aircraft Mechanic, Boilermaker, Bricklayer, Building Construction Crane and Hoist Operator, Carpenter, Construction Electrician, Cook, Glazier, Heavy-Duty Equipment Mechanic, Industrial Electrician, Industrial Instrument Mechanic, Industrial Mechanic, Industrial Pipe Fitter, Industrial Welder, Landscape Technician, Lather and Drywaller, Machinist Tool and Die, Miner, Motor Vehicle Body Repairer, Motor Vehicle Mechanic, Painter and Decorator, Parts Person, Plasterer, Plumber, Power Electrician, Refrigeration and Air Conditioning Mechanic, Roofer, Sheet Metal Worker, Sprinkler and Fire Protection Installer, Steamfitter, Tool and Die Maker)

WAGES BOARDS
Greater Winnipeg Building Construction Wages Board
Heavy Construction Wages Board
Rural Building Construction Wages Board
607, 401 York Ave., Winnipeg, R3C 0P8

The three boards listed above were established under *The Construction Industry Wages Act*, S.M. 1964, Chapter 9.

Each board makes recommendations to the minister on wages and working hours for employees in its own area of the construction industry. The boards report not less than once each year with recommendations on the following:

a) the minimum rates of wages that the employees should receive for regular and for overtime working hours;

b) the maximum number of regular working hours that they should be required to work in any day, week, or month; and

c) any other matters relating to such wages or hours of work that the Board thinks advisable, or in respect of which the minister has requested it to make a recommendation.

Each board consists of two employee representatives, two employer representatives and one public representative, who is the chairman of the Board. These members are appointed by an Order-in-Council. The secretary is appointed by the Minister of Labour.

Chairman, Prof. W.N. Fox-Decent
Secretary, M. Dziewit

DEPARTMENT OF MUNICIPAL AFFAIRS
800 Portage Ave., Winnipeg, R3G 0N4
(except where otherwise indicated)

MINISTER'S OFFICE
330 Legislative Bldg., Winnipeg, R3C 0V8
Minister, The Hon. J. Glen Cummings

DEPUTY MINISTER'S OFFICE
332 Legislative Bldg., Winnipeg, R3C 0V8
Dep. Minister, Gerald D. Forrest
Administration
Manager, Anna Fuller

MUNICIPAL ASSESSMENT
Provincial Municipal Assessor, R.L. Brown
Dep. Director, K. Graham
Municipal Advisory and Financial Services
Director, F.R. Dennis, C.A.
Dep. Director, R.F. Robson
Municipal Finance Officer, R. Gray
Municipal Planning Director, J.N. Whiting
Dep. Director, N. Carroll
Provincial Planning Director, David Johns
Research and Systems Director, Marie Elliott

AGENCIES, BOARDS AND COMMISSIONS

Interdepartmental Planning Board
405, 800 Portage Ave., Winnipeg, R3G 0N4

The Interdepartmental Planning Board is appointed under *The Planning Act* and is also assigned duties under the *Environment Act*. It plays an important role in:
1) providing interdepartmental and interagency co-ordination in the development and implementation of land use policies and programs;
2) providing an interdisciplinary context within which various land use proposals can be reviewed and adjusted before being recommended to the Provincial Land Use Committee;
3) providing one point of contact for municipalities, utilities, private developers, etc. when they are developing plans or projects which ultimately require provincial approval or review;
4) determining the terms of reference for environmental assessments and reviewing assessments once they are complete;
5) providing an arena for information exchange where deputies and departments can be kept up to date on a number of land resource management and environmental issues;
6) reviewing municipal development proposals including those of the City of Winnipeg; and
7) providing co-ordination with the federal government and with other provinces when necessary.

Chairman, Gerald D. Forrest
Secretary, David Johns

Leaf Rapids Town Properties Ltd.
646, 800 Portage Ave., Winnipeg, R3G 0N4
Chairman, Gerald D. Forrest
Sec.-Treasurer, Doug G. Mitchell

The Municipal Board of Manitoba
408, 800 Portage Ave., Winnipeg, R3G 0N4

The Municipal Board is a quasi-judicial body established by the provisions of *The Municipal Board Act*. Composed of the chairman and 12 part-time members, the Board functions as an appeal tribunal, handles matters of local government finance, and carries out other responsibilities assigned to it under the *Municipal Board Act* or any other Act of the legislature.

Chairman, J.G. Donald
Secretary, R.G. Clarke
Asst. Secretary, Irene Hinks
Members: Gunnar Helgason, W.J. Hicks,
H. Jany Keenan, Joyce Lawson,
Everett Leader, Dr. Meir Serfaty,
Garth Berry, Catherine M. Auld,
Jake Reimer, Aimé Gauthier,
Andy Maharaj, Dorothy Hamilton,
William Greenaway, Gordon Peitsch,
Kenneth Porter, Edward Swain,
Douglas S. Martindale

Municipal Employees Benefits Board
308, 131 Provencher Blvd.
Winnipeg, R2H 0G2

The Municipal Employees Benefits Board was established under *The Municipal Act* in 1975, including Regulations thereunder, and has been responsible for administering the pension and group life insurance plans for some 265 municipal and quasi-municipal organizations in the province of Manitoba since Jan. 1, 1977. There are 205 employers participating in the LTD part of the pension plan established June 1, 1981.

Chairman, Gerald D. Forrest
Gen. Manager, W.R. Worosz

Surface Rights Board
408, 800 Portage Ave., Winnipeg, R3G 0N4

The Surface Rights Board administers and enforces the *Surface Rights Act*. Members are appointed by the Lieutenant-Governor in Council and represent the various geographic, social, and economic sectors of the province. The Board's mandate is to provide for the concerns of both the land owners and the oil industry in Manitoba. Activities of the Board include the conducting of surveys, hearings, and investigations. As well, the Board implements research programs and provides mediation services upon request of a party to a dispute concerning surface rights.

Chairman, J.D. McNairnay, Q.C.
Secretary, B. Sheridan
Members: Thomas Cowan, Cromer Ashcroft,
Ivan Carey, Geneva Chipelski

DEPARTMENT OF NATURAL RESOURCES
314 Legislative Bldg., Winnipeg, R3C 0V8

MINISTER'S OFFICE
Minister, The Hon. Jack Penner

DEPUTY MINISTER'S OFFICE
314 Legislative Bldg., Winnipeg, R3C 0V8
Dep. Minister, Dale Stewart
Garrison Focus Office
1495 St. James St., Box C
Winnipeg, R3H 0W9
Special Projects, R.N. Clarkson

ASSISTANT DEPUTY MINISTERS' OFFICE
1495 St. James St., Winnipeg, R3H 0W9
Asst. Dep. Minister, Derek Doyle
Asst. Dep. Minister, Rich Goulden

ADMINISTRATIVE SERVICES DIVISION
500, 191 Broadway, Winnipeg, R3C 4B2
General Inquiry: (204) 775-0221
Exec. Director, W.J. Podolsky
Financial Services
Director, P. Lockett

Personnel Services
Director, K.A. Reimer
Communications, Economics and Planning
1495 St. James St., Box 38
Winnipeg, R3H 0W9
Director, Jim Potton
Regional Services Branch
1495 St. James St., Winnipeg, R3H 0W9
Director, Harvey Boyle
Forestry Branch
300, 530 Kenaston Blvd., Winnipeg, R3N 1Z4
Director, D. Rannard
Wildlife Branch
1495 St. James St., Winnipeg, R3H 0W9
A/Director, Lorne Colpitts
Fisheries Branch
1495 St. James St., Winnipeg, R3H 0W9
Director, W. Hayden
Parks Branch
280 Smith St., Winnipeg, R3C 1T5
Director, Gordon Prouse
Engineering and Construction Branch
1577 Dublin Ave., Winnipeg, R3E 3J5
Director, Umendra Mital
Lands Branch
1495 St. James St., Winnipeg, R3H 0W9
Director, R.W. Winstone
Water Resources Branch
1577 Dublin Ave., Winnipeg, R3E 3J5
A/Director, Derek Doyle
Surveys and Mapping Branch
1007 Century St., Winnipeg, R3H 0W4
Director, D.W. Crandall

AGENCIES, BOARDS AND COMMISSIONS

Conservation Districts Commission
Rm. 800, 1495 St. James St., Box 50
Winnipeg, R3H 0W9

The *Conservation Districts Act,* passed by
Manitoba in 1976, allows municipalities to form
conservation districts in order to manage
resources and to protect the rights of land
owners. Each district is allowed to levy a tax based
on "rate-able" lands and buildings, and also to
receive grants from the provincial government
based on cost-sharing formulae established by
the province to carry out the works and maintenance programs. There are presently five conservation districts, each with a board to conduct its
affairs.

The Conservation Districts Commission, established under the Act, provides advice and guidance to the districts, reviews their operations and
budgets and advises the Minister of Natural
Resources on all matters relating to the Act.

A/Chairman, Derek Doyle
Secretary, L.A. Duguay
Conservation Districts Authority
711, 330 Graham Ave., Winnipeg, R3C 4A5
Exec. Director, Dr. Ian W. Dickson
Sec.-Treasurer, L.A. Duguay
Whitemud Watershed Conservation District #1
Neepawa, R0J 1H0

Chairman, K.W. Schmidt
Manager, S.W. Hildebrand
Sec.-Treasurer, Mrs. G.A. White
*Turtle River Watershed Conservation
District #2*
Ste. Rose du Lac, R0L 1S0
Chairman, B. Durston
Manager, G. Bruce
Sec.-Treasurer, K. Ogg
Alonsa Conservation District #3
Alonsa, R0H 0A0
Chairman, D. Fletcher
Manager, T. Thorleifson
Sec.-Treasurer, Mrs. C. Bruce
Turtle Mountain Conservation District #4
Box 508, Deloraine, R0M 0M0
Chairman, D. Crowe
Manager, W.R. Poole
Sec.-Treasurer, S. Noe
Cooks Creek Conservation District #5
530 Main St., Oakbank, R0E 1J0
Chairman, R. Maciejkow
Manager, B. Lussier
Sec.-Treasurer, Lynn Sellen

Lower Red River Valley Water Commission
Box 336, Carman, R0G 0J0

The Lower Red River Valley Water Commission
was established by an Order-in-Council of the
Government of Manitoba on Aug. 29, 1958. The
Commission consists of 16 representatives
appointed by member municipalities and four
members-at-large appointed by the provincial
government.

The purpose of the Commission is to promote
the use, development, and conservation of water
for the member municipalities. It is the responsibility of the Commission to keep its members
informed and to make representations to governments on their behalf.

Chairman, D.J. Alexander
Sec.-Treasurer, D.L. Fletcher

DEPARTMENT OF NORTHERN AFFAIRS
333 Legislative Bldg., Winnipeg, R3C 0V8
(except where otherwise indicated)
General Inquiries: (204) 945-3944

MINISTER'S OFFICE
Minister, The Hon. James Downey

DEPUTY MINISTER'S OFFICE
Dep. Minister, David Tomasson

Local Government Development
59 Elizabeth Dr., Box 33, Thompson, R8N 1X4
Asst. Dep. Minister, Oliver Boulette
Administrative Support Services
59 Elizabeth Dr., Box 37, Thompson, R8N 1X4
Director, Rene Gagnon

Agreements Management
200, 500 Portage Ave., Winnipeg, R3C 3X1

Asst. Dep. Minister, B. Kustra

DEPARTMENT OF URBAN AFFAIRS
317 Legislative Bldg., Winnipeg, R3C 0V8

MINISTER'S OFFICE

Minister, The Hon. Gerald Ducharme

DEPUTY MINISTER'S OFFICE
311 Legislative Bldg., Winnipeg, R3C 0V8

A/Dep. Minister, James O. Beaulieu

ADMINISTRATION AND FINANCE BRANCH
302, 258 Portage Ave., Winnipeg, R3C 0B6
Manager, Vernon DePape
Admin. Officer, Bob McFee
Sr. Urban Finance Co-ordinator,
Marianne Farag

POLICY CO-ORDINATION BRANCH
302, 258 Portage Ave., Winnipeg, R3C 0B6
Director, Vacant
Sr. Planner, Riverbank Development
Heather MacKnight
Community Planning Officer, Pat Moses
Sr. Urban Development Planner,
Claudette Toupin
Urban Policy and Program Officers:
David Lettner, Jon Gunn
Sr. Community Co-ordinator, Marilyn Walder

INDEPENDENT AGENCIES, BOARDS, COMMISSIONS AND CROWN CORPORATIONS

Civil Service Superannuation Board
600, 400 Tache Ave., Winnipeg, R2H 3C3

The Civil Service Superannuation Board is a nine-member Board composed of a chairman, four government-appointed members, and four members who are elected by contributors to the Superannuation Fund. The Board is the trustee of the Fund and is responsible for administering the pension and group insurance plans for eligible employees of the Province of Manitoba and certain boards, agencies, and commissions.
Minister responsible,
The Hon. Edward Connery

Chairman, R.E. Archer
Gen. Manager, W.R. Worosz

Communities Economic Development Fund
1800, 155 Carlton St., Winnipeg, R3C 3H8

The *Communities Economic Development Fund Act,* passed in July 1971, stipulates that the Fund's objectives are:
- to encourage the economic development of remote and isolated communities within the province of Manitoba;
- to provide financial assistance to establish economic enterprises;
- to encourage and strengthen small and medium enterprises which are locally owned and operated by individuals or community groups; and
- in particular, to assist economically disadvantaged persons.

Financial assistance is limited to loans only — not grants — and the interest rate is the provincial rate applied for loans to Crown corporations. The proposed business enterprise must be a profitable or potentially profitable venture capable of repaying its debts within a reasonable period.

Projects are assessed by staff members and, if deemed viable and suitable, are presented to the board of directors for approval. Management assistance is also provided by the Fund in an attempt to ensure that operations are carried out in a proper manner.

To apply for assistance, the applicant is required to provide personal data, including background, credit history, scope of project, capital cost estimate, operating and revenue expenses, and equity input. If necessary, a member of the Fund will assist in obtaining this information.
Minister responsible, The Hon. James Downey

Chairperson, Barbara Bruce
Gen. Manager, H.J. Jones
Finance Manager, W.E. Chiswell
Corporate Secretary, A.Y. Musgrove

Liquor Control Commission
Box 1023, Winnipeg, R3C 2X1

The Manitoba Liquor Control Commission is responsible for the purchase, sale, and control of beverage alcohol in the province. While it functions essentially as a retailer of regulated products, the Commission strives to combine business effectiveness with a strong awareness of social responsibility.

The Commission seeks to support the efforts of the hospitality industry with realistic enforcement of rules and regulations and an enlightened approach to innovative ideas.

The dissemination of information on matters of interest to the public, in addition to that required by law, is carried out in order to keep the public well informed of Commission and store-level activities.

Minister responsible, The Hon. James McCrae
Chairman, G.W.J. Mercier, Q.C.
Vice-Chairman, Dianne Lambert
Commissioners: Sally Harrison,
Joyce Buffie, Wes Goodspeed
President and CEO, W.E. Emerson
Vice-President, Purchasing, D.V. Lussier
Personnel Director, R. Zubach
Information Systems
Manager, W.D. Bodner
Vice-President, Licensing, I.A. Hamilton
Vice-President, Finance, A.B. Ahoff, C.A.
Retail Operations
Director, F.J. Johnston

Manfor Ltd.

806, 363 Broadway, Winnipeg, R3C 3N9

Manfor Ltd. (Manitoba Forestry Resources) was incorporated under the provisions of Part II of the Manitoba Companies Act on March 23, 1973 and commenced business on Oct. 1, 1973.

Production capacity is: 140,000 tonnes of unbleached kraft paper, and approximately 50 million fbm of random length dimension spruce, pine, or fir lumber.

The Corporation is wholly owned by the Government of the Province of Manitoba.

President and CEO, J.P. Demare, C.A.
Minister responsible, The Hon. James Ernst
Pulp and Paper Division
Box 1590, The Pas, R9A 1L4
Manager, G. Wazny
Lumber and Woodlands Divisions
Box 1590, The Pas, R9A 1L4
Woodlands Manager, W.E. Jonas
Lumber Manager, Al Siemens

Manitoba Civil Service Commission

935, 155 Carlton St., Winnipeg, R3C 3H8

The Manitoba Civil Service Commission provides centralized personnel management services to all departments of government and to agencies, boards, or commissions whose staff is appointed under The Civil Service Act, through three divisions — Personnel Services, Personnel Policy and Audit, and Employee Relations.

The Commission is responsible for recruitment and selection, classification plans, pay plans, personnel policy and benefits administration, management development, staff training, employee health and counselling, and equal employment opportunity programs. Through the Employee Relations Division, the Commission provides for negotiation of collective agreements, contract administration, public sector co-ordination, compensation research, and provision of consultative services.

In addition to responsibility for an appeal function, the Commission performs an audit function and provides advice to the minister responsible on matters concerning personnel administration.

Minister responsible,
The Hon. Edward Connery
FULL-TIME MEMBERS:
Commissioner, Paul Hart
Pay Equity Commissioner,
Roberta Ellis-Grunfeld
PART-TIME MEMBERS:
Chairperson, James Hartry
Members: Beverly Suek, Dr. Ertrice Eddy,
Tom McCartney, Claire Riddle
Secretary, Bob Pollock

Manitoba Hydro

Box 815, Winnipeg, R3C 2P4
General Inquiries: (204) 474-3311

Manitoba Hydro is a provincial Crown corporation established "to provide for the continuance of a supply of power adequate for the needs of the province, and to promote economy and efficiency in the generation, distribution, supply, and use of power."

Manitoba Hydro and Winnipeg Hydro operate as an integrated electrical generation and transmission system interconnected with systems in Saskatchewan, Ontario, and the U.S.

Manitoba Hydro distributes electricity throughout the province except for the core area of the City of Winnipeg which is served by the city-owned Winnipeg Hydro. Manitoba Hydro serves some 320,000 residential and farm customers, and 42,000 power and general-service customers.

Manitoba Hydro's electricity generation in fiscal 1987-88 was 18.2 billion kW/h, made up of 95 per cent hydraulic and 5 per cent thermal. Drought conditions during the year curtailed hydraulic generation which, under optimum water flows, can provide in excess of 99 per cent of the Manitoba system's total requirements. In 1987-88, thermal generation totalled 823.5 million kW/h and an additional 1.2 billion kW/h were imported in order to satisfy the demand from the integrated system.

Minister responsible, The Hon. Harold Neufeld

Chairman, A.B. Ransom
President and CEO, G.H. Beatty
Customer Service and Marketing
Sr. Vice-President, R.O. Lambert
Energy Supply
Sr. Vice-President, R.M. Fraser
Business Development
Vice-President, W.A. Derry
Corporate Relations
Vice-President, L.M. Jolson
Engineering and Construction
Vice-President, D.A. Kilgour
Finance, Vice-President, R.B. Brennan
Operations, Vice-President, W.J. Tishinski
Gen. Counsel and Corp. Secretary, J.F. Funnell
Personnel Division Manager, J.G. Bulloch

Manitoba Lotteries Foundation
830 Empress St., Winnipeg, R3G 3H3

The Foundation is a Crown agency established by the government of Manitoba to manage and conduct all lottery and gaming activities within the province. This includes the licensing of: charitable and religious organizations to conduct bingos, raffles, the sale of breakopen tickets, wheels of fortune, and calcuttas; and also midway operations and agricultural fairs. The Foundation prescribes the terms and conditions for the operation of such gaming activities and inspects for compliance those operations and the expenditure of funds earned.

The Foundation conducts all casino events in Manitoba as well as bingo halls in operation more than five days per week. It is also the provincial marketing organization for all government lottery ticket products.

Minister responsible,
The Hon. Bonnie Mitchelson

Chairman, Glenda Russell
Gen. Manager, Garth Manness
Members: Bill Wilton Sr., Maurice Therrien, Nellie Allen, Ruth Gales, Emily Konopelny, Gordon Mitchell, Les Parry, Howard Robinson, Jane Smith, Bob Solmundson, Bob Swain

The Manitoba Public Insurance Corp.
330 Graham Ave., Winnipeg, R3C 4A4

The Manitoba Public Insurance Corporation, which operates under *The Manitoba Public Insurance Corporation Act,* November 1974, consists of two divisions: the Automobile Insurance Division and the General Insurance Division.

The Automobile Insurance Division provides comprehensive coverage for all motor vehicles registered in the province of Manitoba. This coverage includes an automatic accident compensation plan for injuries or death and major damage to vehicles.

The basic plan, known as Autopac, commenced operations on Nov. 1, 1971 under the old *Automobile Insurance Act.* It provides accident benefit coverage regardless of fault for medical or funeral expenses and makes death payments, weekly payments for total disability, weekly payments for partial disability, and impairment payments.

The General Insurance Division commenced operations in 1975 and markets various fire, property, and casualty general insurance coverages in competition with the private insurance sector.

Minister responsible,
The Hon. James Cummings
President and Gen. Manager, J.W. Bardua
Insurance Operations, Vice-President
and Asst. Gen. Manager, D.R. Kidd

Finance and Administration
Vice-President, B.W. Galenzoski
General Insurance
Vice-President, H.P. Dribnenky
Gen. Counsel and Corporate Secretary,
S.S. Kapoor, Q.C.
Special Projects Asst., T.M. Petrishen
Human and Information Resources
A/Vice-President, R.D. Lynch
Community and Corporate Relations
A/Vice-President, G.D. Newton
Claims
A/Vice-President, J.W. Zacharias

Manitoba Telephone System
489 Empress St., Box 6666
Winnipeg, R3C 3V6
General Inquiries: (204) 941-4111

The Manitoba Telephone System, owned by the government of Manitoba and operated by a board of commissioners, provides telecommunications services and facilities in Manitoba for domestic, business, and defence needs. It is also one of the members of Telecom Canada.

The first telephones in Manitoba were provided by Bell Telephone of Canada in 1877. In 1908, the Bell system was purchased by the province and Manitoba Government Telephones was established. It was later renamed Manitoba Telephone System.

As of March 1985, there were more than 487,440 main-station telephones in the province — all dial-operated. Calling has reached a yearly level of more than 1.6 billion local calls, while the number of long-distance calls exceeds 78.4 million. The System currently has about 4,600 employees.

Minister responsible, The Hon. Glen Findlay

Chairperson, Prof. Paul Thomas
Vice-Chairperson, Patricia Graham
Commissioners: Holly Beard,
Ruth Spletzer, Tom Stefanson,
Helmut Pankratz, Edgar Penner,
Joanne Swayze, Roy McMillan
EXECUTIVE COMMITTEE
President and CEO, Reg Bird
Exec. Vice-President, Dennis H. Wardrop
Eastern Region Manager, E.B. Tinkler
Northern Region Manager, E.M. Scoles
Western Region Manager, D.L. Delgatty
Vice-President, Network Development
and Operations, B.A. Gordon
Vice-President, Customer Service, B.A. Deakin
Gen. Sales Manager, Glenn Brand
Vice-President, Business Communications,
B.B. McCallum
Business
Gen. Sales Manager, Glenn Wilson
Accounts
Gen. Sales Manager, Merv Cavers

Vice-President, Corporate Services,
John Milne
Vice-President, Finance, W.C. Fraser
Vice-President, Marketing and Strategic
Planning, Roger Ballance
Vice-President, Human Resources,
Denis Sutton
Corporate Secretary/Board Analyst
Heather J. Nault

Public Investments Corp.

600, 330 Portage Ave., Winnipeg, R3C 0C4
Minister responsible,
The Hon. Clayton Manness
President and CEO, Stephan R. Barg

Sanatorium Board of Manitoba

629 E. McDermot Ave., Winnipeg, R3A 1P6
General Inquiry: (204) 774-5501

The Sanatorium Board of Manitoba was incorporated in 1906 under the *Sanatorium Board of Manitoba Act*. It is a voluntary non-profit organization that is authorized to establish and administer health and social programs — subject to the approval of the responsible minister. In fulfilling its mandate, the Board currently administers the Provincial Tuberculosis Control Programs, the Manitoba Lung Assn., and the Pelican Lake Training Centre which provides an intensive training program for mentally handicapped adults.

Chairman, J. Marks
Exec. Director, R.F. Marks, C.A.

JUDICIARY AND JUDICIAL OFFICERS

Court of Appeal

Law Courts Bldg.
408 York Ave., Winnipeg, R3C 0P9
General Inquiries: (204) 945-2647

Chief Justice of Manitoba:
The Hon. A.M. Monnin

Justices:
The Hon. Mr. Justice G.C. Hall
The Hon. Mr. Justice J.F. O'Sullivan
The Hon. Mr. Justice C.R. Huband
The Hon. Mr. Justice A.R. Philp
The Hon. Mr. Justice A.K. Twaddle
The Hon. Mr. Justice S.R. Lyon

Registrar: B.T. Cadger

Court of Queen's Bench

Law Courts Bldg.
408 York Ave., Winnipeg, R3C 0P9
Criminal: (204) 945-5382
Civil: (204) 945-3014
Family: (204) 945-5383

Chief Justice: The Hon. B. Hewak

Assoc. Chief Justice: The Hon. R.J. Scott

Justices:
The Hon. Mr. Justice J.E. Wilson*
The Hon. Mr. Justice W.S. Wright
The Hon. Mr. Justice P.S. Morse
The Hon. Mr. Justice G.J. Kroft
The Hon. Mr. Justice J.A. Scollin
The Hon. Mr. Justice V. Simonsen
The Hon. Mr. Justice K.R. Hanssen
The Hon. Mr. Justice M.A. Monnin
The Hon. Mr. Justice G.J. Barkman
The Hon. Mr. Justice B.R. Coleman*
The Hon. Mr. Justice A. Dureault
The Hon. Mr. Justice W.M. Darichuk
  (Dauphin)
The Hon. Mr. Justice G.O. Jewers
The Hon. Mr. Justice G.H. Lockwood
The Hon. Mr. Justice D.P. Kennedy
The Hon. Mr. Justice A.C. Miller
  (Portage la Prairie)
The Hon. Madam Justice R. Krindle
The Hon. Mr. Justice J.G. Smith
The Hon. Mr. Justice S. Schwartz
The Hon. Mr. Justice T. Glowacki
The Hon. Mr. Justice J.J. Oliphant
  (Brandon)
The Hon. Mr. Justice A.A. Hirschfield
The Hon. Mr. Justice W.R. DeGraves

FAMILY DIVISION
Assoc. Chief Justice: The Hon. A.C. Hamilton

Justices:
The Hon. Madam Justice B.M. Helper
The Hon. Madam Justice C.M. Bowman
The Hon. Mr. Justice R.M. Carr
The Hon. Mr. Justice G.R. Goodman
The Hon. Mr. Justice J.A. Mullally

Director (Winnipeg): R.L. Giasson

Sr. Master: M.E. Goldberg, Q.C.
Masters: G. Richardson, Q.C., L. Ring, Q.C.,
  F. Lee

Provincial Court

Law Courts Bldg.
408 York Ave., Winnipeg, R3C 0P9

A/Chief Judge: Ian V. Dubienski
Assoc. Chief Judges: E.C. Kimelman,
  C. Murray Sinclair

Judges: J.J. Enns, L.R. Mitchell,
  R.A. Johnston, R.L. Kopstein, G.B. McTavish,
  R.J.B. Cramer, S. Minuk, R.H. Harris,
  C.N. Rubin, T.J. Lismer, P.L. Ashdown,
  R.J. Meyers, R.J. Morlock, A.J. Conner,
  K.F. Stefanson, M. Garfinkel, C.K Newcombe,
  W.E. Norton, F. Allen, W.H. Swail,
  B.M. Corrin, S.V. Devine, L.A. Duval,
  L.M. Giesbrecht

Director: A.M. Ziemianski

BRANDON
Court House, 1104 Princess Ave., R7A 0P9
Judges: R. Mykle, B.D. Giesbrecht, A. James

DAUPHIN
Court House, 114 W. River Ave., R7N 0J7
Judges: K.P. Peters, R.W. Thompson

PORTAGE LA PRAIRIE
Court Office, 25 Tupper St., R1N 3K1
Judge: B.P. McDonald

THE PAS
Court House, 300 E. 3rd St., R9A 1L2
Judge: W.R. Martin

THOMPSON
Court Office, 59 Elizabeth Dr., R8N 1X4
Judges: J.P. Drapack, M.W. Howell

---

* Supernumerary

Rural Courts
(Administrative & Judicial Centres)

Director, P.D. Chambers

BEAUSEJOUR
Asst. Deputy Registrar: E. Puchlik

BRANDON
Deputy Registrar: D. Karnes
Clerk of Court: D. Karnes

DAUPHIN
Deputy Registrar: Peter Chomiak
Clerk of Court: Peter Chomiak

FLIN FLON
Asst. Deputy Registrar: C.E. Hume

KILLARNEY
Asst. Deputy Registrar: J. Cyr

MINNEDOSA
Asst. Deputy Registrar: C.P. Hopkins

MORDEN
Asst. Deputy Registrar: L. McDonald

PORTAGE LA PRAIRIE
Deputy Registrar: Vacant
Clerk of Court: Wm. Munn

RUSSELL
Asst. Deputy Registrar: F. Keller

ST. BONIFACE
Deputy Registrar: P. Beaulieu
Clerk of Court: Vacant

SELKIRK
Deputy Registrar: Vacant
Clerk of Court: Vacant

STEINBACH
Clerk of Court: D. Chambers

SWAN RIVER
Asst. Deputy Registrar: M. Dennis

THE PAS
A/Deputy Registrar: S. Koshowski
A/Clerk of Court: S. Koshowski

THOMPSON
Deputy Registrar: B. Hallam
Clerk of Court: B. Hallam

VIRDEN
Asst. Deputy Registrar: H.G. Effler

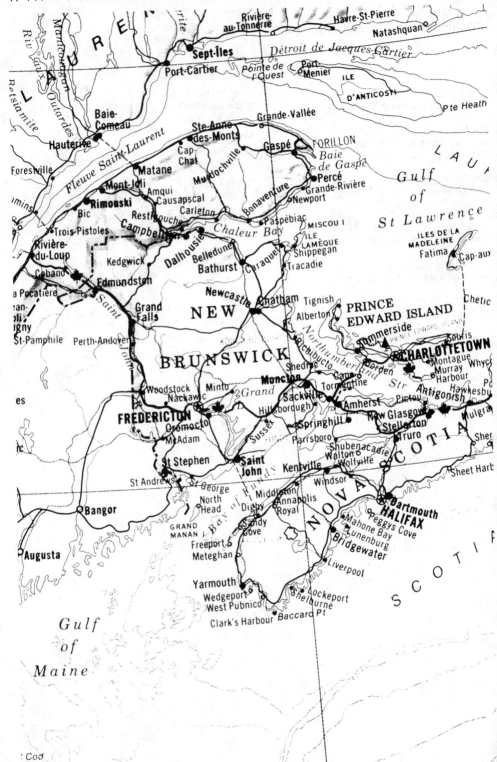

PROVINCE OF NEW BRUNSWICK

Purple Violet
(*Viola cucullata*)

Entered Confederation: July 1, 1867
Capital: Fredericton
Motto: Spem Reduxit (Hope was restored)
Flower: Purple violet
Area: 73,437 km²
  percentage of Canada's total area: 0.7
  LAND: 71,569 km²
  FRESHWATER: 1,868 km²
Elevation:
  HIGHEST POINT: Mount Carleton (820 m)
  LOWEST POINT: northern & eastern coastal
    area at sea level
Population (April 1988): 713,500
  five-year change: +1.7%

per square kilometre: 10.0
percentage of Canada's total
  population: 2.8
  URBAN: 49%
  RURAL: 51%
Gross domestic product, 1987: $10.6 billion
Government Finance:
  REVENUE, 1987/88: $3.1 billion
  EXPENDITURE, 1987/88: $3.5 billion
  DEBT PER CAPITA (March 1987): $3,430
Personal income per capita, 1986: $12,878
Unemployment rate, 1988
  (annual average): 12.0%

HISTORY

New Brunswick was first explored in 1604 by Samuel de Champlain, who claimed the land for France. It was ceded by the French in the Treaty of Utrecht in 1713 and became a permanent British possession in 1763. New Brunswick became a province in June 1784, following the great influx of United Empire Loyalists. Responsible government came in 1847, consisting of an Executive Council, a Legislative Council (later abolished), and a House of Assembly. New Brunswick was given its name from the House of Brunswick, ruling England at the time the province was established. In 1867, it became one of the four charter members of the Canadian Confederation.

THE LAND

New Brunswick is the largest of the three

Maritime provinces, bordering Nova Scotia, Quebec, and the State of Maine. Almost rectangular in shape, extending about 322 km from north to south and 242 km from east to west, New Brunswick is surrounded by water on most of three sides.

Beginning at the north, the province's boundaries are the Province of Quebec, the Restigouche River, and Chaleur Bay. Its eastern boundary is entirely water, made up of the Gulf of St. Lawrence and Northumberland Strait. In the south, the boundary is the Bay of Fundy and Chignecto Bay, with a 21-km stretch of land boundary at its southeast corner, where the province is joined to Nova Scotia by the Isthmus of Chignecto. Its western boundary runs along the side of Quebec and the State of Maine.

Mountainous terrain is predominant in the north. The interior of the province is mostly rolling plateau; the north and east are fairly flat; the south is rugged. The principal rivers are: Miramichi, Nepisiguit, Restigouche, Salmon, St. Croix, Saint John, and Tobique. The main lakes are: Grand, Chiputneticook, Magaguadavic, and Oromocto.

THE PEOPLE

Approximately one third of New Brunswick's people are French-speaking, and the influence of their Acadian background has blended with that of the modern-day descendants of the United Empire Loyalists (those who migrated north during the American Revolution).

The settled areas of the province are principally along the coasts and in the river valleys. New Brunswick's two largest cities are Saint John and Moncton, with a population of 76,381 and 55,468 respectively.

THE ECONOMY

New Brunswick's economy is based upon traditional primary industries. Forest products, farming, and fishing are major contributors to its gross domestic product.

Forestry. Eighty-five per cent of New Brunswick's land mass is considered to be productive forest, a higher percentage than any other Canadian province. Pulp and paper mills, saw mills, plywood plants, furniture factories, and other forestry-based businesses are the mainstays of the province's economy, accounting for approximately 8 per cent of the gross domestic product.

Agriculture. Investment in agriculture in New Brunswick has reached the $658 million mark. In 1987, total farm cash receipts were $247 million.

Two major sources of income for provincial farmers are potatoes and dairy operations, providing respectively about 23 and 22 per cent of farm cash income (five-year average). In 1987, the dairy industry brought in returns to a value of $54 million.

Horticulture and field crops represent 35 per cent of farm cash income. The commodities include landscaping, apples, blueberries, strawberries, greenhouse products, vegetables, forage, and grain.

Fisheries. New Brunswick fisheries remain tributary to foreign markets, particularly the U.S. In 1987, approximately 6,500 fishermen harvested close to 147,000 tonnes of fish and shellfish valued at $115.8 million.

The most landed species is herring, at 89,300 tonnes. However, lobster represents 36.5 per cent of the total value of landings; crab, 20 per cent; and herring, 14 per cent.

Exports of fish products climbed to 80,900 tonnes worth $352.4 million. Shellfish exports accounted for 55 per cent of the total, or $195 million. More than 61 per cent of the total was exported to the U.S. and 21 per cent to Japan.

New Brunswick continued to import fish in 1987. Total imports of 146,000 tonnes amounted to $36 million. Over 68 per cent of fish product imports were from the U.S., 13 per cent from Cuba, and seven per cent from Nicaragua.

Mining. New Brunswick's mines and quarries yield a variety of minerals, and the industry ranks second in economic importance following forestry. In 1987, the total value of minerals produced was $701 million, a 40 per cent increase from 1986. Two potash mines are currently in production, while a mining lease for the Millstream Area could lead to a third producer in the early 1990s. Exploration in the province is concentrated on the search for gold in the Bathurst and the St. John-Moncton area. A gold mine near Saint John is successfully using a Heap leaching method of recovery, long considered unprofitable in a cold climate.

Electricity. New Brunswick Power has over 3 million kW of installed capacity at 14 generating facilities. These include one gas turbine, one diesel, one nuclear, five thermal, and six hydro generating stations. NB Power is also electrically interconnected with neighbouring utilities in Quebec, Nova Scotia, P.E.I., and New England.

Atlantic Canada's first nuclear generating station consists of a single CANDU 600 unit with a total net capacity of 630,000 kW. The Station is located on the Lepreau peninsula, overlooking the Bay of Fundy, 40 km southwest of Saint John.

Point Lepreau reached the top of the international performance standings for all CANDU reactors in 1985, and ranked second among over 200 similar-sized world reactors in 18 countries. Performance of this world-class CANDU-600 has been exceptional with a capacity factor of 97.4 per cent for the 1985 calendar year. Nuclear energy from Point Lepreau supplies over 30 per cent of New Brunswick's electrical energy and is a major source of revenue from export sales to a number of New England utilities.

Electricity export sales accounted for about 34 per cent of revenue in 1986/87; energy purchases came mainly from the large Hydro-Québec system, supplying about 28 per cent of in-province energy load.

Manufacturing. In 1987, total manufacturing shipments reached $4.9 million and new capital investment in manufacturing totalled $208.8 million. The paper and allied industries group ranks first among the manufacturing industries in terms of value of products, followed by the food and wood industries.

Tourism. Tourism is a major industry in New Brunswick. In excess of 4.4 million tourists spent approximately $464 million in the province for 1986.

Text provided by the New Brunswick Information Service.

GOVERNMENT OF NEW BRUNSWICK

Seat of Government:
Legislative Bldg., Fredericton, E3B 5H1

Lieutenant-Governor,
The Hon. Gilbert Finn
Box 6000, Fredericton, E3B 5H1

EXECUTIVE COUNCIL

Premier, Minister responsible for Status of Women, Minister responsible for Regional Development,
The Hon. Frank McKenna
President of the Executive Council, Minister of Intergovernmental Affairs, A/Minister of Fisheries and Aquaculture,
The Hon. Aldéa Landry, Q.C.
Minister of Advanced Education and Training,
The Hon. Russell King, M.D.
Minister of Agriculture,
The Hon. Alan Graham
Attorney General, Minister of Justice,
The Hon. James Lockyer, C.D., Q.C.
Minster of Commerce and Technology,
The Hon. Alfred Lacey
Minister of Education,
The Hon. Shirley Dysart
Minister of Finance,
The Hon. Allan Maher
Minister of Health and Community Services,
The Hon. J. Raymond Frenette
Minister of Housing,
The Hon. Peter Trites
Minister of Income Assistance,
The Hon. Laureen Jarrett
Minister of Labour, Minister responsible for Multiculturalism,
The Hon. Michael McKee
Chairman of the Board of Management,
The Hon. Gérald Clavette
Minister of Municipal Affairs and Environment,
The Hon. Vaughn Blaney
Minister of Natural Resources and Energy,
The Hon. Morris Green
Chairman, N.B. Power,
The Hon. Rayburn Doucett
Solicitor General,
The Hon. Conrad Landry
Minister of Supply and Services,
The Hon. Bruce Smith
Minister of Tourism, Recreation and Heritage,
The Hon. Roland Beaulieu

Minister of Transportation,
The Hon. Sheldon Lee

EXECUTIVE COUNCIL OFFICE

President, The Hon. Aldéa Landry, Q.C.
Clerk of the Executive Council and Secretary to Cabinet, Harry A. Nason
Asst. Deputy Minister, Paul M. O'Connell

LEGISLATIVE ASSEMBLY

51st Legislature, 2nd Session
Last general election: Oct. 13, 1987
 (Maximum 5 years and 2 months)
Majority party: Liberal
Total number of seats: 58
Party standings:
 Liberals: 58

Salaries, Indemnities and Allowances

MEMBERS: $34,099 Member's Sessional Indemnity, plus cost of living clause and $13,640 expense allowance.
MINISTERS: $31,069 salary, plus Member's Sessional Indemnity and expense allowance.
PREMIER: $46,601 salary, plus Member's Sessional Indemnity and expense allowance incidental to the discharge of duties as premier.
SPEAKER: $31,069 allowance, plus Member's Sessional Indemnity and expense allowance, plus $1,000 annual expense allowance and reimbursement for expenses incidental to the discharge of duties.
LEADER OF THE OPPOSITION: $31,069 salary, plus Member's Sessional Indemnity and expense allowance.

Officers

Speaker: Frank Branch
Clerk of the Assembly: David Peterson
Clerk Assistant: Loredana Catalli Sonier
Sergeant-at-Arms: Leo F. McNulty

For further information regarding any aspect of the Government of New Brunswick, contact:
New Brunswick Information Service
Box 6000, Fredericton, NB E3B 5H1
(506) 453-2240

Members

Constituency	Member and Affiliation
Albert	Harold Terris (Lib)
Bathurst	Paul Kenny (Lib)
Bay du Vin	Reginald MacDonald (Lib)
Campbellton	Edmond Blanchard (Lib)
Caraquet	Bernard Thériault (Lib)
Carleton Centre	Allison DeLong (Lib)
Carleton North	Fred Harvey (Lib)
Carleton South	The Hon. Bruce Smith (Lib)
Charlotte Centre	The Hon. Sheldon Lee (Lib)
Charlotte Fundy	Eric Allaby (Lib)
Charlotte West	Reid Hurley (Lib)
Chatham	The Hon. Frank McKenna (Lib)
Dalhousie	The Hon. Allan Maher (Lib)
Edmundston	The Hon. Roland Beaulieu (Lib)
Fredericton North	James Wilson (Lib)
Fredericton South	The Hon. Russell King (Lib)
Grand Falls	Paul Duffie (Lib)
Kent Centre	The Hon. Alan R. Graham (Lib)
Kent North	The Hon. Conrad Landry (Lib)
Kent South	Camille Thériault (Lib)
Kings Centre	Dr. Killem Seaman (Lib)
Kings East	Pius A. (Pete) Dalton (Lib)
Kings West	The Hon. Laureen Jarrett (Lib)
Madawaska Centre	The Hon. Gérald Clavette (Lib)
Madawaska South	Pierrette Ringuette-Maltais (Lib)
Madawaska-les-Lacs	Georges Corriveau (Lib)
Memramcook	Greg O'Donnell (Lib)
Miramichi Bay	Donald (Danny) Gay (Lib)
Miramichi/Newcastle	John McKay (Lib)
Southwest Miramichi	The Hon. Morris Green (Lib)
Moncton East	The Hon. J. Raymond Frenette (Lib)
Moncton North	The Hon. Michael McKee (Lib)
Moncton West	The Hon. James Lockyer (Lib)
Nepisiguit/Chaleur	The Hon. Frank R. Branch (Lib)
Nigadoo/Chaleur	Pierre Godin (Lib)
Oromocto	Tom Gilbert (Lib)
Petitcodiac	Hollis Steeves (Lib)
Queens North	Douglas Tyler (Lib)
Queens South	The Hon. Vaughn Blaney (Lib)
Restigouche East	The Hon. Rayburn Doucett (Lib)
Restigouche West	Jean-Paul Savoie (Lib)
Riverview	Hubert Seamans (Lib)
Saint John East	The Hon. Peter Trites (Lib)
Saint John Fundy	Stuart Jamieson (Lib)
Saint John Harbour	Louis Murphy (Lib)
Saint John North	Leo A. McAdam (Lib)
Saint John Park	The Hon. Shirley Dysart (Lib)
Saint John South	John Patrick Mooney (Lib)
Saint John West	Jane Barry (Lib)
St. Stephen/Milltown	Anne Breault (Lib)
Shediac	Azor Leblanc (Lib)
Shippegan-les-Iles	The Hon. Aldéa Landry (Lib)
Sunbury	Doug Harrison (Lib)
Tantramar	Dr. Marilyn Trenholme (Lib)
Tracadie	Denis Losier (Lib)
Victoria/Tobique	Dr. Larry Kennedy (Lib)
York North	Robert Simpson (Lib)
York South	The Hon. Alfred Lacey (Lib)

Lib — Liberal

Office of the Premier

Centennial Bldg.
Box 6000, Fredericton, E3B 5H1

Premier, The Hon. Frank McKenna
Exec. Assistant (Scheduling), Ruth McCrea

Deputy Minister's Office
Deputy Minister, Fernand Landry

Office of Economic Development
Asst. Commissioner, Janice LeBlanc

Policy Secretariat
Deputy Minister, Claire Morris

Women's Directorate
Deputy Minister, Ellen King

Job Protection Unit
Kings Place, Rm. 646, Fredericton, E3B 5H1
Administrator, W.H. Bryden

Advisory Council on the Status of Women
95 Foundry St., Ste. 207, Moncton, E1C 5H7

The Advisory Council on the Status of Women is an agency for consultation and study on the status of women. Its purpose is to advise the New Brunswick government on matters relating to its field. The Council, which consists of 12 appointed members, reports directly to the premier of the province. The chairperson has the status of a deputy minister. Members, including the chairperson and the vice-chairperson, are appointed for a term of three years. The Council meets at least four times per year.

Chairperson, Jeanne d'Arc Gaudet

Premier's Council on the Status of Disabled Persons
105 Prospect St., Fredericton, E3B 2T7
General Inquiries: (506) 452-1112
1-800-442-4412

The legislation to create the Premier's Council on the Status of Disabled Persons was passed in 1982. The council is a body for consultation and study which was created to advise the provincial government on matters relating to the status of disabled persons. The Council reports directly to the premier of the province.

The act governing the Premier's Council states that the Council shall (among other things):
- advise the Premier on matters relating to the status of disabled persons;
- bring before the government and the public matters of interest and concern to disabled persons;
- promote prevention of disabling conditions;
- promote employment opportunities for disabled persons; and
- promote access by disabled persons to all services offered to the citizens of New Brunswick.

To carry out its function, the Council will:
- receive briefs and suggestions from individuals and groups concerning the status of disabled persons;

- undertake research on matters relating to disabled persons;
- recommend programs concerning the status of disabled persons;
- make referrals to, and consult and collaborate with universities and individuals on matters which affect disabled persons;
- propose legislation, policies, and practices to improve the status of disabled persons;
- publish any reports, studies, and recommendations as the Council considers necessary;
- appoint special committees when needed;
- maintain an information library on subjects related to disabled persons and on any services/programs likely to be of interest to disabled persons; and
- offer advice and/or intervention in cases where disabled persons are having difficulties in gaining access to needed services.

Chairperson, Paul Bourque
Exec. Director, Randy Dickinson

Youth Council of New Brunswick
Box 6000, Fredericton, E3B 5H1

Chairperson, Dirk Bouwer
Exec. Director, Monique LeBlanc

Office of the Ombudsman

703 Brunswick St.
Box 6000, Fredericton, E3B 5H1
General Inquiries: (506) 453-2789

The Office of the Ombudsman was established in New Brunswick in 1967, the second in Canada. The Ombudsman is appointed by the Lieutenant-Governor in Council on the recommendation of the Legislative Assembly and reports to the Assembly. The role of the Ombudsman is to investigate complaints on behalf of those who have a grievance against a governmental department or agency, or a municipality for which the provincial statutes provide no right of appeal or review, or until a right of appeal has been exercised or until the time prescribed for the exercise of that right has expired.

Any person who believes that he has suffered an injustice through the act of a department, agency, organization, or official of the Government of New Brunswick or a municipality may make a complaint to the Ombudsman. A complaint is made in written form; a person may write, call, or visit the Office of the Ombudsman. Under the *Right to Information Act,* the *Family Services Act,* and the *Archives Act,* the Ombudsman may, upon request, review a minister's decision to deny information to an applicant.

Ombudsman, Joseph E. Bérubé
Assistant, Magella St-Pierre
Solicitor, Charles Ferris

Legislative Library

Legislative Bldg.
Box 6000, Fredericton, E3B 5H1

The Legislative Library operates primarily as a library to serve the information needs of the members of the Legislative Assembly and the civil servants of the various departments and agencies. Because of its large collection of New Brunswickana, the Library also offers research services to people doing studies on New Brunswick.

The Legislative Library is the official depository of New Brunswick government documents and has one of the most complete collections of these. An annual checklist entitled *New Brunswick Government Documents* has been published by the Library since 1955.

The Legislative Library reports all its acquisitions to the National Library, and sends it the government publications of New Brunswick.

Legislative Librarian, Eric L. Swanick

DEPARTMENT OF ADVANCED EDUCATION AND TRAINING
Box 6000, Fredericton, E3B 5H1
General Inquiries: (506) 453-2597

MINISTER'S OFFICE
Minister, The Hon. Russell King

DEPUTY MINISTER'S OFFICE
Dep. Minister, Leonard J. Arsenault

Administrative Services
Asst. Dep. Minister, Bill Smith

Educational Services Division—Anglophone
Asst. Dep. Minister, Byron James
Curriculum and Evaluation
Director, J.P. Kilburn
Program Co-ordination and Apprenticeship
Training Director, C. Ramsey

Educational Services Division—Francophone
Asst. Dep. Minister, Raymond Daigle
Curriculum and Evaluation
Director, Claude Savoie
Program Co-ordination and Apprenticeship
Training Director, André Ferlatte
Apprenticeship and Trade Certification
Director, J. Sidney Harris

NEW BRUNSWICK COMMUNITY COLLEGES

Bathurst
Postal Drawer 1, Bathurst, E2A 3Z2
Principal, Maurice Roy

Campbellton
Box 309, Campbellton, E3N 3G7
Principal, Edouard Maltais

Edmundston
Box 70, Edmundston, E3V 3K7
Principal, Rodrigue Arsenault

Dieppe
27 John St., Moncton, E1C 2G7
Principal, Michel Richard

Miramichi
Box 1053, 80 University Ave.
Chatham, E1N 3W4
Principal, Albert Heckel

Moncton
Box 2100, Stn. A, Moncton, E1C 8H9
Principal, A. Sobey

St. Andrews
Box 427, St. Andrews, E0G 2X0
Principal, Gene Tatton

Saint John
Box 2270, Saint John, E2L 3V1
A/Principal, Robert Maybey

Woodstock
Box 1175, Woodstock, E0J 2B0
Principal, James Cromwell

DEPARTMENT OF AGRICULTURE

Box 6000, Fredericton, E3B 5H1
General Inquiries: (506) 453-2666
Fax: (506) 453-7170; Telex: 014-46221

MINISTER'S OFFICE
Minister, The Hon. Alan Graham

DEPUTY MINISTER'S OFFICE
Dep. Minister, Robert W. Saintonge
Asst. Dep. Minister, Marketing and Financial Services, John K. McKay
Asst. Dep. Minister, Technical and Regional Services, Gilbert Ouellette

PLANNING AND DEVELOPMENT BRANCH
Exec. Director, Peter Schousboe

ADMINISTRATIVE SERVICES
Director, Roger Hunter
Human Resources Manager, Lorraine Leger

TECHNICAL AND REGIONAL SERVICES
Agricultural Resource Development Branch
Director, Dr. Chesley Smith
Engineering Services, W.E. Durant
Farm Management Services, G. Maicher
Provincial 4-H Supervisor, Sharon Nussey
Animal Industry Branch
Director, Franklin Johnson
Red Meat Production Manager, Robert Colpitts
Commissioner of Poultry, Donald Ramey
Veterinary Services
Chief Provincial Veterinarian,
Dr. D.L.M. Maloney
Plant Industry Branch
Director, E.T. Pratt
Land Section, A. Ghanem
Fruit and Vegetable Section, Brian Dykeman

MARKETING AND FINANCIAL SERVICES
Agricultural Finance Branch
Director, Jamie Morrison
Agricultural Development Board
Chairman, E.D. Gilchrist
Sec. Manager, Paul Cooper
Special Projects Branch
Director, Dewitt Lister
Market Development Branch
Director, Michael Healy
Market Organization and Inspection Branch
Director, Wayne Buffett

AGENCIES, BOARDS AND COMMISSIONS

MARKETING BOARDS

Marketing boards for agricultural products in Canada are created by a number of different pieces of legislation. National wheat and dairy products plans flow from the *Canadian Wheat Board Act* and the *Canadian Dairy Commission Act* respectively. Egg and poultry boards derive their authority from the *Farm Products Marketing Agencies Act.* As well, many have their own provincial statutes and are normally within the jurisdiction of an umbrella provincial agency. The individual boards are, however, non-governmental and made up largely of elected farmer representatives.

There is also a variety of types. The Economic Council of Canada's study on marketing boards identified five: promotional and developmental boards with little power; selling-desk boards that handle marketing but do not set prices; boards that negotiate prices; boards that set prices; and full-fledged boards that establish quotas. These last are known as supply-management marketing boards. Currently, there are more than 100 active boards in Canada.

FARM PRODUCTS MARKETING COMMISSION
Box 6000, Fredericton, E3B 5H1
General Inquiries: (506) 453-3647

The Farm Products Marketing Commission operates under the *Farm Products Marketing Act* of May 15, 1977. At the 1985 session of the N.B. Legislature, the *Farm Products Marketing Act* and the *Dairy Products Act* were amended. These amendments provided for the Farm Products Marketing Commission to take over the responsibilities of the Dairy Products Commission as well as to establish a Farm Products Appeal Panel to deal with pricing disputes between marketing boards, processors, and other buyers.

The Act delegates several powers to the Commission. Some of these powers relate to investigating and arbitrating disputes; investigating the cost of producing, processing, and distributing farm products; recommending any marketing plan or the amendment of a plan to the minister; and making orders and issuing directives consistent with a plan or regulation. In addition, the Commission has the powers of commissioners under the *Inquiries Act* while conducting an investigation pertaining to any agricultural product.

The Farm Products Marketing Commission's major role is to supervise marketing boards established under the Act, of which there are 12 at the present time, and to ensure that the powers given to them are used in a way that is compatible with the intent of the law and in the best interest of the commodity in question. The Farm Products Marketing Commission may amend or revoke any order, decision, or determination of a commodity marketing board.

Chairman, Benoit Belzile
Vice-Chairman, Robert Keenan
Secretary, Wayne Buffett

Crop Insurance Commission
Box 6000, Fredericton, E3B 5H1

The Crop Insurance Commission of New Brunswick was established in 1974 under the *Crop Insurance Act.* The Commission is composed of seven crop producers, including a chairman, and typically meets six to eight times a year. The development of new crop insurance plans and the administration of existing insurance programs are the responsibility of the general manager and sales manager, along with five part-time field agents.

Crop insurance is offered on apples, strawberries, wheat, barley, oats, potatoes, beans, and Brussels sprouts for processing. The Commission is working towards making crop insurance available on other crops, and on maintaining a high level of service for insured farmers.

Chairman, Dennis Foreman
Gen. Manager, Paul Smith

New Brunswick Grain Commission
Box 6000, Fredericton, E3B 5H1
General Inquiries: (506) 453-2185

The New Brunswick Grain Commission was created in 1981 to administer the *Grain Act.*

The Commission is charged with the effective development of the N.B. grain industry. It promotes, controls, and regulates the production and marketing of grain and establishes quality standards. It regulates grain handling to ensure a dependable commodity for markets.

Membership in the Commission is composed of four producer members: one is appointed chairman and the other three represent the pedigreed seed trade, the feed industry, and the New Brunswick Dept. of Agriculture. Meetings are held six to eight times per year to discuss and review various programs which are prepared and administered by a general manager and a grain officer.

Implemented programs include the establishment of a grading system for grain, the identification of grain producers and dealers, the publication of a grains newsletter with advice on grain elevator operation and grain marketing, and the reviewing of federal and provincial policies related to grain.

Chairman, George T. Trueman
Sec.-Manager, Paul Smith

OFFICE OF THE AUDITOR GENERAL
Carleton Place, 6th Flr., Box 758
Fredericton, E3B 5B4
General Inquiries: (506) 453-2243
Auditor General, John S. Astle, F.C.A.
Dep. Auditor General, G.H. MacLeod, C.A.
Asst. Dep. Auditor General,
K.D. Robinson, C.A.
Audit Directors: P.E. Jewett, C.A.,
P.L. Vessey, C.A., M.W. Gill, C.M.A.

BOARD OF MANAGEMENT
Centennial Bldg., Fredericton, E3B 5H1

CHAIRMAN'S OFFICE
Chairman, The Hon. Gérald Clavette
Secretary to Board of Management,
E.L. MacKinnon

HUMAN RESOURCE ADMINISTRATION
Exec. Director, David Ferguson
Pensions and Insured Benefits
Director, Cyril Theriault
Employee Relations Services
Economic and Central Agency
Director, Harry Stirling
A/Social Director, David Pugh
Part II Director, David Pugh
Part III Director, Andrew Kitchen
Pay Equity Bureau Director, Vacant
Management Compensation
Director, John Cunningham
Human Resource Development
Director, Kevin Malone
Official Languages
Director, Bernard Poirier
Budgets Director, John St. Pierre
Management Improvement
Director, Don McCrea
HRIS Project
A/Director, Gail Wylie
Information Resource Director, Gerry Henry
Departmental Services
Chris Godbout

DEPARTMENT OF COMMERCE AND TECHNOLOGY
Centennial Bldg., Box 6000
Fredericton, E3B 5H1

MINISTER'S OFFICE
Minister, The Hon. Alfred Lacey

DEPUTY MINISTER'S OFFICE
Dep. Minister, L.S. Armstrong

Special Projects
Exec. Director, John Adams

**DEPARTMENTAL RESOURCES AND
ADMINISTRATIVE SERVICES BRANCH**
Director, Michael MacBride

Financial Programs Branch
Asst. Dep. Minister, G.S. Wheatley
Financial Analysis and Account Management
Director, Ken Hamilton
Regional Development and Small Industry
Director, Art Goodwin

SCIENCE AND TECHNOLOGY
Exec. Director, G.S. Wheatley
Planning and Agreements
A/Director, Dick Burgess
Science and Technology
Director, Bill Paterson

Industrial Development Branch
Asst. Dep. Minister, George Bouchard
Management Services
Director, Larry Marshall
Industry Services Director, Vacant
Trade and Investment Director, Jim Lovett
*NEW BRUNSWICK REGIONAL ECONOMIC
DEVELOPMENT COMMISSIONS*
*Economic Expansion Commission of the
Peninsula Inc.*
Box 940, Tracadie, E0C 2B0
Industrial Commissioner, Roland Cormier
Restigouche Industrial Commission Inc.
Box 825, Campbellton, E3N 3H3
Gen. Manager, Claude Lapointe
Chaleur Regional Industrial Commission Inc.
Box 640, Bathurst, E2A 3Z6
Industrial Commissioner, Don Bishop
Northwest Industrial Commission Inc.
Box 490, Edmundston, E3V 1J9
Industrial Commissioner, Rino Pelletier
Kent Industrial Commission Inc.
Box 490, Buctouche, E0A 1G0
Gen. Manager, Bernard Bourque
*Grand Falls Region Development
Commission Inc.*
139 Court St., Box 2754, Grand Falls, E0J 1M0
Industrial Commissioner, Clarence Surette
Miramichi Region Development Corp. Inc.
Stothart Bldg., Ste. 201, 295 Pleasant St.
Newcastle, E1V 1Y7
Gen. Manager, Ernest MacMillan
Capital Region Development Commission Inc.
618 Queen St., Fredericton, E3B 1C2
Gen. Manager, Linda Furlought
*Saint John Fundy Region Development
Commission Inc.*
15 Market Sq., Box 1971, Saint John, E2L 4L1
Gen. Manager, Bill Thompson
Moncton Industrial Development Ltd.
95 Foundry St., 4th Flr., Moncton, E1C 5H7
Gen. Manager, Peter Billiveau

Dieppe Industrial Park Ltd.
1067 Champlain St., Dieppe, E1A 1P9
Gen. Manager, Ferdinand Malenfant
South East Economic Commission Inc.
C.P. 578, Main St., Shediac, E0A 3G0
Industrial Commissioner, Raymond LeBlanc
*Carleton Regional Development
Commission Inc.*
Box 1929, Woodstock, E0J 2B0
Industrial Commissioner, Wayne Carpenter
*Greater Moncton Economic Development
Authority*
Central Trust Bldg., 860 Main St., Box 725
Moncton, E1C 1G2
Exec. Director, Arthur McDermott

AGENCIES, BOARDS AND COMMISSIONS

N.B. Research and Productivity Council
921 College Hill Rd., Box 20000
Fredericton, E3B 6C2

The Research and Productivity Council operates independently as an industrial research organization funded by contract work to private businesses and government. The Council's headquarters in Fredericton has an office-laboratory-engineering complex for problem solving, industrial research and development, techno-economic studies, and production engineering. Branch offices and subsidiary companies, such as Enhanced Recovery Systems Ltd. for mineral processing, are established as required.

RPC does research, engineering and consulting in the areas of product development, manufacturing technology, quality control, process innovations, renewable resource development, environmental protection, and analysis and testing. Services are available for clients in New Brunswick, elsewhere in Canada, and abroad.

Chairman, Knut Grotterod
Exec. Director, Dr. Roy Boorman
Applied Sciences Head, Dr. D. Abbott
Chemistry Department Head, Dr. Peter Silk
Electrochemistry Department
Dr. David Desjardins
Industry Services Head, Dr. Peter Lewell
Food Head, Dr. Gordon D. Brown
Food, Fisheries and Aquaculture
Head, Dr. Gordon B. Bacon
Mineral Development and Processing
Head, Dr. Michael Chalkley
Engineering Services
Head, Hugh Drummond
Engineering Materials Department
Head, Dr. Andrew Mitchell
Administration Head, Stephen Fox, C.A.
Library, Virginia Jackson
Comptroller, Stephen Fox, C.A.

Provincial Holdings Ltd.
Box 6000, Fredericton, E3B 5H1

Provincial Holdings Ltd. (PHL) is a Crown-owned corporation established to hold and administer the province's equity position in various companies. The agency is prepared to take an equity position in industrial enterprises wishing to locate in New Brunswick. The extent of the equity taken by PHL is negotiable and depends upon the various factors of each individual proposal.

In addition, PHL administers the Venture Capital Support Program whereby interest-free loans are provided to venture capital firms in order to encourage investment in N.B. companies.

Chairman, Hon. Alfred Lacey
Sec.-Treasurer, A.L. Barkhouse

DEPARTMENT OF EDUCATION
Box 6000, Fredericton, E3B 5H1

MINISTER'S OFFICE
Minister, The Hon. Shirley Dysart

DEPUTY MINISTER'S OFFICE
Dep. Minister, Earle W.H. Wood
Dep. Minister, Normand Martin

Finance and Support Services Division
A/Asst. Dep. Minister, J. Galvin
Finance and Services Director, J. Galvin
Human Resources Director, Simon Caron
Instructional Resources
Director, Gerald Breau

Educational Services Division — Anglophone
Asst. Dep. Minister, R.E. Elliott
Instruction
Exec. Director, Gerald Keilty
Student Services
Director, Marion Cosman
Program Development
Director, E.J. Owens
Professional Development and Evaluation
Exec. Director, R.J. Harvey
Professional Development
Director, B. Lydon
Evaluation Director, D. Hodgkinson
District Financial Services
Director, Ray Wilson

Services francophones d'éducation
Asst. Dep. Minister, A.-A. Pinet
Direction développement pédagogique
Directeur-exéc., N.-G. Bérubé
Développement des programmes d'études
Directeur, Keith Coughlan
Services aux élèves
Directeur, Pierre Dumas
Direction générale de l'évaluation
et du perfectionnement
Directeur-exéc., Robert Chouinard
Direction l'évaluation
Directeur, Sylvio Chenard
Service du perfectionnement professionel

Directeur, Eudore Lavoie
Services financiers aux districts
Directeur, Jean-Pierre Boudreau

DEPARTMENT OF FINANCE
Centennial Bldg., Fredericton, E3B 5H1
General Inquiry: (506) 453-2511

MINISTER'S OFFICE
Minister, The Hon. Allan Maher

DEPUTY MINISTER'S OFFICE
Dep. Minister, Ian D. MacBain
Administration
A/Director, Preston Hawkins
Tax Administration
Director, Glenn E. Kitchen
Taxation and Fiscal Policy
Exec. Director, Robert W. Kelly
Treasury and Debt Management
Exec. Director, Gerald MacGarvie
Statistics Agency Director, Clifford Marks

AGENCIES, BOARDS, COMMISSIONS AND CROWN CORPORATIONS

Lotteries Commission of New Brunswick

The Lotteries Commission of New Brunswick was established in 1976 under the *Lotteries Act* with the ongoing responsibility of formulating lottery policy for the province and of representing provincial interests in the Atlantic Lottery Corp. and the Interprovincial Lottery Corp.

The Commission also has the responsibility of regulating and licensing all other gaming, such as the operation of bingos, raffles, and casinos.

Chairman, The Hon. Allan E. Maher
Secretary, Brian Steeves

New Brunswick Municipal Finance Corp.
364 Argyle St., 520 King St.
Fredericton, E3B 5H1

The New Brunswick Municipal Finance Corporation was established by the *New Brunswick Municipal Finance Corporation Act,* R.S.N.B. 1982, Chapter N-6.2, which came into force on Feb. 1, 1983. The Corporation's purpose is to provide financing for municipalities and municipal enterprises.

The Corporation borrows money on the Canadian bond market with the guarantee of the Province of New Brunswick and then loans the money to the municipalities and municipal enterprises at the rate of interest paid by the Corporation.

The Corporation has marketed $184.5 million to July 31, 1988 for the municipalities.

Chairman, Ian D. MacBain
Sec.-Treasurer, Paul H. Inman

DEPARTMENT OF FISHERIES AND AQUACULTURE

King's Place, Box 6000, Fredericton, E3B 5H1

MINISTER'S OFFICE

A/Minister, Aldéa Landry

DEPUTY MINISTER'S OFFICE

Dep. Minister, Sylvestre McLaughlin
Administration
Exec. Director, J. Alfred Losier
Asst. Dep. Minister, Policy, Planning and Training, J.E.H. Légaré
Asst. Dep. Minister, Operations and Services, David H. MacMinn

AGENCIES, BOARDS AND COMMISSIONS

Fisheries Development Board

Box 6000, Fredericton, E3B 5H1

The Fisheries Development Board was created in 1978 pursuant to the *Fisheries Development Act, 1977.* Its purpose is to advise the Minister of Fisheries and Aquaculture on the granting of financial assistance to fishermen.

Such assistance can take the form of direct loans, guarantee of repayment of loans, guarantee of bonds or debentures, or forgiveable loans and grants. Financial assistance may be granted for such purposes as the construction or purchase of fishing vessels, gear, and equipment. Aquaculture and other fisheries development projects may be financed as the minister sees fit.

Chairman, Frank McLaughlin
Exec. Director, Yvon Belliveau

Information Systems
Director, Jean-Claude Haché
Vital Statistics
Registrar-Gen., Marianne Wiezel

Institutional Services Division

Asst. Dep. Minister, James Carter
Hospital Services Director, W. Waller
Nursing Home Services
Director, Ronald Crawford
Program Standards and Support Services
Director, Linda Jackson
Ambulance Services
Director, Carolyn MacKay

Insured Health Benefits Division

A/Asst. Dep. Minister, Pam Breau
Medicare Director, Don Chevarie
Prescription Drug Program
A/Director, Stephen Chase
Program Planning and Support
Director, Pamela Breau
Planning and Evaluation Division
Exec. Director, Laura Freeman

Community Services Division

Asst. Dep. Minister, Gérard Doucet
Public Health Services
Chief Medical Health Officer,
Dr. David Allison
Program Support Services
Director, Joy Haines Bacon
Community Services South
Exec. Director, Peter Alderman
Community Social Services North
Exec. Director, Bernard Paulin

DEPARTMENT OF HEALTH AND COMMUNITY SERVICES

Carleton Place, Box 5100
Fredericton, E3B 5G8
General Inquiries: (506) 453-2536

MINISTER'S OFFICE

Minister, The Hon. J. Raymond Frenette

DEPUTY MINISTER'S OFFICE

Dep. Minister, Jean-Guy Finn

MEDICAL DIVISION

Sr. Medical Advisor, Dr. Omer Doiron

Administration Division

Asst. Dep. Minister, Robert Gamble
Human Resources Director, Roger Arseneau
Financial Services Director, Brian Alexander
Communications Services
Director, Dave Gibbs
Construction Services
Director, Gerard LeBlanc

DEPARTMENT OF INCOME ASSISTANCE

Box 6000, Fredericton, E3B 5H1

MINISTER'S OFFICE

Minister, The Hon. Laureen Jarrett

DEPUTY MINISTER'S OFFICE

Dep. Minister, Mavis Hurley
Asst. Dep. Minister, Vacant
Planning and Evaluation
Director, Flora Jeane Kennedy
Corporate Services
Exec. Director, Michael O'Rourke

AGENCIES, BOARDS AND COMMISSIONS

Social Welfare Appeals Board

Box 6236, Saint John, E2L 4R7

The New Brunswick Social Welfare Appeals Board is a quasi-judicial tribunal created in 1970 under the *Social Welfare Act,* S.N.B. 1966, Chapter 27, to permit applicants and recipients to seek a review of a departmental decision.

The Appeals Board is the final step, after two internal administrative reviews, in a three-tiered appeal process. Required by its quasi-judicial nature to conduct hearings according to the rules of natural justice, the Board must provide a fair and unbiased assessment of the facts presented to it during a hearing.

The Appeals Board hears cases at the request of appellants relating to matters under the jurisdiction of the *Social Welfare Act* and Regulations initiated in the Department of Health and Community Services or the Department of Income Assistance. The Board may also investigate and report on any matter under the Act or Regulations that may be referred to it by the minister.

Appeals may be filed by an applicant or recipient under the following circumstances: application for assistance has been denied; financial assistance granted is insufficient or inappropriate; financial assistance has been discontinued or reduced; or there has been an unreasonable delay in making a decision which affects receipt of financial assistance.

The chairperson is required to convene a hearing within 30 days of receipt of an appeal. Hearings are conducted in an informal manner but procedures rigidly conform to the rules of natural justice. Each applicant is entitled to be accompanied by one person or to be represented by legal counsel or another individual acting on behalf of the appellant. The Department also sends its representative to the hearing. An appeal is always conducted by a chairperson and two board members. The decision of the Appeals Board is final and there can be no minority report.

The Regulations ensure that the Appeals Board shall be composed of a chairperson, two vice-chairpersons and not more than 16 members to be appointed by the Lieutenant-Governor in Council.

Chairperson, Patricia Donihee

DEPARTMENT OF INTERGOVERNMENTAL AFFAIRS
Box 6000, Fredericton, E3B 5H1

Dep. Minister, Francis McGuire
Asst. Dep. Minister, Intergovernmental Affairs, Donald Dennison
Asst. Dep. Minister, Intergovernmental Co-operation, Jean-Guy Vienneau

DEPARTMENT OF JUSTICE
Centennial Bldg., Box 6000
Fredericton, E3B 5H1
General Inquiries: (506) 453-7417

MINISTER'S OFFICE
Attorney General and Minister of Justice,
The Hon. James Lockyer, Q.C.

DEPUTY MINISTER'S OFFICE
Dep. Minister, Paul M. LeBreton, Q.C.

ADMINISTRATIVE SERVICES DIVISION
Exec. Director, Carolyn Lovely
Financial Services
A/Director, Duane Pond
Human Resources Services
Director, Jacques Nadeau
Research and Planning
Director, Zena Vigod

ATTORNEY GENERAL'S DIVISION
Law Reform Branch
Director, Basil Stapleton, Q.C.
Legislative Counsel, Elaine Doleman
Assoc. Legislative Counsel, Bruno Lalonde
Legal Services Branch
Director, Richard P. Burns
Public Prosecutions Branch
Director, Robert Murray
Asst. Directors of Public Prosecution:
Special Projects, Manubhai Patel
Family Law, Mary Elizabeth Beaton
Special Prosecutors:
Graham Sleeth, J.T. Keith McCormick

Justice Services Division
Asst. Dep. Minister, Robert L. Scammell
Consumer Affairs Branch
Consumer Affairs
Director, Jolène A. LeBlanc
Chief Rentalsman, Judy Budovitch
Credit Unions and Co-operatives
Director, Wallace Church
Corporate and Trust Affairs
Director, Charles McAllister
Insurance Branch
Sup't, Réginald Richard
Dep. Sup't, George Poirier
Registrar of Deeds Branch
Chief Registrar, R.J. Flemming

COURTS
(See judiciary listings)

LEGAL AID NEW BRUNSWICK
Director, Edward F. McGinley

EXPROPRIATIONS
Expropriations Advisory Officer, John Larlee
74 Roseberry Rd., Campbellton, E3N 2G7

DEPARTMENT OF LABOUR
Chestnut Complex, 470 York St.
Box 6000, Fredericton, E3B 5H1

MINISTER'S OFFICE
Minister, The Hon. Michael McKee

DEPUTY MINISTER'S OFFICE
Dep. Minister, John Roushorne

PLANNING AND ADMINISTRATION DIVISION
Exec. Director, Melbourne McGuigan
Planning and Evaluation Branch
Director, J. Michael O'Brien
Human Resource Services
Director, G.W. Stillwell
Finance and Accounting
Director, Kay Harding
Information Planning and Processing Services
Director, Stuart Oulton
Workers' Advocate (Saint John): (506) 658-2472

Technical and Inspection Services Division
Asst. Dep. Minister, Donald R. Boudreau
Building Inspection Branch
Director, Bill Hall
Mechanical Inspection Branch
Director, Dale Ross
Design Registration and Plans Review Branch
Director, Carroll Kimball
Technical and Engineering Support Branch
Director, Peter Fitzpatrick
Chief Elevator Inspector, Archibald Cameron
Chief Electrical Inspector, Calvin Duncan
Chief Plumbing Inspector, Fred Holland
Chief Structural Inspector, Vacant
Chief Motor Vehicle Inspector, Grant Harding
Chief Boiler Inspector, John Fowles

Labour Division
Asst. Dep. Minister, John Chenier
Conciliation and Mediation
Director, J. Armand Thomas
Labour Policy Branch Director, Vacant
Registrar of Pensions, Danielle Metivier
Employment Standards
Director, Maurice Boucher

Employment Division
Asst. Dep. Minister, Guy Thibodeau
Employment Development
Director, Mike McIntosh
Employment Adjustment Services
A/Director, Mike McIntosh
Manager, Lori Moran

AGENCIES, BOARDS AND COMMISSIONS

Board of Examiners for Compressed Gas
c/o Box 6000, Fredericton, E3B 5H1

The Board of Examiners consists of a chairman and at least four members drawn equally from management and labour. The members of the Gas Board are appointed for a term of three years.

The Board examines all persons applying for licences to: install heating equipment using compressed gas as a fuel source; operate a compressed gas delivery truck or filling station; or install compressed gas piping in a building. As well, the Board may suspend or cancel the licence of anyone guilty of an offence against the Boiler and Pressure Vessels Act or the Regulations.

Chairman, Dale Ross

Board of Examiners for Stationary Engineers
c/o Box 6000, Fredericton, E3B 5H1

The New Brunswick Boiler and Pressure Vessel Act, proclaimed in 1937, provides for the formation of a board of five first class stationary engineers. The Board's members represent the power plant industry, the pulp and paper industry, small heating plants, and the private sector. Under the Act, the Lieutenant-Governor in Council has the power to appoint boiler inspectors with first class stationary engineer licences as examiners.

Chairman, Dale Ross

Electrical Installation and Inspection Advisory Board
c/o Box 6000, Fredericton, E3B 5H1

The function of the Board is to advise the minister on all matters pertaining to the requirements of the Electrical Installation and Inspection Act.

The Act regulates the sale of appliance devices and machinery, and the installation of electrical equipment and lightning rods on or about a consumer's premises.

Appointees to the Board include the minister, the N.B. Electric Power Commission, the Fire Marshal, the Insurers' Advisory Organization of Canada (New Brunswick), the Electrical Contractors' Assn. of New Brunswick Inc., the Int'l Brotherhood of Electrical Workers, the Canadian Manufacturers' Assn., Professional Engineers of New Brunswick, Edmundston Power Commission and such other person or persons as the Lieutenant-Governor in Council considers advisable.

Chairman, Douglas Wilson

Employment Standards Tribunal
Box 6000, Fredericton, E3B 1B0

The Employment Standards Tribunal was established under the provisions of the Employment Standards Act which came into force on Dec. 1, 1985. The Tribunal consists of a chairman and two other members, one of whom is representative of employees while the other is representative of employers.

The Director of Employment Standards may investigate complaints concerning employment standards dealing with minimum wages, hours of work, vacations, notice of termination, prompt payment of wages, and other matters; and make orders directing compliance with the Act.

The function of the Tribunal is to conduct hearings to consider the director's orders when requested to do so by persons affected thereby. The Tribunal has exclusive jurisdiction to determine all questions of fact and law that arise in any matter before it. Decisions of the Tribunal are final except on grounds of an excess of jurisdiction or a denial of natural justice.

Chairman, Vacant
Vice-Chairman, Robert Basque
CEO, Ralph Boyd

Fishing Industry Relations Board
200 Prospect St., Box 908
Fredericton, E3B 1B0

The Fishing Industry Relations Board of New Brunswick is a quasi-judicial tribunal established under the *Fisheries Bargaining Act*. The Act, effective Sept. 15, 1982, applies to buyers, buyers' organizations, fishermen's organizations, councils of fishermen's organizations, and fishermen.

The Board deals with matters which include the certifying of fishermen's organizations which bargain collectively with buyers or buyers' organizations. It also deals with termination of bargaining rights; successor rights, as applied to either fishermen's organizations or to sales of businesses; complaints of unfair practices; and the accreditation of buyers' organizations.

Applications may be made for declarations of unlawful boycotts by fishermen or fishermen's organizations or by buyers or buyers' organizations, as the case may be. Consent to prosecute may be made, in addition to various referrals and miscellaneous applications.

Chairman, Vacant
Vice-Chairman, Vacant
CEO, Ralph Boyd
Secretary, Shara Golden

Human Rights Commission
Box 6000, Fredericton, E3B 5H1

The New Brunswick Human Rights Commission is the agency charged with the responsibility of enforcing the *New Brunswick Human Rights Code,* first passed by the New Brunswick Legislature in 1967.

This law prohibits discrimination in all aspects of employment, housing, public services, accommodations and facilities, advertising, property, and membership in professional, business or trade associations, on the basis of race, colour, religion, national origin, ancestry, place of origin, age (19 and over), physical disability, marital status, or sex. Persons claiming to be aggrieved are asked to contact any office located in Fredericton, Saint John, Campbellton, or Moncton. An officer will be assigned to the case and an investigation will begin immediately.

Chairman, Vacant
Education Director, Karen Taylor
Compliance Director, Janet Cullinan

Industrial Relations Board
200 Prospect St., Box 908
Fredericton, E3B 1B0

The Industrial Relations Board of New Brunswick is a quasi-judicial tribunal established under the provisions of the *Industrial Relations Act*. The Act applies to persons, trade unions, councils of trade unions, employers, and employer organizations.

The Board consists of a General and a Construction Division. The chairman of the board presides over the General Division, while the vice-chairman is responsible for the Construction Division. Employers and employees have equal representation in each division.

The Board addresses matters which pertain to the private sector of the economy as opposed to the public sector. Such matters include the certification of trade unions for the purpose of collective bargaining with the employer, termination of bargaining rights, successor rights as applied to trade unions and to sales of businesses, complaints of unfair practices, and the accreditation of employer organizations. In addition, applications may be made for declarations of unlawful strikes or lockouts.

Chairman, Weldon Graser, Q.C.
Vice-Chairmen:
Wallace Turnbull, Q.C., Thomas Kuttner
CEO, Ralph Boyd
Secretary, Shara Golden

Minimum Wage Board
c/o Box 6000, Fredericton, E3B 5H1

The Minimum Wage Board was established under the *Employment Standards Act*. It comprises a chairman and six members representing management and labour equally. Their mandate is to study and make recommendations to the Lieutenant-Governor in Council on matters dealing with the minimum wage, taking into account the social and economic effects of minimum wage rates in the province.

Chairman, R.P. Campbell
Secretary, Mrs. C. Sheppard

New Brunswick Workers' Compensation Board
1 Portland St., Box 160, Saint John, E2L 3X9

The *Workers' Compensation Act* of New Brunswick came into force on Jan. 2, 1919. The Act underwent many amendments in 1981 (loss of earnings concept) and in 1987 (restructuring of the board, i.e. part-time board members).

The New Brunswick Workers' Compensation Board governs and administers the Act to ensure that workers who are injured during the course of their employment receive the entitled benefits. In addition, the Board establishes an annual assessment to be levied against employers with three or more employees in each class of industry. The rates of assessment vary depending on the type of industry and the accident experience of each group. The Board also administers a 155-bed rehabilitation centre which is available to injured workers.

The Board reports to the Legislative Assembly through the Minister of Labour. Members are appointed by the Lieutenant-Governor in Council. The structure of the Corporate Board is as follows: one chairman who is chief executive officer, one vice-chairman who is the chief adjudicator of the

Appeals Board, four part-time board members representing employees, four part-time board members representing employers, and an ex officio board member who is the chairman of the Occupational Health and Safety Commission.

Chairman, Theo Gagnon
Vice-Chairman, Barbara L. Fulton
Exec. Director, Brian E.H. Baxter
Board Secretary, Alana M. Small
Director of Review Committee,
William E. McNulty
Director of Financial Services, Eric H. Rector
Director of Medical Services,
Dr. Eric D. McCartney
Director of Claims, C. Irvine Robertson
Director of Benefit Services, Andrew G. Rauska
Director of Vocational Rehabilitation,
L. Allan Cromwell
Director of Information Systems, Victor A. Morin
Workers' Rehabilitation Centre
Administrator, M. Dianne Ormandy

Plumbing Advisory Board
c/o Box 6000, Fredericton, E3B 5H1

The Plumbing Advisory Board advises the Minister of Labour on matters pertaining to the Plumbing Installation and Inspection Act. The Board recommends changes to the Act and its Regulations, adoption of plumbing codes and standards, and new applications of material and equipment. Its membership is representative of plumbing contractors, plumbers, consumer interest groups, and enforcing authorities.

Chairperson, Eileen Pike

DEPARTMENT OF MUNICIPAL AFFAIRS AND ENVIRONMENT
364 Argyle St., Box 6000
Fredericton, E3B 5H1
General Inquiries: (506) 453-3700

MINISTER'S OFFICE
Minister, The Hon. Vaughn Blaney

DEPUTY MINISTER'S OFFICE
Dep. Minister, Pierre Marquis

POLICY, ADMINISTRATION AND COMMUNICATIONS BRANCH
Exec. Director, Lowell Boyle
Planning and Program Evaluation
Manager, K.B. Marshall
Administrative Services
Manager, F. Gordon McLeod
Productivity Improvement and
Human Resource Development
Manager, Brian N. Mills
Communications Manager, Gerald Hill

Land and Water Use
Asst. Dep. Minister, Ronald E. Searles

ENVIRONMENTAL PROTECTION BRANCH
Director, David R. Silliphant
Air Quality Section Chief, James Knight
Industrial Wastes Section
Chief, James K.D. Hayden
Sanitary Engineering Section
Chief, R.G. Lutes
Toxic Substances Section
Chief, K.W. Browne
Petroleum Storage Management Section
Chief, Dr. W.J. Shaffner

ENVIRONMENTAL SCIENCES BRANCH
A/Director, W.C. Ayer
Environmental Quality Section
Chief, J.S. Choate
Scientific Studies and Analytical
Services Section
Co-ordinator, W.C. Ayer
Chief Inspector, David Williams

WATER RESOURCE PLANNING BRANCH
Director, Nabil Elhadi
Ground Water Section
Chief, Lawrence P. Peters
Surface Water Section
Chief, James Anderson

LAND USE PLANNING BRANCH
Director, T.J. Jellinek
Land and Water Use Planning
Co-ordinator, Dr. David I. Besner

Local Government Services Division
Asst. Dep. Minister, André Lanteigne
Assessment Branch
Exec. Director, E.A. Cronk
Local Government Administration Branch
Director, Gerald B. Hawkins
Emergency Measures Organization
Director, Jim O. Stith
Fire Marshal's Office
Fire Marshal, Medley Carr
Elections Branch
A/Chief Electoral Officer, Scovil Hoyt

AGENCIES, BOARDS AND COMMISSIONS

Environmental Council
Box 6000, Fredericton, E3B 5H1

Established in 1972 under the authority of the Clean Environment Act, R.S.N.B. 1971, Chapter 3, the Council advises the Minister of Municipal Affairs and Environment, studying, investigating, and reporting on appropriate matters at his request or with his approval. It also receives submissions and prepares an annual report for the legislature.

Under the Ecological Reserves Act, the Council advises the Minister of Natural Resources on ecological reserves.

Chairman, Dr. Louis LaPierre

Vice-Chairman, Donald S. Smith
Exec. Secretary, Gail Darby

Municipal Capital Borrowing Board
Carleton Place, Box 6000
Fredericton, E3B 5H1

The Municipal Capital Borrowing Board was established under the *Municipal Capital Borrowing Act* in 1963. Six members are appointed by the Lieutenant-Governor in Council. The chairman is the Deputy Minister of Municipal Affairs and Environment. The Board authorizes municipalities to borrow money for capital expense.

The Board may authorize a municipality to borrow money by way of a loan or an issue of debentures or to guarantee repayment of any loan or issue of debentures. Such Board authorization must be ratified by an order of the Lieutenant-Governor in Council.

The *Municipalities Act* limits the capital borrowing of a municipality to two per cent of its assessed valuation in any one year. Total borrowing must not exceed six per cent of the tax base. These restrictions do not apply to capital expenditures for water and sewer facilities, repayment of which is on a user-charge basis. However, authority to borrow capital for water and sewer services must be obtained from the Board and the Lieutenant-Governor in Council in the same manner as for other capital expenditures.

Chairman, Pierre Marquis
Secretary, Paul Inman

Provincial Municipal Council
108 Prospect St., Ste. 2, Fredericton, E3B 2T9

Incorporated in 1973, the Provincial Municipal Council is the agency which represents the interest of all municipalities in the province of New Brunswick on issues and problems of common concern. The Council consists of 12 municipal elected officials. It holds monthly meetings and provides direction to a secretariat in the follow-up of resolutions and requests to the provincial government to amend or introduce legislation affecting the general administration and financial responsibilities of all municipalities in the province. The provincial Minister of Municipal Affairs and Environment or his/her designate usually attends each meeting.

Chairman, Councillor Deborah R. Warren
Exec. Director, David W. Ellis

Provincial Planning Committee
Kings Place, Box 6000, Fredericton, E3B 5H1

The Provincial Planning Committee is appointed pursuant to the *Community Planning Act.* It consists of members, appointed by Order-in-Council, drawn from the departments of Municipal Affairs and Environment, Health and Community Services, Transportation, Agriculture, and Natural Resources and Energy.

The Committee is responsible for the following: approval of variances from the normal requirements of building, subdivision, and zoning regulations; approval of subdivisions outside municipal jurisdictions; recommendations to the Minister of Transportation for new public streets in subdivisions; approval of recreational type subdivisions fronting on non-designated highways or other accesses; and review of provincial regulations pertaining to the above and the recommendation of changes where necessary.

Chairman, Paul Rouse
Vice-Chairman, William Ayer

DEPARTMENT OF NATURAL RESOURCES AND ENERGY
Mailing Address:
Box 6000, Fredericton, E3B 5H1

MINISTER'S OFFICE
Minister, The Hon. Morris Green

DEPUTY MINISTER'S OFFICE
Dep. Minister, Bryan J. Walker

Asst. Dep. Minister, Forest Resources,
R.A. Redmond

Asst. Dep. Minister, Minerals and Energy,
Vacant

DEPARTMENTAL SUPPORT SERVICES BRANCH
Exec. Director, W. Alexander Pert
Financial Services
Director, Hayward C. Stewart
Human Resources Services
Director, Daryl O. Barr
Technical Services Director, D. Grant
Information Systems
Director, Lyndon Fairweather
Policy and Planning Branch
Exec. Director, R.S. Watson
Communication Section
A/Director, W. MacKenzie
Crown Lands Branch
Director, Dianne Kent-Gillis
Timber Management Branch
Director, M.D. MacFarlane
Forest Extension Services Branch
Director, Joakim Hermelin
Fish and Wildlife Branch
Exec. Director, Barry B. Meadows
Fish and Wildlife Law Enforcement
Director, Richard C. Monroe

MINERALS AND ENERGY DIVISION
Mineral Development Branch
Director, G.J. Greer
Recorder, V. Eugene Jackson
Geological Surveys Branch
Director, Dr. J. Leslie Davies
Energy Branch Director, Donald E. Barnett

DEPARTMENT OF THE SOLICITOR GENERAL

Centennial Bldg., Rm. 671
Fredericton, E3B 5H1

MINISTER'S OFFICE

Solicitor General, The Hon. Conrad Landry

Dep. Solicitor General, William B. Connor

Asst. Dep. Solicitor General, Grant S. Garneau

ADMINISTRATION DIVISION
A/Director, Bruce Jamieson
Financial Services
Director, Bruce Jamieson
Human Resources Director, Venia Peddie

CORRECTIONAL SERVICES DIVISION
Exec. Director, Ian R. Culligan
Institutions Director, James Tremblett
Community and Young Offenders Services
Director, Yves Boutot

POLICING SERVICES DIVISION
A/Director, Jay Clifford
Asst. Director/Chief Inspector, Jay Clifford
Gun Control
Chief Provincial Firearms Officer,
Harold Steeves
Sheriff-Coroners Division
Chief Sheriff-Coroner, John Evans
Dep. Chief Sheriff-Coroner, Peter Dickens

AGENCIES, BOARDS AND COMMISSIONS

New Brunswick Police Division
98 Prospect St. W.
Fredericton, E3B 2T8
Chairman, Hon. Justice Adrien J. Cormier
Exec. Director, Henry LeBlanc

Parole Board
Box 6000, Fredericton, E3B 5H1
Chairman, Daniel M. Hurley

DEPARTMENT OF SUPPLY AND SERVICES

Centennial Bldg., Box 6000
Fredericton, E3B 5H1
General Inquiries: (506) 453-2525

MINISTER'S OFFICE
Minister, The Hon. Bruce Smith

DEPUTY MINISTER'S OFFICE
Dep. Minister, Max Lewis
Special Projects, Dugald Richford
Finance and Administration
Exec. Director, Pauline Roy
Human Resources Director, Eric White
Finance Director, Richard Burnett

Departmental Services
Co-ordinator, Karen Rice
Central Records Supervisor, Patricia Moxon

Services
Asst. Dep. Minister, J.H. Fowler
Communications
Exec. Director, Fernand Lévesque
A/Director, Andre Carriere
Graphic Design Director, Naoto Kondo
Publications and Distribution
Director, Bill Hall
Printing Services
A/Manager, Weldon Carr
Mail Services Manager, Marty Forsythe
Systems and Technology Services
Exec. Director, Vacant
Client Services Manager, Tony Pavely
Special Projects Manager, Keith Murray
Consulting Services
Manager, Richard Dunphy
Training and Technology Transfer
Manager, Charles Chiasson
Data Centre Services
Exec. Director, Robert Ellis
Computer Operations Manager, Gary Andrews
Network and Office Systems
Director, Rod Mills
Technical Services
Director, Danny MacCallum
Database Administration
Manager, Don MacDonald
Technical Support Manager, Shirley Totten
Marketing Services
Director, John Cuthbert
Supply
Director, Kevin Burns
Purchasing Manager, Arnold Murray
Supervisor of Services, Gregory Hamilton
Central Stores Supervisor, Gary Chase

Buildings Division
Asst. Dep. Minister, Neil Coy
Support Services
Director, John A.M. Rutter
Design and Construction
Exec. Director, Paul Leger
Capital Planning (Hospitals)
Exec. Director, Doug Colwell
Facilities Management
Exec. Director, Gregory S. Cook
Properties Acquisition and Disposal
Director, Glen Trail

DEPARTMENT OF TOURISM, RECREATION AND HERITAGE

Box 12345, Fredericton, E3B 5C3
General Inquiries:
Tourism: (506) 453-2377
Sport and Recreation: (506) 453-2928
Culture: (506) 453-2555
Heritage: (506) 453-2324

Toll-free tourism information:
(out-of-province) 1-800-561-0123
(in-province) 1-800-442-4442
Fax: (506) 453-2416; Telex: 014-46230

MINISTER'S OFFICE
Minister, The Hon. Roland Beaulieu

DEPUTY MINISTER'S OFFICE
Dep. Minister, Paul J. Daigle
Asst. Dep. Minister, David W. Jennings
Asst. Dep. Minister, Vacant

ADMINISTRATION
Exec. Director, Lois J. Sandwith
Culture, Sport and Recreation
Exec. Director, Roger Levesque

SPORT AND RECREATION
Recreation Director, Donat Thériault
Sports Director, Suzanne Mason
Community and Regional Development
Director, Laureat Thériault

RESEARCH AND PLANNING
Exec. Director, Dean Mundee
Research and Evaluation
Director, Evelyn Briggs
Policy Planning Director, William Leonard

PROVINCIAL PARKS AND HISTORIC SITES
Exec. Director, A.P. Peterson
Field Services Director, Wayne Burley
Historic Sites and Museums
Director, Karen Mann
Provincial Archaeologist,
Dr. Christopher Turnbull
DISTRICT TOURISM OFFICES:
Box 639, Campbellton, E3N 3H1
Dist. Manager, Clayton Allison
270 Dalton Ave., Newcastle, E1V 3C4
Dist. Manager, Rhéal Savoie
Sub-Post Office 13, Riverview, E1B 1R0
Dist. Manager, Gilles Pelletier
Box 3637, Saint John, E2M 4Y2
Dist. Manager, Lee French
Mactaquac Provincial Park
R.R. 1, Mouth of Keswick, E0H 1N0
Dist. Manager, Bob Armstrong
Box 180, St. Jacques, E0L 1K0
Dist. Manager, Regis Daigle

DEVELOPMENT
Exec. Director, D. John Archibald
Regional Development
Director, Gordon Smith
Business Services
Director, Ronald Loughrey

MARKETING
Information Services
Director, Hazen T. Gorman
Advertising and Communications

Director, Rod Cunningham
Market Development
Director, Paul-Emile Thériault

CULTURAL DEVELOPMENT
Director, John Saunders
PROVINCIAL ARCHIVES
Provincial Archivist, Marion Beyea

NEW BRUNSWICK LIBRARY SERVICE
Director, Jocelyne LeBel
REGIONAL LIBRARIES:

Albert-Westmorland-Kent Regional Library
Box 708, Moncton, E1C 8M9
Reg. Librarian, Claude Potvin

Bibliothèque régionale du haut Saint-Jean
50 Queen St., Edmundston, E3V 3M4
Reg. Librarian, Guy LeFrançois

Chaleur Regional Library
Box 607, Campbellton, E3N 3H1
Reg. Librarian, G. Chiasson

Saint John Regional Library
One Market Sq., Saint John, E2L 4Z6
Reg. Librarian, M.E. Travis

York Regional Library
4 Carleton St., Fredericton, E3B 5P4
Reg. Librarian, Katherine LeButt

NEW BRUNSWICK MUSEUM
277 Douglas Ave., Saint John, E2K 1E5
Director, Vacant

KING'S LANDING HISTORICAL SETTLEMENT
Box 522, Fredericton, E3B 5R5

Chairman, David W. Jennings
A/Gen. Manager, Greg Finley

VILLAGE HISTORIQUE ACADIEN
C.P. 820, Caraquet, E0B 1K0
Director, Jean-Yves Thériault

AGENCIES, BOARDS AND COMMISSIONS

Fredericton Military Compound Board

The Military Compound Board was established by Order-in-Council in 1966, and is charged with the restoration, preservation, and use of the former British military buildings within the compound, which takes up two central downtown blocks. The Board is also responsible for the overall administration of the compound.

The original remaining structures in the compound are the Officers' Quarters (1851), the Militia Arms Store (1832), the Soldiers' Barracks (1827), and the Guard House (1828). These buildings are owned by the Province and have been declared of national significance by the Historic Sites and Monuments Board of Canada. The Military Compound Board also has administrative responsibility for a more recent structure, the John Thurston Clark Memorial Building (1881), which houses the Fredericton National Exhibition Centre and the

New Brunswick Sports Hall of Fame.
Chairman, David W. Jennings
Sec.-Treasurer, Karen Mann

New Brunswick Film Classification Board
110 Charlotte St., G12, Box 5001
Saint John, E2L 4Y9

Director and Chairman, Edward H. Bringloe

DEPARTMENT OF TRANSPORTATION
Kings Place, 2nd Flr., Box 6000
Fredericton, E3B 5H1

MINISTER'S OFFICE

Minister, The Hon. Sheldon Lee

DEPUTY MINISTER'S OFFICE
Dep. Minister, David L. Seheult
Human Resources Branch
Director, Paul Theriault
Personnel Officer, Herbert Thompson

ASSISTANT DEPUTY MINISTER'S OFFICE
Asst. Dep. Minister and Chief Engineer,
Lyle W. Smith

ENGINEERING SERVICES
Exec. Director, Keith Hicks
Design Branch Director, Herb Page
Asst. Directors: James Knox, Guy Doiron
Right of Way Branch
Director, Malcolm V. MacFadyen
Asst. Director, Paul Nicholson
Traffic Engineering Branch
Director, Gerald Goguen
Planning Branch Director, Paul E. Rouse
Asst. Directors: Brian McEwing, Charles French

OPERATIONS
Exec. Director, James C. Fraser
Structures Branch
Director, Garth A. Rushton
Asst. Directors: George Dayton, Kent Calhoun
Highway Construction Branch
Director, Malcolm S. McInnis
Asst. Directors: William Hicks, Ken Lawson
Soils and Materials Branch
Director, Gerard Keenan
Technical Services Branch
Director, Donald F. Hallet
Asst. Directors: Henry Palmer, John Mossman
Safety Co-ordinator, Kenneth Hall
Communications
System Operation, John W. Palmer

ADMINISTRATION AND POLICY
Exec. Director, R. Douglas MacIntosh
Administration Branch
Director, Douglas B. Stillwell
Admin. Supervisor, Vacant

Accounting Supervisor, Lloyd Penney
Information Systems
Co-ordinator, Emilia Sousa
Transportation and Communications Policy
Director, Walter Steeves
Asst. Director, Gilbert Oldham

MOTOR VEHICLE BRANCH
Registrar of Motor Vehicles, Douglas H. Seely
Vehicle Licensing and Registration
Supervisor, Tom Walton
Highway Safety and Driver Records
Supervisor, Claude Cyr

VEHICLE MANAGEMENT
Exec. Director, Antoine Richard
Asst. Directors: George Caissie, George Burtt

AGENCIES, BOARDS AND COMMISSIONS

Corporation Securities Registration
Provincial Bldg., 110 Charlotte St.
Saint John, E2L 2J4

Corporation Securities Registration is a filing and registration facility for every mortgage or charge created by a corporation in New Brunswick.

Registrar, Donne W. Smith, Jr.

License Suspension Appeal Board
Kings Place, 5th Flr., Box 6000
Fredericton, E3B 5H1

The License Suspension Appeal Board is a quasi-judicial tribunal provided for under section 311 (1) of the *Motor Vehicle Act,* and is set up to hear applications for remissions of licence suspensions under section 312, subject to subsection 7 of the *Motor Vehicle Act.*

The heaviest workload of the Board is eased by granting single member hearings whereby applications are processed and mailed directly from the chairman's office to the concerned board members. Single member hearings are given by four members of the Board in their respective districts: Edmundston, Moncton, Grande-Anse, and Saint John.

Single member hearings are granted for loss of licences under the *Motor Vehicle Act,* section 300, and for first offenders under three sections of the *Criminal Code* (234, 235 and 236). All Board sittings are held in Fredericton during the third week of each month.

The driving records of applicants brought before the Board show major infractions such as: impaired driving, two or more suspensions, or a previous reinstatement by the License Suspension Appeal Board.

Chairman, Edmond Landry

New Brunswick Motor Carrier Board
Provincial Bldg., 110 Charlotte St.
Saint John, E2L 2J4

The New Brunswick Public Utilities Board also constitutes the Motor Carrier Board. This Board is responsible for the regulation and licensing of all for-hire carriers in the province of New Brunswick, both intra- and extra-provincially.

Chairman, David C. Nicholson
Vice-Chairman, Antonio J. Robichaud, Q.C.
Secretary, Donne W. Smith, Jr.
Asst. Secretary, D.W. Sanders
Commissioners: J. Edward Murphy, Q.C.,
Lloyd McAllister, Paul F. Kierstead,
A. Edison Stairs, Aurele Young

New Brunswick Public Utilities Board
Provincial Bldg., 110 Charlotte St.
Saint John, E2L 2J4

The Board and chairman are appointed by the Lieutenant-Governor in Council and by virtue of their appointment are also members of the Motor Carrier Board.

The Public Utilities Board has general supervision over all public utilities in New Brunswick. In practice, the Board regulates the New Brunswick Telephone Co. Ltd., auto insurance rates, and a small gas and electric utility. New Brunswick Power is exempt from regulation.

The *Pipe Line Act* also comes under the Board's jurisdiction, but to date the Board has had no occasion to take action regarding this Act. *(The list of officers and members of this board is identical to that of the Motor Carrier Board.)*

New Brunswick Transportation Authority
Kings Place, Rm. 282, Box 6000
Fredericton, E3B 5H1

The New Brunswick Transportation Authority is a provincial Crown corporation established by the New Brunswick *Transportation Authority Act,* 1972. The purposes of the Authority are as follows:

a) to promote, develop, maintain, operate, and manage transportation terminals in the province;

b) to develop and encourage the development of services associated with transportation terminals; and

c) to carry out any directions given by the Lieutenant-Governor in Council with respect to transportation terminals and services.

Chairman, David L. Seheult
Vice-Chairman, R. Douglas MacIntosh

Securities Act
Provincial Bldg., 110 Charlotte St.
Saint John, E2L 2J4

The administrator of the *Securities Act* licenses the investment dealers, brokers, and salesmen who deal with the public in New Brunswick and investigates complaints to determine any fraudulent practices. The administrator may refer any appeal or investigation to the Public Utilities Board.

All public offerings of securities are cleared by a certificate of registration issued by the administrator.

Administrator, Donne W. Smith, Jr.

Unsatisfied Judgment Fund
Box 6000, Fredericton, E3B 5H1

The New Brunswick Unsatisfied Judgment Fund is a motor vehicle claims fund administered by the Motor Vehicle Division of the Department of Transportation under the authority of the New Brunswick *Motor Vehicle Act.* The fund compensates innocent victims of motor vehicle accidents occurring in New Brunswick in which responsibility for damages rests with the uninsured party.

Liability is determined after an investigation, either through admission of responsibility on the part of the uninsured person or through legal action.

Claims for both personal injury and property damage are eligible for payment and funding is provided from a designated portion of each driver licence fee and recoveries from the responsible uninsured parties.

Administrator, Elaine Patton

INDEPENDENT AGENCIES, BOARDS, COMMISSIONS AND CROWN CORPORATIONS

Alcoholism and Drug Dependency Commission of New Brunswick
65 Brunswick St., Box 6000
Fredericton, E3B 5H1
General Inquiries: (506) 453-2136

The Alcoholism and Drug Dependency Commission of New Brunswick was established by a provincial Order-in-Council in February 1978 to oversee the development of treatment and rehabilitation programs for individuals suffering from any forms of alcoholism or other drug dependencies.

Under the direction of a chairman and a 10-member board of commissioners drawn from all areas of the province, the Commission has established or maintained treatment and rehabilitation facilities for men and women in all regions of the province. As part of this service, the Commission provides out-patient counselling for clients not requiring in-patient treatment in any of the 196 beds around the province.

A Community Services Division provides guidance for all programs of an educational or preventive nature. This service incorporates such areas as employee assistance programs, justice intervention, courses for individuals convicted of impaired driving, and programs for special interest groups which deal with specific concerns of women, disabled persons, youth, or elderly persons in the substance abuse field.

The Support Services Division is made up of all programs identified as complementary to the Commission's role in the province and includes administration, finances, personnel, training, research, and public relations.

Minister responsible,
The Hon. J. Raymond Frenette
Chairman, Dr. G. Everett Chalmers, O.C.
Exec. Director, Joseph E. MacIntyre
Community Services
Program Director, D. Achille Maillet
Treatment Services
Program Director, Ronald J. McHugh
Support Services
Program Director, Wayne Weagle
FREDERICTON REGION
Co-ordinator, Gordon Skead
Victoria Treatment Centre
15 Woodstock Rd., Box 6000
Fredericton, E3B 2H4
Head Nurse, Joan Burt
EDMUNDSTON REGION
Co-ordinator, Luc St. Laurent
Edmundston Treatment Centre
62 Queen St., Edmundston, E3V 1A1
Head Nurse, Carol Le Blanc-Moreau
BATHURST REGION
Co-ordinator, Aurèle Doucet
Bathurst Regional Office
350 St. George St., Bathurst, E2A 1B9
Tracadie Treatment Centre
St. Joseph's Hospital, Box 700
Tracadie, E0C 2B0
Head Nurse, Jeanne d'Arc Comeau, R.N.
Campbellton Treatment and Rehabilitation Centre
31 Prince William St., Campbellton, E3N 1X5
Centre Director, Roger McRae
MONCTON REGION
Co-ordinator, Reg Evans
Moncton Treatment Centre
125 Mapleton Rd., Moncton, E1C 9G6
Head Nurse, Moril Leger, R.N.
Newcastle Treatment Centre
675 King George Hwy., Newcastle, E1V 1N9
Centre Director, Terry McEachreon
Head Nurse, Rosemary Cincurak
SAINT JOHN REGION
Co-ordinator, Patrick Donahoe
Ridgewood Treatment and Rehabilitation Centre
Box 3566, Stn. B, Saint John West, E2M 4Y1
Centre Director, Patrick Donahoe
Lonewater Farm
R.R. 2, Westfield, E0G 3J0
Centre Director, Edwin A. Thomas

Civil Service Commission

Box 6000, Fredericton, E3B 5H1

The Civil Service Commission is appointed pursuant to the New Brunswick *Civil Service Act* of 1984. It consists of a full-time chairman and two part-time commissioners.

The Commission is an independent agency accountable to the Legislative Assembly. It ensures that the merit principle is preserved in all civil service staffing activities and audits adherence to the *Civil Service Act.* It hears appeals and conducts investigations arising from staffing processes. The Commission submits an annual report to the Legislative Assembly.

Chairman, Jean-Paul LeBlanc
Staffing Audits and Administration
Director, F.J. MacKinley

Comptroller, Office of the

Box 6000, Fredericton, E3B 5H1

Pursuant to the *Financial Administration Act,* the Comptroller is required: (a) to co-ordinate the central processing and accounting activities for all financial transactions of the Province and to prepare financial information reports thereon for the Minister of Finance; and (b) to provide independent assurance that management systems, procedures, and internal controls operate economically and efficiently, and that program results are achieved through effective compliance with established legislative authority, policies, plans, and regulations.

Comptroller, Carol E.A. Loughrey
Asst. Comptroller, Edward L. Mehan

Liquor Licensing Board

191 Prospect St., Box 20264
Fredericton, E3B 5V3
General Inquiries: (506) 453-3728

The Liquor Licensing Board was established on April 1, 1976 under the *Liquor Control Act,* Chapter L-10, R.S.N.B. 1973. The Board holds hearings for applicants seeking permanent liquor licences, issues and controls temporary permits and special events licences, issues waiter's licences, and holds hearings for alleged violations of the Act. It is also responsible for the identification card program.

The staff of the Board regularly inspects licensed premises to ensure compliance with the Act and Regulations. A pre-investigation program informs people of the requirements for particular types of licences.

Minister responsible, The Hon. Allan Maher

Chairman, Wendell J. Firlotte
Exec. Director and Secretary to the Board,
Mrs. Georgette Roy
Administrator, Bruce Currie
Inspection and Investigations
Director, John L. Clifford

New Brunswick Coal Ltd.

Box 520, Minto, E0E 1J0

New Brunswick Coal Limited, incorporated in 1969, is engaged in the exploration and mining of bituminous coal in and around the area of Chipman and Minto in central New Brunswick.

The company's strip mining process uses large earth-moving draglines and associated heavy equipment to expose the coal seams lying about 22.5 metres below the surface.

The coal is sold almost entirely to the province's utility, New Brunswick Power, where it fuels thermal generating stations at Dalhousie and Grand Lake.

President and Gen. Manager, Andy Cormier
Mine Administrator, Paul Rollins
Office Administrator, Armand Caterini
Controller, Neil DuPlessis
Asst. Controller, Mark Jardine

New Brunswick Forest Products Commission

Hugh John Flemming Forestry Centre
Core Section, Ste. 215, Box 6000
Fredericton, E3B 5H1

The object of the New Brunswick Forest Products Commission is to expand markets and secure equitable prices for both producers and consumers of purchased primary forest products — especially pulpwood and logs. The Commission has a dual role: (1) to oversee the marketing relationships between consumers and producers of primary forest products produced from private woodlots; and (2) to oversee the establishment and operation of forest products marketing boards in rather the same way that the *Companies Act* oversees the operations of companies.

The Commission was established in 1971 under the *Forest Products Act.* It has broad powers of investigation and reports directly to the Minister of Natural Resources and Energy. It also has the power and authority of the N.B. Farm Products Marketing Commission under the *Farm Products Marketing Act* when the regulated product is any natural product of the forest. Annual agreements between producers and processors concerning forest fibre are negotiated under this Act.

Seven forest products marketing boards (which are independent organizations) now represent all of the 34,000 private woodlot owners in the province. Private woodlot ownership represents 30 per cent of the source of supply of this province's forest fibre resources. All of the 10 major forest industries and many of the approximately 100 smaller forest industries depend, in part, upon wood supplied by these forest products marketing boards. In addition, approximately 150 other wood-using mills depend on the private-woodlot sector for their wood supply. The annual value of fibre from this sector exceeds $90 million.

Chairman, R.L. Bishop
Secretary, J. Ian MacDonald

New Brunswick Housing Corp.

Box 611, Fredericton, E3B 5B2

A Crown corporation established in 1967, the New Brunswick Housing Corporation administers the *New Brunswick Housing Act.*

The Corporation is the provincial policy development and implementation agency for residential housing programs, maintaining nine regional offices throughout the province. All programs offered are directed to low-income households and include loans for home improvement, loans for the construction or purchase of basic shelter units, subsidized rental housing, and administration of non-profit and rent supplement programs. Many of the programs delivered by the Corporation are cost-shared with the federal housing agency, Canada Mortgage and Housing Corp.

Minister and Chairman, The Hon. Peter Trites
President and CEO, Georgio Gaudet
Vice-president, Operations, R. Murray
Vice-president, Finance and Administration, R.E. Naugler
Planning and Research
Exec. Director, R. Macdonald

New Brunswick Liquor Corp.

Box 20787, Fredericton, E3B 5B8

The New Brunswick Liquor Corporation operates 76 retail liquor outlets which sell all spirits, wine, and beer for off-premise consumption as a beverage.

The purpose of the Corporation, as identified in the New Brunswick *Liquor Corporation Act,* is to "carry on the general business of manufacturing, buying, importing, and selling liquor of every kind and description." The Corporation is not responsible for licensing and control functions.

Chairman, B.L. Kinney
Gen. Manager, Roger J.E. Landry
Asst. Gen. Manager, Finance, Administration, and Human Resources, D.J. Dorcas
Asst. Gen. Manager, Operations, Ralph Hicks

New Brunswick Police Commission

98 Prospect St., Fredericton, E3B 2T8

The New Brunswick Police Commission is mandated to promote the prevention of crime, the efficiency of police services, and the development of effective policing within the province. Toward this end, Commission staff are involved in assessing the adequacy of police departments through a system of studies and inspections. Recommendations with regard to manpower needs, training requirements, facilities, equipment, etc. are made by the Commission.

The Commission is also involved in the handling of citizen complaints against police officers within the province. The Commission may investigate complaints received by it or refer the complaint to the appropriate chief of police (or commanding officer of the RCMP) for investigation and appropriate disciplinary action, if necessary. Where the Commission is not satisfied with the investigation conducted by the chief of police or the commanding officer, it may conduct its own investigation into the incident.

The Commission is also involved in the establishment of minimum training standards for the appointment and promotion of police officers within municipal and regional police forces.

Chairman, Hon. Justice Adrien J. Cormier
Exec. Director, Henry E. LeBlanc

New Brunswick Power

515 King St., Fredericton, E3B 4X1
General Inquiries: (506) 458-4444
Telex: 014-46285; Twx: 506-458-4390

New Brunswick Power is a publicly owned provincial Crown corporation established in 1920 under the *Electric Power Act* passed by the provincial legislature (revised in 1973). The Act's stated objective is "to provide for the continuous supply of energy, adequate for the needs and future development of New Brunswick and to promote economy and efficiency in the generation, distribution, supply, sale, and use of power."

N.B. Power currently serves more than 297,000 customers and employs over 2,400 employees. Total assets of over $2.8 billion include over 3.1 million kilowatts of installed capacity from 14 generating facilities located throughout the province. A 630-megawatt CANDU generating unit was placed in commercial operation early in 1983.

Major interconnections with neighbouring utilities in Quebec, Nova Scotia, P.E.I., and New England provide increased reliability and an opportunity for energy transactions.

Chairman, The Hon. Rayburn Doucett
President, A.J. O'Connor
Exec. Vice-President, F.C. MacLoon
Administration
Sr. Vice-President, R.A. Toner
Operations
Sr. Vice-President, G.L. Titus
Vice-President, Legal, and Secretary,
P.J. Dykeman
Corporate Economic Studies
Director, F.H. Ryder
Finance
Vice-President, K.B. Little
Public Affairs and Marketing
Director, T.S. Thompson, Ph.D.

New Brunswick Well Drilling Advisory Board

109 Pitt St., Saint John, E2L 2W2

The New Brunswick Well Drilling Advisory Board has been set up under the Water Well Regulation of the *Clean Environment Act* to advise the minister on the administration of that Regulation. In operation since 1973, it has been involved in making several changes to the Regulations and clarifying important practical points of interest to the New Brunswick water well industry. It is composed of nine people of whom five are department representatives, three are drillers, and one is a member at large.
Minister responsible, The Hon. Vaughn Blaney

Chairman, J. Saab

Occupational Health and Safety Commission

Box 6000, Fredericton, E3B 5H1
General Inquiries: (506) 453-2467

The Occupational Health and Safety Commission administers the *Occupational Health and Safety Act* and its Regulations. The objective is to eliminate health and safety hazards in the workplace and to reduce the frequency and severity of occupational accidents.

The Commission's policies and priorities are determined by a seven-person corporate board. The chairman represents government, three members represent workers, and three represent employers. The powers and responsibilities of the corporate board and the Commission are defined in the *Occupational Health and Safety Commission Act.*
Minister responsible, The Hon. Michael McKee

Chairperson and CEO,
Madeleine Delaney-LeBlanc
Health and Safety Services
Director, R. Brian Connell
Policy, Planning, and Administration
Director, Bryan M. Whitfield

Public Service Labour Relations Board

Box 146, Fredericton, E3B 4Y2

The Public Service Labour Relations Board administers, among other things, a system of collective bargaining in the public service of New Brunswick. Its responsibilities include all facets of certification, negotiation, conciliation, arbitration, and the adjudication of grievances affecting employees of the New Brunswick government, its agencies, public schools, and hospitals. Separate employers under the law are New Brunswick Power, the New Brunswick Liquor Corp., and the Workers' Compensation Board.

Chairman, Douglas Stanley
Vice-Chairman, Donald MacLean
Sr. Exec. Officer, Ralph Boyd
Secretary to the Board, Shara L. Golden

Regional Development Corp.

377 York St., Box 428, Fredericton, E3B 5R4
General Inquiries: (506) 453-2277

The Regional Development Corporation is a provincial Crown corporation which plans, negotiates, administers, and co-ordinates the implementation of all subsidiary agreements under the Economic Regional Development Agreement. It was signed in 1984 between the Province of New Brunswick and the Government of Canada which was represented by the Department of Regional Economic Expansion.

The administration of these subsidiary agreements involves co-chairing management committees with federal representatives, as well as maintaining financial control. Line departments usually implement individual projects sponsored by the agreements, but the Corporation retains considerable responsibility for financing.

The Corporation also administers and implements such activities as the Community Adjustment program, the Kouchibouguac Area Socio-Economic Adaptation program, and the Development Assistance program.

Gen. Manager, K.C. Scott
Asst. Gen. Manager, William Mallory
Exec. Officer, Elsie Gardner

Bathurst Office
Box 20, Bathurst, E2A 3Z1
Exec. Director, Charles-Edouard Landry

Richibucto Office
Box 5001, Richibucto, E0A 2M0
Research and Planning Officer, Donald Savoie

JUDICIARY AND JUDICIAL OFFICERS

Court of Appeal

Justice Bldg.
Box 6000, Fredericton, E3B 5H1
General Inquiries: (506) 453-2452

Chief Justice of New Brunswick:
The Hon. Stuart G. Stratton

Judges (in order of seniority):
The Hon. Jean-Claude Angers
The Hon. William L. Hoyt
The Hon. Robert C. Rice
The Hon. Lewis C. Ayles
The Hon. Patrick A.A. Ryan

A/Registrar: A.M. DiGiacinto, Q.C.
Deputy Registrars: L.C. Dubé, Barbara Baird

Court of Queen's Bench of New Brunswick

(Composed of the Judges of the Trial Division and Family Division)

Box 5001, Moncton, E1C 8R3
General Inquiries: (506) 453-2452

Chief Justice: The Hon. Guy André Richard

Judges (in order of seniority):
The Hon. Adrien J. Cormier (Moncton)*
The Hon. David Masterson Dickson
  (Fredericton)*
The Hon. John Paul Barry (Saint John)*
The Hon. Claudius Ignatius de Loyola Leger
  (Moncton)*
The Hon. Ronald Charles Stevenson
  (Fredericton)
The Hon. Bernard Jean (Bathurst)
The Hon. Hugh Edward Montgomery
  (Fredericton)
The Hon. Richard Laurence Miller (Moncton)
The Hon. William Lawrence Marven Creaghan
  (Fredericton)*
The Hon. Robert J. Higgins (Saint John)
The Hon. Joseph Z. Daigle (Edmundston)
  —Family Division
The Hon. J. Turney Jones (Saint John)
The Hon. Rodman E. Logan (Saint John)
The Hon. Jacques Sirois (Edmundston)
The Hon. Guy Boisvert (Bathurst)
The Hon. Alexandre Deschenes (Bathurst)
The Hon. John Turnbull (Saint John)
The Hon. Raymond Guerette (Saint John)

The Hon. David Russell (Fredericton)
The Hon. Paul Creaghan (Moncton)
The Hon. J. Alfred Landry (Moncton)
The Hon. Margaret Larlee (Campbellton)
The Hon. Hugh H. McLellan (Woodstock)
The Hon. Roger Savoie (Moncton)
The Hon. Thomas W. Riordon (Newcastle)

A/Registrar: A.M. DiGiacinto
Deputy Registrars: L.C. Dubé, Barbara Baird
Director of Court Services (Family Division):
  Barbara Baird

BANKRUPTCY
Box 6000, Fredericton, E3B 5H1
Registrars: A.M. DiGiacinto, Ashwin Mehta,
  L.C. Dubé, Barbara Baird

PROBATE COURT OF NEW BRUNSWICK
(Judges of the Court of Queen's Bench are *ex officio* Judges of the Probate Court.)
A/Registrar: A.M. DiGiacinto
Deputy Registrars: L.C. Dubé, Barbara Baird

Judges of the Provincial Court

Chief Judge: The Hon. H. Hazen Strange
  Box 94, Oromocto, E2V 2G4

Associate Chief Judge:
  The Hon. J. Frederic Arsenault
  Box 5001, Bathurst, E2A 1E1

Judges (in order of seniority):
The Hon. Henry J. Murphy (Moncton)
The Hon. Ian P. Mackin (Richibucto)
The Hon. Douglas E. Rice (St. Stephen)
The Hon. Gaetan S. Bertrand (Tracadie)
The Hon. Frederic S. Taylor (Saint John)
The Hon. Thomas M. Bell (Saint John)
The Hon. James McNamee (Saint John)
The Hon. James D. Harper (Fredericton)
The Hon. George Perusse (Edmundston)
The Hon. C. Blake Lynch (Fredericton)
The Hon. Jacques Desjardins (Grand Falls)
The Hon. Camille Dumas (Bathurst)
The Hon. Andrew Stymiest (Newcastle)
The Hon. J. Robert Martin (Newcastle)
The Hon. William Cockburn (Fredericton)
The Hon. Roger McIntyre (Moncton)
The Hon. Patricia Cumming (Woodstock)
The Hon. Gladys J. Young (Campbellton)
The Hon. Murray F. Cain (Hampton)
The Hon. Paul J. Thériault (Moncton)
The Hon. Gerald Casey (Saint John)

---

* Supernumerary

Director of Provincial Court Services:
Anne McKay

Judicial Officials

BATHURST (Gloucester County)
Court House, E2A 3Y9
Clerk of Probate: R. Grégoire Boudreau
Clerk of Court: R. Grégoire Boudreau
Administrator (Family Division):
Donald Arsenault
Regional Sheriff (Campbellton):
Walter Thompson
Sheriff: Edgar Aubé
A/Registrar of Deeds: Lilianne Boudreau

CAMPBELLTON (Restigouche County)
Court House, E3N 3G9
Clerk of Probate: Lucien LeBlanc
Clerk of Court: Lucien LeBlanc
Administrator (Family Division):
Lucien LeBlanc
Sheriff: W.R. Thompson
Registrar of Deeds: Murielle Charest

EDMUNDSTON (Madawaska and Victoria
Counties)
Box 5001, E3V 3L3
Clerk of Probate: George Thériault
Clerk of Court: George Thériault
Administrator (Family Division):
George Thériault
District Sheriff: Bertrand LeBrun
Deputy Sheriffs: Gerald Plourde,
Gerald Chouinard
Registrar of Deeds: Gisèle Toussaint

FREDERICTON (York, Sunbury & Queens
Counties)
Justice Bldg., E3B 4Y1
Clerk of the Court: Ashwin Mehta
Administrator (Family Division):
Janet McIntosh
Chief Sheriff/Coroner: John Evans
Deputy Chief Sheriff/Coroner: Peter Dickens
Sheriff: Vaughan Fraser
Registrars of Deeds:
Eileen Ames (York County)
I.V. Scott (Sunbury County)
Marilyn Scott (Queens County)

Clerk of Probate: Ashwin Mehta

MONCTON (Westmorland, Kent & Albert
Counties)
770 Main St., E1C 1E8
Clerk of Probate: C.J. Gillespie, Q.C.
Clerk of Court: C.J. Gillespie, Q.C.
Administrator (Family Division): David Leger
Regional Sheriff: J.R. Wolfe
Sheriff: Rhéal LeBlanc
Registrars of Deeds:
Theresa LeBlanc (Westmorland County)
P. Arsenault (Kent County)
Donna Tower (Albert County)

NEWCASTLE (Northumberland County)
Court House, E1V 3M1
Clerk of Probate: George Martin
Clerk of the Court: George Martin
Administrator (Family Division): George Martin
Regional Sheriff: James R. Wolfe
Sheriff: James Muck
Registrar of Deeds: Deborah Frost

SAINT JOHN (Saint John, Kings & Charlotte
Counties)
Court House, E2L 3W9
Clerk of Probate: Richard Hatchette
Clerk of Court: Richard Hatchette
Administrator (Family Division):
Janet Steeves
Sheriff: Harold Gillespie
Registrars of Deeds:
Marie Melanson (Saint John County)
Maxine Robinson (Kings County)
Dalton E. Johnson (Charlotte County)

ST. STEPHEN
(Probate Court of New Brunswick only)
Clerk of Probate: Richard Hatchette
Deputy Clerk of Probate: Fred Nicholson, Q.C.

WOODSTOCK (Victoria & Carleton Counties)
Court House, E0J 2B0
A/Clerk of the Court: Ian MacInnis
A/Clerk of Probate: Ian MacInnis
A/Administrator (Family Division):
Ian MacInnis
Sheriff: Robert C. Dickinson
Registrars of Deeds:
Mrs. Marjorie Cote (Victoria County)
Mrs. Catherine Donovan (Carleton County)

This map is based on information taken from map MCR 4032. © Her Majesty in Right of Canada with permission of Energy, Mines and Resources.

PROVINCE OF NEWFOUNDLAND

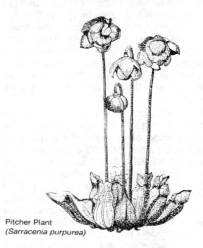

Pitcher Plant
(Sarracenia purpurea)

Entered Confederation: March 31, 1949
Capital: St. John's
Motto: Quaerite Prime Regnum Dei
(Seek ye first the Kingdom of God)
Flower: Pitcher plant
Area: 405,720 km²
  percentage of Canada's total area: 4.1
  LAND: 371,690 km²
  FRESHWATER: 34,030 km²
Elevation:
  HIGHEST POINT: Mt. Caubvick (1,707 m)
  LOWEST POINT: coastal area at sea level
Population (1986 census): 568,349
  five-year change: +0.1%

per square kilometre: 1.4
percentage of Canada's total
  population: 2.2
  URBAN: 57%
  RURAL: 43%
Gross domestic product, 1987: $7.1 billion
Government Finance:
  REVENUE, 1986/87 est.: $2.5 billion
  EXPENDITURE, 1986/87 est.: $2.6 billion
  DEBT PER CAPITA (March 1987): $1,956
Personal income per capita,
  1986: $11,620
Unemployment rate, 1988
  (annual average): 16.4%

HISTORY

Although discovered by the Norse around 1000 A.D., it was John Cabot who claimed discovery of the "new founde lande" in 1497 on behalf of the King of England. From 1504, the Newfoundland fishery was largely monopolized by the French and Portuguese. It was not until 1560 that the English, realizing the potential of the waters, sent fishing vessels and crews in larger numbers. Then, in 1583, Sir Humphrey Gilbert formalized the establishment of Britain's first overseas colony by claiming Newfoundland for England.

Colonies were started around the island; Cupids was settled in 1610 and Ferryland in 1621. The first court of justice in North America was held in Trinity in 1615, while the strife between England and France resulted in the occupation of St. John's by the French in 1662 and 1762.

In 1800, the first North American smallpox vaccination was administered in Newfoundland. The landing of the first successful transatlantic cable took place at Heart's Content in 1866. In 1901, Guglielmo Marconi received the first transatlantic wireless signal on Signal Hill. During the early part of the 1900s, transatlantic flights departed from Harbour Grace and St. John's. In 1949, Newfoundland became the tenth province of Canada.

THE LAND

The most easterly province of Canada has an area of 405,720 km², the island of Newfoundland being 111,390 km² and the mainland portion, Labrador, 294,330 km². The province covers an area more than three times the combined size of the other three Atlantic provinces.

The long arm of Labrador on the eastern boundary of Quebec belongs to the Canadian Shield; the island of Newfoundland is a continuation of the Appalachian Highlands. The island's surface dips generally east and northeast, with rugged coasts in the south and east, fringed with islets. Peninsulas, bays, lakes, and river basins on the island all lie in a northeast to southwest direction.

Newfoundland's temperature is moderate, with frequent high winds. Precipitation is heavy and nearly constant, with rain or snow on an average of 190 days a year at St. John's.

THE PEOPLE

The dialects and rich folklore of Newfoundland reveal predominantly English, Irish and Scottish ancestry. In some areas, the Devon and the Dorset origins of the speech are readily apparent, with many of the words and phrases, long vanished in England, still in use. Labrador is the home of the Inuit, Montagnais and Nascopi. With the discovery of Indian relics, its history can be traced back 9,000 years.

More than 92 per cent of the population traces its roots to the British Isles, which is by far the largest proportion of a single ethnic group in Canada. Placing a distant second are persons of French origin, 2.7 per cent; followed by part-British, part-French, 1.8 per cent; British and other, 0.6 per cent; and native peoples, 0.5 per cent. It follows that Newfoundland is almost completely anglophone, with 97.6 per cent of the population unilingual in English. A tiny fraction (less than 0.1 per cent) speak only French, 2.3 per cent speak both official languages, and 0.1 per cent speak neither.

Newfoundland and Labrador's population is approximately 57 per cent urban and 43 per cent rural. The capital and major city is St. John's, with a metro area population of 161,901 (1986 census).

THE ECONOMY

Newfoundland experienced relatively strong real growth in 1988. Producers of primary goods in the fishery and mining sectors continued to experience increased demand for their products.

Oil and gas. The offshore oil and gas industry is currently in the exploration phase off the Grand Banks of Newfoundland. A number of exploratory wells are currently being drilled, spurred on by the celebrated Hibernia discovery in 1979.

The oil and gas sector is also moving into the development phase with the Hibernia Development Project — which is scheduled for first oil production in the 1990s. It will add a significant stimulus to economic growth within the province. As well, the re-activated Come-by-Chance oil refinery has renewed expectation of processing and refining investment to complement existing exploration and production activities.

Mining. Newfoundland and Labrador's mineral wealth is a significant resource component of the economy of the province, accounting for 7 per cent of the province's work force in both direct and indirect employment related to the mining industry. As a mineral-producing province, Newfoundland is responsible for 10 per cent of the nation's total production of metallic and just over 1 per cent of non-metallic minerals, both on a value basis; it ranks first in iron ore commodities and sixth among all the provinces in mineral

resources. Newfoundland and Labrador currently mines 55 per cent of Canada's production of iron ore and also exploits a variety of non-ferrous and precious metals including copper, lead, zinc, silver, cadmium, and gold. The recently activated gold mine at Hope Break, on the south coast, is expected to yield 126,000 ounces annually. The province's principal non-metal production is concentrated in asbestos, gypsum, limestone, pyrophyllite and shale deposits, in addition to structural material and construction stone.

Hydro. The province's watershed is capable of producing a vast amount of hydroelectric power, an inexhaustible, renewable resource. Research has shown that Newfoundland's electrical energy future is inextricably linked with the Churchill River system in Labrador, indicating that interconnecting Labrador hydroelectric sites to the island of Newfoundland is the most economical means of meeting long-term energy requirements.

The Churchill River's total hydroelectric potential, large by international standards, may be exploited by developing only three sites. Together, these sites have a potential equivalent of 27 million barrels of oil per year or 75,000 barrels of oil per day.

The fishery. The fishing industry will always be the single most important sector of the Newfoundland economy. In 1986, approximately $400 million worth of fish products was exported to the U.S., which remains the province's primary market. Japan, however, is showing great potential. Opportunities exist for investment in secondary manufacturing and in the utilization of certain species other than the traditional cod and herring, an area in which there are great possibilities for joint ventures between foreign investors and Newfoundland firms.

Forestry. Throughout the twentieth century, the forest wealth of Newfoundland and Labrador has supported a healthy forestry industry, annually providing 5,000 man-years of employment directly and another 5,000 man-years indirectly.

The pulp and paper industry forms the major economic base of the large towns, several of which have a paper mill employing many people. In addition, numerous smaller communities derive a significant portion of their livelihood from logging and other forest-related activities.

During the past five years, over $60 million has been spent to ensure that the forests continue to flourish and sustain a very important industry. Programs in silviculture, forest access road construction, insect and disease control, fire protection, and inventory were carried out. In addition, programs aimed at stimulating the forest economy were developed.

Text provided by Newfoundland Information Service and the Department of Development and Tourism, Government of Newfoundland and Labrador, and updated from Statistics Canada figures.

GOVERNMENT OF NEWFOUNDLAND

Seat of Government:
Confederation Bldg., St. John's, A1C 5T7
Lieutenant-Governor,
The Hon. James McGrath, P.C., LL.D
Government House, St. John's, A1C 5W4

EXECUTIVE COUNCIL

(In order of precedence, as of March 20, 1989)

Premier, Minister of Fisheries,
The Hon. Thomas G. Rideout
Deputy Premier, Minister of Health,
The Hon. Dr. John F. Collins
Minister of Finance,
The Hon. H. Neil Windsor
President of the Council, President of the Treasury Board, House Leader, Minister responsible for the Status of Women,
The Hon. Leonard A. Simms
Minister of Intergovernmental Affairs,
The Hon. Ronald G. Dawe
Minister of Transportation,
The Hon. Norman Doyle
Minister of Mines,
The Hon. Jerome W. Dinn
Minister of Consumer Affairs and Communications,
The Hon. D. Haig Young
Minister of Justice, Attorney General,
The Hon. Lynn Verge, Q.C.
Minister of Public Works and Services,
The Hon. Dr. Hugh M. Twomey
Minister of Forestry,
The Hon. Robert J. Aylward
Minister of Social Services,
The Hon. Glen Tobin
Minister of Environment and Lands,
The Hon. James Russell
Minister of Development and Tourism,
The Hon. Harold Barrett
Minister of Culture, Recreation and Youth,
The Hon. John C. Butt
Minister of Education,
The Hon. Loyola Hearn
Minister of Career Development and Advanced Studies,
The Hon. Bill Matthews
Minister of Labour,
The Hon. Ted A. Blanchard
Minister of Municipal Affairs,

The Hon. Charles R. Brett
Minister responsible for Housing,
The Hon. Milton Peach
Minister of Labrador Affairs,
The Hon. Garfield Warren
Minister of Rural, Agricultural and Northern Development,
The Hon. Rick Woodford

CABINET COMMITTEES

Planning and Priorities
Chairman, Vacant

Resource Policy
Chairman, The Hon. H. Neil Windsor

Social Policy
Chairman, The Hon. Loyola Hearn

Committee on Memorial University
Chairman, The Hon. Bill Matthews

Special Committee
Chairman, The Hon. Jerome W. Dinn

Research and Development
Chairman, The Hon. Harold Barrett

Appointments
Chairman, The Hon. Bill Matthews

CABINET SECRETARIAT

Clerk of the Executive Council and Secretary to Cabinet, H.H. Stanley
Deputy Clerk and Asst. Secretary to Cabinet, J.L. Thistle
Asst. Secretary to Cabinet (Resource Policy and Planning), D.J. Oake
Asst. Secretary to Cabinet (Social Policy), Wayne Green
Director of Administration, W. Vincent
Economic Research & Analysis Division
Director, Ms. Beverly Carter
Resource Policy Analysis and Planning
Director, John Scott
Newfoundland Statistics Agency
Director, G. Courage

TREASURY BOARD SECRETARIAT

President, The Hon. Leonard A. Simms
Secretary, A.L. White
Asst. Secretary (Financial), Bruce Peckford
Asst. Secretary (Personnel), Lloyd Powell

Organization and Management
Director, Ralph Alcock
Budgeting Division Director, E. Kent
Collective Bargaining Division
Director, A. Andrews
Insurance Division Director, Tony Lannon
Classification and Pay Division
Director, A.E. Meadus
Personnel Policy Division
Director, Noreen Holden

INTERGOVERNMENTAL AFFAIRS SECRETARIAT

Minister, The Hon. Ronald G. Dawe
Deputy Minister, Peter Kennedy
Asst. Deputy Ministers, F. Way, Ms. B.E. Knight
Native Policy Issues
Exec. Director, Raymond Hawco
Economic and Social Programs
Director, John Abbott
Resource Programs Director, D. Brown
Regional Development Programs
Director, W. Barfoot
Protocol Director, G. Korbai

DETAILS OF DISTRICT CATEGORIES

Category 1:
Conception Bay South, Gander, Grand Falls, Humber West, Kilbride, Menihek, Mount Pearl, Pleasantville, St. John's Centre, St. John's East, St. John's East Extern, St. John's North, St. John's South, St. John's West, Stephenville, Waterford/Kenmount.

Category 2:
Bellevue, Carbonear, Ferryland, Harbour Grace, Harbour Main, Humber East, Mount Scio, Port de Grave, Trinity-Bay de Verde.

Category 3:
Bay of Islands, Bonavista North, Bonavista South, Burin-Placentia West, Exploits, Fogo, Grand Bank, Green Bay, Humber Valley, Lewisporte, Naskaupi, Placentia, Port au Port, St. Barbe, St. George's, St. Mary's-the Capes, Strait of Belle Isle, Terra Nova, Trinity North, Twillingate, Windsor-Buchans.

Category 4:
Bay Verte-White Bay, Burgeo-Bay d'Espoir, Fortune-Hermitage, La Poile.

Category 5:
Eagle River, Torngat Mountains.

HOUSE OF ASSEMBLY

40th General Assembly, 4th Session
Last election: April 2, 1985
    (Maximum duration 5 years)
Majority Party: Progressive Conservative
Total number of seats: 52
Party standings:
    Conservatives: 34
    Liberals: 14
    New Democrats: 2
    Vacant: 2

Salaries, Indemnities and Allowances

Premier's Salary $46,742
Ministers, Leader of Opposition &
    Speaker $33,888
M.H.A. Sessional Allowance $26,543
M.H.A. Travel Allowance *(see Schedule below):*
    16 Districts (Category I). $14,425
    9 Districts (Category II) $15,578
    21 Districts (Category III) $16,731
    4 Districts (Category IV) $17,883
    2 Districts (Category V) $19,037
Speaker's Official Entertainment $3,000
Chairman of Committee Allowance $11,300
Deputy Chairman of Committee
    Allowance $5,650
Government Whip Allowance $5,330
Opposition Whip Allowance $5,330
Per Diem Rate $75.00

Officers of the House

Speaker, The Hon. Dr. Patrick McNicholas
Deputy Speaker, Glenn Greening
Clerk of the House, Elizabeth M. Duff
Law Clerk, John Noel

Members

Constituency	Member and Affiliation
Baie Verte/ White Bay	The Hon. Thomas Rideout (PC)
Bay of Islands	The Hon. Ted Blanchard (PC)
Bellevue	Wilson Callan (Lib)
Bonavista North	Tom Lush (Lib)
Bonavista South	Vacant
Burgeo/ Bay d'Espoir	David Gilbert (Lib)
Burin/ Placentia West	The Hon. Glen Tobin (PC)
Carbonear	The Hon. Milton Peach (PC)
Conception Bay South	The Hon. John C. Butt (PC)
Eagle River	R.E. Hiscock (Lib)
Exploits	The Hon. Dr. Hugh Twomey (PC)
Ferryland	Charles J. Power (PC)
Fogo	R. Beaton Tulk (Lib)
Fortune/Hermitage	Vacant
Gander	Winston Baker (Lib)
Grand Bank	The Hon. Bill Matthews (PC)
Grand Falls	The Hon. Leonard A. Simms (PC)
Green Bay	The Hon. Brian Peckford (PC)
Harbour Grace	The Hon. D. Haig Young (PC)

Constituency	Member and Affiliation
Harbour Main/ Bell Island	The Hon. Norman Doyle (PC)
Humber East	The Hon. Lynn Verge (PC)
Humber Valley	The Hon. Rick Woodford (PC)
Humber West	Raymond Baird (PC)
Kilbride	The Hon. Robert J. Aylward (PC)
LaPoile	Calvin Mitchell (PC)
Lewisporte	The Hon. M. James Russell (PC)
Menihek	Peter Fenwick (NDP)
Mount Pearl	The Hon. H. Neil Windsor (PC)
Mount Scio/ Bell Island	Leo D. Barry (Lib)
Naskaupi	Jim Kelland (Lib)
Placentia	Bill Patterson (PC)
Pleasantville	The Hon. Jerome Dinn (PC)
Port au Port	Jim Hodder (PC)
Port de Grave	John Efford (Lib)
St. Barbe	Chuck Furey (Lib)
St. George's	The Hon. Ronald G. Dawe (PC)
St. John's Centre	The Hon. Dr. Patrick McNicholas (PC)
St. John's East	Gene Long (NDP)
St. John's East (Extern)	Kevin Parsons (PC)
St. John's North	John A. Carter (PC)
St. John's South	The Hon. Dr. John Collins (PC)
St. John's West	The Hon. Harold Barrett (PC)
St. Mary's/ The Capes	The Hon. Loyola Hearn (PC)
Stephenville	Kevin Aylward (Lib)
Strait of Belle Isle	Chris Decker (Lib)
Terra Nova	Glenn Greening (PC)
Torngat Mountains	The Hon. Garfield Warren (PC)
Trinity North	The Hon. R. Charles Brett (PC)
Trinity/Bay de Verde	Jim Reid (PC)
Twillingate	Walter Carter (Lib)
Waterford/ Kenmount	David Gullage (Lib)
Windsor/Buchans	Clyde Wells (Lib)

Lib — Liberal
NDP — New Democrat
PC — Progressive Conservative

Office of the Premier

Confederation Bldg., St. John's, A1C 5T7

Premier, The Hon. T. Rideout
Press Secretary, Frank Petten
Chief of Staff, Wayne Clarke
Registrar, Olive White

Western Regional Office:
Sir Richard Squires Bldg.
Corner Brook, A2H 6J8
Central Regional Office:
Provincial Bldg., Grand Falls, A2A 1W9

Offices of the Official Opposition

Confederation Bldg., St. John's, A1C 5T7

Leader of the Official Opposition, Clyde Wells
Chief of Staff, Edsel Bonnell

Office of the Auditor General

Confederation Bldg., St. John's, A1C 5T7
Auditor General, J.F. McGrath, C.A.
Deputy Auditor General, C.R. Hart, C.A.

Office of the Ombudsman

Prudential Bldg., 49-55 Elizabeth Ave.
St. John's, A1C 5T7
General Inquiries: (709) 753-7730
   The legislation providing for the establishment of the Office of the Ombudsman was passed in 1970; however, it was not proclaimed until June 16, 1975, when the first Parliamentary Commissioner (Ombudsman) was appointed. The appointment is made by the Lieutenant-Governor in Council on the recommendation of the House of Assembly.
   The role of the Ombudsman is to receive and investigate the complaints of citizens who feel that they have been unjustly treated by a department or agency of the provincial government. If a complaint is found to be valid, the Commissioner will recommend redress to the appropriate department or agency.
   The Ombudsman is required to report annually to the House of Assembly.

Ombudsman, Ambrose Peddle
Investigators: Cyril King, Nancy Lundrigan

DEPARTMENT OF CAREER DEVELOPMENT AND ADVANCED STUDIES
Box 4750, St. John's, A1C 5T7

MINISTER'S OFFICE
Minister, The Hon. Bill Matthews

DEPUTY MINISTER'S OFFICE
Dep. Minister, Dr. G. Keith Winter

ASSISTANT DEPUTY MINISTERS' OFFICES
Asst. Dep. Minister, Planning and Administration, Robert F. Smart
Asst. Dep. Minister, Advanced Studies, Cyril J. McCormick
Asst. Dep. Minister, Employment and Careers, Catherine Gogan

ADMINISTRATION DIVISION
Director, Jack Thompson
Financial Analyst, Vacant
Personnel Specialist, Leonard Tulk
Federal/Provincial Claims Officer, Lloyd Laing
Chief Accountant, Wilfred Knee
Asst. Accountant, Mike Dawe

Audit Officer, Vacant
Inventory Control Officer, Winston Butt
Registrar, O.J. Darris
Systems Manager, Craig Slaney
EDP Systems Officer, Sandra Sparrow
Computer Programmer, Carl Noseworthy

POST-SECONDARY EDUCATION
Director, Malachy Mandville
Operations
Asst. Director, E. Yetman
Private Training Supervisor, Nellie Burke
Physical Plant Co-ordinator, Vacant
Programs
Asst. Director, Fintan Costello
Program Consultants: M. Dillon,
John Tremblett, Mrs. Patricia Davis,
Al Lessner, Pat Murray, Munden Batstone,
Margo Dobbin, Arthur Leung,
Carolyn Bennett, Rene Enguehard

PLANNING AND RESEARCH DIVISION
Director, Robert Thompson
Post-secondary Education
Analyst, Andrea Dicks
Research Officer, Ron Abbott
Offshore Support Manager, Christine Hollett
Statistician, Bruce Gellately
Labour Market Programs
Analyst, Rosemarie Langhout
Labour Market Analyst, Rachelle Cochrane
Statistician, Robert Collins

EMPLOYMENT SERVICES DIVISION
Director, Ed McCann
Employment Services Officers:
Paul Dinn, Janet Short
Work Programs
Co-ordinator, Bob Carew
Project Manager, Clayton Johnson
Project Officers: Marbeth Andrews,
Jeannie Martin, Suzanne Wiseman,
Anita Armstrong, Stella Hayes, Walt Mavin,
Allan Drover, Gerard Griffin,
Sandra McIntosh, Brett Thornhill

CAREER SUPPORT SERVICES DIVISION
Director, Lorraine Moores
Public Information Officer, Kevin Pittman
Career Development Specialists:
Christopher Smith, Elizabeth Bungay,
Sharon Knott, Veronica Breen
Education/Training Industry Liaison
Officer, Terry Hynes

OFFICE OF THE POLICY ADVISOR
Policy Advisor, Wayne Taylor

STUDENT AID
Supervisor, Norm Snelgrove
Asst. Supervisor, Vacant
Verification and Recovery Officer,
Lloyd Matchem
Student Appeals Officer, Barb Byrne

INDUSTRIAL TRAINING DIVISION
Director, Cyril Carter
Examination Co-ordinator, Kevin Collins
Library Technician, Daphne Hoyles
St. John's
Reg. Manager, Hubert Locke
Registrar of Apprentices, James Welsh
Grand Falls
Reg. Manager, Maxwell F. Davis
Corner Brook
Reg. Manager, Herman J. Bartlett
Labrador City
Sr. Industrial Training Officer, Vacant

DEPARTMENT OF CONSUMER AFFAIRS AND COMMUNICATIONS
Box 4750, St. John's, A1C 5T7

MINISTER'S OFFICE
Minister, The Hon. D. Haig Young

DEPUTY MINISTER'S OFFICE
Dep. Minister, Alistair Kinsman
Asst. Dep. Minister, Robert J. Barter

Administration
Director, A. Douglas Burry
Chief Accountant, Gary King
Registrar, Sandra Hudson
Commercial Relations Director, Paul Tapper
Asst. Director, Douglas J. Connolly
Communications Director, E. Hunter Rowe
Consumer Affairs Director, J. Diane Driscoll
Supervisor, Harry Mitchell
Trade Practices Director, John G. Housser

LANDLORD-TENANT RELATIONS
Director, Clyde E. Bradbury
Asst. Director, Philip E. Moore
Residential Tenancies Boards
St. John's and Eastern
Chairman, Gerald J. O'Reilly
Secretary, Nancy Lowthian

REAL ESTATE
Sup't, Robert LeGrow

LICENSING AND ENFORCEMENT
Supervisor, Gerald O'Neill

REGISTRY OF BILLS OF SALE
Registrar, Elmer Evans
Dep. Registrar, Doug Evans
REGIONAL OFFICES
Gander Office
The Burden Bldg., Gander, A1V 1K6
Grand Falls Office
Provincial Bldg., Grand Falls, A2A 2M4
Corner Brook Office
Sir Richard Squires Bldg.
Corner Brook, A2H 6E5

Happy Valley-Goose Bay Office
Mitchelmore Bldg.
Happy Valley-Goose Bay, A0P 1E0

DEPARTMENT OF CULTURE, RECREATION AND YOUTH

Confederation Bldg., West Blk.
Prince Philip Dr., Box 4750
St. John's, A1C 5T7
(except where otherwise indicated)

MINISTER'S OFFICE
Minister, The Hon. John C. Butt

EXECUTIVE OFFICERS
Dep. Minister, Robert J. Jenkins
Asst. Dep. Minister, Cultural Affairs, Historic Resources and Youth, W.B. Frost
Asst. Dep. Minister, Parks, Recreation and Wildlife, Vacant

ADMINISTRATION
Director, Kevin Dicks
Director of Personnel, Kay Mullins

WILDLIFE DIVISION
Bldg. 810, Pleasantville
Box 4750, St. John's, A1C 5T7
Director, D.G. Pike
Research and Development
Chief, Eugene Mercer
Chief of Protection, A.O. MacPhee
Salmonier Nature Park
Manager, Kevin Moore
Box 190, Holyrood, A0A 2R0
Information Education Program
Co-ordinator, D. Minty

PARKS DIVISION
Confederation Bldg., West Blk.
Box 4750, St. John's, A1C 5T7
Director, D.G. Hustins
Chief of Planning and Development, Glen Ryan
Chief of Operations, W. Pinsent

HISTORIC RESOURCES DIVISION
Newfoundland Museum, Duckworth St.
St. John's, A1C 1G9
Director, M. Bowe
Asst. Director and Chief of Historic Sites, David Mills
Provincial Archivist, David Davis

CULTURAL AFFAIRS DIVISION
Box 1854, St. John's, A1C 5P9
Director, John C. Perlin
Arts and Culture Centres:
Manager, Heather Morgan
Box 1854, St. John's, A1C 5P9
Manager, Una Joseph
50 Airport Blvd., Gander, A1V 1K6

Manager, Reginald Pye
Cromer Ave., Grand Falls, A2A 1W9
Manager, Diane Butt
University Dr., Box 100, Corner Brook, A2H 6C3
Manager, Janet White
380 Massachusetts Dr., Stephenville, A2N 3A5
Manager, John Fleet
Box 69, Labrador City, A2V 2K3

COMMUNITY RECREATION SPORT AND FITNESS DIVISION
Director, Robert Hillier
Sport Services
Supervisor, Jamie Schwartz
Consultants:
Jim Tee, Kathy Coughlan, Tom Godden
Fitness
Supervisor, Vic Janes
Fitness Specialists:
David Doyle, Patti Clarke, Lesley Tomblin
Community Recreation
Supervisor, Sandy Hickman
Consultants:
Facilities, David Molloy
Community Recreation, Jane Fitzgerald
Recreation Capital Grants
Administrator, Mac Blondon
Recreation Specialists:
Goronwy Price
Box 26, Stn. C
Happy Valley-Goose Bay, A0P 1C0
John Sharpe
Box 397, Habour Grace, A0A 1W0
Randy White
Box 646, Lewisporte, A0G 3A0
Clayton Welsh
Grand Bank, A0A 1W0
Ed Flood
Box 596, Corner Brook, A2H 6G1
Notre Dame Bay-Bonavista North, Randy White
Box 646, Lewisporte, A0G 3A0
Provincial Training Centre
Bldg. 25, Torbay Airport, St. John's, A1C 5T7
Manager, A. Miller
Provincial Training Centre Residence
Bldg. 25, Torbay Airport, St. John's, A1C 5T7
Manager, A. Fitzgerald
West Coast Training Centre
383 Massachusetts Dr., Stephenville, A2N 3A9
Manager, Gerald Boland
Newfoundland and Labrador High School Athletic Federation
Bldg. 25, Torbay Airport, St. John's, A1C 5T7
Exec. Secretary, Vacant
Newfoundland and Labrador Parks/Recreation Association
Exec. Secretary, Gary Milley
Newfoundland and Labrador Amateur Sports Federation
Box 1597, St. John's, A1C 5P3
Exec. Secretary, Dee Murphy

YOUTH SERVICES DIVISION
Director, William Wilson
4-H Supervisor, Mervie Ford

4-H Curriculum Consultant, Heather Griffen
4-H Reg. Consultant, Terry Mallay
Special Programs Co-ordinator,
Betty Lou Elford
Youth Services
Administrator Officer, Roger Mackey
Youth Programs Supervisor, Rose Daley
Youth Programs Consultant, Sidney Witcher
4-H Special Programs Co-ordinator,
Ramona Crane
Travel Co-ordinator, Marie Chippett

AGENCIES, BOARDS AND COMMISSIONS

Canada Games Park Commission
c/o Canada Games Park, 15 Westerland Rd.
St. John's, A1B 3R7

The Commission is a seven-member board constituted under the provisions of the *Canada Games Park Commission Act.*

The Commission is responsible for the operation and programming of a large aquatic facility and a track and field, soccer, and rugby complex. This includes sponsoring and promoting recreational programs, sporting events and competitions, and fitness. In addition to this, the Commission has also developed programs for health, welfare, and the well-being of the aging, handicapped, and disabled people of the province. The operating budget is presently in the vicinity of $2 million and the staff numbers approximately 125 people.

Chairman, D.S. Johnson
Secretary, Mrs. Laura Lynch

Newfoundland and Labrador Youth Advisory Council
Bldg. T851, Pleasantville
Box 4750, St. John's, A1C 5T7

The Youth Advisory Council (YAC) offers a voice for the youth of Newfoundland and Labrador. Its mandate, as set out in a special Act of the Newfoundland House of Assembly, is to provide a forum for youth expression; to provide the opportunity for dialogue and exchange among youth, and between youth and government; and to research and investigate matters relating to youth.

The YAC fulfils this mandate by meeting regularly with executives in the premier's office; by representing youth's point of view to all levels of government; and through regular meetings of youth from all regions of the province.

Chairman, Paul Lahey
Exec. Secretary, David Brazil

Newfoundland Public Library Services
Provincial Headquarters
Library Administration Offices
Arts and Culture Ctr., Allandale Rd.
St. John's, A1B 3A3
(709) 737-3964/66/67; Envoy: ADMIN.NPL
Chairman, Agnes Richard

Provincial Director, Pearce J. Penney
Dep. Director, Diana Rose
(See also Library listings in Sources of Information, Volume 1)

Provincial Public Libraries Board
Arts and Culture Ctr., Allandale Rd.
St. John's, A1B 3A3

The Provincial Public Libraries Board, established as a corporation under the *Public Libraries Act,* develops and controls the public library service in Newfoundland and Labrador. The Board comprises 15 members — 8 appointed by the Lieutenant-Governor in Council, one from each of six regional boards, and one from the St. John's Library Board — who hold office for a three-year period and are eligible for reappointment.

The Board is responsible for 106 public libraries throughout the province. Of these, 101 are established under six regional library systems; four are under the St. John's Library System; and a Provincial Resource Library, located at headquarters, supplements the collections in the regional system and specializes in a collection of Newfoundland material. Also, there is a Provincial Books-By-Mail Service, operated from Grand Falls, serving communities without libraries by a mail service program.

There is a centralized Technical Services Division with an automated system for catalogue support. Business Administration is centralized also, avoiding duplication of accounting at the regional level.

Chairman, Agnes Richard

DEPARTMENT OF DEVELOPMENT AND TOURISM
Confederation Bldg., W. Block, 4th Flr. S.
St. John's, A1C 5T7

MINISTER'S OFFICE
Minister, The Hon. Harold Barrett

DEPUTY MINISTER'S OFFICE
Dep. Minister, C.C. Granter
Asst. Dep. Minister, Trade, Investment and Promotion, B. Wakeham
Asst. Dep. Minister, Small Business and Technology, G. Greenland
Asst. Dep. Minister, Tourism, E.T. Burden
Asst. Dep. Minister, Offshore/Marine Industries, M. Staple

ADMINISTRATION
Director, D. Butler
Management Analyst, C. Phillips
Registrar, C. Anderson
Accountant, Mrs. Minnie Long
Asst. Accountant, Randy Snelgrove

PROSPECT DEVELOPMENT
A/Director, D. Hallett
Industrial Development Officers:
Brian Murray (Trade)
E. Trickett (Trade)
H. Bishop (Investment)
Clyde Woodward (Investment)
Brian Collins (Investment)
D. Doull
E. Collins (Trade)
Promotions Co-ordinator, Kay Coxworthy

PHYSICAL PLANNING SUPPORT
Director, M. Ruelokke
Engineer, John Hudson
Draughting Technician, P. Benson
Engineering Technician, D. O'Neill
Marine Industries Director, L. Clarke

OCEAN INDUSTRIES
Manager, R. Robinson
Development Officers: L. Spurrell, W. Pumphrey
Marine/Coastal Zone Development
Manager, N. Creighton

INDUSTRIAL OPERATIONS
Director, Vacant
Development Officer, P. Tobin

SPECIAL PROJECTS
Director, D. Hallett
Development Officer, R. Nanayakkara

FINANCIAL SERVICES
Director, B. Condon
Development Officers: N. Burggraaf, J. King

LOCAL INDUSTRY SUPPORT SERVICES
Director, T.W. Strickland
Development Officers: A. Sheppard,
D. Hancock, D. Davis, P. Morris

TECHNOLOGY DEVELOPMENT
Director, D. Moody
Development Officers:
R. Newhook, J. Woodman, T. Johnstone

ECONOMIC RESEARCH AND ANALYSIS
Development Officers: A. Patey, P. Maher,
A. Ryan, T. Fallon

PROMOTION SERVICES
Director, P. Sowdon
Development Officer, P. Smith
Promotion Technician, M. Barry
Photographic Specialist, J. Byrne
Promotions, Production
Manager, Wayne Stockwood
Audio-Visual Specialist, W. Sturge
Graphic Artist, D. Warren
Information Officers: Paul Murphy, C. Shea

OFFSHORE BUSINESS DEVELOPMENT
Director, F. Murrin
Petroleum Engineer, C. Dyer
Development Officers: F. Smyth, K. Hawley,
B. Dyke, M. Shinkle, T. Courish

TOURISM MARKETING
Marketing Director, J. Keel-Ryan
Departmental Program Co-ordinator, Vacant
Development Officers: B. Metcalfe, C. Langdon
Market Specialist, Vacant
Promotions Co-ordinator, M. May

INDUSTRY SERVICES
Director, M. Joy
Manager, D. Johnston
Information Officers: H. Hollett, K. Spencer
Distribution Officer, J. Barrett
Licensing and Inspection
Manager, E. Vincent
Engineer, Dennis Martin
Inspector, C. Way
Development Officers: G. Dodd, D. Garland
Financial Incentives
Financial Incentives Officer, D. Moore
Program Co-ordinator, P. Burggraff
Development Counselling Sector
Manager, M. Clair
Events and Attractions Co-ordinator,
Norm Morris
Marketing Services Counsellor, C. Murphy
Financial Counsellor, Vacant
Package Tours Counsellor, Sharon Grouchy
Hospitality Services Counsellor, Vacant

PLANNING AND EVALUATION
Director, M. Singleton
Statisticians: J. Quigley, R. Haynes
Planning and Evaluation Officer,
Annette Stuckless
Corner Brook Office
Herald Towers, 5th Flr., Herald Ave.
Corner Brook, A2H 6J8
Reg. Development Manager, J. Sweetland
Regional Tourism Development
Co-ordinator, Vacant
Development Officer, L. Rich
Gander Office
Box 472, Gander, A1V 1W8
Reg. Development Manager, J. Curran
Development Officers:
T. Fudge, Ross Goldsworthy, J. McLennon
Labrador Office
Box 490, Wabush, A0R 1B0
Reg. Development Manager, D. Lough
Development Officers: C. Simms, R. Bowers

AGENCIES, BOARDS AND COMMISSIONS

**Economic Council of Newfoundland and
Labrador**
Box 5098, St. John's, A1C 5V3

   The Economic Council of Newfoundland and

Labrador is a provincial Crown corporation that was established in late 1983. It is comprised of a 15-member voluntary board of directors who represent diverse business and labour interests throughout the province. The board is supported by a small, permanent staff which operates in St. John's.

The Economic Council has a mandate to provide the provincial cabinet with independent and responsible advice on major social and economic issues, and to recommend appropriate policies and strategies to address these concerns. The Council is also required to contribute to informed public debate on these major issues.

Chairman, H.W. Lundrigan
Box 2002, Corner Brook, A2H 6J5
Vice-Chairman, A.A. Brait
Exec. Director, Paul B. Bugden

Newfoundland and Labrador Development Corp. Ltd.

136 Crosbie Rd., St. John's, A1B 3K3

Newfoundland and Labrador Development Corporation Limited (NLDC) was formed in 1973 to assist in the development and expansion of small and medium-sized provincial businesses.

The Corporation offers financial assistance to entrepreneurs and businesses through its Term Loan, Young Entrepreneur, Equity, and Venture Capital programs. It also administers the provincial Stock Savings Plan and Venture Capital Tax Credit Program. In addition, the Corporation provides business support services through its Business Resource Centre. This business and technical library located at St. John's provides information through a books-by-mail service and on-line electronic database searches. The technical expertise of staff members of the National Research Council's Industrial Research Assistance Program can also be accessed at all of the Corporation's offices.

President, Ira J. Bridger
Vice-President, P. Kennedy
Sr. Financial Advisor, Stock Savings Plan, Ray Sparkes
Gen. Manager, Business Development, Bruce Saunders

Corner Brook
4 Herald Tower, Ste. 503
Corner Brook, A2H 4B4
Reg. Manager, Dave Tizzard

Grand Falls
Tourist Chalet, TCH, Box 780
Grand Falls, A2A 2M4
Project Manager, Roy Boone

DEPARTMENT OF EDUCATION

Confederation Bldg.
Box 4750, St. John's, A1C 5T7

MINISTER'S OFFICE
Minister, The Hon. Loyola Hearn

DEPUTY MINISTER'S OFFICE
Dep. Minister, Lorne Wheeler
Asst. Dep. Minister, Finance and Administration, Donald L. Sansome
Asst. Dep. Minister, Educational Programs, Dr. Edna Turpin-Downey
Asst. Dep. Minister, Educational Operations, Dr. Boyce T. Fradsham
Women's Educational Services
Consultant, Barbara Hopkins

ADMINISTRATION AND PERSONNEL DIVISION
Director, Aubrey Halfyard
Systems Manager, Joan McCarthy-Wiseman
A/Personnel Specialist, Gary Greene
Teacher's Pensions
Supervisor, T. Jones
Central Registry, Vacant

EDUCATIONAL FINANCE DIVISION
Director, Horace Noseworthy
Teacher's Payroll, D. Whalen
Accountant, V. Simmons
School Supplies Manager, Chesley Welcher
Bus Transportation Supervisor, A. Feltham
Educational Finance Officer, John Berniquez

INSTRUCTION DIVISION
Director, Wayne Oakley
Asst. Director (Instructional Materials), N. Harris
Asst. Director (Curriculum), O. Lawrence
Instructional Materials Production Studio
Supervisor, Louise Nugent
Libraries Consultant, Calvin Belbin
Testing Section
Asst. Director (High School Certification), Len Badcock
Consultants:
Social Studies, Smita Joshi
Home Economics, Joan Casey
Music Specialist, Ivan Hibbs
Art Specialist, Heather Moore
French Programs
Assistant Director, Glen Loveless
French Consultant, Patrick Balsom
French Programs Officer, Frank Cholette
Health and Physical Education
Consultant, Sheila Anderson
Mathematics, Wilbert Boone
Vocational Education, S. Marshall
Primary, Delphene Brake
Science, Harold Elliott
French Immersion, Marie Louise Greene
French as a First Language
Education Consultant, Sr. Gladys Bozec
English Consultant, E.A. Jones
Early Childhood Education
Consultant, Bernadette Coady-Condon

SPECIAL EDUCATION SERVICES DIVISION
Director, Gwenda Jablonski
Asst. Director, Ann Power

Consultants:
Edith Furey, Ben Dalton, Doug Young
Consultant for Visually Impaired,
Geraldine Doherty

SCHOOL SERVICES DIVISION
Director, Gary Hatcher
Field Services
Asst. Director, Edward L. Mackey
Student Services
Asst. Director, Sam McGrath
Teacher's Certification
A/Registrar, R. Parsons
Asst. Registrar, Vacant
Teachers' Records Officer, Rose Fitzgerald
Information and Publications
Co-ordinator, Bob Forsey
School Construction Engineer, Robert Kenny
Pupil Retention Consultant, Hayward Harris

EVALUATION AND RESEARCH DIVISION
Director, Dr. Lenora Perry Fagan
Asst. Director (Research and Statistics),
Harold Press
Asst. Director (Evaluation and Testing),
H. Clifford Penney
Statistician, Jill Andrews
Student Evaluation and Testing
Consultant, Russell Blagdon
School Program Systems Consultant,
Allen Wright

DEPARTMENT OF ENERGY
Atlantic Place, Water St., Box 4750
St. John's, A1C 5T7

MINISTER'S OFFICE
Minister, Vacant

DEPUTY MINISTER'S OFFICE
Dep. Minister, Gordon Gosse
Asst. Dep. Minister, Petroleum Resources,
Martin Sheppard
*Asst. Dep. Minister, Petroleum and
Energy Economics,* Lorne Spracklin
*Asst. Dep. Minister, Petroleum and
Energy Programs,* Irene Baird
Community Relations and Social Monitoring
Director, Vacant
Financial Analysis Director, C. Sturge
Economic Analysis Director, D.C. Inkster
Energy Programs Director, P. Graham
Policy Research Director, C. Lester
Petroleum Resource Development
Director, D. Hawkins

DEPARTMENT OF ENVIRONMENT AND LANDS
Confederation Bldg., W. Block
Box 4750, St. John's, A1C 5T7

MINISTER'S OFFICE
Minister, The Hon. M. James Russell

DEPUTY MINISTER'S OFFICE
Dep. Minister, Gilbert Pike
Asst. Dep. Minister, Environment,
David Jeans
Asst. Dep. Minister, Lands, Robert Winsor

ADMINISTRATION
Director, Frank Harris
Accountant, John Byrne

POLLUTION CONTROL
Civil/Sanitary Environmental
Engineering Division
Director, K. Dominie
Environmental Investigations Division
Director, C.W. Strong
Grand Falls Office, R. Conway
Corner Brook Office, Roger Saunders
Clarenville Office, G. Perry
Industrial Environmental Engineering Division
Director, Dr. L. Hulett
Water Resources Management Division
Director, Dr. Wasi Ullah
Environmental Assessment Division
Director, David Taylor

LANDS
Lands Surveys Division
Director, N. MacNaughton
Land Management Division
Director, R. Warren
Crown Lands Administration Division
Director, J. Power

DEPARTMENT OF FINANCE
Confederation Bldg., St. John's, A1C 5T7
General Inquiry: (709) 576-2924
Telex: 016-4132

MINISTER'S OFFICE
Minister, The Hon. Neil Windsor

DEPUTY MINISTER'S OFFICE
Dep. Minister, Gilbert Gill

ADMINISTRATION
Director, Mary Mansfield
Departmental Management Analyst,
Max Baldwin
Accountant, Fred Lyall
Registrar, William Moores

Debt Management and Pensions
Asst. Dep. Minister, Philip Wall

DEBT MANAGEMENT
Director, Winston Morris

Investments
Manager, Cyril Bambrick
Sr. Financial Officer, Linda Holloway
Investment Officer, Eric Noseworthy
Accountant, Tom Lawlor

Loan Administration
Manager, Brian Condon
Sr. Crown Corporations Officer, Stephen Lush
Government Loans Officers: Vacant
Accountant, Don Furlong

Debt Research
Manager, Earl Saunders
Prospectus Officer, Vacant
Debt Analyst, Kirk Tilley

Special Projects
Manager, Douglas Laing

Bond Registry
Supervisor, Terry Dalton
Asst. Supervisor, Robert Royle

PENSIONS
Pension Administration Director, John Bennett
Pensions Financial Manager,
Maureen McCarthy
Pension Policy Director, Tim McGrath

Fiscal Policy
Asst. Dep. Minister, Robert Vardy

FISCAL POLICY
Federal/Provincial Relations
Director, Bruce Hollett
Tax Policy Director, Vacant

Comptroller General's Office
Comptroller Gen., Bernard G. Carew

TAX COMPLIANCE AND AUDIT
Asst. Comptroller Gen., R.G. Clarke
Director, Regional Offices, William Kean
Director, St. John's Region, Howard Hillier
Tax Information and Rulings
Manager, Robert Constantine
Audit Managers:
Anthony McAllister, Jackie Power
Support Services Director, Bernard Cook
Appeals Officer, Oswald Tilley

GOVERNMENT ACCOUNTING
Asst. Comptroller Gen., Raymond Gruchy
Director, Ronald Williams
Asst. Director, John Martin
Exchequer Manager, Vacant
Central Accounts Manager, Robert Harnum
Central Cashier Manager, Michael Spearns
Public Accounts Manager, Robert Stone
Pre-Audit Manager, Thomas Hopkins
Payrolls Manager, Harold Grandy
Systems Development Manager, David Schell

INTERNAL AUDIT
Director, Keith Healey
Manager, George Butt

DEPARTMENT OF FISHERIES
Confederation Bldg. Complex, Prince Philip Dr.
Box 4750, St. John's, A1C 5T7
General Inquiry: (709) 576-3723
Telex: 016-4732

MINISTER'S OFFICE
Minister, The Hon. Thomas G. Rideout

DEPUTY MINISTER'S OFFICE
Dep. Minister, Ray Andrews

Policy/Planning
Asst. Dep. Minister, Leslie Dean
Administration Division
Director, Joseph Dunphy
Public Relations Specialist, Elizabeth Lundrigan
Planning Services Director, Karl Sullivan
Field Services Division Director, L.C. Shirley

Support Services
Asst. Dep. Minister, Harold Murphy
Harvesting Operations
Director, Alastair O'Rielly
Processing Operations Director, Frank Pinhorn
Market Research and Development
Director, Vacant

Facility Services
Asst. Dep. Minister, Vacant
Facility Operations Director, Brett Wareham
Engineering Services Director, Harry Meadus

AGENCIES, BOARDS AND COMMISSIONS

Fisheries Loan Board
Atlantic Place, 5th Flr., Water St.
St. John's, A1C 5T7

The Fisheries Loan Board was established and funded by the Newfoundland Government in 1950 under *An Act to provide for loans for fishermen and to create a Fisheries Loan Board for Newfoundland.*

The Board provides loans of up to $50,000 at a rate of interest three per cent below bank prime lending rates; this is adjusted semi-annually to coincide with current bank rates. Loans are available to fishermen to acquire boats and equipment to be used in the catching or taking of fish from the sea.

Loans over $50,000 and up to $1 million for the same purposes are made through the chartered banks. The Newfoundland Government guarantees the principal to the banks while the Board subsidizes the difference between the interest charged by the banks and the interest charged by the Board.

The Board also administers bounty (grant) programs for the construction of new fishing vessels and the rebuilding/repairing of used fishing ships. In addition to the outlay of funds, this entails strict supervision of new vessel

construction and rebuilding/repair work.
Chairman, Reg Kingsley
Dep. Chairman, Eric D. Wells
Comptroller, Gordon Kane

Fishing Industry Advisory Board

Box 8101, Stn. A, St. John's, A1B 3M7

This statutory provincial agency, created under the *Fishing Industry Advisory Board Act, 1975,* reports directly to the Minister of Fisheries. The Board collects current, ongoing information about costs and operations from both fishermen and processing plants. The resulting statistical data is available during collective bargaining and for use by government in making policy decisions about the fishing industry and its development.

As well, the Board monitors major market areas for seafood products, and supplies regular or special reports to government departments and to official fishermen's and processors' organizations.

The Board also sponsors or carries out special studies into various business aspects of the fishing industry as may be required from time to time.

Chairman, Marylou Peters
Secretary to Board, Maureen Bolger

DEPARTMENT OF FORESTRY

Confederation Bldg., W. Blk., 5th Flr.
Box 4750, St. John's, A1C 5T7
General Inquiries: (709) 576-3245
Fax: (709) 576-5798; Telex: 016-4732

MINISTER'S OFFICE
Minister, The Hon. Robert J. Aylward

DEPUTY MINISTER'S OFFICE
Dep. Minister, R.D. Peters
Asst. Dep. Minister, Forestry, Dr. M. Nazir
Asst. Dep. Minister, Administration and Support Services, K.J.S. Beanlands
Special Projects
Exec. Director, S.W. Hoddinott

ADMINISTRATION
Director, R. Chafe
Accounting and Financial Manager, Bernard F. McGuire

SUPPORT SERVICES
Director, Albert King
Information and Education
Supervisor, P. Peddle

FORESTRY BRANCH
Herald Bldg., Box 2006, Corner Brook, A2H 6J8
Forest Management Director, R.D. Mercer
Resource Roads and Forest Protection
Director, G. Fleming

Forest Products Development
Director, B. Garland
Silviculture and Research Director, G. Ross
REGIONAL OFFICES:
Reg. Resource Directors:
Charles John (Eastern)
Box 4750, St. John's, A1C 5T7
Richard M. Carroll (Central)
30 Airport Blvd., Gander, A1V 1T5
Ivan Downton (Western)
Box 2006, Corner Brook, A2H 6J8
Ken Colbert (Labrador)
Box 370, Goose Bay, A0P 1C0

DEPARTMENT OF HEALTH

Confederation Bldg., W. Blk.
Box 4750, St. John's, A1C 5T7

MINISTER'S OFFICE
Minister, The Hon. Dr. John F. Collins

EXECUTIVE OFFICES
Dep. Minister, Ronald Penney
Assoc. Dep. Minister, Medical Services and Community Health, Dr. Robert Williams
Asst. Dep. Minister, Institutions, Brian Lemon
Asst. Dep. Minister, Policy, Planning and Special Programs, Gerald White
Program Co-ordinator, Brenda Andrews

ROYAL COMMISSION IMPLEMENTATION COMMITTEE
Exec. Director, Duncan Howell

WELFARE INSTITUTIONS LICENSING AND INSPECTION AUTHORITY
A/Chairperson, Margaret MacDonald

GENERAL ADMINISTRATION
Exec. Director, Cecil Templeman
Financial Manager, Earl Aker
Accountant, Max Osmond
Business Management Director, Paul Andrews
Personnel Services Manager, David Roberts
Registry and Records
Registrar, Rosella Evans
Health Care Supply Centre
Manager, Gerald Whalen

POLICY, PLANNING, AND SPECIAL PROGRAMS
Health Policy and Special Programs
Director, Aubrey Osborne
Drug Programs and Services
Director, John Downton
Health Manpower Planning
Director, Jeffrey Young

HEALTH STATISTICS AND RESEARCH
Director, Catherine Ryan

Disability Information System
Manager, Geraldine Spurrell
Systems Management
Manager, Frank Dawe
Transportation and
Special Assistance Programs
Director, Edward Hollett
Vital Statistics
Registrar, Norman Parker

INSTITUTIONAL SERVICES
Hospital Services Director, Primrose Bishop
Services to Senior Citizens
Director, Reg Gabriel
Facilities Planning Director, Gerald Gover
Personal Care Home Program
Director, Nancy Knight
Institutional Financial Services
Director, David Saunders

MEDICAL SERVICES AND COMMUNITY
HEALTH
Emergency Health Services
Director, Richard Conrad
Mental Health Services
Director, Debbie Sue Martin
Mental Health Services for Children
Director, Dr. David Aldridge
Rural Medical Care and Recruitment
Director, Cyril Galway
Public Health Laboratories
Director, Dr. Sam Ratnam

COMMUNITY HEALTH SERVICES
Director, Dr. Kevin Hogan
Disease Control and Epidemiology
Director, Dr. Faith Stratton
Reproductive Health
Consultant, Joanne MacKinnon
Health Education, Promotion and Nutrition
Director, Eleanor Swanson
Parent and Child Health
Consultant, Lynn Vivian-Book
Public Health Inspection
Director, Warrick Swyers
Public Health Nursing Director, Helen Lawlor
Occupational Health Nurse, Loretta Jeddry
St. John's and District Health Unit
Reg. Medical Officer, Dr. Gordon Noseworthy
Eastern Nfld. Health Unit, Holyrood
Reg. Medical Officer, Dr. Gordon Noseworthy
Central Nfld. Health Unit, Gander
Reg. Medical Officer, Dr. Jane Pickersgill
Western Nfld. Health Unit, Corner Brook
Reg. Medical Officer, Dr. Minnie Wasmeier

DEPARTMENT OF JUSTICE
Confederation Bldg., St. John's, A1C 5T7

MINISTER'S OFFICE
Minister and Attorney General,
The Hon. Lynn Verge, Q.C.

EXECUTIVE OFFICES
Dep. Minister and Dep. Attorney General,
Ronald Richards, Q.C.
Assoc. Dep. Minister of Justice, Deborah Fry
Assoc. Dep. Attorney General,
Robert Hyslop, Q.C.
Gen. Counsel, John Cummings
Administration Director, Garland Mouland
Financial Manager, Leonard Clarke
Accountant, Gerald Crocker

PUBLIC PROSECUTIONS
Asst. Director, Colin Flynn
Eastern
Mount Scio House, St. John's, A1C 5T7
Sr. Crown Attorney, Frank Gronich
Central
151 Airport Blvd., 2nd Flr., Gander, A1V 1W8
Sr. Crown Attorney, J. Thomas Eagan
Western
Sir Richard Squires Bldg.
Corner Brook, A2H 6C3
Sr. Crown Attorney, Gregory Brown
Labrador
Box 24, Stn. C
Happy Valley-Goose Bay, A0P 1C0
Crown Attorney, Dougald Gillis
Clarenville
Box 1163, Clarenville, A0E 1J0
Crown Attorney, Vacant
Grand Falls
Provincial Bldg., Grand Falls, A2A 1W9
Sr. Crown Attorney, Wayne Gorman
Harbour Grace
Box 479, Harbour Grace, A0A 2M0
Crown Attorney, Vacant
Stephenville
506 Montana Dr., 2nd Flr., Rm. 51
Stephenville, A2N 2T4
Crown Attorney, Vacant

OFFICE OF THE LEGISLATIVE COUNSEL
Sr. Legislative Counsel, John Noel
Legislative Counsels:
Calvin Lake, Lorna Proudfoot, Wendy Kipnis

CIVIL DIVISION
Director, John McCarthy
Sr. Solicitor, Herbert Buckingham
Solicitors: Alphonsus Faour, Mary Mandville,
Adrian Battcock, Greg Crockett,
Lynn Spracklin, Q.C., Ronald Stevenson,
Anne Marie Rose, Reg Locke,
Deborah Paquette, Lisa Byrne, Brian Furey,
Katherine J. Crosbie, Heather Young

ADMINISTRATION
Librarian, Mona B. Pearce
Personnel Specialist, L.M. Dingwell
Systems Analyst, Karen Hibbs
Registrar, Phyllis Cahill

COURTS
(See judiciary listings)

LICENSING DIVISION
Prudential Bldg., St. John's, A1C 5T7
Director, H. Vivian
REGISTRY OF DEEDS, COMPANIES AND
SECURITIES
Confederation Bldg., St. John's, A1C 5T7
Registrar, William Gillies, Q.C.
ELECTORAL OFFICE
278 LeMarchant Rd., St. John's, A1E 1P7
Chief Electoral Officer, D. Whelan
ROYAL NEWFOUNDLAND CONSTABULARY
Fort Townshend, St John's, A1E 3Y4
Chief of Police, Edward J. Coady

ADULT CORRECTIONS
Box 6084, St. John's, A1V 2E1
Director, M. McNutt

H.M. Penitentiary
Forest Rd., St. John's, A1C 5W4
Asst. Sup't, D. Saunders
HUMAN RIGHTS DIVISION
Exec. Director, Gladys Vivian

AGENCIES, BOARDS AND COMMISSIONS

Human Rights Commission
Box 4750, St. John's, A1C 5T7

The Human Rights Commission is appointed under the authority of the *Newfoundland Human Rights Code,* passed in 1969. The Commission's dual responsibility involves administering and enforcing the Code, and promoting a general awareness of human rights through education. It also reviews affirmative action programs. If approved by the Commission, such programs do not violate the Code.

The Code prohibits discrimination in the areas of accommodation, services, occupancy of dwelling units, employment, and publications on the basis of race, religion, religious creed, sex, marital status, physical disability, mental disability, political opinion, colour, or ethnic, national, or social origin. Harassment on any of these grounds is also prohibited in the area of occupancy and in places of business. In addition, age discrimination is forbidden in the area of employment.

The Commission receives and investigates complaints of discrimination. If the parties cannot reach agreement informally, it may recommend that a hearing be held and the Commission has been granted wide-ranging powers to compel persons to appear and to obtain necessary information and documents.

The Commission is composed of seven commissioners and an administrative staff.

Chairperson, Gillian Butler
Box 5457, St. John's, A1C 5W4
Exec. Director, Gladys Vivian
345-347 Duckworth St., 6th Flr.
St. John's, A1C 1H6

Newfoundland Crimes Compensation Board
Box 4750, St. John's, A1C 5T7

Newfoundland Law Reform Commission
Centre Bldg., 21 Church Hill
St. John's, A1C 3Z8
General Inquiries: (709) 739-9686

The Newfoundland Law Reform Commission was established pursuant to the provisions of *The Newfoundland Law Reform Commission Act,* S.N. 1971, Chapter 38. The first commissioners were appointed in April 1981.

Under the enabling statute, the Commission is mandated to inquire into and to consider matters relating to reform of the province's laws, including statute law, the common law, judicial decisions, judicial and quasi-judicial procedures under any Act, and any subject referred to it by the Minister of Justice. The Commission receives sustaining funding jointly from the Province and The Law Foundation of Newfoundland. The Commission is responsible to the provincial Minister of Justice, who is charged with the administration of the Act. Copies of the Commission's Working Papers and Reports are available upon request.

Chairman, J. Derek Green, Q.C.
Exec. Director, Christopher P. Curran
Research Officer, Marie I. Donovan
Secretary, Jackie P. Youden

DEPARTMENT OF LABOUR
Confederation Bldg., W. Blk., 2nd Flr.
Prince Philip Dr., Box 4750
St. John's, A1C 5T7

MINISTER'S OFFICE
Minister, The Hon. Ted A. Blanchard

DEPUTY MINISTER'S OFFICE
Dep. Minister, Howard Noseworthy
Director of Administration, Robert Learning
Accountant, H.E. Tansley

Occupational Health and Safety Division
Asst. Dep. Minister, Robert K. Langdon
Chief Occupational Medical Officer,
Dr. J. Martin
Engineering and Technical Services
Director, A.W. Diamond
Electrical Inspection Services
A/Director, R. Layden
Occupational Health and Safety
Inspection Services
Director, Roger March
Occupational Health and Safety
Education and Committees
A/Director, David Clark

Labour
Asst. Dep. Minister, Linda Hunt Black
Labour Relations
Director, Joseph O'Neill
Labour Standards Division
Director, G.H.D. Jackman
Asst. Director, David Kerr

AGENCIES, BOARDS AND COMMISSIONS

Labour Relations Board
Confederation Bldg., St. John's, A1C 5T7

The Labour Relations Board administers certain provisions of *The Labour Relations Act, 1977; The Fishing Industry Collective Bargaining Act, 1971; The Public Service Collective Bargaining Act, 1973;* and *The Newfoundland Teacher Collective Bargaining Act, 1973.*

These provisions include: (a) the certification of unions as bargaining agents for units of employees; (b) the issuance of orders of revocation of certification; (c) the termination of bargaining rights of unions who have been voluntarily recognized by employers but who no longer represent a majority of employees in the unit; and (d) the investigation of complaints of unfair labour practices, such as the failure to negotiate in good faith, and discrimination against employees because of their membership in a union.

Chairman, Gordon Easton, Q.C.
CEO, J.M. Noel

Labour Standards Board
Confederation Bldg., St. John's, A1C 5T7

The Labour Standards Board is established under authority of section 55 of *The Labour Standards Act, 1977,* and consists of three members, one representative of management, one representative of labour, and one who is independent.

The principal function of the Board is to investigate rates of pay and terms and conditions of employment of persons receiving less than subsistence wages and to recommend minimum rates of wages for such employees to the Lieutenant-Governor in Council. The end result here is the proclamation of a Minimum Wage Order.

Chairman, Emerson Barbour
Secretary, David Kerr

Labour Standards Tribunal
Confederation Bldg., St. John's, A1C 5T7

The Labour Standards Tribunal was established under the *Labour Standards Act, 1977.* It reviews and decides upon matters referred to it by: (1) the Director of Labour Standards; (2) any person aggrieved by a determination of the director; or (3) any person alleging a breach of the Act.

The Tribunal may order the payment of wages due employees by employers, or compliance with any obligations imposed upon employers and employees under the Act.

Chairman, David G. Andrews, LL.B.
Secretary, C. Allen

DEPARTMENT OF LABRADOR AFFAIRS
Confederation Bldg., St. John's, A1C 5T7

MINISTER'S OFFICE
Minister, The Hon. Garfield Warren

DEPUTY MINISTER'S OFFICE
Dep. Minister, Harold Stone

DEPARTMENT OF MINES
Box 4750, St. John's, A1C 5T7

MINISTER'S OFFICE
Minister, The Hon. Jerome W. Dinn

DEPUTY MINISTER'S OFFICE
Dep. Minister, John McKillop
Asst. Dep. Minister, Mines, John Fleming
Asst. Dep. Minister, Energy, Vacant
Administration Director, Kevin Whelan
Accountant, Felix Croke

MINERAL DEVELOPMENT DIVISION
Director, Bryan Greene
Administrative Officer, D. Wayne Ryder
Laboratory Services Director, H. Wagenbauer
Regional Mapping
Sr. Geologists:
R. Wardle (Labrador)
S. Coleman-Sadd (Newfoundland)
Sr. Geochemist, P.H. Davenport
Mineral Evaluation
Sr. Geologist, Paul Dean
Publications and Information
Sr. Geologist, R. Gibbons
Quarternary Geology
Sr. Geologist, D. Vanderveer
Mapping Service (Draughting)
Supervisor, K. Byrne

MINERAL LANDS AND MINES DIVISION
Director, Norman Kipnis
Mineral Development Engineering
Manager, F. Morrissey
Mineral Policy and Project Analysis
Manager, B. Hynes
Mineral Rights Administration
Manager, Noel Gover
Quarry Materials Administration
Manager, John Sullivan

ENERGY POLICY DIVISION
Director, D.C. Inkster
Economic and Program Analysis
Manager, Arch Hutchings

ENERGY PROGRAMS DIVISION
Director, P. Graham
Energy Audit and Management
Manager, D. Driscoll

Energy Demonstrations and Development
Manager, D. Drover
Energy Information Co-ordinator, Vacant

DEPARTMENT OF MUNICIPAL AFFAIRS

Confederation Bldg. Complex
St. John's, A1C 5T7

MINISTER'S OFFICE
Minister, The Hon. R. Charles Brett

DEPUTY MINISTER'S OFFICE
Dep. Minister, S.F. Manuel
Asst. Dep. Minister, Finance, Planning
and Administration, D. Peckham
Asst. Dep. Minister, Municipal Services,
A.R. Colbourne

ADMINISTRATION
Director, W. Hiscock
Chief Accountant, D. Sheppard
Registrar, Joan Hibbs

LOCAL GOVERNMENT ADMINISTRATION
Director, A. Brown
Asst. Director, S. Ivany
Municipal Finance
Director, C. Goodland

MUNICIPAL ENGINEERING SERVICES
Director, E. Mercer
REGIONAL ENGINEERS:
Eastern, R. Dillon
Confederation Bldg. Complex, Main Flr.
St. John's, A1C 5T7
Central-Gander, J. Harty
Burden Bldg., 70 Airport Blvd.
Gander, A1V 1K6
Western-Corner Brook, W. Cheater
Sir Richard Squires Bldg.
Corner Brook, A2H 6K6
Labrador-Goose Bay, M. Edge
Bldg. 480, Box 370
Goose Bay Airport, A0P 1C0

URBAN AND RURAL PLANNING
Director, D. Hurd
Asst. Director, S. Clinton
Chief Reg. Planners:
Ron Ozon (East), M. Burns (West)
Sr. Planners: Alice Graesser (East)
Y. Lam (East), Vacant (West)

DEVELOPMENT CONTROL
Director, D.J. Ryan
St. John's Office
Confederation Bldg. Complex
St. John's, A1C 5T7
Reg. Development Control Officer, Bruce Pike

Corner Brook Office
Sir Richard Squires Bldg.
Corner Brook, A2H 6K6
Reg. Development Control Officer, L. Pike
Grand Falls Office
Provincial Bldg., Cromer Ave.
Grand Falls, A2A 1W9
Reg. Development Control Officer, R. Peaty

ASSESSMENT DIVISION
Confederation Bldg. Complex
St. John's, A1C 5T7
Director, N. Mullett
REGIONAL OFFICES
Gander
70 Airport Blvd., Gander, A1V 1K6
Reg. Municipal Affairs Administrator, R. Lush
Labrador
Bldg. 480, Box 370
Goose Bay Airport, A0P 1S0
Reg. Municipal Affairs Administrator, E. McLean

EMERGENCY MEASURES
Prudential Bldg., 47-55 Elizabeth Ave.
St. John's, A1C 5T7
Director, J. Greer
REGIONAL OFFICES
Sir Richard Squires Bldg., Mt. Bernard Ave.
Corner Brook, A2H 6K6
Regional Municipal Affairs Administration
T. Dunphy

ST. JOHN'S FIRE DEPT.
Central Fire Stn., St. John's, A1C 2G2
Fire Chief, S. Stanley

AGENCIES, BOARDS AND COMMISSIONS

Provincial Fire Commissioner
Fire Commissioner's Office
Pleasantville, St. John's, A1C 5T7
Fire Commissioner, Francis Ryan

DEPARTMENT OF PUBLIC WORKS AND SERVICES

Confederation Bldg., St. John's, A1C 5T7
General Inquiries: (709) 576-3439

MINISTER'S OFFICE
Minister, The Hon. Dr. Hugh Twomey

DEPUTY MINISTER'S OFFICE
Dep. Minister, Wayne Mitchell

Government Services
Asst. Dep. Minister, Sid Blundon, C.A.
Finance and Administration
Director, W. Delaney
Chief Accountant, A. English

Personnel and Pay Director, G. Conran
Registrar, J. Kelsey
Newfoundland Information Services
Director, R. Callahan
Realty Services Division
Director, K. Brocklehurst

Technical Services Branch

Assoc. Dep. Minister, Thomas E. Bursey, P.Eng.
Tendering and Contracts
Director, R. Hoyles

Property and Accommodations

Asst. Dep. Minister, G.W. Smith
Accommodations Manager, L. Newhook
Support Services Director, D. Taylor
Director of Security, John Clarke
Project Management Director, R. Brophy
Director of Design, E. Snook

GOVERNMENT PURCHASING AGENCY
Atlantic Place, 5th Flr., St. John's, A1C 5T7
Exec. Director, E.E. Rowe

AGENCIES, BOARDS AND COMMISSIONS

C.A. Pippy Park Commission
Nagles Place, Box 8861, St. John's, A1B 3T2

Established as a Crown corporation in 1968 under the *Pippy Park Commission Act,* the Commission is charged with the administration and control of 1,619 hectares of natural woodland in the northwest section of St. John's. It has two broad mandates: the provision of "recreational" land, and land-banking for future institutional construction.

The Commission consists of eight members who are appointed as follows: six by the Lieutenant-Governor in Council, one of whom shall be by recommendation of the C.A. Pippy family; one by the City of St. John's; and one by the Memorial University of Newfoundland.

Chairman and CEO, D.C. Barter
Operations Manager, C.M. Manning
Financial Administrator, J. Balram

Public Service Commission
146-148 Forest Rd., St. John's, A1A 1E6

The Public Service Commission operates under authority of the *Public Service Commission Act* (1973). It provides for the appointment of three commissioners and a professional staff who are responsible for carrying out certain duties in support of selected personnel programs for government departments and several agencies.

The principal programs include: recruitment and selection of candidates for appointment to or promotion within the Public Service based upon the "merit principle"; provision of Service-wide staff training and development activities including training for municipal governments and support for non-government hospitals; personnel plan-

ning advisory services; staff evaluation advisory services; the employee assistance program; long-service awards; and employee relocation benefits.

Chairman, P. Withers
Vice-Chairman, V.J. Rossiter
Commissioner, D. Whitten

Queen's Printer
Confederation Bldg. Annex
St. John's, A1C 5T7

The Office of the Queen's Printer responds to the printing and publishing needs of the Newfoundland Legislature and departments and agencies of the Government of Newfoundland and Labrador.

The Office ensures that printing and publishing requests meet existing guidelines. It then seeks the most effective means of handling those requests placing strong emphasis on cost, quality, service, and security.

Required printing is either carried out internally by the Printing and Micrographics Division of the Department of Public Works and Services or externally by a firm selected through a public tendering process.

The Office provides a subscription service to *The Newfoundland Gazette* (published weekly), *The Statutes of Newfoundland* (published yearly in bound volumes), Bills of the House of Assembly, and individual chapters of the Statutes.
Queen's Printer, D. Dawe
Printing Services
A/Director, W. Hudson

DEPARTMENT OF RURAL, AGRICULTURAL AND NORTHERN DEVELOPMENT
Confederation Bldg., W. Blk., 4th Flr.
St. John's, A1C 5T7

MINISTER'S OFFICE
Minister, The Hon. Rick Woodford

DEPUTY MINISTER'S OFFICE
Dep. Minister, Harold Stone

Asst. Dep. Minister, Rural Development,
T.C. Healey

Asst. Dep. Minister, Labrador Branch,
John McGrath

ADMINISTRATION
Director, Margaret Power
Accountant, P. Costigan
Information Specialist, I. Mullett
Registrar, G. Costello

Business Development
Director, F. Cook

BUSINESS DEVELOPMENT OFFICES:

Eastern Region
Box 239, Clarenville, A0E 1J0
Business Development Specialist, Lloyd Powell
Box 598, Harbour Grace, A0A 2M0
Business Development Specialist, Ernie Pynn

Central Region
Provincial Bldg., Grand Falls, A2A 1W9
Business Development Supervisor, Tom Fagan
Box 352, Gander, A1B 1W5
Business Development Specialist,
Percy Chaytor

Western Region
Sir Richard Squires Bldg.
Corner Brook, A2H 6J8
Business Development Supervisor,
Derek Stratton

Labrador
Box 280, Stn. B, Happy Valley, A0P 1E0
Business Management Consultant, Eric Flynn

REGIONAL DEVELOPMENT
Director, Neville Squire
REGIONAL DEVELOPMENT OFFICES:

Eastern Region
Confederation Bldg., St. John's, A1C 5T7
Eastern Reg. Supervisor, George Green

Central Region
Box 352, Gander, A1B 1W5
Central Reg. Supervisor, Frank McDonald

Western Region
Sir Richard Squires Bldg.
Corner Brook, A2H 6J8
Western Reg. Supervisor, Martin Lowe

RESEARCH AND ANALYSIS
Director, Richard Fuchs
CO-OPERATIVE DIVISION
Director, S.M. Kean

Agriculture Branch

Asst. Dep. Minister, Martin Howlett
Soil and Land Management
Director, D. Sudom
Provincial Veterinarian, Dr. Hugh Whitney
Extension and Veterinary Services
Director, Kevin Aucoin
Production and Market Planning
Director, Phil Macarthy
Crop and Livestock Insurance Programs
Co-ordinator, Vacant
Farm Business and Evaluation
Director, Vacant

AGENCIES, BOARDS, COMMISSIONS AND CROWN CORPORATIONS

MARKETING BOARDS

Marketing boards for agricultural products in Canada are created by a number of different pieces of legislation. National wheat and dairy products plans flow from the *Canadian Wheat Board Act* and the *Canadian Dairy Commission*

Act respectively. Egg and poultry boards derive their authority from the *Farm Products Marketing Agencies Act*. As well, many have their own provincial statutes and are normally within the jurisdiction of an umbrella provincial agency. The individual boards are, however, non-governmental and made up largely of elected farmer representatives.

There is also a variety of types. The Economic Council of Canada's study on marketing boards identified five: promotional and developmental boards with little power; selling-desk boards that handle marketing but do not set prices; boards that negotiate prices; boards that set prices; and full-fledged boards that establish quotas. These last are known as supply-management marketing boards. Currently, there are more than 100 active boards in Canada.

AGRICULTURAL PRODUCTS MARKETING
BOARD
Provincial Agriculture Bldg., Brockfield Rd.
Mount Pearl, St. John's, A1C 5T7

The Agricultural Products Marketing Board is a provincial supervisory board that has been in operation since 1970. It protects consumers against producers who abuse the authority given them through their own commodity marketing boards. This Board has authority under legislation to control and direct the operations of provincial commodity marketing boards. It consists of a chairman, a secretary, and seven members.

Chairman, Art Jackman
Program Co-ordinator, Reg King

NEWFOUNDLAND CHICKEN MARKETING
BOARD
49-55 Elizabeth Ave., St. John's, A1C 5P9

The Newfoundland Chicken Marketing Board, established in 1980, consists of five to seven members appointed by the Minister of Agriculture under section 13 of the *Natural Products Marketing Act,* S.N. 1973, Chapter 79.

The purpose of the Newfoundland Chicken Marketing Scheme is to promote, control, regulate, or prohibit the production and marketing of chicken within the province. The scheme applies to all producers and processors who produce or market chicken, but does not apply to those who produce and market fewer than 100 chickens at any one time.

Chairman, Joseph Smallwood
Manager, William Slade

NEWFOUNDLAND EGG MARKETING BOARD
49-55 Elizabeth Ave., St. John's, A1A 2Y3

Incorporated on Jan. 1, 1971, the Newfoundland Egg Marketing Board formulates and implements policies for the egg industry in accordance with the *Provincial Agricultural Products Marketing Act,* within the guidelines set down by the Newfoundland Egg Marketing Scheme, 1970, as amended.

The Board is comprised of six directors, including a chairman, who are elected every two years by and from among egg producers. The Board is supported financially by the egg producers of the province through the collection of a service charge on all eggs produced and marketed. There is no financial assistance from either the provincial or federal governments.

The purpose of the Board is to provide stability to the industry. The Board regulates the supply and pricing of eggs in the province at the farm gate level, operating within the established quota policy of the Canadian Egg Marketing Agency (CEMA).

The Board also participates in other facets of the egg industry, such as the monitoring of pullet replacements; the surveillance of the quality, handling, and display of the product in the market place; and the advertising and promotion of the use of eggs, especially in the food service industry.

Chairman, Hollis Duffett
Manager, M.F. Dicks

NEWFOUNDLAND MILK MARKETING BOARD
653 Topsail Rd., St. John's, A1E 2E3

The purpose of the Board is to promote, control, and regulate or prohibit the production and marketing of milk within the province. The Board, which was formed in 1983, consists of seven members appointed by the Minister of Agriculture; five are producers and two are independent consumers. The chairman and vice-chairman are elected by the members.

Chairman, Eric Rumbolt
Manager, Martin Hammond

Farm Development Loan Board of Newfoundland
Provincial Agriculture Bldg.
Brookfield Road, Mt. Pearl, A1C 5T7

The Farm Development Loan Board was established and funded by the Newfoundland Government in 1953 under *An Act to Create a Farm Loan Board and to Provide Loans for Farm Development.*

The Board provides loans of up to $75,000 at a rate of interest three percentage points below the prime lending rate charged by commercial banks. The repayment period is determined by the Board but does not exceed 20 years unless there are exceptional circumstances. The loans are chiefly for land purchase and improvements, farm equipment purchases, farm buildings, livestock, and working capital (maximum $30,000).

Chairman, Martin Howlett
Manager, D. Dicks

Newfoundland Farm Products Corp.
Bldg. 902, Pleasantville
Box 9457, Stn. B, St. John's, A1A 2Y3

Newfoundland Farm Products Corporation is a Crown corporation, established under the *New-foundland Farm Products Corporation Act,* S.N. 1964, Chapter 62, for the purpose of processing locally produced poultry and hogs for major markets. The Corporation is under the general supervision of the Minister of Rural, Agricultural and Northern Development, and is operated under a board of directors, consisting of five to nine members who are appointed by the Lieutenant-Governor in Council on a year to year basis.

The Board is responsible for broiler and hog processing plants in St. John's and for broiler plants in Corner Brook. The administration and accounting divisions are centralized at the head office in St. John's.

Chairman, G.J. O'Reilly
President and CEO, J.E. McDonald
Vice-President, Operations, Tom Burke
Secretary, R.J. McGrath

DEPARTMENT OF SOCIAL SERVICES
Confederation Bldg., Box 4750
St. John's, A1C 5T7
General Inquiry: (709) 576-2478
Fax: (709) 576-6996; Telex: 016-4197

MINISTER'S OFFICE
Minister, The Hon. Glenn Tobin

DEPUTY MINISTER'S OFFICE
Dep. Minister, Elizabeth Marshall
Asst. Dep. Minister, Income and Rehabilitative Services, Calvin Payne
Asst. Dep. Minister, Finance and Regional Operations, David Roberts
Asst. Dep. Minister, Children and Youth Services, Sheila Devine

SERVICES
Administration
Director, E. Johnson
Asst. Director, Vacant
Personnel and Labour Relations
Director, Patrick Hamilton
Accounting
Financial Manager, David Miller
Accountant, L. Hatcher
Registrar, Howard Butt
Planning and Research
Director, Ronald G. Day
Child Welfare
Director, Frank Simms
Asst. Director, Elizabeth Crawford
Youth Corrections
Director, Sharron Callahan
Asst. Director, Bryan Purcell
Social Assistance
Director, Terry Haire
Asst. Director, Roy Barbour
Employment Opportunities
Director, Terry Stapleton
Asst. Director, Peter Harvey

Regional Services
Director, Roy Tiller
Emergency Welfare Services
Director, Roy Tiller
Day Care and Homemaker Services
Director, Vivian Randell
Asst. Director, Sandra Morris
Mental Retardation Services
Director, Noel Browne
Asst. Director, Donald Gallant
Rehabilitation Services
Director, Jerome Quinlan
Asst. Director, Melvin Duffett
REGIONAL OFFICES
Central Region
Reg. Director, Fred Granville
Provincial Bldg., Cromer Ave.
Grand Falls, A2A 1W9
Eastern Region
Reg. Director, Harvey Reid
Box 580, Harbour Grace, A0A 2M0
Labrador Region
Reg. Director, Wayne Penney
Box 820, Happy Valley, Labrador, A0P 1E0
St. John's Region
Reg. Director, Gordon Dunn
Box 4750, St. John's, A1C 5T7
Western Region
Reg. Director, John Jenniex
Sir Richard Squires Bldg.
Corner Brook, A2H 6J8

AGENCIES, BOARDS AND COMMISSIONS

Social Assistance Appeal Board
c/o Dept. of Social Services
Confederation Bldg., St. John's, A1C 5T7
    The Social Assistance Appeal Board is an independent, non-partisan body appointed by the Lieutenant-Governor in Council. It consists of a chairman and two members, who are appointed for a three-year term and are eligible for reappointment. They are not employees of the government.
    The Board hears appeals by persons who are not satisfied with the decisions of Regional Directors or Administrative Review Committees to whom they had appealed their treatment by officials of the Department of Social Services. At present, these appeals relate to matters of financial assistance provided under the *Social Assistance Act.*
Chairman, Edward Mifflin
Exec. Secretary, Mary Codner

DEPARTMENT OF TRANSPORTATION

Confederation Bldg. Complex, 6th Flr.
St. John's, A1C 5T7

MINISTER'S OFFICE
Minister, The Hon. Norman Doyle

DEPUTY MINISTER'S OFFICE
Dep. Minister, A.J. Goss
Asst. Dep. Minister, Finance and Administration, Vacant
Asst. Dep. Minister, Technical, J.F. O'Reilly

ADMINISTRATION/PERSONNEL
Director of Personnel, G. Murphy
Department Systems Manager, L. Hayley
Registrar, J. Anthony

FINANCIAL SERVICES
Director, F. Delaney
Departmental Budget Analyst, E. McCormack
Accountant, P. Browne
Purchasing Services Manager, R. Harris

MOTOR REGISTRATION DIVISION
Viking Bldg., Crosbie Rd., St. John's, A1C 5T7
Registrar, G.M. Hussey
Dep. Registrar, G. Barbour

TECHNICAL SERVICES DIVISION
Maintenance Director, A.E. Arklie
Transportation Services Director, T. Prim
Vehicle Fleet Manager, N. Payne
Highway Design Director, T. McCarthy
Construction Director, W. Spencer
Chief Bridge Engineer, P. Lester
Marine Operations Manager, J. Hanlon

POLICY DEVELOPMENT AND PLANNING DIVISION
Director, W.T. Beckett

AIR SERVICES DIVISION
Air Operations Manager, H. Hillier
Air Services Co-ordinator, Vacant

INDEPENDENT AGENCIES, BOARDS, COMMISSIONS AND CROWN CORPORATIONS

Alcohol and Drug Dependency Commission of Newfoundland and Labrador

Prince Charles Bldg., Ste. 105
120 Torbay Rd., St. John's, A1A 2G8
    The Alcohol and Drug Dependency Commission (ADDC) is a corporation that was established by an Act of the provincial legislature in 1982. Its mandate is to co-ordinate a plan for implementing treatment, rehabilitation, education, and prevention programs to reduce problems related to abuse of alcohol and other drugs.
    The ADDC provides counselling and referral services for individuals and families affected by

alcoholism or other drug abuse problems. Public education is provided through schools, the media, and by presentations to community groups. Seminars and workshops are conducted for professionals, such as teachers and law enforcement officers, whose work involves them in the field of alcohol and drug abuse. The ADDC also provides Employee Assistance Programs and an Information Centre. It sponsors the Provincial Allied Youth Program.

Chairman, George W.N. Skinner

REGIONAL OFFICES:

St. John's Region
49-55 Elizabeth Ave., Prudential Bldg.
Box 10072, Stn. B, St. John's, A1A 4L5
Reg. Administrator, Donna Simms

Eastern Region
Box 339, Harbour Grace, A0A 2M0
Reg. Administrator, Kimberly Grant

Central Region
Box 724, Grand Falls, A2A 2K2
Reg. Administrator, Betty Pye

Western Region
Box 684, Corner Brook, A2H 6G1
Reg. Administrator, William Haynes

Labrador Region
Box 1060, Stn. B, Goose Bay, A0P 1E0
A/Reg. Administrator, Delia Halbot

Churchill Falls (Labrador) Corp. Ltd.
Philip Place, Elizabeth Ave.
Box 9200, St. John's, A1A 2X8
General Inquiries: (709) 737-1450

This Corporation is a subsidiary of Newfoundland and Labrador Hydro and operates a hydroelectric generating plant (5,225 megawatts) at Churchill Falls, Labrador.

Chairman and CEO, Cyril J. Abery
President, John P. Henderson
Vice-President, Finance, and CFO, R.A. Grant
Vice-President, Operations and Engineering, David Reeves
Vice-President, Gen. Counsel and Corporate Secretary, Maureen Greene
Public Relations Director, C.W. Bursey

Lower Churchill Development Corp.
Box 9800, St. John's, A1A 3W3
General Inquiries: (709) 737-1400

The Lower Churchill Development Corporation is a Crown corporation which is owned 51 per cent by Newfoundland and Labrador Hydro, the designate for the Government of Newfoundland and Labrador, and 49 per cent by the Government of Canada.

The Corporation was established on Dec. 15, 1978 with an option to develop the hydroelectric potential of the Lower Churchill River in Labrador. Studies carried out by the Corporation have confirmed that 2,300 megawatts of power could

be generated at two locations on the river and serve as an economical source of energy for the eastern North American market.

The board of directors for the Corporation consists of twelve persons: six nominees of Newfoundland, five nominees of Canada and the chief executive officer.

Chairman, Cyril J. Abery
President and CEO, David W. Mercer
Vice-President, Gen. Counsel and Corporate Secretary, Maureen Greene
Public Relations Director, C.W. Bursey

Newfoundland and Labrador Computer Services Ltd.
Box 9308, Stn. B, St. John's, A1A 2Y3
(709) 737-6100; Fax: (709) 737-6155

Newfoundland and Labrador Computer Services is a Crown corporation, wholly owned by the provincial government, which provides a range of electronic data processing services to government, its agencies, and Memorial University.

Incorporated under the *Companies Act* in 1969, the organization has three shareholders: the Minister of Health, the Minister of Public Works and Services, and the President of Treasury Board, with a ten-member board of directors appointed on an annual basis. The board is composed of five representatives from government, two from the university, and three from Crown agencies.

The corporation employs approximately 225 people and is located in St. John's. The centre operates 24 hours a day supporting over 1,000 on-line terminals, with average production runs in the order of 1,000 batch jobs per day. Support services include systems consulting and development, and facilities management.

President, H.S. Miller
Operations
Vice-President, C.R. Horwood
Finance and Administration
Vice-President, J.K. Murphy
Systems Development
Vice-President, H.M. Grant
Planning and Client Services
Vice-President, E.K. Drodge

Newfoundland and Labrador Hydro
Philip Place, Elizabeth Ave.
St. John's, A1A 2X8

Newfoundland and Labrador Hydro was created by an *Act respecting the Newfoundland and Labrador Hydroelectric Corporation No. 3* (March 27, 1975). Its objective is to develop the use of power on an economical and efficient basis.

The Corporation engages in the development, generation, production, transmission, distribution, delivery, supply, sale, and use of power. It also supplies power for domestic, commercial, industrial or other uses within and, subject to the prior approval of the Lieutenant-Governor in Council, outside the province.

Chairman and CEO, Cyril J. Abery
President, D.W. Mercer
Exec. Vice-President, John P. Henderson
Vice-President, Engineering and Construction, Leo J. Cole
Vice-President, Finance, and CFO, R.A. Grant
Vice-President, Rates and Corporate Services, Derek Osmond
Vice-President, Operations, T. David Collett
Vice-President, Gen. Counsel and Corporate Secretary, Maureen Greene
Vice-President, Employee Relations, S. Dicks
Director, Public Relations, C.W. Bursey

Newfoundland Commission of Public Utilities

Prince Charles Bldg., Box 9188
St. John's, A1A 2X9

The Newfoundland Commission of Public Utilities consists of five members appointed by the Lieutenant-Governor in Council, and a support staff of 22.

The Board administers the following statutes: *The Public Utilities Act, The Electrical Power Control Act, The Public Utilities (Acquisition of Lands) Act, The Motor Carrier Act, The Motor Vehicle Transport Act (Canada)* and *The Automobile Insurance Act.*

Chairman, J.A. Gordon MacDonald
Vice-Chairman, R.E. Good
Commissioners:
G.F. Lawrence, T.E. Williams, A.H. Wells
Exec. Director, E.H. Hodder

Newfoundland Liquor Corp.

Box 8750, Stn. A, St. John's, A1B 3V1

The Newfoundland Liquor Corporation was created in June 1973 by the *Liquor Corporation Act.*

The Corporation controls the purchase and sale of alcohol in the province. Its main objective is to provide the most efficient system of distribution of alcoholic products to the public with the highest possible level of customer service, resulting in the maximizing of revenues to the provincial treasury.

The Corporation now operates 37 liquor stores and has established 55 liquor agency stores. The Corporation also operates a bottling plant which bottles approximately 20 per cent of all the liquor sold in the province.
Minister responsible,
The Hon. H. Neil Windsor, P.Eng.
Kenmount Rd., St. John's, A1B 3V1

President, Douglas M. Chafe, CMA, FSMAC
Finance and Administration
Vice-President, Gerard Adams, C.A.
Operations
Vice-President, K. Griffiths

Newfoundland Liquor Licensing Board

Box 8550, St. John's, A1B 3P2

The Newfoundland Liquor Licensing Board, established in 1973, is a Crown corporation responsible for the administration of the *Liquor Control Act* and the Liquor (Licensing) Regulations. Its main function is to control the possession, sale, and delivery of alcohol within the province of Newfoundland.

Chairman, Edward White
Members: Douglas M. Chafe, Anne Picco, Frances Lalonde, Walter Downey

Newfoundland Medical Care Commission

Elizabeth Towers, Elizabeth Ave.
St. John's, A1C 5J3

The Newfoundland Medical Care Commission, established under the *Newfoundland Medical Care Insurance Act* (1968), was made responsible for the establishment and administration of a plan to cover the cost of medically required physician services to all residents of Newfoundland and Labrador.

This medical care plan, known as MCP, covers a wide range of insured services which are specified in the Newfoundland Medical Care (Insured Services) Regulations. Recently, the Commission also assumed responsibility for administration of the provincial dental program. The main purpose of the organization is to evaluate claims from providers and beneficiaries with respect to insured services and to process these for prompt and accurate payment.

There are four major departments within the Commission: Finance and Administration, Systems and Information, Claims Processing, and Medical Affairs. These departments are responsible to the executive director who in turn reports to the board of commissioners.
Minister responsible,
The Hon. Dr. John Collins

Chairman, Roger Crosbie
Exec. Director, Robert Peddigrew
Medical Director, Dr. G. Russell
Dental Director, Dr. Bruce Bowden

St. John's Metropolitan Area Board

Kenmount Rd., St. John's
Box 8897, Stn. A, St. John's, A1B 3T2

The St. John's Metropolitan Area Board, established by legislation enacted in June 1963, was initially responsible for the administration, development, and control of rural land surrounding the City of St. John's and the Town of Mount Pearl.

With the passing of the *Municipalities Act* in 1980, the St. John's Metropolitan Area Board was assigned the powers and authority of a "Town" and became the municipal authority for an area covering approximately 86,538 hectares with a population of 6,254 at that time. The Board provides a variety of municipal services to properties within its municipal boundaries, depending on the urban or rural nature of the area.

Membership on the Board is through appointment by the Lieutenant-Governor in Council.

Chairman, J.R. O'Dea
Vice-Chairman, William Dalton
Members: James Fagan, Thomas J. Greene, Joan Roberts, Mayor Harvey Hodder, P.G. Withers, David Barrett, Patrick Lockyer
Town Clerk, Nancy D. Caines
Town Engineer, Paul Mackey
Planner, Stephen B. Jewczyk

Twin Falls Power Corp.

Philip Pl., Elizabeth Ave., St. John's, A1A 2X9
General Inquiries: (709) 737-1450

Twin Falls Power Corporation is incorporated under the laws of Canada and has developed a 225-megawatt hydroelectric generating plant on the Unknown River, a tributary of the Churchill River in Labrador. Twin Falls holds a sublease from Churchill Falls (Labrador) Corp., but certain rights under the sublease were suspended effective June 30, 1974, with the result that Churchill Falls is diverting the flow of water from the Twin Falls plant. Churchill Falls is required, under those rights, to deliver the equivalent amount of energy to the installed capacity at Twin Falls. The Twin Falls plant was developed to supply the mining industry of Labrador North.

President, John P. Henderson
Vice-President, Finance, R.A. Grant
Secretary, Maureen Greene

Workers' Compensation Commission

146-148 Forest Rd., St. John's, A1A 3B8

The purpose of the *Workers' Compensation Act* is to provide recompense to the worker for wage loss due to disability from personal injury by accident arising out of employment, without recourse to litigation. It ensures promptness and certainty of payment to the worker or dependents without unduly burdening the employer.

The Act also: (1) extends the worker's protection to *all* accidents arising out of and in the course of employment, not only those caused by the negligence of the employer; (2) places the adjudication of claims in the hands of the Workers' Compensation Commission rather than the courts; and (3) in the industries to which it applies, makes the employer's liability collective rather than individual.

Minister responsible,
The Hon. Ted A. Blanchard

Chairman, Gary Reardon
Vice-Chairperson, Dr. Catherine Penney
CEO, Ed Maynard
Corporate Services
Exec. Director, Derek W. Forsey
Claims Services
Exec. Director, Norman Kennedy
Policy and Special Services
Exec. Director, M.J. Bursey
Financial Services Director, Eric Bartlett
Claims Department Director, John Bambrick
Rehabilitation Department
Director, Donald P. Myron
Information Services Director, Merv Andrews
Medical Services Director, Dr. Graham Cook
Administration Director, Jim Casey

JUDICIARY AND JUDICIAL OFFICERS

Supreme Court of Newfoundland

Court House, Duckworth St.
Box 5144, St. John's, A1C 5V5
General Inquiries: (709) 726-4482

APPEAL DIVISION
Chief Justice: The Hon. Noel H.A. Goodridge

Judges:
Hon. Justice J.R. Gushue
Hon. Justice J.W. Mahoney
Hon. Justice W. Marshall
Hon. Justice A.S. Mifflin*

---

* Supernumerary

Hon. Justice H.B. Morgan
Hon. Justice J.J. O'Neill

TRIAL DIVISION
Chief Justice: The Hon. T.A. Hickman

Judges:
Hon. Justice F.J. Aylward
Hon. Justice M. Cameron
Hon. Justice R.J. Halley
Hon. Justice G. Lang
Hon. Justice N.S. Noel
Hon. Justice D.L. Russell
Hon. Justice G. Steele
Hon. Justice R. Wells
Hon. Justice William G. Adams
Hon. Justice David G. Riche
Hon. Justice Lloyd Soper*
Hon. Justice Denis M. Roberts
Hon. Justice H. James Puddester, Q.C.
Hon. Justice Abraham Schwartz, Q.C.

Registrar, Supreme Court: Cyril J. Goodyear
Deputy Registrar: Henry J. Thorne
Clerk: William Parsons
High Sheriff: Leslie R. Thoms
   Kampa Bldg., 210 Water St.
   St. John's, A1C 5W2

JUDICIAL CENTRES

BRIGUS
Box 100, A0A 1K0
Judge: His Hon. Rupert W. Bartlett

CORNER BROOK
Box 2006, A2H 6J8
Judges: His Hon. P.L. Soper,
   His Hon. F.R. Woolridge

GANDER
Box 40, A1V 2E1
Judge: His Hon. Kevin Barry

GRAND BANK
Box 910, A0E 1W0
Judge: His Hon. H.H. Cummings

GRAND FALLS
Provincial Bldg., A2A 1W9
Judge: His Hon. S.H. Inder

HAPPY VALLEY/GOOSE BAY
Box 301, Labrador, A0P 1C0
Judge: His Hon. S. O'Regan

Provincial Court, St. John's

Court House, Duckworth St.
Box 5144, St. John's, A1C 5V5
General Inquiries: (709) 726-7181

Chief Judge and Clerk of the Peace:
His Hon. C.P. Scott
Assoc. Chief Judge: His Hon. E.J. Langdon
Judges: J.P. Trahey, J. Woodrow,
   G. Seabright, L.W. Wicks

YOUTH COURT
Judge: L.W. Wicks

TRAFFIC COURT
Judge: Chester C. Stone

SMALL CLAIMS
Judge: M.R. Reid

Unified Family Court

355 Duckworth St., St. John's, A1C 1H6
General Inquiries: (709) 753-5873

Judge: Hon. Justice M. Noonan
Administrator: J. Berkley Reynolds

Court Officials

SHERIFFS
Sheriff of Newfoundland: Leslie R. Thoms
Kampa Bldg., 210 Water St.
St. John's, A1C 5W2

Sub-Sheriff: A. Downey
Sir Richard Squires Bldg.
Corner Brook, A2H 6J8

BAILIFFS
Supreme Court, St. John's:
David Carrol, William Chafe, Earl Colbert

REGISTRAR OF DEEDS, COMPANIES
AND SECURITIES
William Gillies, Q.C.
Confederation Bldg., St. John's, A1C 5T7

REGISTRARS AND RECEIVERS IN
BANKRUPTCY
Registrar in Bankruptcy: Henry J. Thorne
(Official Receiver for Atlantic Provinces
V. Arthur Sibley, Sheriff
Box 235, Halifax, NS B3J 2M4)

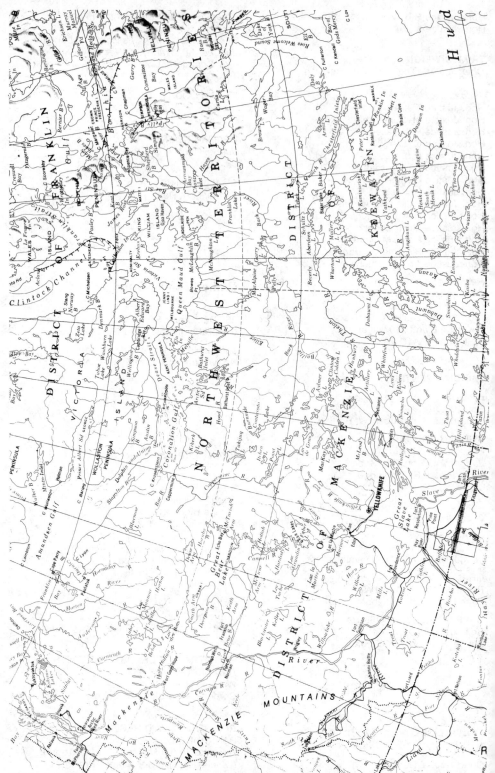

This map is based on information taken from map MCR 4032. © Her Majesty in Right of Canada with permission of Energy, Mines and Resources.

NORTHWEST TERRITORIES

Mountain Avens
(Dryas integrifolia)

Reconstituted: Sept. 1, 1905
Capital: Yellowknife
Motto: None
Flower: Mountain avens
Area: 3,426,320 km²
   percentage of Canada's total area: 34.4
   LAND: 3,293,020 km²
   FRESHWATER: 133,300 km²
Population (October 1988): 51,900
Elevation:
   HIGHEST POINT: Mount Sir James MacBrien
     (2,773 m)
   LOWEST POINT: Arctic shore at sea level

five-year change: +7.5%
per square kilometre: 0.01
percentage of Canada's total
   population: 0.2
   URBAN: 46%
   RURAL: 54%
Government Finance:
   REVENUE, 1986/87: $702.9 million
   EXPENDITURE, 1986/87: $693.0 million
   DEBT PER CAPITA (March 1987): $1,923
Personal income per capita, 1986: $17,395
Unemployment rate, 1987
   (estimated average): 17%

HISTORY

Before Confederation in 1867, the Northwest Territories was a part of a vast tract of land known as Rupert's Land, administered by the Hudson's Bay Company. In 1870, the British government transferred full title of these lands to Canada. The Canadian *Northwest Territories Act* of 1875, with amendments, still serves as the "constitution" of the Northwest Territories.

After 1905, when the provinces of Saskatchewan and Alberta were created, the residual N.W.T. was left with a federally-appointed Commissioner and Council in Ottawa. In 1951, the first elected members from the Mackenzie District joined the Territorial Council. Finally in 1967, the N.W.T. obtained a resident Commissioner and administration.

By 1975, the Territorial Council was fully elected, rather than partially appointed, and included representation from the Eastern Arctic as well as the West. Now, the Territorial Legislative Assembly is made up of 24 elected members.

An executive council made up of eight members of the Legislative Assembly, one of whom is elected Government Leader, is responsible for decisions on policy and programs, for relations with federal or provincial governments, and for the general conduct of government in the N.W.T.

The territorial government maintains a departmentalized public service similar to those of the provincial governments. The public service handles administrative duties in the Territories. The federal government controls and administers all the Territories' natural resources, except game and forestry, because their development requires substantial government investment in exploration, communications and transportation.

THE LAND

The physiographic areas in the Northwest Territories are varied. Just over half of the N.W.T. and the Arctic Archipelago is occupied by the Precambrian Shield. The Plains area can be divided into the Interior or Western Plains, the Arctic Lowlands, the Arctic Coastal Plain, and the Hudson Bay Lowland. The Interior Plains are a continuation of the Great Plains that stretch from the Gulf of Mexico northward. Mountains and basins similar to those of the Cordilleran and Appalachian areas of western and eastern Canada comprise the Innuitian area. A small portion of the Cordilleran region is contained in the western N.W.T. — part of the great mountain barrier which extends along the western part of the continent.

The Northwest Territories is not a land of eternal ice and snow, although there are permanent icecaps on the far northern islands and a large percentage of the land is permanently frozen (a condition termed permafrost). For the most part, however, the climate of the N.W.T. can be described as dry and cold.

THE PEOPLE

The population of the Northwest Territories can be divided into three ethnic groups: Inuit, or Eskimo, comprise 35.5 per cent of the total population; Dene (or native Indian) and Métis, 22.4 per cent; and non-native, 42.1 per cent, about half of whom are of British descent. (The preceding percentages were based on 1986 figures).

The Northwest Territories has the largest proportion of people who cannot speak French or English, with 13.9 per cent speaking neither official language. Unilingual anglophones make up 79.9 per cent of the population, while unilingual francophones constitute only 0.1 per cent; 6 per cent are bilingual. This is in addition to Inuktitut and Inuvialuktun (spoken by the Inuit); the Dene languages, which include Chipewyan, Dogrib, South Slavey, North Slavey, and Loucheux; and certain European and Asian languages.

Of the total Northwest Territories population aged 15 years or older, 64.6 per cent participate in the labour force. The city of Yellowknife has one of the highest participation rates in Canada, at 82.7 per cent. Within the labour force, paid workers account for 96.7 per cent of the total, self-employed workers for 3.1 per cent, and the remainder consists of unpaid family workers.

THE ECONOMY

Renewable and non-renewable resources provide the main base for the economy of the Northwest Territories, which has been experiencing a 4 per cent growth rate recently. Fish, marine mammals, game, forestry, and some agricultural developments contribute to the employment of N.W.T. residents and to the territorial economy.

Tourism, community co-operatives and government also contribute to the economy. The territorial and federal governments are the two largest employers in the Northwest Territories.

Public sector employment accounts for about 21 per cent of the labour force, while the service sector accounts for the largest portion of the work force, employing some 25 per cent.

Fishing and hunting. Sport fishing, net fishing for domestic purposes, and a small commercial fishery are an important sector of the economy. Most residents who undertake net fishing are native people and/or others who live primarily off the land.

A significant component of the economy in most Inuit communities is the Arctic marine mammal harvest, while a wide variety of game in other parts of the N.W.T. is hunted for sport and for domestic use. A great many residents use hunting and trapping as a primary or secondary source of livelihood.

Forestry. The area below the tree line in the N.W.T. is sufficiently timbered to support a modest commercial forest industry. In the more northerly forested areas, wood is usually used domestically for fuel rather than building.

Agriculture. The relatively harsh climate in most areas of the N.W.T. has precluded any large-scale agricultural development, but several privately-run market gardens are located in communities situated south of Great Slave Lake.

Mining. In the non-renewable resource sector, mineral exploration and development is by far the largest independent economic operation in the Northwest Territories. Gold, silver, zinc, lead, and copper are all mined in the N.W.T. In 1987, the N.W.T. had six operating mines, providing direct employment for 2,500 people. Due to inadequate increases in tungsten prices, the Cantung mine at Tungsten was not reopened. The Salamita mine and the Terra Mines Bullmoose project closed during 1987. However, the effect of mine closures was eased as employment by other mines increased.

The value of mineral production in 1987 is estimated at $795 million, compared with $826 million the previous year. Exploration activity increased to an estimated 60 to 65 million.

Oil and gas finds at Norman Wells (the Territories' only producing oilfield), the Arctic Islands, Beaufort Sea, and Mackenzie Delta also contribute to the northern economy. Oil and gas exploration activity declined in 1986 and 1987, due primarily to a drop in world oil prices. However, the outlook for development of some discovered reserves in the Beaufort Sea/Mackenzie Delta region remains promising. The Northern Oil and Gas Action Program (NOGAP) was created to help examine and prepare for the effects of major northern hydrocarbon development in this area.

Information provided by the Department of Culture and Communications, Government of the Northwest Territories.

GOVERNMENT OF THE NORTHWEST TERRITORIES

Seat of Government: Yellowknife, X1A 2L9

NORTHWEST TERRITORIES ACT

The *Northwest Territories Act*, R.S.C. 1970, Chapter N-22, provides for the government of the Northwest Territories by a Commissioner under instructions given from time to time by the Governor in Council or the Minister of the Department of Indian Affairs and Northern Development. *The Northwest Territories Act*, as amended, also provides for a Legislative Assembly of 24 elected members.

The Commissioner of the Legislative Assembly has legislative powers on such matters as: direct taxation within the Territories in order to raise revenue, maintenance of municipal institutions, licences, solemnization of marriages, property and civil rights, administration of justice, education, public health, welfare, and generally all matters of a local nature. The resources, with the exception of game, forestry, and fire suppression are under the control of the federal government.

N.W.T. EXECUTIVE

OFFICE OF THE COMMISSIONER
Commissioner, John H. Parker, O.C.

Executive Members of the Legislative Assembly

Government Leader, Minister responsible for the Executive, Minister of Intergovernmental Affairs, Minister responsible for the NWT Science Institute, Minister responsible for the Devolution Office,
The Hon. Dennis Patterson
Minister of Culture and Communications, Minister of Renewable Resources, Associate Minister of Aboriginal Rights and Constitutional Development,
The Hon. Titus Allooloo
House Leader, Minister of Finance, Minister of Justice, Minister of Safety and Public Service,
The Hon. Michael Ballantyne

Minister of Health, Minister of Energy, Mines and Resources, Minister of Public Works and Highways, Minister responsible for the Public Utilities Board, Minister responsible for the Workers' Compensation Board,
The Hon. Nellie Cournoyea
Minister of Education, Aboriginal Rights and Constitutional Development,
The Hon. Stephen Kakfwi
Minister of Social Services, Minister of Personnel, Minister of Equal Employment Directorate, Minister responsible for Women's Secretariat, Highway Transport Board,
The Hon. Jeannie Marie-Jewell
Minister of Government Services, Minister responsible for the NWT Housing Corporation,
The Hon. Tom Butters
Minister of Municipal and Community Affairs, Minister of Economic Development and Tourism,
The Hon. Gordon Wray

EXECUTIVE COUNCIL SECRETARIAT

Box 1320, Yellowknife, X1A 2L9
Deputy Minister of the Executive Council,
Louis Vertes
Deputy Secretary to the Executive Council,
Richard Abernethy
Territorial Statistician, Ralph Joyce
Protocol Director, Terri Boldt

Ottawa Office:
350 Sparks St., Ste. 912, Ottawa, ON K1R 7S8
Deputy Minister, Federal/Provincial Relations,
George Braden

ABORIGINAL RIGHTS AND CONSTITUTIONAL DEVELOPMENT SECRETARIAT
Secretary, Charles Overvold

REGIONAL OPERATIONS SECRETARIAT
Asst. Deputy Minister, Dennis Lowing
Secretary to the Priorities and Planning Committee/Asst. Deputy Minister, Policy, Jim Sellers

AUDIT BUREAU
Exec. Manager, Doug Hill

PUBLIC UTILITIES BOARD AND HIGHWAY TRANSPORT BOARD
Exec. Secretary, Dale Thomson

WOMEN'S SECRETARIAT
Exec. Director, Kate Irving

For further information regarding any aspect of the Government of the Northwest Territories, contact:
Department of Culture and Communications
Box 1320, Yellowknife, X1A 2L9
(403) 873-7556

OFFICE OF DEVOLUTION
Exec. Director, Lee Horn

Territorial Government Regional Offices

BAFFIN REGION
Iqaluit, X0A 0H0
Exec. Regional Director, Ken MacRury
Asst. Regional Director, David Gilday
Baffin Divisional Board of Education
Director, Brian Menton
Renewable Resources
Regional Sup't, Jim Noble
Municipal and Community Affairs
Regional Sup't, Michael Ferris
Economic Development and Tourism
Regional Sup't, Katherine Trumper
Public Works and Highways
Regional Engineer, Stewart Kennedy
Social Services
Regional Sup't, Val Haas
Personnel
Regional Manager, Mary Wilman
Finance
Regional Comptroller, Allan Sanderson
Government Services
Regional Sup't, Ralph Goodbody
Culture and Communications
Regional Manager, Andrew Tagak
Baffin Regional Hospital
Administrator, Trevor Pollitt
N.W.T.H.C.
District Manager, Maureen Cochrane
Arctic College
Vice-President, Don Couch
Justice
Regional Sup't, Anne Crawford

FORT SMITH REGION
Fort Smith, X0E 0P0
Regional Director, Don Ellis
Education
Regional Sup't, Vacant
Renewable Resources
Regional Sup't, Don Boxer
Municipal and Community Affairs
Regional Sup't, Vacant
Economic Development
Regional Sup't, Ian McRae
Personnel
Regional Manager, Vacant
Government Services
Regional Manager, Ralph Shelton
Public Works
Regional Engineer, Lloyd Henderson
Finance
Regional Comptroller, John Mageean
Social Service
Regional Sup't, Vacant
Arctic College—Thebacha Campus
Vice-President, Ron Holtorf
Culture and Communications
Language Bureau
Regional Manager, Tony Buggins

INUVIK REGION
Inuvik, X0E 0T0
Regional Director, Dan Norris
Asst. Regional Director, Roger Connelly
Education
Regional Sup't, Jim Maher
Renewable Resources
Regional Sup't, John Bailey
Economic Development
Regional Sup't, John Colford
Personnel
Regional Sup't, Dale Saulis
Social Services
Regional Sup't, Robie MacIntosh
Government Services
Regional Sup't, Don Smithson
Finance
Regional Sup't, Wayne Coghill
Municipal and Community Affairs
Regional Sup't, Mike O'Rourke
Department of Public Works and Highways
Regional Engineer, Dave Ramsden
Development Activity
Manager, Doug Matthews
Field Exec. Officers:
Max Melnyk (Norman Wells),
Dennis Thrasher (Tuktoyaktuk)
Department of Health
Regional Sup't, George Gillies
Housing Corporation
District Manager, David Kravitz
Arctic College
Vice-President, Jay Goman

KEEWATIN REGION
P.O. Bag Service 002, Rankin Inlet, X0C 0G0
Regional Director, Micheal Vaydik
Asst. Regional Director, Vacant
Board of Education
Director, Metro Solomon
Renewable Resources
Regional Sup't, Alex Illasiak
Municipal and Community Affairs
Regional Sup't, Tom Sammurtok
Social Services
Regional Sup't, Greg Cummings
Personnel
Regional Sup't, Don Palfrey
Finance
Regional Comptroller, Eric de Miel
Economic Development and Tourism
Regional Sup't, Bill Graham
Government Services
Regional Sup't, Doug Edey
Public Works and Highways
Regional Sup't, Micheal O'Floinn
Culture and Communications
Regional Manager, Vacant

KITIKMEOT REGION
Cambridge Bay, X0E 0C0
Regional Director, Helen Adamache
Asst. Regional Director, Dan O'Neill
Culture and Communications
Manager, Connie McCrae

Economic Development and Tourism
Sup't, Charlie Evalik
Education
Asst. Sup't, Carl Isnor
Finance
Comptroller, Vacant
Government Services
Regional Manager, Nick Carter
Municipal and Community Affairs
Sup't, John Borkowic
Personnel
Manager, Donna Laing
Public Works and Highways
Regional Sup't, Derek Lovlin
Health Board
Director, Frank Butter
COPPERMINE OFFICE
Coppermine, X0E 0E0
Education
Director, Tom Stewart
Supervisor of Schools, Mel Pardy
Social Services
Sup't, Judy Forbister
Renewable Resources
Sup't, Don Vincent

LEGISLATIVE ASSEMBLY

Legislative Assembly Bldg.
Yellowknife, X1A 2L9

11th Assembly, 4th Session
Date of Last Election: Oct. 5, 1987
Total number of Seats: 24

Salaries, Indemnities and Allowances

MEMBERS: $33,720 Member's Annual Indemnity,
$17,100 Member's Annual Guaranteed Constit-
uency Indemnity for member's without portfolio, plus constituency expense allowances
ranging from $15,140 to $26,180 annually,
depending on location.
MINISTERS WITH PORTFOLIO: $56,415 salary
plus Member's Annual Indemnity, Annual Guaranteed Constituency Indemnity of $5,700 and
applicable constituency expense allowance.
GOVERNMENT LEADER: $62,655 salary plus
Member's Annual Indemnity, Annual Guaranteed Constituency Indemnity of $5,700 and
applicable constituency expense allowance.
SPEAKER: $15,000 Indemnity plus Member's
Annual Indemnity, Annual Guaranteed Constituency Indemnity of $17,100 and applicable
constituency expense allowance. The Speaker
is entitled to $2,500 in expenses each fiscal
year, however all expenses must be supported
by receipts.
DEPUTY SPEAKER: $6,000 Indemnity plus Mem-
ber's Annual Indemnity, Annual Guaranteed
Constituency Indemnity of $17,100 and applica-
ble constituency expense allowance, plus $65

per day when the Deputy Speaker performs the
duties of either the Chairperson of the Committee
of the Whole or those of Speaker during a session.
The Deputy Speaker is also entitled to an expense
allowance of $1,500 in each fiscal year, however
expenses must be supported by receipts.

Officers

Speaker, The Hon. Red Pedersen
Clerk, David Hamilton
Clerk Assistant, Rhoda Perkison
Sergeant-at-Arms, Harry Finnis
Research Officer, Gary Juniper
Public Affairs Officer, Ann Taylor

Members

Constituency	Member and Community
Aivilik	Peter Ernerk (Rankin Inlet)
Amittuq	The Hon. Titus Allooloo (Yellowknife)
Baffin Central	Ipeelee Kilabuk (Pangnirtung)
Baffin South	Joe Arlooktoo (Lake Harbour)
Deh Cho	Samuel Gargan (Fort Providence)
Hay River	John Pollard (Hay River)
High Arctic	Ludy Pudluk (Resolute Bay)
Hudson Bay	Charlie Crow (Sanikiluaq)
Inuvik	Tom Butters (Inuvik)
Iqaluit	The Hon. Dennis Patterson (Iqaluit)
Kitikmeot West	The Hon. Red Pedersen (Coppermine)
Kivallivik	The Hon. Gordon Wray (Baker Lake)
Mackenzie Delta	Richard Nerysoo (Fort McPherson)
Nahendeh	The Hon. Nick Sibbeston (Fort Simpson)
Natilikmiot	Michael Angottitauruq (Gjoa Haven)
Nunakput	The Hon. Nellie Cournoyea (Inuvik)
Pine Point	Bruce McLaughlin (Yellowknife)
Rae/Lac La Martre	Henry Zoe (Yellowknife)
Sahtu	The Hon. Stephen Kakfwi (Yellowknife)
Slave River	The Hon. Jeannie Marie-Jewell (Fort Smith)
Tu Nedhe	Don Morin (Fort Resolution)
Yellowknife Centre	Brian Lewis (Yellowknife)
Yellowknife North	The Hon. Michael Ballantyne (Yellowknife)
Yellowknife South	Tony Whitford (Yellowknife)

DEPARTMENT OF CULTURE AND COMMUNICATIONS

Box 1320, Yellowknife, X1A 2L9
Minister, The Hon. Titus Allooloo

Dep. Minister, Vacant
Asst. Dep. Minister, Communications,
Ross Harvey
Asst. Dep. Minister, Culture, Vacant
Finance and Administration
Director, William Setchell
Language Bureau Director, Sabet Biscaye
Dene Section Manager, Vacant
Inuktitut Section Manager, Rassi Nashalik
French Section Manager, Bob Galipeau
Audio-Visual Communications Program
Manager, Bill Crossman
Publications and Production
Production Co-ordinator, Yvonne Lynn
Territorial Printer, John Moss
Printing Supervisor, Laurence Nelson
Prince of Wales Northern Heritage Centre
Director, Chris Stephens
Cultural Affairs Program Officer, Allice Legat
Library Services Director, Marion Pape
Government Librarian, Vera Raschke

DEPARTMENT OF ECONOMIC DEVELOPMENT AND TOURISM

Box 1320, Yellowknife, X1A 2L9
Telex: 034-4-5528
Minister, The Hon. Gordon Wray
Dep. Minister, Dwight Noseworthy
Asst. Dep. Minister, Tourism and Parks,
Alan Vaughan

Business Development

Asst. Dep. Minister, Peter Allen
Trade, Investment and Industrial Development
Director, Larry Adamson
Natural Resources Director, Syd Kirwan
Arts and Crafts Head, Glenn Wadsworth
Loans Fund
Co-ordinator, Helen Loraas-Harding
Small Business Development
Director, John McGregor
Policy and Planning
Director, Eric Christensen
Product Development and Parks
Director and Sup't, J.H. MacKendrick
Program Development
Director, Peter Neugebauer
Marketing Director, Alan Kaylo
Economic Development Agreement Secretariat
Manager, Altaf Lakhani
Finance Administration
Director, Jim Kennedy
Finance Officer, Jean Sanderson

DEPARTMENT OF EDUCATION

Box 1320, Yellowknife, X1A 2L9
Minister, The Hon. Stephen Kakfwi
Dep. Minister, Joseph L. Handley
Policy and Evaluation Director, Gail Joyce
Financial and Management Services
Director, Paul Devitt

Advanced Education

Asst. Dep. Minister, Ken Lovely

School Programs

Asst. Dep. Minister, Eric Colbourne
Arctic College, Yellowknife
President, Mark Cleveland

EQUAL EMPLOYMENT DIRECTORATE

Box 1320, Yellowknife, X1A 2L9
Minister, The Hon. Jeannie Marie-Jewell
Exec. Director, Darryl Bohnet
Manager, Russ Look
Co-ordinator, Charles Gaudet

DEPARTMENT OF FINANCE

Box 1320, Yellowknife, X1A 2L9
Minister, The Hon. Michael Ballantyne
Dep. Minister, Eric Nielsen
Comptroller-Gen., Jim Nelson
Asst. Comptroller-Gen., Fred Barrett
Fiscal Policy Director, Jean Guertin
Finance and Administration Director, Tom Liss
Revenue and Asset Management
Director, Vacant
Taxation Director, Jay Saint
Government Accounting Director, Vacant
Management Accounting Services
Director, Jim Winsor

FINANCIAL MANAGEMENT SECRETARIAT

Box 1320, Yellowknife, X1A 2L9
Secretary, Eric Nielsen
Dep. Secretary, Lew Voytilla

DEPARTMENT OF GOVERNMENT SERVICES

Box 1320, Yellowknife, X1A 2L9
Minister, The Hon. Tom Butters
Dep. Minister, John Quirke
Asst. Dep. Minister, Don Johnston
Finance Director, Henry Dragon
Supply Services Director, Norm Phillpot
Petroleum Products Director, Merv Homenuik
Policy and Planning
Director, James E. Harding
Motor Vehicles Director, Richard MacDonald
Systems and Computer Services
Director, Peter Bourke
Liquor Commission
Box 1130, Hay River, X0E 0R0
Gen. Manager, Ron Courtoreille

DEPARTMENT OF HEALTH

Box 1320, Yellowknife, X1A 2L9
Minister, The Hon. Nellie Cournoyea
Dep. Minister, Bob Cowcill
*Asst. Dep. Minister, Insurance/
Institutional Health,* Michael Pontus
*Asst. Dep. Minister, Standards/Community
Health,* Elaine Berthelet
Nursing Services Director, Vacant
Medical Services Director, Dr. Ian Gilchrist
Dental Services Director, Dr. Michael Lewis
Capital Planning and Maintenance
Director, Ed Norwich
Human Resources Management
Director, Wendy Sheridan
Health Facilities Operations
Director, Nelson McClelland
Community Health Director, Sandra McKenzie
Health Insurance Services Director, Vacant
Finance and Administration
Director, Darrell Bower
Legislation and Policy
Director, Stella Van Rensburg

DEPARTMENT OF JUSTICE

Box 1320, Yellowknife, X1A 2L9
Telex: 034-4-5528
Minister, The Hon. Michael Ballantyne
Dep. Minister, Geoffrey Bickert
Asst. Dep. Minister, Justice, Jeff Gilmour
Constitutional Law Division
Director, Bernard Funston
Finance and Administration
Director, R. Louise Dundas-Matthews
Policy and Planning Director, Nora Sanders
Legal Division Director, Robert Kasting
Legislation Division
Director, Giuseppa Bentivenga
Legal Services Board
Exec. Director, W. Douglas Miller
Land Titles/Legal Registries
Registrar, Gary MacDougall

COURTS
Court Services Director, Bud Harvey
(See also Judiciary listings)

DEPARTMENT OF MUNICIPAL AND COMMUNITY AFFAIRS

Box 1320, Yellowknife, X1A 2L9
Minister, The Hon. Gordon Wray
Dep. Minister, Al Menard
Asst. Dep. Minister, Hal Gerein
Emergency Measures Organization
Director, Eric Bussey
Finance and Administration
Director, Jim France
Policy and Evaluation
Director, Gary Vanderhaden
Municipal Affairs Director, John Argue
Lands Director, Richard Ashton
Arctic Airports Director, Doug Howard
Sport and Recreation Director, Dennis Adams

Community Planning Director, Brian Render
Community Works and Capital Planning
Director, Vern Christensen
Surveys and Mapping
Director, Wayne Barraclough

DEPARTMENT OF PERSONNEL

Box 1320, Yellowknife, X1A 2L9
Minister, The Hon. Jeannie Marie-Jewell
Dep. Minister, G. Tanner
Finance and Administration
Director, Sue Cunningham
Staff Relations Director, Herb Hunt
Staffing and Classification
Director, Michael Balaski
Human Resources Planning
Director, Carole Powell
Yellowknife Regional Office
Personnel Sup't, John Suliak

DEPARTMENT OF PUBLIC WORKS AND HIGHWAYS

Box 1320, Yellowknife, X1A 2L9
Minister, The Hon. Nellie Cournoyea
Dep. Minister, Larry Elkin
Asst. Dep. Ministers:
Bob Doherty, Gord Barber
Policy, Planning and Training Division
Director, Dave Murray
Contracts and Capital Planning
Director, David Aikens
Finance Division Director, Dave Waddell
Architectural Division
Director, Nicholas Marach
Engineering Division Director, Emery Wilson
Operations Division Director, Les Clegg
Equipment Management
Head, Dan Costache
Accommodations Services Head, Vacant
Buildings and Works Head, Manu Khemani
Energy Conservation Division
Director, Ron Hawkins

DEPARTMENT OF RENEWABLE RESOURCES

Box 1320, Yellowknife, X1A 2L9
Minister, The Hon. Titus Allooloo
Dep. Minister, Jim Bourque
Asst. Dep. Minister, Management, Vacant
Asst. Dep. Minister, Operations, Bob Wooley
Finance and Administration
Director, Rick Feil
Pollution Control Division
Director, Mel Smith
Wildlife Management
Director, Kevin Lloyd
Conservation Education and
Resource Development
Director, Doug Stewart
Policy and Planning
Director, Ron Livingston

Land Use Planning
Director, Ian Robertson
Fire Operations
Director, Bob Bailey
Forest Management
Director, Bob Larson

DEPARTMENT OF SAFETY AND PUBLIC SERVICES

Box 1320, Yellowknife, X1A 2L9
Minister, The Hon. Michael Ballantyne
Dep. Minister, Vacant
Safety Division
Director, Robbie Robinson
Fire Safety
Fire Marshall: (403) 873-7469
Mining Inspection Services
Director, W. Skelly
Labour Division
Labour Standards Officer, Eric Smith
Labour Standards Board: (403) 873-7924
Consumer Services
Director, Dorothy Mellor

DEPARTMENT OF SOCIAL SERVICES

Box 1320, Yellowknife, X1A 2L9
Minister, The Hon. Jeannie Marie-Jewell
Dep. Minister, B.I. Doyle
Asst. Dep. Ministers:
Blair Dunbar, Bronwyn Watters
Finance and Administration
Director, Phyllis Sartor
Policy and Planning
Director, Richard Clarke
Corrections Service
Young Offenders Program
Director, Will Drake
Family and Children's Services
Director, Diane Doyle
Alcohol, Drug and Community
Mental Health Services
Director, Andrew Langford
Community and Family Support Services
Director, Ron MacLellan

DEPARTMENT OF TRANSPORTATION

Box 1320, Yellowknife, X1A 2L9
Minister, The Hon. Nellie Cournoyea
Dep. Minister, Larry Elkin
Transportation Planning Division
Director, John Bunge
Transportation Engineering Division
Director, Andrew Gamble
Community Program
Head, Vacant
Highways Program
Head, Vacant
Highways Structure

Head, Jivko Jivkov
Design Services
Head, Peter Vician
Marine Operations Division
Director, Russ Wiggs
Highways Operations Division
Director, Terry Pollock
Yellowknife District Office
Dist. Sup't, Bruce Rattray
Arctic Airports Division
Director, Doug Howard
Motor Vehicles Division
Director, Richard MacDonald

INDEPENDENT AGENCIES, BOARDS AND COUNCILS

Akaitcho Hall Advisory Board

Box 1320, Yellowknife, X1A 2L9
Akaitcho Hall is a student residence built in 1958 by the federal government. Students from Northwest Territories communities where high school is unavailable must attend high school in Yellowknife and live in the residence. A staff of 14 provides administrative, custodial, laundry, and meal services to the students. A staff of 12 provides round-the-clock supervision in the dormitories.
The residence has the capacity to provide housing for up to 120 students.
Contact, Eric Colbourne

Alcohol and Drug Co-ordinating Council

Box 1320, Yellowknife, X1A 2L9
The Council serves as an advisory committee to the Territorial Alcohol and Drug Program. It is also the regional board for the National Native Alcohol Abuse program, and is responsible for allocating grants under the community Alcohol Problems Grants Program.
Contact, Andrew Langford

Apprenticeship and Trade Certification Board

Box 1320, Yellowknife, X1A 2L9
The Board is responsible for recommending trade designations, reviewing recommendations on training and certification of apprentices, and hearing appeals under the *Apprentices and Tradesmen Act.*
Director, Brian Carr

Arctic College Board of Governors

Box 1769, Yellowknife, X1A 2P3

Arctic College has grown in the last 20 years from a small adult vocational training centre to a community college system which now provides effective services to the entire Northwest Territories. With five campuses located throughout the N.W.T. (at Inuvik, Iqaluit, Fort Smith, Yellowknife, and Rankin Inlet), Arctic College is committed to delivering high-quality educational programs for adults in or near their home communities. An additional campus is planned for Cambridge Bay to allow even greater accessibility to College programs.

In addition to campus-based programs, Arctic College's Community Education division offers courses in many N.W.T. communities. This ensures that those students who can't attend an Arctic College campus still have access to a range of adult education and training opportunities.

Arctic College offers a full range of programs including academic preparation, trades and technology, and two- and three-year diploma programs. Core programs, such as academic studies, are delivered at each campus, while unique programs are developed for specific campus locations. Programs are designed for maximum accessibility, but those graduating from Arctic College achieve standards equal to similar programs across Canada.

Chairperson, Robert Hanson
Box 1000, Iqaluit, X0A 0H0
Vice-Chairperson, Larry Gordon
Box 1008, Inuvik, X0E 0T0
President, Mark Cleveland

Arts Advisory Council

Box 1320, Yellowknife, X1A 2L9
Contact, Ethel Blondin-Townsend

Commissioner's Awards Committee

Box 1320, Yellowknife, X1A 2L9

The Commissioner's Awards were instituted in 1965, whereby awards would be presented to persons who distinguished themselves by acts of bravery or exceptional deeds of public service in the Northwest Territories.

The highest level of award consists of a medal accompanied by a scroll signed by the Commissioner and describing the deeds of the recipient(s). The scroll without the medal may be awarded and a third level is a letter of commendation from the Commissioner.

The Committee, comprised of three members (one of whom acts as a chairman) and a secretary, meets as required to consider submissions and make recommendations to the Commissioner on the number and level of awards to be given.

Chairman, Dr. Walter Kupsch (Saskatoon)
Members:
Archdeacon Michael Gardener (Iqaluit),
Jane Dragon (Fort Smith)
Secretary, Tony Whitford

Denendeh Conservation Board

Box 1320, Yellowknife, X1A 2L9

The Denendeh Conservation Board was established in 1987 to provide advice to the Minister of Renewable Resources about wildlife and environmental issues in the western N.W.T.

The Board consists of ten members and a chairman. Five members are nominated by the Dene Nation and Métis Assn., and five members are appointed directly from the general public by the minister.

This joint management board has a mandate to deal with wildlife and environmental issues in the area encompassed by the Dene/Métis land claims.

Chairman, John Bayly
Exec. Director, Larry Hagen
Recording Secretary, Shirley Bohnet

Eskimo Loan Fund Advisory Board

Box 1320, Yellowknife, X1A 2L9

The Board administers the N.W.T. Eskimo Loan Fund, which is a federal government fund established to finance Inuit entrepreneurs, individuals, groups, and co-operatives by providing term loans, contributions, and bank loan guarantees.

Contact, Helen Loraas-Harding

Highway Transport Board

Box 697, Yellowknife, X1A 2N5

The Board regulates public service vehicles in accordance with the *Public Service Vehicles Act* and its Regulations. Approximately 300 "for-hire" trucking companies are regulated, with the prime objective to ensure that all persons associated with transportation in the Northwest Territories — truckers, shippers, and the public — receive high-quality, reliable service at reasonable rates. The Board is composed of five members, including a chairman and vice-chairman, and it meets monthly, holding disciplinary and general application hearings at various locations as required.

Contact, Dale Thomson

Labour Standards Board of the N.W.T.

Box 2804, Yellowknife, X1A 2R1

The Board was established primarily to hear appeals from decisions and orders of the Labour Standards Officer. It also has minor administrative functions in connection with the *Labour Standards Act* of the Northwest Territories and is empowered to make binding decisions with only a limited right of appeal to the Supreme Court of the Northwest Territories.

Contact, Karyn Dick

Legal Services Board of the N.W.T.
Box 1320, Yellowknife, X1A 2L9

The Board is responsible for ensuring that legal services are provided to all eligible persons; for ensuring that the legal services provided and the various systems for providing those services are the best that circumstances permit; and for developing and co-ordinating Territorial or local programs aimed at reducing and preventing the occurrence of legal problems among the people, and increasing their knowledge of the law, legal processes, and the administration of justice.
Contact, W. Douglas Miller

Liquor Licensing Board
Box 1320, Yellowknife, X1A 2L9

The Board grants, renews, and transfers licences; suspends and cancels licence permits; controls the conduct of licensees; and prescribes rights, privileges, conditions, and obligations to licences and permits by authority of the *Liquor Act.*
Contact, Margaret Strang

Medical Registration Committee
c/o Department of Justice
Box 1320, Yellowknife, X1A 2L9

The Medical Registration Committee of the Northwest Territories was established in 1983 under the *Medical Profession Act,* Chapter 10. The Committee is responsible for the review and evaluation of applications submitted for licensing to practice medicine.

It consists of six members, three members of the N.W.T. Medical Assn., one representative of the Department of Health, one lay person, and the registrar. Three persons make a quorum.
Registrar, Helen Roberts

Mine Occupational Health and Safety Board
Box 1320, Yellowknife, X1A 2L9

The Mine Occupational Health and Safety Board is a five-member board created under the provisions of the *Mining Safety Act* to advise the Minister of Justice on matters pertaining to the Act and its Regulations, including the possible amendment of the legislation. It also advises on issues concerning the occupational health and safety of persons in or about a mine.
Contact, Dale Vitone

N.W.T. Advisory Council on the Status of Women
c/o Women's Secretariat
Box 1320, Yellowknife, X1A 2L9

This Council was established in 1983 to advise the Minister responsible for the Status of Women on matters of concern and to research, report, and publish on issues of concern to women.
Contact, Ruth Utatnaq

N.W.T. Affirmative Action Advisory Committee
Box 1320, Yellowknife, X1A 2L9
Telex: 034-4-5528

The N.W.T. Affirmative Action Advisory Committee was established in April 1986 under the Territories' Native Employment Policy to provide guidance and advice to the government on matters associated with equal opportunity and affirmative action in the territorial public service. All members are appointed by the Executive Council.

The Committee is representative of a cross-section of organizations throughout the Territories. This includes native organizations, the Union of Northern Workers, employee associations, the Council for the Status of Women, and the N.W.T. Council for Disabled.

The Committee meets approximately every three months and is briefed on all activities of the Equal Employment Directorate. The Committee reports to the Executive Council through the Minister responsible for Equal Employment.
Minister responsible,
The Hon. Jeannie Marie-Jewell
Equal Employment
Exec. Director, Darryl Bohnet

N.W.T. Business Council
Box 1320, Yellowknife, X1A 2L9
Contact, Jim Britton

N.W.T. Committee on Law Reform
Box 1320, Yellowknife, X1A 2L9

The Northwest Territories Committee on Law Reform was founded in 1986 to study the laws of the N.W.T. and to advise the government of ways in which those laws could be reformed.

The members of the Committee are all volunteers and come from both within and outside government bodies. The Northwest Territories Department of Justice provides research and administrative support.
Contact, Ralph Armstrong

N.W.T. Housing Corp.
Box 2100, Yellowknife, X1A 2P6

The Corporation was established by an Order of the Commissioner on March 1, 1973. The first official meeting of the board of directors was held Aug. 22, 1973 and the Corporation began its operations on Jan. 1, 1974 at its head office in Yellowknife.

In February 1983, the board of directors stated that the overall objectives of the Corporation would be "to develop, co-ordinate, and direct social housing programs, so as to make an adequate standard of housing available to residents in need, in the Northwest Territories."

Currently, the Corporation has an inventory of approximately 4,100 units, managed by 48 Housing Associations/Authorities. The Corporation maintains a staff of 164 employees, of whom approximately 70 are directly involved in field operations. The total annual budget of the Corporation exceeds $130 million.

The programs of the Corporation can be split into two basic areas, homeownership and rental accommodation.

Homeownership Programs: The Housing Corp. offers, on a one-time only basis, assistance in the form of a materials package to approved applicants who wish to build their own home. The cost of the assistance is forgiven over a period of five years. The Corporation also offers assistance for repairs to eligible homeowners, with repayment geared to income.

Rental Programs: The Corporation operates Public Housing Programs. Rent is based on income. The N.W.T.H.C. and the Canadian Mortgage and Housing Corp. share the operating costs.

President, J.A. Heron
Corporate Relations
Manager, Don Routledge
Exec. Officer, Tanis Stirling

Finance and Corporate Services
Vice-President, Jim Pratt
Comptroller, Emil Homenuik
Corporate Services
Manager, Chris Lupiano
Human Resources
Director, Jack Conroy

Construction/Development Division
Vice-President, Norman Ridgely
Contract Services
Manager, Elsa Mogensen
Design Services
Director, Dick Bushell
Construction Services
Director, Joe Solowy
Lands Section
Manager, Peter Cook

Community and Program Services
Vice-President, Hal Logsdon
Property Management and Program Operations
Director, Jalal Toeg
Community and Program Development
Director, Gary McLellen

N.W.T. Land Use Planning Commission

Goga Cho Bldg., 3rd Flr.
Box 2280, Yellowknife, X1A 2P7

The principal responsibility of the Northwest Territories Land Use Planning Commission is the preparation of draft land use plans. It provides direction to the Land Use Planning Office; monitors implemented plans; co-ordinates land use planning with other public planning activities in the Northwest Territories; and ensures that there is public input into the planning process.

The federal Minister of Indian Affairs and Northern Development and the territorial Minister of Renewable Resources appoint the members of the Commission, eight private citizens from diverse backgrounds, on recommendations from both levels of government and from the major native organizations.

When planning land development and use, factors taken into consideration include the environment, the traditional pursuits of the people, and the potential economic benefits for all Canadians. To balance local and national needs and interests, and to provide accountability to the permanent residents of each region, a community-based planning process was developed. Accordingly, regional land use planning commissions have been established. The final draft plan from the Lancaster Sound Regional Land Use Planning Commission was expected at the end of 1988, while the first draft plan from the Mackenzie Delta-Beaufort Sea Regional Commission is due to be released in June 1989. A new Denendeh Regional Commission is expected to be established for the Dene/Métis Settlement Area.

The members of the regional commissions are also appointed by the ministers, chosen from the territorial commission and from within the planning region in question.

Chairman, Ben Hubert
Vice-Chairman, George Barnaby
Contact, Ian Robertson

LANCASTER SOUND REGIONAL LAND USE PLANNING COMMISSION
Box 1320, Yellowknife, X1A 2L9

Chairman, David Mablick
Vice-Chairman, Kik Shappa
Contact, Ian Robertson

MACKENZIE DELTA-BEAUFORT SEA REGIONAL COMMISSION
Box 1320, Yellowknife, X1A 2L9

Chairman, Alex Aviugana
Vice-Chairman, Charlie Snowshoe
Contact, Ian Robertson

N.W.T. Power Corporation

Box 5700, Stn. L, Edmonton, AB T6C 4J8

The Northwest Territories Power Corporation is a territorial Crown corporation operating under authority of the *Northwest Territories Power Corporation Act.* It is concerned with the planning, construction and management of public utilities, primarily electrical, on a commercial basis. For this purpose, it is empowered to survey utility requirements and to construct utility plants in the Northwest Territories.

The Commission is the principal producer of electricity north of 60° and operates the main transmission networks in the Northwest Territories. Heat, water and sewerage service utilities are operated at Inuvik. Wholesale heat supply is provided to the Northwest Territorial Government for distribution at Iqaluit. The Commission's head office is located at Edmonton, Alberta. Regional offices will be located at Hay River with regional offices in Yellowknife and Iqaluit.

Chairman, Jack Beaver

N.W.T. Social Assistance Appeal Board
Box 1320, Yellowknife, X1A 2L9

Where a decision by a local appeal committee is in question, the Board is authorized to make a final decision pursuant to the *Social Assistance Act.*
Contact, Ron MacLellan

N.W.T. Teacher Certification Board
Box 1320, Yellowknife, X1A 2N2

The Board advises the minister with respect to any matters pertaining to teacher certification and is responsible for safeguarding appropriate certification standards in the Northwest Territories.
Contact, Alana Jacobs

N.W.T. Water Board
Box 1500, Yellowknife, X1A 2R3

The Water Board provides for the conservation, development, and utilization of the water resources of the Northwest Territories. Under the *Northern Inland Waters Act,* 1972, an application must be made to the Board for authorization or a licence to use water or dispose of wastes into the water. Domestic use of water is exempted from this Regulation, as well as the use of water in emergency situations such as fire.

The Board has three to nine members appointed by the Minister of Indian Affairs and Northern Development. Included are: at least one member from each federal department that, in the opinion of the Governor-in-Council, is directly concerned with the management of water resources in the Northwest Territories; and at least three persons named by the Commissioner-in-Council of the Northwest Territories.

Chairman, Dave Nickerson
Vice-Chairman, D.E. Arden
Contact, Pamela LeMouel

Public Records Committee
Box 1320, Yellowknife, X1A 2L9
Contact, Richard Valpy

Public Utilities Board of the N.W.T.
Box 697, Yellowknife, X1A 2N5

The Board regulates utility companies operating in the Northwest Territories in accordance with the terms and conditions established by the *Public Utilities Act.* The Board's mandate is to ensure that public utilities provide high-quality services at fair and equitable rates. There are five members, including a chairman.
Contact, Dale Thomson

Regional Health Boards
The Regional Health Boards were established pursuant to the *Territorial Hospital Insurance Act.* Board membership comprises representatives from the communities within each region plus a representative from each of the major Inuit associations. Board administrative offices are located at the regional centres.

Each Board provides primary health care, dental care, and community health services to residents of its region. Medical and dental services are provided by various provincial institutions and physicians and dentists from the provinces regularly visit the communities. Access to secondary and tertiary facilities in the south is also provided. For this purpose, transient centres are maintained for patients travelling to the south for diagnostic services and medical treatment.

BAFFIN REGIONAL HEALTH BOARD
Postal Bag 200, Iqaluit, X0A 0H0
Contact, Trevor Pollitt

KEEWATIN REGIONAL HEALTH BOARD
Box 298, Rankin Inlet, X0C 0G0
(819) 645-2171; Fax: (819) 645-2329
Exec. Director, Frank Russell
Regional Nursing Officer, Rosemary Brown
Finance and Administration
Director, Gerry Mullen

KITIKMEOT REGIONAL HEALTH BOARD
c/o Government of N.W.T.
Cambridge Bay, X0C 0C0
Contact, Helen Adamache

MACKENZIE REGIONAL HEALTH SERVICES
Box 520, Yellowknife, X1A 2N5

Science Institute
Box 1617, Yellowknife, X1A 2P2

The Science Institute was established in the spring of 1985 by the Northwest Territories Legislative Assembly to replace the N.W.T. Science Advisory Board. The Board's responsibilities include assessing the scientific, engineering, and technological requirements and the potential

of the territories in order to help solve social and economic problems, and to recommend research and development programs.
Contact, Laurie Nowakowski

Special Rural Development Act (ARDA) Committee
Box 1320, Yellowknife, X1A 2L9

The Committee administers the special ARDA (Agricultural and Rural Development Agreement) program, which is a joint federal/territorial program operating under the authority of the Canada/Northwest Territories Special ARDA Agreement. This program provides people of the Northwest Territories, particularly those of Indian and Inuit ancestry, with financial contributions and other assistance for projects which will open up new jobs, increase income, and improve living conditions.
Contact, Ron Kungl

Student Financial Assistance Review Board
Box 1320, Yellowknife, X1A 2L9

The Student Financial Assistance Review Board is constituted under the provisions of the *Student Financial Assistance Act,* assented to May 21, 1982.

The Board is responsible for awarding student grants to applicants and recommending to the Minister of Education the amount of student loans to be provided to applicants. The Board is also responsible for recommending to the minister guidelines and policies respecting the administration of student financial assistance. The Board currently reviews over 1,300 applications for student financial assistance from northern residents. Approximately 75 per cent receive some form of financial aid. The revolving loan fund has a maximum limit of $8.5 million and about $2 million is provided to northern students annually in the form of grants.

Chairman, Ken Lovely
Asst. Dep. Minister, Advanced Education
EASTERN ARCTIC STUDENT FINANCIAL ASSISTANCE BOARD
Resolute Bay, X0A 0V0
Contact, Walter Audla
KITIKMEOT/YELLOWKNIFE STUDENT FINANCIAL ASSISTANCE BOARD
Box 1830, Yellowknife, X1A 2P4
Contact, J.C. Poston
MACKENZIE VALLEY STUDENT FINANCIAL ASSISTANCE BOARD
Department of Education, Inuvik, X0E 0P0
Contact, Jim Maher
SOUTH MACKENZIE VALLEY STUDENT FINANCIAL ASSISTANCE BOARD
Department of Education, Fort Smith, X0E 0P0
Contact, George Demeule

Territorial Business Loans Board
Box 1320, Yellowknife, X1A 2L9

The Business Loans and Guarantees Fund was created in 1970 by the federal Department of Indian Affairs and Northern Development to provide business financing to those unable to obtain commercial debt financing from conventional lenders at reasonable terms and conditions.

Loans and guarantees may be made to finance the purchase, installation, renovation, improvement, or expansion of equipment, inventory, or premises used or to be used in the course of carrying on a business enterprise. In addition, loans and guarantees may be made to provide working capital for the acquisition of current assets and as security in lieu of bonding for specified construction projects.

Interest rates for the Business Loan Fund are set quarterly at 2 per cent above the chartered banks' prime rate. Loan terms are available for a maximum of five years; maximum amortization of a loan is 25 years. Since 1977, when the Fund was transferred to the Government of the Northwest Territories, the loan and guarantee limits have increased from an aggregate $50,000 to $500,000.

There are seven Regional Business Loan Boards in addition to the Territorial Business Loan Board. Members of the Territorial Board are business community leaders representing the geographic and cultural diversity of the Northwest Territories.
Loans Co-ordinator, Helen Loraas-Harding

Territorial Health Board
Box 1320, Yellowknife, X1A 2L9

The Board is responsible for the administration of the *Territorial Hospital Insurance Services Act* and Regulations and oversees the operation of all hospitals and health facilities.
Contact:
Director, Hospitals and Health Facilities
FORT SMITH HEALTH CENTRE BOARD OF MANAGEMENT
Box 1080, Fort Smith, X0E 0P0
Contact, Joyce Balla
H.H. WILLIAMS MEMORIAL HOSPITAL
Box 1280, Hay River, X0E 0R0
Contact, James Tyler
INUVIK LONG-TERM CARE FACILITY
Box 1158, Inuvik, X0E 0T0
Contact, Frank Schikurski
STANTON YELLOWKNIFE HOSPITAL BOARD OF MANAGEMENT
Box 10, Yellowknife, X1A 2N1
Contact, Lawrence Todd

Trade Advisory Committees
Box 1320, Yellowknife, X1A 2L9

The legislation governing the Trade Advisory Committees is the *Training and Certification of Apprentices and Tradesmen Act,* assented to Nov. 25, 1982. There are currently eight Committees in force. Their purpose is to advise the Apprenticeship and Trade Certification Board on all matters pertaining to the specific trade or groups of trades for which they were formed. Membership is comprised of an equal number of employees and employers and an attempt is made to achieve a good cross-section of the industry by location and type of work.

Contact, Joanne Skeates

Workers' Compensation Board

Box 8888, Yellowknife, X1A 2R3
(403) 873-7745; 1-800-661-0792
Fax: (403) 873-4596

The Board determines eligibility for compensation, the amount of compensation, and the provision of medical, surgical, and rehabilitative treatment to workers injured in workplace accidents. It also decides on the classification of employers, the setting of assessment rates, the collection of assessment revenue, and the administration of the Accident Fund from which workers' compensation payments are made.

Chairman, Barney Dohon
Dep. Chairperson, Jo-Anne Allison
Members: Violet Beaulieu, Okalik Eegeesiak, James Evoy, Arnold Hope, Dale Johnston, Wilfrid MacDonald, Steve McAlpine, Bert Stromberg, John Todd, Mike Zubko
Gen. Manager, Vacant
Claims Services
Director, Bryan C. Roberts
Financial and Administrative Services
Director, James B. White
Secretary, Lynne Green

FEDERAL GOVERNMENT DIRECTORY

Canada Oil and Gas Lands Administration
Reg. Engineer, Maurice Thomas

Canadian Broadcasting Corp.
Northern Service
250 Lanark Ave., Box 3220, Stn. C
Ottawa, K1Y 1E4
Reg. Director, Brian Cousins

Department of Environment
Canadian Wildlife Service
Biologist, K. McCormick
Box 637, Yellowknife, X1A 2N5

Water Survey of Canada
Officer-in-Charge, Murray Jones
Box 43, Fort Smith, X0E 0P0
Officer-in-Charge, Patrick Wood
Box 377, Fort Simpson, X0E 0N0
Officer-in-Charge, Herbert Wood
Inuvik, X0E 0T0
Officer-in-Charge, Derrick Curtis
Baker Lake, X0C 0A0

Parks
Northern Parks Establishment
Dist. Manager, Gordon Hamre
Box 1166, Yellowknife, X1A 2N8

Department of Fisheries and Oceans
Field Services
Manager, Don H. Dowler
Box 2310, Yellowknife, X1A 2P7

Department of Indian Affairs and Northern Development
Box 1500, Yellowknife, X1A 2R3

NORTHERN AFFAIRS PROGRAM
Director Gen., Dr. A.H. Macpherson
Corporate Affairs
Director, Judy Wilson
Personnel
Director, Paul Lizée
Land Use Planning
Director, Hal Mills
Communication Services
Director, Lynne Boyer
Regional Finance and Administration
Director, Colin McEwan
Renewable Resources and Environment
Director, William Stephen
Environment and Conservation
Reg. Manager, Rick Hurst
Land Resources
Reg. Manager, Floyd Adlem
Water Resources
Reg. Manager, Jennifer Letourneau
Fort Smith District
Dist. Manager, Odiel Vandenberghe
Fort Simpson District
Dist. Manager, Bernie Gauthier
Inuvik District
Dist. Manager, Rudy Cockney
Yellowknife District
Dist. Manager, Bob Lynn
Iqaluit District
Dist. Manager, Andy Theriault
Rankin Inlet District
Dist. Manager, Guy Saint-Andre
Minerals and Economic Analysis
Director, Pierre Laporte
Economic Development and Northern Benefits
Reg. Manager, Helen Young
Geology
Reg. Manager, Bill Padgham
Mining Lands
Reg. Manager, Ed Cook

INDIAN AND INUIT AFFAIRS PROGRAM
Reg. Director, Lorne Tricoteux
Community Affairs
Director, Wayne Balanoff
Band Financial Advisor, John Ivey
Training and Development Officer, Vacant
Economic Development
Director, Vacant
Dist. Sup't, Hugh Richardson
Reg. Program Activities Manager, John Metcalfe

JUDICIARY AND JUDICIAL OFFICERS

Court of Appeal and Court Officials

Court House, Box 550, Yellowknife, X1A 2N4
General Inquiries: (403) 920-8759
The Judges of the Court of Appeal comprise:
a) the Justices of Appeal of Alberta;
b) a Justice of Appeal of Saskatchewan; and
c) the Justices of the Supreme Court of the Northwest and Yukon Territories.

Chief Justice: The Hon. J.H. Laycraft

Judges:
The Hon. Justice R.P. Foisy
The Hon. Justice N.D. McDermid
The Hon. Justice C.F. Tallis
The Hon. Justice C.W. Clement
The Hon. Justice S.L. Lieberman
The Hon. Justice A.M. Harradence
The Hon. Justice R.P. Kerans
The Hon. Justice A.F. Moir
The Hon. Justice W.A. Stevenson
The Hon. Justice W.J. Haddad
The Hon. Justice J.W. McClung
The Hon. Justice H.C.B. Maddison
The Hon. Justice R.H. Belzil
The Hon. Justice M.M. de Weerdt
The Hon. Justice T.D. Marshall
The Hon. Justice H.L. Irving
The Hon. Justice M.M. Hetherington
The Hon. Justice J. Edward Richard

Registrar: M. Melinchuk

The Hon. K.H. Fogarty (Ottawa)
The Hon. W.D. Griffiths (Toronto)
The Hon. J.K. Hugesson (Ottawa)
The Hon. S.S. Lieberman (Edmonton)
The Hon. A. Lutz (Calgary)
The Hon. D. MacKinnon (Vancouver)
The Hon. J.L. MacPherson (Calgary)
The Hon. E. McFadyen (Edmonton)
The Hon. D. Medhurst (Calgary)
The Hon. T.H. Miller (Edmonton)
The Hon. W. Oppal (Vancouver)
The Hon. R.F. Paul (Montreal)
The Hon. J.H. Potts (Toronto)
The Hon. P. Power (Calgary)
The Hon. M.L. Rothman (Montreal)
The Hon. M. Shannon (Calgary)
The Hon. W. Sinclair (Edmonton)
The Hon. W.A. Stevenson (Edmonton)
The Hon. C.F. Tallis (Regina)
The Hon. C. Tourigny (Quebec)
The Hon. P. Trudeau (Quebec)
The Hon. C. Virtue (Alberta)
The Hon. W. Wallace (Vancouver)

Clerk of the Court: M. Melinchuk
Sheriff: M. Melinchuk

REGISTRAR IN BANKRUPTCY
Court House, Box 550, Yellowknife, X1A 2N4
General Inquiries: (403) 920-8759
Registrar: M. Melinchuk

Supreme Court and Court Officials

Court House, Box 550, Yellowknife, X1A 2N4
General Inquiries: (403) 920-8759

Judges:
The Hon. M.M. de Weerdt
The Hon. T. David Marshall
The Hon. J. Edward Richard

Ex-officio Judge:
The Hon. H.C.B. Maddison

Deputy Judges:
The Hon. J-G. Boilard (Montreal)
The Hon. J.D. Bracco (Edmonton)
The Hon. J.C. Cavanagh (Edmonton)
The Hon. G. Cumming (Vancouver)
The Hon. J. Ducros (Montreal)

Territorial Court and Court Officials

Court House, Box 550, Yellowknife, X1A 2N4
General Inquiries: (403) 873-7600
Chief Judge: The Hon. J.R. Slaven

Judges:
The Hon. R.W. Halifax
  Box 1276, Hay River, X0E 0R0
The Hon. R.M. Bourassa
The Hon. T. Davis
The Hon. O.J.T. Troy
  Box 297, Iqaluit, X0A 0H0

Clerks of the Court:
  Vacant (Yellowknife)
  Shirley Klause (Hay River)
  Jacques Fortier (Iqaluit)

Administrator: Diane Rogers

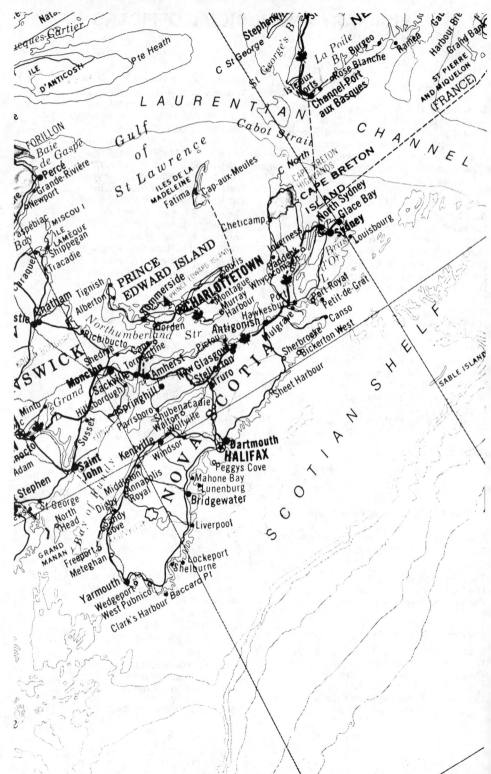

This map is based on information taken from map MCR 4032. © Her Majesty in Right of Canada with permission of Energy, Mines and Resources.

PROVINCE OF NOVA SCOTIA

Mayflower
(*Epigaea repens*)

Entered Confederation: July 1, 1867
Capital: Halifax
Motto: Munit Haec et Altera Vincit
(One defends and the other conquers)
Flower: Mayflower
Area: 55,490 km²
   percentage of Canada's total area: 0.6
   LAND: 52,840 km²
   FRESHWATER: 2,650 km²
Elevation:
   HIGHEST POINT: Cape Breton highlands
   (554 m)
   LOWEST POINT: sea level
Population (June 1986): 873,199

   five-year change: +3.0%
   per square kilometre: 16.5
   percentage of Canada's total
     population: 3.4
   URBAN: 54%
   RURAL: 46%
Gross domestic product, 1987: $13.4 billion
Government Finance:
   REVENUE (gross), 1986/87: $3.0 billion
   EXPENDITURE (gross), 1986/87: $3.5 billion
   DEBT PER CAPITA (March 1987): $2,403
Personal income per capita, 1986: $13,899
Unemployment rate, 1988
(annual average): 10.2%

HISTORY

In 1783, United Empire Loyalists from the newly-independent New England states began to arrive. The influx of colonial refugees loyal to Britain doubled the province's population and created strong ties with both Britain and the New England states. The War of 1812 between Canada and the U.S. consolidated Halifax as a main defence garrison, and trading and shipbuilding port.

In 1820, Cape Breton Island lost its status as a separate colony and became part of Nova Scotia. In 1848, largely through the efforts of Joseph Howe, Nova Scotia became the first British colony to win responsible government.

Nova Scotia was one of the four provinces that joined the federation called the Dominion of Canada in 1867. At that time, the province was in the forefront of international shipbuilding, lumber, and fish trade. However, Nova Scotia's economic prosperity did not survive for long, its fall furthered by the decline of wooden ships and the vigorous growth in Quebec and Ontario.

The first and second world wars restored the importance of Halifax as one of the world's major military ports. Postwar expansion in European and American markets, and improved transportation revived Nova Scotia's lagging economy.

THE LAND

Nova Scotia juts into the North Atlantic, and is the most easterly point on the North American mainland. As such, it offers ports which are the first stop for vessels from Europe. The province is bounded by the Northumberland Strait and the Gulf of St. Lawrence to the north, the Atlantic Ocean to the south and east, and the Bay of Fundy to the west. The only land boundary is the 22-km Isthmus of Chignecto, shared with New Brunswick. The 579-km length of the province is less than a day's drive, and because it is so narrow one is never more than 60 km from the sea.

The province's landscapes are varied. The Fundy shore includes the wide valleys of the Annapolis and Cornwallis rivers, and the broad dykelands and salt marshes of the Minas Basin. Here, the highest tides in the world, up to 16.6 metres, interest Nova Scotians and tourists alike, as well as financiers and engineers from around the world, who come to view the first tidal river project in the western hemisphere. Glaciers left rich soil deposits in the lowlands of the Annapolis Valley and the Cumberland along the north coast. They also carved out the rugged highlands that rise 554 metres on Cape Breton Island, the large island to the north which represents 20 per cent of Nova Scotia's land mass.

About 177 km to the east of Nova Scotia lies Sable Island, the notorious "Graveyard of the Atlantic", where recent commercial gas finds have awakened international interest in the island's undersea potential.

THE PEOPLE

Sixty-three per cent of Nova Scotians reported British origins according to the 1986 Census. The largest ethnic group after the British (including those who were only partially British) was the French, whose members constituted 6.1 per cent of the population. Germans were the original settlers of the Lunenberg area, and their descendants made up 2.4 per cent of the total. For those that reported multiple origins, 9.4 and 9.3 per cent respectively were of mixed British and other, and British and French background. Nova Scotia is also the home of a long-established black community, whose 0.92 per cent of the population surpassed the Canadian average.

At the time of the 1986 Census, 814,000 or 93.2 per cent of the population of Nova Scotia reported English as their only mother tongue; 31,000 or 3.5 per cent reported French as their only mother tongue; and 16,000 or 1.8 per cent reported a non-official language as their only mother tongue. The most prevalent non-official languages included Dutch, German, and Chinese.

THE ECONOMY

Fish and fish products represent 35 per cent of exports, forest products 24 per cent, and the remainder includes transportation equipment, non-metallic minerals, and a variety of other products. In 1987, Nova Scotia experienced a growth rate of 7.3 per cent, compared to 26.6 per cent growth in 1986.

Fishing. Most of Nova Scotia's fishing fleet are inshore boats which take much of the lucrative catch of lobsters and scallops species. These account for 48 per cent of the value of the annual catch, which was worth $423.6 million in 1986. Cod, haddock, herring, and pollock make up the balance of the catch. In 1986, Nova Scotia

contributed 31.9 per cent of Canada's fishing effort, which is marketed worldwide, particularly in the northeastern U.S.

Forestry. Three-quarters of the province's land mass is covered by forest — 4.1 million hectares that produced 1.1 million m^3 of sawlogs and 3.1 million m^3 of pulpwood in 1987. About 75 per cent of the woodlands is owned by small woodlot owners or forest product companies, while the Crown owns the rest. Of the 30 varieties of trees native to Nova Scotia, only 12 are used industrially and most of them are softwoods — balsam fir, spruce, pine, and hemlock. Principal hardwoods are birch, maple, aspen, and oak.

Mining and Energy. For many years, Nova Scotia's mineral industry has been dominated by the production of coal and industrial minerals. Tin, gold, copper, and silver are now being produced and there is considerable potential for the development of other metals, minerals, and mineral fuels in the future.

On a province by province basis, N.S. is the largest producer of gypsum in Canada. Salt, anhydrite, barite, limestone, dolomite, peat moss, building stone, silica, and clay products are also produced. In recent years, large quantities of aggregates have been shipped to ports in the Caribbean area and substantial increases in production of this material are forecast.

Nova Scotia has North America's only primary tin mine which also produces base metals (copper, zinc, and silver). Several gold mines are also in the final stages of exploration and development.

Nova Scotia currently produces more than 3.0 million tonnes per year of metallurgical and thermal coal; mostly from underground mines in Cape Breton. Coal reserves, in place, are estimated to be in the order of 3.0 billion tonnes. Most of the Province's electricity is generated from indigenous coal.

There has been a considerable amount of petroleum-gas exploration in the Province's offshore area. Since 1959, drilling to date has revealed discovered resources of 5.7 trillion cubic feet of natural gas and 144 million barrels of oil and condensate. Development awaits higher world oil and gas prices.

Agriculture. The most concentrated farming region is the Annapolis Valley stretching from Windsor to Annapolis Royal. There are 158,000 hectares of improved farm land in the province. Dairying is the largest farm sector, accounting for 28 per cent of farm sales and utilizing a third of the land in farm production. In 1987, farm returns from dairy products totalled $82.0 million. Other major farm sectors include horticulture ($51.5 million), poultry and eggs ($51.4 million), hogs ($34.4 million), cattle and calves ($29.7 million), and fur ($16.3 million). Total farm cash receipts in 1987 were $287.1 million.

Text provided courtesy of the Nova Scotia Information Service.

GOVERNMENT OF NOVA SCOTIA

Seat of Government:
Province House, Halifax, B3J 2T3
Lieutenant-Governor,
The Hon. Alan R. Abraham
Government House, 1451 Barrington St.
Halifax, B3J 1Z2

EXECUTIVE COUNCIL

(In order of precedence, as of Jan. 1, 1989)
Premier, President of the Executive Council, Chairman of the Policy Board, Minister responsible for the Cabinet Secretariat,
The Hon. John M. Buchanan, P.C., Q.C.
Minister of Housing, Deputy Premier, Minister responsible for the Emergency Measures Organization,
The Hon. Roger S. Bacon
Minister of Mines and Energy, Chairman of the Senior Citizens Secretariat, Minister responsible for the Communications and Information Act,
The Hon. John A. MacIsaac
Minister of Tourism and Culture, Minister responsible for the Heritage Property Act,
The Hon. Roland J. Thornhill
Minister of Industry, Trade and Technology, Minister responsible for the Administration of the Nova Scotia Research Foundation Corporation Act, Minister responsible for the Advisory Council on Applied Science and Technology,
The Hon. Donald W. Cameron
Minister of Small Business Development, Minister responsible for the Nova Scotia Business Capital Corporation Act,
The Hon. Kenneth Streatch
Minister of Education,
The Hon. Ronald C. Giffin, Q.C.
Chairman of the Management Board, Minister of Government Services, Minister of Intergovernmental Affairs, Chairman of the Economic Development Committee of Cabinet, Minister responsible for the Civil Service Act,
The Hon. Terence R.B. Donahoe, Q.C.
Attorney General, Minister responsible for the Administration of the Human Rights Act, Chairman of the Social Development Committee of Cabinet,
The Hon. Thomas J. McInnis
Minister of Advanced Education and Job Training,
The Hon. Joel R. Matheson, Q.C.
Minister of Labour, Minister responsible for the

Administration of the Liquor Control Act,
The Hon. Ronald S. Russell
Minister of Finance, Minister responsible for the Administration of the Nova Scotia Sport and Recreation Commission, Minister in charge of the Lottery Act,
The Hon. J. Greg Kerr
Minister of the Environment,
The Hon. John G. Leefe
Minister of Transportation and Communications,
The Hon. George C. Moody
Minister of Health and Fitness, Registrar General, Minister in charge of the Drug Dependency Act, Minister responsible for reporting on the handicapped,
The Hon. G. David Nantes
Minister of Community Services, Minister responsible for Acadian Affairs,
The Hon. Guy J. LeBlanc
Minister of Municipal Affairs,
The Hon. Brian A. Young
Minister of Fisheries, Minister responsible for the Advisory Council on the Status of Women Act,
The Hon. Donald P. McInnes
Minister of Consumer Affairs, Minister in charge of the Residential Tenancies Act,
The Hon. R. Colin D. Stewart
Minister of Agriculture and Marketing,
The Hon. George Archibald
Minister of Lands and Forests,
The Hon. Charles W. MacNeil
Solicitor General, Provincial Secretary, Minister in charge of the Regulations Act, Minister responsible for Youth,
The Hon. Neil J. Leblanc

EXECUTIVE COUNCIL OFFICE
Secretary to the Executive Council,
Michael A. Kontak
One Government Place, 5th Flr.
1700 Granville St., Halifax, B3J 3N7
Clerk of the Executive Council,
H.F.G. Stevens, Q.C.
One Government Place, Barrington Level
Box 2125, Halifax, B3J 3B7

Protocol Office
One Government Place, 7th Flr.
1700 Granville St., Box 1617, Halifax, B3J 2Y3
Chief of Protocol, Marilyn Atkinson

For further information regarding any aspect of the Government of Nova Scotia, contact:
Nova Scotia Information Service
Box 608, Halifax, B3J 2R7
(902) 424-2700

PRINCIPAL COMMITTEES OF THE EXECUTIVE COUNCIL

Cabinet Secretariat
1700 Granville St., 5th Flr.
Box 1617, Halifax, B3J 2Y3
Minister responsible,
   The Hon. John M. Buchanan, P.C., Q.C.
Deputy Minister, L. Jerry Redmond

Management Board
1700 Granville St., 4th Flr.
Box 1619, Halifax, B3J 2Y3
Chairman, The Hon. Terence R.B. Donahue, Q.C.
Ex officio Officers:
Exec. Director of the Civil Service
   Commission, George L. Hall
Deputy Minister, Douglas T. Tobin

LEGISLATIVE ASSEMBLY

55th General Assembly, 1st Session
Date of last election: Sept. 6, 1988
   (Maximum duration 5 years)
Majority party: Progressive Conservative
Total number of seats: 52
Party standings (as of Jan. 1, 1989):
   Conservatives: 28
   Liberals: 21
   New Democrats: 2
   Independent: 1

Salaries, Indemnities and Allowances

MEMBERS: $28,695 Member's Sessional Indemnity and $12,450 expense allowance.
MINISTERS: $35,290, plus Member's Sessional Indemnity and expense allowance.
PREMIER: $45,535, plus Member's Sessional Indemnity and expense allowance.
LEADER OF THE OPPOSITION: $35,290, plus Member's Sessional Indemnity and expense allowance.
LEADER OF RECOGNIZED PARTY: $17,650, plus Member's Sessional Indemnity and expense allowance.
SPEAKER: $35,290, plus Member's Sessional Indemnity and expense allowance.
DEPUTY SPEAKER: $17,650, plus Member's Sessional Indemnity and expense allowance.

Officers

Speaker, The Hon. Arthur R. Donahoe, Q.C.
Chief Clerk of the House, R.K. MacArthur
Asst. Clerk, Mrs. C.G. Fergurson
Sergeant-at-Arms, Maj. H.C. Long
Chief Legislative Counsel,
   Graham Walker, Q.C.

Members

Constituency	Member and Affiliation
Annapolis East	Earle Rayfuse (Lib)
Annapolis West	The Hon. J. Greg Kerr (PC)
Antigonish	J. William Gillis (Lib)
Argyle	The Hon. Neil J. LeBlanc (PC)
Bedford-Musquodoboit Valley	The Hon. Kenneth J. Streatch (PC)
Cape Breton Centre	Wayne Connors (Lib)
Cape Breton East	John MacEachern (Lib)
Cape Breton North	The Hon. Brian A. Young (PC)
Cape Breton Nova	Paul W. MacEwan (Ind)
Cape Breton South	Vincent J. MacLean (Lib)
Cape Breton West	Russell MacKinnon (Lib)
Cape Breton-The Lakes	Bernie Boudreau (Lib)
Clare	The Hon. Guy J. LeBlanc (PC)
Colchester North	Edward Lorraine (Lib)
Colchester South	Dr. R. Colin D. Stewart (PC)
Cole Harbour	The Hon. G. David Nantes (PC)
Cumberland Centre	Guy A.C. Brown (Lib)
Cumberland East	The Hon. Roger S. Bacon (PC)
Cumberland West	Ross Bragg (Lib)
Dartmouth East	Dr. James A. Smith (Lib)
Dartmouth North	Sandra Jolly (Lib)
Dartmouth South	The Hon. Roland J. Thornhill (PC)
Digby	Joseph Casey (Lib)
Guysborough	The Hon. C.W. (Chuck) MacNeil (PC)
Halifax Atlantic	The Hon. John M. Buchanan, Q.C. (PC)
Halifax Bedford Basin	The Hon. Joel Matheson, Q.C. (PC)
Halifax Chebucto	Alexa A. McDonough (NDP)
Halifax Citadel	The Hon. Arthur R. Donahoe, Q.C. (PC)
Halifax Cornwallis	The Hon. Terence Donahoe, Q.C. (PC)
Halifax Eastern Shore	The Hon. Thomas J. McInnis (PC)
Halifax Needham	Gerald O'Malley (Lib)
Halifax St. Margaret's	Gerald Lawrence (PC)
Hants East	Jack Hawkins (Lib)
Hants West	The Hon. Ronald S. Russell (PC)
Inverness North	Charles MacArthur (Lib)
Inverness South	Danny Graham (Lib)
Kings North	The Hon. George G. Archibald (PC)
Kings South	Derrick Kimball (PC)
Kings West	The Hon. George C. Moody (PC)
Lunenburg Centre	Al Mosher (PC)
Lunenburg East	James A. Barkhouse (Lib)
Lunenburg West	Marie Dechman (PC)
Pictou Centre	The Hon. John A. MacIsaac (PC)
Pictou East	The Hon. Donald W. Cameron (PC)
Pictou West	The Hon. Donald P. McInnes (PC)
Queens	The Hon. John G. Leefe (PC)
Richmond	Richard Mann (Lib)
Sackville	John E. Holm (NDP)
Shelburne	Harold M. Huskilson (Lib)
Truro-Bible Hill	The Hon. Ronald Giffin, Q.C. (PC)
Victoria	Kenneth MacAskill (Lib)
Yarmouth	Leroy Legere (PC)

Ind — Independent

Lib — Liberal
NDP — New Democrat
PC — Progressive Conservative

Office of the Premier

Province House, Box 726, Halifax, B3J 2T3
Premier, The Hon. John M. Buchanan,
   P.C., Q.C.
Press Secretary, John O'Brien

Offices of the Official Opposition

Centennial Bldg., Ste. 1009, 1660 Hollis St.
Box 723, Halifax, B3J 2T3
Leader of the Official Opposition,
   Vincent J. MacLean
Director of Communications, Al Hollingsworth

Offices of the New Democratic Party

Roy Bldg., Ste. 422
1657 Barrington St., Halifax, B3J 2Y3
Leader, Alexa A. McDonough
Chief of Staff and Communications Director,
   Dan O'Connor

Offices of Independent Members

Dennis Bldg., 4th Flr.
1740 Granville St., Halifax, B3J 1X5

Nova Scotia Legislative Library

Province House, Box 396, Halifax, B3J 2P8
General Inquiries: (902) 424-5932

   The primary function of the Legislative Library is to provide library and information services to the legislature. It also provides these services to the provincial public service, members of the judiciary, and representatives of federal and foreign governments in the province. To do this, the Legislative Library acquires and maintains a collection of provincial and federal government publications, books, newspapers, periodicals, microforms, and other materials to assist MLAs and other government officials with their legislative and official responsibilities. The Library also houses a definitive collection of books and pamphlets relating to Nova Scotia. As the depository library for Nova Scotia official publications, the Library publishes a monthly and annual catalogue of Nova Scotia government publica-

tions. The general public may use the facilities of the Legislative Library, but they do not have borrowing privileges.

Legislative Librarian, Margaret Murphy

Office of the Ombudsman

5161 George St., Ste. 1100
Box 2152, Halifax, B3J 3B7
   The Office of the Ombudsman was established in Nova Scotia in 1971. The Ombudsman is empowered to hear and investigate personal complaints from individuals who feel they have been done a disservice by municipal or provincial government departments in Nova Scotia. The Ombudsman may use his investigatory powers to correct the injustice or to guide the complainant in the right direction in order to have the grievance rectified. He may also recommend appropriate measures to government departments.
   The Ombudsman can only help settle those grievances arising from the administration of laws and regulations by government departments and agencies. These may be in the form of unreasonable delays, administrative errors, oversight, negligence, abuse of authority, inefficiency, etc. The Ombudsman has no jurisdiction over decisions made by judges, magistrates or justices; by the cabinet or its committees; or by private companies and individuals.
   Requests for help may be made in writing, by telephone, or in person at the address listed above. The complaint will be given written form in the early stage of an investigation.

A/Ombudsman and Investigator,
Gerald F. DeYoung

DEPARTMENT OF ADVANCED EDUCATION AND JOB TRAINING

Founders Sq., 5th Flr., 1701 Hollis St.
Box 2086, Stn. M, Halifax, B3J 3B7

MINISTER'S OFFICE
Minister, The Hon. Joel R. Matheson, Q.C.

DEPUTY MINISTER'S OFFICE
Dep. Minister, Joseph H. Clarke
Management Information Services
Co-ordinator, A. Cornwall

FINANCE AND ADMINISTRATION
Exec. Director, N.N. Graham
Planning and Evaluation
Exec. Director, Wayne Doggett
Program Development
Exec. Director, Peter Woods

PROGRAMS
Exec. Director, Dermot Mulrooney
Area Directors:
Cape Breton, E.C. MacLean
Metro Area, J.M. Murley
Northern Area, Georgina Burns
Valley/South Shore Area, J.D. Anthony

Student Aid Office
Director, Elizabeth Ann Macdonald

Youth Initiatives
Exec. Director, Kathie Swenson

AGENCIES, BOARDS AND COMMISSIONS

Nova Scotia Council on Higher Education
Founders Sq., 6th Flr., 1701 Hollis St.
Box 2086, Stn. M, Halifax, B3J 3B7

Chairman, Gerald J. McCarthy
Secretary, Betty-Ann Pothier
Sr. Policy Advisor, Dr. Peter M. Butler
Sr. Financial Advisor, Andrew C. Carras

DEPARTMENT OF AGRICULTURE AND MARKETING
World Trade and Convention Ctr., 5th Flr.
1800 Argyle St., Box 190, Halifax, B3J 2M4

MINISTER'S OFFICE
Minister, The Hon. George Archibald

DEPUTY MINISTER'S OFFICE
Dep. Minister, Ralph E. Morehouse

ADMINISTRATION BRANCH
Exec. Director, Richard J. Huggard
Policy and Research
Co-ordinator, Kevin Grant
Personnel Officer, H.J. Masterman
Box 550, Truro, B2N 5E3
Accounting
Director, Robert Mosher
Marketing and Economics Branch
Director, Brian Smith
Extension Branch
Director, Rolland Hayman
Livestock Services Branch
Director, Jack Johnson
Soils and Crops Branch
Director, Jim Goit
Horticulture and Biology Services Branch
Director, D.M. Sangster

Nova Scotia Agricultural College
Principal, Dr. H.F. MacRae

AGENCIES, BOARDS AND COMMISSIONS

MARKETING BOARDS

Marketing boards for agricultural products in Canada are created by a number of different pieces of legislation. National wheat and dairy products plans flow from the *Canadian Wheat Board Act* and the *Canadian Dairy Commission Act* respectively. Egg and poultry boards derive their authority from the *Farm Products Marketing Agencies Act.* As well, many have their own provincial statutes and are normally within the jurisdiction of an umbrella provincial agency. The individual boards are, however, non-governmental and made up largely of elected farmer representatives.

There is also a variety of types. The Economic Council of Canada's study on marketing boards identified five: promotional and developmental boards with little power; selling-desk boards that handle marketing but do not set prices; boards that negotiate prices; boards that set prices; and full-fledged boards that establish quotas. These last are known as supply-management marketing boards. Currently, there are more than 100 active boards in Canada.

NATURAL PRODUCTS MARKETING COUNCIL
Box 550, Truro, B2N 5E3

The Natural Products Marketing Council was established in 1946 under the *Natural Products Act.* Its objective is to provide for the orderly marketing of designated natural products. Under the Act, the Council has wide-ranging powers, including the investigation of any activities concerning the marketing of natural products and the establishment of price-negotiating agencies. The Council may delegate certain of these powers to commodity boards.

In brief, the Council arbitrates disputes between processors and producers of natural products. It supervises the operation of existing marketing plans and assists in the development of new marketing plans as requested by producers. The Council co-operates with other marketing agencies at the federal and provincial levels. It also develops marketing policies for the consideration of the minister.

The Lieutenant-Governor in Council determines the number of persons on the Council (currently five). The Nova Scotia Department of Agriculture and Marketing supplies a secretary (professional agriculturist) and secretarial services. The Council reports to the Lieutenant-Governor in Council through the minister.

Chairman, Stuart Allaby
Secretary, G. Brian Smith

NOVA SCOTIA DAIRY COMMISSION
Box 782, Truro, B2N 5E8

The Nova Scotia Dairy Commission was established in 1967 to administer Part XVIII of the *Agriculture and Marketing Act.* The Commission is composed of five members, three of whom are required to have no direct association with the dairy industry; the other two members represent the production and processing sectors of the industry.

The Commission is involved in producer and processor licensing; price control at producer, wholesale, and retail levels; farm inspection; milk production and quality standards; central testing processor audits; industry statistics; and fluid quota and market sharing quota administration.

Chairman, Vacant
Manager, Roger Mason

PROVINCIAL GRAIN COMMISSION
Kentville Agricultural Centre
Box 785, Kentville, B4N 3X9

Chairman, Ted Ueffing
Sec.-Manager, Robert Dechman

Farm Loan Board
Box 550, Truro, B2N 5E3

The Farm Loan Board was established as the successor to the Nova Scotia Land Settlement Board under the *Agriculture and Rural Credit Act, 1967,* to provide development loans to Nova Scotia farmers. The Board provides long-term credit primarily for the purchase and development of farm operations, including farm acquisition, land purchases, building construction, land development, land drainage, and other long-term development requirements. The Board is also authorized to acquire and hold land for leasing to farmers and generally to service the long-term credit needs of the farm community.

Offices are maintained in Kentville, serving western Nova Scotia, and in Truro, serving central and eastern Nova Scotia.

Chairman, Lawrence Coldwell
Director, Arnold A. Rovers

Nova Scotia Crop and Livestock Insurance Commission
Box 1092, Truro, B2N 5G9

The Crop and Livestock Insurance Commission is responsible for administering nine crop insurance plans and a dairy livestock insurance plan. The program is under the authority of the Minister of Agriculture and Marketing for the Province of Nova Scotia. The Government of Canada provides financial assistance to the crop insurance program by contributing 50 per cent of the total premium required each year. The Province of Nova Scotia pays all of the administration costs.

Chairman, Peter Van Oostrum
Manager, Donald MacNeil

DEPARTMENT OF THE ATTORNEY GENERAL
Bank of Montreal Bldg., 10th Flr.
5151 George St., Box 7, Halifax, B3J 2L6

ATTORNEY GENERAL'S OFFICE
Attorney General, The Hon. Thomas J. McInnis

DEPUTY ATTORNEY GENERAL'S OFFICE
Dep. Attorney General,
D. William MacDonald, Q.C.

LEGAL SERVICES DIVISION
Exec. Director, R. Gerald Conrad, Q.C.
Solicitor Services
Director, B. Davidson, Q.C.
Civil Litigation
Director, R.M. Endres
Criminal
Director, G. Gale, Q.C.
Prosecutions
Director, M.E. Herschorn
COURT AND REGISTRY SERVICES
Exec. Director, R.A. MacDonald
Finance and Administration
Director, Clarence Guest
Field Operations
Director, A.E. Rennie
Revenue and Audit
Co-ordinator, Bernard Conrad
Staff Services
Co-ordinator, John Budden

PUBLIC TRUSTEE
Central Trust Twr., Ste. 220, 1801 Hollis St.
Box 685, Halifax, B3J 2T3
Public Trustee, Martin H. Bushell, Q.C.
COMPANIES BRANCH
Centennial Bldg., 1660 Hollis St.
Box 1529, Halifax, B3J 2Y4
Registrar of Joint Stock Companies,
C.B. Alcorn

Registry of Deeds
Centennial Bldg., 5th Flr., 1660 Hollis St.
Box 2205, Halifax, B3J 3C4
Registrar, R.A. Hickey
Dep. Registrar, A. Stuart

AGENCIES, BOARDS AND COMMISSIONS

Criminal Injuries Compensation Board
Centennial Bldg., 10th Flr., 1660 Hollis St.
Box 985, Halifax, B3J 2V9

The Criminal Injuries Compensation Board considers payment of compensation to persons who are injured or killed in Nova Scotia by another person committing a criminal offence, as described in the schedule to the *Compensation for Victims of Crime Act.* The offences referred to are generally violent and do not include theft or loss or damage to property.

Compensation is awarded for expenses actually and reasonably incurred, for pecuniary loss or damages affecting a victim's capacity for work, and for pain and suffering and the maintenance of a child born as the result of a sexual assault. In the event of a victim's death, compensation is made to the dependents.

The conduct of the victim is always considered to ascertain whether the victim may have contributed to his/her own misfortune. The Nova Scotia statute was proclaimed May 12, 1981; only victims of crime after that date are eligible to receive compensation.

Chairman, D.J.C. Waterbury, Q.C.

Expropriations Compensation Board

Centennial Bldg., 9th Flr., 1660 Hollis St.
Box 2071, Halifax, B3J 2Z1

The Exropriations Compensation Board of Nova Scotia consists of four members. It hears and determines questions of compensation with respect to all expropriations coming under the provisions of the *Expropriation Act, 1973*. The Board holds hearings in various parts of the province where land is expropriated from time to time.

Chairman, S. David Bryson, Q.C.
Clerk, Mrs. Laura Delaney

Nova Scotia Horse Racing Commission

Belmont House, Ste. 202
33 Alderney Dr., Dartmouth
Mailing Address:
Box 1073, Halifax, B3J 2X1

The Nova Scotia Horse Racing Commission is appointed under the provisions of the *Nova Scotia Horse Racing Commission Act*. It has the power to govern, direct, regulate, and control horse racing in Nova Scotia.

Its activities include holding hearings and inquiries, conducting investigations, licensing racing participants, making and enforcing rules and regulations, employing and supervising race officials, and promoting horse racing.

Chairman, Vacant
Director, Gerald G. Grant

Nova Scotia Legal Aid Commission

5212 Sackville St., Ste. 300, Halifax, B3J 1K6

The Nova Scotia Legal Aid Commission is responsible for all matters relating to legal aid in the province of Nova Scotia. The Commission is a body corporate established by the *Legal Aid Act*, S.N.S. 1977, Chapter 11.

With few exceptions, legal aid may be granted for any proceeding and at any stage of a proceeding before any court. A barrister providing such legal aid may give legal advice, draw documents, and negotiate settlements.

Where the Commission determines that the claim of the applicant has merit, legal aid will be granted where part or all of the applicant's income is being received from municipal or provincial social assistance, or where the applicant is in an equivalent position to that of a provincial social assistance recipient. Where the applicant is found eligible, legal aid is furnished free of charge to any individual who is unable to pay; there may be a partial charge to any individual who is able to pay a portion of the cost.

Legal services are normally provided by lawyers employed on a full-time basis by the Commission. These lawyers staff a network of offices throughout the province. There are 11 regional offices and, where appropriate, sub-offices are operated. There are currently 61 lawyers employed by the Commission.

Chairman, J. Mark McCrea
Exec. Director, Gordon Murray, Q.C.
215 Provost St., New Glasgow, B2H 2R2

Nova Scotia Securities Commission

Joseph Howe Bldg., 2nd Flr., 1690 Hollis St.
Box 458, Halifax, B3J 3J9
Registrar, M.A. Pittas

AUDITOR GENERAL'S OFFICE

Hollis Bldg., 2nd Flr., 1649 Hollis St.
Box 793, Halifax, B3J 2V2
General Office: (902) 424-5855/5907

Auditor General, O.P. Cormier, F.C.A.
Dep. Auditor General, R.S. Gunn
Asst. Auditor General, J.R. Butler
Director, Vacant
Director, C.D. Carter
Audit Managers: R.L. Bowes, A.D. Horgan, D.E. Perry, D.C. Hicks, E.M. Morash
Audit Supervisors: T.E. Edwards, R.E. Edmonds, S.M. Lacusta, D.P. Hendsbee

DEPARTMENT OF COMMUNITY SERVICES

Johnston Bldg., 5th Flr., 5182 Prince St.
Box 696, Halifax, B3J 2T7

MINISTER'S OFFICE
Minister, The Hon. Guy J. LeBlanc

DEPUTY MINISTER'S OFFICE
Dep. Minister, Carmen F. Moir
A/Co-ordinator of Appeals, Mike Johnston
Indian Affairs
Co-ordinator, Allan Clark

AUDIT SERVICES
Director, George Hudson
Supervisor, Paul Palmer

FAMILY AND CHILDREN'S SERVICES
Administrator, W.D. Greatorex
Director, Rosemary Rippon
Child and Adolescent Services
Director, Trevor Townsend
Child Abuse Register
Supervisor, Debra Burris
Day Care Services
Director, Greg Gammon
Young Offender and Court Services
Director, John T. MacKinnon

FIELD SERVICES AND PERSONNEL
Director, J.A. MacKinnon
Sr. Departmental Consultant, Michael Craig
Personnel Manager, David MacEachern
Personnel Services
Supervisor, Barbara Bromke

Psychological Services
6061 Young St., Ste. 320, Box 8715
Halifax, B3K 5M4
A/Co-ordinator, Alan Cuvelier

FINANCIAL SERVICES
Director, Arnold R. Jones
Fiscal Planning and Control
Co-ordinator, Clement Hennebury
FAMILY BENEFITS DIVISION
Director, Bill Campbell
Diabetic Assistance
Supervisor, C. Fraser
Senior Citizens Financial Aid Programs
Supervisor, S. MacLean

REHABILITATION AND COMMUNITY
SERVICES
Administrator, J.A. McIsaac
Services to the Mentally Handicapped
Director, Ross Thorpe
Rehabilitation and Community Services
Director, Ron L'Esperance
Classifications and Assessments
Supervisor, Dr. M. MacFarlane
Municipal Assistance
Director, Peter Barteaux
Classification and Assessment
Supervisor, Carolyn Rushton-Conrad
Homes for Special Care
Chief Supervisor, Barb Millar
Adult Protection Services
Co-ordinator, Nancy Cochrane

POLICY, PLANNING AND MANAGEMENT
INFORMATION SERVICES
Director, Bessie Harris
Policy, Planning and Research
Director, Liz McNaughton
Management Information Systems
Director, Tom Conrad
Librarian, Jane Phillips
Staff Training
Supervisor, Joan Parks

CO-ORDINATED HOME CARE
Provincial Co-ordinator, Bob Moody
Asst. Provincial Co-ordinator, Joan Redmond
Homemaker Services
Director, A.S. Brown

AGENCIES, BOARDS AND COMMISSIONS

Nova Scotia Senior Citizens Commission
Johnston Bldg., 3rd Flr., 5182 Prince St.
Box 696, Halifax, B3J 2T7

The Nova Scotia Senior Citizens Commission, established in 1972 under the *Senior Citizens' Social Services Act*, is an advisory body to the Minister of Community Services. The Commission consists of 19 private citizens, many of them seniors, who come from all parts of the province. They are appointed by the Executive Council for a three-year term. Representatives from the departments of Education, of Health and Fitness, and of Advanced Education and Job Training, and from the Senior Citizens Secretariat also participate in Commission meetings.

The mandate of the Commission is to:
1) conduct, direct, and promote fact-finding studies and research related to aging;
2) seek out and encourage persons interested in providing voluntary services to citizen groups concerned with aging;
3) promote new activities and social services for senior citizens through voluntary agencies and all levels of government;
4) review existing legislation and government programs and make recommendations as to how these may be improved to provide better services for senior citizens; and
5) perform any duties assigned by the Governor in Council or the Minister of Community Services.

Chairman, John Glassey
Co-ordinator, Allan Clark

Nova Scotia Senior Citizens Secretariat
Dennis Bldg., 4th Flr., 1740 Granville St.
Box 2065, Halifax, B3J 2Z1
(902) 424-4649/4737/5329/6322

The Nova Scotia Senior Citizens Secretariat was established by legislation introduced in 1980. The Act named the ministers of Social Services, Health, and Municipal Affairs, and the Minister responsible for the *Housing Development Act* to the Secretariat, with the Governor in Council having authority to add other persons as may be determined from time to time. In 1982, the ministers of Education and of Culture, Recreation and Fitness were added, since their departments provide programs of interest and benefit to seniors.

The purpose of the Secretariat is to facilitate the planning and development of services and programs for seniors by developing and co-ordinating plans, policies, and programs for and with seniors in partnership with the responsible government departments, other provincial bodies, and voluntary seniors' groups.

Director, Dr. Fred R. MacKinnon
Co-ordinator, Valerie White
Special Consultant, John A. MacKenzie

Nova Scotia Social Services Council
Johnston Bldg., 3rd Flr., 5182 Prince St.
Box 696, Halifax, B3J 2T7

The Nova Scotia Social Services Council is a 15-member advisory board to the Minister of Community Services. Established under the *Social Services Councils Act,* S.N.S. 1970-71, Chapter 22, the Council has a broad mandate to provide information and advice to the minister on issues and concerns relating to all aspects of social services.

In order to achieve its objective, the Council regularly holds meetings with community groups, organizations, and individuals. As well, the Council reviews established social service programs, conducts small research studies, and participates, at the minister's request, on various committees studying and discussing specific program-related matters.

The Council's chairman and members are appointed by an Order-in-Council for two-year terms which are renewable upon expiry.

Chairman, Rev. Vincent Ihasz
Exec. Secretary, Bessie Harris

DEPARTMENT OF CONSUMER AFFAIRS
5151 Terminal Rd., 2nd Flr.
Box 998, Halifax, B3J 2X3

MINISTER'S OFFICE
Minister, The Hon. R. Colin D. Stewart

DEPUTY MINISTER'S OFFICE
Dep. Minister, Cathy MacNutt
Policy and Planning
Co-ordinator, Barbara Jones-Gordon

CONSUMER AND COMMERCIAL RELATIONS
Director, Robert G. Martin
Licensing, Anne Merry
Consumer Services, Ron Whiting
Inspection and Compliance, Greg Mitchell
FINANCIAL INSTITUTIONS AND REVENUE
Director, Paul LeBlanc
Sup't of Insurance, Lawrence Umlah

RESIDENTIAL TENANCIES AND
CONDOMINIUMS DIVISION
Landlord/Tenant Relations
Director, Howard Delano
RENT REVIEW AND ADMINISTRATION
Director, Dennis Holland
AMUSEMENTS REGULATION
Chief Inspector and Admin. Officer,
Dennis Smith

AGENCIES, BOARDS AND COMMISSIONS

Amusements Regulation Board
5151 Terminal Rd., 7th Flr.
Box 607, Halifax, B3J 2R7

The Amusements Regulation Board has responsibility for the classification of films and videos exhibited, sold, or rented in Nova Scotia. It ensures that theatre owners, video store operators, and distributors adhere to the rules regarding the advertising, sale, renting, and exhibition of films. The Board also examines and licenses projectionists.

Chairman, D.F.L. Trivett

Rent Review Commission
5151 Terminal Rd., 7th Flr.
Box 820, Halifax, B3J 2V2
Chairman, J. Romans

Residential Tenancies Board
5151 Terminal Rd., 1st Flr.
Box 820, Halifax, B3J 2V2
Landlord/Tenant Relations
Director, Howard Delano

DEPARTMENT OF EDUCATION
Trade Mart Bldg., Brunswick at Cogswell
Box 578, Halifax, B3J 2S9

MINISTER'S OFFICE
Minister, The Hon. Ronald C. Giffin, Q.C.

DEPUTY MINISTER'S OFFICE
Dep. Minister, Blenis J. Nicholson
Learning Disabilities, Research and Information
Director, Dr. Joan Backman

EDUCATION PROGRAMS
Chief Director, B. Robert Haines
CURRICULUM DEVELOPMENT
Director, LaJune Naud
Special Services
Asst. Director, Grace Beuree
Elementary Education
Co-ordinator, Shirley Sangster
French Language Programs
Director, Kenneth Gaudet
INSPECTION SERVICES
Director, Peter Lawson
TEACHER CERTIFICATION
Registrar, D. Brett Woodbury

Nova Scotia Teacher's College
Box 810, Truro, B2N 5G5
Principal, Margaret A. Swan

EDUCATION RESOURCE SERVICES
PROGRAM
1747 Summer St., Halifax, B3H 3A6
Director, Candace Stevenson

Education Media Services
6955 Bayers Rd., Halifax, B3L 4S4
Asst. Director, B.F. Hart

Nova Scotia Provincial Library
6955 Bayers Rd., Halifax, B3L 4S4
A/Provincial Librarian, Bertha Higgins

Nova Scotia Museum Complex
1747 Summer St., Halifax, B3H 3A6
Asst. Director, R.W. Frame

PUBLICATION AND REFERENCE
Director, Fay P. Lee
FINANCE AND BUDGETING PROGRAM
Chief Director, J.R. Levangie
Public Education Grants
Director, Richard Morris

Research
Director, Bette Kelly
Nova Scotia School Book Bureau
Supervisor, M.A. Reinhardt
School Planning and Conveyance
Director, D.E. Nauss

AGENCIES, BOARDS AND COMMISSIONS

Teachers' Pension Commission
Box 578, Halifax, B3J 2S9

The Teachers' Pension Commission, as presently constituted, was established in 1949 under the *Teachers' Pension Act*, S.N.S. 1949, Chapter 8. The Act was subsequently amended and is now cited as the *Teachers' Pension Act*, R.S.N.S. 1967, Chapter 301, as amended by legislation up to and including 1984.

The Commission is responsible for the overall administration of the Act including the provision of pension benefits to approximately 4,000 retired teachers and dependents; the collection of contributions from approximately 11,000 active teachers; and the processing of refunds, purchases of prior service, and transfers to and from other funds. The Act empowers the Commission to make Regulations under the Act, subject to the approval of the Lieutenant-Governor in Council. All applications for full-service, reduced-service, disability and dependents' pensions must receive the approval of the Commission, as must all applications for purchase of prior service. The plan at present has reciprocal transfer arrangements with the Nova Scotia Public Service Superannuation Fund and all other provincial teacher pension plans except British Columbia's. The plan is a unit benefit plan and the fund is subject to actuarial valuation every five years.

The Commission has five members. Three are appointed by the Lieutenant-Governor in Council and two by the Nova Scotia Teachers' Union. Each member serves for a term of three years and may be reappointed.
Secretary, R.W.C. Jack

DEPARTMENT OF THE ENVIRONMENT
5151 Terminal Rd., 5th Flr.
Box 2107, Halifax, B3J 3B7

MINISTER'S OFFICE
Minister, The Hon. John G. Leefe

DEPUTY MINISTER'S OFFICE
Dep. Minister, Armand F. Pinard
Administration and Office Services
Director, Earl Stone
Field Services Division
Director, J.A. Turner, P.Eng.
Environmental Assessment Division
Director, A.J. Crouse, P.Eng.

Policy Advisor, J.F. Jones, P.Eng.
Utilities Division
Director, R.J. Porter, P.Eng.

AGENCIES, BOARDS AND COMMISSIONS

Environmental Control Council
Box 2107, Halifax, B3J 3B7

The Environmental Control Council, a citizens' advisory board to the Minister of the Environment, is established under the *Environmental Protection Act*, S.N.S. 1973, Chapter 6.

The Council has broad responsibility to advise the minister on environmental policies, programs, and standards for the preservation and protection of the environment. In addition, the Council may review and evaluate programs and activities of government or the private sector in light of their environmental impact, and make recommendations to the minister.

In special or continuing situations, the Council may appoint a committee of its members, possibly with citizen representation, to investigate or monitor environmental conditions.

The Environmental Control Council is composed of 12 to 15 members with regional representation. Under the Act, the Council must include representation from the following areas: health, law, engineering, industry, labour, municipalities, conservation or ecology groups, agriculture, the academic community, forestry, and fisheries. The Council is supported by an executive secretary and a research co-ordinator, and includes the Deputy Minister of the Environment as an ex officio member.

Chairman, Jim Harrison
Secretary and CEO, Jim MacDonald

DEPARTMENT OF FINANCE
Provincial Bldg., 4th Flr., 1723 Hollis St.
Box 187, Halifax, B3J 2N3

MINISTER'S OFFICE
Minister, The Hon. J. Greg Kerr

DEPUTY MINISTER'S OFFICE
Dep. Minister, Allan G. Manuel, C.A.

CONTROLLER'S OFFICE
Controller, S.L. Wile, C.A.
Financial Counsel, Jim Spurr
Personnel Office
Manager, Doug Low
Federal-Provincial Taxation and Fiscal Relations Division
Director, Marilyn Gaudet
Revenue Division
Director, Ivan K. Richardson, R.I.A.

ACCOUNTING AND FINANCIAL REPORTING SERVICES
Director, Richard Noble, R.I.A.
Payment of Accounts
Manager, Don Woods
Data Entry and Verification
Supervisor, B. LaPierre
Audit and Control
Supervisor, C. Phair
Co-ordinator of Accounting, B. MacDonald
Collection Procedures
Supervisor, G. Hughes
Appropriations Analyst, G. Delouchry

MANAGEMENT INFORMATION SYSTEMS
Director, C.H. Bert Loveless, C.A.
Systems and Programs
Co-ordinator, Holly Fancy
Data Processing
Manager, James Mak
Data Controller, C. Bastable

INTERNAL AUDIT DIVISION
Director, George Perrin, C.A.
Programs and Special Assignments
Auditor, Lynn Burrows
PAYROLL DIVISION
Director, Steve MacDonald
Co-ordinator, Ken Cameron
PENSIONS DIVISION
Director, Gordon Sturdy
Registration
Sup't, P.J. Fleet

TRUSTS AND DEBT MANAGEMENT
Chief Director, H.W.V. Matthews
Investments Manager, Vacant
Debt Management
Manager, Keith Mumford
Cash, Banking and Accounting
Manager, Thomas Collins
Securities Officer, Mary Fougere
Trusts and Financing
Manager, Richard McAloney, C.A.

AGENCIES, BOARDS AND COMMISSIONS

Provincial Tax Commission
Provincial Bldg., 2nd Flr., 1723 Hollis St.
Box 755, Halifax, B3J 2N3

The Provincial Tax Commission is responsible for administering the *Health Services Tax Act,* the *Gasoline and Diesel Oil Tax Act,* and the *Homeowners' Incentive Act.*

The various sections of the Commission promulgate tax information and rulings, perform audits on taxpayer accounts, collect outstanding accounts, deal with various requests for refunds and rebates, and generally monitor compliance with the legislation and Regulations.

Commissioner, Eric Lavers, C.G.A.
Secretary, S.A. MacDonald

Health Services Tax Division
Box 755, Halifax, B3J 2V4
Audit Section
Manager, Paul Curran
Account Monitoring Section
Manager, C.G. Arnold
Tax Information Services
Manager, D.V. Quaintance
Gasoline and Diesel Oil Tax Division
Box 2212, Halifax, B3J 3C4
Manager, R.S. Hubley

DEPARTMENT OF FISHERIES
Purdy's Wharf, 3rd Flr., 1959 Upper Water St.
Box 2223, Halifax, B3J 3C4

MINISTER'S OFFICE
Minister, The Hon. Donald P. McInnes

DEPUTY MINISTER'S OFFICE
Dep. Minister, D.A. (Sandy) MacLean

FINANCE AND ADMINISTRATION
Administration
Director, John A. Marsters
Management Support Services
Co-ordinator, Kenneth R. Weston
Administrative Services
Supervisor, Charles G. Allen
MARKETING
Director, Janis L. Raymond
Seafood Consultant, A. Estelle Bryant
Home Economist, Marilyn C. O'Neill

MARINE RESOURCES
Director, Arthur A. Longard
Marine Advisor, Invertebrates,
S. Gregory Roach
Marine Advisor, Groundfish,
Peter C.C. Underwood
Marine Advisor, Pelagics,
Dr. Robert H. Crawford

AQUACULTURE AND INLAND FISHERIES
Director, L.L. MacLeod
Aquaculture Co-ordinator,
Dr. Catherine T. Enright
Aquaculture
Administrator, Clarrie F. MacKinnon
Inland Fisheries Supervisor, G. Murray Hill
Pleasant Point Field Station
Biologist, Andrew G. Bagnall
Box 84, Musquodoboit Harbour, B0J 2L0
Fraser's Mill Trout Hatchery
Manager, Donald A. MacLean
McGowan Lake Trout Hatchery
Manager, Michael G. McNeil

TRAINING AND FIELD SERVICES
Director, James J. McLevey
School of Fisheries
Supervisor, Donald F. Robertson

INDUSTRIAL DEVELOPMENT
Director, George R. Richard
Development and Inspection Programs
Supervisor, David F. Hansen
Development Programs
Asst., Vacant
Fisheries Inspectors: Mary E. Meagher,
Dana M. Rodgers, Thomas A. LeBlanc
Fisheries Technician, Olafur E. Egilsson
Plants and ERDA Programs
Supervisor, Gary B. Scott
Product and Process Development
Supervisor, Michael A. Drebot
Marine Facilities
Supervisor, Marshall F. Giles
Fisheries Technician, William J. MacDonald

AGENCIES, BOARDS AND COMMISSIONS

Nova Scotia Fisheries Loan Board
Purdy's Wharf, 3rd Flr., 1959 Upper Water St.
Box 2223, Halifax, B3J 3C4

The Nova Scotia Fisheries Loan Board makes loans at subsidized interest rates to fishermen, associations of fishermen, and fishing companies to build new boats, buy used boats, install engines and other equipment on boats, and modify and convert one type of fishing to another. Loans are also available for aquaculture. Loans cannot be made for less than $1,000 or for boats under 6.7 metres in length. The maximum term of a loan is 12 years.

The Fisheries Loan Board is comprised of 11 members, plus a chairman, and meets approximately once a month to consider applications which are approved under the *Fisheries Development Act*. The Fisheries Loan Fund, from which loans are made, is funded to the extent of $150 million. Loans up to $100,000 may be approved by the Board, but anything over $100,000 must obtain the approval of the Governor in Council.

To be eligible for a loan, a fisherman must be a Canadian citizen and a resident of Nova Scotia, be of the age of majority at the time of application, have at least two years fishing experience out of the last five, demonstrate to the Board that the larger portion of time spent or income earned directly relates to commercial fishing, and satisfy the Board that the security for the loan (a first mortgage on the boat) will be adequately protected during the term of the loan.

Chairman, Robert A. Inglis
Exec. Director, John A. Marsters
Fisheries Loans
Manager, Eldon A. MacIntosh
Sr. Loan Officer, James P. Sarty
Chief Accountant, Malcolm R. Everett
Technical Services Officer, Michael Myketyn

DEPARTMENT OF GOVERNMENT SERVICES
Maritime Ctr., 14th Flr., 1505 Barrington St.
Box 54, Halifax, B3J 2L4

MINISTER'S OFFICE
Minister, The Hon. Terence R.B. Donahoe, Q.C.

DEPUTY MINISTER'S OFFICE
Dep. Minister, Michael T. Zareski
Special Projects
Co-ordinator, Charles Cook

DESIGN AND CONSTRUCTION DIVISION
Exec. Director, Brian Stonehouse
Architecture Services
Director, John Way
Engineering Services
Director, Gerry Cullinan
Project Management
Director, Dave Seller
Construction Services
Director, Ted Keddy

PROPERTY AND OPERATION SERVICES
Exec. Director, Darrell Hiltz
Property Services
Director, John MacLean
Building Services
Director, Norman Atkinson
Operations Services
Director, Tim Olive
Queen's Printer
6176 Young St., 1st Flr., Halifax, B3K 2A6
Queen's Printer, Bernard K. Hamm

SYSTEMS AND COMPUTER SERVICES
Exec. Director, David Beaulieu
Client Services
Director, Ernie Englehart
System Development and Support
Director, Wayne Champniss
Telecommunications
Director, Terry Hallett

FINANCE AND ADMINISTRATION
Exec. Director, Bill Hogg
Personnel and Administration
Director, Vacant
Financial Management
Director, Jack McNaughton
Publishing Director, Vacant
Insurance and Risk Management
Director, Ellery A. Dakin

DEPARTMENT OF HEALTH AND FITNESS
Joseph Howe Bldg., 12th Flr., 1690 Hollis St.
Box 488, Halifax, B3J 2R8

MINISTER'S OFFICE
Minister, The Hon. G. David Nantes

DEPUTY MINISTER'S OFFICE
Dep. Minister, Wayne J. Grady
Legal Counsel, Wayne Cochrane

HEALTH CARE INSTITUTIONS
A/Administrator, John Malcolm
A/Admin. Co-ordinator, Bob St. Laurent
Psychiatric Mental Health Services
Administrator, Dr. D.W. Archibald
Construction
Director, Gerald Brennan

COMMUNITY HEALTH PROGRAMS
Administrator, Dr. Wayne Sullivan
Nursing
Director, Janet Braunstein
Health Promotion and Fitness
Director, Theresa Marie Underhill
Nutrition
Director, Carole Milligan
ENVIRONMENTAL HEALTH
Public Health Engineering
Director, Peter Casey

FINANCE
Administrator, A.V. Rowland
Hospital Budgets and Auditing
Manager, A. Little
Accounting Manager, Fred Canavan
Capital Financing
Manager, Don Sweete
Third Party Liability
Supervisor, Kay Delaney
Office Services
Supervisor, Paul Pottie

INFORMATION SYSTEMS AND RESEARCH
Administrator, D. Rice
Health Manpower
Co-ordinator, R. Cameron
Statistics and Information
A/Director, Carolyn McDonald
Hospital Systems
Engineer, J. Phillips

REGISTRATION SERVICES
Provincial Bldg., 1723 Hollis St.
Box 157, Halifax, B3J 2M9
Dep. Registrar General, Betty Etter
Asst. Dep. Registrar General, Stella Fogarty

AGENCIES, BOARDS AND COMMISSIONS

Nova Scotia Health Services and Insurance Commission
Joseph Howe Bldg., 2nd Flr., 1690 Hollis St.
Box 760, Halifax, B3J 2V2

The Health Services and Insurance Commission was established Sept. 1, 1973 under *The Health Services and Insurance Act*, S.N.S. 1973, Chapter 8. The Commission is responsible to the Minister of Health and Fitness for the administration of a number of health services insurance programs in Nova Scotia, including the following:
(a) physicians' services (Medicare);
(b) surgical-dental services rendered by dentists in hospitals;
(c) vision analyses by optometrists;
(d) prescription drugs for residents 65 years of age and over;
(e) dental services for children born on or after Jan. 1, 1967, and who have not attained their sixteenth birthday, and for students registered with the School for the Blind;
(f) prescribed drugs and equipment for cystic fibrosis patients;
(g) dental services for patients with cleft lip/cleft palate;
(h) drugs required by those suffering from diabetes insipidus;
(i) drugs for cancer patients;
(j) prosthetic services — replacement of and repairs to standard arm and leg prostheses;
(k) intra-oral and extra-oral prostheses required as a result of maxillofacial surgery; and
(l) synthetic growth hormone drugs for patients with a certified growth hormone deficiency.

The Commission consists of 12 members appointed by the Lieutenant-Governor in Council, and meets monthly. Committees of the Commission meet as required throughout the year.

Chairman, C.E. Larsen
Exec. Director, Derek Dinham
Admin. Asst., Glen McClare

Medical Services Insurance
7 Spectacle Lake Dr.
Burnside Industrial Park
Box 2200, Halifax, B3J 3C6
Gen. Manager, D.L. McAvoy
Medical Director, Dr. Henry Bland
Operations Manager, Allen Murray
Inquiries Section
Manager, Gerry Martin

DEPARTMENT OF HOUSING
Royal Bank Bldg., 5th Flr., 46 Portland St.
Box 815, Dartmouth, B2Y 3Z3

MINISTER'S OFFICE
Minister, The Hon. Roger S. Bacon

DEPUTY MINISTER'S OFFICE
Dep. Minister, Louis Stephen
Housing Development Board
Chairman, M.H. Frank Harrington
Office Services
Director of Administration, Murray MacGray
Administrative Services
Manager, Betty Falle
Solicitor, Noella Fisher
Planning Services
Director, Ernest Clarke
Financial Services
Director, R.E. Boyd
Program and Property Management
Director, Dennis Kerr
Program Administration
Manager, Kathleen Spicer

Property Administration
Manager, James D. Graham
REGIONAL OFFICES:
Metro Regional Office
Bedford Twrs., Ste. 304, Box 280
Bedford, B4A 2X2
Reg. Manager, Clint Schofield
Cape Breton Regional Office
Provincial Bldg., 360 Prince St.
Box 1267, Sydney, B1P 6J9
Reg. Manager, R.C. Hines
Central Regional Office
176 Archimedes St., Box 481
New Glasgow, B2H 5E5
Reg. Manager, Thomas Moore
Western Regional Office
166 Commercial St., Box 1000
Middleton, B0S 1P0
Reg. Manager, Gordon MacPherson

DEPARTMENT OF INDUSTRY, TRADE AND TECHNOLOGY
World Trade and Convention Ctr., 7th Flr.
1800 Argyle St., Box 519, Halifax, B3J 2R7
General Inquiries: (902) 424-8920
Telex: 019-22548

MINISTER'S OFFICE
Minister, The Hon. Donald W. Cameron

DEPUTY MINISTER'S OFFICE
Dep. Minister, Thomas G. Merriam
Internal Auditor, Harry Lamont
Departmental Solicitor, Elizabeth Cuddihy
Information Services
Sr. Information Officer, Carole MacDonald

OFFICE OF THE AGENT GENERAL
14 Pall Mall, London, SW1Y 5LU England
Telex: 51-915867
Agent General in the United Kingdom and
Representative in Europe, Donald M. Smith

ECONOMIC PLANNING AND TECHNOLOGY
DIVISION
Exec. Director, Carol Conrad
Economic Analysis
Chief Economist, Charles Pye
Sr. Planner, Richard Shaffner
Program and Evaluation Branch
Director, Bob Doherty
Sr. Planner, Greg Bent
Policy Analyst, Richard Shaffner
Statistics and Research Services
Director, Paul Dober
Technology and Industrial Innovation Branch
Director, Ivor Harrington

INDUSTRIAL DEVELOPMENT DIVISION
Exec. Director, Richard Fletcher
Industrial Benefits Office
Director, Richard Butler

Trade Development Centre
Director, Fred Were
Industrial Promotion Branch
Director, Robert Baillie

FINANCE AND ADMINISTRATION DIVISION
Exec. Director, Philip Peapell
Financial Services
Manager, Donald Reardon
Systems and Administration
Manager, Ernie MacCulloch
Human Resources Branch
Manager, Frank MacLean
Technical Services Branch
A/Director, Gary Campbell
Business Advisory Services
Director, Andrew Hare
Director of Co-operatives, Fred Pierce
640 Prince St., Box 9, Truro, B2N 1G4

DEPARTMENT OF LABOUR
5151 Terminal Rd., 6th Flr.
Box 697, Halifax, B3J 2T8

MINISTER'S OFFICE
Minister, The Hon. Ronald S. Russell, Q.C.

DEPUTY MINISTER'S OFFICE
Dep. Minister, Hugh Macdonald

INDUSTRIAL RELATIONS
Director, William McCallum
ADMINISTRATION AND ACCOUNTING
Director, P.G. Horne
FIRE MARSHAL'S OFFICE
Fire Marshal, Thomas S. Makin
Dep. Fire Marshals: J. Forshner, G. Smith,
T. Gates, J. Holesworth, R. Shephard
Chief L.P. Gas Inspector, Vic Perry
Sr. Building Plan Examiner, R. Claridge
Chief Electrical Inspector, D. Bennicke
LABOUR STANDARDS
Director, Ross Mitchell
Chief Labour Standards Officer, Syd A. Cyr
Provincial Bldg., Sydney, B1P 5L1
RESEARCH
Director, Jean Dobson

OCCUPATIONAL HEALTH AND SAFETY
Exec. Director, Jack Noonan
Occupational Safety
Director, Dave Todd
Accident Prevention
Director, John F. Herbin
Mine Safety
Director, Claude White
Occupational Health
Director, Jim LeBlanc

AGENCIES, BOARDS AND COMMISSIONS

Construction Industry Panel
5151 Terminal Rd., 7th Flr.
Box 697, Halifax, B3J 2T8

The Construction Industry Panel of the Labour Relations Board exercises all the powers and jurisdictions of the Board with respect to the construction industry and in addition has the power to accredit an employers' organization. Part II of the *Trade Union Act* which set up the Panel was passed in 1972 by the Nova Scotia legislature.

Chairman, Judge Robert J. McCleave, Q.C.
CEO, Ken Horne
Secretary, Cecile O'Reilly

Labour Relations Board
5151 Terminal Rd., 7th Flr.
Box 697, Halifax, B3J 2T8

The Labour Relations Board is composed of two employer representatives, two union representatives, and an independent chairperson appointed by the Governor in Council. An alternate member for each member of the Board may also be appointed.

The Board holds the powers of a commissioner under the *Public Inquiries Act*. It may receive and accept evidence and information — on oath, affidavit, or otherwise — which it may deem admissible as evidence in a court of law.

The Board's authority extends to: the certification of trade unions as bargaining agents; the revocation of certification; unfair labour practices; voluntary recognition; the determination of successor rights; union succession; jurisdictional assignments; and the power to order any employer, employee, or trade union to cease and desist certain activities when an illegal work stoppage occurs.

Chairman, Judge Robert J. McCleave, Q.C.
CEO, K. Horne
Secretary, Jane Dickey

Labour Standards Tribunal
5151 Terminal Rd., 7th Flr.
Box 697, Halifax, B3J 2T8

The Labour Standards Tribunal first commenced hearing appeals in September 1973, in accordance with amendments to the *Labour Standards Code* in 1972. The Tribunal is a quasi-judicial body designed to provide an opportunity to employees and employers for appealing orders of the Director of Labour Standards.

All complaints filed pursuant to the *Labour Standards Code* must first be investigated by an officer of the Labour Standards Division. The employee or employer has the right to appeal to the Tribunal. Hearings are then conducted, with the concerned parties allowed to present evidence and argue in support of their respective claims.

Chairman, Stephen Mont
Exec. Officer, Gary Ross

Minimum Wage Board
5151 Terminal Rd., 7th Flr.
Box 697, Halifax, B3J 2T8

The Minimum Wage Board is appointed under provision of the *Labour Standards Code* of Nova Scotia to make recommendations to the Governor in Council concerning the appropriate level of minimum wages in the province. Special rates for specific occupational groups may be set. There are presently four Minimum Wage Orders in force: general; road building and heavy construction industry; beauty parlour; and logging and forest operations. Unless there is a specific order, the General Order applies. The Board has limited control over hours of work as well.

The recommendations of the Board must be approved by the Governor in Council.

Chairman, J. McIntyre
Secretary, Pat Slate

Stationary Engineers Board
5151 Terminal Rd., 6th Flr.
Box 697, Halifax, B3J 2T8

The Stationary Engineers Board is appointed under the provisions of the *Stationary Engineers Act, 1980* and Regulations which rescinded the *Engine Operators Act* of 1967.

The Board is composed of four members and a chairperson who meet approximately once a month to determine whether applicants for certificates of qualification have the necessary experience and education to become candidates for examination. The Board sets the date, hour, and place for the writing of the examination, and approves the questions. The Board assigns a value to all answers made by candidates, or delegates this task to a qualified employee of the Department of Labour assigned by the minister. At its discretion, the Board may review and consequently revise any value ascribed to such answers.

Chairman, Clarence Purcell
Inspector-Registrar, Wayne Nowlan
Inspector-Examiner, Kenneth Daniels

Workers' Compensation Appeal Board
Lord Nelson Bldg., 8th Flr.
5675 Spring Garden Rd.
Box 3311, Halifax, B3J 3J1

Chairman, L.F. Scaravelli
Exec. Officer, J.J. O'Brien

Workers' Compensation Board
Workers' Compensation Ctr., 5668 South St.
Box 1150, Halifax, B3J 2Y2

The Workers' Compensation Board (WCB) is a corporate body established under authority of the *Workers' Compensation Act* to administer and develop all aspects of workers' compensation in the province of Nova Scotia.

Workers' compensation is basically a mutual accident assurance scheme. It serves Nova Scotia employers and employees in the provision of workers' compensation insurance coverage and in the prevention of accidents.

The activities of the WCB include collecting assessments; handling claims; paying time-loss compensation, permanent disability benefits, and survivors' benefits; and providing all aspects of medical and rehabilitation aid.

Chairman, R.J. Allen
Commissioner, J.H. Vaughan
Finance and Administration
Exec. Director, R.L. Shedden
Human Resources and Administration
Director, M.J. MacNeil
Medical Services
Director, Dr. T.E. Dobson
Claims Director, J.W. Langille
Assessment and Collections
Manager, J.O. Skerry
Rehabilitation Director, C.S. Hipson
Management Information Services
Director, P.A. Kent
Public Affairs
Director, A. Bruce Collins

DEPARTMENT OF LANDS AND FORESTS

Founder's Sq., 7th Flr., 1701 Hollis St.
Box 698, Halifax, B3J 2T9

MINISTER'S OFFICE
Minister, The Hon. Charles W. MacNeil

DEPUTY MINISTER'S OFFICE
Dep. Minister, John Mullally

POLICY AND PROGRAM DEVELOPMENT
Sr. Director, John D. Smith
Program Development and Evaluation
Manager, G. Peter MacQuarrie
Extension Services
Director, Gerald T. Joudrey
Parks and Recreation
R.R. 1, Belmont, B0M 1C0
Director, Barry Diamond
Wildlife
Box 516, Kentville, B4N 3X3
Director, Merrill Prime

FORESTRY
Sr. Director, Dan Graham
Reforestation and Silviculture
Box 68, Truro, B2N 5B8
Director, Ed Bailey
Reforestation
Manager, Brian F. White
Forest Resources Planning and Mensuration
Box 68, Truro, B2N 5B8
Director, Fred Wellings
Forest Protection
Box 130, Shubenacadie, B0N 2H0
Director, Ed MacAulay

LAND SERVICES
Sr. Director, J. Douglas Bancroft
Surveys, Land Resources and Provincial Crown Land Record Centre
Torrington Pl., 780 Windmill Rd.
Dartmouth B3B 1T3
Director, Keith AuCoin
Asst. Director, Murray Banks
Land Resources
Director, C. Alan Steele
Provincial Crown Land Record Centre
Director, Ron Dunn

OPERATIONS
Sr. Director, Robert G. MacGregor
Forest Management, Private Lands
Director, Arden Whidden
Forest Management, Crown Lands
Director, Dan Eidt
Enforcement and Hunter Safety
Manager, Casey Pendergast
Private Lands Forestry
Specialist, Brian Gilbert

ADMINISTRATION
Sr. Director, Gary E. Rix
Financial Management
Director, James Morrison
Air Services
Box 130, Shubenacadie, B0N 2HO
Co-ordinator, Len Crocker
Personnel and Payroll
Manager, John Peers
Computer Services
Co-ordinator, Graham Gagne

AGENCIES, BOARDS AND COMMISSIONS

Forest Enhancement
Sun Alliance Bldg., Ste. 201, 640 Prince St.
Box 1830, Truro, B2N 5Z5
Commissioner, Donald L. Eldridge

Nova Scotia Primary Forest Products Marketing Board
Metropolitan Pl., Ste. 470, 99 Wyse Rd.
Dartmouth, B3A 1L9

The Nova Scotia Pulpwood Marketing Board, predecessor to the Nova Scotia Primary Forest Products Marketing Board, was established in 1972 under the *Nova Scotia Pulpwood Marketing Act.* The main activities of the Board were the registration of bargaining agents and supervision of collective bargaining between groups of pulpwood producers and large pulpwood mills in the province.

In 1986, the Act was amended to give the Board jurisdiction over additional primary forest products including sawmill chips, hogfuel, and Christmas trees; the purposes of the Act were broadened to include the support and encouragement of the continued development of forest resources held by private woodlot owners, and to enable private woodlot owners to have a fair share of the available market for primary forest products and receive a reasonable return for those products sold.

The Board has limited price-fixing power, but cannot finally resolve disputes.

The Board is appointed by and is responsible to the Minister of Lands and Forests. It is funded partially by the Province and partially by a levy on wood sold by producers.

Chairman, Graham Langley
Exec. Officer, Diane Findlay

DEPARTMENT OF MINES AND ENERGY

Founders Sq., 3rd Flr., 1701 Hollis St.
Box 1087, Halifax, B3J 2X1

MINISTER'S OFFICE
Minister, The Hon. John A. MacIsaac

DEPUTY MINISTER'S OFFICE
Dep. Minister, John J. Laffin
Asst. Dep. Minister, Mines and Minerals,
Dr. Richard Potter
Asst. Dep. Minister, Energy, P. Carey Ryan
Communications and Information
Manager, Harry Chapman
Legal Services
Solicitor, Nancy Hood

FINANCE AND ADMINISTRATION
Director, Carroll James
Accounting
Manager, Kenneth Faulkner
Personnel Manager, Paul Edwards
Office Services
Supervisor, Christine Squires
Cartographic Services
Manager, Joseph Campbell

MINERAL RESOURCES
Director, Dr. Peter Giles
Regional Surveys
Manager, Dr. Duncan Keppie
Mineral Deposits
Manager, Dr. A.K. Chatterjee
Geochemistry
Manager, Dr. Peter Rogers
MINERAL DEVELOPMENT
Director, Daniel Murray
Resource Geology
Manager, James Bingley
Mineral and Petroleum Titles
Registrar, Richard Ratcliffe
Library Supervisor, Valerie Brisco
MINING ENGINEERING
Director, Patrick W. Phelan
Manager, Donald Jones

ENERGY MANAGEMENT
Director, Greg Haverstock

Public Programs
Manager, James Gordon
Provincial Energy Analysis
Co-ordinator, Terry Tomney
Energy Engineering
Supervisor, Allan Parker
ENERGY RESOURCES
Director, Andrew Batcup
Coal Development
Manager, Edward Bain
Petroleum Resources
Manager, Andy Parker
Economics and Statistics
Director, Vicki Harnish

DEPARTMENT OF MUNICIPAL AFFAIRS

Maritime Ctr., 13th Flr., 1505 Barrington St.
Box 216, Halifax, B3J 2M4

MINISTER'S OFFICE
Minister, The Hon. Brian A. Young

DEPUTY MINISTER'S OFFICE
Dep. Minister, Gordon D. Gillis
Solicitors: F. Robertson, Janet Willwerth
Personnel Manager, Susan Crandall

ASSESSMENT
Director, Robert F. Warren
Asst. Director, John MacKay
Solicitor, Randall Duplak
COMMUNITY PLANNING
Director, Ronald Simpson
Asst. Director, Provincial Planning,
David Darrow
Administration and Implementation
Asst. Director, Jack Leedham

FINANCE, ADVISORY SERVICES AND ADMINISTRATION
Director, E.G. Cramm
Finance and Advisory
Asst. Director, V.T. Smith
Administration
Asst. Director, William McKee
Municipal Training
Co-ordinator, Vacant
POLICY DEVELOPMENT AND RESEARCH
Director, Vacant

DEPARTMENT OF SMALL BUSINESS DEVELOPMENT

Joseph Howe Bldg., Ste. 700, 1690 Hollis St.
Halifax, B3J 3J9

MINISTER'S OFFICE
Minister, The Hon. Kenneth Streatch
Special Projects Co-ordinator,
Douglas MacLeod

DEPUTY MINISTER'S OFFICE
Dep. Minister, Ann Janega

VOLUNTARY PLANNING
Exec. Director, Elizabeth Mills
FINANCE AND ADMINISTRATION
Director, David McNamara
Personnel Manager, Frank MacLean
Regional Offices Branch
Director, Lance Hale
REGIONAL OFFICES:
Central Region Small Business Service Centre
Metropolitan Place, Ste. 950
99 Wyse Rd., Dartmouth, B3A 1L9
Manager, Doug Nicholson
Southwestern Region Small Business
Service Centre
13 First St., Yarmouth, B5A 1S9
Gen. Manager, R. Maillet
Northeastern Regional Small Business
Service Centre
Sun Alliance Bldg., 640 Prince St.
Truro, B2N 1G4
Gen. Manager, Charles Eastman
Strait of Canso Regional Small Business
Service Centre
Professional Bldg., Church St.
Box 219, Port Hawkesbury, B0E 2V0
Gen. Manager, Alex Harris
Cape Breton Regional Small Business
Service Centre
Commerce Twr., 1st Flr., 15 Dorchester St.
Sydney, B1P 5Y9
Gen. Manager, Drummond Fraser
Valley Regional Small Business Service Centre
Industrial Park Mall, Box 524
Kentville, B4N 3X3
Manager, Donald Cameron
Community Economic Development
52 Queen St., Box 9020, Stn. A
Dartmouth, B3K 5M6
Director, John Chiasson

AGENCIES, BOARDS AND COMMISSIONS
Small Business Development Corp.
Metropolitan Pl., Ste. 940
99 Wyse Rd., Dartmouth, B3A 1L9

The Small Business Development Corporation was established in Nova Scotia by An Act Respecting Development of Small Business, S.N.S. 1981, Chapter 12, on June 24, 1981. The purpose of the Corporation is to promote the economic well-being of the province by rendering to small businesses financial assistance or such other assistance as may be determined by the Lieutenant-Governor in Council.

The Corporation may, subject to the Regulations, render to small business financial assistance, or such other assistance as may be determined by the Regulations, which in the opinion of the Board will encourage, sustain, improve, or develop small business in the province. The Act applies to businesses with fewer than 50 employees and an annual sales volume of less than $2 million unless determined otherwise by Regulations.

The Corporation consists of a board of directors composed of a chairman and other directors appointed by the Lieutenant-Governor in Council. The minister responsible for this Act is the Minister of Small Business Development.
Director, Harold Clarke
Secretary to the Board, Vacant
Asst. Director, Dennis Holland
Solicitor, Margaret Howie
Loan Administrator, William Sitland
Accountant, Nadine Heisler

DEPARTMENT OF SOLICITOR GENERAL
Joseph Howe Bldg., 1690 Hollis St.
Box 2599, Stn. M, Halifax, B3J 3N5

SOLICITOR GENERAL'S OFFICE
Solicitor General and Provincial Secretary,
The Hon. Neil J. LeBlanc
Dep. Solicitor General and Provincial Secretary,
Nadine Cooper-Mont

FINANCE AND ADMINISTRATION
Director, Audrey Harmer
POLICY PLANNING AND RESEARCH
Director, Kit Waters
Research and Planning
Co-ordinator, Donna Smith

CORRECTIONAL SERVICES
Exec. Director, James L. Crane
Community Corrections
Director, Fred W. Honsberger
Adult Institutions
Director, N.T. MacKenzie
Young Offender Institutions
Director, William A. Baldwin
Temporary Absence Program
Administrator, David W. White

AGENCIES, BOARDS AND COMMISSIONS
Nova Scotia Police Commission
Queen's Sq., 10th Flr., 45 Alderney Dr.
Box 1573, Dartmouth, B3J 2Y3
A/Chairman, Murray J. Ritch

Provincial Firearms Office
Belmont House, Ste. 200, 33 Alderney Dr.
Box 1254, Dartmouth, B2Y 4B9
Chief Provincial Firearms Officer,
Garth M. Burbridge

DEPARTMENT OF TOURISM AND CULTURE

1601 Lower Water St., 4th Flr.
Box 456, Halifax, B3J 2R5

MINISTER'S OFFICE
Minister, The Hon. Roland J. Thornhill

DEPUTY MINISTER'S OFFICE
Dep. Minister, Robert E. Geraghty

ADMINISTRATION
Director, Brian McDonough
Accounting
Manager, David MacKay
Personnel
Manager, Judy Sullivan-Corney
BLUENOSE II
Operations Manager, Peter Brown

MARKETING AND PROMOTION
Director, Daniel G.M. Brennan
Market Development
Manager, Michele McKenzie
Attractions and Events
Manager, Patricia Lynch
Travel Trade
Manager, David Townsend
Outdoor Promotions
Supervisor, W.R. Bryson
Research Analyst, Gary Young

INDUSTRY DEVELOPMENT
Director, B. Gallivan
Planning and Development
Manager, Bernard LeBlanc
Training and Inspection Services
Manager, Douglas Matthews
Tourism Development Officer, Fred Tibbet
Architect, C. Hollebone
Planner, Kim McNutt

RESORT HOTELS
Director, Jose Cabrita
Keltic Lodge
Manager, Alex MacClure
The Pines
Manager, Maurice Thiebaut
Liscombe Lodge
Manager, David Evans
TRAVEL INFORMATION
Director, J. Alex MacLean
Travel Information Centres
A/Manager, S. Martin
OUTSIDE OFFICE:
Portland, Maine
136 Commercial St., Portland, ME 04101 U.S.A.
Manager, Robert Boyd

CULTURAL AFFAIRS
Director, Allison Bishop
Production Crafts
Head, Chris Tyler

Heritage
Head, Brian Cuthbertson
Librarian, Gwen Whitford
Performing Arts
Head, Ted Bairstow
Visual Arts
Head, Susan Lowery

AGENCIES, BOARDS AND COMMISSIONS

Art Gallery of Nova Scotia
1741 Hollis Rd., Box 2262, Halifax, B3J 3C8

The Art Gallery of Nova Scotia, legislated in 1975, evolved from a volunteer organization which has been in existence since the first decade of the century.

The Gallery has an internationally recognized collection of regional folk art, as well as historical and contemporary works by such well-known European artists as Jacopo Bassano, Rembrandt, Salvador Rosa, and Picasso. Important donations of special collections include the Hiroshige, Tokaido, and British contemporaries.

A historic building in downtown Halifax is currently undergoing renovations to replace interim facilities and to house a developing collection.

Chairman, Robert Radchuk
Director, Bernard Riordon

DEPARTMENT OF TRANSPORTATION AND COMMUNICATIONS

Provincial Bldg., 6th Flr., 1723 Hollis St.
Box 186, Halifax, B3J 2N2
General Inquiries: (902) 424-5837

MINISTER'S OFFICE
Minister, The Hon. George C. Moody

DEPUTY MINISTER'S OFFICE
Dep. Minister, Luigi L. Centa

ADMINISTRATION
Transportation
Chief Engineer, C.J. Smith
Operations
Chief Engineer, A.E. King
Asst. Chief Engineer, L. Rankin
Services
Chief Engineer, R.M. MacDonald

DIVISION HEADS
Communications Policy
Director, D. Colville
Construction Director, J. Gavin
Engineering Director, D. MacIntosh
Maintenance
Director, K.A. MacDermid
Planning Director, R.W. Spares

Right of Way Claims
Director, C.E. Caines
Staff Services
Director, B.G. Jay
Registrar, S.M. Ali
Traffic Engineering
Director, F.C.S. Lee
Transportation Policy
Director, D. MacDougall
REGIONAL MANAGERS:
M. Morash
107 Dakmount Dr., Box 214, Bedford, B4A 2X2
D. Jenkins
Jubilee Rd., Hebbville, Box 409
D. Fraser
Jubilee Rd., Hebbville, Box 409
Bridgewater, B4V 2X6
M.P. Miller
61 Main St., Box 820, Middleton, B0S 1P0
R.G. Hanes
MacLellans Brook Rd., Box 459
New Glasgow, B2H 5E5
P.A. Wright
St. Davids Ave., Box 218, Truro, B2N 5C1
T.C. Hackett
Keltic Dr., Sydney River, Box 1180
Sydney, B1P 6J9
REGISTRY OF MOTOR VEHICLES
6061 Young St., Box 1652, Halifax, B3J 2Z3
Registrar, S.M. Ali
Dep. Registrar, G.L. Allen
Regulations Development
Director, C.E. Pass
Accounts
A/Chief Accountant, D. Doncaster
Licences and Registration Division
Director, G.D. Duff
Workstation/Dealer Licensing
A/Supervisor, D. Whittier
Prorate Registration
A/Supervisor, D. Estabrooks
Mail/Workstation Support
Supervisor, S. Tarr
Systems Administration
Administrator, C. Henderson
A/Supervisor, J. Sullivan
Highway Safety and Field Programs Division
Director, G.L. Allen
Chief Supervisor, C. Miller
Record Processing
Supervisor, A.M. Hanrahan
Driver Qualifications
Supervisor, L. Searle
Driver Record Evaluations
Supervisor, Don Brown
Safety Programs
Supervisor, George Mansfield
Driver Education and Motorcycle Training
Provincial Co-ordinator, Ken Cogan
Motor Vehicle Inspection Division
Director, A. Tony Tucker
Motor Vehicle Inspection
A/Sr. Inspector, S. Lowther
Road Transport and Motor Vehicle Inspection
Supervisor, L. MacArthur

INDEPENDENT AGENCIES, BOARDS, COMMISSIONS AND CROWN CORPORATIONS

Advisory Council on the Status of Women

Purdy's Wharf Bldg., Ste. 207
1959 Upper Water St.
Box 745, Halifax, B3J 2T3
(902) 424-8662

The Council was established in 1977 in response to the recommendations of a task force appointed during International Women's Year (1975). The Council was established to monitor women's issues and to act as an advisory body to the provincial government.

Members of the Council are appointed by government and collectively represent the regional, cultural, and ethnic diversity of the province. With the exception of the full-time president, all members are unsalaried. The Council consists of various committees that meet regularly to discuss and deal with numerous different issues.

The executive of the Council consists of a president, a chairperson, a vice-chairperson and the Standing Committees' chairpersons.
Minister responsible,
The Hon. Donald P. McInnes

President, Debi Forsyth-Smith
Researcher, Jane Wright
Regional Services
Co-ordinator, Marily Berry

Board of Commissioners of Public Utilities

1526 Dresden Row, Box 3058 South
Halifax, B3J 3G7

The Nova Scotia Board of Commissioners of Public Utilities regulates the service provided and the rates charged by various publicly owned services. It licenses public motor carriers within the province by authority of the *Motor Carrier Act* and extra-provincial traffic to and from Nova Scotia under the federal *Motor Vehicle Transport Act*. It regulates and licenses salvage yards. It regulates the sale of gasoline and fuel oil, sets prices, and licenses service stations and wholesalers under the authority of the *Gasoline and Fuel Oil Licensing Act.*
Minister responsible,
The Hon. Thomas J. McInnis

Chairman, John Stewart Drury, Q.C.
Vice-Chairman, R.A. Robertson, F.C.A.
Clerk of the Board, Bernadine Dempsey
Board Administrator, Paul Allen
Regulation and Finance
Sr. Advisor, John Murphy, P.Eng.
Gasoline and Fuel Oil Licensing
Supervisor, Lloyd W. Gibbs

Salvage Yards Licensing
Supervisor, Lloyd W. Gibbs
Motor Carrier—Freight Division
Supervisor, Reid MacVicar
Motor Carrier—Public Passenger Division
Supervisor, David White

Civil Service Commission

One Government Pl., 1700 Granville St.
Box 943, Halifax, B3J 2V9

The Commission's function is personnel management. It offers administrative services to the various departments, boards, agencies, and commissions of government regarding staffing, affirmative action, training and development, human resource planning, classification, collective bargaining, contract administration, grievance handling, salary and fringe benefit research, and compensation for employees excluded from the collective bargaining process.
Minister responsible,
The Hon. Terence R.B. Donahoe, Q.C.

Dep. Minister, Douglas T. Tobin
Exec. Secretary, Antoinette MacDonald
Exec. Director, George L. Hall
Exec. Secretary, Barbara Armstrong
Compensation Director, B.B. MacCharles
Compensation Manager, A.F. Walker
Staffing Director, E.W. Pace
Human Resources Development
Manager, Cynthia Gorman
Affirmative Action
Officer, E. McDougall-Salchert
Affirmative Action Officer, Mary Macnab
Staff Relations Director, John Puchyr
Office Services
Supervisor, Pat Thomson

Council of Applied Science and Technology

Box 519, Halifax, B3J 2R7

The Council of Applied Science and Technology first met in October 1987. Its members are drawn from industry, labour, the research and academic communities, and government. Its main functions are to:
- advise the government on the application of science and technology for economic development; and
- raise awareness of the importance of applied science and technology.
Minister responsible,
The Hon. Donald W. Cameron

Chairman, Dr. Robert O. Fournier
Secretariat: Technology Transfer Office

Emergency Measures Organization (N.S.)

Joseph Howe Bldg., 2nd Flr.
1690 Hollis St., Box 1502, Halifax, B3J 2Y3

The Emergency Measures Organization is a co-ordinating agency of the Government of Nova Scotia with the responsibility of assisting municipalities to plan and prepare for emergencies. In an emergency, EMO (NS) co-ordinates the efforts of provincial and federal departments and agencies as well as private health and social services to provide assistance to the disaster areas. Additionally, EMO (NS) sponsors the RCMP Auxiliary Program and the Ground Search and Rescue Program. The agency maintains a small staff of professional planners at the head office in Halifax and at the zone offices located in Truro, Kentville, and Sydney.
Director, Michael R. Lester
Headquarters Zone Controller, John Perkins
Western Zone Controller, John A. Andersen
Central Zone Controller, Joseph E. Saunders
Cape Breton Zone Controller,
Winston A. Musgrave

Halifax Infirmary

1335 Queen St., Halifax, B3J 2H6

The Halifax Infirmary Hospital was founded in 1886 by the Sisters of Charity. In 1973, ownership of the hospital was transferred to the Province of Nova Scotia. At present, the Halifax Infirmary is a teaching hospital and provides community, regional, and referral health services. It is also a major referral point for the investigation and treatment of diabetes, and the location of the first medical/surgical gastroenterology unit in eastern Canada. The Infirmary is a hospital of the Camp Hill Medical Centre.
Exec. Director, J.N. Roberts
Asst. Exec. Director, Patient Services,
M.M. Hope
Asst. Exec. Director, Administrative Services,
G.Y. FitzGerald
Asst. Exec. Director, Hospital Services,
J.R. Orlando
Chief of Staff, Dr. K.J. MacKinnon

Human Rights Commission

Lord Nelson Bldg., 7th Flr.
5675 Spring Garden Rd.
Box 2221, Halifax, B3J 3C4

The Nova Scotia Human Rights Commission performs the following functions:
a) administers and enforces provisions of the *Nova Scotia Human Rights Act;*
b) develops programs of public information and education to forward the principle that every person is free in dignity and rights without

regard to race, religion, creed, colour, sex, age, physical or mental disability, ethnic or national origin, marital status, or source of income;

c) conducts and encourages research by universities in the general field of human rights;

d) advises and assists government departments to co-ordinate activities which concern human rights;

e) advises the government on suggestions, recommendations, and requests made by private organizations and individuals;

f) co-operates and assists any person, organization, or body concerned with human rights;

g) reports its business and activities to the minister; and

h) considers, investigates, or administers any matter or activity referred by the Governor in Council or the minister.

The Nova Scotia Human Rights Commission carries out its broad mandate mainly through investigation and conciliation of discrimination complaints, boards of inquiry, public education, community relations, and affirmative action in the areas of employment, services, education, and housing.
Minister responsible,
The Hon. Thomas J. McInnis

Chairman, Dr. Donald E. Curren
Exec. Secretary, Lois Smith
Exec. Director, Dr. P.A. Johnstone
Chief Human Rights Officer, Francine Comeau-Godin
Exec. Secretary, Patricia Grosse
Public Education Officer, May Lui
Administration and Operations Co-ordinator, P.A. Comeau
Affirmative Action Programs Co-ordinator, Carolyn Thomas
Ethic Services Officer, David States
Regional Supervisor, Sydney, David Beaton
Human Rights Officer, Sydney, Gordon Hayes
Regional Supervisor, Digby, Cherry Paris
Regional Office, New Glasgow
Secretary, Beverley Bonvie
Human Rights Officers: Gerald Boudreau, Francine Comeau-Godin, Ed Russell, Norma Williams, Janet McKinnon

Metropolitan Authority/Metropolitan Area Planning Commission
Ferry Terminal Bldg., 2nd Flr.
5077 George St., Halifax, B3J 1M3

The Metropolitan Area Planning Commission of Halifax, Dartmouth, Bedford and Halifax County is a district planning commission established pursuant to section IV of the *Planning Act,* S.N.S. 1969, Chapter 16, to provide a forum whereby the objectives of the metro area, in terms of urban reform, environmental quality and economic growth, can be articulated in such a fashion as to allow all levels of government to play a supportive role.

It advises the Minister of Municipal Affairs in the revision of the Regional Development Plan, acts as a vehicle for consultation between the participating municipalities and between the municipalities and provincial departments, and studies opportunities for co-operative action in the provision of municipal services.

The Commission consists of a Board composed of: the chief magistrates and one elected representative from each of Halifax, Dartmouth, and the county; one elected representative from Bedford; and one representative appointed by the Minister of Municipal Affairs.

Chairman, Mayor Keith Roberts
Exec. Secretary, R. Mort Jackson
Planning Director, Brian T. Smith

Nova Scotia Boxing Authority
Box 864, Halifax, B3J 2V2

The Nova Scotia Boxing Authority is composed of five to nine members who are appointed by the Governor in Council. The Boxing Authority is involved in a wide number of concerns ranging from regulation of licensing and contracts to determining what entertainment is defined as boxing. The Boxing Authority is authorized and empowered to hold hearings relating to the carrying out of its objects or powers. In addition, its authority covers both professional and amateur boxing.
Minister responsible, The Hon. J. Greg Kerr

Chairman, Eric Thomson
Sec.-Treasurer, Charles Campbell

Nova Scotia Business Capital Corp.
Joseph Howe Bldg., Ste. 500
1690 Hollis St., Halifax, B3J 3J9
President and CEO, Norman S. MacNeil

Chairman, Robert W. Shaw
Vice-Chairman, Dr. Joseph Zatzman
Vice-President and Sr. Engineering
Project Manager, Arthur Abbott
Industrial Parks
Manager, Frank LeTourneau

Nova Scotia Commission on Drug Dependency
Lord Nelson Tower, 6th Flr.
5675 Spring Garden Rd., Halifax, B3J 1H1

The Nova Scotia Commission on Drug Dependency is the provincial agency responsible for treatment, rehabilitation, education, and prevention in the field of chemical substance abuse. The Commission operates under the *Drug Dependen-*

cy Act and reports directly to the Minister of Health and Fitness.

Operating in close co-operation with relevant government departments, the Commission offers a highly decentralized comprehensive program in both inpatient and outpatient services, and takes a unique decentralized approach to community development in the field of education and prevention through the organization of citizen committees at the local level in towns and villages throughout the province. The Commission maintains a research division, offers audio-visual and library services, and runs a highly organized Employee Assistance Program.

Minister responsible, The Hon. G. David Nantes
Exec. Director, Marvin M. Burke
Secretary, Valerie Tingley
Prevention and Community Education
Co-ordinator, Brian Wilbur
Research
Co-ordinator, Vacant
Employee Assistance Programs
Co-ordinator, E.T. Fitzpatrick
Education Officer, Margaret Duncan
Youth and School Services
Representative, Nancy Comeau
Training Supervisor, Eleanor Cardoza
Sr. Public Information Officer,
Kevin MacPherson
Special Liaison Officer, Rick Anderson
Admin. Services Manager, Zane O'Brien
Librarian, Patricia MacNeil
Pharmacology Programs
Supervisor, Wenda MacDonald

Metro Drug Dependency Program, Dartmouth
Pleasant St., Box 896, Dartmouth, B2Y 3Z6
Reg. Co-ordinator, R.J. Power

North Shore Drug Dependency Program
Denoon St., Box 359, Pictou, B0K 1H0
Reg. Co-ordinator, Donald J. MacDonald

Cape Breton Addiction Rehabilitation Centre
115 Alexandra St., Box 640, Sydney, B1P 6H7
Reg. Co-ordinator, Wayne Yorke

Western Regional Drug Dependency Program
Yarmouth Regional Hospital
50 Vancouver St., Yarmouth, B5A 2P5
Reg. Co-ordinator, Stan MacDougall

Valley Health Services Assn.
Miller Hospital, Crosbie Ctr., Kentville, B4N 1C4
Reg. Co-ordinator, Gaston d'Entremont

Nova Scotia Government Employees Union

6080 Young St., Ste. 509, Halifax, B3K 5L2

President, Greg Blanchard
Administrator/Negotiator, Laraine Singler
Employee Relations Officers: W.J. McMullin, Steve MacDonald, Gerry Beck, Dane Percy, Linda Cormier, Jim Ryan
Research Officer, Reg Lownie
Education Officer, Norm Hebert

Nova Scotia Government Purchasing Agency

Queen's Sq., 10th Flr., 45 Alderney Dr.
Box 787, Dartmouth, B3J 2V2

The Nova Scotia Government Purchasing Agency is a branch of the public service of the Province of Nova Scotia, established in accordance with the *Government Purchases Act*. This Agency constitutes a centralized procurement service with the responsibility to purchase all materials, supplies, and equipment on behalf of all departments, agencies, boards, commissions, etc., of the government of Nova Scotia.

The Agency is headed by a director of purchases (deputy minister status) who is responsible directly to an appointed minister of the Crown for all aspects of its operation.

Director, Allan Timmins

The Nova Scotia Hospital

300 Pleasant St., Box 1004
Dartmouth, B2Y 3Z9

The Nova Scotia Hospital is the major psychiatric hospital in Nova Scotia providing assessment and treatment services for persons with mental and/or emotional problems. In addition to accepting referrals from all parts of the province, it also acts as a teaching hospital and provides specialized services for a wide range of patient needs.

Exec. Director, Vacant
Assoc. Exec. Director, David Chase
Medical Director, Vacant
Nursing
Asst. Exec. Director, Vacant
Support Services
Asst. Exec. Director, M. Townsend
Finance
Asst. Exec. Director, Vacant
Human Resources
Asst. Exec. Director, Elsie Hill

Nova Scotia Information Service

One Government Pl., Ground Flr.
1700 Granville St., Box 608
Halifax, B3J 2R7

Nova Scotia Information Service, established in 1965, is a provincial government agency reporting to the chairman of the Management Board. It is comprised of four divisions responsible for: communications and public inquiries; advertising; still photography; and films.

Collectively, these divisions supplement communications and information services provided by provincial government departments, agencies, commissions, and Crown corporations.

Specifically, the communications and public inquiries division provides creative writing services and operates a government wire service for the transmission of government news releases, feature stories, and statements. This division also monitors print and electronic media, and maintains a customized client service for articles and radio and television stories pertaining to the provincial government. The public inquiries service responds to inquiries from government departments and the general public on government-related programs and services.

The advertising, still photography, and film divisions provide internal, central services for each respective function.

The Nova Scotia Bookstore is also a division of the Information Service and has available a wide variety of government reports, maps and publications, as well as a variety of Nova Scotia-related publications.

Exec. Director, Rob Smith
Communications
Director, Sandra M. Phillips

Nova Scotia Liquor Commission

Bayers Lake Industrial Pk., 93 Chainlake Dr.
Box 8720, Stn. A, Halifax, B3K 5M4

The Liquor Commission was formed in 1930 under the *Liquor Control Act* to regulate and control the purchase and sale of all alcoholic beverages. The first controlled liquor store opened Aug. 18, 1930. In addition to the Distribution Centre/Head Office Complex, there are 94 retail outlets to serve the public.

The Commission maintains a staff of approximately 684 permanent employees. The total listing of products on the General and Port of Wines lists exceeds 1,600.

Minister responsible,
The Hon. Ronald S. Russell

Chief Commissioner, Peter J. MacKeigan
Commissioners:
A. Angus MacIsaac, Hanson D. Jovey
Secretary, Karen Campbell-Stevens
Gen. Manager and CEO, D.W. Pulsifer
Secretary, Kathy Smith

Nova Scotia Liquor License Board

Darmouth Professional Ctr., Ste. 401
277 Pleasant St., Box 857, Dartmouth, B2Y 3Z5

The Nova Scotia Liquor License Board receives and processes applications from private clubs, taverns, beverage rooms, lounges, dining rooms, restaurants, and cabarets to sell beer, wine, and spirits.

The Board exercises a quasi-judicial function. It is presided over by the chairman in addition to two board members, and it grants or denies a licence to sell alcohol after a hearing has taken place. Special occasion licences are also issued through the Board, though with less formal requirements.

In addition to regular office staff, the Board maintains in its employ 19 full-time inspectors who enforce the regulations.

Minister responsible,
The Hon. Ronald S. Russell
Chairman and CEO, C. William Singer
Exec. Director and Counsel,
Margaret A.M. Shears
Sr. Director, R.S. Durling

Nova Scotia Lottery Commission

Metropolitan Pl., Ste. 930
99 Wyse Rd., Dartmouth
Mailing Address:
Box 545, Dartmouth, B2Y 3Y8
(902) 424-4520

The Lottery Commission was established in 1976 by the Government of Nova Scotia to administer, issue, and control all applications for lottery licences for bingos, games of chance, and ticket draws. The Commission processes and monitors the transfer of revenue from the Atlantic Lottery Corporation for the sale of all lottery products.

In addition to these responsibilities, the Lottery Commission enforces the *Nova Scotia Lottery Act,* as well as sections 189 and 190 of the *Criminal Code* of Canada.

Chairman, Douglas T. Tobin
Exec. Director, Clyde M. Horner
Lottery Officer, Terry Kelly

Nova Scotia Municipal Board

Bank of Commerce Bldg., Ste. 510
1809 Barrington St., Box 1587, Halifax, B3J 2Y3

The Nova Scotia Municipal Board is a provincial tribunal established under the *Municipal Board Act,* which came into effect June 1, 1982. The Board performs such duties as are conferred upon it under this Act and other legislation, as well as those conferred upon it by the Governor in Council.

The Board currently consists of three members, all of whom or any one of whom may sit at any particular hearing, as determined by the chairman.

Minister responsible, The Hon. Brian A. Young
Chairman, Michael G. Johnson, C.A.
Vice-Chairman, Linda Garber
Member, Richard Weldon
Clerk, Doreen Friis
Secretary, Sharon Prizeman

Nova Scotia Municipal Finance Corp.

Founders Sq., Ste. 302, 1701 Hollis St.
Box 850, Stn. M, Halifax, B3J 2V8

The Corporation was established by an Act of the legislature in 1979. Its function is to provide financing of capital requirements for the cities, towns, municipalities, school boards, and hospitals in the province. The debentures and securities issued by the Corporation are guaranteed by the Province, and the funds thus raised are loaned to individual municipal units to finance their approved capital projects. The Board of Directors is appointed by the Governor in Council.

Chairman and CEO, R.S. Brookfield, F.C.A.
Secretary, G. Harding
Treasurer, Shirley Carras, C.A.
Asst. Treasurer, Richard McAloney, C.A.
Secretary, R. Mark Gilbert
Gen. Counsel, Jim Spurr

Nova Scotia Power Corp.
Barrington Tower, 18th Flr., Scotia Sq.
Box 910, Halifax, B3J 2W5

The Nova Scotia Power Corporation is a wholly-owned Crown corporation of the province, established in 1919 by an Act of the provincial legislature.

The objective of the Corporation is to provide power to Nova Scotians on an economical and efficient basis. It may engage, in Nova Scotia and elsewhere, in the development, generation, production, transmission, distribution, supply, and use of electricity, water, steam, gas, oil, or other products or things used or useful in the production of power.

The Corporation's system is province-wide and serves approximately 373,600 customers. The Corporation operates 33 hydroelectric, six thermal, and three gas turbine plants with a total nameplate generating capacity of 1,964 MW. The Corporation maintains a distribution system consisting of 28,370 circuit km.
Office of the President

President and CEO, Louis R. Comeau
Corporate Relations Manager,
Maurice MacDonald
Vice-Presidents:
Planning, T.F. MacDonald
Finance, O.P. O'Rourke
Personnel and Corporate Services, W.L. Fraser
Engineering and Production, G.D. Lethbridge
Customer Services, L.J. Sweett
Directors:
Customer Service, W.R. Bailly
Management Information Services, K.W. Butler
Engineering, P.N. Sidebottom
Treasurer, H. Green
Controller, R.E. Johnson
Secretary, R.J. Smith
Transmission/Distribution, L.A. LeBlanc
Industrial Relations, R.N. McArel
Thermal Production, J.A. Parker
System Operations, W.V. Wallace
System Planning, R.W. Brown
Financial Planning and Budgeting, L.A. White
Organization and Employee Development,
J.M. Woods

Nova Scotia Research Foundation Corp.
100 Fenwick St., Box 790, Dartmouth, B2Y 3Z7
(902) 424-8670
Fax: (902) 424-4679; Telex: 019-22719

Nova Scotia Research Foundation Corp. was established in 1946 by the Province of Nova Scotia to use science and technology to assist in the province's economic development.

A staff of 125 scientists, engineers, technicians, and support staff occupy a well-equipped 5,670 m^2 laboratory building and a 560 m^2 pilot plant on the Corporation's four-hectare Dartmouth site.

The Corporation pursues two main goals: assistance to industry in the solution of today's technical problems, and product/process innovation in anticipation of tomorrow's opportunities. While the Corporation serves all sectors of Nova Scotia's industrial economy, it emphasizes technological support for the secondary manufacturing industry and takes a special interest in developing Nova Scotia's ocean industry potential.

Three operating divisions — Applied Science, Industry Services, and Product Development — carry out technical assignments for 600 companies and government departments each year. Applied Science assists government and industry with R & D and scientific services related to Nova Scotia's natural resources. Industry Services provides technical assistance to small- and medium-sized manufacturers to improve productivity and technological capabilities. Product Development specializes in ocean-related engineering, manufacturing, and marketing to develop Nova Scotia products for international markets.
Minister responsible,
The Hon. Donald W. Cameron

President, T.B. Nickerson
Secretary, Norma Gerogiannis
Finance and Administration
Vice-President, R.F. MacNeill
Applied Science
Vice-President, Dr. D.E.T. Bidgood
Industry Services
Vice-President, J.R. Helliwell
Product Development
Vice-President, C.R. Tyner
Marketing
Director, D.S. Rankin
Library
Librarian, Helen Hendry

Nova Scotia Resources Ltd.
1718 Argyle St., Ste. 600
Box 2111, Halifax, B3J 3B7

Nova Scotia Resources Ltd., a corporation owned by the Province of Nova Scotia, began operations in 1981. It was established to invest in and manage the Province's interests in petroeum, energy, and mineral projects. As of December 1987, the assets of NSRL and its subsidiaries included the following:

- working interests of 2.5 to 10 per cent in petroleum exploration rights covering almost 500,000 hectares in the Sable Island region;
- a 10 per cent working interest in the Venture Gas Project near Sable Island;
- an approximate 20 per cent working interest in the Cohasset oil-bearing structure;
- an approximate 39 per cent interest in the Panuke oil-bearing structure; and
- an approximate 25 per cent interest in the Scotian Mineral Exploration Joint Venture managed by Inco Ltd.

NSRL also has the right to acquire up to a 50 per cent equity interest in Sable Gas Systems Ltd., a company which, if the necessary certification is obtained, will construct and operate a regional pipeline for the transmission of offshore natural gas to export markets. In addition, the corporation holds interests in oil and gas assets in western Canada.

NSRL is provided with up to $25 million in federal funding to defray half of its eligible exploration and development costs under the Canada/Nova Scotia Offshore Petroleum Resources Accord of August 1986. The corporation has also received cost reimbursements under the Petroleum Incentives Program. As of March 31, 1987, NSRL had current assets of $15 million.

President and CEO, Peter A. Outhit
Marketing and Business Development
Director, John D. French
Treasurer, Robert B. MacDiarmid
Exec. Secretary, Mary A. Conrod
DIRECTORS:
Halifax
Peter A. Outhit (Chairman), D. Ashworth,
T. Lynch, J. MacPherson, J.E. Blanchard,
A. Manuel, J.A.F. Macdonald (Secretary)
Montreal, P. Crawford
Port Williams, J.E. Shaffner
Calgary, R.B. Coleman
Toronto, J.L. Stoik

Nova Scotia Sport and Recreation Commission

Terminal Bldg., 8th Flr., 5151 Terminal Rd.
Box 864, Halifax, B3J 2V2
Minister responsible, The Hon. J. Greg Kerr
Exec. Director, Duff Montgomerie
Secretary, Carolyn Newcombe
Personnel
Manager, Mrs. Brenda J. Manning
Financial Management
Supervisor, Mary Dauphinee
Publications/Promotions Co-ordinator,
Marsha Andrews
SPORT
Co-ordinator, Blaise Landry
Consultants: Bob Book, Allan Wilson

Program Liaison Officer, Liz Pace
Community Recreation
Director, Michael Arthur
Outdoor Recreation
Co-ordinator, Richard Gilbert
Program Consultant, Ted Scrutton
Facility Development
Co-ordinator, Bill Mackie
Municipal and Special Recreation Services
Co-ordinator, Richard Hayden
REGIONAL REPRESENTATIVES:
Central Region
45 Alderney Dr., Ste. 813, Dartmouth, B2Y 2N6
Nelson Ellsworth
Valley Region
Box 2140, Windsor, B0N 2T0
William R. Spurr
Fundy Region
542 Prince St., Truro, B2N 1E8
James Campbell
Highland Region
274 Main St., Antigonish, B2G 2C4
Gary Boone
Cape Breton Region
Provincial Bldg., Sydney, B1P 5L1
Frank McNamara
Box 989, Port Hawkesbury, B0E 2V0
Reg. Asst., Jim Coady
South Shore Region
Box 470, Bridgewater, B4V 2X6
John MacLean

Novaco Ltd.

18 King St., Box 147, Sydney Mines, B1V 1Y3

Novaco Ltd. was incorporated in 1970 under the *Companies Act.* Novaco is a provincial Crown corporation mandated to undertake any surface coal-mining operations that the Government of Nova Scotia wishes to do on its own behalf. Novaco also acts in an advisory role to the provincial government with respect to all current and proposed coal-mining operations, providing independent advice on technical and physical aspects, and social and environmental matters. Novaco will undertake any activity that may be required by the government to assist in the exploration, production, transportation, and marketing of the province's coal resources.

Chairman, Malcolm Turner, P.Eng.
Vice-Chairman, Dr. Nordau Goodman
President, Vacant
Sec.-Treasurer, Carroll James

Province House Credit Union Ltd.

1724 Granville St., Ground Flr.
Box 1083, Halifax, B3J 2X1

Province House Credit Union Ltd. is a co-operative savings and loan association incorporated under charter in 1937. Membership is open to full-time employees of departments, boards, and commissions of the Province of Nova Scotia, and the Nova Scotia Technical College, Nova Scotia Power Corp., Nova Scotia Government Employees Assn., Province House Credit Union Ltd., and The Halifax Infirmary.

Treas.-Manager, Stephen M. McManus
Office Manager, Rosalina Benteau

Public Archives of Nova Scotia

6016 University Ave., Halifax, B3H 1W4

Established in 1857, the Archives' objectives are to preserve the documentary record of the province of Nova Scotia, which is of permanent value for research; to make its archival resources available to the general public; and to contribute to a better appreciation of the history, heritage, and archival resources of Nova Scotia through special programs. As well as manuscripts and government records, the Archives contain a library of Novascotiana; photo, map, and architectural collections; and a film and sound department.

Provincial Archivist, Mr. Carman Carroll
Asst. Provincial Archivist, Allan Dunlop

Sydney Steel Corp. (SYSCO)

Box 1450, Sydney, B1P 6K5

Sydney Steel Corporation is a Crown corporation incorporated by special Act of the House of Assembly of Nova Scotia. Familiarly known as Sysco, the Corporation operates a fully integrated steel plant at Sydney. Production facilities are located on a 265-hectare site on the south arm of Sydney Harbour, a fine natural port open for shipping throughout the year. Annual capacity is 910,000 tonnes of raw steel.

Railroad rails have been the principal product of Sysco for more than 80 years. Other products include slabs, blooms, forging and slab ingots, tie plates, and mine arch. Sydney Steel serves both domestic and export markets.

Chairman, Michael H. Cochrane
A/President, John Strasser
Vice-President of Finance/Secretary,
R.J. Skinner
Vice-President of Marketing, Vacant
Works Manager, Vacant
Director, Corporate Affairs, H.S. MacLeod
Director, Engineering, L.A. Chaisson
Metallurgical Services
Manager, Steve H. Didyk
Management Information Services
Director, K. Garland
Industrial Relations
Manager, D. Coleman
Technical Development
Manager, B.E. Britten
Primary Operations
Manager, R.N. MacInnis

Rolling Mills
Manager, B.W. Kokoska
Maintenance
Manager, E.B. Parsons
Purchasing Agent, R. Peddle
Controller, J.B. MacArthur
Accounting Supervisor, Jim Rudderham
General Services
Manager, G. Ryan

Technology Transfer Office

Box 519, Halifax, B3J 2R7

The Technology Transfer Office was established in August 1987 under a federal-provincial agreement to facilitate the transfer of technology between industry and university and government research establishments. The Office provides information, advice, and contacts to industrialists and members of the research community wishing to commercialize technology.

Director, Kay Crinean

Tidal Power Corp.

Duke St. Twr., Ste. 1109, 5251 Duke St.
Halifax, B3J 1P3
General Inquiries: (902) 423-8467

The mandate of the Tidal Power Corporation, under the *Tidal Power Corporation Act,* is to derive benefit from the exploitation of tidal power. This provincial Crown corporation carries on activities connected with or arising from such exploitation, and promotes the development of tidal power as well.

As a result, North America's first tidal generating station is operating at Annapolis Royal, using the world's largest straflo turbine.

The Corporation has a board of directors composed of a chairperson, a president, and four to eleven members appointed by the Governor in Council, who also defines the length of term. One of them is designated as chief executive officer.

President and CEO, Ronald Barkhouse

Chairman, Dr. Gerald Sheehy, D.V.M., MLA
Vice-President, Dr. L.F. Kirkpatrick, P.Eng.
Exec. Vice-President, G.C. Baker, P.Eng.
Directors: Ronald Barkhouse,
Dr. Gerald Sheehy, D.V.M., MLA,
Dr. L.F. Kirkpatrick, P.Eng.,
G.C. Baker, P.Eng., C.A.E. Fowler,
A.M. McCrea, P.Eng., Dr. J.C. Callaghan,
J.C. Turner, Wm. D. Casey, G.K. Mitchell,
Louis R. Comeau
Treasurer, R.C. Fraser, F.C.A.
Secretary, J.T. MacQuarrie, Q.C.

Victoria General Hospital
1278 Tower Rd., Halifax, B3H 2Y9

The Victoria General Hospital, located in the heart of peninsular Halifax, is the largest tertiary acute-care institution in the province. It serves the entire Atlantic region, including the Maritime provinces, Newfoundland, and the French colonies of St. Pierre and Miquelon, and has been ranked among the top ten hospitals in Canada.

Among its more outstanding accomplishments are: a Kidney Transplantation Program which is the largest of any hospital in Canada; the development of a Liver Transplant Program, realized in 1985 when its first efforts were successful; one of the finest and most progressive cardiac bypass surgery departments in the country; and a radiology department which is among the largest in the nation.

The acquisition of a walk-in, multi-place hyperbaric oxygen treatment chamber has placed the Hospital in the forefront of the field of medical use of pressurized oxygen.

Exec. Director, Dr. B.W.D. Badley
Medical Director, Dr. E.V. Haldane
Interim CFO, Andrew Boehme
President, Medical Staff, Dr. R.H. Lea
Director, Nursing Services, M.A. Grantham
Director, Special Services, J.A. Stewart
Director, Educational Services, M.J. Magee
Public Relations
Director, Chris Hansen

Waterfront Development Corp. Ltd.
The Cable Wharf, 2nd Flr.
1751 Lower Water St., Halifax, B3J 1S5

The Waterfront Development Corp. Ltd. is a provincial Crown corporation established in 1976 to implement the Metropolitan Halifax and Dartmouth Area Development Subsidiary Agreement, entered into by the federal and provincial governments. The Corporation's purpose is to co-ordinate the process of "Bringing Back the Waterfront" as recreational, commercial, and cultural extensions of the downtown cores of both Halifax and Dartmouth.

The Subsidiary Agreement provided $31 million in shared costs and the provincial government provided an additional $4 million by way of grants for planning, land acquisition, site preparation, and infrastructure construction in the areas designated for redevelopment. A further $3.4 million was provided for construction of a new ferry system serving the two port cities. All funding under this Agreement ended March 31, 1981, and the Corporation now operates on revenues generated from its real estate holdings.

Much-needed improvements to the public infrastructure, including new water and sewer lines and underground electrical and telephone systems, have permitted more intensive and modern development of the waterfront areas, and encouraged businesses to locate there.

Two private-sector projects were pioneered by the Corporation: Admiralty Place, a 114-unit condominium project in Dartmouth, and the Sheraton/Lundrigan Group's 365-room convention hotel in Halifax. Several major projects are presently underway in the downtown waterfront areas.

The Corporation's future plans are to explore the development opportunities for its 80,770 m² land bank and to encourage more private-sector involvement in the restoration and revitalization of the Halifax and Dartmouth waterfronts.

Chairman of the Board, Alan MacDonald
President and CEO, Harvey W. Doane, P. Eng.
Vice-Chairman, Stephen Thompson
Controller, Philip Peapell
Administration Manager, John Wright
Property Manager, Patrick Kennedy

World Trade and Convention Centre (Trade Centre Limited)
1800 Argyle St., Box 955, Halifax, B3J 2V9

President and CEO, Kenneth M. Mounce
Marketing Director, S. Patrick McCabe
Canadian Sales
Manager, Carole Ann Michael
Reg. Sales Manager, Paul Cody
Sales Co-ordinator, Sheila Blair
World Trade Centre
Manager, Chris Thornley
Finance Director, Donald Larlee
Metro Centre
Manager, David Stevenson
Building Services
Manager, Darrell Hardy
Convention Services
Manager, Vacant
Promotions Manager, Colin Craig

JUDICIARY AND JUDICIAL OFFICERS

Supreme Court

The Law Courts, 1815 Upper Water St.
Halifax, B3J 1S7
General Inquiries: (902) 424-4900

Chief Justice of Nova Scotia:
The Hon. Mr. Justice Lorne O. Clarke

APPEAL DIVISION
Chief Justice:
The Hon. Mr. Justice Lorne O. Clarke

Judges:
The Hon. Mr. Justice Ian M. MacKeigan*
The Hon. Mr. Justice Angus L. Macdonald
The Hon. Mr. Justice Leonard L. Pace
The Hon. Mr. Justice Gordon L.S. Hart
The Hon. Mr. Justice Malachi C. Jones
The Hon. Mr. Justice Kenneth M. Matthews
The Hon. Mr. Justice David R. Chipman

Registrar: A. Martin Smith, Q.C.

TRIAL DIVISION
(ex officio members of Appeal Division)

Chief Justice:
The Hon. Madam Justice Constance R. Glube

Judges:
The Hon. Mr. Justice A. MacIntosh*
The Hon. Mr. Justice J. Doane Hallett
The Hon. Mr. Justice William J. Grant
The Hon. Mr. Justice K. Peter Richard
The Hon. Mr. Justice C. Denne Burchell
The Hon. Mr. Justice R. MacLeod Rogers
The Hon. Mr. Justice D. Merlin Nunn
The Hon. Mr. Justice Hilroy S. Nathanson
The Hon. Mr. Justice Robert MacDonald
The Hon. Mr. Justice F.B. William Kelly
The Hon. Mr. Justice Gordon Tidman
The Hon. Mr. Justice John McNab Davison

Prothonotary: A. Martin Smith, Q.C.
Taxing Master: Arthur E. Hare, Q.C.

County Court

The Law Courts, 1815 Upper Water St.
Halifax, B3J 1S7
General Inquiries: (902) 424-4900

JUDGES
(also local Judges of the Trial Division of the
Supreme Court of Nova Scotia, and Judges of the
Probate Court)

District No. 1: (Halifax)
Judges: Felix A. Cacchione,
  Robert Anderson, Ian H.M. Palmeter

District No. 2: (Liverpool)
Judge: Gerald B. Freeman

District No. 3: (Digby)
Judge: Charles E. Haliburton

District No. 4: (Berwick)
Judge: Donald M. Hall

District No. 5: (New Glasgow)
Judge: Hugh MacDonnell

District No. 6: (Antigonish)
Judge: Hugh J. MacPherson

District No. 7: (Sydney)
Judges: Murray James Ryan,
  Simon J. MacDonald

Provincial Court

5250 Spring Garden Rd., Halifax, B3J 1E7
General Inquiries: (902) 421-1316
Chief Judge: His Hon. Harry W. How, Q.C.

AMHERST
Judges: David Cole, Ross Archibald

BEDFORD
Judge: Patrick H. Curran

BRIDGEWATER/LUNENBURG
Judges: Hiram J. Carver, Joseph P. Kennedy

DARTMOUTH
Judges: Frances K. Potts, Reginald B. Kimball

DIGBY
Judge: John R. Nichols

HALIFAX
Judges: G. Hughes Randall, W.J.C. Atton,
  Sandra E. Oxner, Elmer J. MacDonald

---

* Supernumerary

KENTVILLE/WINDSOR/MIDDLETON
Judges: R.E. Kimball, Kenneth Crowell,
   John Alexander MacLellan

NEW GLASGOW/ANTIGONISH
Judges: H. Russell MacEwan,
   Ronald Angus MacDonald

PICTOU
Judge: Robert A. Stroud

PORT HAWKESBURY
Judge: D. Lewis Matheson

SHUBENACADIE
Judge: John G. MacDougall

SYDNEY
Judges: J. Charles O'Connell,
   George R. LeVatte, Stanley D. Campbell

TRURO
Judge: Charles W. Archibald

YARMOUTH
Judge: James D. Reardon

Relief Judge: Phillip Woolaver

Family Court

C: Clerk, Court Officer &/or Supervisor
CJ: Chief Judge
J: Judge(s)

AMHERST
24 Crescent Ave., Box 399, B4H 3Z5
J: David Milner
C: Archie St. Peter

ANTIGONISH
11 James St., B2G 1R6
J: Robert White
C: Donald Keigan

ARICHAT
Box 359, Port Hawkesbury, B0E 2V0
J: Robert Ferguson
C: Fulton MacPherson

BADDECK/INGONISH
Box 760, Sydney, B1P 6J1
J: Vernon MacDonald
C: Stan Reppa

BARRINGTON/SHELBURNE
10 Starrs Rd., Box 460, Yarmouth, B5A 4B4
J: John Comeau
C: Douglas Mosley

DARTMOUTH
(East Shore, Preston, Waverly Road)
45 Alderney Dr., Box 1253, B2Y 4B9
J: Paul Niedermayer, James Williams
C: Peter Roberts

DIGBY
10 Starrs Rd., Box 460, Yarmouth, B5A 4B4
J: John Comeau
C: Douglas Mosley

GUYSBOROUGH/SHERBROOKE
11 James St., B2G 1R6
J: Robert White
C: James Hahnen

HALIFAX
(Lower Sackville, Bedford, South Shore)
3380 Acadia St., Box 1473 N., B3K 5H7
J: Elizabeth Roscoe, Louis Moir,
   Robert Butler, Timothy Daley
C: Len Lipsett

KENTVILLE
120 Exhibition St., Box 816, B4N 4E5
CJ: Marshall Black
J: Margaret Stewart
C: Perry Bishop

LIVERPOOL
120 Townsend St., Box 57
Lunenburg, B0J 2C0
J: Robert Hebb
C: Fraser Dorman

LUNENBURG
120 Townsend St., Box 57, B0J 2C0
J: Robert Hebb
C: Fraser Dorman

MIDDLETON
120 Exhibition St., Kentville, B4N 4E5
J: Margaret Stewart
C: Perry Bishop

NEW GLASGOW
Box 518, B2H 5E7
J: Corrine Sparks, Robert White
C: James Hahnen

PORT HOOD/PORT HAWKESBURY
Box 359, B0E 2V0
J: Darryl Wilson
C: Fulton MacPherson

SHUBENACADIE
Box 950, Truro, B2N 5G7
J: Corrine Sparks
C: Ted Lohnes

SYDNEY
Box 760, B1P 6J1
J: Robert Ferguson, Vernon MacDonald,
   Darryl Wilson
C: Stan Reppa

TRURO
Box 950, B2H 5G7
J: Corrine Sparks, David Milner
C: Ted Lohnes

WINDSOR
120 Exhibition St., Kentville, B4N 4E5
CJ: Marshall Black
C: Perry Bishop

YARMOUTH
10 Starrs Rd., Box 460, B5A 4B4
J: John Comeau
C: Douglas Mosley

County Court Officials

C: Prothonotary of the Supreme Court,
  or Clerk of the County Court
R: Registrar of Probate
D: Registrar of Deeds
S: Sheriff

ANNAPOLIS
Box 129, Annapolis Royal, B0S 1A0
C/R: Patricia A. Connell
D: Catherine Lowe
  Box 88, Lawrencetown, B0S 1M0
S: Theresa McNeil

ANTIGONISH
C/S: Gerald MacDonald
  Box 1342, B2G 2L8
R/D: Marion MacPherson
  42 West St., B2G 2H5

CAPE BRETON
County Court House, Sydney, B1P 6H4
C: William Bungay
R: Shauna Wilson
D: Melvin Moraff
S: Wayne Magee

COLCHESTER
Court House, Truro, B2N 5E7
C: Gail Miller
R: H.K. Starratt
D: R.L. Pearson
S: Ronald Conrad

CUMBERLAND
Court House, Amherst, B4H 3Y6
C: Walter Maltby
R: William Fairbanks
D: Nancy Harrison
S: Aubrey M. Chapman

DIGBY
C/S: J.R. Patrick McIntyre
  Box 668, Digby, B0V 1A0
R: Lynn Durkee
  Box 463, B0V 1A0

GUYSBOROUGH
General Delivery, Guysborough, B0H 1N0
C: Lorraine Ehler
R: Lorna M. Chisholm
D: Josephine O'Connor
  Box 123, B0H 1N0

HALIFAX
1815 Upper Water St., Halifax, B3J 1S7
C: A. Martin Smith, Q.C.
R: V.P. Allen, Q.C.
D: Robert A. Hickey
  Box 2205, B3J 3C4
S: Keith Roberts

HANTS
C/S: Robert Mack
  Box 2170, Windsor, B0N 2T0
R: Mary Louise Rippey
  Box 177, Windsor, B0N 2T0
D: Vincent R. Bwigess
  Box 2349, Windsor, B0N 2T0

INVERNESS
C: Mary T. MacDonald
  Box 83, Port Hood, B0E 2W0
R/D: Reynelda MacDonald
  Box 178, Port Hood, B0E 2W0
S: Alex Sutherland
  Box 24, Port Hood, B0E 2W0

KINGS
Court House, Kentville, B4N 3X3
C: Yvonne Bezanson
R: K.N. James
D: Ross Watkins
S: George Menzies

LUNENBURG
Box 760, B0J 2C0
C/R: Arthur Hebb
D: Jean E. Litt (Bridgewater),
  Elaine Smith (Chester)
S: Carl Odegard

PICTOU
C: Wayne Canam
  Box 569, B0K 1H0
R: Mrs. D.M. Robinson
  Box 1199, B0K 1H0
D: Edward MacLaren
  Box 490, B0K 1H0
S: Alex Sutherland
  Box 189, B0K 1H0

QUEENS
C: Robert Brogan
  Box 569, Liverpool, B0T 1K0
R/D: Gloria Pentz
  Box 727, Liverpool, B0T 1K0

RICHMOND
C/S: J. Richard MacKay
  Box 234, Arichat, B0E 1A0
R/D: Arthur A. Bowen
  Box 231, Arichat, B0E 1A0

ST. MARY'S
Box 166, Sherbrooke, B0J 3C0
R/D: Margaret MacIntosh

SHELBURNE
C: Carol Lynn Strang
  Box 106, B0T 1W0

R/D: Robert Robertson (Shelburne)
    Box 421, B0T 1W0
  M. Aileen Smith (Barrington)
S: Kendall Stoddard
    Box 106, B0T 1W0

VICTORIA
C/S: Winston F. Cameron
    Box 305, Baddeck, B0E 1B0
R/D: Anne Marie Campbell
    Box 353, Baddeck, B0E 1B0

YARMOUTH
Court House, B5A 4B2
C: Diane Bullerwell
R/D: Bruce Murray
S: Basil Pero

Registrars and Receivers in Bankruptcy

Division No. 1: (Halifax, Hants, Lunenburg, Queens, Annapolis, and Kings Counties)
Law Courts, Box 2288, Halifax, B3J 3C8
Registrar: Linden M. Smith, Q.C.

Division No. 2: (Pictou, Guysborough, Cumberland, Colchester and Antigonish Counties)
Court House, Pictou, B0K 1H0
Registrar: Wayne Canam

Division No. 3: (Cape Breton, Inverness, Richmond, and Victoria Counties)
Box 475, Sydney, B1P 6H4
Registrar: A.D. Muggah

Division No. 4: (Digby, Yarmouth, and Shelburne Counties)
Box 188, Yarmouth, B5A 4B2
Registrar: Diane Bullerwell

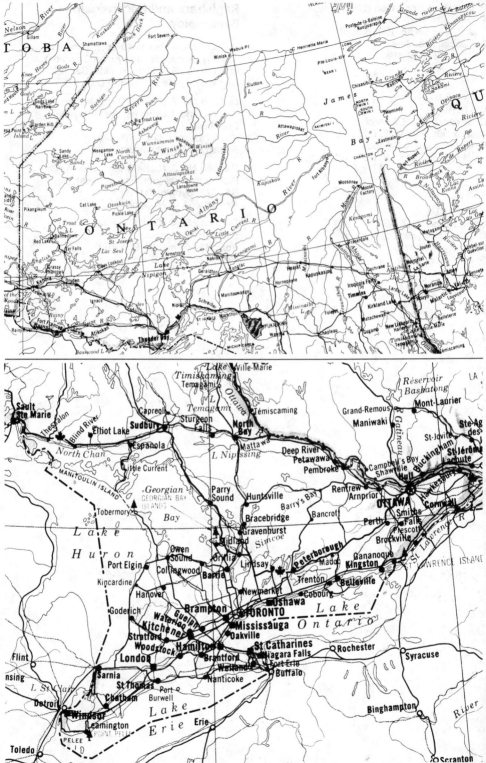

This map is based on information taken from map MCR 4032. © Her Majesty in Right of Canada with permission of Energy, Mines and Resources.

PROVINCE OF ONTARIO

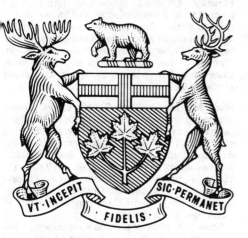

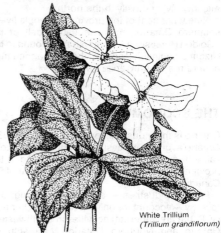

White Trillium
(*Trillium grandiflorum*)

Entered Confederation: July 1, 1867
Capital: Toronto
Motto: Ut Incepit Fidelis Sic Permanet
(Loyal it began, loyal it remains)
Flower: White trillium
Area: 1,068,582 km²
  percentage of Canada's total area: 10.7
  LAND: 891,192 km²
  FRESHWATER: 177,390 km²
Elevation:
  HIGHEST POINT: Mount Whatnot (693 m)
  LOWEST POINT: Hudson Bay shore
Population (1986): 9,100,000

five-year change: +5%
per square kilometre: 8.5
percentage of Canada's total
  population: 36.0
  URBAN: 82%
  RURAL: 18%
Gross domestic product, 1987: $224.7 billion
Government Finance:
  REVENUE, 1987/88 est.: $33,866 million
  EXPENDITURE, 1987/88 est.: $34,846 million
  DEBT PER CAPITA (March 1987): $1,899
Personal income per person, 1986: $18,882
Unemployment rate, 1988
  (annual average): 5.0%

THE LAND

Ontario is the second largest of Canada's ten provinces. The province covers 1,068,582 km², bounded on three sides by water. It extends from Hudson Bay and James Bay in the north to the St. Lawrence River and the Great Lakes in the south, and from Manitoba in the west to the Ottawa River and Quebec in the east. The longest distance in Ontario east to west is 1,690 km; the longest distance north to south is 1,730 km.

The land is vast and varied, changing quite suddenly from the flat bogs and coniferous forest of the Hudson Bay lowlands to the rocky plateau of the Precambrian Shield, or Canadian Shield, and then to the rolling hills and fertile agricultural soil of the Great Lakes-St. Lawrence lowlands.

Ontario's climate ranges from humid continental in the south to subarctic in the far north. It is moderated by the presence of the Great Lakes, and Hudson and James bays, which cool the summers, lessen the severity of the winters, delay autumn frosts, and reduce the difference between day and night temperatures.

THE PEOPLE

In the four decades since the end of the Second World War, Ontario's population has doubled and the tide of immigration has contributed to a flowering of diversity which has affected every aspect of daily life, from the languages heard on the street, the food available in homes and restaurants, to the issues spoken of in public life.

The language spoken by most of Ontario's people is English, with French the mother tongue of half a million Ontarians. In fact, this population represents the largest French-speaking minority group living in one province.

Many immigrants continue to speak the language they learned as children. According to the 1981 census, major language groups are Italian (338,980), German (174,545), Portuguese (114,280), Chinese (89,355), Ukrainian (81,600), Netherlandic and Flemish (78,515), Polish (73,765), and Greek (65,400).

There are four Indian groups within Ontario: Algonkian-speaking in the eastern half of the province, Iroquoian-speaking in the south, Ojibwa scattered throughout most parts, and Cree, the majority, living mostly in the north.

Ninety per cent of the province's people live in southern Ontario, in the industrial belt of the "Golden Horseshoe", from Oshawa around to the Niagara peninsula, and in the rich agricultural area of the St. Lawrence lowlands.

THE ECONOMY

Ontario is the industrial core of Canada. In 1987, Ontario's gross domestic product — the total value of all goods and services produced in the province — was $224 billion, or 42 per cent of the Canadian total.

Primary industries — agriculture, mining, and forestry — account for only 4 per cent of Ontario's GDP, but are important activities in southwestern Ontario and Northern Ontario. Manufacturing contributes 26 per cent of Ontario's GDP, and is heavily concentrated in Southern Ontario's "Golden Horseshoe" centered around Metropolitan Toronto. Service industries such as retailing, banks, insurance, and government make up the remaining 70 per cent of Ontario's GDP.

Agriculture. Ontario has 3.5 million hectares of cropland and some 73,000 farms. Its farm production amounted to $5.6 billion in 1987, or 27% of the national total, making it Canada's leading agricultural province. It is Canada's largest producer of poultry products, fluid milk, fruit, tobacco, corn, and soybeans.

Mining. Some 30 different minerals are mined in Ontario, but the most important in terms of 1987 value of production are: gold, $1,029 million; nickel, $902 million; copper, $675 million; and uranium, $509 million. Ontario's mineral production amounted to $5.7 billion in 1987, or some 16 per cent of Canada's total.

Forestry. Ontario's productive forest lands amount to 42.6 million hectares or 16 per cent of Canada's total. Approximately 30 million cubic meters of roundwood were harvested from these lands in 1987, with an estimated value of $1 billion. This wood was used by pulp and paper mills, sawmills, and other wood industries to produce almost $10 billion worth of forest products.

Manufacturing. Ontario is Canada's leading manufacturing province, accounting for some 52 per cent of the country's total value of manufacturing shipments. The Province's largest manufacturing industry is motor vehicle parts and assembly, whose value of shipments totalled $33.7 billion in 1987, or nearly one quarter of all Ontario manufacturing shipments. Ontario accounts for some 90 per cent of Canadian manufactured motor vehicles and parts.

Some two-thirds of Canada's machinery, electrical and electronics manufacturing takes place in Ontario. Chemicals, rubber, and plastics constitute another large industry, particularly in the Sarnia area where crude oil and natural gas from Western Canada are refined into a variety of products. Forest products and primary metals are also important industries, particularly in Northern Ontairo.

Services. The service sector, including construction, is the largest component of Ontario's economy. Service activities are geographically distributed more or less according to population, but a large number of industrial and financial head offices are located in Metropolitan Toronto. The provincial government is also centered in Toronto, while the national capital is in Ottawa.

Text provided by the Information Services Branch, Ontario Ministry of Government Services.

For further information regarding any aspect of the Government of Ontario, contact:
Citizen's Inquiry Bureau
M151, Macdonald Block, 900 Bay St., Toronto, M7A 1N3
(416) 965-3535

GOVERNMENT OF ONTARIO

Seat of Government:
  Parliament Bldgs., Toronto, M7A 1A1

Lieutenant-Governor,
  The Honourable Lincoln M. Alexander
  Queen's Park, Toronto, M7A 1A1

EXECUTIVE COUNCIL

(In order of precedence, as of Jan. 1, 1989)

Premier, President of the Council, Minister of Intergovernmental Affairs,
  The Hon. David Peterson
Treasurer of Ontario, Minister of Economics, Deputy Premier,
  The Hon. Robert Nixon
Minister of Mines, Government House Leader,
  The Hon. Sean Conway
Minister of the Environment,
  The Hon. James Bradley
Attorney General, Minister responsible for Native Affairs,
  The Hon. Ian G. Scott
Minister of Agriculture and Food,
  The Hon. Jack Riddell
Minister of Municipal Affairs,
  The Hon. John Eakins
Minister of Natural Resources,
  The Hon. Vincent Kerrio
Minister of Tourism and Recreation,
  The Hon. Hugh O'Neil
Minister of Community and Social Services,
  The Hon. John Sweeney
Chairman of the Management Board, Minister of Financial Institutions, Chairman of Cabinet,
  The Hon. Murray Elston
Minister of Consumer and Commercial Relations,
  The Hon. William Wrye
Minister of Revenue, Minister responsible for Francophone Affairs,
  The Hon. Bernard Grandmaître
Minister of Skills Development,
  The Hon. Alvin Curling
Minister of Transportation,
  The Hon. Edward Fulton
Minister of Industry, Trade and Technology,
  The Hon. Monte Kwinter
Minister of Culture and Communications,
  The Hon. Lily Munro
Minister of Labour, Minister responsible for Women's Issues,
  The Hon. Greg Sorbara
Minister of Health,
  The Hon. Elinor Caplan
Minister of Northern Development,
  The Hon. René Fontaine
Minister of Correctional Services,
  The Hon. David Ramsay
Solicitor General,
  The Hon. Joan Smith
Minister of Education,
  The Hon. Chris Ward
Minister of Housing,
  The Hon. Chaviva Hosek
Minister of Colleges and Universities,
  The Hon. Lyn McLeod
Minister of Government Services,
  The Hon. Richard Patten
Minister of Citizenship, responsible for Race Relations and the Ontario Human Rights Commission,
  The Hon. Gerry Phillips
Minister of Energy,
  The Hon. Robert Wong
Minister without Portfolio, responsible for Disabled Persons,
  The Hon. Remo Mancini
Minister without Portfolio, responsible for Senior Citizens' Affairs,
  The Hon. Mavis Wilson

CABINET COMMITTEES

Economic Policy
Chairman, The Hon. Robert Nixon
Exec. Co-ordinator, Sherry Yundt

Emergency Planning
Chairman, The Hon. Joan Smith
Exec. Co-ordinator, Wil Vanderelst

Justice
Chairman, The Hon. Ian Scott
Exec. Co-ordinator, Wil Vanderelst

Legislation
Chairman, The Hon. Ian Scott
Secretary, Suzanne Wilson

Management Board
Chairman, The Hon. Murray Elston
Secretary, John Sloan

Native Affairs
Chairman, The Hon. Ian Scott
Policy Advisor, Laura Metrick

Northern Development
Chairman, The Hon. René Fontaine
Exec. Co-ordinator, Sherry Yundt

Policy and Priorities
Chairman, The Hon. David Peterson
Secretary, Andrew Szende

Race Relations
Chairman, The Hon. Gerry Phillips
Policy Advisor, Laura Metrick

Regulations
Chairman, The Hon. Greg Sorbara
Secretary, Suzanne Wilson

Social Policy
Chairman, The Hon. Elinor Caplan
Exec. Co-ordinator, Jane Marlatt

CABINET OFFICE

Secretary of the Cabinet and Clerk of the Executive Council, Robert D. Carmen
Admin. Asst., Felicia Bigford

OPERATIONS
Assoc. Secretary of the Cabinet, Tom Coleman
Director, J.E. Tangney

OFFICE OF FRANCOPHONE AFFAIRS
Exec. Director, Rémy Beauregard

LEGISLATIVE ASSEMBLY

34th Parliament, 1st Session
Last election: Sept. 10, 1987
  (Maximum legal duration 5 years)
Government party: Liberal
Total Number of seats: 130
Party standings:
  Liberals: 94
  New Democrats: 19
  Progressive Conservatives: 17

Salaries, Indemnities and Allowances

MEMBERS: Member's Sessional Indemnity, $39,229 per annum, plus $13,171 per annum expense allowance.
PREMIER: Member's Sessional Indemnity and expense allowance; Ministerial salary, $40,957, plus $7,098 leader's allowance.
LEADER OF THE OFFICIAL OPPOSITION: Member's Sessional Indemnity and expense allowance; additional indemnity, $28,743, plus $4,733 leader's allowance.
LEADER OF THE THIRD PARTY*: Member's Sessional Indemnity and expense allowance; additional indemnity, $14,432, plus $2,366 leader's allowance.
CABINET MINISTERS: Member's Sessional Indemnity and expense allowance; ministerial salary, $28,743.
CABINET MINISTERS WITHOUT PORTFOLIO: Member's Sessional Indemnity and expense allowance; ministerial salary, $14,433.
PARLIAMENTARY ASSISTANTS: Member's Sessional Indemnity and expense allowance; $8,880 salary.
SPEAKER: Member's Sessional Indemnity and expense allowance; additional indemnity, $21,217.
CHAIRMAN OF THE COMMITTEES OF THE WHOLE HOUSE: Member's Sessional Indemnity and expense allowance; additional indemnity, $8,880.
DEPUTY CHAIRMAN OF THE COMMITTEES OF THE WHOLE HOUSE: Member's Sessional Indemnity and expense allowance; additional indemnity, $6,168.
CHAIRMAN OF STANDING COMMITTEES: Member's Sessional Indemnity and expense allowance; additional indemnity, $4,810.

CHIEF GOVERNMENT WHIP: Member's Sessional Indemnity and expense allowance; additional indemnity, $10,979.
HOUSE LEADER OF THE OFFICIAL OPPOSITION: Member's Sessional Indemnity and expense allowance; additional indemnity, $10,979.
HOUSE LEADER OF THE THIRD PARTY*: Member's Sessional Indemnity and expense allowance; additional indemnity, $8,264.
CHIEF WHIP OF THE OFFICIAL OPPOSITION: Member's Sessional Indemnity and expense allowance; additional indemnity, $7,524.
CHIEF WHIP OF THE THIRD PARTY*: Member's Sessional Indemnity and expense allowance; additional indemnity, $6,168.

* Leader of the Party with recognised membership of 12 or more in the Assembly.

Officers

Speaker, The Hon. Hugh Edighoffer
Deputy Speaker, Jean Poirier
Sergeant-at-Arms, Thomas Stelling
Clerk of the House, Claude DesRosiers
Hansard Office, Chief, P. Brannan
Chief Election Officer, Warren Bailie

Members

Constituency	Member and Affiliation
Algoma	Bud Wildman (NDP)
Algoma/Manitoulin	Mike Brown (Lib)
Beaches/Woodbine	Marion Bryden (NDP)
Brampton North	Carman McClelland (Lib)
Brampton South	Bob Callahan (Lib)
Brant/Haldimand	The Hon. Robert Nixon (Lib)
Brantford	Dave Neumann (Lib)
Bruce	The Hon. Murray Elston (Lib)
Burlington South	Cameron Jackson (PC)
Cambridge	Mike Farnan (NDP)
Carleton	Norman Sterling, Q.C. (PC)
Carleton East	Gilles Morin (Lib)
Chatham/Kent	Maurice Bossy (Lib)
Cochrane North	The Hon. René Fontaine (Lib)
Cochrane South	Alan W. Pope, Q.C. (PC)
Cornwall	John Cleary (Lib)
Don Mills	Murad Velshi (Lib)
Dovercourt	Tony Lupusella (Lib)
Downsview	Laureano Leone (Lib)
Dufferin/Peel	The Hon. Mavis Wilson (Lib)
Durham Centre	Allan Furlong (Lib)
Durham East	Sam Cureatz (PC)
Durham West	Norah Stoner (Lib)
Durham/York	Bill Ballinger (Lib)
Eglinton	Dianne Poole (Lib)
Elgin	Marietta Roberts (Lib)
Essex South	The Hon. Remo Mancini (Lib)
Essex/Kent	Jim McGuigan (Lib)
Etobicoke West	Linda LeBourdais (Lib)
Etobicoke/Humber	Jim Henderson (Lib)
Etobicoke/Lakeshore	Ruth Grier (NDP)
Etobicoke/Rexdale	Ed Philip (NDP)

Constituency	Member and Affiliation
Fort William	The Hon. Lyn McLeod (Lib)
Fort York	The Hon. Bob Wong (Lib)
Frontenac/ Addington	Larry South (Lib)
Grey	Ron Lipsett (Lib)
Guelph	Rick Ferraro (Lib)
Halton Centre	Barbara Sullivan (Lib)
Halton North	Walt Elliot (Lib)
Hamilton Centre	The Hon. Lily Munro (Lib)
Hamilton East	Bob Mackenzie (NDP)
Hamilton Mountain	Brian Charlton (NDP)
Hamilton West	Richard Allen (NDP)
Hastings/ Peterborough	Jim Pollock (PC)
High Park/Swansea	David Fleet (Lib)
Huron	The Hon. Jack Riddell (Lib)
Kenora	Frank Miclash (Lib)
Kingston and The Islands	Ken Keyes (Lib)
Kitchener	David Cooke (Lib)
Kitchener/Wilmot	The Hon. John Sweeney, Q.C. (Lib)
Lake Nipigon	Gilles Pouliot (NDP)
Lambton	David Smith (Lib)
Lanark/Renfrew	Douglas J. Wiseman (PC)
Lawrence	Joseph Cordiano (Lib)
Leeds/Grenville	Robert Runciman (PC)
Lincoln	Harry Pelissero (Lib)
London Centre	The Hon. David Peterson, Q.C. (Lib)
London North	Dianne Cunningham (PC)
London South	The Hon. Joan Smith (Lib)
Markham	W. Donald Cousens (PC)
Middlesex	Douglas Reycraft (Lib)
Mississauga East	John Sola (Lib)
Mississauga North	Steven Offer (Lib)
Mississauga South	Margaret Marland (PC)
Mississauga West	Steve Mahoney (Lib)
Muskoka/ Georgian Bay	Ken Black (Lib)
Nepean	Hans Daigeler (Lib)
Niagara Falls	The Hon. Vincent Kerrio (Lib)
Niagara South	Ray Haggerty (Lib)
Nickel Belt	Floyd Laughren (NDP)
Nipissing	Michael D. Harris (PC)
Norfolk	Gordon Miller (Lib)
Northumberland	Joan Fawcett (Lib)
Oakville South	Doug Carrothers (Lib)
Oakwood	The Hon. Chaviva Hosek (Lib)
Oriole	The Hon. Elinor Caplan (Lib)
Oshawa	Mike Breaugh (NDP)
Ottawa Centre	The Hon. Richard Patten (Lib)
Ottawa East	The Hon. Bernard Grandmaître (Lib)
Ottawa South	Dalton McGuinty (Lib)
Ottawa West	Bob Chiarelli (Lib)
Ottawa/Rideau	Yvonne O'Neil (Lib)
Oxford	Charlie Tatham (Lib)
Parkdale	Tony Ruprecht (Lib)
Parry Sound	Ernie Eves (PC)
Perth	The Hon. Hugh Edighoffer (Lib)
Peterborough	Peter Adams (Lib)
Port Arthur	Taras Kozyra (Lib)
Prescott and Russell	Jean Poirier (Lib)
Prince Edward/ Lennox	Keith MacDonald (Lib)
Quinté	The Hon. Hugh P. O'Neil (Lib)
Rainy River	Howard Hampton (NDP)
Renfrew North	The Hon. Sean Conway (Lib)
Riverdale	David Reville (NDP)

Constituency	Member and Affiliation
St. Andrew/ St. Patrick	Ron Kanter (Lib)
St. Catharines	The Hon. James Bradley (Lib)
St. Catharines/ Brock	Mike Dietsch (Lib)
St. Georges/ St. David	The Hon. Ian Scott, Q.C. (Lib)
Sarnia	Andrew Brandt (PC)
Sault Ste. Marie	Karl Morin-Strom (NDP)
Scarborough Centre	Cindy Nicholas (Lib)
Scarborough East	The Hon. Ed Fulton (Lib)
Scarborough North	The Hon. Alvin Curling (Lib)
Scarborough West	Richard Johnston (NDP)
Scarborough/ Agincourt	The Hon. Gerry Phillips (Lib)
Scarborough/ Ellesmere	Frank Faubert (Lib)
Simcoe Centre	Bruce Owen (Lib)
Simcoe East	Allan McLean (PC)
Simcoe West	George McCague (PC)
Stormont, Dundas and Glengarry	Noble Villeneuve (PC)
Sudbury	Sterling Campbell (Lib)
Sudbury East	Shelley Martel (NDP)
Timiskaming	The Hon. David Ramsay (Lib)
Victoria/Haliburton	The Hon. John Eakins (Lib)
Waterloo North	Herbert Epp (Lib)
Welland/Thorold	Peter Kormos (NDP)
Wellington	Jack Johnson (PC)
Wentworth East	Shirley Collins (Lib)
Wentworth North	The Hon. Chris Ward (Lib)
Willowdale	Gino Matrundola (Lib)
Wilson Heights	The Hon. Monte Kwinter (Lib)
Windsor/Riverside	David Cooke (NDP)
Windsor/Sandwich	The Hon. William Wrye (Lib)
Windsor/Walkerville	Michael C. Ray (Lib)
York Centre	The Hon. Greg Sorbara (Lib)
York East	Christine Hart (Lib)
York Mills	Brad Nixon (Lib)
York North	Charles Beer (Lib)
York South	Bob Rae, Q.C. (NDP)
Yorkview	Claudio Polsinelli (Lib)

Lib — Liberal
NDP — New Democrat
PC — Progressive Conservative

Commission on Election Finances
151 Bloor St. W., Ste. 800, Toronto, M5S 1S4

The Commission was established to administer the provisions of the *Election Finances Act,* which requires the registration of political parties, constituency associations, candidates, and leadership contestants; limits contributions that may be accepted; limits campaign expenditures; requires the filing of audited annual financial statements by political parties and constituency associations; and requires audited statements of campaign period income and expenses by political parties, constituency associations, candidates, and leadership contestants. The commission also studies and recommends changes in the indemnity and allowances of the members of the Assembly and submits an annual report to the Speaker of the Assembly.

Chairman, Donald C. MacDonald

Exec. Director, Gordon H. Kushner
Secretary and Legal Counsel, Anna Ker
Registrar, Edward W. Allen
Compliance Officers, Daphne E. Check
Administrative Assistant to Chairman/Office
    Manager, Donna Aceto
Communications Officer, Jean Ouellet

Office of the Premier

Queen's Park, Toronto, M7A 1A1

Premier, The Hon. David Peterson
Principal Secretary to the Premier,
    Vince Borg
Exec. Director, Gordon Ashworth
Director of Press Office and Press Secretary,
    Guy Côté

Ontario Office for Disabled Persons

700 Bay St., 3rd Flr., Toronto, M5G 1Z6

The Ontario Office for Disabled Persons was established in 1978 to act as a liaison between the Government of Ontario and the disabled community.

In this role the Office promotes an awareness of government programs and ensures that the needs of disabled persons are being met through a responsible policy process. The Office has three major roles: to act as a central information source for policies, programs, and services for disabled persons; to identify and promote public awareness of disabled persons, programs, and needs; and to develop, in conjunction with other ministries, policies responding to the needs of the disabled community.

Programs of the Office include the Premier's Awards for Accessibility and the Minister's Award, which encourage barrier-free design in Ontario buildings and environments. The Community Action Awards honour outstanding achievements of disabled Ontarians and persons involved with the disabled community. The Access Fund provides grants to community-based facilites to increase physical accessibility for disabled persons and senior citizens. The Community Action Fund assists groups in promoting equality and full participation of disabled Ontarians.

Other projects carried out by the Office's staff include the publication of the "Guide to Ontario Government Programs and Services for Disabled Persons", the "Guide for Disabled Drivers in Ontario", the "Statistical Profile of Disabled persons in Ontario" and "Courier", the Office's quarterly newsletter.

Minister responsible, The Hon. Remo Mancini

Ontario Advisory Council for Disabled Persons

700 Bay St., Ste. 203, Toronto, M5G 1Z6
General Inquiry: (416) 965-9537

The Ontario Advisory Council for Disabled Persons was established on February 5, 1975 by Order-in-Council. The Council consists of a chairman, three vice-chairmen, and 13 members who are drawn from across the province. Over half of the members are physically handicapped and all possess experience with agencies or organizations that work for and with people with disabilities.

The mandate of the Council is generally to advise the Minister responsible for Disabled Persons on matters pertaining to disabled persons in our society. The Council seeks to:
a) identify and study issues of concern to physically handicapped persons and, on the basis of the knowledge and experience of Council Members, to recommend action where appropriate;
b) encourage residents of Ontario to express their views on matters relating to the physically handicapped;
c) promote opportunities for self-help for the physically handicapped in the context of family and community;
d) review programs and policies affecting physically handicapped persons;
e) advise the Minister responsible for Disabled Persons on a regular basis of progress in the Council's work; and
f) submit to the Minister responsible for Disabled Persons an annual report outlining the Council's activities and achievements.

Chairman, Ron McInnes
Exec. Officer, Mary Tate

Office for Senior Citizens' Affairs

76 College St., 6th Flr., Toronto, M7A 1N3
(416) 965-5106

The Office of Senior Citizens' Affairs, established in 1985 to provide policy support to the Minister for Senior Citizens' Affairs, has two primary roles: policy development and information services. Although the office does not administer any legislation, it is responsible for developing an aggregate policy framework for seniors' services and for ensuring co-ordination of policies affecting the elderly. It has specific responsibilities for selected initiatives in the white paper *A New Agenda* on health and social services.

The office provides information to senior citizens through an information line. The office also publishes the "Guide for Senior Citizens" (in English and French) and the "Directory of Accomodation for Seniors in Ontario"; promotes research support for eligible projects; offers financial support to the Crane Memorial Library on geriatric and gerontological literature; and maintains links with a wide variety of seniors' organizations and professional groups in the private/voluntary sector.

Minister responsible for Senior
    Citizens' Affairs, The Hon. Mavis Wilson
Special Advisor to the Minister, Glen Heagle
Policy Development Manager, Dorothy Singer

Strategic Planning Manager, Bob Youtz
Finance and Administration Manager,
  Anna-Maria Adamiw
Communications and Information Manager,
  Suzanne Beaubien
Co-ordinator of Information Services,
  Beverley J. Nickoloff

Ontario Advisory Council on Senior Citizens

700 Bay St., Ste. 203, Toronto, M5G 1Z6
General Inquiry: (416) 965-2324

The Ontario Advisory Council on Senior Citizens was established by an Order-in-Council of the Government of Ontario in April 1974. Its mandate calls for the promotion and development of opportunities for self-help for the aged, and the review of current policies which have a bearing on aging and the economy. The Council reports to the government through the Minister for Senior Citizens' Affairs.

The 16-member body is composed of men and women from various age groups, professions, lifestyles, interests and geographic locations across Ontario.

While the Council meets at regular intervals and all recommendations are discussed and passed by the general membership, much of the work is done in committees and task groups. The Council has no funding power nor is it involved in grant distribution. Its primary function is to relay to the Government of Ontario the opinions and suggestions made by senior citizen organizations, community agencies, associations, and individuals concerned with the aged in this province. The Council also receives input from government ministries and there is a mutual consultation process.

Chairman, Mrs. Ivy St. Lawrence
Exec. Officer, Mary Tate

Offices of the Official Opposition

Main Parliament Bldgs., Queen's Park
Toronto, M7A 1A2
Leader of the Official Opposition, Bob Rae
Principal Secretary, Robin Sears
Public Liaison Asst., Richard McLellan
Opposition House Leader, Dave Cooke
Caucus Whip, David Reville

Offices of the Progressive Conservative Party

Legislative Bldg., Rm. 116
Queen's Park, Toronto, M7A 1A2
*Leader of the Ontario Progressive
  Conservative Party,* Andrew S. Brandt
Principal Secretary, Peter Clute
P.C. House Leader, Michael D. Harris

Whip, Ernie Eves
Research Director, David Lindsay
Communications Director, Fred Biro

Ontario Legislative Library

Legislative Bldg., Toronto, M7A 1A2
General Inquiries: (416) 965-4545

The goal of the Legislative Library is to provide information, reference and research services to the Members of the Legislative Assembly. It strives to achieve this goal by selecting, acquiring, cataloguing, and servicing the books, periodicals, newspapers, government publications, reports, microforms, and other materials in order to enable MPPs to carry out their legislative responsibilities in the most efficient manner. The Library also provides research services to MPPs as well as a press clipping service and is responsible for the compiling and editing of monthly and annual catalogues of Ontario government publications.

Exec. Director, R. Brian Land

Office of the Ombudsman

125 Queen's Park, Toronto, M5S 2C7
General Inquiry: (416) 586-3300
Toll-free: 1-800-263-1830
French Language Service: 1-800-387-2620

The Office of the Ontario Ombudsman was established in 1975. The Ombudsman, appointed by the Lieutenant-Governor in Council on the address of the Legislative Assembly, is an officer of the Legislature. His function, with specified exceptions, is to investigate any decision, recommendation, act or omission made in the course of the administration of a governmental organization of Ontario.

Complaints to the Ombudsman are to be made in writing; however, if the complainant is unable to do so, he or she may telephone or visit his office.

The Ombudsman is afforded broad powers of investigation and access to information.

After investigation, should the Ombudsman be of the opinion that the complaint submitted to him is a valid one, he reports his opinion and his reasons therefor to the appropriate governmental organization, and may make such recommendations as he thinks fit. A copy of the report is also submitted to the minister concerned and, if necessary, to the Premier and the Legislative Assembly.

The Ombudsman must report at least annually upon the affairs of his office to the Speaker of the Assembly, who lays the report before the Assembly.

Ombudsman, Dr. Daniel Hill

Exec. Director, Eleanor Meslin
Gen. Counsel, Michael Zacks
Director of Investigations, Gail Morrison
Controller, Allan Mills
Communications and Publications
Director, Milan Then
Community Relations Unit
Co-ordinator, Karen Wheeler-McSweeney
Administration Manager, Sharon Chambers
Personnel Officer, Joan Harrison
Regional Services Manager, David Sora

REGIONAL OFFICES:
Kenora:
223-1st St. S., P9N 1C2
District Officer, Harry Shankowsky
London:
London Urban Resource Centre
388 Dundas St., 2nd Flr., N6B 1V7
District Officer, Jackie Yuen
North Bay:
Box 508, P1B 8J1
District Officer, Marie Marchand
Ottawa:
151 Slater St., Ste. 702, K1P 5H3
District Officer, Klaus Bylsma
Sault Ste. Marie:
500 Bay St., P6A 1X5
District Officer, Johanna Bischoping
Thunder Bay:
213 Red River Rd., P7B 1A5
District Manager, Inez Knudson
Timmins:
32 Balsam St. S., Ste. 30, P4N 2C6
District Officer, Gilbert Cheechoo
Windsor:
United Way Bldg., Unit B
1695 University Ave. W., N9B 1C3
District Officer, Pamela Young

MINISTRY OF AGRICULTURE AND FOOD

801 Bay St., Toronto, M7A 1A3
(unless otherwise indicated)
General Inquiries: (416) 965-1421
Fax: (416) 965-8370; Telex: 06-22546

MINISTER'S OFFICE
801 Bay St., 11th Flr., Toronto, M7A 1A3
Minister, The Hon. Jack Riddell

DEPUTY MINISTER'S OFFICE
801 Bay St., 11th Flr., Toronto, M7A 1A3
Dep. Minister, Dr. Clayton M. Switzer
Communications Branch
Director, Lee Allison
Planning and Publications
Manager, Deborah Etsten
Media and Editorial Services
Manager, Nigel Atkin
Legal Services Director, Carl Dombek

Economics and Policy Co-ordination
Director, Bob Seguin
Media Relations Officer, Charles Coon
Guelph Development Project
Director, Bob Kalbfleisch
French Language Services
Co-ordinator, Rodrigue Hurtubise

Finance and Administration
Asst. Dep. Minister, Elizabeth McLaren
Projects Co-ordinator, Laura Jamieson
Audit Services Branch
Director, R. Stroeter
Human Resources Branch
Director, Sharyn Carlson
Financial and Support Services Branch
Director, Michael Keith
Freedom of Information and Library Services
Manager, Mindy Ginsler
Freedom of Information
Program Officer, Alma Beard

FOODLAND PRESERVATION AND FINANCIAL PROGRAMS
Exec. Director, Henry Ediger
Foodland Preservation Branch
Director, Donald Dunn
Crop Insurance and Stabilization
Director and Gen. Manager, Keith Pinder
Farm Assistance Programs Branch
Director and Livestock Commissioner,
Norm MacLeod
Management Systems Branch
Director, John Galloway

Marketing and Standards
Asst. Dep. Minister, Dr. George H. Collin
MARKETING DIVISION
Exec. Director, Russell Duckworth
Farm Products Marketing Branch
Director, Kenneth W. Knox
Market Development Branch
Director, Grahame Richards
Food Processing Branch
Director, Brian Slemko
QUALITY AND STANDARDS DIVISION
Exec. Director, Vacant
Livestock Inspection Branch
Director, Dr. John Henry
Dairy Inspection Branch
Director, Dr. J. Ashman
Fruit and Vegetable Inspection Branch
Director, James H. Wheeler

Technology and Field Services
Asst. Dep. Minister, Dr. J.C. Rennie
EDUCATION AND RESEARCH DIVISION
Guelph Agriculture Ctr.
Box 1030, Guelph, N1H 6N1
Exec. Director, Dr. Robert McLaughlin
Rural Organizations and Services Branch
Director, Jack Hagarty
Horticultural Research Institute of Ontario
Vineland Station, L0R 2E0
Director, Dr. Frank C. Eady

Alfred College of Agriculture and Food Technology
Box 580, Alfred, K0B 1A0
Principal, M. Paulhus

Centralia College of Agricultural Technology
Huron Park, N0M 1Y0
Principal, William Allen

Kemptville College of Agricultural Technology
Kemptville, K0G 1J0
Principal, John D. Curtis

New Liskeard College of Agricultural Technology
Box G, New Liskeard, P0J 1P0
Principal, David Beattie

Ridgetown College of Agricultural Technology
Ridgetown, N0P 2C0
Principal, Don Taylor

Ontario Agricultural Museum
144 Town Line, Box 38, Milton, L9T 2Y3
Gen. Manager, John Wiley

ADVISORY AND TECHNICAL SERVICES DIVISION
Guelph Agriculture Ctr.
Box 1030, Guelph, N1H 6N1
Exec. Director, David George
Animal Industry Branch
Guelph Agriculture Ctr., 1st Flr.
Box 1030, Guelph, N1H 6N1
Director, Dr. James Pettit
Plant Industry Branch
Director, Ralph Shaw
Veterinary Lab Services
Director, Dr. J.N. Henry
Agricultural Representatives Branch
Director, Norris Hoag
Soil and Water Management Branch
Director, Vernon Spencer
Guelph Agriculture Centre
Box 1030, Guelph, N1H 6N1
Agricultural Laboratory Services
(Pesticide Laboratory)
Bldg. 43, McGilvray St.
c/o University of Guelph, Guelph, N1G 2W1
Director, Dr. R. Frank

AGENCIES, BOARDS AND COMMISSIONS

MARKETING BOARDS

Marketing boards for agricultural products in Canada are created by a number of different pieces of legislation. National wheat and dairy products plans flow from the *Canadian Wheat Board Act* and the *Canadian Dairy Commission Act* respectively. Egg and poultry boards derive their authority from the *Farm Products Marketing Agencies Act*. As well, many have their own provincial statutes and are normally within the jurisdiction of an umbrella provincial agency. The individual boards are, however, non-governmental and made up largely of elected farmer representatives.

There is also a variety of types. The Economic Council of Canada's study on marketing boards identified five: promotional and developmental boards with little power; selling-desk boards that handle marketing but do not set prices; boards that negotiate prices; boards that set prices; and full-fledged boards that establish quotas. These last are known as supply-management marketing boards. Currently, there are more than 100 active boards in Canada.

ONTARIO FARM PRODUCTS MARKETING COMMISSION
33 Yonge St., Ste. 800, Toronto, M7A 1A6

The Ontario Farm Products Marketing Commission was established in January 1988 under the *Ministry of Agriculture and Food Act*. This major amendment to the legislation brought together into one body the former Farm Products Marketing Board and the Milk Commission of Ontario.

The Commission's responsibilities include supervising existing marketing boards established under the *Farm Products Marketing Act*, assisting in the development of new marketing plans as requested by producers, co-operating with various groups involved in the marketing of the designated commodities, and licensing processors and dealers of some regulated commodities.

The Commission's responsibilities also include supervision of the Ontario Milk Marketing Plan and the Ontario Cream Marketing Plan, developing and formulating dairy policy for consideration by the minister and co-operating with the Canadian Dairy Commission or any other agency of Canada or the provinces on dairy matters.

The Commission is also responsible for the administration of the fund for milk and cream producers under the *Farm Products Payments Act*.

Commission members are appointed by the Lieutenant-Governor in Council. Currently, there are 14 members.

Chairman, Kenneth W. Knox

ONTARIO GRAIN CORN COUNCIL
Co-operators Bldg., Ste. 303A
130 MacDonell St., Guelph, N1H 2Z6
General Inquiries: (519) 837-2053

The Ontario Grain Corn Council was established by Order-in-Council on Dec. 21, 1971.

The 15 members of the Council are appointed by the Minister of Agriculture and Food and represent producers, elevator operators, the feed trade, distillers, processors, and exporters. The objectives of the Council are to work with all segments of the industry to promote sales at the national and international levels and to support and initiate new uses and value-added products. The Council acts as a clearing-house for information on quality, quantity, and source, but does not merchandise corn.

Chairman, H.A. Krech
St. Lawrence Starch Co.
Box 1050, Port Credit, L5G 1G8
Sec.-Treasurer, W.D. Taylor

Agricultural Licensing and Registration Review Board
801 Bay St., Toronto, M7A 2B2

Chairman, Jamie A. McQuarrie, Q.C.

Agricultural Rehabilitation and Development Directorate (ARDA)
Guelph Agriculture Ctr.
Box 1030, Guelph, N1H 6N1

ARDA Ontario began in 1962 as a federal-provincial initiative to remove low-capability land from agricultural production and to expand off-farm income opportunities in Ontario. The initial Agreement, which terminated in 1965, placed its program emphasis on improving the viability of farm units through farm consolidation, development of community pastures, and the upgrading of agricultural land by soil and water conservation.

ARDA II (1965-70) added to this endeavour programs for outlet drainage and field enlargement in a continued drive to upgrade farm productivity and income. A new objective, that of broadening employment opportunities for rural people, was added at this time with parks and tourism projects.

In the next five-year period, ARDA III (1970-75), under the auspices of the federal Department of Regional Economic Expansion, continued the emphasis on diversifying the rural employment base and expanding farm units with programs geared to farm consolidation, parks development, and industrial incentives.

The final Agreement, ARDA IV (1975-79), continued to put priority on job-creating programs and improving farm productivity through drainage projects. The Agreement was not renewed after March 31, 1979.

To summarize its major achievements in Ontario, ARDA has:
- brought about the maintenance and cultivation of some 17,000 hectares of farm land;
- assisted over 2,000 farmers to establish viable farming enterprises;
- upgraded productivity of farm lands; and
- created an estimated 1,000 direct jobs and 375 part-time jobs through rural development projects since 1970.

Chairman, Vernon Spencer

Agricultural Research Institute of Ontario
801 Bay St., 2nd Flr., Toronto, M7A 1A3

Under the *Agricultural Research Institute of Ontario Act* (1962), the Institute was formed to report to the Minister of Agriculture and Food on ministry-funded research and to fulfil the following duties and responsibilities:
- to review research programs concerning agriculture, veterinary medicine, and consumer studies;
- to select and recommend areas of research for the betterment of agriculture, veterinary medicine, and consumer studies;

- to stimulate interest in research as a means of developing a high degree of efficiency in the production and marketing of agricultural products in Ontario.

The ARIO is composed of not more than 15 producers and agri-business representatives, appointed by the Lieutenant-Governor in Council. The director of research and the comptroller are employees of the Ministry of Agriculture and Food.

Chairman, Dr. Janice Aluin
Director of Research, Dr. J.C. Rennie
Comptroller, M. Toivonen

Co-operative Loans Board of Ontario
801 Bay St., Toronto, M7A 2B2

The Co-operative Loans Board does not make any new loans. At this time, there are only a small number of loans outstanding (fewer than 10). As a result, the board is inactive except for the collection of payments.

Chairman, Henry Ediger

Crop Insurance Arbitration Board
801 Bay St., Toronto, M7A 1B7

The Ontario Crop Insurance Arbitration Board is established pursuant to the *Crop Insurance Act*, R.S.O. 1980, Chapter 104, and Regulations pursuant thereto. The Board has exclusive jurisdiction to hear and determine all disputes between the Crop Insurance Commission and an insured person arising out of the adjustment of a loss under a contract of insurance.

The Board membership consists, at present, of a chairman and three members appointed by the Lieutenant-Governor in Council.

Chairman, Susan Mather

Crop Insurance Commission of Ontario
801 Bay St., 5th Flr., Toronto, M7A 2B2

The Commission, charged with the administration of the *Crop Insurance Act,* makes available to farmers crop insurance plans to insure about four dozen commercially grown crops against natural disaster.

The Commission's activities include the functions of selling, underwriting, claims adjustment, and accounting. It also conducts surveys and research programs relating to crop insurance to obtain statistics.

Chairman, Gordon Hill

Farm Income Stabilization Commission of Ontario
801 Bay St., Toronto, M7A 2B2

The Commission administers farm income stabilization plans to provide financial assistance during times of low prices for the following crops: oats, canola, potatoes, soybeans, barley, winter wheat, and corn. The plans guarantee producers a price equal to 95 per cent of the market price over the previous five years, adjusted for cash costs.

The Commission also conducts surveys and research relating to farm income stabilization to obtain statistics for Commission purposes.

Chairman, Keith Pinder

Farm Products Appeal Tribunal
Co-operators Bldg., Ste. 303A
130 MacDonell St., Guelph, N1H 2Z6

The Farm Products Appeal Tribunal came into operation Feb. 1, 1979. Constituted under section 10 of the *Ministry of Agriculture and Food Act,* as amended, it provides an independent, accessible avenue of appeal in matters relating to the *Farm Products Marketing Act* and the *Milk Act.* The Tribunal also serves as a licence review board under the *Milk Act,* the *Farm Products Marketing Act,* the *Edible Oil Products Act,* and the *Oleo Margarine Act.* It has additional authority to review the conduct of commodity board members under the *Commodity Board Members Act.*

Under farm products marketing legislation, extensive regulatory powers are conferred on local producer boards by the Farm Products Marketing Commission of Ontario. The Tribunal was established to make an impartial appeal mechanism available to any person who feels that a decision, direction, policy, or order of the Commission, a producer board, or a director appointed under the *Milk Act* is unfair. Regulations made by producer marketing boards under the *Farm Products Marketing Act* or the *Milk Act* may also be appealed.

Chairman, Dr. K.A. McEwen
Secretary, Miss Dagny Ingolfsrud

Farm Tax Rebate Appeal Board
c/o Farm Assistance Programs Branch
801 Bay St., 10th Flr., Toronto, M7A 2B2

The Farm Tax Rebate Appeal Board is a seven-member tribunal constituted under Order-in-Council 406/83 which came into force on Nov. 10, 1983.

The Board is responsible for hearing appeals of decisions of the Farm Tax Rebate Program Administration. This program rebates 100 per cent of the tax levied on farm land and eligible outbuildings. Appeals may be heard on the eligibility of the property or the applicant, or on the issue of whether an application has been submitted in the prescribed manner. Over 170,000 eligible properties have rebates paid on them each year, for an annual disbursement of over $150 million.

Chairman, Debbie Steele

Ontario Crop Introduction and Expansion Program
Box 587, Simcoe, N3Y 4N5

The Crop Introduction and Expansion Program provides financial assistance to groups, corporations, institutions, and organizations to encourage testing, processing, and marketing of crops and production technologies with commercial potential in Ontario. This five-year Program was begun in 1985.

The Program provides funding up to two-thirds of the total eligible cost of a project to a maximum of $100,000 per year.

Exec. Secretary, A. Loughton

Ontario Drainage Tribunal
801 Bay St., Toronto, M7A 2B2

The Ontario Drainage Tribunal was established in 1977 pursuant to the *Drainage Act.* The Ontario Drainage Tribunal functions as a review agency with respect to drainage undertakings authorized by the Act. The Tribunal's panel consists of a minimum of three members and meetings are held in local municipalities across the province.

Chairman, Delbert A. O'Brien, Q.C.
Box 487, Pembroke, K8A 6X7

Ontario Family Farm Interest Rate Reduction (OFFIRR) Appeal Board
c/o Farm Assistance Programs Branch
801 Bay St., 10th Flr., Toronto, M7A 2B2

The OFFIRR Appeal Board is a nine-member tribunal constituted under Order-in-Council 1915/85 which came into force on Aug. 7, 1985.

The Board is responsible for hearing appeals of decisions of the administration of the Ontario Family Farm Interest Rate Reduction Program. This program, originally introduced as a one-year program in 1985, was extended for a further three years in 1986. It pays grants to farmers to cover interest paid in excess of 8 per cent on eligible farm debt. Approximately 12,000 grants are paid each year for an annual disbursement of $50-60 million. Appeals may be heard on the eligibility of the applicant or the debt submitted.

Chairman, Martin Schneckenburger

Ontario Farm Machinery Board
801 Bay St., 2nd Flr., Toronto, M7A 2B2

The Ontario Farm Machinery Board was established by Order-in-Council 2843/77 on Oct. 12, 1977 and reports to the Minister of Agriculture and Food.

The purpose of this program is to encourage the resolution of problems encountered by farmers and the farm machinery industry arising out of the sale of farm machinery, its repair, maintenance, and use.

The Board may:
a) investigate any complaint referred to it respecting farm machinery;
b) hold meetings and conduct hearings for the purpose of resolving new farm machinery problems and disputes involving farmers and manufacturers, certified distributors, and certified dealers of farm machinery;
c) administer a voluntary code of practice and the certification of distributors and retail dealers of farm machinery; and
d) provide education regarding farm machinery purchase, operation, maintenance, and safety.

Chairman, W. Benson
Sec.-Manager, J. Kessler

Ontario Food Terminal Board
165 The Queensway, Toronto, M8Y 1H8

The Ontario Food Terminal Board enforces all Regulations laid down under the *Ontario Food Terminal Act.* The Board is comprised of seven persons appointed by the Lieutenant-Governor in Council.

The Ontario Food Terminal is the largest market, in volume, of wholesale fresh fruit and produce in Canada. It plays a major role in the orderly marketing of fruits and vegetables, as price trends in Toronto are a major determining factor of prices in other parts of Ontario and Canada.

Chairman, A. Collins
Gen. Manager, C.E. Carsley

Ontario Stock Yards Board
590 Keele St., Toronto, M6N 3E3

The Stock Yards Board owns the Ontario Stock Yards, Canada's largest livestock market. The stock yard operation is governed by Regulations under the *Livestock and Livestock Products Act* (Canada). The yard provides facilities for the trading of all types of livestock. Since the board is neither buyer nor seller, it acts as the independent third party in all transactions.

Agencies operating on the market are licensed by the Stock Yards Board. The Livestock Exchange, an official body of licensed sales agencies and individuals, is properly constituted to conduct buying and selling in an ethical manner and to take action, if required, to assure the financial security of those doing business.

Chairman, Ross Beattie
R.R. 4, Stayner, L0M 1S0
Gen. Manager, D. McDonell

Wolf Damage Assessment Board
c/o Farm Assistance Programs Branch
801 Bay St., 10th Flr., Toronto, M7A 2B2

The Wolf Damage Assessment Board was established in 1975 by authority of the *Dog Licensing and Live Stock and Poultry Protection Act.*

Municipalities apply to this Board for reimbursement of compensation they have paid to livestock owners for losses or damages caused by wolves. If the livestock commissioner (who administers the Act) feels there is insufficient evidence to conclude that wolves were responsible for any claim, he can refer the application to the Wolf Damage Assessment Board, which then holds a hearing and makes a binding decision.

Board membership consists of a chairman and two members. Board members are appointed by the Lieutenant-Governor in Council.

Chairman, Vacant

MINISTRY OF THE ATTORNEY GENERAL
18 King St. E., Toronto, M5C 1C5
(except where otherwise indicated)
General Inquiries: (416) 965-2831

MINISTER'S OFFICE
Attorney General, The Hon. Ian G. Scott, Q.C.

DEPUTY ATTORNEY GENERAL'S OFFICE
Dep. Attorney General, Richard Chaloner, Q.C.
Communications Branch
Director, Bob Wyatt
French Language Services
Co-ordinator, Dorais Therese
10 King St. E., 8th Flr., Toronto, M5C 1C3
LEGISLATIVE COUNSEL
Main Parliament Bldg., Queen's Park
Toronto, M7A 1A2
Sr. Legislative Counsel, Donald Revell
Registrar of Regulations, Russell Yurkow
POLICY DEVELOPMENT DIVISION
Director, J. Douglas Ewart

Criminal Law
A/Asst. Dep. Attorney General,
Douglas C. Hunt
Director of Crown Attorneys, Michael E. Martin
Dep. Director of Crown Attorneys,
Lloyd M. Budzinski
Sr. Crown Counsel, H. Morton
Crown Law Office, Criminal
A/Director, E. Then, Q.C.

Civil Law
Asst. Dep. Attorney General,
John M. Johnson, Q.C.
Crown Law Office, Civil
Director, T.C. Marshall, Q.C.
Constitutional Law
Director, J. Cavarzan, Q.C.
Legal Services Branches
Exec. Co-ordinator, Brock Grant, Q.C.

OFFICIAL GUARDIAN'S BRANCH
180 Dundas St. W., 6th Flr., Toronto, M5G 1Z8
Official Guardian, Willson A. McTavish
Estates and Maintenance
Estates Counsel, G.R. Hodgson
Child Representation Program
Director, Vacant

PUBLIC TRUSTEE GENERAL
ADMINISTRATION
145 Queen St. W., Toronto, M5H 2N8
Public Trustee, Hugh S.D. Paisley
Legal Services Director, G.K. McClure

PROGRAMS AND ADMINISTRATION
18 King St. E., Toronto, M5C 1C5
Gen. Manager, Julia Bass

Administrative Services
Manager, G.R. Cowie
Computer and Telecommunications
Services Branch
36 Toronto St., 6th Flr., Toronto, M5C 2C5
Director, Mrs. Maria Moore
Office of the Accountant of the
Supreme Court of Ontario
123 Edward St., Ste. 610, Toronto, M5G 1E3
Accountant, E.J. McGann
Finance Management and Program
Planning Branch
Director, Oliver Carroll
Human Resources Management
Director, P.W. Clendinneng
Audit Services Branch
101 Bloor St. W., 4th Flr., Toronto, M5S 1P7
Director, Anton M. Odeh

Courts Administration

Asst. Dep. Attorney General and Director of
Courts Administration, D.R. Peebles
Courts Administration
Exec. Director, Nestor Yurchuk
Supreme District Court Services Branch
18 King St. E., Mezz., Toronto, M5C 1C5
Director, David G. Henderson
Court Reporting Manager, T. Moran
Provincial Court Services Branch
18 King St. E., Mezz., Toronto, M5C 1C5
Director, Matt Veskimets
Small Claims Court Services Branch
18 King St. E., Mezz., Toronto, M5C 1C3
Director, Peter Jackson

AGENCIES, BOARDS, COMMISSIONS AND TRIBUNALS

Assessment Review Board
80 Bloor St. W., Ste. 705, Toronto, M5S 1L9
General Inquiry: (416) 965-7574

The Assessment Review Board was established under *The Assessment Act, 1968-69* and continues the *The Assessment Review Court Act, 1972*, as amended. This Board is an administrative tribunal which draws its jurisdiction from *The Assessment Act, The Municipal Act,* and *The City of Ottawa Act, 1962*. The responsibility of the Board is to hear and determine as soon as may be practicable:

- complaints of errors in or omissions from real property assessment and school support, which are the basis of municipal taxation in Ontario at the lowest cost to the taxpayer;
- appeals arising from the refusal of assessment commissioners to amend the list showing school support for school-board taxation;
- the apportionment of municipal taxes or rates applicable to individual parcels where land has been assessed in block;
- when authorized by a municipal by-law (or by way of an appeal from the decision of a municipal council), applications for the cancellation, reduction, or refund of municipal taxes and when authorized by a municipal council (or by way of an appeal from the decision of a municipal council), applications for an increase in municipal taxes where gross or manifest errors have been made in the collector's roll;
- when authorized by a municipal by-law, appeals from special redevelopment charges.

Chairman, Z.J.C. Prattas, LL.M.
Vice-Chairman, Zita D. Bury
Provincial Registrar, T.G. Murphy
Reg. Registrar-at-large, James Eadie
REGIONAL OFFICES:
Eastern Area
2378 Holly Lane, Rm. 208, Ottawa, K1V 7P1
Regional Registrar, J.E. Crawford
Metro Toronto North
Sheppard Ctr., Ste. 605
2 Sheppard Ave. E., North York, M2N 5Y7
Regional Registrar, Reg Michor
Metro Toronto South
80 Bloor St. W., Ste. 701, Toronto, M5S 1L9
Regional Registrar, Mohamed S. Manji
Central, Georgian Bay and Lake Huron Area
390 Davis Dr., Newmarket, L3Y 2R3
Regional Registrar, P.B. Pudge
Lake Ontario Office
277 George St. N., Peterborough, K9J 3G9
Regional Registrar, Mrs. Chris Harris
Grand River/Niagara
678 Main St. E., Hamilton, L8M 1K2
Regional Registrar, E.J. Kingma
Southwestern Area
426-3rd St., 1st Flr., London, N5W 4W6
Regional Registrar, M. Gamble
Northeastern Area
Northgate Sq., North Bay, P1B 2H3
Regional Registrar, James Boyd
Northwestern Branch Office
85 Great Northern Rd.
Sault Ste Marie, P6B 4Y8
Regional Registrar, Mrs. C. Archambault

Board of Negotiation
439 University Ave., Ste. 1800
Toronto, M5G 1Y8

The Board of Negotiation was created by the provisions of the *Expropriation Act, 1968-69*. It provides an informal tribunal which, without prejudice to any subsequent arbitration procedures, may negotiate in a summary and informal manner the settlement of a compensation in expropriation cases.

The Board, upon receiving a written request from either party, arranges meetings between the expropriated party and the expropriating authority. A formal notice is issued to both parties, advising them of the time and place of the meeting, which can be held anywhere throughout the province without cost to either party. A unique provision of the Act provides that the Board shall view the property in question.

An individual may appear on his own behalf to present his compensation claim. If no agreement follows these informal negotiations, the parties are free to proceed to arbitration to the Ontario Municipal Board.

Chairman, G.W. Swayze
Office Administrator, Miss Mary Begey

Board of Valuation
439 University Ave., Ste. 1800
Toronto, M5G 1Y8

Where a power exercised under the *Power Corporation Act* does not constitute an expropriation or injurious affection, compensation shall be paid to the real property owner for all damage, and when no agreement is arrived at as to the amount of compensation to be paid to the owner, the Board of Valuation shall determine compensation for such property damage. If either the owner or the power corporation is dissatisfied with the amount fixed, appeals may be made to the Ontario Municipal Board.

Chairman, Vacant
Office Administrator, Miss Mary Begey

Criminal Injuries Compensation Board
439 University Ave., 17th Flr.
Toronto, M5G 1Y8

The Board decides whether applicants for compensation are eligible under the legislation and, if so, on the amount to be awarded. Compensation is for personal injury only, when a person is injured or killed in Ontario as a result of a crime of violence. The crime of violence must be an offence under the *Criminal Code* (Canada) but any offence involving a motor vehicle is excluded unless the vehicle was used as a weapon of assault. Compensation may also be awarded when a person is injured while lawfully arresting or attempting to arrest someone for an offence against another person; when a person is injured while assisting a peace officer in the performance of his duties; or when a person is injured while preventing or attempting to prevent an offence against another person.

The Board is appointed by the Lieutenant-Governor in Council and has a full-time chairman and 12 part-time members.

Chairman, Wendy L. Calder
CAO, V.P. Giuffre
Chief of Investigation, J.H. Sheard
Compensation Claims
Manager, F.G. Suter
Chief Clerk, Ms. L. Smith

Drinking/Driving Countermeasures
101 Bloor St. W., Toronto, M5S 1P7

The Drinking/Driving Countermeasures Office was created to develop and implement province-wide strategies designed to reduce deaths and injuries due to impaired driving.

The Office has fostered the establishment and growth of over 70 community-based groups and associations devoted to the prevention of drinking and driving, and has produced a variety of educational materials, including a film, posters, pamphlets, and associated items designed to increase public awareness of the problem.

Drinking/Driving Countermeasures sponsors and conducts research on drinking drivers and advises the Attorney General of Ontario on this issue.

A/Director, Gerry Conroy

Metropolitan Toronto Forensic Service (METFORS)
1001 Queen St. W., Toronto, M6J 1H4

The Metropolitan Toronto Forensic Service (METFORS) was established by Order-in-Council on May 15, 1977. It is responsible to the Ministry of the Attorney General and is operated by the Clarke Institute of Psychiatry.

This service within the Division of Forensic Psychiatry at the University of Toronto provides clinical services primarily to the courts of metropolitan Toronto. It consists of: (1) a Brief Assessment Unit (B.A.U.) to provide rapid psychiatric assessments for those appearing in the courts who are identified as possibly having serious psychiatric and emotional problems. Such assessments assist the judges in determining the most appropriate manner in which to proceed; and (2) a 23-bed inpatient unit is available for those patients who require a more extensive psychiatric assessment. A small number of outpatient referrals are available to the courts.

Chairman, Douglas C. Hunt
Director, S.J. Hucker
Administrator, M.S. Phillips

Office of the Public Complaints Commissioner
157 Bloor St. W., Toronto, M5S 1P7

The Office of the Public Complaints Commissioner was established as a permanent agency with the proclamation of the *Metropolitan Police Force Complaints Project Act, 1981.*

The Office is totally separate from the police. Its civilian investigators receive, record, and investigate complaints concerning allegations of misconduct by police officers. The Office was created to monitor and review investigations done by the Metropolitan Police Force. Upon review, the Public Complaints Commissioner has the power to resolve complaints, recommend changes in police practices and procedures, and, if in the public interest, to order Board of Inquiry hearings.

A complaint can be made directly at the Office of the Public Complaints Commissioner, the police department's in-house Public Complaints Investigation Bureau, or any police station.

Commissioner, Clare E. Lewis
Director of Investigations, E.R. Singleton
Office Administrator, Mary Lasica
Boards of Inquiry Registrar, P. Bartley

Ontario Law Reform Commission
18 King St. E., 15th Flr., Toronto, M5C 1C5

The Ontario Law Reform Commission is a provincial statutory commission established in

1964. Under its founding statute, the function of the Commission is to inquire into and consider any matter relating to: reform of the law having regard to the statute law, the common law, and judicial decisions; the administration of justice; judicial and quasi-judicial procedures under any Act; or any subject referred to it by the Attorney General.

To carry out its mandate, the Commission institutes and directs legal research, and reports, with recommendations for remedial legislation, to the Attorney General of Ontario. Commission reports are available at the Ontario Government Book Store, 880 Bay St., Toronto, M7A 1N8.

Chairman, James R. Breithaupt, Q.C.
Vice-Chairman, H. Allan Leal, O.C., Q.C.
Counsel, Mel A. Springman
Admin. Officer, Anne McGarrigle

Ontario Municipal Board
180 Dundas St. W., Toronto, M5G 1E5
Information: (416) 598-2266

The Municipal Board, an independent administrative tribunal, was created in 1932 by the enactment of the Ontario Municipal Board Act. That Act repealed the Ontario Railway and Municipal Board Act and The Bureau of Municipal Affairs Act, and incorporated many of the provisions and powers of those Acts in the Board. Most of the powers bestowed upon it in 1932 have been retained by the Board to this date, although many other statutes have established jurisdiction or conferred authority on the Board, notably The Assessment Act, The Planning Act, The Municipal Act, and the Expropriation Act.

When the Board holds a hearing, it is governed by any applicable statute, but it is also subject to the rules of natural justice and the requirements of the Statutory Powers Procedure Act.

The administration of justice could be said to be divided between the judicial arm of government (the courts) and the executive arm, of which this Board is a branch. The courts operate under strict rules and interpret and follow statutes and precedents. Administrative boards, such as this one, administer what is sometimes called "discretionary justice" having a minimum of rules and a wide spectrum of discretion.

In matters of law, there is provision for appeal from decisions of the Board to the courts. In a limited number of matters dealt with by the Board, there is provision for appeal from the Board's decisions to cabinet by way of a petition to the Lieutenant-Governor in Council. The Board has authority under section 42 of the Ontario Municipal Board Act to review any of its decisions or orders.

Chairman, H.E. Stewart
Vice-Chairmen: D.S. Colbourne,
P.M. Brooks, Q.C., H.H. Lancaster, Q.C.,
Dorothy H. McRobb
CAO and Secretary of the Board,
James G. Malcolm
Asst. Secretary and Manager of
Administration, B. Cindy Alty

MINISTRY OF CITIZENSHIP
77 Bloor St. W., 6th Flr., Toronto, M7A 2R9

MINISTER'S OFFICE
Minister, The Hon. Gerry Phillips

DEPUTY MINISTER'S OFFICE
Dep. Minister, Maureen O'Neil
Citizenship Development Branch
Director, Clive Joakim
Native Community Branch
Director, Robert Dickson
Policy Services Branch
Director, Bunny Segal

AGENCIES, BOARDS AND COMMISSIONS

Ontario Advisory Council on Multiculturalism and Citizenship
10 St. Mary St., 2nd Flr., Toronto, M7A 2R9

The Advisory Council was first established in 1973 following a recommendation of the June 1972 Congress of Heritage Ontario. In October 1979, the mandate was broadened to include citizenship. The Council currently advises the government through the Minister of Citizenship.

The Council has a membership of up to 60 persons, representing a wide range of ethnocultural backgrounds, professions, and socio-economic levels from all regions of the province. The members and the full-time chairman are appointed by Orders-in-Council.

The Council is responsible for the following:
• responding to specific government requests for advice relating to policy formulation and program development and delivery;
• examining and commenting on the effectiveness in a multicultural society of the policies, programs, and service-delivery mechanisms of the ministries and agencies of the government of Ontario; and
• assisting in the promotion of the concept of a multicultural Ontario as set out in the government's multicultural policy with reference to equality, access and participation, cultural retention, and sharing.

President, Dr. Shiu Loon Kong
Exec. Co-ordinator, H.J. McErlean

Ontario Human Rights Commission
400 University Ave., 12th Flr.
Toronto, M7A 1T7

The Ontario Human Rights Commission administers the Ontario Human Rights Code. The Code prohibits: discrimination in employment, accommodation, contracts, goods, services and facilities, membership in trade unions, trade or occupational associations, and self-governing professions; and reprisal actions on the grounds of race, creed, colour, age, sexual orientation, marital status, nationality, ancestry, place of origin, ethnic origin, citizenship, record of offences (employment only), family status, handicap, and receipt of public assistance (accommodation only).

The Commission investigates and conciliates complaints of discrimination, and conducts a human rights public education program.

Chief Commissioner, Raj Anand
Commissioners: Elizabeth Kishkon,
Robert Paris, Shirley O'Connor,
John Cochrane, Catherine Frazee,
Jack Diamond, Reva Devins,
Louis Lenkinski, George Bancroft
Ontario Human Rights Branch
400 University Ave., 12th Flr.
Toronto, M7A 2R9
Exec. Director, Mike Gage

Race Relations Directorate
400 University Ave., 11th Flr., Toronto, M7A 1T7
Commissioner for Race Relations,
Dan McIntyre

MINISTRY OF COLLEGES AND UNIVERSITIES
101 Bloor St. W., 13th Flr., Toronto, M5S 1P7

MINISTER'S OFFICE
Minister, The Hon. Lyn McLeod

DEPUTY MINISTER'S OFFICE
101 Bloor St. W., 14th Flr., Toronto, M5S 1P7

Dep. Minister, Dr. Thomas A. Brzustowski

Asst. Dep. Minister, Colleges and

Student Support, Dr. Ralph Benson

Asst. Dep. Minister, Universities and

Research Support, Brian Goodman
Corporate Planning and Services
790 Bay St., 11th Flr., Toronto, M5G 1N8
Exec. Co-ordinator, David Lyon
Communications Branch
790 Bay St., 11th Flr., Toronto, M5G 1N8
Director, Vacant
Research Support and International Activities
790 Bay St., 11th Flr., Toronto, M5G 1N8
Director, Dr. Maria Cioni
University Relations
Mowat Blk., 9th Flr.
900 Bay St., Toronto, M7A 1L2
Director, R.L. Cummins
Student Awards
230 Park Ave., Thunder Bay, M7B 5L4
Director, Vacant
College Affairs
Mowat Blk., 10th Flr.
900 Bay St., Toronto, M7A 1L2
Director, Peter Wright
Private Vocational Schools
790 Bay St., 11th Flr., Toronto, M5G 1N8
Sup't, Carolyn Barrett

AGENCIES, BOARDS AND COMMISSIONS

College Relations Commission
111 Avenue Rd., Ste. 400, Toronto, M5R 3J8

The College Relations Commission was established in 1975 to oversee collective bargaining between the Ontario Council of Regents for CAATs (Colleges of Applied Arts and Technology) and the Ontario Public Service Employees Union, which represents both academic and support staff. The Commission monitors and assists in negotiations, supervises staff votes, and advises the Lieutenant-Governor in Council when a strike or lockout is jeopardizing student education.

Chairman, Katherine E. Swinton
CEO, R.E. Saunders
Information Services
A/Director, Sharon McElroy
Field Services Director, Dr. E.M. Aim

Francophone Affairs
Mowat Block, 9th Flr.
900 Bay St., Toronto, M7A 1L2

The *French Language Services Act, 1986* received Royal Assent on Nov. 18, 1986. It guarantees to all persons and corporate entities the right to communicate with the government and to receive services in French. The guarantee comes into effect three years after Royal Assent, and, therefore, all services to the public covered by the Act must be in place by Nov. 18, 1989.

In order to respect the letter and the spirit of the Act, the Ministry of Colleges and Universities established Francophone Affairs in April 1987. Its role is:

• to co-ordinate the implementation process of the *French Language Services Act, 1986* in support of the ministry's organization and programs;

• to provide policy, planning, and information services to support the planning and development of French-language post-secondary educational policies and programs at the program branch level and at the ministry level; and

• to ensure that the French-language services and programs fully and competently meet the ministry's priorities and needs.
Exec. Co-ordinator, Lionel Poirier

Ontario Council of Regents for Colleges of Applied Arts and Technology
790 Bay St., 10th Flr., Toronto, M5G 1N8

The Ontario Council of Regents is a provincial agency established under the *Ministry of Colleges and Universities Act*. The Council is responsible and accountable to the Minister of Colleges and Universities.

The Council's primary role is to provide informed policy advice for consideration by the minister that will promote and encourage the well-being and effectiveness of Ontario's system of colleges of applied arts and technology.

Medium- and long-term planning leadership, then, is the major role of the Council. It also performs other ad hoc responsibilities as assigned by the minister.

The Council also has executive authority to appoint governors to college boards. As such, the Council has a responsibility to provide support to the Ministry of Colleges and Universities and the Assn. of Colleges of Applied Arts and Technology of Ontario in the area of orientation and development of individual boards.

Currently, the Council has responsibility for collective bargaining with college support staff and faculty (Ontario Public Service Employees Union) and for making recommendations to the minister regarding salaries for college administrative staff. These responsibilities are pending a review by the minister in the wake of the report of the Colleges Collective Bargaining Commission.

At present, the Council of Regents consists of 16 members plus the chairperson. Members are appointed by Order-in-Council and provide balanced representation with respect to region, sex, language, occupation, and cultural background. The Council's work is assisted by a permanent secretariat and research staff, supplemented by secondments from the college system.

Chairman, Dr. Charles Pascal

Ontario Council on University Affairs

700 Bay St., 7th Flr., Toronto, M5G 1Z6

The Ontario Council on University Affairs (OCUA) was established by Order-in-Council in 1974 and is an advisory body to the Minister of Colleges and Universities and the Lieutenant-Governor in Council. The Council may advise on any matters pertaining to the university system but regularly advises on the funding required, the allocation of funds, graduate and professional program approval, and the Ontario Graduate Scholarship Funding. In many ways, OCUA acts as a buffer between government and the 15 provincially-assisted universities, Ryerson Polytechnical Institute, The Ontario College of Art, The Ontario Institute for Studies in Education, and the Bar Admission Course (Law Society of Upper Canada).

The Council is composed of a full-time chairman and 19 members who serve on a part-time basis. A small research staff supports the work of the Council.

Chairman, Dr. H. Vivian Nelles
Research and Policy Analysis
Manager, P. Stenton
Research Officer, Diana Royce

MINISTRY OF COMMUNITY AND SOCIAL SERVICES

Hepburn Blk., 80 Grosvenor St.
Toronto, M7A 1E9
(unless otherwise indicated)
General Inquiries: (416) 965-7825

MINISTER'S OFFICE
Minister, The Hon. John Sweeney

DEPUTY MINISTER'S OFFICE
Dep. Minister, Peter Barnes
Communications and Marketing Branch
Director, Robert L. Gregson
Legal Services Branch
Director, Andrea Walker
STRATEGIC PLANNING
/INTERGOVERNMENTAL RELATIONS
Exec. Director, Colin Evans

Community Services Division
Asst. Dep. Minister, Michael Mendleson
Children's Services Director, Sandra Scarth
Elderly Services A/Director, Sandy Lang
Services for the Disabled
A/Director, Jon Kelly

Family Services and Income Maintenance Division
Asst. Dep. Minister, Michele Noble
Income Maintenance Director, Bob Cooke
Child Care Director, Kay Eastham
Family Support Director, Vicki Bales

Finance and Administration Division
Asst. Dep. Minister, John Burkus
Financial Planning and Corporate Analysis
Director, Barbara Stewart
Capital and Administrative Services
Director, Mike Basich
Financial Services Director, Jim Tighe
Human Resources Branch
Director, Timo Hytonen
Operations Evaluation and Audit
Director, Bob Glass

Information Systems and Applied Technology Division
Asst. Dep. Minister, Ola Berg
Strategic Systems Development Branch
Director, Vacant
Technology Support Branch
Director, Sam Marafioti
Program Technology Branch
Director, George Abrahamsohn

Operations Division
Asst. Dep. Minister, Randolph C. Norberg
Operational Co-ordination
Director, Joe McReynolds
French Language Services
Co-ordinator, Rejean Nadeau
CENTRAL REGIONAL OFFICES
2195 Yonge St., 10th Flr., Toronto, M7A 1G2
Reg. Director, Michael Ennis
Toronto Area Office
2195 Yonge St., 9th Flr., Toronto, M7A 1G1
Area Manager, Agnes Samler
Barrie Area Office
34 Simcoe St., Box 910, Barrie, L4M 1A1
Area Manager, L.E. Strang

Mississauga Area Office
1140 Burnhamthorpe Rd. W., Ste. 212
Mississauga, L5C 4E9
Area Manager, B. Whalen

SOUTHWEST REGIONAL OFFICES
195 Dufferin Ave., 5th Flr., London, N6A 1K7
Reg. Director, Murray Hamilton

Hamilton Area Office
119 King St. W., 6th Flr.
Box 2112, Hamilton, L8N 3Z9
Area Manager, Don Cornish

London Area Office
495 Richmond St., 6th Flr., London, N6A 5A9
Area Manager, F.J. Capitano

Waterloo Area Office
75 King St. S., 5th Flr., Waterloo, N2J 1P2
Area Manager, M. Stephenson

Windsor Area Office
250 Windsor Ave., Windsor, N9A 6V9
Area Manager, Shari Cunningham

SOUTHEAST REGIONAL OFFICES
336 Alfred St., Kingston, K7L 3S5
A/Reg. Director, Ernie Nelson

Peterborough Area Office
60 Hunter St. E., Peterborough, K9H 1G5
Area Manager, Fred Purificati

Kingston Area Office
1055 Princess St., Kingston, K7L 5T3
A/Area Manager, Dennis Ferenc

Ottawa Area Office
10 Rideau St., Ottawa, K1N 9J1
Area Manager, Pierre Lalonde

NORTH REGIONAL OFFICES
473 Queen St. E., Ste. 202
Sault Ste. Marie, P6A 1Z5
Reg. Director, John Rabeau

North Bay Area Office
222 McIntyre St. W., North Bay, P1B 2Y8
Area Manager, J.H. Pride

North Bay District Office
222 McIntyre St. W., North Bay, P1B 2Y8
A/Dist. Manager, Barney Owens

Timmins District Office
11 Elm St. N., Timmins, P4N 6A3
Dist. Manager, Denis Lozier

Sudbury Area Office
111 Larch St., 8th Flr., Sudbury, P3E 4T5
Area Manager, Richard Rivard

Sudbury District Office
111 Larch St., 8th Flr., Sudbury, P3E 4T5
Dist. Manager, Dan Lafranier

Sault Ste. Marie District Office
123 March St., Sault Ste. Marie, P6A 2Z5
Dist. Manager, David Zuccato

Thunder Bay Area Office
710 Victoria Ave., 3rd Flr.
Thunder Bay, P7C 5P7
Area Manager, Doug Hayman

Thunder Bay District Office
710 Victoria Ave., 3rd Flr.
Thunder Bay, P7C 5P7
Dist. Manager, Kie Delgaty

Kenora District Office
20 Main St., Kenora, P9N 1S7
A/Dist. Manager, Sue Braun

AGENCIES, BOARDS AND COMMISSIONS

Child and Family Services Review Board
700 Bay St., Rm. 212, Toronto, M5G 1Z6

The Child and Family Services Review Board is established under section 3 of the *Children's Residential Services Act*. The Board conducts hearings related to a director's decisions with regard to:
- licences to operate day nurseries (under the *Day Nurseries Act*);
- licences of private adoption agencies and approvals of adoption placements generally (under the *Child Welfare Act*);
- licences to operate children's residences or to provide more than one location (under the *Children's Residential Services Act*).

The Board is involved in reviewing two types of decisions of the respective directors: 1) decisions to impose terms and conditions upon licences; and 2) decisions to refuse to issue, to refuse to renew, and to revoke licences.

The Board consists of a chairman and ten members (maximum number: eleven) who are appointed by Order-in-Council.

Chairperson, Dr. Robert Seim

Custody Review Board
700 Bay St., Rm. 212, Toronto, M5G 1Z6

Chairperson, Joan Riches

Social Assistance Review Board
Macdonald Blk., Rm. M1-56
Queen's Park, Toronto, M7A 1E9
1-800-387-5619

The Social Assistance Review Board is a quasi-judicial body operating as a tribunal to review decisions relating to social assistance in the province of Ontario. The members of the Board, who are appointed by the cabinet, act independently of any provincial or municipal social service department.

The Board has jurisdiction to hear appeals regarding the refusal to grant a benefit, the suspension or cancellation of a benefit, the reduction of a benefit, or the amount of the benefit as set out in the *Family Benefits Act*, the *General Welfare Assistance Act* and the *Vocational Rehabilitation Act*.

Hearings are held throughout the province and can be in either English or French. The hearing will be convened by the presiding Board member who will chair the hearing and who will usually be assisted by one or two other members of the Board. The Board members will review the person's Notice of Request for Hearing and the submission of the municipal social services administrator or the provincial director. At the hearing, the person requesting the appeal has an opportunity to present his/her own case, including the calling of witnesses. Evidence of persons testifying at the hearing is taken under oath. The person requesting the hearing has the option to be represented by a legal agent or counsel. The Board members will ask questions in order to clarify the information set before them. The Board's decision following the appeal is given in writing to the parties involved in the appeal.

Chairperson, Joanne Campbell
Gen. Manager, Valerie March

MINISTRY OF CONSUMER AND COMMERCIAL RELATIONS

555 Yonge St., Toronto, M7A 2H6
(except where otherwise noted)
General Inquiries: (416) 963-1111
Consumer Information Centre: 1-800-268-1142
TTY/TDD: (416) 963-0808

MINISTER'S OFFICE
Minister, The Hon. William Wrye

DEPUTY MINISTER'S OFFICE
Dep. Minister, Valerie Gibbons
Legal Services
Director, Robert Stupart
10 Wellesley St. E., 5th Flr., Toronto, M7A 2J3
Policy and Planning Branch
Director, Dr. Joyce S. Feinberg
Policy and Analysis Section
Manager, Bonnie Foster
Agency Manager, Denise Evans
Program Evaluation and Strategic Planning
Co-ordinator, Cliodhna McMullin

SUPPORT SERVICES DIVISION
Exec. Director, W.E. Steinkrauss
French Language Services
Co-ordinator, Aline Desjardins
Communications Services Branch
Director, A.W. Campion
News and Information Section
Manager, Sid Rodeway
Consumer Information Centre
A/Manager, Robert Bourassa
Ministry Librarian, Mrs. E. Morgan

FINANCE AND ADMINISTRATIVE SERVICES BRANCH
Financial Services Branch
10 Wellesley St. E., 4th Flr., Toronto, M7A 2J3
Director, Mrs. D. Nagel
Expenditure and Revenue Accounting
Chief Accountant, H. Hergash
Expenditure Office Manager, H. Workman
Revenue Office Manager, Anne Brown
Planning and Budgeting Services
Manager, Mary Spencer

Administrative Services
10 Wellesley St. E., 6th Flr., Toronto, M7A 2H8
Sr. Manager, L. Ted Brathwaite
Accommodations and Telecommunications
Services Manager, Maurice Shrubb
Supply and Allied Services
Manager, D.A. Vaillancourt
Records Management
Manager, Emilia Petrozzi

Human Resources Branch
10 Wellesley St. E., 7th Flr., Toronto, M7A 2J6
Director, J. Walter
Personnel Services
Sr. Manager, Tony Sharp
Personnel Standards and Administration
Manager, Dianne Wilson
Employee Information and Payroll
Manager, Vivian Robinson
Organizational Development
Manager, Greg Yarrow
Employment Equity
Co-ordinator, M. Loesgen

Internal Audit and Operation Review Branch
101 Bloor St. W., 3rd Flr., Toronto, M7A 2H8
Director, J.H. Macpherson
Asst. Director, E. Stephens

INFORMATION TECHNOLOGY DIVISION
543 Yonge St., Toronto, M7A 2H8
Exec. Director, B.A. McKinnon
Information Technology Planning Branch
Director, R. Binsell
Information Systems Services Branch
Director, W. Baxter
Information Systems Development Section
Manager, Ali Curban
SUPPORT SERVICES DIVISION
Business Practices and Technical
Standards Branch
Services Manager, Dan Edwards
Technical Support, J. Murphy
End User Support Section
Manager, Les Solman
Quality Assurance and Standards Section
Manager, James Murphy

COMMERCIAL STANDARDS PROGRAM

Business Practices Division
555 Yonge St., 5th Flr., Toronto, M7A 2H6

Asst. Dep. Minister, Bernard Webber
Program Administration Section
Management Services Co-ordinator,
Stewart Smith
Business Regulation Branch
Director, E. Tappenden
Central Registration
A/Manager, Katheryn Smith
Motor Vehicle Dealers Act
Registrar, Stephen Moody
Real Estate and Business Brokers Act
Registrar, Gordon Randall
Travel Industry Act
Registrar, Hal Burns

Consumer Protection Act
Registrar, W. Stoddart
Cemeteries Regulation
Manager, Marie Fitzgerald
Consumer Services Branch
Director, D. Mitchell
Investigations Section: (416) 963-0302
Consumer Services Bureau: (416) 963-0321
Entertainment Standards Branch
555 Yonge St., 5th Flr., Toronto, M7A 2H6
Director, D. Brown
Gen. Manager, Elaine Gugins

Technical Standards Division
3300 Bloor St. W., 4th Flr., Toronto, M8X 2X2

Asst. Dep. Minister, Grant H. Mills
Exec. Director, John Peck
Pressure Vessels Safety Branch
Director, G. Grodecki
Elevating Devices and Special Devices Branch
Director, T.G. Smith
Fuels Safety Branch
Director, R.H. Clendining
Upholstered and Stuffed Articles Branch
Registrar, M. Fitzpatrick

PUBLIC ENTERTAINMENT STANDARDS PROGRAM

Registration Division
393 University Ave., 4th Flr., Toronto, M7A 2H6

Asst. Dep. Minister, Art Daniels
Finance and Administration Group
Manager, Mrs. Brenda Cowley
Northern Relocation Project
543 Yonge St., 2nd Flr., Toronto, M7A 2J8
Director, Randy Wall
Real Property Registration Branch
Director, R.A. Logan
Dep. Director, Leon Dorff
Land Registry Offices
595 Bay St., Toronto, M5G 2C2
Surveys, Mapping and Title Examination Office
Manager, T.C. Seawright
Property Law Branch
Director, T.M. Rundle
Property Law
Dep. Director, Barbara Levasseur
Real Property, Program Improvement
Dep. Director, R. Blomsma
Personal Property Registration Branch
Director and Registrar, Rosemarie Gage
Dep. Director, Peter Preager

COMPANIES BRANCH
Director, O.S. Nagel
Operations
Dep. Director, M.R. Lottamoza
Compliance
Dep. Director, A.A. Coleclough
Controller of Records, R. McLeod
Registrar of Partnerships, M.E. Magnus

Registrar General
Macdonald Blk., 2nd Flr., Rm. M2-25

900 Bay St., Queen's Park, Toronto, M7A 1Y5
General Inquiry: (416) 965-1687

Registrar General, The Hon. William Wrye
Dep. Registrar General, Mrs. Despina Georgas
Administration Support Services
Manager, A.B. Thorne
Registration Vital Events
Manager, R. Ventresca
Customer Services Manager, G. Hall

AGENCIES, BOARDS AND COMMISSIONS

Commercial Registration Appeal Tribunal
1 St. Clair Ave. W., 10th Flr., Toronto, M4V 1K6

The Tribunal holds public hearings when appeals are made against administrative decisions which deny, refuse to renew, suspend, or revoke the current or tentative registration of individuals or corporations. It also reviews government-originated cease and desist orders respecting advertising, selling, and unfair business practices.

The Tribunal acts under the following legislation: *Bailiffs Act, Business Practices Act, Collection Agencies Act, Consumer Protection Act, Discriminatory Business Practices Act, Mortgage Brokers Act, Motor Vehicle Dealers Act, Ontario New Home Warranties Plan Act, Real Estate and Business Brokers Act, Travel Industry Act,* and *Upholstered and Stuffed Articles Act.*

The Tribunal hears appeals of: credit unions regarding orders for the takeover of management of the Ontario Share and Deposit Insurance Corp.; trustees' decisions under the *Travel Industry Act;* corporation decisions under the *Ontario New Home Warranties Plan Act;* and Liquor Licence Board decisions.

Chairman, Vacant
Vice-Chairmen: Richard F. Stephenson,
David Appel, Mary G. Critelli,
Ronald J. Poirier, James Leslie
Registrar, Audrey Verge

Liquor Control Board of Ontario
55 Lakeshore Blvd. E., Toronto, M5E 1A4

The *Liquor Control Act* describes the role and responsibilities of the chairman who is also the chief executive officer and reports to the Ministry of Consumer and Commercial Relations.

A summary of the functions of the Board is as follows:
1) to provide outlets for the distribution of beverage alcohol throughout the province;
2) to provide outlets through which the producers of beverage alcohol can offer their products for sale to the public;
3) to generate revenues for the provincial government.

In addition, the Liquor Control Board provides certain administrative services for the Liquor Licence Board.

Chairman, J.W. Ackroyd

Part-time Board Members:
Dr. Katy Driver-Radhakrishnan, John L. Fryer,
C.R. (Dick) Sharpe, Steven A. Stavro
Exec. Vice-President, L.F. Pitura
Sr. Vice-President, Operations, L.C. Lee

Liquor Licence Board of Ontario
55 Lakeshore Blvd. E., Toronto, M5E 1A4

The Liquor Licence Board of Ontario was
established in 1946 and reorganized in 1976 as a
provincial Crown corporation under the *Liquor
Licence Act, 1975* by O. Reg. 1008/75, now O.
Reg. 581/80.

The Board is responsible for issuing liquor
licences to restaurants, hotels, resorts, recreational facilities, clubs, and to manufacturers of
beer, wine and liquor and their sales agents. It also
issues special-occasion permits and Ontario
photo cards. All forms of alcoholic beverage
advertising in the province are monitored and
approved by the Board.

Ontario's Liberal government reviewed the
Board's regulations and operation in 1986.
Among the changes considered was whether the
province's approximately 11,000 liquor outlets
should be allowed to operate longer hours.

A/Chairman, Andromache Karakatsanis
Exec. Director, Barry D. Tocher
Policy and Research Analyst, John Kiedrowski
Vice-Chairman, Andromache Karakatsanis
Board Members: J.H. Aitken, F.M. D'Andrea,
G. Solursh, W.L. Yenson
Legal and Advertising Services
Director, D. Russell
Legal Services, S.A. Grannum
Counsel, P. Ballantyne
Advertising and Promotional Services
Manager, K. Klas
Hearings and Support Administrator,
Teri McIver
Financial and Administrative Services
Chief Accountant, J.J. Scarnati
Administrative Services
Supervisor, K. Palmer
Personnel Services Manager, G. Harmer
Licensing and Permits
Director, L. Griffiths
Operation Support Manager, W. Jackson
Ontario Photo Card, D. Keeling
Licensing Records Manager, P. James
Licensing and Permits Operation
Manager, Ms. S. Wilson
Inspection
Director, Bob Aldous
Managers:
District 1, K. Brooks
District 2, R. Oliver
District 3, K. Collard
Intelligence Liaison, C. Rycroft
Investigation and Enforcement
Manager, John Fournier

Ontario Racing Commission
180 Dundas St. W., 14th Flr., Toronto, M5G 1Z8

The Racing Commission was established under
The Racing Commission Act, 1950. The responsibilities of the seven-member Commission involve
the regulation of horse racing in any or all of its
forms. Included are the following:
- regulating the operation of race tracks in
  Ontario;
- holding hearings relating to the carrying out of
  its objects or powers;
- enforcing the Regulations, rules, and conditions established under the Act;
- licensing race track operators as well as
  owners, trainers, drivers, jockeys, and all such
  other persons in or about race tracks;
- setting terms and conditions for licences;
- fixing and collecting licence fees, fines, and
  penalties;
- making and promulgating rules for the conduct
  of horse racing;
- approving the appointment of race track officials and employees;
- requiring licensed operators of race tracks to
  keep books of account and inspecting such
  books; and
- doing such things relating to horse racing in
  any or all of its forms, or to the operation of race
  tracks at which horse racing is carried on, as
  are authorized or directed by the Lieutenant-Governor in Council.

Chairman, Frank Drea
Director, W.R. McDonnell
Sec.-Treasurer and Supervisor
of Administration, Gregory Fernandes
Thoroughbred Racing
Dep. Director, Dr. R.D. Roelofson
Standardbred Racing
Dep. Director, Terry Stone
Supervisor, Vic Gould
Sires Stakes
A/Supervisor, T. Iwanciw

Theatres Branch
1075 Millwood Rd., Toronto, M4G 1X6

The jurisdiction of the Theatres Branch is the
administration of the *Theatres Act.*
Its objectives are as follows:
- to regulate the film and cassette industry in
  Ontario by ensuring that films are classified and
  approved for public screening and commercial
  distribution on the basis of community standards, and that safety and age requirements are
  observed in theatres in the province;
- by careful classification of films, to protect
  children from harmful or anti-social content;
- to prohibit the public exhibition or commercial
  distribution of material which is totally unacceptable to the community as a whole by
  applying representative guidelines; and
- to help the public make knowledgeable choices
  of films and video cassettes by providing
  information on film content.

To achieve these goals, the Branch licenses
and monitors more than 400 theatres in the

province for observance of *Theatres Act* requirements, tests and licenses over 1,000 projectionists and licenses almost 500 items of projection equipment. Through the Film Review Board, it screens, classifies, and approves standard, 16mm, 8mm, and videotape films for public exhibition and home use.

Through continual community liaison, the Board's rotating members study and research current community standards to determine criteria and to define content as acceptable or unacceptable for public screens. These criteria are the basis for flexible guidelines which are applied in the classification and approval of over 1,500 films a year.

In keeping with the philosophy of open decision-making and public accountability, Board members participate in numerous public meetings and media interviews to explain the role of the Board and to assess specific areas of public concern in classifying and approving film for public exhibition. The procedures and guidelines followed by the Board, as well as information on particular decisions, are available to the public on request.

Director, D. Brown
Ontario Film Review Board
Chairman, Anne Jones

MINISTRY OF CORRECTIONAL SERVICES

2001 Eglinton Ave. E., Scarborough, M1L 4P1
General Inquiry: (416) 750-3333

MINISTER'S OFFICE
Whitney Blk., Rm. 5320
99 Wellesley St. W., Toronto, M7A 1A2

Minister, The Hon. David Ramsay
Minister's Advisory Committee on Corrections
Chairman, Rev. Massey Lombardi

DEPUTY MINISTER'S OFFICE
2001 Eglinton Ave. E., Scarborough, M1L 4P1

Dep. Minister, Robert M. McDonald
Operational Review Audit and Investigation
Director, Judy Sutcliffe
Legal Services Director, Murray Chitra

Corporate Services Division
2001 Eglinton Ave. E., Scarborough, M1L 4P1

Asst. Dep. Minister, William Gibson
Policy and Corporate Planning
Exec. Co-ordinator, Judi Richter
Human Resources Management
Director, Vacant
Management Information Systems Branch
Director, W.D. Gray
Financial and Administrative Services
Branch Director, Keith Wylie
Communications Branch Director, D.W. Kerr
Employment Equity Program

Co-ordinator, Monika Campbell
Freedom of Information
Co-ordinator, C. Mahaffy

Operations Division

Asst. Dep. Minister, Leonard Crispino
Offender Programs
Director, Neil McKerrel
Health and Professional Services
Sr. Medical Advisor and Manager,
Dr. P.W. Humphries
Social Work Chief, M. Briks
Psychology
Sr. Advisor, Dr. W. Coons
Program Development and Implementation
A/Manager, Adam Borgida
Policy Development and Co-ordination
Manager, G.A. Nancekivell
Offender Education and Training
Sr. Advisor, William Tilden
Program Support and Co-ordination
Manager, Tom Watson

Community Corrections
Exec. Co-ordinator, Don Page
Community Residential Services
Manager, Kurt Jensen
Probation, Community Services
Manager, Frances McKeague
Industrial Programming
Sr. Advisor, John Pahapill

REGIONAL OFFICES:

Metro Region
2 Dunbloor Rd., Ste. 312, Islington, M9A 2E4
Reg. Director, David Parker

Central Region
6711 Mississauga Rd., Ste. 406
Mississauga, L5N 2W3
Reg. Director, J.L. Main

Western Region
80 Dundas St., Box 5600, Terminal A
London, N6A 2P3
Reg. Director, V.J. Crew

Eastern Region
1055 Princess St., Ste. 404, Kingston, K7L 1H3
Reg. Director, Sydney Shoom

Northern Region
199 Larch St., 9th Flr., Sudbury, P3E 5P9
Reg. Director, G.F. Tegman

AGENCIES, BOARDS AND COMMISSIONS

Ontario Board of Parole
2195 Yonge St., Ste. 201, Toronto, M4S 2B1

Following passage of the *Ministry of Correctional Services Act* in June 1978, the Ontario Board of Parole increased from one central board to five regional boards, providing more effective service to the province.

The Ontario Board of Parole exercises parole jurisdiction for all inmates sentenced to provincial institutions (sentences up to two years less one day). All members of the Board are appointed by the Lieutenant-Governor in Council. The Board consists of a chairman, 20 full-time members, and 103 part-time or community members.

Parole is a means of releasing an offender into the community under supervision while he serves the remaining portion of his sentence. An inmate is eligible for parole consideration after serving one third of his sentence. Inmates serving sentences of six months or more are automatically scheduled for parole consideration, while those inmates serving sentences of under six months must apply for consideration. The Board may grant, defer, or deny parole and considers information from a wide variety of sources in the process of its decision-making. It sets regular and special conditions of release and is empowered to revoke parole should there be failure to comply with the parole program.

The protection of society is enhanced with the supervised return of prisoners to the community. Those who are granted parole receive support and encouragement through parole supervision as they seek to re-establish themselves in the community.

In early 1988, the Board released its "Mission Statement and Values and Principles" which will help the Board to set its future direction. During the 1987-88 fiscal year, the Board released 3,718 inmates on parole. Eighty-four per cent completed parole successfully.

Chair, S.P. Henriksen
Exec. Vice-Chairman, K.S. Sandhu
Program and Projects Administrator,
D. Sepejak
Sr. Policy Analyst, M. McGuire
Operational Services
Supervisor, S. Taneja
REGIONAL BOARDS:
Central Region
2195 Yonge St., Ste. 204, Toronto, M4S 2B1
Vice-Chairman, G.G. McFarlane
West-Central Region
35 Crawford Cres., D Blk.
Campbellville, L0P 1B0
Vice-Chairman, John Spriggs
Northern Region
128 Larch St., Ste. 502, Sudbury, P3E 5J8
Vice-Chairman, W.E. Peters
Western Region
785 York Rd., Box 1716, Guelph, N1H 6Z9
Vice-Chairman, W. Taylor
Eastern Region
1055 Princess St., Kingston, K7L 1H3
Vice-Chairman, Genevieve Blais

MINISTRY OF CULTURE AND COMMUNICATIONS
77 Bloor St. W., Toronto, M7A 2R9
General Inquiries: (416) 965-0615

MINISTER'S OFFICE
Minister, The Hon. Lily Oddie Munro

DEPUTY MINISTER'S OFFICE
Dep. Minister, David P. Silcox
Corporate Policy Services
Sr. Advisor, Phillip Baker
Communications and Marketing Branch
A/Director, Michael Langford

Finance and Administration Division
Asst. Dep. Minister, Lynn M. MacDonald
French Language Services
Co-ordinator, Léo Desmarteau
Management Systems and Services Branch
A/Director, Daryl Novak
Library/Resource Centre
A/Manager, Renata Grodski
Freedom of Information and Privacy
Co-ordinator, Sharon Fleming
Finance Branch Director, J.E. Parker
Human Resources Branch
A/Director, G.A. Berry
Employment Equity Program
Manager, Judith Ridley
Legal Services Director, Maureen Simpson
Internal Audit Branch
Director, Brian Boyd
REGIONAL SERVICES
A/Exec. Co-ordinator, Brian David

Northern Region
Ontario Government Bldg., Box 3000
479 Government Rd., Dryden, P8N 3B3
General Information: (807) 223-3331
1825 East Arthur St., Thunder Bay, P7E 5N7
General Information: (807) 475-1683
Elgin Twr., 3rd Flr., 390 Bay St.
Sault Ste. Marie, P6A 1X2
General Information: (705) 759-8652
Sudbury City Ctr., 4th Flr.
200 Elm St. E., Sudbury, P3C 5N3
General Information: (705) 675-4383
22 Wilcox St., 2nd Flr., Timmins, P4N 3K6
General Information: (705) 267-8018

Eastern Region
1 Nicholas St., Ste. 612, Ottawa, K1N 7B7
General Information: (613) 566-3728
280 Pinnacle St., Ste. 3, Belleville, K8N 3B1
General Information: (613) 968-3474

Central Region
10 St. Mary St., 2nd Flr., Toronto, M4Y 1P9
General Information: (416) 965-6597
114 Worsley St., Barrie, L4M 1M1
General Information: (705) 737-0543

Western Region
119 King St. W., 8th Flr., Hamilton, L8N 3Z9
General Information: (416) 521-7229
15 Church St., #406, St. Catharines, L2R 3B5
General Information: (416) 685-7397
30 Duke St. W., 4th Flr., Kitchener, N2H 3W5
General Information: (519) 578-8200
Duff-Baby House, 221 Mill St.
Windsor, N9C 2R1
General Information: (519) 256-5486
255 Dufferin Ave., Ste. 601, London, N6A 5K6
General Information: (519) 679-7146

Culture Division

Asst. Dep. Minister, Linda Stevens
Arts Branch Director, Linda Loving
Libraries and Community Information Branch
Director, Morris Zbar
Heritage Branch
Director, Robert Montgomery
Cultural Industries and Agencies Branch
Director, Angela Longo

COMMUNICATIONS DIVISION
Exec. Director, David Barr
Operations and Technology Office
Manager, R.P. Bulger
Telecommunications Branch
Director, Joan McCalla
Broadcasting and Cable Branch
Director, Karen Lilley

AGENCIES, BOARDS AND COMMISSIONS

Archives of Ontario
77 Grenville St., Toronto, M7A 2R9

The Archives of Ontario, established in 1903, operates under *The Archives Act.* Under the mandate provided by this Act, it acquires significant unpublished documents to preserve Ontario's historical heritage and to retain information of long-term operational value to government ministries. It obtains from Ontario government agencies important non-current records, and through donation or purchase, it obtains important historical manuscripts, maps, pictures, photographs, early newspapers, etc. It welcomes information on the location of historical material.

A conservation laboratory is maintained for document restoration of Archives holdings, and a library (telephone 416-965-4039) and public reading room are available for those doing historical, administrative, legal, or other research. Archives staff members also advise and assist ministries and government agencies on cost-efficient records management, including forms control, microrecording, correspondence, and reports. They co-ordinate a records management training course for ministries and government agencies.

Archivist of Ontario, Ian E. Wilson

Art Gallery of Ontario
317 Dundas St. W., Toronto, M5T 1G4

In 1911, The Grange and its surrounding parkland became the first permanent site for the Gallery, which had been incorporated in 1900 as The Art Museum of Toronto. The first galleries were built in 1918; additions were made in 1926, 1935, 1974, and 1977. Under the *Provincial Government Act* of 1966, the Gallery became the Art Gallery of Ontario.

Today, the Gallery owns more than 10,000 works of art, and its collections and exhibitions are complemented by a variety of lectures, films, public tours, and concerts available at the Gallery. Although the collections include paintings by the old masters, the impressionists, and early twentieth-century artists, over half of the Gallery's permanent collection is by Canadian artists. The four second-floor galleries of the Canadian wing house a wide variety of paintings and sculptures from the early nineteenth century through to the present.

Sculpture of the nineteenth and twentieth centuries is featured in the Walker Court and in the Henry Moore Sculpture Centre. The Gallery owns the largest public collection of works by Henry Moore in the world based on an unprecedented gift from the artist. Related drawings, prints, studio material, and photography donated by Henry Moore are also displayed.

The Print and Drawing Gallery exhibits range from sixteenth-century watercolours to examples of present-day graphic techniques, while the Walter Trier Gallery displays satirical and illustrative prints and drawings.

President, Board of Trustees
Margaret H. Bindhardt
Director, William J. Withrow
Chief Curator, Dr. Roald Nasgaard
Chief of Administration and
Corporate Secretary, Vacant
Controller, Timothy Hopcraft
Education Services
Head, Sheila Greenspan
Marketing/Communications
Head, Elizabeth Addison
Development Head, Douglas Todgham
Volunteer Activity
Manager, Joyce Turner
Art Support
Head, Noni Regan

CJRT-FM Inc.
297 Victoria St., Toronto, M5B 1W1

Chairman, M.A. Stuart
President and Gen. Manager, C.R. Finley
Program Director, E. Toppings
Asst. to the Director of Open College,
Shirley Gibson
Music Director, Paul Robinson
Operations Manager, A. Markow
Chief Engineer, K. Poling

Conservation Review Board
77 Bloor St. W., 2nd Flr., Toronto, M7A 2R9

The Conservation Review Board, established under the *Ontario Heritage Act,* holds hearings at the request of a municipality if owners object to the municipal designation of property for historical or architectural conservation. The Board reports its opinion to the municipal council. Hearings are also held if there are appeals against the minister's designation of archeological or historic sites or against the minister's refusal of archeological licences.

Chairman, Michael Vaughan

The McMichael Canadian Art Collection
10365 Islington Ave., Kleinburg, L0J 1C0

The McMichael Canadian Art Collection was begun in 1955 by Robert and Signe McMichael, who donated their home and art collection to the provincial government in 1965. The Collection has grown to become one of the most important collections of Canadian art in the world. Featured are the works of Tom Thomson, the Group of Seven, Emily Carr, David Milne, and Clarence Gagnon. Inuit, Woodland, and Northwest Coast Indian art are also part of the Collection.

Chairman of the Board, H. Michael Burns
Director and CEO, Barbara A. Tyler
Operations
Asst. Director, Dennis Jones
Public Services
Asst. Director, John Ryerson
Development and Marketing
Asst. Director, Jill Planche
Chief Curator, Jean Blodgett
Assoc. Curator, Megan Bice
Finance and Human Resources
Manager, Christopher Brown
Public Programs Manager, Bonnie Gordon
Security, William Plant
Promotions Manager, Sue-Ellen Boyes
Gallery Shop Manager, Lee Guscott
Food Services Manager, Mary-Anne White
Registrar, Sandy Cooke
Exhibitions Co-ordinator, Lisa Landreth
Librarian, Linda Morita
Conservator, Catherine Stewart
Technical Services
Head, Steven Lemon
Librarian, Linda Morita
Group Bookings, June Côté

Ontario Arts Council
151 Bloor St. W., Ste. 500, Toronto, M5S 1T6

Established in 1963, the Ontario Arts Council is an independent agency of the Ontario Ministry of Culture and Communications. It is composed of 12 people from different regions of the province, who are selected for their knowledge and support of the arts. Appointed to three-year terms, these members meet quarterly to consider grant requests from a variety of arts organizations and recommendations from its juries.

In addition to promoting the study and enjoyment of the arts, the OAC encourages the production of works in all arts disciplines. It provides financial and other assistance to professional artists and arts organizations, and administers a range of special projects.

The Council is assisted in its work by a staff which processes more than 3,000 grants through 10 discipline offices: Arts Education; Community Arts Development; Dance; Film, Photography, and Video; Franco-Ontarian; Literature; Music; Touring; Theatre; and Visual Arts. Detailed information about individual programs is available from the specific discipline office.

Chairperson, Nalini Stewart
Exec. Director, Norman B. Walford
Special Projects Director, Ron Evans

Operations Director, Robert Sirman
Personnel Manager, Linda England
Office Manager, Mo Chung
Communications Director, Mary Jolliffe
Officers:
Arts Education, Susan Habkirk
Community Arts Development,
Naomi Lightbourn
Community Arts Development
Sr. Assoc., Walter Sunahara
Film, Photography, and Video, David Craig
Franco-Ontarian, Mme Jeanne Sabourin
Franco-Ontarian Assoc., Jean Malavoy
Literature, Margaret McClintock
Music, Gwenlyn Setterfield
Music Assoc., Michael LaLeune
Theatre, Tim Leary
Theatre Assoc., Jan McIntyre
Dance, Susan Cohen
Touring, Helen Billington (Acting)
Visual Arts, Nancy Hushion
Visual Arts Assoc., Nataley Nagy

Ontario Educational Communications Authority (TVOntario)
2180 Yonge St., Toronto, M4S 2C1
Mailing Address:
Box 200, Stn. Q, Toronto, M4T 2T1
General Inquiry: (416) 484-2700
Fax: (416) 484-2725

TVOntario, a provincial Crown corporation, is responsible for educational broadcasting in Ontario. It designs and produces TV-based learning systems in English and French designed for in-school, pre-school and adult education.

The TVOntario educational television network broadcasts via Anik C3 satellite to transmitters in Toronto (Channel 19), Ottawa (Channel 24), London (Channel 18), Chatham (Channel 59), Windsor (Channel 32), Kitchener (Channel 28), Thunder Bay (Channel 9), Sault Ste. Marie (Channel 20), Sudbury (Channel 19), Timmins (Channel 7), Owen Sound (Channel 12), North Bay (Channel 6), Penetanguishene (Channel 51), Huntsville (Channel 13), Peterborough (Channel 18), and surrounding communities, many of which receive TVO's full service on their local cable systems.

TVO also broadcasts via the Anik C3 satellite to more than 160 low-power rebroadcast transmitters in northern Ontario communities.

With the extension of TVO's broadcast service to transmitters in Kingston and Belleville in 1986, and in the Bancroft, Tobermory, Parry Sound, and Kenora areas in 1987, TVO reaches more than 96 per cent of the Ontario population.

Videotapes, audiotapes, and print materials to accompany educational programming are distributed by TVOntario. Schedules and information on programs are available on request.

Chairman and CEO, Bernard Ostry
Director General, Mimi Fullerton
COO, Peter G. Bowers
Policy, Research and Planning
Man. Director, Howard Krosnick

External Relations
Sr. Man. Director, Bill Roberts
English Programming Services
Man. Director, Donald Duprey
Human Resources Director, Bill Milliken
Information and Publications
Director, Beverley Roberts
Finance Director, Jan Shah
Corporate Relations Director, Ross Mayot
Ontario Policy Relations
Manager, Micheline McKay-Camparey
Project Revenue Manager, Nadia Shafto

Ontario Film Development Corp.
81 Wellesley St. E., Toronto, M4Y 1H6

Fourteen representatives of Ontario's arts, entertainment, and business communities have been appointed directors of the Ontario Film Development Corporation, an agency created to assist the film industry in Ontario. The Corporation began operations on Nov. 1, 1985.

A/CEO, Jonathan Barker
Legal Counsel, Michael Fleisher
Exec. Co-ordinator, Corporate Management, Wendy MacKeigan
Exec. Co-ordinator, Production and Development, Louise Clark
Manager, Location, Promotion and Services, Gail Thomson
Manager, Sales and Distribution, Shane Kinnear

Ontario Heritage Foundation
77 Bloor St. W., 2nd Flr., Toronto, M7A 2R9

The Ontario Heritage Foundation advises the Minister of Culture and Communications on the issuance of archeological licences and on the designation of significant archeological and historic sites.

Further, the Foundation:
- provides grants to encourage innovative work in archeology and to help complete artifact analysis;
- provides grants or loans for architectural conservation to encourage renovation of buildings of historical or architectural significance;
- provides grants to assist historians with the preparation and printing of manuscripts of local, regional, or specialized interest related to Ontario's heritage;
- erects historical plaques which recognize people, places, buildings, and events in the province's history; and
- acquires, usually by donation, heritage properties, parkland, works of art, and historical artifacts.

Chairman, Richard M. Alway
Vice-Chairman, Gay Evans

Ontario Science Centre
770 Don Mills Rd., Don Mills, M3C 1T3

Opened in 1969, the internationally recognized Ontario Science Centre aims to promote science and modern technology to the general public. Visitors are invited to tour 800 original exhibits and participate in demonstrations, workshops, and theatre presentations.

Chairman, George A. Cohon
Director Gen., Dr. Mark Abbott
Controller, G.R. Gillman
Administrative Services
Supervisor, Peter Osborne
Science Chief, G. Vanderkuur
Education Chief, John Fowles
Communications Chief, J.W. Bell
Editor, C. Gold
Information and Promotion
Manager, Martha McGloin
Exhibits Co-ordinator, John Voskuil
Production Chief, G. McLennan
A/Enterprises Chief, Josie Szczasiuk
Human Resources Chief, D. Powell
Design Chief, J. Krause
Ontario Film Institute
Director, Gerald Pratley

Ontario Telephone Service Commission
3625 Dufferin St., Ste. 200
Downsview, M3K 1Z2

The Ontario Telephone Service Commission regulates 30 independent telephone systems in Ontario under the authority of the *Telephone Act,* R.S.O. 1980, Chapter 496.

Chairman, Mrs. V.W. Bielski, Q.C.
Vice-Chairman, Ms. A.E. Stahmer
Members: L.A. Green, R. Grzela, G.E. Kaiser, G.C. Rennick
Manager of Operations, H.A. Lyons
Sr. Financial Analyst, R.W. Olenick
Financial Analyst, K. Sharma
Rates Analyst, J.A. Veloce
Secretary/Registrar, L. Corbeil
Research Officer, Vacant
Communications Officer, L. Mathur

Royal Botanical Gardens
Box 399, Hamilton, L8N 3H8

The plant collections of the Royal Botanical Gardens (RBG) in Hamilton-Wentworth and Halton regions are world-renowned. The RBG, which occupies 1,000 hectares, has extensive natural areas served by 48 km of interpretive nature trails.

Educational programs, which range from instruction to school classes to university credit courses, include courses on horticulture, botany, and design with plants. The RBG offers to the public extensive information on ornamental plants of all types, and is also a Resource Centre for the study of the flora and fauna of southern Ontario. The RBG participates in Outreach Ontario and Festival Ontario, and will arrange tours on request.

Chairman, J.G. Sheppard
Director, Allen P. Paterson
Asst. Director, Scientific, Dr. J.S. Pringle
Asst. Director, Conservation, Dr. P.F. Rice

Director of Development, Cathie Korhonen
Manager, Horticulture Services,
Chris R. Graham
Buildings and Equipment
Manager, Mark Runciman
Manager, Education Services
(including Outreach Ontario), J.B. Lord
Plant Breeder, H. Pearson
Manager, Administrative Services,
H.J. Vandermaas
Curator of Collections, F. Vrugtman
Environmental Biologist, W. Leonard Simser
Librarian, Ina Vrugtman
Public Relations Officer, Susan Malcolm

Royal Ontario Museum

100 Queen's Park Cres., Toronto, M5S 2C6
General Inquiry: (416) 586-5549
Fax: (416) 586-5863

The Royal Ontario Museum (ROM), founded in 1912, is now the largest public museum in Canada. With collections in 18 science, art, and archeology departments, the museum is also a major research institution. Since 1968, the ROM has been established as a corporation without shares that receives the major portion of its operational money as direct grants from the Government of Ontario. The Museum is controlled by a board of 21 trustees, 15 of whom are appointed by the Lieutenant-Governor in Council.

The ROM, incorporating the adjacent McLaughlin Planetarium and the Sigmund Samuel Canadiana Building at 14 Queen's Park Cres. W., offers a variety of public educational programs, reference and identification services, and popular and scholarly publications. Its Outreach Department circulates travelling exhibits to institutions throughout Ontario and across Canada. Education Services (telephone 416-586-5801) offers a variety of programs for school visits to the ROM.

The ROM continues to open new, permanent galleries in phases. Galleries now open include, among others: the Greeks and Etruscans Gallery, the Bat Cave, the Later Imperial China Gallery, the Hardwood Forest Gallery, the Astrocentre, the Dinosaur Gallery, the Ming Tomb Gallery, and the keystone to the ROM's galleries, the Mankind Discovering Gallery. Many more galleries are scheduled to open in the next few years. In addition, a full range of special exhibitions and temporary exhibitions will be on view at the ROM.

Chairman, Edwin A. Goodman, O.C., Q.C., D.U.
Secretary to the Board, Robert Barnett
Director, Dr. T. Cuyler Young, Jr.
Assoc. Director, Membership and Development, Robert Howard
Assoc. Director, Curatorial, Dr. David Barr
Assoc. Director, Exhibits, Dr. Louis Levine
Assoc. Director, Public Programs,
Ken MacKeracher
Asst. Director, Administration and Finance,
Mike Shoreman
Asst. Director, Human Resources, Nancy Hood

Science North

100 Ramsey Lake Rd., Sudbury, P3E 5S9
General Inquiry: (705) 522-3700
Fax: (705) 522-4954

Chairman, Robert Gougeon
Exec. Officer, James Marchbank
Director of Science, Tom Semadeni
Controller, Carolyn Thain
Physical Services Manager, Daryl Potvin

MINISTRY OF EDUCATION

Mowat Blk., 900 Bay St., Toronto, M7A 1L2
(unless otherwise noted)

MINISTER'S OFFICE
Minister, The Hon. Chris Ward

DEPUTY MINISTER'S OFFICE
Dep. Minister, Bernard Shapiro

Franco-Ontarian Education

Asst. Dep. Minister,
Mrs. Mariette Carrier-Fraser

Administration

Asst. Dep. Minister, Dina Palozzi
Human Resources Director, Bob Beninati
Policy, Planning and Development
Manager, June Fukushima
Equal Opportunity/Affirmative Action
Co-ordinator, Carol Westcott
Internal Audit Director, Joan St. Rose-Haynes
Administrative Services
Director, Andy Glendenning
Financial Services Director, Peter Brown
Information Technology and Systems
Director, D. Thornton
Communication Services
Director, Bernadette Sulgit

Corporate Planning and Financial Management

Asst. Dep. Minister, Mark Larratt-Smith
Policy Analysis and Research
Director, Howat Noble
Legislation Director, Jim B. Doris
Education Liaison and Exchange
Director, W.E.P. Fleck
Corporate Planning and Financial Management
Director, Katharine Smith

Learning Programs

Asst. Dep. Minister, Wally Beevor
Centre for Early Childhood and Elementary
Education
Director, Shannon Hogan
Centre for Secondary and Adult Education
Director, Sheila Roy
Special Education and Provincial Schools
Director, Dave McKee
Computers in Education Centre
Director, Maurice Poirier

Independent Learning Centre
A/Director, R. Cussons
Professional Development
Director, Julie Lindhout

Learning Services

Asst. Dep. Minister, Roy Houghton
Program Implementation and Review
Director, William Lipischak
School Business and Finance
Director, R. Trbovich
REGIONAL OFFICES:
Northwestern Ontario Region
435 James St. S., Box 5000
Thunder Bay, P7E 5G6
Reg. Director, Margaret A. Twomey
Midnorthern Ontario Region
199 Larch St., Sudbury, P3E 5P9
Reg. Director, William Boivin
Northeastern Ontario Region
477 McKeown Ave., Box 3020
North Bay, P1B 8K7
Reg. Director, J.J. Sullivan
Western Ontario Region
759 Hyde Park Rd., London, N6H 3S6
Reg. Director, Michael F. Cyze
Central Ontario Region
2025 Sheppard Ave. E., Ste. 3201
Willowdale, M2J 1W4
Reg. Director, Joe Rees
Eastern Ontario Region
Merivale Shopping Fair, 1580 Merivale Rd.
Ottawa, K2B 4B5
Reg. Director, Jean Comtois
School Board Services Unit
Exec. Manager, N. Parker

AGENCIES, BOARDS AND COMMISSIONS

Conseil de l'éducation franco-ontarienne
880 Bay St., Ste. 203, Toronto, M7A 1L2

The purpose of the Council for Franco-Ontarian Education is to advise the Minister of Education and the Minister of Colleges and Universities on all matters concerning French-language education in Ontario.

Chairman, Marc P. Godbout
Sec.-General, Alfred Abouchar

Education Relations Commission
111 Avenue Rd., Ste. 400, Toronto, M5R 3J8

The Education Relations Commission (ERC) was established in 1975 to administer the collective bargaining process between teachers and school boards and to further harmonious relations between the parties. The Commission monitors and assists in negotiations, supervises teachers' votes, and advises the Lieutenant-Governor in Council when a strike or a lockout is jeopardizing the students' education.

Chairperson, Katherine E. Swinton
CEO, R.E. Saunders

Information Services
A/Director, S. McElroy
Field Services Director, Dr. E.M. Aim

Languages of Instruction Commission of Ontario
George Drew Bldg., 17th Flr.
25 Grosvenor St., Toronto, M4Y 1A9

The Languages of Instruction Commission of Ontario was established by the Lieutenant-Governor in Council in 1973, on the recommendation of the government of Ontario, to help resolve disputes between school boards and parents over the provision of educational programs in English or French.

Since its inception, the Commission has been presented with a number of problems, many long-standing, relating to minority-language education. In the majority of cases, it has brought about solutions and it is continuing to work on the remaining problems.

The main role of the Commission is to:
- consider any problems dealing with languages of instruction that are brought to its attention by school boards, advisory committees, or ratepayer groups;
- consider all matters, referred by the minister, that relate to French-language or English-language instruction, when the students receiving such instruction form a minority;
- determine, when there is doubt, which linguistic group — English-speaking or French-speaking — should establish an advisory committee or whether in certain situations each group should form an advisory committee;
- investigate any alleged irregularity in the election of an advisory committee; and
- provide information on minority-language rights to all parties concerned in order to prevent potential problems.

As outlined in the *Education Act,* the Commission is composed of five members, at least two French-speaking and at least two English-speaking.

Chairman, Keith Rielly

Planning and Implementation Commission
1200 Bay St., 11th Flr., Toronto, M5R 2A5

The Planning and Implementation Commission was established on July 26, 1984 by Order-in-Council. Its duties relate to the extension of funding for Roman Catholic secondary schools as provided for under the *Education Amendment Act* of 1986.

Prior to the proclamation of the Act, the Commission advised the Minister of Education on how to implement the new policy, on new and altered school zones and districts, and on the legislation that would be required to arbitrate disputes. It also received and evaluated implementation plans from separate school boards and consulted with various groups of education professionals about employment concerns.

The Commission is now responsible for supervising the extension of separate secondary school grades, one year at a time. This includes ensuring that full programs are available at separate schools while maintaining the public secondary system and, as enrolment shifts from the latter, ensuring that all employees are treated fairly and that facilities are well utilized and shared equitably.

Chairman, W.J. McCordic
CEO, R.H. Desjardins

Teachers' Superannuation Commission
5650 Yonge St., Ste. 400
North York, M2M 4H5

The Teachers' Superannuation Commission of Ontario provides pensions for retired teachers in the province of Ontario under the *Teachers' Superannuation Act*, R.S.O. 1980, Chapter 494. All teachers employed at the elementary and secondary level of education must contribute to the fund. In addition, certificated teachers from private schools may become members of the plan. Pensions are payable for the lifetime of the retired teacher and are continued in half the amount to a spouse. There is provision for limited escalation of pensions, which are adjusted annually in keeping with cost of living changes.

Chairman, C. Peter Honey
Director, Dan F. McArthur
Divisional Directors:
W.G. Foster, A.H. McKellar

MINISTRY OF ENERGY
56 Wellesley St. W., 12th Flr.
Toronto, M7A 2B7
General Inquiries: (416) 965-2459

MINISTER'S OFFICE
Whitney Blk., Rm. 6323
99 Wellesley St. W., Toronto, M7A 1W3
Minister, The Hon. Robert Wong

DEPUTY MINISTER'S OFFICE
Dep. Minister, Daniel J. Gagnier
Intergovernmental Liaison/Energy Relations, Anne Buntic
Legal Services Group
Director, Edward Ciemiega
French-Language Services
Co-ordinator, Lionel Forestier

POLICY DEVELOPMENT BRANCH
Exec. Co-ordinator, George Davies
ENERGY LIAISON AND PLANNING BRANCH
Exec. Co-ordinator, Jean Lam
Oil and Gas Manager, George Dominy
A/Electricity Manager, Cliff Jutlah
Energy Management
A/Manager, Bunli Yang
Economics and Forecasts
A/Manager, Duncan Taylor

ENERGY PROGRAMS AND TECHNOLOGY BRANCH
Exec. Co-ordinator, Paul Shervill
Industry Programs Manager, Linda Ploeger
Energy Technology Research
Manager, Bob Greven

FINANCE AND ADMINISTRATION BRANCH
Director, Victor A. Bailey
Evaluation and Audit, Vacant
Information Systems Services
Manager, Dee Phillips
Staff Services Manager, Goldie Spencer
CORPORATE RELATIONS BRANCH
Director, Arthur Dickinson
Administration
Manager, James Walker
Communications Manager, Brian Edwards
Client Relations Manager, Steve Gray

AGENCIES, BOARDS, COMMISSIONS AND CROWN CORPORATIONS

Ontario Energy Board
Maple Leaf Mills Tower, Ste. 2601
2300 Yonge St., Box 2319, Toronto, M4P 1E4
General Inquiries: (416) 481-1967

The Ontario Energy Board regulates all natural gas utilities in Ontario except those municipally owned and controlled. It is responsible for establishing rates and charges for the transmission, storage, distribution, and sale of natural gas in the province, and for the designation and authorization of storage areas, construction of transmission lines, expropriation for natural gas pipelines, and franchises for natural gas companies to serve designated areas. The Board acts upon references from the Minister of Energy regarding Ontario Hydro wholesale rates and other rate-related matters, and from the Lieutenant-Governor in Council on any question about energy. The Board answers to the legislature through the Minister of Energy.

Chairman, Stephanie Wychowanec, Q.C.
Vice-Chairman, J.C. Butler
Members: D.A. Dean, O.J. Cook, C.A. Wolf, M. Jackson, M. Daub, R.M. Higgin, M.P. O'Farrell
TECHNICAL AND ADMINISTRATIVE STAFF
Energy Returns Officer, R.A. Cappadocia
A/Director, Technical Operations, P. Coroyannakis
Board Secretary, S.A.C. Thomas
Project Manager, Engineering, C.J. Mackie
Special Projects Officer, D.R. Cochran

Ontario Energy Corp.
56 Wellesley St. W., 12th Flr.
Toronto, M7A 2B7
General Inquiry: (416) 926-4200

Ontario Energy Corporation was established by the government of Ontario in 1975 to implement government energy policies through investments in energy ventures. This mandate was reassessed in 1986 and the Corporation commenced disinvesting its portfolio. As of mid-1988, all assets and holdings of the Corporation had been liquidated or sold with the exception of a 25 per cent equity interest in Suncor.

President and CEO, Duncan M. Allan
Finance and Administration
Manager, Joe Geoghegan

Ontario Hydro

700 University Ave., Toronto, M5G 1X6
Switchboard: (416) 592-5111

One of the largest public power utilities in North America, Ontario Hydro is a special statutory corporation of the Province of Ontario. It was created in 1906 by the *Hydro-Electric Power Commission of Ontario Act* to generate, supply, and deliver electric power throughout Ontario. Ontario Hydro operates under the *Power Corporation Act* and reports to the government of Ontario through the Minister of Energy.

Ontario Hydro is responsible for the wholesale supply of electricity to more than 300 municipalities whose utilities, in turn, retail it to consumers in their service areas. It delivers electricity over 131,000 km of transmission and distribution lines, providing 95 per cent of Ontario's power.

Ontario Hydro generates electricity in hydro-electric, fossil-fired, and nuclear generating stations. Nuclear generation supplies about 50 per cent of Ontario's electricity requirements; hydraulic and fossil-fired generation each supply about 25 per cent. A construction program will add 3.6 million kilowatts of capacity, primarily nuclear, to the system between now and 1992. By that time, nuclear energy will provide almost two-thirds of the province's electricity. This added capacity will meet the electrical needs of the province through the 1990s.

The Corporation is financially self-sustaining with revenues derived through the rates charged to customers. Payment of the principal and interest on bonds and notes issued to the public by Ontario Hydro is guaranteed by the Province of Ontario.

Ontario Hydro is administered by a board of directors consisting of a chairman, a vice-chairman, a president, and not more than 10 other directors.

Chairman, Robert C. Franklin
Executive Office
Director, D.A. Dack
Gen. Counsel and Secretary, L.E. Leonoff
OFFICE OF THE PRESIDENT
President, Robert C. Franklin
Audit Director, F.A. Knautz
Corporate Planning
Vice-President, L.G. McConnell
Corporate Relations
Vice-President, N. Simon
Energy Management
Vice-President, D.B. MacCarthy

FINANCE AND SERVICES GROUP
Sr. Vice-President, E.H. Burdette
Treasurer, F.P. Chee
Supply and Services
Vice-President, A.R. Holt
Property Development
Vice-President, J.G. Matthew
Pension Fund Division
Director, Peter de Auer
HUMAN RESOURCES GROUP
Sr. Vice-President, S.G. Horton
OPERATIONS GROUP
Sr. Vice-President, A. Niitenberg
Design and Construction
Vice-President, W.G. Morison
Production
Vice-President, R.W. Bartholomew
Regions
Vice-President, H.K. Wright

MINISTRY OF THE ENVIRONMENT

135 St. Clair Ave. W., Toronto, M4V 1P5
General Inquiries: (416) 323-4321

MINISTER'S OFFICE

Minister, The Hon. James Bradley
Sr. Policy Advisor, Gary Gallon

DEPUTY MINISTER'S OFFICE

Dep. Minister, Gary S. Posen
Communications Branch
A/Director, Tim Nau
Legal Services Branch
Director, Bonnie Wein

Environmental Services Division

Asst. Dep. Minister, D. Balsillie
Air Resources Branch
Director, Ed Piché
Water Resources Branch
Director, Jim Bishop
Waste Management Branch
Director, Hardy Wong

Laboratory Services Branch
Resources Rd., Box 213, Rexdale, M9W 5L1
Director, G.C. Ronan

Intergovernmental Relations and Strategic Projects Division

Assoc. Dep. Minister, J.W. Giles
Hazardous Contaminants Branch
Director, Ivy Wile
Intergovernmental Relations and Strategic Projects
Co-ordinator, Ken Richards
Technical Advisor, W. Steggles
Strategic Project: Niagara River
Co-ordinator, Vacant
119 King St., Hamilton, L8N 3Z9
Strategic Project: St. Clair/Detroit

River Improvement
Co-ordinator, Vacant
Acid Precipitation Office
A/Co-ordinator, Walter Chan

Operations Division

Asst. Dep. Minister, J. Reid
Investigations and Enforcement Branch
Director, Alex Douglas
Northwestern Region
435 James St. S., Box 5000
Thunder Bay, P7C 5G6
Reg. Director, W. Scott
Northeastern Region
199 Larch St., Sudbury, P3E 5P9
Reg. Director, R. Hore
Southwestern Region
985 Adelaide St. S., London, N6E 1V3
Reg. Director, D. McTavish
Southeastern Region
133 Dalton St., Box 820, Kingston, K7L 4X6
Reg. Director, D. Guscott
West Central Region
119 King St., 12th Flr., Box 2112
Hamilton, L8N 3Z9
Reg. Director, Boris Boyko
Central Region
7 Ferrand Dr., Ste. 700, Don Mills, M3C 3C3
Reg. Director, G. Mierzynski
Approvals and Engineering
Exec. Director, C.E. McIntyre
Environmental Assessment Branch
Director, Brian Ward
Environmental Approvals and Land Use
Planning Branch Director, W. Balfour
Project Engineering Branch Director, J. Bray

CORPORATE RESOURCES DIVISION
Exec. Director, A. Castel
Policy and Planning Branch
Director, J.V. Merritt
Research and Technology Branch
Director, Jane Pagel
Human Resource Branch
A/Director, Ron Clark
Financial and Capital Management Branch
Director, Fausto Saponara
Systems Information and Technology Branch
Director, V. Rudik
Administrative Services Branch
A/Director, N. Vakharia
Management Audit Branch
Director, C.D. Mialkowsky
French Language Services
Asst. Director, N. Vakharia

AGENCIES, BOARDS AND COMMISSIONS

Board of Negotiation (Environment)
1 St. Clair Ave. W., Toronto, M4V 1K7

Chairman, M.I. Jeffery, Q.C.

Environmental Appeal Board
40 St. Clair Ave. W., 6th Flr., Toronto, M4V 1M2

Established under *The Environmental Protection Act, 1971,* the Environmental Appeal Board provides an appeal mechanism for persons affected by certain decisions made by the Ministry of the Environment or local health units.

The Board consists of 12 part-time members, including the chairman and vice-chairman, drawn from various occupations and parts of the province.

Chairman, Prof. Alan Bryant
Vice-Chairman, Knox M. Henry
Board Secretary, Yvette Dick

Environmental Assessment Advisory Committee
1 St. Clair Ave. W., 9th Flr., Toronto, M4V 1K6

The Environmental Assessment Advisory Committee provides advice to the Minister of Environment on requests for exemptions from the provisions of *The Environmental Assessment Act, 1975* and on requests or proposals for the designation of undertakings so as to render them subject to the Act. The Committee advises and comments on the reasons provided by the proponent for the exemption of an undertaking, in particular those reasons relating to public health and safety, economic necessity, and significance of environmental effects.

Chairman, Dr. P. Byer

Environmental Assessment Board
2300 Yonge St., Ste. 1201
Box 2382, Toronto, M4P 1E4

The Environmental Assessment Board was established on April 20, 1976, on the proclamation of *The Environmental Assessment Act, 1975.* The Board was given, at that time, the responsibility of conducting public hearings under the new Act as well as those required under *The Ontario Water Resources Act* and *The Environmental Protection Act, 1971.* Hearings under the latter two Acts had previously been conducted by the Environmental Hearing Board, which was absorbed into the Environmental Assessment Board. Under the Acts, the Board's basic purpose is to ensure, to the fullest extent possible, the participation of the public in the consideration of all environmental matters associated with the major development proposals which become the subject of such public hearings.

Under *The Consolidated Hearings Act, 1981,* passed on July 3, 1981, the Board may hold joint hearings with the Ontario Municipal Board on undertakings where more than one hearing by more than one tribunal is required under one or more of the Acts set out in the schedule to this piece of legislation.

Board membership consists, at present, of four full-time and six part-time members. Board members are appointed by the Lieutenant-Governor in Council.

Chairman, M.I. Jeffery, Q.C.
Vice-Chairmen: R.B. Eisen, Q.C.,
Mary G. Munro, Grace Patterson,
Dr. D.J. Kingham, Elie W. Martel
Board Secretary/Hearings Registrar,
Yvonne Lane
Asst. Board Secretary/Dep. Hearings
Registrar, Nada Davidovic

Environmental Compensation Corp.
2300 Yonge St., Ste. 1203
Box 2382, Toronto, M4P 1E4

The Environmental Compensation Corporation was created to administer compensation paid out by the government under Part IX of *The Environmental Protection Act, 1971,* the "Spills Bill". Compensation is paid by the Corporation to third-party victims of spills of environmentally damaging materials.

Among the types of loss or damage that the fund is intended to compensate for are property damage, bodily injury, cleanup cost, and economic loss. Before receiving assistance from the Corporation, the victim is required to exhaust all regular avenues of recourse such as insurance and civil litigation.

Chairman, Marjory Loveys
Director, John G.W. Manzig
Director, Geoffrey T.G. Scott

Farm Pollution Advisory Committee
R.R. 4, Hagersville, N0A 1H0

The Farm Pollution Advisory Committee was established by Order-in-Council in 1973, under the *Environmental Protection Act.*

The Committee consists of four farmers who are designated Provincial Officers under the Act. This Committee provides objective assessments of environmental situations as requested by ministry officials.

The Committee visits farms to investigate complaints and make recommendations concerning manure storage and spreading, cultivation, yard drainage, and ventilation of livestock and poultry buildings.

Chairman, Otto Crone

MISA Advisory Committee
112 St. Clair Ave. W., Toronto, M4V 2Y3

Chairman, Jim McLaren
Vice-Chairman, T. Vigod
Co-ordinator, Doug Vallery

Ontario Waste Management Corp.
2 Bloor St. W., 11th Flr., Toronto, M4W 3E2

The Ontario Waste Management Corporation (OWMC) was formally created by the *Ontario Waste Management Corporation Act,* S.O. 1981, Chapter 21, which received Royal Assent on July 3, 1981. The OWMC's primary responsibility is to design, construct, and operate a province-wide system for the treatment and disposal of liquid industrial and hazardous waste, and to develop a long-term program to assist in the reduction and recycling of such wastes.

Chairman and President, Dr. D.A. Chant
Director of Communications, Michael G. Scott
Operations Director, R.V. Griffiths
Facilities Development
Project Manager, Edgar H. Schmidt
Environmental Projects
Project Manager, Jim G. Micak
Finance and Administration
Director, L.K. Bentley
Marketing and Sales
Director, W.R. Lightowlers

Pesticides Advisory Committee
1 St. Clair Ave. W., 9th Flr., Toronto, M4V 1K6

The Pesticides Advisory Committee was established in 1971 on the proclamation of the *Pesticides Act,* R.S.O. 1980, Chapter 376. The Committee acts in an advisory capacity to the Minister of the Environment, and its functions, as defined in the Act, are as follows:
a) to review annually the content and operation of the Act and the Regulations, and recommend to the minister changes or amendments thereto;
b) to inquire into and consider any matter concerning pesticides and the control of pests that is considered advisable by the Committee or that is referred to it by the minister, and report thereon to the minister;
c) to review publications of the government of Ontario respecting pesticides and the control of pests, and report thereon to the minister; and
d) to perform such other functions as the Regulations prescribe.

Included among such other functions is the Committee's work in overseeing the funding of an annual research program. The objectives of this program are to find alternative pesticides for those deemed environmentally hazardous and thus restricted in use; to determine the potential environmental hazards of pesticides currently in use; and to reduce pesticide input into the environment. An annual assessment of the research projects is published each year.

Another important function of the Committee is to recommend a classification for all registered pesticides for storage, sale, and use in Ontario, in accordance with the Regulations.

The Committee currently consists of 14 members appointed by the Lieutenant-Governor in Council.

Chairman, Dr. K.A. Howard

Recycling Advisory Committee
119 King St. W., 9th Flr.
Box 2112, Hamilton, L8N 3Z9

Chairman, Wendy Cook

MINISTRY OF FINANCIAL INSTITUTIONS

555 Yonge St., Toronto, M7A 2H6
(except where otherwise noted)
General Inquiries: (416) 963-1111
Telex: 06-219786

MINISTER'S OFFICE
Minister, The Hon. Murray Elston

DEPUTY MINISTER'S OFFICE
Dep. Minister, Robert A. Simpson

FINANCE AND ADMINISTRATION
Exec. Co-ordinator, Daniel H. Rivet
Administration
Manager, Valerie St. Onge
Investigations Branch
Director, Philip Yakubovich
Policy and Planning Branch
Director, Colleen Parrish
Legal Services Branch
Director, Marie Rounding

INSURANCE OPERATIONS
Sup't of Insurance, James J. Wilbee
Director, E.J. Wells
Licencing and Examinations
Director, G. Swanson
Agents, Brokers and Adjusters
Registrar, William G. Stride
Motor Vehicle Accident Claims
Director, Barbara Dudzinski
DEPOSIT INSTITUTIONS
Sup't, B. Cass
Loan and Trust Corporations Branch
Director, T.T. Robins
Credit Unions and Co-operatives Branch
Director, Norm Wilson

AGENCIES, BOARDS AND COMMISSIONS

Ontario Automobile Insurance Board
5 Park Home Ave., 4th Flr.
North York, M2N 6L4

Chairman, John Kruger
Gen. Manager, George L. Cook
Finance and Rate Review
Exec. Director, Norm Seeny
Sr. Legal Counsel, Cheryl Cottle
Research and Communication
Manager, Thomas Vares

Ontario Securities Commission
20 Queen St. W., Ste. 1800
Box 55, Toronto, M5H 3S8
General Inquiries: (416) 597-0681

The Ontario Securities Commission is responsible for the administration of the following Acts: *The Securities Act, The Commodity Futures Act, The Toronto Stock Exchange Act,* and *The Deposits Regulation Act.* In addition, it is vested with certain exempting and enforcing powers under *The Business Corporations Act.*

The Commission's goal is to maintain and foster confidence in the capital markets of Ontario. In administering the legislation and in articulating the policies it has the discretionary power to develop according to the legislation, it strives:

* through its investigatory and enforcement powers, to protect the public from fraud, manipulation, or misconduct in the securities and futures markets;
* to ensure that investors have full, true, and plain disclosure of material facts in the disclosure documents relating to publicly offered securities and have accurate and timely continuing information about reporting issuers to assist them in arriving at informed investment decisions;
* through its powers to grant, suspend, or cancel registration, to ensure that only persons who have achieved a minimum standard of honesty, good reputation, and competence are admitted as registrants and to supervise the various standards imposed upon registrants by the Acts, Regulations, and self-regulatory bodies; and
* increasingly, in recent years, to impose a standard of fair conduct in dealings between parties in the market place through the issuance of policy statements to deal with perceived abuses.

The Securities Act, The Commodity Futures Act, and respective Regulations thereunder are the work of the Commission. Of necessity, in such complex and technically opaque fields, great reliance has to be placed on the draftsmanship of the Commission and on its monitoring of the continuing stream of economic, financial, and technological developments in order that Acts, Regulations, and policies are up-to-date and realistic.

Chairman, Stanley M. Beck, Q.C.
Vice-Chairman, Charles R.B. Salter, Q.C.
Secretary to the Commission,
Julie-Luce B. Farrell
Exec. Director, Ermanno Pascutto
Legal Advisor, Priscilla H. Healy
Corporate Finance
Director, Robert E. Steen
Capital Markets
Director, Jamie Scarlett
Registration
A/Dep. Director, Mary Kelly
Enforcement Branch
Director, J. Groia
Commodity Futures
Dep. Director, David D. Walters
Chief Accountant, Michael Meagher
Gen. Counsel, Frank R. Allen

Pension Commission of Ontario
101 Bloor St. W., 9th Flr., Toronto, M7A 2K2

The Pension Commission of Ontario was established in 1963 to administer *The Pension*

Benefits Act, which came into force Jan. 1, 1965. The Commission sets ground rules for private pension plans to ensure that they are properly funded, safely invested, and paid out according to law. The role of the Pension Commission is to promote the establishment, extension, and improvement of pension plans throughout Ontario; to register the pension plans that qualify for registration; to administer and enforce *The Pension Benefits Act;* to conduct surveys and research programs; and to assess and collect fees for Annual Returns, new plans, and the Pension Benefits Guaranty Fund, which is administered by the Commission.

Chairman, John Kruger
Sup't of Pensions, Robert Hawkes, Q.C.
Pension Plans
Director, Barrie Entwistle
Secretariat Director, Vacant
Operations Director, Leonard Lu
Pensions Managers: Mirko Slak, Nurez Jiwani

MINISTRY OF GOVERNMENT SERVICES
Ferguson Blk., 77 Wellesley St. W.
Toronto, M7A 1N3
(except where otherwise indicated)
General Inquiry: (416) 965-3535

MINISTER'S OFFICE
Ferguson Blk., 12th Flr.
77 Wellesley St. W., Toronto, M7A 1N3
Minister, The Hon. Richard Patten

DEPUTY MINISTER'S OFFICE
Ferguson Blk., 12th Flr.
77 Wellesley St. W., Toronto, M7A 1N3
Dep. Minister, Dennis Caplice
Communications Services Branch
Director, Joan Krantzberg
Northern Ontario Relocation Program
Exec. Co-ordinator, Arnold Bock

SUPPLY AND SERVICES DIVISION
Ferguson Blk., 12th Flr.
77 Wellesley St. W., Toronto, M7A 1N3
Exec. Director, Anne Beaumont
CHRIS Project
101 Bloor St., 2nd Flr., Toronto, M5S 1P7
A/Director, David Ritcey
Employee Services Branch
880 Bay St., 5th Flr., Toronto, M7A 1N3
Director, Gary Browne
Employee Benefits and Data Services Branch
George Drew Bldg., 17th Flr.
25 Grosvenor St., Toronto, M7A 1R1
Director, David Ferguson
General Services Branch
George Drew Bldg., 16th Flr.
25 Grosvenor St., Toronto, M7A 1R2
Director, Alan Leslie

Purchasing Services Branch
Ferguson Blk., 6th Flr.
77 Wellesley St. W., Toronto, M7A 1N3
Director, Larry Loop
Information Services Branch
Ferguson Blk., 7th Flr.
77 Wellesley St. W., Toronto, M7A 1N3
Director, Eric Steeves

COMPUTER AND TELECOMMUNICATION SERVICES
155 University Ave., 8th Flr., Toronto, M5H 3B7
Customer Service and Technology
Gen. Manager, Kam Jain
Operations and Energy
Gen. Manager, Robert Beatty
Technologies Branch Director, Vacant
User Services Branch Director, Vacant
Operations Branch Director, Vacant

FINANCE AND ADMINISTRATIVE SERVICES DIVISION
Ferguson Blk., 12th Flr.
77 Wellesley St. W., Toronto, M7A 1N3
Exec. Director, Margaret Rodrigues
Audit Branch
George Drew Bldg., 13th Flr.
25 Grosvenor St., Toronto, M7A 1Y6
Director, Margaret Shiu
Finance and Office Services Branch
Ferguson Blk., 9th Flr.
77 Wellesley St. W., Toronto, M7A 1N3
Director, Vern Chaves
Systems Branch
Ferguson Blk., 4th Flr.
77 Wellesley St. W., Toronto, M7A 1N3
Director, Michael Roach
Legal Services Branch
Ferguson Blk., 3rd Flr.
77 Wellesley St. W., Toronto, M7A 1N3
Director, David Bernstein
Human Resources Service Branch
Ferguson Blk., 8th Flr.
77 Wellesley St. W., Toronto, M7A 1N3
Director, Maria Wacyk

Realty Group
Ferguson Blk., 12th Flr.
77 Wellesley St. W., Toronto, M7A 1N3
Asst. Dep. Minister, Robert W. Riggs
Land Management Branch
777 Bay St., 15th Flr., Toronto, M5G 2E5
Director, David McHugh
Land Development Branch
777 Bay St., 16th Flr., Toronto, M5G 2E5
Director, Andrew Beattie
Land Marketing Branch
777 Bay St., 16th Flr., Toronto, M5G 2E5
Director, Peter Johansen

PROGRAM DEVELOPMENT AND MANAGEMENT DIVISION
Ferguson Blk., 13th Flr.
77 Wellesley St. W., Toronto, M7A 1N3

Exec. Director, Ron Gotts
Client Services Branch
Director, Virginia West
Portfolio Management
Director, Barry Gutteridge
Corporate Management and Mortgage Branch
Director, Ralph Grant

DESIGN AND CONSTRUCTION DIVISION
Ferguson Blk., 13th Flr.
77 Wellesley St. W., Toronto, M7A 1N3
Exec. Director, Robert Lowry
Project Management Branch
Macdonald Blk., Rm. M1B-90
Queen's Park, Toronto, M7A 1N3
Director, Brian Jewitt
Design Services Branch
Ferguson Blk., 11th Flr.
77 Wellesley St. W., Toronto, M7A 1N3
Director, Peter Crabtree
Contract Management Branch
Director, John Mair

PROPERTY MANAGEMENT DIVISION
Ferguson Blk., 5th Flr.
77 Wellesley St. W., Toronto, M7A 1N3
Exec. Director, John Jackson
Central Operations Branch
Director, Mike Lukacko
Leasing Services Branch
Director, Delbert Jackson

REGIONS:

Toronto Region
880 Bay St., 7th Flr., Toronto, M5S 1Z8
Reg. Director, Albert Côté

Northern Region
Ontario Government Bldg., 6th Flr.
199 Larch St., Sudbury, P3E 5P9
Reg. Director, Andy Gibson

Southwestern Region
380 Wellington St., Ste. 1803
London, N6A 5B5
Reg. Director, Bill Minion

Eastern Director
780 Midpark Dr., Rm. 205, Kingston, K7M 7P6
Reg. Director, Brian Bellinger

DISTRICT AND AREA OFFICES:

Lakeshore District
171 Judson St., Toronto, M8Z 1A4
Manager, Ed Menezes

Orillia District
24 James St. E., Box 790, Orillia, L3V 6K7
Manager, Charles Schaab

Guelph District
53 Victoria Rd. S., Guelph, N1E 5P7
Manager, Harry Higgins

Kemptville District
Postal Bag 2008, Kemptville, K0G 1J0
Manager, Wallis Cousineau

Kingston District
1055 Princess St., Postal Bag 8000
Kingston, K7L 5A8
Manager, Bill Graham

London District
900 Highbury Ave., Box 5452, London, N6A 4L6
Manager, Jim Gill

Sudbury District
Hwy. 69, South McFarlane Lake
Box 2520, Stn. A, Sudbury, P3A 4S9
Manager, Rod Fabbro

Sault Ste. Marie Area
445 Albert St. E., Sault Ste. Marie, P6A 2J9
Manager, Dave Campbell

Timmins Area
Hollinger Lane, Box 520
Schumacher, P0N 1G0
Manager, Omer Bazinet

North Bay District
1353 Gorman St., North Bay, P1B 2Y3
Manager, Doug Brown

Thunder Bay District
500 Algoma St. N., Box 3020
Thunder Bay, P7B 5G5
Manager, Carl Westerback

Kenora Area
720 Robertson St., Box 2840, Kenora, P9N 3X8
Manager, Bruce Lawrence

AGENCIES, BOARDS AND COMMISSIONS

Ontario Mortgage Corp.
62 Wellesley St. W., Toronto, M7A 1N3

The Ontario Mortgage Corporation was created in 1974 to provide mortgage assistance under a variety of government initiatives aimed at making home ownership available to low and moderate income groups.

The Corporation administers various mortgage programs established to assist in the provision of both rental and ownership accommodation and to stimulate the construction industry by encouraging employment.

President and Chairman, Robert Lynch
Vice-President and Gen. Manager,
Robert W. Riggs

Provincial Judges Benefits Board
George Drew Bldg., 17th Flr.
25 Grosvenor St., Toronto, M7A 1R1

Chairman, Michael Wadsworth
120 Bloor St. E., Toronto, M4W 1B8

Public Service Superannuation Board
George Drew Bldg., 17th Flr.
25 Grosvenor St., Toronto, M7A 1R1

The Board was first established in 1920 under an Act of the legislature of Ontario. It now operates under *The Public Service Superannuation Act,* R.S.O. 1980, Chapter 419. Its members are appointed by the Lieutenant-Governor in Council.

The Board advises the minister responsible for the administration of the Act (now the Chairman of Management Board) and approves disability and certain survivor pension benefits. It evaluates eligibility in special cases and hears appeals against routine decisions made by the Employee Benefits and Data Services Branch of the Ministry of Government Services.

Chairman, Miss S.J. Wychowanec, Q.C.
2300 Yonge St., 26th Flr., Toronto, M4P 1E4
Secretary, Basil Cooke
George Drew Bldg., 17th Flr.
25 Grosvenor St., Toronto, M7A 1R1

MINISTRY OF HEALTH

Hepburn Blk., 80 Grosvenor St.
Toronto, M7A 2C4
(unless otherwise indicated)
General Inquiries: (416) 965-3101
1-800-268-1153

MINISTER'S OFFICE
Minister, The Hon. Elinor Caplan

DEPUTY MINISTER'S OFFICE
Dep. Minister, Dr. Martin Barkin
Communications and Information Branch
Director, D. Rimstead
Legal Services Branch
Director, Gilbert Sharpe

Planning and Programs
Asst. Dep. Minister, D. Corder
Sr. Policy Advisor, Dr. Bruce Buchanan
HEALTH PROGRAMS DIVISION
Exec. Co-ordinator, C. Bigenwald
Co-ordinators:
Mental Health and Addictions, D. Macfarlane
AIDS, Dr. E. Wallace
Emergency Services, J. Wong
Cardiovascular Health, G. Kumagni
Systems, H. Spence
Native Health, D. Stuart
Cancer, Vacant
POLICY DEVELOPMENT AND RESEARCH
Exec. Co-ordinator, A.E. LeBlanc
DISTRICT HEALTH COUNCIL PROGRAM
Exec. Co-ordinator, D. Mauro
FRENCH-LANGUAGE HEALTH SERVICES
Exec. Co-ordinator, D. Fortin

Women's Health Bureau
880 Bay St., 2nd Flr., Toronto, M5S 1Z8
Manager, J. Hill

Community Health
Asst. Dep. Minister, Dr. R.M. MacMillan
Laboratory Services Branch
81 Resources Rd., Islington, M9W 5K9
Director, Dr. D.S. Willoughby
Health Promotion Branch
700 Bay St, 14th Flr., Toronto, M5G 1Z6
Director, Myrna Francis
COMMUNITY HEALTH PROGRAMS DIVISION
15 Overlea Blvd., 5th Flr., Toronto, M4H 1A9
Exec. Co-ordinator, G. Eisenstein

Community Health Programs Branch
15 Overlea Blvd., 6th Flr., Toronto, M4H 1A9
Director, D. Loranger
Community Mental Health Branch
A/Director, L. Hessey
Public Health Branch
15 Overlea Blvd., 5th Flr., Toronto, M4H 1A9
Director and Chief Medical Officer
of Health, Dr. Richard Schabas

Institutional Health
Asst. Dep. Minister, J. Kaufman
Teaching and Specialty Hospitals Branch
15 Overlea Blvd., 7th Flr., Toronto, M4H 1A9
Director, P. McGee
Psychiatric Hospitals Branch
Director, T. Firestone
Nursing Homes Branch
15 Overlea Blvd., 5th Flr., Toronto, M4H 1A9
Director, H. Boon
Community Hospitals Branch
15 Overlea Blvd., 7th Flr., Toronto, M4H 1A9
Director, R. Sapsford
Hospital Planning Branch
15 Overlea Blvd., 7th Flr., Toronto, M4H 1A9
Director, M. Tino

Personal Health
Asst. Dep. Minister, M.C. Lindberg
Ambulance Services Branch
7 Overlea Blvd., 7th Flr., Toronto, M4H 1A8
Director, G. Brand
Professional Relations Branch
7 Overlea Blvd., 1st Flr., Toronto, M4H 1A8
Director, A.R. Barrows
DRUGS AND DEVICES DIVISION
Exec. Director, F. Lortie
Drug Programs Branch
7 Overlea Blvd., 6th Flr., Toronto, M4H 1A8
Director, Y.S. Drazin
Assistive Devices Branch
7 Overlea Blvd., 6th Flr., Toronto, M4H 1A8
Director, Donna Segal

Corporate Administration
Asst. Dep. Minister, R. LeNeveu
Audit Branch
7 Overlea Blvd., 7th Flr., Toronto, M4H 1A8
Director, K. Amin
FINANCE AND ADMINISTRATION DIVISION
Exec. Director, P. Donoghue
Freedom of Information
Program Co-ordinator, Eric Novick
Health Boards Secretariat
Registrar, J. Colangeli

Contact the Health Boards Secretariat for all of the following boards: Denture Therapists Appeal Board, Funeral Services Review Board, Health Disciplines Board, Health Services Appeal Board, Health Facilities Appeal Board, Health Protection Appeal Board, Hospital Appeal Board, Laboratory Review Board, Nursing Homes Review Board, Psychiatric Review Boards (Review of involuntary admissions to psychiatric facilities)

Lieutenant Governor's Board of Review
A/Registrar, H. Tyrell
Library
15 Overlea Blvd., 1st Flr., Toronto, M4H 1A9
Supervisor, V. Brunka
Finance and Accounting Branch
7 Overlea Blvd., 5th Flr., Toronto, M4H 1A9
Fiscal Resources Branch
Director, J. Leggatt
Supply and Services Branch
15 Overlea Blvd., 4th Flr., Toronto, M4H 1A9
Director, R.L. Brethour
Human Resources Branch
Director, R. Oss

Claims Payment and Systems

Asst. Dep. Minister, D. McNaughton
HEALTH INSURANCE DIVISION
Macdonald-Cartier Bldg., 2nd Flr.
49 Place d'Armes, Box 48, Kingston, K7L 5J3
Gen. Manager, M.H. Gibson
Special Services Unit
7 Overlea Blvd., 1st Flr., Toronto, M4H 1A8
Manager, H. D'Rozario
Membership Programs
Director, P. Malcolmson
Professional Services Branch
Director, Dr. J.D. Proud
Operations Branch Director, D. Buchanan

INFORMATION AND SYSTEMS DIVISION
Exec. Director, D. Harry
Information Resources and Services Branch
15 Overlea Blvd., 2nd Flr., Toronto, M4H 1A9
Director, D. Bogart
Insurance Systems Branch
Macdonald-Cartier Bldg., 5th Flr.
49 Place d'Armes, Kingston, K7K 5J3
Director, P. Burgess
Management Systems Branch
15 Overlea Blvd., 2nd Flr., Toronto, M4H 1A9
Director, S. Russell

OHIP DISTRICT OFFICES AND DIRECTORS:
Hamilton
119 King St. W., Hamilton, L8P 4T9
A.W. Board
Kingston
1055 Princess St., Ste. 401, Kingston, K7L 5T3
F. Feld
London
227 Queens Ave., London, N6A 1J8
C. Mee
Mississauga
201 City Centre Dr., Mississauga, L5B 2T4
W.R. Josiah
Oshawa
419 King St. W., Oshawa, L1J 7J2
A.J. Arkelian
Ottawa
75 Albert St., 7th Flr., Ottawa, K1P 5Y9
S. St. Germain
Sudbury
199 Larch St., 8th Flr., Sudbury, P3E 5R1
E. Mahood

Thunder Bay
435 James St. S., 2nd Flr.
Thunder Bay, P7E 6E3
G. Friday
Toronto
2195 Yonge St., Toronto, M4S 2B2
I. Searle

AGENCIES, BOARDS AND COMMISSIONS

Alcoholism and Drug Addiction Research Foundation
33 Russell St., Toronto, M5S 2S1
General Inquiries: (416) 595-6000

The Alcoholism and Drug Addiction Research Foundation is a Crown corporation which operates specialized research, educational, clinical, and service development programs throughout the province. The Foundation, established by an Act of the Ontario legislature, is supported by the Ministry of Health through direct annual grants.

Responsibility for the Foundation's overall policies rests with the members of the Foundation, a group of community representatives appointed by the Lieutenant-Governor in Council. The members, who serve voluntarily, appoint the president who is the chief executive officer. A professional advisory board is appointed by the members with the concurrence of the Lieutenant-Governor in Council.

The Foundation's provincial headquarters at 33 Russell St., Toronto, house the following divisions: Social and Biological Studies, the Clinical Institute, Prevention and Health Promotion Programs, Administrative and Support Services, and part of the Regional Programs Division. Across Ontario, the Foundation maintains 29 regional offices which assist communities to develop appropriate community-based services for the treatment and prevention of alcohol and other drug problems. The guiding principle is to relate such community programs to Ontario's developing system of regional and district health councils and education, justice, and social-service networks.

The Foundation's School for Addiction Studies, located at 8 May St., Toronto, offers training and educational courses to professionals whose work involves dealing with alcoholics and other drug-dependent persons.

Chairman, William P. Moher
President, Dr. J.A. Marshman
Sr. Secretary, J. Crawford
Clinical Institute Division
Director, E.F. Watson
Social and Biological Studies Division
Director, Dr. H. Cappell
Community Services Division
Director, J.C. La Rocque
Administration, Finance and Support
Operations Division
Director, A.P. Charles
School for Addiction Studies
Director, Dr. D.E. Meeks

Office of Corporate Communications
Director, J. Soulodre
Inter-organizational Affairs
Director, H.J. Schankula
Prevention and Health Promotion
Director, L. Hershfield

Healing Arts Radiation Protection (HARP) Commission

7 Overlea Blvd., 6th Flr., Toronto, M4H 1A8

The Healing Arts Radiation Protection (HARP) Commission was established under the provisions of the *Healing Arts Radiation Protection Act* to ensure that the exposure of Ontario residents to radiation from medical x-ray sources is as low as possible, consistent with the production of high-quality diagnostic images.

In consultation with its six advisory committees representing the disciplines of chiropractic medicine, dentistry, medical radiology, physics, podiatry, and radiological technology, the Commission develops regulations and guidelines to ensure the safe use of x-rays. In addition, the HARP Commission advises the Minister of Health on matters relating to x-ray safety and approves training courses for all personnel involved in the use of medical x-rays.

The activities of the HARP Commission, as well as information relating to the creation of the Commission and its advisory committees, are detailed in the Commission's annual report.

Chairman, Gerard P. Charette

Ontario Cancer Institute

500 Sherbourne St., Toronto, M4X 1K9

Chairman, Kenneth R. Clarke
CEO, Dr. D. Carlow
Administrator, Johanne E. Ratz

The Ontario Cancer Treatment and Research Foundation

7 Overlea Blvd., 2nd Flr., Toronto, M4H 1A8

The Ontario Cancer Treatment and Research Foundation supports programs of diagnosis, treatment, and research in cancer, and operates seven regional cancer treatment centres (associated with hospitals) and 31 consultative and follow-up clinics. It is affiliated with the Ontario Cancer Institute (incorporating the Princess Margaret Hospital) in Toronto.

Services and rehabilitation programs funded include speech therapy, prosthetic devices, colostomy patients' program, transportation of patients travelling over 40 km, and chemotherapeutic drugs for needy Ontario patients. The Foundation maintains and operates six lodges where out-of-town ambulatory patients receiving treatment can be accommodated, and supports undergraduate and postgraduate study in oncology for medical, paramedical, and scientific personnel. It also supports career scientists, awards research scholarships, and funds clinical cancer investigation.

The statistical section promotes adequate reporting of cancer cases and compiles statistical data.

Chairman, M.A. Meighen
Exec. Director, Dr. J.W. Meakin
Sec.-Treasurer, R.D. Gray

Ontario Mental Health Foundation

365 Bloor St. E., Ste. 1708, Toronto, M4W 3L4

The Ontario Mental Health Foundation was established by a special Act of the legislature of the province of Ontario.

The Foundation provides support for mental health research. It has two programs: (1) grants for specific research projects and major equipment; and (2) research fellowships.

Chairman, M. Longdon
Exec. Director, Dr. D. Campbell

MINISTRY OF HOUSING

777 Bay St., Toronto, M5G 2E5
General Inquiries: (416) 585-7041

MINISTER'S OFFICE
Minister, The Hon. Chaviva Hosek

DEPUTY MINISTER'S OFFICE
Dep. Minister, Bryan Davies

Social Housing

Asst. Dep. Minister, Tim Casey
HOUSING FIELD OPERATIONS
Exec. Director, Dr. A.M. Wilson
Social Housing Programs Branch
Director, David Martin
Tenant Support Services Branch
Director, Mary Tate
Technical Support Branch
Director, P.G. Stonehouse

Housing Policy

Asst. Dep. Minister, Rita Burak
Corporate Resources Management
Gen. Manager, Arnie Temple
Housing Supply Policy Branch
Director, Crom Sparling
Rent Review Policy Branch
A/Director, Susan Gillespie

Rent Registry
415 Yonge St., 19th Flr., Toronto, M5B 2E7
Registrar, David Braund

AGENCIES, BOARDS AND COMMISSIONS

Ontario Housing Corp.

777 Bay St., Toronto, M5G 2E5

The Ontario Housing Corporation is the provincial agency which provides subsidized rental housing to qualified lower-income families, senior citizens, and the physically, developmentally, and psychiatrically handicapped.

The Corporation was formed on Aug. 11, 1964 as a Crown corporation in the provincial Department of Economics and Development. The Corporation underwent a major reorganization in November 1983, which involved a substantial expansion of the OHC mandate. Today, virtually everything connected with social housing in Ontario is under the mandate of the Corporation, including responsibility for all social housing programs and policies of the ministry.

The powers of the Ontario Housing Corp. are drawn from the *Ontario Housing Corporation Act,* and from the *Housing Development Act. The Ministry of Municipal Affairs and Housing Act, 1981,* confers responsibility on the minister for housing and related matters.

Family housing is available to parent(s) aged 18 years or more with at least one dependent child under 18 years of age. Those attending learning institutions on a full-time basis are considered dependents, even if they are more than 18 years of age.

Senior citizen accommodation is provided for couples when at least one spouse is aged 60 or more and for individuals aged 60 or more.

Physically handicapped persons under the age of 60 are also eligible to apply for subsidized housing, provided they are able to cope on their own.

Developmentally and psychiatrically handicapped persons under the age of 60 are eligible for subsidized housing. Such persons must be capable of living on their own based on the assessment of a professional agency.

OHC is providing housing for about 200,000 people in more than 300 communities. The Corporation's portfolio is made up of more than 84,000 public housing units, about 48,000 allocated to families and more than 36,000 to senior citizens.

Chairman, David B. Greenspan
Vice-Chairman and CEO, Tim Casey

Rent Review Hearings Board
77 Bloor St. W., 10th Flr., Toronto, M5S 1M2

In 1986, the Ontario legislature introduced the *Residential Rent Regulation Act.* The Rent Review Hearings Board was established under this Act.

The Board is an appeal board. Tenants or landlords directly affected by, and disagreeing with, a decision of the Minister of Housing may appeal to the Board. These decisions may relate to the determination of rent, disputed rent, rent rebate, and standards of rental units. As the result of a hearing, the Board will affirm, vary, or substitute its own order for the order of the minister.

The Board's appeal process, including the public hearing, is subject to the *Statutory Powers Procedure Act,* except for preferred conferences.

Twenty members, including the chairman and vice-chairman, were appointed in March 1987 to serve the Board's four regions in London, Sudbury, Ottawa, and Toronto.

Chairman, Dr. Ratna Ray
Vice-Chairman, P.P. Chadha
Sr. Legal Counsel, D. Burnside

MINISTRY OF INDUSTRY, TRADE AND TECHNOLOGY
Hearst Blk., 900 Bay St., Toronto, M7A 2E1
General Inquiry: (416) 965-1586

MINISTER'S OFFICE
Minister, The Hon. Monte Kwinter

DEPUTY MINISTER'S OFFICE
Dep. Minister, Gordon W. Gow
Audit Services Director, Mike Chang
Legal Services Director, Ingrid Peters
Communications Director, R. Stephens
Premier's Council Technology Fund
Director, M.F. Walmsley
Premier's Council Secretariat
Dep. Secretary, Helen Burstyn

Small Business, Services and Capital Projects
Asst. Dep. Minister, J.D. Girvin
Business Development
A/Director, Peter Tanaka
Small Business Director, P. Friedman
Service Sector Secretariat
Director, C. Kirsh

Industry and Trade Expansion
Assoc. Dep. Minister, D. Blair Tully
INVESTMENT AND REGIONAL OPERATIONS
Director, B.M. Hildebrand

Eastern Ontario
56 Sparks St., Ste. 404, Ottawa, K1P 5A9
Reg. Director, R. Wagner

Central East
5 Fairview Mall Dr., Ste. 480
Willowdale, M2J 2Z1
Reg. Director, Vacant

Central West
305 King St. W., Ste. 507, Kitchener, N2G 1B9
Reg. Director, D.M. Grant

Southwestern Ontario
195 Dufferin St., Ste. 607, London, N6A 1K7
Reg. Director, W.G. Long

UNITED STATES AND LATIN AMERICA
Director, John Ardagh

New York
Government of Ontario, Canada
800 Third Ave., Ste. 2800
New York, NY 10022 U.S.A.
Agent General, Walter Stothers
Sr. Representative, D. Benfield

Boston
Government of Ontario, Canada
Prudential Twr., Ste. 4066
800 Boylston St., Boston, MA 02199 U.S.A.
Sr. Representative, J. Brady

Chicago
Government of Ontario, Canada
Ste. 1806, 208 S. LaSalle St.
Chicago, IL 60604 U.S.A.
Sr. Representative, D. Counsell

Los Angeles
Government of Ontario, Canada
Ste. 1420, 700 S. Flower St.
Los Angeles, CA 90017 U.S.A.
Sr. Representative, Susan MacDonald

Dallas
Government of Ontario, Canada
Ste. 835, 14901 Quorum Dr.
Dallas, TX 75240 U.S.A.
Sr. Representative, E. Vita-Finzi

Atlanta
Government of Ontario, Canada
Ste. 620, 1100 Circle
75 Parkway, Atlanta, GA 30339 U.S.A.
Sr. Representative, J.B. Donoghue

EUROPE, MIDDLE EAST AND AFRICA
Director, H.L. Duerr

Frankfurt, Germany
Government of Ontario, Canada
Bockenheimer Landstr. 51/53
D-6000 Frankfurt/Main 1, Germany
Sr. Representative, Vacant

Paris, France
Ontario House, 109, rue du Faubourg
St. Honoré, 75008 Paris, France
Agent General, Gerald W. Doucet
Sr. Representative, Vacant

London, England
Government of Ontario
21 Knightsbridge, London SW1X 7LY, England
Agent General, Thomas Wells
Sr. Representative, J.B. Blanchard

PACIFIC RIM
Director, D.G. Jure

Tokyo, Japan
Government of Ontario, Canada
World Trade Center Bldg., Rm. 1219
4-1 Hamamatsu-cho 2-chome, Minato-ku
Tokyo 105, Japan
Agent General, Thomas E. Armstrong
Sr. Representative, D. Bond

Singapore
Government of Ontario, Canada
541 Orchard Rd., Liat Towers, Ste. 10-03
0923 Singapore
Sr. Representative, D. Cooper

Seoul, Korea
Government of Ontario, Canada
Canadian Embassy, C.Box 6299
Seoul 100, Korea
First Secretary, R. McCague

CHINA AND SOUTH ASIA
A/Director, H.L. Duerr

Hong Kong
Government of Ontario, Canada

Admiralty Ctr., Twr. I, Ste. 1303
18 Harcourt Rd., Hong Kong
Sr. Representative, R.H. Smart

New Delhi, India
Government of Ontario, Canada
N-104 Panchshila Park
New Delhi - 100 017, India
Sr. Representative, R. Halfnight

Ontario-Jiangsu Science and Technology Ctr.
Taipingmenwai, Suojincun, Nanjing, Jiangsu
People's Republic of China
Co-Director, C.K. Pan

Northern Ontario Industry
500 Bay St., 2nd Flr., Sault Ste. Marie, P6A 1X4
Asst. Dep. Minister, J.D. McClure
Reg. Director, R.C. Sawchuk
ADMINISTRATION
Exec. Director, Amber J. Armitage
Human Resources
Director, Tom Clark
Management Services
Director, John Chapman
Finance and Systems
Director, Brian Wood

Policy and Technology
Asst. Dep. Minister, D. Redgrave
Technology Policy Director, Vacant
Industry and Trade Policy
Director, D.S. Barrows
Strategic Planning Secretariat
Sr. Manager, T. Melnyk

Ontario Centre for Microelectronics
30 Colonnade Rd., Nepean, K2E 7J6
General Inquiries: (613) 723-7499
A/President, C. Williams

*Ontario Centre for Automotive Parts
Technology*
80 King St., Ste. 804, St. Catharines, L2R 7G1
General Inquiries: (416) 688-2600
President, G. Lacy

*Ontario Centre for Farm Machinery and Food
Processing Technology*
870 Richmond St., Chatham, N7M 5J5
President, G.B. Fossenier

Ontario Centre for Advanced Manufacturing
743 Monaghan Rd., Peterborough, K9J 5K2
President, Ken Jones

*Ontario Centre for Resource Machinery
Technology*
127 Cedar St., 4th Flr., Sudbury, P3E 1B1
General Inquiries: (705) 673-6606
President, John Dodge

**AGENCIES, BOARDS, COMMISSIONS AND
CROWN CORPORATIONS**

Ontario Development Corp.
56 Wellesley St. W., 5th Flr., Toronto, M7A 2E7

The Government of Ontario encourages economic development and employment growth by providing selective financial assistance for the establishment and expansion of manufacturing and tourism facilities. This assistance is channelled regionally to business and industry through three Crown corporations: the Ontario Development Corp. (serving central and southwestern Ontario), the Northern Ontario Development Corp., and the Eastern Ontario Development Corp. A fourth Crown corporation, Innovation Ontario, was recently established to provide venture capital assistance to small and emerging high-technology firms.

By directing the province's financial assistance programs through these separate but co-ordinated agencies, Ontario can respond flexibly to the unique characteristics and demands of the province's distinct economic regions.

Business proposals are assessed by the Corporation against regional, technical, export, and social considerations to ensure overall compatibility with the province's economic priorities and the need of the applicant for ODC participation.

Chairman, Peter White
President and CEO, David C. MacKinnon
Corporate Affairs
A/Director, Gary Sullivan
Legal Services Director, Ingrid Peters
Loan Administration
Director, K.G. MacMillan
Loan Applications Director, J. Mitchell
Finance and Administration
A/Director, Robert Winter
Special Financial Services
Director, F.R. Winter
INNOVATION ONTARIO CORP.
56 Wellesley St. W., 7th Flr., Toronto, M7A 2E7
Chairman, D. Green
Director, Michael St. Amant
EASTERN ONTARIO DEVELOPMENT CORP.
Chairman, C. Ian Ross
Loan Applications Director, Vacant
NORTHERN ONTARIO DEVELOPMENT CORP.
Ontario Government Bldg.
199 Larch St., 4th Flr., Sudbury, P3E 5P9
Chairman, Pierre Belanger
Loan Applications
A/Director, J. Symington

Ontario International Corp.
56 Wellesley St. W., 7th Flr., Toronto, M7A 2E4

Created in 1980, the Ontario International Corporation (OIC) is a primary marketing agency whose principal functions are to facilitate the marketing and sale of Ontario services, expertise, and related capital goods overseas and to co-ordinate public- and private-sector skills for international capital projects. Government direction of the Corporation is exercised through the Ministry of Industry, Trade and Technology. In 1986, the Corporation was reorganized into three groups: Eastern Division, Western Division, and Corporate Development Division.

The Corporation's primary functions are as follows:

1) to assist Ontario's private sector in selling its consulting expertise, capital goods, and training services in the world market for capital and training projects;
2) to promote and support the marketing of Ontario's public-sector expertise and systems internationally, in conjunction with the private sector; and
3) to provide intergovernment contact and an Ontario government presence in support of exports of services, capital goods, and training for international capital projects.

In pursuing this role, OIC has established a broad range of global contacts including Canadian federal posts abroad, foreign government ministries, private-sector overseas capital projects, and international financial institutions such as The World Bank, Asian Development Bank, Inter-American Development Bank, and The African Development Bank. Canadian contacts include the Canadian International Development Agency, the Export Development Corp., and the Canadian Commercial Corp.

To assist in the promulgation of Ontario-based company expertise, the Corporation maintains listings of Ontario engineering, architectural, construction, educational, management, specialty, and engineering consulting firms, as well as existing consortia of these types of companies, which are available to foreign buyers.

Although the Corporation is not primarily a funding agency, and does not compete with the private sector, it can provide forgivable loans on a shared basis against the agreed costs of pursuing an identifiable foreign project. OIC constantly explores appropriate foreign markets, identifying and co-ordinating transactions that will benefit both the foreign client and Ontario business. It can provide a contractual relationship when it supports private-sector activities.

Chairman, Frank S. Miller
President and CEO, D. Blair Tully

EASTERN DIVISION
A/Vice-President, W.A. Rathbun
Director, South Asia, Colin Macfarlane
Director, Middle East, Aladin M. Wahba
Director, Africa, Kim F. Harris
Director, Europe, Sandra E. Bruce
International Market Development Officer, Rowena E. Dias

WESTERN DIVISION
Vice-President, H.L. Wood
Director, Southeast Asia, Robert L. Decent
Director, South America, Fred A. Sheehy
Director, Caribbean and Central America, James D. Thompson
Director, China, Vacant

CORPORATE DEVELOPMENT DIVISION
Vice-President, W.A. Rathbun
Finance and Administration
Manager, Verne M. Coates
Development Officer, Sonya H. Lambert

ORTECH International

Sheridan Park, 2395 Speakman Dr.
Mississauga, L5K 1B3

As an independent, non-profit, contract research organization formerly known as the Ontario Research Foundation, ORTECH provides comprehensive technological capabilities to small and medium companies that are not large enough to have their own research and development facilities, and technological specialization to larger companies to complement their own in-house resources. Services offered include research, product and process development, and innovation, testing and analytic services related to production and to products. All ORTECH services are conducted on a confidential basis. Patents resulting are assigned to the client.

ORTECH's professional and technical support staff form project teams on the basis of related scientific disciplines. Areas of major emphasis include energy, environment, materials, products and processes, and resources.

ORTECH's president reports to a board of governors consisting of 18 prominent industrialists and scientists. These governors serve without fee and are appointed by the Lieutenant-Governor of Ontario for a five-year term. Each member of the board is eligible for re-appointment.

President, W.P. Midghall
Marketing
Vice-President, W.D. Heaslip
Finance
Vice-President and Sec.-Treasurer, B.T. Porter
Advanced Manufacturing and Engineering
Vice-President, R.W. Neville

MINISTRY OF INTERGOVERNMENTAL AFFAIRS

Mowat Blk., 900 Bay St., Toronto, M7A 1C2
General Inquiries: (416) 965-4706
Fax: (416) 965-2096; Telex: 06218562

MINISTER'S OFFICE

Minister, The Hon. David Peterson

DEPUTY MINISTER'S OFFICE

Dep. Minister, David Cameron
Communication Branch
Director, Larry Kent
Information Officer, Patricia MacDonell
Chief of Protocol, Gabrielle Kirschbaum
Planning and Management Group
Exec. Co-ordinator, Sam J. Clasky

Office of Federal/Provincial Relations Branch

Asst. Dep. Minister, Peter Sadlier-Brown
International Relations Branch
Exec. Co-ordinator, Horst Intscher

MINISTRY OF LABOUR

400 University Ave., Toronto, M7A 1T7

MINISTER'S OFFICE

Minister, The Hon. Greg Sorbara

DEPUTY MINISTER'S OFFICE

Dep. Minister, Glenn R. Thompson
Legal Branch
Director, Judith Wolfson

FINANCE AND ADMINISTRATION DIVISION
Exec. Director, Fred Peters
Internal and Management Audit
A/Director, Pat Cummings
Administrative Operations Branch
Director, R.R. Hogarth
Financial Management and Analysis Branch
Director, Linda Petterson
Communications Branch
Director, R. Cohen
Human Resources Branch
Director, N.E. Mayne
Management Information Systems Branch
Director, Vacant

Labour Policy and Programs

Asst. Dep. Minister, Vacant
Labour Programs
Exec. Director, Arthur Gladstone
Labour Policy and Communications
Exec. Co-ordinator, Cindy Morton
Policy Branch
A/Director, Nick Ignatieff
Handicapped Employment Program
A/Manager, John Rae
Employment Standards Branch
Director, Penny Dutton
Employment Adjustment Branch
Director, H. Shardlow

Occupational Health and Safety Division

Asst. Dep. Minister, Tim Millard
Policy and Regulations Branch
Director, Dr. N. Shulman
Construction Health and Safety Branch
Director, W. Melinyshyn
Industrial Health and Safety Branch
Director, Vic Pakalnis
Health and Safety Support Services Branch
Director, Dr. P. Pelmear
Mining Health and Safety Branch
Director, Paavo Kivisto

Industrial Relations Division

Asst. Dep. Minister, L.V. Pathe
Conciliation and Mediation Services Branch
Director, Romain Verheyn
Preventive Mediation Programs
Asst. Director, Fraser Kean
Office of Arbitration
400 University Ave., 25th Flr., Toronto, M7A 1T7
Director, Jean Read

AGENCIES, BOARDS AND COMMISSIONS

Advisory Council on Occupational Health and Occupational Safety
400 University Ave., 11th Flr., Toronto, M7A 1T7

The Advisory Council on Occupational Health and Occupational Safety was formed in October 1977 and replaced the former Labour Safety Council and the Advisory Council on Occupational and Environmental Health. Its primary objective is to advise the Minister of Labour on matters relating to occupational health and safety in Ontario. Membership currently stands at 17 and, in accordance with section 10 of *The Occupational Health and Safety Act,* is made up of management, labour, technical and professional persons, and the public who are concerned with and have knowledge of occupational health and occupational safety.

Advice given to the minister by the Council, together with the minister's response, is published in the Council's annual report; copies are available in university, community college, and other resource libraries, and through the Ontario Government Book Store.

Chairman, Dr. Dennis McCalla
Exec. Co-ordinator, V. Biggar
Research Officers: P.L. Chan, S. Spencer

Grievance Settlement Board
180 Dundas St. W., Ste. 2100
Toronto, M5G 1Z8

Pursuant to the *Crown Employees Collective Bargaining Act,* the Grievance Settlement Board became the forum for the hearing of employee/union grievances from ministry and Crown agency personnel. The Board has exclusive jurisdiction to determine such matters as dismissal, discipline, working conditions, compensation, and interpretation of the appropriate collective agreements.

Under section 20 of the Act, the Board sits in panels of three, with a chair and two members. Each member is a nominee of one of the parties before it.

Decisions are final, subject to judicial review on procedural matters.

Chair, Owen B. Shime
Registrar, Joan Shirlow

Ontario Labour Relations Board
400 University Ave., 4th Flr., Toronto, M7A 1T7
General Inquiries: (416) 965-4151

The Ontario Labour Relations Board has authority, conferred by the *Labour Relations Act,* over many important areas in collective bargaining in the private sector, such as certification of trade unions, unfair labour practices, unlawful strikes and lock-outs, jurisdictional disputes, and arbitration of grievances. The Board's role is limited with respect to the public sector. While it has full jurisdiction over employees of municipalities and hospitals, it has none over Crown employees, police officers, and firefighters, and has only a limited jurisdiction with respect to teachers, for whom special Acts apply.

The Board is also given an important role under the *Occupational Health and Safety Act,* and is occasionally required to determine the impact of the *Canadian Charter of Rights and Freedoms* and other legislation on the rights of parties before it.

An independent, quasi-judicial body, combining administrative and judicial functions, the Board encourages settlements without the need for formal hearings and it strives to keep its procedures expeditious and fair. All decisions are available to the public, with many published in a Monthly Report. There is also an Annual Report of Board activities.

The Board has exclusive jurisdiction to exercise the powers conferred upon it and to determine all questions of fact or law that arise during any hearing before it. Decisions are not appealable and there is only limited scope for judicial review. However, the Board may reconsider any of its decisions.

The Board is composed of a chairman and an alternate chairman, several vice-chairmen and equal numbers of members representing labour and management. These appointments are made by the Lieutenant-Governor in Council.

Chair, Rosalie Silberman Abella
Alternate Chair, R.O. MacDowell
Registrar/CAO, Theresa Inniss
Field Services
Manager, J.A. MacDonald
Solicitors: C. Edwards, Kathleen A. MacDonald, Marilyn Nairn

Ontario Public Service Labour Relations Tribunal
180 Dundas St. W., Ste. 2100
Toronto, M5G 1Z8

The Tribunal is responsible for the administration of the *Crown Employees Collective Bargaining Act* in matters affecting the relationship between the employer and the union in ministry and Crown agency bargaining units of the Ontario Government.

Union rights, representation rights and relationship, bargaining units, determination of bargaining unit positions, fair representation and collective bargaining are among the subjects put before the Tribunal.

Each panel consists of a chair, a union nominee, and a management nominee.

Decisions are final, although the Tribunal may review its own decisions should circumstances warrant. Its decisions are subject to judicial review on procedural matters.

Chair, Pamela C. Picher
Registrar, Joan Shirlow

Public Service Classification Rating Committee
180 Dundas St. W., Ste. 2010
Toronto, M5G 1Z8

Job evaluation grievances from Ontario ministry personnel related to positions outside the bargaining unit are decided by a three-person panel, which is comprised of a chair, one member with no affiliation with government, and one member who is in personnel/staff relations but is not in the grievor's ministry. *See also Public Service Grievance Board.*

Rating Committee decisions are final, subject to judicial review on procedure by the courts.

Chair, Gail Brent

Public Service Grievance Board
180 Dundas St. W., Ste. 2010
Toronto, M5G 1Z8

The Public Service Grievance Board was established in 1959 by Order-in-Council. Its mandate to adjudicate employee grievances is contained in the Public Service Regulation, R.R.O. 1980, Reg. 881. The Public Service Grievance Board's jurisdiction is mainly limited to grievances from certain management-excluded personnel in Ontario Government ministries. Subject matter includes appeals against dismissal, promotion/demotion, discrimination and the like. *See also Public Service Classification Rating Committee.*

Hearings are usually held in Toronto by a three-person board. Panels are non-representative of the parties before them. Decisions are final, subject to judicial review on procedural matters.

Chairman, Gail Brent

Workers' Compensation Board
2 Bloor St. E., Toronto, M4W 3C3
General Inquiries: (416) 927-9555

The *Workmen's Compensation Act* was passed by the Ontario Legislature in 1914. It came into effect on Jan. 1, 1915, the same day the Board was established. Over the years, that which is now called the *Workers' Compensation Act* has been amended to keep its provisions in line with current needs and to improve and extend its benefits.

The Act provides for the following:

- compensation payments for Ontario workers who are prevented from earning full wages due to disability caused by work-related accidents or diseases;
- health-care benefits, including payments of doctor's bills, hospitalization costs, etc.;
- rehabilitation services, including therapy and job training to help injured workers re-establish themselves;
- pensions for workers who are permanently disabled by accidents on the job;
- pensions for widows (or widowers) and children of workers who die as a result of work accidents or industrial diseases; and
- financial support for Ontario safety education programs, the mission of which is the prevention of industrial accidents and diseases.

The Act is administered by the Workers' Compensation Board, which maintains its head office in Toronto, local offices in 12 other Ontario cities, and a hospital and rehabilitation centre in Downsview, a suburb of Toronto.

Chairman, Dr. Robert G. Elgie
Vice-Chairman, Administration, and
President, Alan D. Wolfson
Client Services
Vice-President, Michael Czetyrbok
Corporate Services
Vice-President, Sam Van Clieaf
Policy and Specialized Services
Vice-President, Dr. Elizabeth Kaegi
Strategic Policy and Analysis
Vice-President, Robert Coke
A/Gen. Counsel, Susan Naylor
Secretary of the Board, Linda Angove
Board Actuary, John Neal

CLIENT SERVICES
Exec. Director, Henry McDonald
Exec. Director, George Picken
Communications Director, David Stones
DIVISIONAL MANAGEMENT SERVICES
Exec. Director, Peter Landolt
Employment Equity
Co-ordinator, Josephine Grayson
FINANCIAL SERVICES
Exec. Director, Robert Barnett
Human Resources
Director, Andrea Hagan
Internal Audit
Board Director, Gordon Russell
Legal Services
Director, Elizabeth Kosmidis
Board Solicitor, Jim Carter

MANAGEMENT INFORMATION SERVICES
Exec. Director, Brian Bailey
Occupational Health and Safety Education
Authority
A/Chairman, R.D. Reilly
Administrators: Stewart Cooke, John Ridout
POLICY AND PROGRAM DEVELOPMENT
DEPARTMENT
Exec. Director, Irwin Glasberg
Research and Evaluation Branch
Director, Richard Allingham

REVIEW SERVICES
A/Exec. Director, Joe D'Andrea
SPECIALIZED MEDICAL SERVICES
Exec. Director, Dr. J. Tinie van Schoor
SPECIALIZED VOCATIONAL REHABILITATION
SERVICES
Exec. Director, Vacant
Strategic Policy Branch
A/Director, Ian Welton

REGIONAL OPERATIONS AND AREA OFFICES
Exec. Director, Art Darnbrough

Hamilton Regional Office
120 King St. W., Hamilton, L8P 1J3
Director, Chris Hornberger

London Regional Office
200 Queens Ave., London, N6A 1J3
Director, Dick Miller
Ottawa Regional Office
360 Albert St., Ste. 200, Ottawa, K1R 7X7
A/Director, Pat Lamanna
Sudbury Regional Office
30 Cedar St., Sudbury, P3E 1A4
Director, Ron M. Farrell
Thunder Bay Regional Office
410 Memorial Ave., Thunder Bay, P7B 3Y5
Director, Carl Autio
Windsor Region
235 Eugenie St. W., Windsor, N8X 2X7
Director, Heather Sheriff
Downsview Rehabilitation Ctr.
115 Torbarrie Rd., Downsview, M3L 1G8
Exec. Director, Tom Schonberg
Administrator, Vacant

MANAGEMENT BOARD OF CABINET

Frost Bldg. S., 7th Flr.
Queen's Park, Toronto, M7A 1Z6

OFFICE OF THE CHAIRMAN
Chairman, The Hon. Murray Elston

MANAGEMENT BOARD SECRETARIAT
Secretary of the Management Board,
John R. Sloan

PROGRAMS AND ESTIMATES DIVISION
Frost Bldg. S., 6th Flr.
Queen's Park, Toronto, M7A 1Z6
Asst. Secretary of the Management Board,
M. Mottershead
Education and Social Services Branch
Director, P. Hundeck
Justice and General Government Branch
Director, L. Steele
Expenditure Policy and Divisional Services
Branch Director, P.A. Gelinas
Resources Development Branch
Director, J. Halstead
Government Activity Review Branch
Director, M.W. Cox

MANAGEMENT POLICY DIVISION
Frost Bldg. S., 6th Flr.
Queen's Park, Toronto, M7A 1Z6
Exec. Co-ordinator, M. Jordan
Policy Development and Administration Branch
Director, J. Barry Gardiner
Review of Agencies, Boards and Commissions
Project Director, R. Macaulay
Freedom of Information and Privacy Branch
56 Wellesley St. W., 18th Flr., Toronto, M5S 2S3
Director, F. White
Advertising Review Board
102 Bloor St. W., 12th Flr., Toronto, M5S 1M8
Gen. Manager, S. Sellen

INFORMATION TECHNOLOGY DIVISION
56 Wellesley St. W., 4th Flr., Toronto, M5S 2S3
Exec. Co-ordinator, D. McGeown
Policy Administration Branch
Director, H. Nickels
Strategic Policy Branch
Director, M. Nahon
Systems Development Manager, B. Jardine

HUMAN RESOURCES SECRETARIAT

Frost Bldg. S., 7th Flr.
Queen's Park, Toronto, M7A 1Z5
Dep. Minister, Elaine M. Todres
EXECUTIVE MANAGEMENT BRANCH
A/Exec. Co-ordinator, L. Kahn
Northern Ontario Relocation Program
Exec. Co-ordinator, T. Dawes
Strategic Planning and Projects
Director, L. Lewis
French Language Co-ordinator,
Monique Levert

Corporate Services
Asst. Dep. Minister, R.M. Monzon
EXECUTIVE DEVELOPMENT INSTITUTE
Exec. Co-ordinator, D. Evans
Education Services
A/Director, D. Heming
Staffing Services Director, P. Mooney
Administrative Services
Director, R. Ferguson
Employment Equity Director, S. Wilkinson
Marketing and Corporate Information Services
Manager, A. Welsh
Communications Section
A/Manager, V. Thorne
Technology and Human Resources Project
Director, D. McGee
Human Resources Management
Audit Project
Manager, J. Hunter

Employee Relations and Compensation
Asst. Dep. Minister, J.R. Thomas
PENSIONS AND BENEFITS POLICY GROUP
Exec. Director, R. Lundeen
Pensions Policy Branch
Director, P. Clark
Benefits Policy Director, B. Rooke
Staff Relations Director, W. Gorchinsky
Pay and Classification Branch
Director, C. Farr

AGENCIES, BOARDS AND COMMISSIONS

Civil Service Commission
Frost Bldg. S., Queen's Park, Toronto, M7A 1Z5

The Civil Service Commission is responsible to the Chairman, Management Board of Cabinet (Minister) for the administration of the *Public Service Act* under which the Commission is established.

The Commission monitors and reports on the

performance of the government as an employer with particular emphasis on maintaining the merit principle. In addition, the Commission is responsible for developing corporate values on matters such as conflict of interest and employee ethics. The Commission's responsibility for policy development and administration in respect of human resources management has been delegated to the Human Resources Secretariat and the ministries.

Chairman, G.J.M. Raymond
Commissioners: J.R. Sloan, A.F. Daniels, V.A. Gibbons
Secretary to the Commission, C. Bedborough

MINISTRY OF MUNICIPAL AFFAIRS

777 Bay St., Toronto, M5G 2E5
General Inquiries: (416) 585-7041

MINISTER'S OFFICE
Minister, The Hon. John Eakins

DEPUTY MINISTER'S OFFICE
Dep. Minister, Donald Obonsawin
Ontario Municipal Audit Council
Exec. Director, Elizabeth Patterson
Municipal Education and Training Secretariat
Director, Ron Farrow

CORPORATE RESOURCES
Exec. Co-ordinator, Lawrence J. Close
Corporate Planning and Co-ordination
Manager, Jim Pine
Municipal Information and Technology Branch
Director, G.R. Jamison
French-Language Services Branch
Director, Gilbert Héroux
Communications and Information Services
Exec. Co-ordinator, Robert Nykor

Community Planning
Asst. Dep. Minister, Vacant
Office of Local Planning Policy
Policy Co-ordinator, G. Fitzpatrick
Plans Administration Branches:
North and East
Director, Pauline Morris
Central and Southwest
Director, Les J. Fincham
Community Renewal Branch
Director, Peter Boles
Community Planning Advisory Branch
A/Director, Bruce McLeod
Research and Special Projects Branch
Director, Bill Mackay

Municipal Affairs
Asst. Dep. Minister, Marcia Sypnowich
Local Government Organization Branch
Director, M. Lesurf
Subsidies Branch
A/Director, Paul Burton

Housing Development
Special Advisor, Milt G. Farrow
Municipal Finance Branch
Director, Nancy Bardecki

MUNICIPAL OPERATIONS DIVISION
Exec. Director, Vacant
Municipal Management Practices Branch
Director, Bryan Isaac
Field Services Branch
Director, Don Malpass
Municipal Boundaries Branch
Director, Doug Barnes

AGENCIES, BOARDS AND COMMISSIONS

Niagara Escarpment Commission
232 Guelph St., Georgetown, L7G 4B1

The Niagara Escarpment Commission, an agency of the Ontario government, was established in 1973 by *The Niagara Escarpment Planning and Development Act.* The Commission has been responsible for the preparation of the Niagara Escarpment Plan which is intended to maintain the Niagara Escarpment and land in its vicinity substantially as a continuous natural environment and to ensure its balanced future use.

The minister's recommended plan was released in July 1984, and received cabinet approval in 1985.

Provision has been made in the Plan for the eventual delegation of development control authority to regions and counties. Until such delegation occurs, however, development permit applications for Dufferin County and the regional municipalities of Halton and Peel continue to be handled by the Commission's Georgetown office; for the counties of Bruce, Grey and Simcoe, by the Clarksburg office; and for the regional municipalities of Hamilton-Wentworth and Niagara, by the Grimsby office. The telephone numbers for these offices are listed below.

The Commission also provides an audio-visual presentation, a library, information kits, and a drop-in centre to the general public.

Chairman, G.H.U. Bayly
Director, Frank G. Shaw
Georgetown: (416) 877-5191
Toronto: (416) 453-2468
Clarksburg: (519) 599-3340
Grimsby: (416) 945-9235

MINISTRY OF NATURAL RESOURCES

Whitney Blk., 99 Wellesley St. W.
Toronto, M7A 1W3
General Inquiry: (416) 965-2000

MINISTER'S OFFICE
Minister, The Hon. Vincent Kerrio

DEPUTY MINISTER'S OFFICE
Dep. Minister, George Tough
Corporate Policy Secretariat
Director, P.J. Bryant
Planning and Environmental Assessment
Director, L.A. Douglas

Administration
A/Asst. Dep. Minister, Michael R. Garrett
Communications Services
A/Director, M.L. Welch
Legal Services Director, B.G. Jones
Human Resources Director, R. Gordon

FINANCE AND ADMINISTRATION GROUP
Exec. Co-ordinator, M. Fordyce
Administrative Services
A/Director, T. Kurtz
Systems Services Director, J.A. Queen
Financial Resources
A/Director, T. Pierro
Chief Accountant, I.A. Nott
Internal Audit Services
Director, A.A. Ward
FOREST RESOURCES GROUP
Exec. Co-ordinator, J.F. Goodman
Ontario Tree Improvement and
Forest Biomass Institute
Gen. Manager, D.P. Drysdale
Forest Resources
A/Director, G. Oldford
Timber Sales
A/Director, T.R. Isherwood

LANDS AND WATERS GROUP
Exec. Co-ordinator, Ron J. Vrancart
Land Management
A/Director, J.R. Morton
Surveys, Mapping and Remote Sensing
Director, Dr. J. Zarzycki
Surveyor General, S.B. Panting
Conservation Authorities and Water
Management
Director, M.G. Lewis
OUTDOOR RECREATION GROUP
Exec. Co-ordinator, R.M. Christie
Fisheries Director, G.R. Whitney
Parks and Recreational Areas
Director, N.R. Richards
Provincial Parks Council
Chairman, L. Burridges
Co-ordinator, F. Bishop
Wildlife Director, D.W. Simkin

Ontario Northern Regions
435 James St. S., Box 5000
Thunder Bay, P7C 5G6
Asst. Dep. Minister, G.A. McCormack
Budget and Program Analyst, L. Keller
Operations for Northern Ontario
Director, E.E. Murphy
Aviation and Fire Management Ctr.
747 Queen St. E., Box 310
Sault Ste. Marie, P6A 5L8
Director, L.H. Lingenfelter

REGIONAL DIRECTORS:
Northwestern
Kenora, P9N 3X9
D.R. Johnston
North Central
Thunder Bay, P7C 5G6
G.P. Elliott
Northern
Cochrane, P0L 1C0
D.E. McHale, (Acting)
Northeastern
Sudbury, P3E 5P9
Dr. M.A. Klugman

Southern Regions
Maple, L0J 1E0
Asst. Dep. Minister, R.J. Burgar
Budget and Program Analyst, Anne Cox
Operations for Southern Ontario
Director, A.M. Houser

AGENCIES, BOARDS AND COMMISSIONS

Algonquin Forestry Authority
222 Main St. W., Box 1198, Huntsville, P0A 1K0
General Inquiries: (705) 789-9647

The Algonquin Forestry Authority is an Ontario Crown corporation responsible for production and distribution of forest products harvested from Algonquin Provincial Park.

The annual allowable cut of 588,000 m³ is allocated to 16 individual mills in the region surrounding Algonquin Park. The Authority also conducts forestry and land-management projects authorized by the Minister of Natural Resources.

Vice-Chairman, F. Roberts
Gen. Manager, W.J. Brown
Treasurer, M. Green

Canada-Ontario Rideau-Trent-Severn CORTS Agreement Board
10670 Yonge St., Richmond Hill, L4C 3C9

The Agreement Board co-ordinates implementation of the second Canada-Ontario Rideau-Trent-Severn (CORTS) Agreement signed in December 1983 by the federal Minister of the Environment and the provincial Minister of Natural Resources. The Agreement provides for co-ordinated planning and development of the recreational land corridor and waterway between Ottawa and Georgian Bay. Objectives include a pollution-free environment, adequate public recreation areas, adequate commercial and private development, and co-ordinated implementation of "The CORTS Policies" approved in 1982.

Chairman, R.J. Burgar
CORTS Secretariat
Provincial Co-ordinator, P. White

Mining and Lands Commissioner
700 Bay St., 24th Flr., Box 330
Toronto, M5G 1Z6

The Commissioner exercises administrative and judicial duties under the *Mining Act, Mining Tax Act, Beach Protection Act,* and *Conservation Authorities Act,* and performs duties of the Minister of Natural Resources assigned by Regulation. Examples of such jurisdiction are extension orders, the granting of relief from forfeiture, disputes, hearing of appeals, easements, and vesting orders.

Application forms and supporting abstracts for applications for extension orders and licence renewals may be obtained from the ministry's nine mining recorders. Other applications should be made through the Mining and Lands Commissioner at the above address. Notices of appeal under the *Mining Act* are required by that Act to be filed with the mining recorder. Where practicable, hearings are arranged in local courthouses.

Commissioner, G.H. Ferguson, Q.C.

Ontario Geographic Names Board
c/o Surveys, Mapping and Remote Sensing Branch
90 Sheppard Ave. E., North York, M2N 3A1
Chairman, Prof. J.R. Pitblado
Exec. Secretary, M.B. Smart

MINISTRY OF NORTHERN DEVELOPMENT AND MINES

10 Wellesley St. E., Toronto, M4Y 1G2
General Inquiry: (416) 965-1683

MINISTER'S OFFICE - NORTHERN DEVELOPMENT
Minister, The Hon. René Fontaine

MINISTER'S OFFICE - MINES
Minister, The Hon. Sean Conway

DEPUTY MINISTER'S OFFICE
Dep. Minister, Brock Smith

Northern Transportation Division
Asst. Dep. Minister, H.J. (Herb) Aiken

Northern Development Division
Asst. Dep. Minister, Bill Lees
56 Wellesley St. W., 3rd Flr., Toronto, M7A 2B7

Mines and Minerals
Asst. Dep. Minister, Dennis Tieman
Mineral Development and Lands
Director, John Gammon
Omep Office Manager, Richard Rose
Ontario Geological Survey
77 Grenville St., 11th Flr., Toronto, M5S 1B3
Director, Dr. Victor Milne
Northwestern Region
Director, John Wood
12 Main St. S., Box 5050, Kenora, P9N 3X9

Northeastern Region
Director, John (Sandy) McIntosh
60 Wilson Ave., Timmins, P4N 2S7
Southern Ontario Region
Manager, Dr. Tony Pitts
10 Wellesley St. E., 1st Flr., Toronto, M4Y 1G2

CORPORATE SERVICES DIVISION
Exec. Director, Vacant
Communications Services
Director, John McHugh
Financial Services Director, Terry Huggins
Legal Services Director, Steve Stepinac
Corporate Planning Secretariat
Director, Bill Stevenson
Information Technology and Office Services
Director, Fran Grant
Human Resources Director, Melanie Goldhar
Ministry Relocation Project
Director, Sheila Willis
Financial Systems Development Project
Director, Ed Bacon
Audit Services (Sudbury)
Manager, Fred Snow
French-Language Services (Sudbury)
Co-ordinator, Robert Ribout

AGENCIES, BOARDS AND COMMISSIONS

Ontario Northland Transportation Commission
555 Oak St. E., North Bay, P1B 8L3

The Ontario Northland Transportation Commission is an agency of the Government of Ontario operating independently under the leadership of a chairman and under the direction of the Ontario Ministry of Northern Development.

The Commission provides rail freight and passenger services to the northeastern area of Ontario and serves the residents of northern Ontario. The Highway Services division offers scheduled motor coach service within northeastern Ontario and charter/tour service from its area of operation.

Tourism operations include: the Polar Bear Express, a summer rail excursion to Moosonee, Ontario's northernmost rail settlement; the *Chief Commanda II* cruise vessel on Lake Nipissing and the French River; and the *M.S. ChiCheemaun,* a modern ferry which operates on Georgian Bay.

The Commission's airline, norOntair, serves over 20 communities throughout northern Ontario, providing local transportation to these communities as well as convenient connections to major centres. Ontario Northland Communications operates three local telephone exchanges in addition to providing long-distance services for local telephone companies by means of a microwave system.

Chairman, Wilf Spooner
Gen. Manager, Peter Dyment
Asst. Gen. Manager, D.E. (Don) MacDougall
Telecommunications Services
Director, Bob Hutton

Passenger Services
Sr. Director, Ernie Marasco
Commission Secretary and Counsel,
Terrence O'Connell

OFFICE OF THE PROVINCIAL AUDITOR

The Atrium on Bay, Ste. 1530
20 Dundas St. W., Box 105, Toronto, M5G 2C2
Provincial Auditor, D.F. Archer
Asst. Provincial Auditor, J.F. Otterman
Human Resources and Support
Services Branch
Director, H. Halvachs
REPORTING AND SPECIAL AUDITS
Exec. Director, K.W. Leishman
Reporting and Standards Branch
Director, G.A. Calderwood
EDP Branch Director, D. Stasila
Special Assignments Branch
Director, N.J. Mishchenko
MINISTRY AND AGENCY AUDITS
Exec. Director, J.R. McCarter
Directors: G.R. Peall, D.P. Amrite, E.M. Osti,
M.R. Teixeira

MINISTRY OF REVENUE

33 King St. W., Oshawa, L1H 8H5
(except where otherwise noted)
General Inquiries: (416) 433-0870

MINISTER'S OFFICE
Hearst Blk., 4th Flr.
Queen's Park, Toronto, M7A 1X7
Minister, The Hon. Bernard Grandmaître

DEPUTY MINISTER'S OFFICE
Hearst Blk., 4th Flr.
Queen's Park, Toronto, M7A 1X7
Dep. Minister, T.M. Russell
Legal Services Branch
Director, Jerry Sholtack
Audit Services Branch
Director, Larry Lindburg

Tax Revenue and Grants Program
Asst. Dep. Minister, Roy Lawrie
Corporations Tax Branch
Director, Claude Dagenais
Motor Fuels and Tobacco Tax Branch
A/Director, Bob Moxley
Retail Sales Tax Branch
Director, Burke Williams
Revenue and Operations Research Branch
Director, John Godden
Special Investigations Branch
Director, Alfred Carr
Tax Appeals Director, Nicole Anidjar

TAX SYSTEM OPERATIONS AND DESIGN
A/Exec. Director, Derek Rowsell
Guaranteed Income and Tax Credit Branch
Director, Noreen Gomes
Taxation Data Centre
Director, Bob Thompson
Taxpayer Services Branch
A/Director, Mary Proc

RETAIL SALES TAX FIELD OFFICES:
Belleville
191 Dundas St. E., Belleville, K8N 1E2
Sr. Service Representative,
Mary Lou Latchford
Hamilton
Ontario Government Bldg.
119 King St., W., Hamilton, L8N 3Z9
Service Manager, Bruce Poynter
Kitchener
449 Belmont Ave. W., Kitchener, N2M 1N2
Service Manager, Linda Doede
London
334 Westminster Ctr., London, N6C 4P6
Reg. Service Manager, Marg Morrison
Mississauga
2 Robert Speck Pkwy., Ste. 350
Mississauga, L4Z 1H8
Service Manager, Cheryl Boniface

North Bay
1500 Fisher St., Northgate Plaza
North Bay, P1B 2H3
Service Manager, Bruce Carmichael
Orillia
438 West St. N., West Way Mall
Orillia, L3V 5E8
Sr. Service Representative, Isabelle McGarvey
Oshawa
33 King St. W., Oshawa, L1H 8K1
Service Manager, Cliff Roach
Ottawa
1355 Bank St., Ottawa, K1H 8K7
Reg. Service Manager, Dan McLeod

Sudbury
Ontario Government Bldg.
199 Larch St., Sudbury, P3E 5P9
Sr. Service Representative, Susan Pitre
Thunder Bay
Ontario Government Bldg.
435 James St. S., Thunder Bay, P7C 5G6
Sr. Service Representative, Sandra Raison
Toronto
2300 Yonge St., Toronto, M4P 1H6
Reg. Service Manager, Don Martin
Windsor
Ontario Government Bldg.
250 Windsor Ave., Windsor, N9A 6V9
Sr. Service Representative,
Anita Groundwater

Property Assessment Program
Asst. Dep. Minister, Jack Lettner
Assessment Policies and Priorities Branch
Director, Vacant

ASSESSMENT SERVICES DIVISION
Exec. Director, Bob Beach
Data Services and Development Branch
Director, Vacant
Field Operations Branch
Director, Earl Winter
Special Properties Branch
Director, Tom Boyd

INFORMATION TECHNOLOGY DIVISION
Exec. Director, John Randolph
Information Systems Development Branch
Director, Tony Loginow
Systems and Facilities Management Branch
Director, Jeff Smith

CORPORATE RESOURCES DIVISION
Exec. Director, John Purdon
Administrative and Financial Services Branch
Director, Jim Ireland
Communications Services Branch
Director, David Stones
Finance and Priorities Planning Branch
Director, Jim Evans
Personnel Services Branch
Director, Ed Farragher
PROVINCE OF ONTARIO SAVINGS OFFICE
Director, John Allen
Branch Operations Manager, Terry Lowes

MINISTRY OF SKILLS DEVELOPMENT

101 Bloor St. W., 13th Flr., Toronto, M5S 1P7

MINISTER'S OFFICE
Minister, The Hon. Alvin Curling

DEPUTY MINISTER'S OFFICE
Dep. Minister, Glenna Carr
Legal Counsel, M. Victoria Vidal-Ribas

Skills Training Division
Asst. Dep. Minister, Vacant
Apprenticeship Branch
Mowat Blk., 9th Flr., 900 Bay St.
Toronto, M7A 2B5
Director, Jim Lanthier
Legislative Policy Analysts:
Rob Easto, Nancy Dow
Support Services
Co-ordinator, Leonard Joki
Training Support Services Branch
Director, J.B.S. Rose
Access Programs
Sr. Manager, Gerry Wright
Community Resources
Sr. Manager, Robert Connors
Training Support
Sr. Manager, Kayla Hoffman
Training Profile Development
Sr. Manager, Doug Jennings

YOUTH EMPLOYMENT SERVICES BRANCH
Director, W.G. Wolfson
Office Manager, Colleen Grozelle
Ontario Summer Employment Program
Manager, Lesley Eyton-Jones
Supervisor, Lisa Flannery

Policy and Development Division
Asst. Dep. Minister, Les Horswill
Policy and Planning Branch
Director, Anne Martin
Corporate Policy
Manager, Malcolm Campbell
Policy Analysts: Daniel Cayen, Pat Spence
Researcher, Colleen Sharon
Policy Development
Manager, Janet Mason
Policy Analysts: Andrew Shepherd,
Kathryn Shaver, Bruce Baldwin
Access Policy
Manager, Walter Tuohy
Policy Analysts: Bobby Siu, Mary Beth Wallace,
Don Bourgeois
Planning and Development
Sr. Manager, Vacant
Program Development and Evaluation
Manager, Linda Pergantes
Management Planning
A/Manager, Linda Pergantes
Federal and Provincial Planning
Sr. Manager, Helmut Zisser
Policy Manager, Rob Swaffield
Policy Analysts: Janet Cox, Paul Evans,
Bruce Pollard
Planning Manager, Vacant

FINANCE AND ADMINISTRATION DIVISION
Exec. Director, Frank J. Kidd
Management Resources Branch
Director, Jim Hansen
Financial Services
CFO, Doug Holder
Audit Branch Director, Paul Foy
Information Systems
Co-ordinator, Dr. Paul Roberts

COMMUNICATIONS AND MARKETING BRANCH
Director, Patricia Werner
Manager, Mike Langford
Manager, Administration, Tracy Samonas
Information Officer, Janet Maxwell
Special Projects, Susan Marcus
Public Inquiry, Jennifer Isaacson
Distribution Co-ordinator, Donna Alberts

MINISTRY OF THE SOLICITOR GENERAL

George Drew Bldg., 11th Flr.
25 Grosvenor St., Toronto, M4Y 1A9
(except where otherwise indicated)

SOLICITOR GENERAL'S OFFICE
Solicitor General, The Hon. Joan Smith

DEPUTY SOLICITOR GENERAL'S OFFICE
Dep. Solicitor General, Stien K. Lal
Legal Services Branch
Director, David Spring
Solicitors: Yan Lazor, Susan Watt
Policy Development and Co-ordination
Director, Jill Hutcheon
Sr. Advisor, Beverly Ward
Communications Services Branch
Director, Vacant

ADMINISTRATION DIVISION
Exec. Director, Lorne Edwards
Internal Audit Director, David Mailer
Information Technology Services Branch
Director, R.L. Fletcher
Financial and Administration Services Branch
Director, Helen Hayward
Human Resources Services Branch
Director, Lynn Ceglar
Accommodation Services Branch
Director, T.A. Thomson

Public Safety Division
Asst. Dep. Minister, Domenic Alfieri
Chief Coroner's Office
26 Grenville St., Toronto, M7A 2G9
Chief Coroner, Dr. R.C. Bennett
Dep. Chief Coroner, Dr. James Young
Provincial Forensic Pathologist,
Dr. J. Hillsdon Smith
Centre of Forensic Sciences
25 Grosvenor St., 2nd Flr., Toronto, M7A 2G8
Director, D.M. Lucas
Dep. Director, G. Cimbura
Office of the Fire Marshal
590 Keele St., Toronto, M6N 4X2
Fire Marshal, J. Bateman
Dep. Fire Marshal, A. Williams

Policing Services
A/Asst. Dep. Minister, R.E. Russell

AGENCIES, BOARDS AND COMMISSIONS

Ontario Police Commission
George Drew Bldg., 9th Flr.
25 Grosvenor St., Toronto, M7A 2H3

The Ontario Police Commission was instituted in 1962 within the enabling legislation of the *Police Act.* The Commission, appointed by the Lieutenant-Governor in Council, is designed to ensure adequacy and promote efficiency of police forces in Ontario through advisory services, crime intelligence, disciplinary procedures, technical services, and police training. The Commission is the operating authority for the Ontario Police College at Aylmer, Ont., where the police officers of the province are trained. The powers of the Commission are quasi-judicial, advisory, and supervisory.

Chairman, Douglas Drinkwalter
Vice-Chairman, Vacant

Ontario Provincial Police
90 Harbour St., Toronto, M7A 2S1
See description in the Law chapter, Volume 1.

Commissioner, Tom O'Grady
Deputy Commissioners:
Services, James Szarka
Field Operations, Peter Campbell
Investigations, A.N. Chaddock

MINISTRY OF TOURISM AND RECREATION

77 Bloor St. W., Toronto, M7A 2R9

MINISTER'S OFFICE
Minister, The Hon. Hugh O'Neil

DEPUTY MINISTER'S OFFICE
Dep. Minister, James Keenan

CORPORATE MANAGEMENT SERVICES DIVISION
Exec. Director, A.S. Young
Finance and Administration
Director, E.M. Mills
Admin. Co-ordinator, J. Boyer
Audit Services Director, A. Harding
Human Resources Director, J. Davidson
Employment Equity Manager, E. Osborne
Freedom of Information
Co-ordinator, N. Pineda
Information Technology Services
Director, D. Wicary
Communications Branch
Director, C.L. Wickson

Division of Tourism
Asst. Dep. Minister, D.M. Jackman
Tourism Marketing Branch
Director, A. McCall
Tourism Development Branch
Director, R.L. Brock
Huronia Historical Parks
Box 160, Midland, L4R 4K8
Gen. Manager, John Barrett-Hamilton
Promotion and Public Relations
A/Supervisor, K. Vodrzanger
Sainte-Marie-among-the-Hurons
Midland, L4R 4K8
Programs Co-ordinator, W. Byrick
Historical Naval and Military Establishments
Penetanguishene, L0K 1P0
Programs Co-ordinator, B. Penny
Old Fort William
Vickers Heights P.O., Thunder Bay, P0T 2Z0
Gen. Manager, A. Weber
Programs Manager, J. Robertson
Marketing and Communications
A/Manager, J. Sims

Recreation Division
Asst. Dep. Minister, Bob Secord
Sports and Fitness Branch
Director, Gerry Ker
Recreation Branch
Director, Ray R. Wittenberg

TOURISM AND RECREATION OPERATIONS
Exec. Director, T. Adamchick
Program Co-ordinator, J. Blain
Grants Administration, R. O'Connor

FIELD SERVICES:
Central Ontario
700 Bay St., 8th Flr., Toronto, M5G 1Z6
Reg. Director, C. Bouskill
Eastern Ontario
10 Rideau St., 4th Flr., Ottawa, K1N 9J1
Reg. Director, J.T. Johnston
Southwest Ontario
255 Dufferin Ave., Ste. 601, London, N6A 5K6
Reg. Director, T. Rankin
Northeastern Ontario
Ontario Government Bldg.
199 Larch St., 4th Flr., Sudbury, P3E 5P9
Reg. Director, J. Cruickshank
Northwest Ontario
435 James St. S., Lwr. Level
Thunder Bay, P7C 5G6
Reg. Director, R. Zizman

AGENCIES, BOARDS, COMMISSIONS AND CROWN CORPORATIONS

Huronia Historical Advisory Council
Box 160, Midland, L4R 4K8

The Huronia Historical Advisory Council is a ten-person board established on Jan. 1, 1964 by the Province of Ontario. It is composed of individuals from various parts of the province with a common interest in the preservation of our cultural heritage. The Council's stated purpose is to advise the minister on matters relating to historical sites operated by the Ministry of Tourism and Recreation (e.g. Sainte-Marie among the Hurons and the Historic Naval and Military Establishments) and generally on the cultural heritage of "Old Huronia" and the enhancement of developed and developing historical sites.

Chairman, Rev. J.J. Farrell, S.J.
Exec. Secretary, John Barrett-Hamilton

Metro Toronto Convention Centre Corp.
255 Front St. W., Toronto, M5V 2W6

The Metro Toronto Convention Centre Corporation, established by Order-in-Council on Jan. 29, 1981 is charged with managing the facility, which was completed and officially opened in the fall of 1984.

The Convention Centre features a main exhibit hall with 18,580 m², direct access from the loading docks and multiple access by escalator banks

from various levels. In addition, the Centre offers: the Constitution Hall Ballroom, which will accommodate 3,000 for dinner, or seating for 4,000, or 3,250 m² of additional exhibition space; a 1,350-seat multi-purpose theatre/auditorium; 40 meeting rooms; kitchen facilities; a large registration area; a press conference area; indoor parking for 1,200 cars; instantaneous translation facilities; and 10,000 first-class hotel rooms within walking distance. The entire centre is air-conditioned.

Chairman of the Board, Thomas N. Davidson
President and CEO, J.O. Maxwell
Sales
Vice-President, Michael Prescott
Finance and Administration
Vice-President, Syd Widdowson
Controller, Barbara Henderson
Operations
Vice-President, Terry Sim
Public Relations Manager, C. Moir
Food and Beverage Director, Bernd Gabel

The Niagara Parks Commission
Oak Hall Administration Bldg.
Box 150, Niagara Falls, L2E 6T2
General Inquiries: (416) 356-2241

The Niagara Parks Commission is Ontario's first Provincial Park and was established by an Act of the Ontario legislature on March 30, 1885. However, the Park was not officially opened to the public until May 24, 1888, in the area adjacent to the Falls known as Queen Victoria Park.

Initially only 62.2 hectares in size, the Niagara Parks Commission today includes slightly more than 1,254 hectares extending along the entire length of the Niagara River, a distance of 56 km. Included in this system are historic sites, golf courses, a marina, campgrounds, swimming beaches, picnic areas, restaurants, gift shops, horticultural gardens and school, significant natural areas, and scenic attractions.

Chairman, Pamela Verrill Walker
Gen. Manager, D. Schafer

Old Fort William Advisory Committee
Vickers Heights P.O., Thunder Bay, P0T 2Z0

The Old Fort William Advisory Committee is a ten-person board established by the Province of Ontario to advise the Minister of Tourism and Recreation on general policy concerning the Fort's capital development and program expansion. The Committee also works to build community awareness of Ontario's fur-trade heritage.

Old Fort William is a reconstruction of the original Fort William which operated from 1801 to 1821 as the inland fur-trading headquarters of the North West Company's western exploration. It was reconstructed beginning in 1971 and today includes 54 buildings. The facility employs 270 people and hosts more than 100,000 visitors each year.

Chairman, Ruth Armstrong

Ontario Lottery Corp.
2 Bloor St. W., Ste. 2400, Toronto, M4W 3H8

The Ontario Lottery Corporation was established in February 1975 with a mandate to develop and operate provincial government lotteries.

Though a Crown corporation reporting to the Minister of Tourism and Recreation, the Ontario Lottery Corp. is structured and operated in a manner similar to a private business. Corporate policy is directed by a nine-member board of directors, appointed by the Lieutenant-Governor in Council.

Lottery profits are paid into the Consolidated Revenue Fund of the Province of Ontario. From there, Corporation profits are made available for the promotion and development of physical fitness, sports, recreation, and cultural activities.

Proceeds from the interprovincial lotteries (Lotto 6/49 and the Provincial) are used to assist health and environmentally-related health research, hospital construction and equipment purchase, senior citizens' housing, the Trillium Foundation, and other emerging priorities.

Chairman, W.G.D. Stothers
President, Vacant
Exec. Vice-President, A.J. Hawkins
Vice-President, Corporate Communications, Kathy Petrik
Vice-President, Sales and Distribution, J.M. Holroyde
Vice-President, Marketing, Murray Dodd
Vice-President, Computer Services, John MacNabb
Controller, John Van Camp

Ontario Place Corp.
955 Lakeshore Blvd. W., Toronto, M6K 3B9
General Inquiries: (416) 965-7711

Ontario Place is an internationally acclaimed culture, leisure, and entertainment parkland complex extending throughout three man-made islands on Lake Ontario along the Toronto waterfront.

Ontario Place covers some 39 hectares and includes the following attractions and features: a children's village; several waterslides; two nine-hole miniature golf courses; the Cinesphere, an IMAX movie theatre; the Forum, a large amphitheatre where live entertainment is offered; the World War II Canadian destroyer HMCS Haida; a theme pavilion, "Ontario North Now"; restaurants, snack bars, and boutiques; and a 360-slip marina.

Ontario Place is open from mid-May until early September. Many attractions are free with admission. Banquet and function facilities are available year-round. Special film screenings may be arranged for conventions or other groups. During the fall and winter months, Ontario Place presents film festivals at the Cinesphere.

Ontario Place is a Crown corporation of the Government of Ontario and reports to the Ministry of Tourism and Recreation. Ontario Place first opened to the public on May 22, 1971. Since then, over 47 million people have visited the site.

Chairman, E. Cieszkowski
Gen. Manager, Vacant
Finance and Operations
Director, Joel Shapiro
Chief Accountant, Bill Ferguson
Purchasing and Office Services
Manager, Mike Shaver
Attractions Manager, D. Moore
Food Services Manager, Jim Kemp
Retail Sales Manager, M. Horkins
Trillium Restaurant Manager, R. Groebner
Marketing and Public Relations
Sr. Manager, Katherine Holmes
Programming
Sr. Manager, Lou Seiler
Maintenance and Construction
Sr. Manager, W. Tracy

Ontario Sports Medicine and Safety Advisory Board
1220 Sheppard Ave. E., Willowdale, M2K 2X1
Chairman, Linda Thom
Vice-Chairman, D. Ferguson
A/Exec. Director, Ted Baker

Ontario Trillium Foundation
15 Prince Arthur Ave., Toronto, M5R 1B2

The Trillium Foundation operates under a voluntary board of directors. An independent organization, it receives its funds from the proceeds of the Ontario Lottery Corp. through the Ministry of Tourism and Recreation. Grants are made to charitable organizations which provide direct social services across the province, or locally in northern Ontario only.

Chairman, J.C. Eaton
Exec. Director, S. Farr

St. Clair Parkway Commission
Box 700, Corunna, N0N 1G0

The St. Clair Parkway Commission operates a joint program of parks development with the Province of Ontario, the counties of Lambton and Kent, and the cities of Sarnia and Chatham. Since its inception in 1966, the Commission's principal goals have been to create a scenic drive along the St. Clair River, to acquire as much of the natural shoreline as possible for public access to the river, and to encourage tourism to "Blue Water Country".

Chairman, John David George
Vice-Chairman, Margaret Stacey
Gen. Manager, R.F. Harrison

St. Lawrence Parks Commission
Box 740, Morrisburg, K0C 1X0
General Inquiries: (613) 543-2951

The St. Lawrence Parks Commission operates and maintains parks, campgrounds, and historic sites from the Ontario-Quebec border to the Bay of Quinte. The historic sites are Old Fort Henry at Kingston, Fairfield House and Fairfield Historical

Park west of Kingston, and Upper Canada Village east of Morrisburg. The Village features operating farms, domestic activities, and a bustling mill complex consisting of a wool factory, a sawmill, and a steam-powered flour mill. Old Fort Henry features multilingual guided tours during the months of July and August, and performances of the Ceremonial Retreat three evenings a week. Other facilities include the Upper Canada Golf Club, an 18-hole golf course, a wildfowl sanctuary, a maple sugar bush operation, Crysler Park Marina, nature trails, Pioneer and Loyalist memorials, and the Queen Elizabeth Gardens, featuring fountains, walking paths, and rose gardens. Winter recreation facilities include cross-country skiing, snowmobiling, tobogganing, and snowshoeing. Skating and horse-drawn sleigh rides operate at Upper Canada Village. A riding stable is operated as a concession on Commission lands in Crysler Farm Battlefield Park.

Chairman, R. Mitton
Gen. Manager, Vacant
Human Resources Manager, M.A. Hart
Finance, Administration Co-ordinator
Manager, S. Gourlay
Upper Canada Village
Manager, P. Deault
Merchandising, Parks and Recreation
Manager, R. Mott
Marketing and Communications
Manager, P.F. Wilson
Engineering and Maintenance
Manager, M. Paradis
Old Fort Henry
Manager, D.H. Clark

Thunder Bay Ski Jumps Limited (Big Thunder National Ski Training Centre)
428 East Victoria Ave., 2nd Flr.
Thunder Bay, P7C 1A5

Thunder Bay Ski Jumps Ltd. is the operator of the hill where Canada's ski-jumping team trains. As well, a World Cup event is held here each year. The facility is equipped with four separate jumps of 90, 70, 50, and 30 metres and can accommodate other winter sports such as luge and cross-country skiing.

Manager, Rob B. McCormack

MINISTRY OF TRANSPORTATION

1201 Wilson Ave., Downsview, M3M 1J8
General Inquiries: (416) 235-2771

MINISTER'S OFFICE
Ferguson Blk., 3rd Flr.
77 Wellesley St. W., Toronto, M7A 1Z8
Minister, The Hon. Ed Fulton

DEPUTY MINISTER'S OFFICE
Dep. Minister, David Hobbs
Communications Services Branch
Director, E. Curlanis-Bart

Office of Legal Services
Director, C.J. McCombe, Q.C.
Internal Audit Branch
Director, Al Anderson
GO Transit Chairman, L.H. Parsons
STRATEGIC POLICY SECRETARIAT
Director, John Menary
Policy Planning Office
Manager, E. Giansante
Corporate Policy and Outlooks Office
Manager, J.L. Thorne

Finance and Administration
Asst. Dep. Minister, J.E. Service
Computer Systems Branch
Director, C. Vervoort
Human Resources Branch
Director, Brent Gibbs
Employment Equity Program
Manager, Carol Murphy
Financial Planning and Administration Branch
Director, A.C. Lennox
Supply and Services Branch
Director, R.J. Cartwright
French-Language Services
Co-ordinator, R.J. Bourque

Safety and Regulation
Asst. Dep. Minister, Margaret Kelch
Transportation Regulation Development Branch
Director, Anne F. Burbidge
Special Projects Co-ordinator, M. Lister

TRANSPORTATION REGULATION
OPERATIONS DIVISION
Exec. Director, H. Kivi
Licensing and Control Branch
Director, Kim Devooght
Program Planning and Evaluation Office
Manager, L. Reypert
Systems Improvement
A/Manager, B. Cheung
Compliance Branch Director, E.P. Merkley
Operational Policy and Standards
Manager, E.E. Kreis
Carrier Control Office
Manager, Bruce Stonehouse
Carrier Licensing Office
Manager, W. Greer
Regulations Systems Office
Manager, M. Aymer

HIGHWAYS OPERATIONS AND MAINTENANCE
Exec. Director, I.V. Oliver
Traffic Management and Engineering
Manager, M.R. Quinton
Equipment Engineering Manager, K.G. Forker
Maintenance Director, R.G. Porter
Government Garage Manager,
Doug McClelland

Engineering and Construction
Asst. Dep. Minister, Alex Kelly

HIGHWAY ENGINEERING
Exec. Director, Ed McCabe
Research and Development
Director, P. Smith
Traffic and Decision Systems
Manager, E.R. Case
Structural Office Manager, R.A. Dorton
Engineering Materials Office
Manager, R.P. Northwood
Surveys and Plans Manager, R.W. Oddson
Highway Design Manager, F. Devisser
Environmental Manager, B. Hodgins
Estimating Manager, J.B. Curtis
Engineering Claims Office
Manager, D. Aspinwall
Contract Manager, D.F. Barnes
Property Manager, D.E. McFarlane
Transportation Capital Branch
Director, Bob Pillar
Highway Program Analysis Office
Manager, M.J. Cook
Highway Capital Administration Office
Manager, Claude Sherwood

Provincial/Municipal Transportation
Asst. Dep. Minister, G.H. Johnston
MUNICIPAL TRANSPORTATION
Exec. Director, R. Puccini
Transit Manager, G. McMillan
Municipal Roads Manager, I. Nethercot
Municipal Transportation Policy Planning
Director, K. Pask
Municipal Transportation Policy Office
Manager, G. Campitelli

PROVINCIAL TRANSPORTATION DIVISION
Exec. Director, N.E. Mealing
Rail Office Manager, I.R. Chadwick
Aviation Office Manager, J.E. Gleason
Marine Office Manager, R. Madill
Passenger Systems Office
Manager, Mike Ernesaks
Goods Distribution Systems
Manager, G. Gera
Transportation Demand Research Office
Manager, P.M. Dalton
Technology and Energy Branch
Director, M. Harmelink
Vehicle Technology
Manager, O. Colavincenzo
Transportation Energy and Productivity
Manager, V. Soots
Transportation Industry Office
A/Manager, V. Soots

REGIONAL DIRECTORS:
Eastern
355 Counter St., Postal Bag 4000
Kingston, K7L 5A3
J.L. Forster
Southwestern
659 Exeter Rd., Box 5338, London, N6A 5H2
G.R. Browning
Northern
447 McKeown Ave., Box 3030

North Bay, P1B 8L2
J. Heffernan
Northwestern
615 S. James St., Box 1177
Thunder Bay, P7C 4X9
R. Carney
Central
5000 Yonge St., Willowdale, M2N 6E9
B.D. Riddell

AGENCIES, BOARDS, COMMISSIONS AND CROWN CORPORATIONS

GO Transit
1120 Finch Ave. W., Downsview, M3J 3J8
General Inquiries: (416) 665-9211
Fax: (416) 665-9006

GO Transit is a comprehensive interregional rail and bus system for Toronto and the surrounding area.

Service began in May 1967 with a single rail line along the shore of Lake Ontario between Oakville and Pickering, with downtown Toronto being the main terminus at the line's midpoint. The service reached the ridership mark predicted for the second year — 15,000 passengers a day — in only three months; weekday ridership now totals more than 89,000 passengers on the combined GO Train and GO Bus system, a total of over 25 million a year.

Rail service has grown to a six-corridor network. The Georgetown line between Georgetown and Toronto was introduced in 1974, the Richmond Hill line between Richmond Hill and Toronto in 1978, the Milton line between Milton and Toronto in 1981, and the Stouffville and Bradford lines between Toronto and Stouffville and Toronto and Bradford in 1982. GO Bus service began in 1970 as an extension of the rail operation and has grown into a full-fledged network in its own right, serving numerous communities within 90 km of Metro Toronto.

To meet the demand into the next century, GO Train service will be expanded using conventional diesel trains. Full rail service is being extended on the Lakeshore East from Pickering to Whitby and was scheduled to begin operating in 1988; meanwhile, studies are underway to determine the best route for service farther east to Oshawa. On the Lakeshore West, service between Oakville and Burlington will be phased up to full schedules by the early 1990s, while planning with that area's municipalities is being carried out to achieve consensus on the best way of providing interregional transit services for the area. Service on the Milton line was also to be expanded in 1988.

Chairman, L.H. Parsons
Man. Director, T.G. Smith
Operations
Exec. Director, J.A. Brown
Engineering, Development and Plant
Exec. Director, H.W. Clelland
Planning, Finance and Administration
Exec. Director, D.A. Sutherland

Licence Suspension Appeal Board
LuCliff Place, 24th Flr., 700 Bay St.
Toronto, M5G 1Z6

The Licence Suspension Appeal Board hears appeals from drivers and operators whose licences have been suspended under sections 18 and 30 of the *Highway Traffic Act*. It can also hear appeals from operators of vehicle inspection stations whose licences have been withdrawn.

Chairman, R. Browning Watts
Vice-Chairman, M. Whitaker

Ontario Highway Transport Board
151 Bloor St. W., 10th Flr., Toronto, M5S 2T5

The Ontario Highway Transport Board, a regulatory tribunal, recommends to the Minister of Transportation the issuance of and changes to licences for bus and truck for-hire services, and the approval or rejection of transfers of operating licences and public-vehicle tariffs. Operating licences are issued by the Minister of Transportation under the following Acts: *Public Commercial Vehicles Act, Public Vehicles Act*, and *Motor Vehicle Transport Act, 1987*. These Acts require that for-hire bus and truck operators hold an operating licence.

Chairman, Barry E. Smith
Vice-Chairmen: Ernie Magee, Margot Priest
Program Advisor and Exec. Officer,
John D. Sanderson

MINISTRY OF TREASURY AND ECONOMICS

Frost Bldg. S., Queen's Park, Toronto, M7A 1Y7
(except where otherwise indicated)
General Inquiries: (416) 965-7171

MINISTER'S OFFICE
Frost Bldg. S., 7th Flr.
7 Queen's Park Cres., Toronto, M7A 1Y7
Treasurer and Minister of Economics,
The Hon. Robert Nixon

DEPUTY MINISTER'S OFFICE
Dep. Minister, Mary Mogford
Ministry Office
Manager, John Taylor
Legal Services
Director, Graham Stoodley, Q.C.

Office of the Budget and Intergovernmental Finance
Asst. Dep. Minister, Michael Gourley
Taxation Policy Branch
Director, T.G. Sweeting
Fiscal Planning Policy Branch
Director, Mark McElwain
Intergovernmental Finance Policy Branch
Director, K. Bouey

Tax Reform
Asst. Dep. Minister, Larry Leonard
Dep. Chairman, C.H. Townsend
Exec. Member, Aubrey LeBlanc

Office of the Treasury
Frost Bldg. N., 2nd Flr., Toronto, M7A 1Y7
Asst. Dep. Minister, D.S. McColl
Financial Information and Accounting Policy Branch
Director, W. Tysall
Finance Operations Branch
Director, R.J. Watson
Finance Policy Branch
Director, Bob Christie

Office of Economic Policy
Frost Bldg. N., 5th Flr., Toronto, M7A 1Y7
A/Asst. Dep. Minister, H. Ploeger
Demographics and Social Economics Branch
Director, J. Tylee
Sectoral and Regional Policy Branch
Frost Bldg. N., 4th Flr., Toronto, M7A 1Y7
A/Director, D. Trick
Economic Forecasting Branch
Frost Bldg. N., 6th Flr., Toronto, M7A 1Y7
Director, Q. Silk

ADMINISTRATION
1075 Bay St., 4th Flr., Toronto, M5S 2B1
Exec. Director, Sharon Cohen
Finance and Management Services Branch
Director, S.I. Ker
Supply and Office Services Branch
Director, S.I. Ker
Internal Audit Branch
Director, D.A. Tovell
Human Resources Branch
Director, D. Gordon
Chief Librarian, B.A.B. Weatherhead
Frost Bldg. N., Main Flr., Toronto, M7A 1Y7
Communications Services
Director, J. Boyle

AGENCIES, BOARDS, COMMISSIONS AND CROWN CORPORATIONS

Stadium Corp. of Ontario Ltd. ("SKYDOME")
277 Front St. W., Ste. 930, Toronto, M5V 2X4
General Inquiries: (416) 963-3663

The Stadium Corporation was formed in 1984 by an order of the Lieutenant-Governor in Council. The Corporation was charged with the development, funding, construction, and operation of a major facility in Metro Toronto to accommodate a variety of sports events, trade shows, exhibitions, rallies, and conventions.

Reporting to the Treasurer and Minister of Economics, the Corporation is joined in this venture by representatives and agencies of both the municipal and federal governments. As well, there is a unique funding agreement with a consortium of private-sector corporations. It is intended that this latter association will evolve into a formal partnership when the stadium commences operation. Completion of construction is targeted for 1989.

President and CEO, Charles Magwood
Exec. Vice-President, Paul D. Colangelo
Finance and Administration
Vice-President, James W.S. MacArthur
Marketing
Vice-President, David E. Garrick
Operations
Vice-President, R.J. Hunter
Corporate Treasurer, John Kravis

INDEPENDENT AGENCIES, BOARDS AND COMMISSIONS

Ontario Advisory Council on Women's Issues

880 Bay St., 5th Flr., Toronto, M7A 1N3

The Council is an advisory body to the Ontario government on all matters pertaining to women. Originally created in 1973 as the Ontario Council on the Status of Women, in 1984, it became the Ontario Advisory Council on Women's Issues.

The mandate of the Council is:

* to monitor and assess existing programs, legislation, and policy related to women;
* to identify specific areas requiring attention;
* to hold discussions and consultations; and
* to respond to requests from the minister for advice and consultation.

The Council is made up of 16 members who serve for three-year terms on a part-time basis.

Minister responsible, The Hon. Greg Sorbara
President, Sandra Kerr
Exec. Officer, Bridget Vianna
Policy Advisor, Elayne Ceifets Osher
Communications Officer, Lydia Oleksyn

Ontario Native Affairs Directorate

18 King St. E., 3rd Flr., Toronto, M5C 1C5
General Inquiries: (416) 965-4827
Fax: (416) 965-9917

The Ontario Native Affairs Directorate is a central agency of the Ontario government that carries out the mandate of the Minister responsible for Native Affairs. That mandate requires that the Directorate develop government policy on issues affecting native people, co-ordinate that policy with other ministries, and engage in the negotiation of corporate native issues such as land claims, self-government, and constitutional matters. The Directorate also monitors the delivery of programs and services to native communities and plays an advocacy role in the resolution of native issues by line ministries and the cabinet.

Minister responsible, The Hon. Ian G. Scott
Exec. Director, Mark Krasnick

Planning and Support Services
Manager, Tim Eger
Policy Asst., Zunaid Moolla
Finance and Administration
Manager, Nick Dybenko
Financial Officer, Marlene Brushett
A/Sr. Researcher, Gwynneth Jones
Corporate Policy
Manager, Wallis Smith
Policy Advisor, Paul Wertman
Lands and Natural Resources
Manager, David McNab
Land Claims Advisor, Lise Hansen
Policy Asst., Victor Lytwyn
Federal/Provincial Relations
Director, Ted Wilson
Justice and Social Policy/Institutions of Self-Government
A/Director, Mark Krasnick
Self-Government Negotiations
Caroline LaChapelle
Policy Advisors: Meish Podlog, Dave Mackey

Ontario Women's Directorate

480 University Ave., Ste. 200
Toronto, M5G 1V2

The Ontario Women's Directorate advises the Minister responsible for Women's Issues on all matters affecting women in Ontario and co-ordinates government policy on women's issues. The major thrust of their work is toward achieving economic, social, and legal equality for women. In recent years, legislative measures relating to family violence and pay equity have resulted from their efforts.

Minister responsible, The Hon. Greg Sorbara
Asst. Dep. Minister, Naomi Alboim
Policy and Research Branch
Director, Celia Denov
Sr. Policy Advisor, Economic Issues,
Margot Trevelyan
Sr. Policy Advisor, Justice Issues,
Rebecca Shamai
A/Sr. Policy Advisor, Social Issues,
Juanita Bay
Provincial Co-ordinator of Family
Violence Initiatives, Betty Notar
Public Education Programs
and Services Branch
Director, Bev Wybrow
Consultative Services Branch
Director, Joan Andrew
Private-Sector Employment Equity Unit
Manager, Mary Helen Spence
Public-Sector Employment Equity
Programs Unit
A/Manager, Sue Varla
Program Development Unit
Co-ordinator, Ann Holmes
Grants Unit
A/Co-ordinator, Jeanne Eddington
French-Language Services
Co-ordinator, Monique Belanger
Corporate Services Branch
Director, Susan Singh

JUDICIARY AND JUDICIAL OFFICERS

Supreme Court of Ontario

Osgoode Hall
130 Queen St. W., Toronto, M5H 2N5
Court of Appeal: (416) 965-5548
High Court of Justice: (416) 363-4101

THE COURT OF APPEAL FOR ONTARIO

Chief Justice of Ontario:
The Hon. William G.C. Howland

Assoc. Chief Justice of Ontario:
The Hon. Charles L. Dubin*
The Hon. M.N. Lacourcière*
The Hon. L.W. Houlden*

Justices:
The Hon. Mr. Justice J.W. Brooke
The Hon. Mr. Justice T.G. Zuber
The Hon. Mr. Justice D.G. Blair
The Hon. Mr. Justice J.W. Morden
The Hon. Mr. Justice D.S. Thorson
The Hon. Mr. Justice A. Goodman
The Hon. Mr. Justice Sydney L. Robins
The Hon. Mr. Justice S.G.M. Grange
The Hon. Mr. Justice W.S. Tarnopolsky
The Hon. Mr. Justice G.D. Finlayson
The Hon. Mr. Justice H. Krever
The Hon. Madam Justice H.M. McKinlay
The Hon. Mr. Justice W.D. Griffiths
The Hon. Mr. Justice Marvin Catzman
The Hon. Mr. Justice James Carthy

THE HIGH COURT OF JUSTICE FOR ONTARIO

Chief Justice: The Hon. William D. Parker

Assoc. Chief Justice: The Hon. F.W. Callaghan

Justices:
The Hon. Mr. Justice S.H.S. Hughes*
The Hon. Mr. Justice J.H. Osler*
The Hon. Mr. Justice E.P. Hartt
The Hon. Mr. Justice P.T. Galligan
The Hon. Mr. Justice T.P. Callon*
The Hon. Mr. Justice J.D. O'Driscoll
The Hon. Madam Justice M.M. Van Camp*
The Hon. Mr. Justice R.E. Holland
The Hon. Mr. Justice D.F. O'Leary
The Hon. Mr. Justice D.H.W. Henry*
The Hon. Mr. Justice R.F. Reid
The Hon. Mr. Justice J.M. Labrosse
The Hon. Mr. Justice J.B.S. Southey
The Hon. Mr. Justice A.W. Maloney
The Hon. Mr. Justice R.C. Rutherford
The Hon. Mr. Justice D.R. Steele
The Hon. Mr. Justice M.A. Craig*
The Hon. Mr. Justice John Holland*
The Hon. Madam Justice Janet L. Boland
The Hon. Mr. Justice R.S. Montgomery

The Hon. Mr. Justice D.H. Carruthers
The Hon. Mr. Justice W.J. Anderson*
The Hon. Mr. Justice E. Saunders
The Hon. Mr. Justice A.H. Hollingworth*
The Hon. Mr. Justice J.E. Eberle
The Hon. Mr. Justice A.M. Linden
The Hon. Mr. Justice G.T. Walsh
The Hon. Mr. Justice C.A. Osborne
The Hon. Mr. Justice R.G. Trainor
The Hon. Mr. Justice W.G. Gray
The Hon. Mr. Justice E.E. Smith
The Hon. Mr. Justice J.W. O'Brien
The Hon. Mr. Justice M.A. Catzman
The Hon. Mr. Justice J.H. Potts
The Hon. Mr. Justice J.G.M. White
The Hon. Mr. Justice J.J. Fitzpatrick
The Hon. Mr. Justice R.A.F. Sutherland
The Hon. Mr. Justice J.C. Sirois
The Hon. Mr. Justice N.D. McRae
The Hon. Mr. Justice John D. Bowlby
The Hon. Mr. Justice J.R. Barr
The Hon. Mr. Justice E.G. Ewaschuk
The Hon. Mr. Justice A.B. Rosenberg
The Hon. Mr. Justice J.M. Donnelly
The Hon. Mr. Justice J. David Watt
The Hon. Mr. Justice Archie G. Campbell
The Hon. Mr. Justice Allan M. Austin
The Hon. Mr. Justice William P. McKeown
The Hon. Madam Justice Judith M. Oyen
The Hon. Mr. Justice George Yates
The Hon. Madam Justice Jean L. MacFarland
The Hon. Madam Justice Louise Arbour
The Hon. Mr. Justice B. Thomas Granger
The Hon. Mr. Justice W. Dan Chilcott
The Hon. Mr. Justice James B. Chadwick
The Hon. Mr. Justice Paul Philp
The Hon. Mr. Justice David Doherty

*Chief Administrative Officer,
Supreme Court of Ontario:* W.J. Dunlop

OFFICERS OF THE SUPREME COURT OF ONTARIO

180 Queen St. W., Toronto, M5H 2N5

Registrar: W.J. Dunlop
Executive Officer to the Chief Justices:
    B. Krivy, Q.C.
Registrar, Court of Appeal: A.P. Bridges
*Registrar, Divisional Court and Sr. Deputy
    Registrar, S.C.O.:* A.P. Bridges
Local Registrar of the Judicial District of York:
    W.J. Dunlop
Sr. Deputy Local Registrar: A.E. Chapman
Deputy Local Registrars: M.E. Dayton,
    A.C. Fernandes, R.O. Robinson

Sr. Master: H.F.H. Sedgwick
Masters:
G.C. Saunders; J.M. Ferron, Q.C.;

---

* Supernumerary

D.H. Sandler; H. Garfield; S.D. Cork;
W.R. Donkin, Q.C.; J.G. Quinn (Windsor);
B. Sischy, Q.C.; D.A. Peppiatt, Q.C.;
E.R. Browne, Q.C. (London); R.B. Linton, Q.C.;
R.B. Peterson; G.E. Schreider (Ottawa);
B.T. Clark, Q.C.

Part-time Master and Assessment Officer:
  S.M. McBride, Q.C.; B.B. Osler, Q.C.;
  G.W. Dunn; D.T. Elliott (Ottawa)

Special Examiners:
M.J. Nimigen (Hamilton),
L.A. Gillespie (Ottawa),
R.J. Penfound (St. Catharines),
E. Paquette (Timmins), Jean Pert (Toronto),
A.C. Devenport (Toronto),
P.W. Rosenberger (Toronto),
R.J. Graham (Toronto),
E.B. Macmillan (Windsor)
(Ex officio: The Registrar, every Local
Registrar, Deputy Registrar of the
County Court)

Official Guardian: Willson A. McTavish, Q.C.
Deputy Official Guardian: Susan Heimel
Accountant of the Supreme Court:
  E.J. McGann, C.A.
Public Trustee, Ontario: Hugh S. Paisley, Q.C.

District Court of Ontario

Chief Judge, District Court of Ontario:
  The Hon. W.D. Lyon
  400 University Ave., Ste. 1803
  Toronto, M5G 1S5

Assoc. Chief Judge: The Hon. P.J. LeSage

Judges: F.E. Dunlap, G.B. Smith,
  J.A. Hoolihan, W.E.C. Colter*,
  W.F.B. Rogers*, James Crossland,
  J.R. Maurice Gautreau, William A. Jenkins,
  Christopher Speyer

COUNTIES AND DISTRICTS

ALGOMA DISTRICT
424 Queen St. E., Sault Ste. Marie, P6A 5M8
Judges: I.A. Vannini, R. Stortini, R.W. Warren,
  M.C. DiSalle, P.S. Fitzgerald*

BRANT DISTRICT
70 Wellington St., Brantford, N3T 2L9
Judges: J.C. Kent, E.V. Fanjoy*

BRUCE COUNTY
215 Cayley St., Walkerton, N0G 2V0
Judge: J.I. McKay

COCHRANE DISTRICT
149-4th Ave., Cochrane, P0L 1C0
Judge: R.P. Boissonneault

48 Spruce St. N., Timmins, P4N 6M7
Judge: R.E. Maranger

DUFFERIN COUNTY
10 Louisa St., Orangeville, L9W 3P9
Judge: R.G. Thomas

DURHAM DISTRICT
605 Rossland Rd. E., Whitby, L1N 5S4
Judges: J.P. Kelly*, D.M. Lawson, W.B. Lane,
  E.R. Lovekin, J.H. Jenkins

ELGIN COUNTY
Box 310, St. Thomas, N5P 3T9
Judge: J.F. McGarry

ESSEX COUNTY
245 Windsor Ave., Windsor, N9A 1J2
Judges: C. Zalev, P.I. Staniszewski,
  J.P. McMahon, R.J. Huneault, K.G. Ouellette,
  A.E. Cusinato

FRONTENAC COUNTY
Court St., Kingston, K7L 2N4
Judges: T.L. Lally, A.R. Campbell*

GREY COUNTY
595-9th Ave. E., Owen Sound, N4K 3E3
Judge: R.E. Zelinski

HALDIMAND DISTRICT
55 Munsee St. N., Cayuga, N0A 1E0
Judges: M.P. Forestell, W.W. Leach*

HALTON DISTRICT
491 Steeles Ave. E., Milton, L9T 1Y7
Judges: J.D. Carnwath, J.H. Clarke,
  T.E. Quinlan

HAMILTON/WENTWORTH DISTRICT
50 Main St. E., Hamilton, L8N 1E9
Judges: G.J. Sullivan, C.S. Lazier,
  J.C. Scime, W.T. Stayshyn, G.E. McTurk,
  P.W. Perras, N. Borkovich

Unified Family Court:
100 James St. S., Hamilton, L8P 2Z3
Judges: J.E. Van Duzer, D.M. Steinberg,
  D. Mendes da Costa, T.A. Beckett,
  P.H. Wallace

HASTINGS COUNTY
235 Pinnacle St., Belleville, K8N 3A9
Judges: R.C. Honey*, R.G. Byers

HURON COUNTY
1 Court House Sq., Goderich, N7A 1M2
Judge: F.G. Carter

KENORA DISTRICT
Water St., Kenora, P9N 1S4
Judge: G.F. Kinsman

KENT COUNTY
21-7th St., Chatham, N7M 4K1
Judges: G.B. Clements, R.M.P. Daudlin

LAMBTON COUNTY
700 Christina St. N., Sarnia, N7V 3C2
Judges: M.R. Meehan, K.F. Ross

LANARK COUNTY
43 Drummond St. E., Perth, K7H 1G1
Judges: C.J. Newton, J.R. Matheson*

LEEDS AND GRENVILLE COUNTIES
Court House Green, Brockville, K6V 5T7
Judge: P.J. Cosgrove

LENNOX & ADDINGTON COUNTY
97 Thomas St. E., Napanee, K7R 1L1
Judge: B.W. Hurley

MANITOULIN COUNTY
155 Elm St. W., Sudbury, P3C 1T9
Judges: C.T. Murphy, G.E. Collins*

MIDDLESEX COUNTY
80 Dundas St., 12th Flr., London, N6A 2P3
Judges: G.P. Killeen, J.A. Winter*,
   J.F. McCart, R.J. Flinn, D.R. McDermid,
   T.G. Street*, D.G.E. Thompson

MUSKOKA DISTRICT
3 Dominion St., Bracebridge, P0B 1C0
Judge: S.B. Hogg

NIAGARA NORTH DISTRICT
59 Church St., St. Catharines, L2R 7A7
Judges: F.J. Kovacs, G.W. Dandie,
   R.T.P. Gravely

NIAGARA SOUTH DISTRICT
102 East Main St., Welland, L3B 3W6
Judges: G.G. Nicholls, E.I. MacDonald,
   J.J. Fleury

NIPISSING DISTRICT
390 Plouffe St., North Bay, P1B 4G1
Judge: R. Perras

NORFOLK COUNTY
No. 3 Highway W., Simcoe, N3Y 4N4
Judge: J.A. Pringle

NORTHUMBERLAND COUNTY
860 William St., Cobourg, K9A 4K2
Judge: J.G. Kerr

OTTAWA/CARLETON DISTRICT
161 Elgin St., Ottawa, K2P 2K1
Judges: K.A. Flanigan, C.F. Doyle,
   K.H. Fogarty*, F.H. Poulin, H. Soublière,
   E.J. Houston, D.L. McWilliam, P. Mercier,
   W.T. Hollinger*, R.C. Desmarais

OXFORD COUNTY
415 Hunter St., Woodstock, N4S 4G6
Judge: C.C. Misener

PARRY SOUND DISTRICT
89 James St., Parry Sound, P2A 1T7
Judge: E. Loukidelis

PEEL DISTRICT
7755 Hurontario St.
Box 8000, Brampton, L6V 2M7
Judges: J.B. Webber, E.F. West, S.N. Filer,
   M.T. Morrissey, H.J. Keenan, M.G. Bolan,
   J.A. Goodearle, B.B. Shapiro*

PERTH COUNTY
1 Huron St., Stratford, N5A 5S4
Judge: J.A. Mullen

PETERBOROUGH COUNTY
470 Water St., Peterborough, K9H 3M3
Judges: S.H. Murphy, G.L. Murdoch*

PRESCOTT AND RUSSELL COUNTIES
Queen St., L'Orignal, K0B 1K0
Judge: R.J. Cusson

PRINCE EDWARD COUNTY
44 Union St., Box 680, Picton, K0K 2T0
Judge: John D. O'Flynn

RAINY RIVER DISTRICT
333 Church St., Fort Frances, P9A 3M5
Judge: B.B. Trembley

RENFREW COUNTY
297 Pembroke St. E., Pembroke, K8A 3K2
Judge: E.R. Millette

SIMCOE COUNTY
114 Worsley St., Barrie, L4M 1M1
Judges: H.D. Logan, A.P. Dilks, P.B. Tobias,
   A.M. Carter*, J.A. Clare*

**STORMONT, DUNDAS & GLENGARRY
COUNTIES**
26 Pitt St., Cornwall, K6J 3P2
Judge: J.A. Forget

SUDBURY DISTRICT
155 Elm St. W., Sudbury, P3C 1T9
Judges: S.D. Loukidelis, M.J. Fortier,
   F.L. Gratton

THUNDER BAY DISTRICT
277 Camelot St., Thunder Bay, P7A 4B3
Judges: S.R. Kurisko, J. de P. Wright
   L.C. Kozak

TIMISKAMING DISTRICT
393 Main St., Haileybury, P0J 1K0
Judge: J.D. Bernstein

VICTORIA COUNTY
440 Kent St. W., Lindsay, K9V 5P2
Judge: Lloyd A. Woods

WATERLOO COUNTY
20 Weber St. E., Kitchener, N2H 1C3
Senior Judge: Michael G. Bolan
Judges: D.F. Mossop, R.E. Salhany,
   F.J. McDonald, F. Costello*, J.V. Scott

---

* Supernumerary

WELLINGTON COUNTY
74 Woolwich St., Box 247, Guelph, N1H 6J9
Judges: E.G. McNeely, W.F. Higgins

YORK REGION
50 Eagle St. W., Newmarket, L3Y 6B1
Judges: J.E. Sheppard, D.J. Taliano,
  E.B. Fedak, D.R. Shearer*

YORK DISTRICT
361 University Ave., Toronto, M5G 1T3
Judges: N.D. Coo, G.F. Moore*, E.F. Wren,
  H.W. Allen, S. Dymond, J.B. Trotter,
  H.R. Locke, J.D. Hudson, G.S.P. Ferguson,
  W.J. Rapson, J.D. Sheard, B.C. Hawkins,
  R.G. Conant, I. Cartwright, S.P. Webb,
  A. Mandel, J. Gilbert, J.C. Kane, A.C. Whealy,
  P.R. German, S. Borins, K.M. Weiler,
  K.A. Hoilet, A.J. Davidson, K.M. Gibson,
  H.J. Smith, D.J. Haley, M. Corbett,
  P.T. Matlow, H.M. O'Connell, D.G. Humphrey,
  L. Gotlib, D.H. Lissaman

Provincial Judges and Provincial Courts

CRIMINAL DIVISION
Old City Hall, 60 Queen St. W.
Toronto, M5H 2M4
General Inquiries: (416) 965-7217

Chief Judge: His Honour F.C. Hayes

ALGOMA DISTRICT
60 Taylor Ave., Box 187, Bruce Mines, P0R 1C0
Judge: W.W. Cohen

Court House, Box 550
Sault Ste. Marie, P6A 5M8
Judges: C.E. Boyd, J.D. Greco

BRANT COUNTY
102 Wellington Sq., Box 608
Brantford, N3T 2M2
Judge: W.A. MacDonald

BRUCE COUNTY
215 Cayley St., Box 39, Walkerton, N0G 2V0
Judge: F.W. Olmstead

COCHRANE DISTRICT
District Court House
Box 2069, Cochrane, P0L 1C0
Judge: G.E. Cloutier

The 101 Mall, Ste. 125, Timmins, P4N 6K6
Judges: J.H. Caldbick, R. Lajoie

DUFFERIN COUNTY
10 Louisa St., Orangeville, L9W 3P9
Assoc. Chief Judge: H.A. Rice

DURHAM JUDICIAL DISTRICT
242 King St. E., Oshawa, L1H 1C7
Judges: D.B. Dodds, N.H. Edmondson,
  D.J. Halikowski

ELGIN COUNTY
30 St. Catharine St.
Box 267, St. Thomas, N5P 3T9
Judge: G.A. Phillips

ESSEX COUNTY
Provincial Court Bldg., City Hall Square
Box 607, Windsor, N9A 6N4
Senior Judge: G.F. DeMarco
Judges: D.A. Ebbs, H. Momotiuk, S. Nosanchuk

FRONTENAC COUNTY
279 Wellington St., Box 400
Kingston, K7L 4W2
Senior Judge: P.E.D. Baker
Judge: P.H. Megginson

GREY COUNTY
1133-2nd Ave. E., Ste. 200
Box 233, Owen Sound, N4K 5P3
Judge: J.F. Laing

HALDIMAND COUNTY
Munsee St., Box 399, Cayuga, N0A 1E0
Judge: D.H. Gowan

HALTON JUDICIAL DISTRICT
491 Steeles Ave. E., Milton, L9T 1Y7
Judges: D.V. Latimer, J.E.C. Robinson,
  W.S. Sharpe

HAMILTON-WENTWORTH JUDICIAL DISTRICT
125 Main St. E., Box 2014, Hamilton, L8N 3S1
Senior Judge: E.A. Fairbanks
Judges: N. Bennett, R.T. Bennett,
  A.J. Marck, P.R. Mitchell, M.J. Perozak,
  C.J. Stiles, A. Zuraw

HASTINGS COUNTY
Provincial Court House
15 Victoria Ave., Belleville, K8N 1Z5
Judge: J. Cassells

HURON COUNTY
Court House, Goderich, N7A 1M2
Judge: R.G.E. Hunter

KENORA DISTRICT
Ontario Government Bldg.
479 Government St., Box 3000
Dryden, P8N 3B3
Judge: R.E. Bogusky

Court House, 216 Water St., Kenora, P9N 1S4
Judge: D.G. Fraser

KENT COUNTY
21-7th St., 2nd Flr., Chatham, N7M 4K1
Judge: C.E. Perkins

---

† denotes judges serving both family and criminal divisions.
†† denotes judges retired and serving per diem.

LAMBTON COUNTY
700 North Christina St., 3rd Flr.
Box 2017, Sarnia, N7T 7L1
Judges: A.L. Eddy, A.M. Lang

LANARK COUNTY
Shopping Plaza, 39 Chambers St., Rm. 307
Box 31, Smith's Falls, K7A 4S9
Judge: D.W. Dempsey

LEEDS & GRENVILLE UNITED COUNTIES
75 Water St. W., Box 1360
Brockville, K6V 5Y6
Judge: R.M. MacFarlane

LENNOX & ADDINGTON COUNTY
Memorial Bldg., 41 Dundas St. W.
Box 386, Napanee, K7R 3P5
Judge: J.P. Coulson

MANITOULIN DISTRICT
District Court House, Box 314
Gore Bay, P0P 1H0
Judge: G. Mahaffy

MIDDLESEX COUNTY
80 Dundas St. E., Box 5600
Terminal A, London, N6A 2P3
Senior Judge: A.J. Baker
Judges: W.E. Bell, J.L. Menzies,
   J.M. Seneshen, J.D.R. Walker, G.A. Guthrie

MUSKOKA DISTRICT
Court House, Dominion St.
Box 1110, Bracebridge, P0B 1C0
Judge: D.G. Bice

NIAGARA JUDICIAL DISTRICT
Niagara North:
59 Church St., Box 1537
St. Catharines, L2R 7J9
Senior Judge: H.W. Edmondstone
Judges: T.R. BeGora, W.D. Morrison

Niagara South:
4300 Queen St., Box 627
Niagara Falls, L2E 6V5
Judge: D.J. Wallace

40 Division St., Box 243, Welland, L3B 3Z6
Judges: M.J. Girard, D.H. Gowan

NIPISSING DISTRICT
Court House
621 Main St. W., North Bay, P1B 2V6
Judge: Jean-Gilles Lebel

NORFOLK JUDICIAL DISTRICT
No. 3 Hwy. W., Box 605, Simcoe, N3Y 4N4
Judge: W.E. Ross

NORTHUMBERLAND COUNTY
1011 William St., Box 910
Cobourg, K9A 4W4
Judges: J.D. Bark, J.D. Evans

OTTAWA-CARLETON JUDICIAL DISTRICT
United Trust Bldg., 4th Flr.
161 Elgin St., Ottawa, K2P 2K1
Senior Judge: P.R. Belanger
Judges: J.P. Beaulne, J.M. Bordeleau,
   R.B. Hutton, J.D. Nadelle, B.T. Ryan,
   P.D. White, J.A. Fontana, B.W. Lennox

OXFORD COUNTY
Court House, 415 Hunter St., Box 910
Woodstock, N4S 4G6
Judge: A.M. Graham

PARRY SOUND DISTRICT
89 James St., Parry Sound, P2A 1T7
Judge: L.S. Geiger

PEEL JUDICIAL DISTRICT
141 Clarence St., Brampton, L6W 3E6
Senior Judge: W.D. August
Judges: K.A. Langdon, J.D. Ord,
   W.G. Richards, J.D. Smith, R.T. Weseloh,
   G.L. Young, J.D. Takach

PERTH COUNTY
17 George St. W., Stratford, N5A 1A6
Judge: W.A. Ehgoetz

PETERBOROUGH COUNTY
70 Simcoe St., Peterborough, K9H 7G9
Judges: R.B. Batten, L.T.G. Collins

PRESCOTT & RUSSELL UNITED COUNTIES
Court House, Box 272, L'Orignal, K0B 1K0
Judge: J.F.R. Levesque

PRINCE EDWARD COUNTY
Box 640, Picton, K0K 2T0
Senior Judge: P.E.D. Baker
Judge: P.H. Megginson

RAINY RIVER DISTRICT
Court House, Box 336, Fort Frances, P9M 3M7
Judge: A.D. McLennan

RENFREW COUNTY
415 Pembroke St. W.
Box 218, Pembroke, K8A 6X3
Judge: C.R. Merredew

SIMCOE COUNTY
Court House, 30 Poyntz St.
Box 284, Barrie, L4M 5L4
Judges: D.R. Inch, N.J. Nadeau, G.V. Palmer

19 Front St. N., Box 218, Orillia, L3V 6J3
Judge: L.T. Montgomery

STORMONT, DUNDAS & GLENGARRY
JUDICIAL DISTRICT
340 Pitt St., Box 56, Cornwall, K6H 5R9
Judge: M.J. Fitzpatrick

Morrisburg Mall, Box 858, Morrisburg, K0C 1X0
Judge: H.B. Hunter

---

† denotes judges serving both family and criminal divisions.
†† denotes judges retired and serving per diem.

SUDBURY JUDICIAL DISTRICT
Court House, 155 Elm St. W.
Sudbury, P3C 1V1
Senior Judge: G.E. Michel
Judges: W.F. Fitzgerald, W.G. Mahaffy,
  G.R. Matte

THUNDER BAY DISTRICT
1805 East Arthur St., Thunder Bay, P7E 5N7
Senior Judge: R.J. Walneck
Judges: R.D. Clarke, F.A. Sargent,
  R.B. Mitchell

TIMISKAMING DISTRICT
Court House, Box 1208, Haileybury, P0J 1K0
Judge: R.N. Fournier

VICTORIA & HALIBURTON COUNTIES
440 Kent St. W., Box 82, Lindsay, K9V 4R8
Judge: G.F.W. Inrig

WATERLOO JUDICIAL DISTRICT
200 Frederick St., Ste. 1000
Kitchener, N2H 6P1
Senior Judge: G.H. McConnell
Judges: D.J. MacMillan, J.F. McCormick,
  R.D. Reilly, D.C. Downie

WELLINGTON COUNTY
36 Wyndham St. S., Box 878, Guelph, N1H 7J5
Judge: B.E. Payne

YORK JUDICIAL DISTRICT
Metro East:
1911 Eglinton Ave. E., Scarborough, M1L 2L6
Senior Judge: A.W. Davidson
Judges: W.L. Camblin, C.E. Purvis,
  Ian MacDonnell

College Park
444 Yonge St., Toronto, M5B 2H4
Senior Judge: C. Scullion
Judges: M.A. Cadsby, E.G. Hachborn,
  T. Mercer, J. Murphy,
  P.B. Pickett, H.D. Porter

Metro North:
1000 Finch Ave. W., Downsview, M3J 2V5
Senior Judge: C.P. Opper
Judges: J. Crossland, C.J. Morrison,
  Lauren Marshall

Metro West:
80 The East Mall, Etobicoke, M8Z 5X1
Senior Judge: Vacant
Judges: C.J. Cannon, W.G. Richards
  A.V. Couto, S.W. Long

Metropolitan Toronto:
Old City Hall, 60 Queen St. W.
Toronto, M5H 2M4
Senior Judge: Gerald Lapkin
Judges: W.J. Babe, J.J. Belobradic,
  J.T. Bernhard (Her Honour), G.E. Carter,
  M.A. Charles, A.E. Charlton, J.S. Climans,
  S. Darragh, L.E. DiCecco, R.B. Dnieper,
  D. Draper, H.D. Foster, W.S. Gonet,
  D.F. Graham, P.A. Grossi, M.H. Harris,
  S.M. Harris, M.L. Hogan (Her Honour),
  D.T. Hogg, W.P. Hryciuk, B.M. Kelly,
  J.P. Kerr, C.H. Paris, W.P. Ross,
  H.W. Silverman, D. Vanek, F.D. White,
  P.J. Wilch, B.J. Young,
  E. Earle-Renton (Her Honour)

YORK REGION
Court House, 2nd Flr.
50 Eagle St. W., Newmarket, L3Y 6B1
Judge: H.E. Zimmerman, D.G. Scott,
  V.A. Lampkin, R.D. Osborne

FAMILY COURT DIVISION
700 Bay St., #2306, Toronto, M5G 1Z6
General Inquiries: (416) 924-0631

Chief Judge: H.T.G. Andrews
Assoc. Chief Judge: R.J.K. Walmsley
Judges: P.W. Dunn, K. Wang

ALGOMA DISTRICT
473 Queen St. E., Ste. 100
Box 909, Sault Ste. Marie, P6A 1Z5
Judge: G.D. Holder

BRANT COUNTY
38 Darling St., 2nd Flr., Brantford, N3T 6A8
Judge: D.S. Cooper

BRUCE COUNTY
215 Cayley St., Box 578, Walkerton, N0G 2V0
Senior Judge: J.M. Gammell
Judge: R.S. MacKenzie†

COCHRANE DISTRICT
149-4th Ave., Box 2069, Cochrane, P0L 1C0
Judge: G.E Cloutier†

Cochrane South:
38 Pine St., #127, Timmins, P4N 6K6
Judges: J.H. Caldbick†, R. Lajoie†

DUFFERIN COUNTY
10 Louisa St., 2nd Flr., Orangeville, L9W 3P9
Judge: F.S. Fisher

DURHAM JUDICIAL DISTRICT
44 Bond St. W., Box 2216, Oshawa, L1H 7V5
Senior Judge: R.H. Donald
Judges: J.B. Allen, R.H. Donald, P.Z. Magda

ELGIN COUNTY
145 Curtis St., Box 327, St. Thomas, N5P 3T9
Judge: J.F. Bennett

ESSEX COUNTY
250 Windsor Ave., 4th Flr.
Box 1508, Windsor, N9A 6R5
Judges: R.J. Abbey, S.G. Zaltz

FRONTENAC COUNTY
469 Montreal St., Kingston, Box 981, K7L 4X8
Judges: R.H. Fair, K.E. Pedlar, W.J. Pickett

GREY COUNTY
347-8th St. E., Box 206
Owen Sound, N4K 5P3
Judge: R.S. MacKenzie

HALDIMAND JUDICIAL DISTRICT
55 Munsee St. Cayuga, Box 399, N0A 1E0
Judge: D.S. Cooper

HALTON JUDICIAL DISTRICT
491 Steeles Ave. E., Milton, L9T 1Y7
Judge: A.J. Fuller

HASTINGS COUNTY
199 Front St., Ste. 402
Box 906, Belleville, K8N 5B6
Judges: D.K. Kirkland, W.J. Pickett

HURON COUNTY
Court House, Goderich, N7A 1M2
Judge: R.S. MacKenzie

KENORA DISTRICT
479 Government St., Box 3000
Dryden, P8N 3B3
Judge: R.E. Bogusky†

216 Water St., Kenora, P9N 1S4
Judge: Ms. J.P. Little†

KENT COUNTY
465 St. Clair St., Box 38, Chatham, N7M 5K1
Judge: L.G. De Koning

LAMBTON COUNTY
700 Christina St. N.
Box 2628, Sarnia, N7T 7V8
Judge: D.F. Kent

LANARK COUNTY
39 Chambers St. E, Box 31
Smiths Falls, K7A 4S9
Judge: A.D. Sheffield

LEEDS & GRENVILLE UNITED COUNTIES
75 Water St. W., Box 1360, Brockville, K6V 5Y6
Judge: R.H. Fair

LENNOX & ADDINGTON COUNTY
41 Dundas St. W., Box 386, Napanee, K7R 3P5
Judge: D.K. Kirkland

MANITOULIN DISTRICT
Court House, Box 314, Gore Bay, P0P 1H0
Senior Judge: R.T. Runciman
Judge: J.A. Cousineau

MIDDLESEX COUNTY
80 Dundas St. E.
Box 5600, Stn. A, London, N6A 2P3
Judges: M.H. Genest, H.A. Vogelsang,
   A.R. Webster

MUSKOKA DISTRICT
3 Dominion St., Box 159, Bracebridge, P0B 1C0
Judge: Vacant

NIAGARA JUDICIAL DISTRICT
Niagara North:

59 Church St., 4th Level
Box 536, St. Catharines, L2R 6V9
Judge: Ms. J.W. Scott

Niagara South:
3 Cross St., Box 383, Welland, L3B 5P7
Senior Judge: R.L. Budgell

NIPISSING DISTRICT
147 McIntyre St. W., North Bay, P1B 2Y5
Judge: Ms. L. Duchesneau-McLachlan

500 Main St. W., North Bay, P1B 2Y5
Judge: G.E. Wallace††

NORFOLK JUDICIAL DISTRICT
Court House, Hwy. #3 W., Box 605
Simcoe, N3Y 4N4
Judge: D.S. Cooper

NORTHUMBERLAND COUNTY
55 King St. W., Box 996, Cobourg, K9A 2M2
Judge: B.C. Thompson

OTTAWA-CARLETON JUDICIAL DISTRICT
161 Elgin St., Ottawa, K2P 2K1
Senior Judge: P.D. Hamlyn
Judges: G.J. Guzzo, J.P. Michel,
   A.D. Sheffield

OXFORD COUNTY
415 Hunter St., Woodstock, N4S 4G6
Judge: A.R. Webster

PARRY SOUND DISTRICT
89 James St., Parry Sound, P2A 1T7
Judge: L.S. Geiger†

PEEL JUDICIAL DISTRICT
7765 Hurontario St., 2nd Flr.
Box 220, Brampton, L6V 2L1
Judges: J.B. Allen, J.D. Karswick, R.E. Stauth

PERTH COUNTY
17 George St. W., Stratford, N5A 1A6
Judge: J.F. Bennett

PETERBOROUGH COUNTY
70 Simcoe St., Peterborough, K9H 7G9
Judges: A.P. Ingram, B.C. Thompson

PRESCOTT & RUSSELL UNITED COUNTIES
Court House, 59 Court St.
Box 272, L'Orignal, K0B 1K0
Judge: R. Lalande

PRINCE EDWARD COUNTY
332 Main St., Box 640, Picton, K0K 2T0
Judge: D.K. Kirkland

RAINY RIVER DISTRICT
333 Church St., Box 336
Fort Frances, P9A 3M7
Judge: A.D. McLennan†

---

† denotes judges serving both family and criminal divisions.
†† denotes judges retired and serving per diem.

RENFREW COUNTY
415 Pembroke St. W., Box 218
Pembroke, K8A 6X3
Judge: L.P. Foran

SIMCOE COUNTY
114 Worsley St., Box 184, Barrie, L4M 4T2
Judge: J.M. Gammell

STORMONT, DUNDAS AND GLENGARRY
UNITED COUNTIES
340 Pitt St., 4th Flr.
Box 56, Cornwall, K6H 5R9
Judge: R. Lalande, G. Goulard

SUDBURY JUDICIAL DISTRICT
40 Larch St., 2nd Flr., Sudbury, P3E 5M7
Senior Judge: R.T. Runciman

100 Tudhope St., 2nd Flr.
Box 1248, Espanola, P0P 1C0
Judge: J.A. Cousineau

THUNDER BAY DISTRICT
1805 Arthur St. E., 1st Flr.
Thunder Bay, P7E 5N7
Senior Judge: P.S. Glowacki
Judge: G.R. Kunnas

TIMISKAMING DISTRICT
4 Kirkland St., Box 253
Kirkland Lake, P2N 3H7
Judge: R.N. Fournier†

VICTORIA COUNTY
440 Kent St. W., Box 4000, Lindsay, K9V 5P2
Judge: A.P. Ingram

WATERLOO JUDICIAL DISTRICT
200 Frederick St., 2nd Flr.
Kitchener, N2H 6N9
Judges: G.A. Campbell, J.T. Robson

WELLINGTON COUNTY
36 Wyndham St. S.
Box 244, Guelph, N1H 6J9
Judge: F.H. Nowak

YORK JUDICIAL DISTRICT
160 Silverhill Dr., Etobicoke, M9B 3W7
Judges: F.S. Fisher, N. Weisman

1911 Eglinton Ave. E., Scarborough, M1L 2L6
Judges: C.R. Ball, D.F. Morrison

311 Jarvis St., Toronto, M5B 2C4
Senior Judge: L.A. Beaulieu
Judges: D.A. Bean, J.C.M. James, L. King,
   D.R. Main, A.P. Nasmith, J.P. Nevins

47 Sheppard Ave. E., North York, M2N 5N1
Judges: J.P. Felstiner, W.E. MacLatchy,
   H.D. Wilkins

YORK REGION
50 Eagle St. W., Newmarket, L3Y 6B1
Judges: W.W. Bradley, M.H. Caney

Bankruptcy Administrators

Bankruptcy proceedings are filed at the following Ontario offices. Please address inquiries to Department of Consumer and Corporate Affairs, Bankruptcy.

HAMILTON
10 John St. S., Rm. 657, L8N 4A7
Manager: David Stewart

LONDON
451 Talbot St., Rm. 302, N6A 5C9
Manager: Evan De Boyce

OTTAWA
255 Argyle Ave., K2P 1B8
Manager: Jean G. Chartrand

SUDBURY
127 Cedar St., Ste. 702, 7th Flr., P3E 1B1
Manager: Denise Leitch

TORONTO
25 St. Clair Ave. E., 7th Flr., M4T 1M2
Manager: William O'Connor

Mining Recorders

(Under the Ontario Ministry of Northern Development and Mines)

Mining Division	Mining Recorder
Kenora	Albert Scott Rivett
	808 Robertson St.
	Box 5200
	Kenora, P9N 3X9
Larder Lake	Michael Weirmeir
	4 Government Rd. E.
	Kirkland Lake, P2N 1A2
Ontario (Southern)	Mrs. R.M. Charnesky
	10 Wellesley St. E., 1st Flr.
	Toronto, M4Y 1G2
Patricia	R. Spooner
	Box 3000
	Sioux Lookout, P0V 2T0
Porcupine	Gary White
	60 Wilson Ave.
	Timmins, P4N 2S7
Red Lake	Ms. Romona Majcher
	Box 324
	Red Lake, P0V 2M0
Sault Ste. Marie	Mrs. Sheila T. Lessard
	875 Queen St. E.
	Sault Ste. Marie, P6A 2B3
Sudbury	V.C. Miller
	200 Brady St.
	Sudbury, P3A 5W2
Thunder Bay	Mrs. C. Allam (acting)
	435 James St. S.
	Box 5000
	Thunder Bay, P7C 5G6

This map is based on information taken from map MCR 4032. © Her Majesty in Right of Canada with permission of Energy, Mines and Resources.

PROVINCE OF PRINCE EDWARD ISLAND

PARVA SUB INGENTI

Lady's Slipper
(Cypripedium acaule)

Entered Confederation: July 1, 1873
Capital: Charlottetown
Motto: Parva Sub Ingenti (The small under
the protection of the great)
Flower: Lady's Slipper
Area: 5,657 km²
  percentage of Canada's total area: 0.1
  LAND: 5,657 km²
  FRESHWATER: 0
Elevation:
  HIGHEST POINT: Queens County (142 m)
  LOWEST POINT: sea level
Population (Oct. 1987): 127,300
  five-year change: +3.7%

per square kilometre: 22.5
percentage of Canada's total
  population: 0.5
  URBAN: 38%
  RURAL: 62%
Gross domestic product, 1987: $1.61 billion
Government Finance:
  REVENUE, 1986/87 est.: $520.2 million
  EXPENDITURE, 1986/87 est.: $538.2 million
  DEBT PER CAPITA (March 1987): $276
Personal income per capita, 1986: $12,071
Unemployment rate, 1988
  (annual average): 13.0%

HISTORY

"The fairest land 'tis possible to see", were the words Jacques Cartier used to describe the island which he discovered in 1534. Before the arrival of Europeans, Indians had inhabited Prince Edward Island for over 10,000 years. They gave it the name "Abegweit" which means cradle on the waves. The French first settled the Island in 1719, but it was taken from them by the English in 1758. Captain Samuel Holland surveyed the Island of St. John, as it was then known, in 1766. He divided it into 67 lots and these were raffled to English landlords in London. For the next 100 years, the Island was plagued with the problem of absentee ownership. In 1799, Prince Edward Island was approved as the colony's name, in honour of Prince Edward, the Duke of Kent.

Charlottetown, the provincial capital, was the site of the 1864 meeting which led to the formation of the Canadian Confederation. Though known as the "Cradle of Confederation" because of this meeting, the Island did not join Confederation until 1873.

THE LAND

Prince Edward Island, one of Canada's four Atlantic provinces, is the smallest of the ten provinces in both size and population. The Island is crescent-shaped and measures 224 km from tip to tip and from 6 to 64 km wide. It is situated in the Gulf of St. Lawrence and is separated from Nova Scotia and New Brunswick by the Northumberland Strait. The province covers 5,657 km², with over 50 per cent of the land devoted to agriculture, so that the Island is often referred to as the "Million Acre Farm."

The Island is sheltered from the Atlantic by Nova Scotia and Newfoundland, and is therefore free from sudden extremes of temperature and from fog. Its average precipitation is 109 cm. The waters around the province are warmer in summer than those of its neighbours, making P.E.I. beaches a popular attraction.

THE PEOPLE

Prince Edward Island's population is almost evenly divided between urban and rural dwellers. Approximately 62 per cent of the population is rural and 19 per cent of the total population lives on farms. Charlottetown, with a population of 15,776, is the only city in the province. Summerside, with a population of 8,020, is the second largest municipality.

Approximately 80 per cent of the population is of British ancestry, the majority of whom are of Scottish descent. About 17 per cent is of French descent, while 8 per cent of the total population speaks French.

Approximately 41.5 per cent of the population is under 25, with 46.5 per cent in the 25-64 age group. The average weekly earnings in the industrial aggregate for 1988 is estimated to be $366. There were an estimated 63,000 people in the labour force in 1988.

THE ECONOMY

Agriculture, tourism, and fishing are the most important industries in Prince Edward Island. However, manufacturing is becoming increasingly important. Service-oriented industries are the largest and fastest growing sectors in terms of employment. The traditional sectors — agriculture and fishing — dominate goods production, while food processing dominates manufacturing. Tourism is an important contributor to the Island economy. The provincial Gross Domestic Product in 1987 was approximately $1.61 billion, with an estimated growth of 5.2 per cent expected for 1988.

Agriculture. Prince Edward Island's rich red soil and moderate climate make it an ideal location for "mixed farming". Approximately 158,000 hectares of the 283,000 hectares devoted to agriculture are in crops. One of the major sources of farm income is potatoes. In 1988, yields rose to 12.4 per cent above the 5-year average. However, 1988 cash receipts were expected to drop due to the poor potato production and declining prices of 1987.

Tourism. Tourism is surpassed only by agriculture in terms of its importance to the provincial economy. In 1988, tourism activity set a new record, in turn encouraging increased growth in key service-oriented sectors.

Fishing. Commercial fishing is the second most important primary industry in the province. The fishing industry and related services contribute approximately $125 million annually to the P.E.I. economy. In 1988, growth in real fishing output is expected to increase by 10 per cent over the previous year.

The most important species is the lobster which accounts for more than half of the total fishery income. More than 30 species are harvested commercially. Species of major importance include groundfish, snowcrab, the famous Malpeque oyster, cultured mussels, herring, and giant bluefin tuna. The seaplant Irish Moss is an important income earner for P.E.I. fishermen; its extract, carrageenan, is used extensively in the food industry.

Manufacturing. A large part of the province's manufacturing sector is involved in the processing of agricultural and fish products, although there has been expansion into light manufacturing. Examples of manufacturing in the province include boatbuilding, commercial printing, dairy and fish processing, fibreglass production, metal fabricating, paint manufacturing, and production of agricultural implements. The provincial government is currently encouraging growth in the business sector in hopes of strengthening P.E.I.'s manufacturing base.

Forestry. There are 270,000 hectares of forested land on Prince Edward Island. Though timber quality has suffered from poor harvesting practices in the past, soil and site capability for forest production are excellent. The primary use of wood is for space heating. The processing sector consists of some 50 sawmills which produce 17 million board feet of lumber annually, at a value of over $6 million. In addition to fuel and sawlogs, some wood is exported as pulpwood.

Energy and Transportation. Prince Edward Island lacks the hydroelectric resources of some other provinces, and so must import power from New Brunswick via undersea cable, supplemented by costly oil-fired generators. Thus, electricity costs more than twice the national average. However, prices are expected to stabilize and then decrease, as less reliance is placed on thermal electricity produced on the Island, and more on New Brunswick hydro power.

Prince Edward Island is also linked to New Brunswick by a year-round car ferry service. The P.E.I.-Nova Scotia ferry operates from April to December. Some ferries carry railway cars as well as automobiles, facilitating the export of agricultural products to offshore markets.

Plans to begin the construction of a fixed link to the mainland have been delayed as the environmental and cultural impact of such a crossing is being further reviewed.

Text provided by Island Information Service, Government of Prince Edward Island.

GOVERNMENT OF PRINCE EDWARD ISLAND

Seat of Government:
  Province House, Box 2000
  Charlottetown, C1A 7N8

Lieutenant-Governor,
  The Hon. Lloyd G. MacPhail
  Government House, Box 846
  Charlottetown, C1A 1N8

EXECUTIVE COUNCIL

In order of precedence, as of Jan. 1, 1989)

*Premier, President of the Executive Council,
Minister of Agriculture,*
  The Hon. Joseph A. Ghiz, Q.C.
*Minister of Finance, Minister of Community and
Cultural Affairs,*
  The Hon. Gilbert R. Clements
Minister of Energy and Forestry,
  The Hon. Allison Ellis
Minister of Industry,
  The Hon. Leonce Bernard
Minister of Fisheries,
  The Hon. Ross (Johnny) Young
Minister of Transportation and Public Works,
  The Hon. Robert Morrissey
Minister of Education,
  The Hon. Betty Jean Brown
*Minister of Justice, Attorney General, Minister
of Labour,*
  The Hon. Wayne D. Cheverie, Q.C.
Minister of Tourism and Parks,
  The Hon. Gordon MacInnis
Minister of Health and Social Services,
  The Hon. Keith Milligan

EXECUTIVE COUNCIL OFFICE

Shaw Bldg., 95 Rochford St.
Box 2000, Charlottetown, C1A 7N8

President of the Executive Council,
  The Hon. Joseph A. Ghiz, Q.C.
Clerk of the Executive Council,
  Diane I. Blanchard
Clerk Asst. of the Executive Council,
  Lynn Ellsworth

Treasury Board

Chairman, The Hon. Gilbert R. Clements
Secretary, Andrew B. Wells
Budget Director, William G. Harper
Employee Relations
Director, Wayne McMillan

LEGISLATIVE ASSEMBLY

57th General Assembly, 4th Session
Last election: April 21, 1986
  (Maximum legal duration 5 years)
Government party: Liberal
Total number of seats: 32
Party standings:
  Liberals: 22
  Conservatives: 9
  Vacant: 1

Salaries, Indemnities and Allowances

MEMBERS: $18,500 Member's Sessional Indem-
  nity, plus expense allowance of $9,100 per
  annum.
MINISTERS: $33,900 per annum, in addition to
  Member's Sessional Indemnity and expense
  allowance.
PREMIER: $44,200 per annum, in addition to
  Member's Sessional Indemnity and expense
  allowance.
SPEAKER: $7,100 per annum, in addition to
  Member's Sessional Indemnity and an expense
  allowance of $2,500.
DEPUTY SPEAKER: $3,600 per annum, in addi-
  tion to Member's Sessional Indemnity and an
  expense allowance of $1,300.
LEADER OF THE OPPOSITION: $33,900 per
  annum, in addition to Member's Sessional
  Indemnity and expense allowance.

Officers

Speaker, The Hon. Edward W. Clark
Deputy Speaker, Barry Hicken
Clerk, Dr. J. Aubin Doiron
Clerk Assistant, Douglas B. Boylan
Law Clerk, M. Raymond Moore
Sergeant-at-Arms, John Richard

Members

Two types of members are elected to the
Legislative Assembly. Each District elects one
Councillor and one Assembly member (both on a
general franchise vote).

---

*For further information regarding any aspect of the
Government of Prince Edward Island, contact:
Island Information Service,
Box 2000, Charlottetown, C1A 7N8
(902) 368-4000*

Riding	Councillor and Affiliation
1st Prince	Robert E. Campbell (Lib)
2nd Prince	The Hon. Allison Ellis (Lib)
3rd Prince	The Hon. Edward W. Clark (Lib)
4th Prince	Vacant
5th Prince	Nancy Guptill (Lib)
1st Queens	Leone Bagnall (PC)
2nd Queens	Ronald MacKinley (Lib)
3rd Queens	Tom Dunphy (Lib)
4th Queens	Lynwood MacPherson (Lib)
5th Queens	Tim Carroll (Lib)
6th Queens	Paul Connolly (Lib)
1st Kings	Albert Fogarty (PC)
2nd Kings	Francis O'Brien (PC)
3rd Kings	Peter MacLeod (PC)
4th Kings	The Hon. Gilbert R. Clements (Lib)
5th Kings	Barry Hicken (Lib)

Riding	Assembly Member and Affiliation
1st Prince	The Hon. Robert Morrissey (Lib)
2nd Prince	The Hon. Keith Milligan (Lib)
3rd Prince	The Hon. Leonce Bernard (Lib)
4th Prince	Stavert Huestis (Lib)
5th Prince	Andrew Walker (PC)
1st Queens	Marion Reid (PC)
2nd Queens	The Hon. Gordon MacInnis (Lib)
3rd Queens	The Hon. Betty Jean Brown (Lib)
4th Queens	Wilbur MacDonald (PC)
5th Queens	The Hon. Wayne D. Cheverie, Q.C. (Lib)
6th Queens	The Hon. Joseph A. Ghiz, Q.C. (Lib)
1st Kings	The Hon. Ross (Johnny) Young (Lib)
2nd Kings	R.B. (Roddy) Pratt (PC)
3rd Kings	A.A. (Joey) Fraser (PC)
4th Kings	Stanley Bruce (Lib)
5th Kings	Rosie Marie MacDonald (Lib)

Lib — Liberal
PC — Progressive Conservative

Office of the Premier

Shaw Bldg., 95 Rochford St.
Box 2000, Charlottetown, C1A 7N8

Premier, The Hon. Joseph A. Ghiz
Principal Secretary and Sr. Policy Advisor,
   Alex MacAulay
Exec. Assistant, Percy Downe
Communications and Co-ordination Officer,
   Kim Devine

Offices of Government Members

Coles Bldg., 100 Richmond St.
Box 2890, Charlottetown, C1A 8C5

Secretary, Hazel Gallant

Offices of the Official Opposition

Coles Bldg., 100 Richmond St.
Box 338, Charlottetown, C1A 7K7

Leader of the Opposition, Leone Bagnall
Leader of the Conservatives, Mel Gass
Research Officer, Maurice Rodgerson
Administrative Asst., Colleen Chipmen

DEPARTMENT OF AGRICULTURE

Jones Bldg., 4th Flr., 11 Kent St.
Box 2000, Charlottetown, C1A 7N8
General Inquiries: (902) 368-4880

MINISTER'S OFFICE

Minister, The Hon. Joseph A. Ghiz, Q.C.

DEPUTY MINISTER'S OFFICE

Dep. Minister, Dale Dewar
Special Projects
Co-ordinator, Marlene Clark
Administration Director, Al Hogan
Planning and Operations Section
Director, David Rogers
Marketing and Extension Branch
Director, Brian Thompson
Production Services
Director, Dr. Wendall Grasse

AGENCIES, BOARDS AND COMMISSIONS

MARKETING BOARDS

Marketing boards for agricultural products in Canada are created by a number of different pieces of legislation. National wheat and dairy products plans flow from the Canadian Wheat Board Act and the Canadian Dairy Commission Act respectively. Egg and poultry boards derive their authority from the Farm Products Marketing Agencies Act. As well, many have their own provincial statutes and are normally within the jurisdiction of an umbrella provincial agency. The individual boards are, however, non-governmental and made up largely of elected farmer representatives.

There is also a variety of types. The Economic Council of Canada's study on marketing boards identified five: promotional and developmental boards with little power; selling-desk boards that handle marketing but do not set prices; boards that negotiate prices; boards that set prices; and full-fledged boards that establish quotas. These last are known as supply-management marketing boards. Currently, there are more than 100 active boards in Canada.

P.E.I. MARKETING COUNCIL
Farm Centre, Box 2000
Charlottetown, C1A 7N8

The *Natural Products Marketing Act*, 1969, through which the Council was established, provides for the promotion, control, and regulation of the marketing of natural products within the province, including the prohibition of any aspect of marketing. The Council also fixes the wholesale and home-delivered prices of fluid or table milk.

The Council consists of not less than three and not more than eight members appointed by the Lieutenant-Governor in Council. It is the supervisory agency of the individual commodity boards. As such, it makes recommendations to the Lieutenant-Governor in Council on the establishment, amendment, or revocation of plans for the marketing of natural products, and on the constitution and powers of commodity boards or marketing commissions to administer such plans.

Chairman, Joseph Gaudin
Manager, Paul Jelley

MILK MARKETING BOARD
173 Belvedere Ave., Box 335
Charlottetown, C1A 7K7

The P.E.I. Milk Marketing Board is a nine-member, producer-elected board formed under the *P.E.I. Natural Products Marketing Act*, R.S.P.E.I. 1974, Chapter N-2. The Board operates under a plan granted by Order-in-Council on the recommendation of the P.E.I. Marketing Council.

The Board has very broad powers which are used to control and regulate milk production, milk quotas, pricing of industrial milk, as well as the buying and selling of raw milk. Milk purchased from producers is sold to industrial and fluid milk processors in P.E.I. as well as to buyers outside the province.

The Board is also responsible for fluid milk promotion within P.E.I. and for industrial milk product promotion in co-operation with the Dairy Bureau of Canada.

Annual sales of raw milk are approximately $20 million, with payments made to over 300 milk producers.

Chairman, Alan McIssac
Administrator, Murray Myles

P.E.I. EGG COMMODITY MARKETING BOARD
Farm Ctr., 420 University Ave.
Charlottetown, C1A 7Z5

Chairman, Eldred Simmons
Manager, Alvin MacDonald

P.E.I. HOG COMMODITY MARKETING BOARD
Farm Ctr., 420 University Ave.
Charlottetown, C1A 7Z5

Chairman, Herman Van Wichen
Manager, Don Mutch

P.E.I. PEDIGREED SEED COMMODITY MARKETING BOARD
Box 2000, Charlottetown, C1A 7N8

The P.E.I. Pedigreed Seed Commodity Market-

ing Board is made up of all pedigreed seed growers in P.E.I. The day-to-day activities of the Board are run by a six-member board with a chairman, vice-chairman, and secretary-treasurer.

The Board is authorized to regulate the marketing of pedigreed seed in interprovincial and export trade. It also makes orders; fixes, imposes and collects levies; suggests prices; and advertises and promotes the sale of pedigreed seed.

Chairman, Fulton Hammill
Sec.-Treasurer, Jim Murphy

P.E.I. POTATO MARKETING COMMISSION
Farm Ctr., 420 University Ave.
Charlottetown, C1A 7Z5

The Potato Marketing Board was formed in the early 1950s and has operated according to its present charter under the federal *Agricultural Products Marketing Act* since then. Its authority derives from the federal government through the provincial Executive Council. The Board answers directly to the provincial Minister of Agriculture.

The P.E.I. Potato Marketing Board's activities are conducted by a board of directors whose members are elected by the growers of P.E.I. by mail vote. It consists of six producer members and three dealer members, all subject to the producers' vote.

The Potato Marketing Board is involved in everything that directly or indirectly affects the potato industry of P.E.I., such as disease and quality control, transportation, promotion, operation of the Elite Seed Farm, negotiation of trade and tariff, and the receiving of trade missions.

Chairman, Jamie Ballem
Gen. Manager, Gordon MacEachern

P.E.I. POULTRY MEAT COMMODITY MARKETING BOARD
Box 2000, Charlottetown, C1A 7N8

The P.E.I. Poultry Meat Commodity Marketing Board was established under the *P.E.I. Natural Products Marketing Act*, R.S.P.E.I. 1974, Chapter N-2, to promote, control, and regulate the marketing of poultry meat within the province.

On Dec. 18, 1982, the P.E.I. Marketing Council assumed the functions, assets, and liabilities of the Board.

Chairman, Joseph Gaudin
Treas.-Manager, Paul Jelley

P.E.I. TOBACCO GROWERS COMMODITY BOARD
Box 602, Montague, C0A 1R0

The P.E.I. Tobacco Marketing Board is legislated under the *Natural Products Marketing Act* of P.E.I. and by the P.E.I. Tobacco Marketing Regulations, EC 162/86.

The Board was established in 1973 and is currently a four-member board. The major functions of the Board are to control production of tobacco within the province of P.E.I. and to facilitate the sale of all tobacco produced within the province. The Board also administers a variety of government programs to assist its members.

Chairman, George Demeulenaere
Sec.-Treasurer, Michael Dougan

DEPARTMENT OF COMMUNITY AND CULTURAL AFFAIRS
Jones Bldg., 11 Kent St.
Box 2000, Charlottetown, C1A 7N8
General Inquiries: (902) 892-0311

MINISTER'S OFFICE
Minister, The Hon. Gilbert R. Clements

DEPUTY MINISTER'S OFFICE
Dep. Minister, Kenneth DesRoches
Management Services
Director, Errol Andrews
Personnel Officer, Stewart Johnston
Planning and Co-ordination
Director, Ron MacNeil
Environmental Management
Exec. Director, William Howard
Community Services
Exec. Director, George Likely
Cultural Affairs
Director, Allan Rankin
Youth, Fitness and Recreation
Director, Don Leclair

PUBLIC ARCHIVES
Coles Bldg., 100 Richmond St.
Charlottetown, C1A 7K7
Provincial Archivist, Nicholas de Jong

DEPARTMENT OF EDUCATION
Shaw Bldg., 95 Rochford St.
Box 2000, Charlottetown, C1A 7N8
General Inquiries: (902) 368-4600

MINISTER'S OFFICE
Minister, The Hon. Betty Jean Brown

DEPUTY MINISTER'S OFFICE
Dep. Minister, Roger Burke

PROGRAMS AND SERVICES BRANCH
Chief Director, Tom Rich
Program Development and Implementation
Director, Allan Hammond
Educational Services
Director, Parnell Garland

ADMINISTRATION AND FINANCE BRANCH
Chief Director, Gar Andrew
Administration Director, Ronald F. Rice

Personnel Manager and Student Aid Supervisor,
David MacPherson
Management Information Co-ordinator, Linda Trenton
Finance Officer, Mike Clow

PROVINCIAL LIBRARY
Box 2000, Charlottetown, C1A 7N8
Provincial Librarian, Donald Scott

DEPARTMENT OF ENERGY AND FORESTRY
Shaw Bldg., 105 Rochford St.
Box 2000, Charlottetown, C1A 7N8
General Inquiries: (902) 368-5010

MINISTER'S OFFICE
Minister, The Hon. Allison Ellis

DEPUTY MINISTER'S OFFICE
Dep. Minister, Douglas Cameron
Administration Director, W.G. Bustard
Energy Branch
A/Director, Wayne MacQuarrie
Forestry Branch
Director of Operations, Jerry Gavin

DEPARTMENT OF FINANCE
95 Rochford St., Shaw Bldg.
Box 2000, Charlottetown, C1A 7N8
General Inquiries: (902) 368-4070

MINISTER'S OFFICE
Minister, The Hon. Gilbert R. Clements

DEPUTY MINISTER'S OFFICE
Dep. Minister, W. Philip MacDougall

ACCOUNTING SERVICES DIVISION
Comptroller, W. Bruce White
Supervisor of Accounting, Arnold Sampson
Supervisor of Operations, Scott Stevens
Supervisor of Claims, Sterling Dennis
A/Employee Benefits Officer,
Robert Ramsay

COMPUTER SERVICES DIVISION
Director, Edward Lawlor
Operations Manager, Lorne Gaudet

ECONOMICS, STATISTICS AND FISCAL ANALYSIS DIVISION
Director, John R. Palmer
Economist, Dennis Stang

REAL PROPERTY RECORDS DIVISION
Director, James Ramsay
Assessment Research Analysis
Chief Assessor, John Squarebriggs

Operations and Systems
Chief Assessor, Herman McQuaid
Registry and Mapping Manager,
Robert Kenny

PURCHASING DIVISION
Director, John E. MacRae
REVENUE DIVISION
Director, W.R. Noonan
Chief Tax Auditor, F. Weatherby
Debt Management and Investments
Director, W.R. Noonan
Investment Officer, R.E. Rossiter

DEPARTMENT OF FISHERIES
Sullivan Bldg., 16 Fitzroy St.
Box 2000, Charlottetown, C1A 7N8
General Inquiries: (902) 368-5240

MINISTER'S OFFICE
Minister, The Hon. Ross (Johnny) Young

DEPUTY MINISTER'S OFFICE
Dep. Minister, Douglas Johnston
Commercial Fisheries
Director, Lewis Creed
Extension Services
Manager, Friend Herring
Resource Utilization and Marketing
Manager, David Younker
Processing and Quality
Manager, Lloyd Murphy
Aquaculture Manager, Irwin Judson
Financial Services
Manager, Donald Judson

DEPARTMENT OF HEALTH AND SOCIAL SERVICES
Sullivan Bldg., 16 Fitzroy St.
Box 2000, Charlottetown, C1A 7N8
(except where otherwise indicated)
General Inquiries: (902) 368-4900

MINISTER'S OFFICE
Minister, The Hon. Keith Milligan

DEPUTY MINISTER'S OFFICE
Dep. Minister, J. Charles Campbell
Asst. Dep. Minister, Verna Bruce
Sr. Policy Analyst, Bob Thompson
Chief Health Officer, Dr. W.R. Stewart

HEALTH SERVICES DIVISIONS
Oncology Services
Director, Dr. Dagny Dryer
Community Hygiene Division
Director, Richard Davies
Dental Public Health Division
Director, Dr. R.G. Romcke
Child and Family Services Division

Director, Steve McQuaid
Management Services Division
Director, Rick Callaghan
Mental Health Division
Director, Dr. Pam Forsythe
Community Mental Health
Director, Bill Lawlor
Nursing Services Division
Director, Ella MacLeod
Pharmacy Division
Director, L. Roger Montigny
Aging and Extended Care Division
Director, Gordon MacKay
Special Services Division
Supervisors: Carl Cooper, Steve Mullin
Home Care and Support Division
Director, Vacant
Vital Statistics Division
Director, Gloria Melanson
Hillsborough Hospital and Special Care Centre
Riverside Dr., Box 4000
Charlottetown, C1A 7P3
Administrator, J.A. Fraser
Director of Nursing, Peter Sudworth
Eric Found Health Centre
65 McGill Ave., Charlottetown, C1A 2K1
Medical Director, Dr. W.R. Stewart
Administrator, Vacant
Director of Nursing, Louise Gillis

DEPARTMENT OF INDUSTRY
Shaw Bldg., Box 2000
Charlottetown, C1A 7N8
General Inquiries: (902) 368-4240

MINISTER'S OFFICE
Minister, The Hon. Leonce Bernard

DEPUTY MINISTER'S OFFICE
Dep. Minister, Michael S. Kelly

DEPARTMENTAL MANAGEMENT
Administration
Director, J. Oswald MacKinnon
Policy and Planning Director, Vacant
Trade Policy and Economic Analysis
Director, W.A. (Sandy) Stewart
Small Business Development
Director, Lorne Driscoll
Business Program Manager, Colin Jackson
Business Development Services
Manager, Terry Hopkins
Human Resource Development
Director, Peter McGonnell
Apprenticeship and Industrial Training
Manager, Louis Dalton
Employment Development
Manager, Daryl MacDonald
Adult and Continuing Education
Manager, Vacant
Research and Analytical Services
Chief, Carol Mayne

COMMUNITY ECONOMIC DEVELOPMENT
Director, Bill Buell
Co-operative Development
Manager, Frank Driscoll
West Prince Regional Services Centre
Box 8, O'Leary, C0B 1V0
General Inquiries: (902) 859-2400
Summerside Regional Services Centre
Box 63, 109 Water St., Summerside, C1N 4P6
General Inquiries: (902) 436-9191
Southern Kings and Queens Regional Services Centre
Box 1500, Montague, C0A 1R0
General Inquiries: (902) 838-2992
Eastern Kings Regional Services Centre
Box 550, Souris, C0A 2B0
General Inquiries: (902) 687-3022
Evangeline Regional Services Centre/Centre de services regional Evangeline
Box 58, Wellington Stn., Wellington, C0B 2E0
General Inquiries: (902) 854-3131

DEPARTMENT OF JUSTICE
Shaw Bldg., 73 Rochford St.
Box 2000, Charlottetown, C1A 7N8
(except where otherwise indicated)
General Inquiries: (902) 368-4550

MINISTER'S OFFICE
Minister, The Hon. Wayne D. Cheverie, Q.C.

DEPUTY MINISTER'S OFFICE
Dep. Minister, Arthur J. Currie, Q.C.
Administration Director, Edison Shea
Consumer Services, Debtor Assistance, and Lotteries Licensing
Director, Eric Goodwin

LEGAL SERVICES
Director, Charles Thompson
Departmental Solicitors: Judith Haldemann, Roger Langille, Valerie Moore
CORPORATIONS
Director, Edison Shea
Corporations Officer, Merrill H. Wigginton
INSURANCE
Sup't, W. Bennett Campbell

CROWN PROSECUTOR
Director, Richard Hubley, Q.C.
Crown Attorneys:
Charlottetown, D.E. Coombs
Charlottetown, Agnes MacDonald
Summerside, David O'Brien
Court House, 108 Central St.
Summerside, C1N 3L4

COMMUNITY CORRECTIONS AND YOUNG OFFENDERS SERVICES
Director, J.P. Arbing
Corrections Manager, John Bruce
Youth Facilities
Administrator, John Picketts

Sr. Probation Officers/Youth Workers:
Carl E. Doucette, Alan Paquet
Supervising Family Counsellor,
Irene MacInnis

ADULT CORRECTIONAL CENTRES
Provincial Correctional Ctr.
Charlottetown, C1A 7N8
Adult Facilities
Administrator, Preston Robbins

LEGISLATION
Box 1628, Charlottetown, C1A 7N3
Legislative Counsel, M. Raymond Moore
LEGAL AID
Criminal Division Director, Kent Brown
Asst., Bert Visser
Family Division Solicitor, Nancy Orr
GUN CONTROL
Chief Provincial Firearms Officer, Valerie Moore

DEPARTMENT OF LABOUR
3 Queen St., Box 2000, Charlottetown, C1A 7N8
General Inquiries: (902) 368-5550

MINISTER'S OFFICE
Minister, The Hon. Wayne D. Cheverie, Q.C.

DEPUTY MINISTER'S OFFICE
Dep. Minister, Robert Crockett
Asst. Dep. Minister, Roger Kennedy
Chief Conciliation Officer, Roger Kennedy

LABOUR STANDARDS DIVISION
Chief Inspector, Wayne S. MacKinnon
Occupational Health and Safety Division
Director, Paul Deveau
Chief Electrical Inspector, Ed Power
Chief Boiler Inspector, Miller West
Women's Division
Director, Heather Orford
Pay Equity Bureau
Director, Faye Martin-Birt

AGENCIES, BOARDS AND COMMISSIONS

Employment Standards Advisory Board
3 Queen St., Box 2000, Charlottetown, C1A 7N8

The Employment Standards Advisory Board was established by the P.E.I. government to make orders, subject to the approval of the Lieutenant-Governor in Council, on matters such as minimum wage rates, hours of work, overtime rates, rates for board and lodging, and pay exemptions.

The Board also acts as a tribunal to resolve disputes involving the interpretation of Regulations, and to hear appeals from employers on any ruling made in relation to employment standards.

Chairman, Michael Hennessey
Secretary, Wayne S. MacKinnon

Labour Relations Board
3 Queen St., Box 2000, Charlottetown, C1A 7N8

The Labour Relations Board is an independent body established under the *P.E.I Labour Act* R.S.P.E.I. 1974, Chapter L-1 and Regulations. The Board consists of a chairman and six members representing employers and employees. The Labour Relations Board is a part-time board, but has a full-time chief executive officer appointed by the Minister of Labour to act as an agent of the Board and carry out such duties as the Board may direct.

The Board has jurisdiction over such matters as determining whether or not:
a) a person is an employer or employee;
b) an organization is a trade union;
c) a collective agreement has been entered into;
d) a group of employees is a unit appropriate for collective bargaining;
e) a person is a member in good standing of a union;
f) a person is to be included or excluded from an appropriate bargaining unit; and
g) an activity constitutes a strike or lockout.

Chairman, Lynn Murray
Vice-Chairman, J.J. Revell
CEO, Roy J. Doucette

Occupational Health and Safety Council
3 Queen St., Box 2000, Charlottetown, C1A 7N8

The Occupational Health and Safety Council was appointed in 1982 by the Executive Council. It consists of a chairman and eight other members who represent agriculture, fishing, manufacturing, construction, labour unions, women/nursing, and the general public. The Deputy Minister of Labour and the Deputy Minister of Health and Social Services are ex officio members.

The mandate of the Council is outlined in the *Occupational Health and Safety Council Act.*

Chairman, Graham W. Stewart

Power Engineers Board of Examiners
3 Queen St., Box 2000, Charlottetown, C1A 7N8

The Power Engineers Board of Examiners is established under the authority of the *Boiler and Pressure Vessels Act, 1981.*

The function of the Board is to report to and advise the minister on the application of the Act and Regulations, any code or body of rules relating thereto, and technical evidence respecting accidents concerning boilers, pressure vessels, or pressure piping systems, or any matter assigned to the Board, by the minister or the chief inspector, pertaining to the Act and Regulations.

Chairman, W.A. Miller West

P.E.I. Labour-Management Relations Council
3 Queen St., Box 2000, Charlottetown, C1A 7N8

The Labour-Management Relations Council is an independent agency made up of five labour and five management representatives. The Department of Labour supplies clerical assistance but no government member normally attends Council meetings.

The Council's purpose is to be an independent body designed to promote labour-management co-operation in all its respects. Its own structure is used as a model for individual committees set up in workplaces across the province. After study and mutual agreement, it may also recommend legislative changes to the Department of Labour.

DEPARTMENT OF TOURISM AND PARKS
Shaw Bldg., 105 Rochford St.
Charlottetown, C1A 7N8
General Inquiries: (902) 368-4444

MINISTER'S OFFICE
Minister, The Hon. Gordon MacInnis

DEPUTY MINISTER'S OFFICE
Dep. Minister, Larry MacPherson
Administration and Finance
Director, Dianne Bradley

PARKS BRANCH
Director, Douglas Murray
Operations East Division
Manager, Harry Simmonds
Operations West Division
Manager, Vacant

TOURISM DEVELOPMENT BRANCH
Director, Doug Smith
Visitor Services Division
Manager, Bruce Garity
Research and Statistics Division
Research Officer, George Ferguson
Extension Services Division
Sr. Development Officer, Gerry Gabriel

TOURISM MARKETING BRANCH
Director, Harvey Sawler
Advertising and Communications Division
Media Co-ordinator, Sheri Coles
Sales Development Division
Travel Sales, Lloyd McKenna

DEPARTMENT OF TRANSPORTATION AND PUBLIC WORKS
Jones Bldg., 11 Kent St.
Box 2000, Charlottetown, C1A 7N8
General Inquiries: (902) 368-5100

MINISTER'S OFFICE
Minister, The Hon. Robert Morrissey

DEPUTY MINISTER'S OFFICE
Dep. Minister, Lorne Moase
Administration Director, P.J. Murphy

HIGHWAY CONSTRUCTION
Chief Engineer, T.W. Walker
Director of Planning, Mike Bailey
Director of Traffic Engineering,
Allan Bartlett
Highway Maintenance
Director, G. Trainor
Mechanical Branch Supervisor,
Herb MacDougall
Buildings and Property Director, Joe Caswell
Transportation Director, Kenneth MacKenzie
Highway Safety Director, Glen Beaton

INDEPENDENT AGENCIES, BOARDS, COMMISSIONS AND CROWN CORPORATIONS

Charlottetown Area Development Corp.

4 Pownal St., Box 786, Charlottetown, C1A 7L9

The Charlottetown Area Development Corporation (CADC) was formed in 1974 with a mandate to improve the economic and social life of the provincial capital area. The activities of the CADC are managed by a board of directors nominated by the Corporation's shareholders, the Province of P.E.I., and the City of Charlottetown. The emphasis of the Corporation has been directed at revitalization of the downtown core and waterfront areas of Charlottetown. Major projects include the Queen Parkade, the Confederation Court Mall, and Harbourside.
Minister responsible,
The Hon. Gilbert R. Clements

Chairman, Stanley H. MacPherson
Gen. Manager, Cliff Campbell
Manager (Finance), Paul Norris
Manager (Property), J. Joseph Condon
Manager (Development), Les R. Parsons

Civil Service Commission

Shaw Bldg., 105 Rochford St.
Box 2000, Charlottetown, C1A 7N8

The Civil Service Commission is the central government agency responsible for the administration of the Civil Service Act and Regulations.

The Staffing Branch recruits for and staffs all permanent positions for departments and agencies.

The Classification Branch is responsible for pay research and for maintaining a classification plan for permanent positions in the civil service.

Personnel Administration provides the centralized control and administration of personnel activities and records. This branch also represents the employer on workers' compensation and alcoholism programs, and monitors disciplinary actions.

The Staff Development and Training Branch provides opportunities for training and development through in-service programs, selected external programs, and financial assistance plans.
Minister responsible,
The Hon. Gilbert R. Clements

Chairman, Donald G. MacCormac
Staff Relations Director, G.K. Cantelo
Staffing Director, J.R. Lewis
Staff Development and Training
Director, Barry M. Curley
Personnel Administration
Director, Barry M. Curley

Energy Corp.

Shaw Bldg., 105 Rochford St.
Box 2000, Charlottetown, C1A 7N8

The P.E.I. Energy Corporation is a provincial Crown corporation established by the Energy Corporation Act in 1978. The board of directors consists of five to seven members and is appointed by the Lieutenant-Governor in Council. The Minister of Energy is an ex officio director of the Corporation.

The objectives of the Corporation are to aid and promote the development of energy systems and the generation, production, transmission and distribution of energy in all its forms on an economical and efficient basis; to provide financial assistance for the development, installation and use of energy systems; and to co-ordinate all government programs in the establishment and application of energy systems in the province.
Minister responsible, The Hon. Allison Ellis

Chairman, Norman F. Stewart
Gen. Manager, Robert J. Brandon

Georgetown Shipyard Inc.

Box 220, Georgetown, C0A 1L0

Georgetown Shipyard was incorporated as a provincial Crown corporation in December 1974 through An Act to Incorporate Georgetown Shipyard Inc.

The Corporation's affairs are conducted by a board of directors appointed by the Lieutenant-Governor in Council.

The Corporation operates as an independent commercial enterprise in the business of shipbuilding, ship repair, and metal fabrication.

Minister responsible, The Hon. Leonce Bernard
Chairman, Gerrard Fitzpatrick
Gen. Manager, Hugh M. Sutherland

Chairperson, J. Leo Trainor
Exec. Director, Thomas W. Klewin
Office Staff, Frances Piercy

Horse Racing and Sports Commission

11 Kent St., Box 3014, Charlottetown, C1A 7N9
Minister responsible,
The Hon. Gilbert R. Clements
Chairman, Ross Lefurgey
Exec. Secretary, David Campbell

Hospital and Health Services Commission

Jones Bldg., 11 Kent St.
Box 4500, Charlottetown, C1A 7P4

The Hospital and Health Services Commission provides payment toward the cost of services that are medically necessary and are provided by physicians to patients in their homes, in doctor's offices, and in hospitals. Certain services provided by dentists in hospitals may also be included.

The Commission maintains a plan of hospitals care insurance for the people of P.E.I. The operating costs of all general hospitals in the province are paid out of the provincial revenue through the Commission in accordance with the provisions of the Hospital and Diagnostic Services Insurance Act and Regulations.
Minister responsible, The Hon. Keith Milligan

Chairman, Melville Campbell, Q.C.
Exec. Director, Barry MacMillan
Medical Director, Dr. D.A.C. MacDonald
Management Services Division
Director, Wayne Hooper
Quality Assurance and Extension Services
Division
Director, Judy Lougheed
Program Development Division
Director, Jeanette MacAulay

Human Rights Commission

180 Richmond St., Box 2000
Charlottetown, C1A 7N8

The P.E.I. Human Rights Commission is the agency responsible for the administration and enforcement of the P.E.I. *Human Rights Act.* This involves the investigation and settlement of formal complaints based on alleged discrimination in the areas of employment, services, accommodations, and facilities. In addition, the Commission is responsible for the development of programs of public information and education in the area of human rights for the entire province.
Minister responsible,
The Hon. Wayne D. Cheverie, Q.C.

Island Information Service

11 Kent St., Box 2000, Charlottetown, C1A 7N8
General Inquiries: (902) 368-4000
Fax: (902) 892-3420; Telex: 014-44154

The Island Information Service answers inquiries about P.E.I. and assists departments, agencies, commissions, and boards with the preparation and distribution of information about government programs to news media and other interested individuals or organizations. It offers assistance in the preparation of brochures, advertising, audio-visual productions and government news items, and provides photographic services and a limited translation service to departments.

It also operates the P.E.I. government telex and facsimile equipment and runs a government bookstore which stocks free and priced publications, including all provincial Acts and Regulations.
Minister responsible,
The Hon. Robert Morrissey
Director, Frank Arsenault

Land Use Commission

3 Queen St., Box 1957, Charlottetown, C1A 7N7

The Land Use Commission was created in 1974 to make recommendations to the Lieutenant-Governor in Council on policies affecting the use and ownership of land within the province. In addition, the Commission approves official plans proposed for adoption by planning boards and considers appeals of decisions made under the *Planning Act.* The Commission reports to the Lieutenant-Governor in Council through the Minister of Community and Cultural Affairs. The terms of reference of the Commission are set out in the *Planning Act, 1974.*

The Commission consists of seven members who are appointed to represent the private sector. There is also an advisory board of two persons, normally civil servants, appointed by the Lieutenant-Governor in Council; these persons participate in the meetings of the Commission but are not eligible to vote on any issue.
Minister responsible,
The Hon. Gilbert R. Clements
Chairman, Leslie MacKay
Exec. Director, John Blakeney

Liquor Control Commission

3 Garfield St., Box 967
Charlottetown, C1A 7M4

The P.E.I. Liquor Control Commission consists of three members appointed by the Lieutenant-Governor in Council and is vested with the powers and duties to administer the *Liquor Control Act,* as well as to exercise general control, management, and supervision of all vendors, stores, and warehouse and office facilities.

The chairman of the Commission is obliged to devote his full time to Commission business, while the remaining officers, one of whom is appointed secretary, are employed on a part-time and consulting basis.

The Commission administers and is fully responsible for the purchase, distribution, and sale of all alcoholic beverages containing more than one-half of one percent of alcohol by volume destined for consumption in P.E.I.

The Commission determines the location of all retail liquor stores; may grant, refuse, or cancel permits and licences for the purchase of alcoholic beverages; and may lease, furnish, and equip buildings and land required for the operation of the *Liquor Control Act.*

Minister responsible, The Hon. Allison Ellis

Chairman, Stanhope Moore
Controller, Wayne A. MacDougall
Licensing and Security
Director, R.R. MacAdam

Office of the Auditor General

Shaw Bldg., 105 Rochford St.
Box 2000, Charlottetown, C1A 7N8
General Inquiries: (902) 368-4520

The Auditor General audits the receipt and disbursement of public money. He may conduct comprehensive audits or examinations as he considers necessary to determine whether an agency of government is carrying out its objectives economically, efficiently, and in accordance with the applicable statutory provisions. He reports his findings annually to the Legislative Assembly.

Auditor General, J. Wayne Murphy

P.E.I. Advisory Council on the Status of Women

180 Richmond St., Box 2000
Charlottetown, C1A 7N8

The P.E.I. Advisory Council on the Status of Women was established by an Act of the P.E.I. Legislature on July 16, 1988.

The Council's functions are as follows:

a) develop public awareness of the issues affecting the status of women;

b) promote a change in attitudes within the community in order that women may enjoy an equality of opportunity;

c) encourage discussion and expression of opinion by Island residents on questions affecting the status of women;

d) advise the minister with respect to such

issues as the minister may refer to the Council for consideration;

e) review policies and legislation affecting women and report its findings to the relevant government departments or agencies;

f) provide assistance to the minister in providing changes to ensure the attainment of equality objectives of women; and

g) provide assistance, as the Council deems appropriate, to organizations and groups whose objectives promote the equality of women.

The Advisory Council consists of nine members who are appointed by the Lieutenant-Governor in Council for a term of not less than two and not more than three years.

Minister responsible,
The Hon. Joseph A. Ghiz, Q.C.

Chairperson, Dianne Porter
Administrator, Muriel Houston

P.E.I. Crop Insurance Agency

11 Kent St., Box 2000, Charlottetown, C1A 7N8

The P.E.I. Crop Insurance Agency is a provincial Crown corporation established by Order-in-Council in 1962. The objective of the Agency is to make available to P.E.I. farmers a comprehensive all-risk Crop Insurance Plan, which, in years of crop losses, will return to the farmer his cost of production.

The responsibilities of the Agency are as follows:

1) administration of the *Crop Insurance Act*; and

2) administration of the Crop Insurance Plans established by Regulations, including the functions of selling, underwriting, claims adjusting, and accounting.

Minister responsible,
The Hon. Joseph A. Ghiz, Q.C.

Chairman, Bill Lewis
Manager, Vacant

P.E.I. Development Agency

West Royalty Industrial Park
Charlottetown, C1E 1B0
General Inquiries: (902) 368-5800
Fax: (902) 566-4030

The P.E.I. Development Agency is a Crown corporation of the Province of P.E.I., established in 1984.

The Agency consists of three divisions: marketing, finance, and business development, offering to the business community the most advanced ideas in creative technology for establishment, expansion and marketing, on a cost-shared basis. The programs of the three divisions vary in content depending on the demand or requirement and, to a company seriously contributing to the

Island economy, it is a "one-stop shop" for assistance.

Minister responsible and Chairman,
The Hon. Leonce Bernard
CEO, Michael Kelly
Exec. Directors:
Business Development, Donald Baker
Finance, Hillard MacKinnon
Marketing, Ron Atkinson
Controller, Reagh Hicken, C.A.

P.E.I. Grain Elevators Corp.
Box 250, Kensington, C0B 1M0
General Inquiries: (902) 836-3605
Minister responsible,
The Hon. Jospeh A. Ghiz, Q.C.

Chairman, Allison McNally
Exec. Gen. Manager, Patrick Gaudet

P.E.I. Housing Corp.
11 Kent St., Box 2000, Charlottetown, C1A 7N8

The P.E.I. Housing Corporation is a provincial Crown corporation established in 1969 to act as the principal agent of the Province in delivering housing programs.

The basic objective of the Corporation is to provide low and moderate income Island residents with increased access to adequate housing. To carry out this responsibility, it has operated programs and projects to provide for home repairs, new-home ownership, senior citizens housing, rent geared-to-income housing, and community residential development.

Minister responsible and Chairman,
The Hon. Wayne D. Cheverie, Q.C.
Gen. Manager, Sterling Breedon
Chief Accountant, George Curley
Planning and Co-ordination
Director, Fred Eberman
Field Services Director, Bill Irwin
Construction and Technical Services
Director, Carl Reynolds
Rentalsman, John Comeau

P.E.I. Land Development Corp.
40 Great George St., Box 1390
Charlottetown, C1A 7N1

The P.E.I. Land Development Corp. purchases, sells, and leases farm land. The objectives of the Corporation are to facilitate the transfer of farm properties and to make available suitable financing arrangements by way of mortgages, agreements of sale, or leases.
Minister responsible,
The Hon. Joseph A. Ghiz, Q.C.

Chairperson, Dianne Balderston
Gen. Manager, Lloyd Palmer

Administrator, Leonard Keefe

P.E.I. Lending Authority
Confederation Court Office Bldg.
134 Kent St., Box 1420
Charlottetown, C1A 7N1

The P.E.I. Lending Authority is a Crown corporation of the provincial government, which was established by an Act of the provincial legislature in June 1969. The Lending Authority provides capital and operating credit to the primary producers of P.E.I.

The Corporation has four divisions, namely agriculture, fisheries and aquaculture, tourism, and small business. Loans and operating credit are extended to individuals and companies in agriculture, fisheries and tourism, and term financing only to small business, on terms and conditions comparable to conventional lenders. Corporation directors are nominated by the Corporation and confirmed by the Lieutenant-Governor in Council.
Minister responsible,
The Hon. Gilbert R. Clements

Chairman, Peggy Coady
Gen. Manager, William M. Jay
Administrator, Eric G. Wood

P.E.I. Lotteries Commission
Box 2000, Charlottetown, C1A 7N8

The P.E.I. Lotteries Commission was established by an Act of the Legislative Assembly in 1976. The Commission authorizes all lottery schemes on behalf of the government of the province, in conjunction with the Atlantic Lottery Corp. and the Interprovincial Lotteries Corp.

Minister responsible and Chairman,
The Hon. Gilbert R. Clements
Vice-Chairman, W. Philip MacDougall
Sec.-Treasurer, Douglas B. Boylan

P.E.I. Museum and Heritage Foundation
Beaconsfield, 2 Kent St.
Charlottetown, C1A 1M6

The P.E.I. Museum and Heritage Foundation is a decentralized provincial museum system active in research, genealogy, exhibitions, publications and distribution, as well as operating a series of branch museums and historic houses.
Minister responsible,
The Hon. Gilbert R. Clements

Chairperson, Dr. Ian MacQuarrie
Exec. Director, David Webber

Public Utilities Commission

Confederation Court Bldg.
134 Kent St., Ste. 501, Box 577
Charlottetown, C1A 7L1

The Public Utilities Commission was established in 1929 and currently has jurisdiction over a number of Acts.

The *Electric Power and Telephone Act* is concerned with the general supervision, regulation and setting of rates for public utilities as defined in the Act and operating in the province of P.E.I. The *Petroleum Products Act* is involved with the licensing and regulation of the wholesale and retail distributors of petroleum products within the province, and with the pricing of petroleum products. The *Motor Carrier Act* is responsible for the general administration and supervision of intra-provincial and extra-provincial trucking operations. The *Motor Vehicle Transport Act (Canada)* gives the Commission responsibility for licensing motor carriers operating to and from the province of P.E.I. The *Water and Sewerage Act* is responsible for the general supervision and control over setting of rates for water and sewerage utilities in the province.

The Public Utilities Commission is composed of three commissioners appointed by Lieutenant-Governor in Council, one of whom is designated chairman.
Minister responsible,
The Hon. Wayne D. Cheverie, Q.C.

Chairman, Linda St. Jean
Commissioners: C.C. Hickey, Anna Carr
Utilities Division
Director, Donald G. Sutherland
Petroleum Division
Director, H. Doris Pursey
Motor Carrier Division
Administrator, Diane Gaudet

Queen's Printer

Shaw Bldg., 105 Rochford St.
Box 2000, Charlottetown, C1A 7N5

The Queen's Printer provides the following services:
a) printing for government departments, boards, and commissions;
b) volume copying for the same agencies; and
c) Xerographic copying for centrally located agencies.

As well, the Queen's Printer distributes and sells the *Royal Gazette*, the *Revised Statutes of P.E.I.*, the *Annual Statutes of P.E.I.*, the *Legislative Journal of P.E.I.*, and the *Revised Regulations of P.E.I.*

Queen's Printer, Gordon Babineau

Summerside Waterfront Development Corp.

120 Water St., Summerside, C1N 1A9

The Summerside Waterfront Development Corporation was incorporated in 1971, with the objective of providing a major enhancement to the town of Summerside, as a growing service and tourism centre, and an attractive community for the development of light industry.

The Corporation has accomplished a number of its objectives to date, having assets which include a yacht club and marina, golf club, office building, East Prince Regional Services Centre, shopping centre, and museum. It has recently completed an infrastructure in the downtown business district consisting of a four-lane traffic corridor and additional parking facilities, and has acquired valuable land sites for development of tourist accommodations and attractions to revitalize the downtown business district.
Minister responsible,
The Hon. Leonce Bernard

President, Brent Schurman
Gen. Manager, Gerald Enman

Workers' Compensation Board

60 Belvedere Ave., Box 757
Charlottetown, C1A 7L7

The Workers' Compensation Board administers the *Workers' Compensation Act*. Employers are protected against liability for injuries suffered by employees in the course of their work. Employees are insured against loss of earnings in the case of injury on the job. The Board awards permanent compensation for permanent disability, and in the case of death, awards benefits to widows, widowers, children, and other dependents.

Revenue for the Board's operations comes from assessment premiums charged against employers.
Minister responsible,
The Hon. Wayne D. Cheverie, Q.C.

Chairman, Arthur J. MacDonald
Exec. Director, C.E. Ready
Claims Division
Chief Claims Officer, T. Dunsford
Finance Division
Supervisor, David Kassner
Assessment Division
Assessment Officer, Greg MacCallum
Rehabilitation Division
Supervisor, John Gallant

JUDICIARY AND JUDICIAL OFFICERS

Supreme Court

Sir Louis Henry Davies Law Courts Bldg.
42 Water St., Box 2200
Charlottetown, C1A 8B9
General Inquiries: (902) 892-9131

APPEAL DIVISION
Chief Justice: The Hon. Norman H. Carruthers
Justices:
The Hon. Mr. Justice Gerard R. Mitchell
The Hon. Mr. Justice Charles R. McQuaid*
The Hon. Mr. Justice G.R. McMahon

TRIAL DIVISION
Chief Justice: The Hon Kenneth R. MacDonald
Justices:
The Hon. Mr. Justice Frederic A. Large*
The Hon. Mr. Justice Alexander B. Campbell
The Hon. Mr. Justice George J. Mullally
The Hon. Madam Justice Jacqueline Matheson

COURT OFFICIALS:
Prothonotary and Chief Judicial Officer:
George E. MacMillan
Deputy Prothonotaries:
Hazel Thompson (Queens County)
F. Wayne Lilly (Prince County)
Howard Kerwin (Kings County)

Registrars:
Estates Division: Collette Vessey
Family Division: Deborah MacKinnon

Provincial Court

Box 2000, Charlottetown, C1A 8B9
General Inquiries: (902) 892-9131

Chief Judge: Ralph C. Thompson

Judges:
Gerald L. FitzGerald (Queens County)
Ralph C. Thompson (Prince County)
Bertrand R. Plamondon (Kings County)

Clerks of the Provincial Court:
E. Dorothy Kitson (Queens County)
Howard Kerwin (Kings County)
Wayne Lilly (Prince County)

Sheriffs:
Kenneth Jenkins (Queens County)
Layton Schurman (Prince County)
John Daly (Kings County)

Registrars of Deeds:
Vacant (Queens County)
Eileen Gaudet (Prince County)
Vacant (Kings County)

---

* Supernumerary

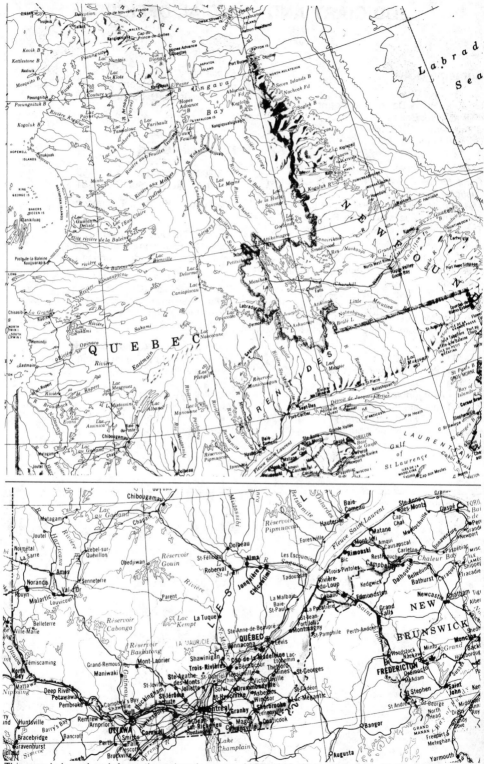

This map is based on information taken from map MCR 4032. © Her Majesty in Right of Canada with permission of Energy, Mines and Resources.

PROVINCE OF QUEBEC

*(The Coat of Arms of the
Province of Quebec was
unavailable for reproduction.)*

White
Garden Lily
(Lilium candidum)

Entered Confederation: July 1, 1867
Capital: Quebec City
Motto: Je me souviens (I remember)
Flower: Fleur-de-lis
Area: 1,540,680 km²
  percentage of Canada's total area: 15.5
  LAND: 1,356,790 km²
  FRESHWATER: 183,890 km²
Elevation:
  HIGHEST POINT: Mont d'Iberville (1,652 m)
  LOWEST POINT: St. Lawrence shore
Population (1986): 6,532,460
  five-year change: +0.84%

per square kilometre: 4.2
percentage of Canada's total
  population: 25.8
URBAN: 78%
RURAL: 22%
Gross domestic product, 1987: $131.8 billion
Government Finance:
  REVENUE, 1986/87 est.: $32.2 billion
  EXPENDITURE, 1986/87 est.: $32.3 billion
  DEBT PER CAPITA (March 1987): $3,715
Personal income per capita, 1986: $16,138
Unemployment rate, 1988
  (annual average): 9.4%

THE LAND

Quebec has three geological regions. (1) The St. Lawrence lowlands, a low-lying plain traversed by the St. Lawrence River, contains most of the populated area, industrial centres, and fertile farm land. (2) The Appalachian region extends south of the St. Lawrence River between Quebec City and the international boundary, and includes the Gaspé Peninsula. It contains mountains and plateaus. Agriculture, chiefly in the form of dairy farming, is confined mainly to the valleys, the uplands being forested. (3) The Canadian Shield covers four-fifths of the province, forming an arc around Hudson Bay. The Shield is rocky and covered with coniferous forest. Only five per cent of this area is arable; most farm land is located in the clay-belt east of Lake Abitibi.

There are no areas of great altitude, though the Laurentians, a division of the Canadian Shield north of the St. Lawrence Valley, rise to 915 metres, and the Torngat Mountains on the Labrador border reach 1,525 metres. South of the St. Lawrence, the extension of the Appalachians reaches heights of 915 to 1,220 metres.

The St. Lawrence River is a major inland waterway, and the life of the province is concentrated along its banks.

The climate is varied. In the north and northwestern parts of the province, it is cold and stable; in the south, it is more temperate but subject to sudden changes. Precipitation is nearly constant throughout the year, ranging from 1,016 mm or more in the St. Lawrence Valley to 381 mm in the north.

THE PEOPLE

Of Quebec's 6.5 million inhabitants, 5.3 million are French-speaking. This is the principal French-language enclave on the North American continent. For over 200 years, it has succeeded, despite its North American environment, in retaining its linguistic and cultural identity. One sixth of Quebec's population is English-speaking, descendants of the English, Irish, and Scots who landed here in the years following the conquest of New France by England in 1760.

A rapid evolution in attitudes and customs

overturned Quebec's demographic pattern. The birth rate has decreased below the point of population replacement; the average Quebec family now has 1.4 children. This uncovers another demographic fact related to the low birth rate: the population of Quebec as a whole, like the rest of Canada, is aging, and senior citizens will make up the largest segment of Quebec society in the next century.

Quebec has been a home for immigrants from its very beginnings. First came the French, who founded New France; after the Conquest came the English; from the early years of this century, it has been the turn of other Europeans. But it was after the Second World War, in response to a need for manpower, that most of Quebec's new citizens arrived. The first great wave came from Italy, the British Isles, eastern Europe, Germany, France, and Greece. Since 1971, more than 50 per cent of the new arrivals have come from the Far East, the West Indies, and Latin America.

The largest ethnic group in Quebec, after the French (80.2 per cent) and the British (7.6 per cent), are the Italians (2.6 per cent). They are followed by the Jews (1.4 per cent), Greeks (0.8 per cent), and Germans (0.5 per cent). Native people in Quebec number approximately 82,000, including almost 6,000 Inuit and 40,000 Métis. Haitians, Vietnamese, and Latin Americans are among the latest arrivals to pass through Quebec's immigration services. About 85 per cent of new Quebeckers settle in the Montreal area.

THE ECONOMY

The vast expanses of land, the forests, fauna, mines, hydroelectric resources, and raw materials that contribute to Quebec's economy are well-known. While not in itself false, this image is incomplete. Natural resources still have a vital, if indirect, impact, but Quebec's economy today is diversified, highly developed, and open to international competition.

Primary Sector. Mining is Quebec's most important primary industry. Many metals have been mined for several decades; more recently, huge quantities of iron were found in central Quebec. The Gaspé yields copper, and most of Canada's asbestos is located in the Eastern Townships. Hydroelectric power ranks second as a primary resource; there is more installed and potential water-power than in any other province. Quebec's forests provide slightly more than one third of Canada's pulp and paper production. Agriculture is centred in the fertile St. Lawrence Valley, but its relative importance has declined in recent years with increased industrial development.

Services Sector. The primary sector — namely the agricultural, forestry, and mining industries — employs less than 5 per cent of the Quebec labour force, whereas the tertiary or services sector accounts for more than 66 per cent of all jobs. This distribution is due not only to the growth of the public services sector, as has been the case in all industrialized countries, but also to a profound change in the development of the entire framework of production.

Quebec is still a top producer of paper and related products, metal ore, wood, clothing, and textiles; but it has also developed expertise and production capabilities with regard to electrical appliances and equipment, chemicals, telecommunications, and transportation equipment — specifically in the fields of aircraft manufacturing, subway construction, and rail and water transportation.

Many firms, specialized in advanced technology and geared to the international market, have sprung up in the services sector in the wake of these thriving new areas of activity. Production-oriented services have developed in all fields, from management, finance, marketing and export to, lately, data processing, telematics, office automation, and general engineering consulting. A number of engineering consulting firms have acquired an international reputation, notably in designing dams, hydroelectric power stations, and transportation and electrical power supply networks. Others still are known for the design and construction of subways, highways, aqueduct and sewer systems, as well as public buildings.

Micro-electronics, the bio-industries, energy, and transportation are sectors in which Quebeckers' skills are being maintained and developed. Quebec is particularly interested in the growth of electrochemistry and electrometallurgy, as it can draw on both an abundance of hydroelectric power and the acknowledged expertise and capabilities of a large core of researchers, businesses, and organizations. Similarly, the transportation sector takes on a new dimension when considered in light of Quebec's geographic position, its territorial expanse, and the scope of its trading, both on the Canadian domestic market and internationally.

Economic Outlook. In terms of expansion in the primary sector, the continuing James Bay project Phase II alone is expected to add $2.2 billion in investment this year. Other projects included Alcan's expansion at Laterrière, Pechiney's at Bécancour, and Northern Telecom's at St. Laurent; two water purification plants in Quebec City; and an expansion of petrochemical facilities in Montreal.

Real growth in 1988 was estimated at 4.3 per cent. The province's forecast growth rate of 2.9 per cent for 1989 could be enhanced if more contracts are negotiated to supply electricity to U.S. customers.

International Trade. The Quebec economy is among the most open in the western world. Over 40 per cent of its gross domestic product is exported, and imports account for about the same proportion. All of the province's industrial groups will be gearing up for the impact of freer trade with the U.S.

Information provided by the Ministère des Affaires internationales. Statistics have been verified through various sources, but the main source was Statistics Canada.

GOVERNMENT OF QUEBEC

Seat of Government:
Hôtel du Parlement, Québec, G1A 1A3

Lieutenant-Governor,
L'hon. Gilles Lamontagne
Cité parlementaire, Québec, G1A 1A1

CONSEIL DES MINISTRES
(Cabinet)

Hôtel du Gouvernement, éd. A
Québec, G1A 1A5

(Ministers are in alphabetical order)

Premier ministre,
    L'hon. Robert Bourassa
Vice-premier ministre, ministre des Affaires culturelles, ministre de l'Environnement,
    L'hon. Lise Bacon
Ministre de la Main-d'oeuvre et de la Sécurité du revenu,
    L'hon. André Bourbeau
Ministre de l'Énergie et des Ressources,
    L'hon. John Ciaccia
Ministre délégué aux Forêts,
    L'hon. Albert Côté
Ministre des Transports, responsable du Développement régional,
    L'hon. Marc-Yvan Côté
Ministre délégué aux Finances et à la Privatisation,
    L'hon. Pierre Fortier
Ministre des Communications,
    L'hon. Richard D. French
Ministre déléguée à la Condition féminine,
    L'hon. Monique Gagnon-Tremblay
Ministre des Affaires internationales,
    L'hon. Paul Gobeil
Ministre du Tourisme, leader parlementaire, ministre délégué à la Réforme électorale,
    L'hon. Michel Gratton
Ministre délégué à l'Administration, président du Conseil du Trésor,
    L'hon. Daniel Johnson
Ministre de la Santé et des Services sociaux,
    L'hon. Thérèse Lavoie-Roux
Ministre des Finances,
    L'hon. Gérard D. Levesque
Ministre de l'Industrie, du Commerce et de la Technologie, ministre du Commerce extérieur et du Développement technologique,
    L'hon. Pierre MacDonald

Ministre de l'Agriculture, des Pêcheries et de l'Alimentation,
    L'hon. Michel Pagé
Ministre des Affaires municipales,
    L'hon. Pierre Paradis
Ministre du Loisir, de la Chasse et de la Pêche, ministre délégué aux Pêcheries,
    L'hon. Yvon Picotte
Ministre de la Justice, ministre délégué aux Affaires intergouvernementales canadiennes, ministre des Relations internationales, ministre de la Sécurité publique,
    L'hon. Gil Rémillard
Ministre délégué aux Affaires culturelles,
    L'hon. Guy Rivard
Ministre des Communautés culturelles et de l'Immigration,
    L'hon. Louise Robic
Ministre des Approvisionnements et Services,
    L'hon. Gilles Rocheleau
Ministre de l'Éducation, ministre de l'Enseignement supérieur et de la Science,
    L'hon. Claude Ryan
Ministre délégué aux Mines et aux Affaires autochtones,
    L'hon. Raymond Savoie
Ministre du Revenu, ministre du Travail,
    L'hon. Yves Séguin

L'ASSEMBLÉE NATIONALE
(National Assembly)

33rd Legislature, 2nd Session
Last election: Dec. 2, 1985
    (Maximum duration five years)
Total number of seats: 122
Party standings (as of Jan. 1, 1989):
    Parti Libéral du Québec: 99
    Parti Québécois: 20
    Independent: 1
    Vacant: 2

Salaries, Indemnities and Allowances

MEMBERS OF THE NATIONAL ASSEMBLY: $52,788, plus $9,211 tax-free expense allowance.
PRIME MINISTER: $55,427, plus Member's salary and expense allowance.

For further information regarding any aspect of the Government of Quebec, contact:
Communication-Québec, 3, complexe Desjardins, Montréal, H5B 1B3
(514) 873-2111

MINISTERS, PRESIDENT, LEADER OF THE OFFI-
CIAL OPPOSITION: $39,591, plus Member's
salary and expense allowance.

Officers

Président de l'Assemblée, Pierre Lorrain
Directeur de cabinet, Richard Labrie
Vice-présidente, Louise Bégin
Directeur de cabinet, Claude Poulin
Vice-président, Jean-Pierre Saintonge
Directeur de cabinet, André Labrecque

BUREAU DU SECRÉTAIRE GÉNÉRAL

Secrétaire gén., Pierre Duchesne
Secrétaires adj.:
    Gérard Laliberté, Mathieu Proulx
Secrétariat du bureau de l'Assemblée
    nationale, Richard Breton
Secrétaire gén. adj. à l'administration,
    Gilbert L'Heureux
Directeur de la bibliothèque, Jacques Prémont
Sergent d'armes, Romain Gauthier
Vérificateur gén., Rhéal Chatelain
Directeur gén. des élections, Pierre-F. Côté

Members

Constituency	Member and Affiliation
Abitibi-Est	L'hon. Raymond Savoie (Lib)
Abitibi-Ouest	François Gendron (PQ)
Anjou	René Serge Larouche (Lib)
Argenteuil	L'hon. Claude Ryan (Lib)
Arthabaska	Laurier Gardner (Lib)
Beauce-Nord	Jean Audet (Lib)
Beauce-Sud	Robert Dutil (Lib)
Beauharnois	Serge Marcil (Lib)
Bellechasse	Louise Bégin (Lib)
Berthier	Albert Houde (Lib)
Bertrand	Jean-Guy Parent (PQ)
Bonaventure	L'hon. Gérard D. Levesque (Lib)
Bourassa	L'hon. Louise Robic (Lib)
Bourget	Claude Trudel (Lib)
Brome/Missisquoi	L'hon. Pierre Paradis (Lib)
Chambly	Gérard Latulippe (Lib)
Champlain	Pierre A. Brouillette (Lib)
Chapleau	John J. Kehoe (Lib)
Charlesbourg	L'hon. Marc-Yvan Côté (Lib)
Charlevoix	Daniel Bradet (Lib)
Châteauguay	Pierrette Cardinal (Lib)
Chauveau	Rémy Poulin (Lib)
Chicoutimi	Jeanne L. Blackburn (PQ)
Chomedey	L'hon. Lise Bacon (Lib)
Crémazie	L'hon. André Vallerand (Lib)
D'Arcy-McGee	Herbert Marx (Lib)
Deux-Montagnes	Yolande D. Legault (Lib)
Dorion	Violette Trépanier (Lib)
Drummond	Jean-Guy St-Roch (Lib)
Dubuc	Hubert Desbiens (PQ)
Duplessis	Denis Perron (PQ)
Fabre	Jean A. Joly (Lib)
Frontenac	Robert Lefebvre (Lib)
Gaspé	André Beaudin (Lib)

Constituency	Member and Affiliation
Gatineau	L'hon. Michel Gratton (Lib)
Gouin	Jacques Rochefort (Ind)
Groulx	Madeleine Bleau (Lib)
Hull	Vacant
Huntingdon	Claude Dubois (Lib)
Iberville	Jacques Tremblay (Lib)
Iles-de-la-Madeleine	George Farrah (Lib)
Jacques-Cartier	Joan Dougherty (Lib)
Jean-Talon	L'hon. Gil Rémillard (Lib)
Jeanne-Mance	Michel Bissonet (Lib)
Johnson	Carmen Juneau (PQ)
Joliette	Guy Chevrette (PQ)
Jonquière	Francis Dufour (PQ)
Kamouraska-Témiscouata	France Dionne (Lib)
Labelle	Damien Hétu (Lib)
L'Acadie	L'hon. Thérèse Lavoie-Roux (Lib)
L'Assomption	Jean-Guy Gervais (Lib)
La Peltrie	Lawrence Cannon (Lib)
Lac St-Jean	Jacques Brassard (PQ)
Lafontaine	Jean-Claude Gobé (Lib)
Laporte	L'hon. André Bourbeau (Lib)
Laprairie	Jean-Pierre Saintonge (Lib)
Laurier	Christos Sirros (Lib)
Laval-des-Rapides	Guy Bélanger (Lib)
Laviolette	Jean-Pierre Jolivet (PQ)
Lévis	Jean Garon (PQ)
Limoilou	Michel Després (Lib)
Lotbinière	Lewis Camden (Lib)
Louis-Hébert	Réjean Doyon (Lib)
Maisonneuve	Louise Harel (PQ)
Marguerite-Bourgeoys	Gilles Fortin (Lib)
Marie-Victorin	Cécile Vermette (PQ)
Marquette	Claude Dauphin (Lib)
Maskinongé	L'hon. Yvon Picotte (Lib)
Matane	Claire-Hélène Hovington (Lib)
Matapédia	Henri Paradis (Lib)
Mégantic/Compton	Madeleine Bélanger (Lib)
Mercier	Gérald Godin (PQ)
Mille-Iles	Jean-Pierre Bélisle (Lib)
Mont-Royal	L'hon. John Ciaccia (Lib)
Montmagny/L'Islet	Réal Gauvin (Lib)
Montmorency	L'hon. Yves Séguin (Lib)
Nelligan	Clifford Lincoln (Lib)
Nicolet	Maurice Richard (Lib)
Notre-Dame-de-Grâce	Harold Thuringer (Lib)
Orford	Georges Vaillancourt (Lib)
Outremont	L'hon. Pierre Fortier (Lib)
Papineau	Vacant
Pontiac	Robert Middlemiss (Lib)
Portneuf	L'hon. Michel Pagé (Lib)
Prévost	Paul-André Forget (Lib)
Richelieu	Albert Khelfa (Lib)
Richmond	Yvon Vallières (Lib)
Rimouski	Michel Tremblay (Lib)
Rivière-du-Loup	L'hon. Albert Côté (Lib)
Robert-Baldwin	L'hon. Pierre MacDonald (Lib)
Roberval	Gaston Blackburn (Lib)
Rosemont	L'hon. Guy Rivard (Lib)
Rousseau	Robert Thérien (Lib)
Rouyn-Noranda/Témiscamingue	Gilles Baril (Lib)
Saguenay	Ghislain Maltais (Lib)
Ste-Anne	Maximilien Polak (Lib)
St-François	L'hon. Monique Gagnon-Tremblay (Lib)
St-Henri	Roma Hains (Lib)
St-Hyacinthe	Charles Messier (Lib)

Constituency	Member and Affiliation
St-Jacques	André Boulerice (PQ)
St-Jean	Pierre Lorrain (Lib)
St-Laurent	L'hon. Robert Bourassa (Lib)
St-Louis	Jacques Chagnon (Lib)
Ste-Marie	Michel Laporte (Lib)
St-Maurice	Yvon Lemire (Lib)
Sauvé	Marcel Parent (Lib)
Shefford	Roger Paré (PQ)
Sherbrooke	André J. Hamel (Lib)
Taillon	Claude Filion (PQ)
Taschereau	Jean Leclerc (Lib)
Terrebonne	Yves Blais (PQ)
Trois-Rivières	Paul Philibert (Lib)
Ungava	Christian Claveau (PQ)
Vachon	Christiane Pelchat (Lib)
Vanier	Jean-Guy Lemieux (Lib)
Vaudreuil-Soulanges	L'hon. Daniel Johnson (Lib)
Verchères	Jean-Pierre Charbonneau (PQ)
Verdun	L'hon. Paul Gobeil (Lib)
Viau	William Cusano (Lib)
Viger	Cosmo Maciocia (Lib)
Vimont	Jean-Paul Théorêt (Lib)
Westmount	L'hon. Richard D. French (Lib)

Ind — Independent
Lib — Libéral
PQ — Parti Québécois

MINISTÈRE DU CONSEIL EXÉCUTIF
(Executive Council)

885, av. Grande-Allée est, éd. J, 3e ét.
Québec, G1A 1A2

75, boul. René-Lévesque ouest, 17e ét.
Montréal, H2Z 1A4

CABINET DU PREMIER MINISTRE
Premier ministre, L'hon. Robert Bourassa
Secrétaire, Jacqueline Boucher
Directeur du cabinet, Mario Bertrand
Attaché de presse, Ronald Poupart

Secrétariat général du Conseil exécutif
Secrétaire gén. et greffier, Benoît Morin
Adj. au secrétaire gén., Suzanne Masson
Greffier adj., Jean-Pierre Vaillancourt

Secrétariat à la Législation
875, av. Grande-Allée est, éd. H, 2e ét.
Québec, G1R 4Y8
Président du Comité de législation,
  L'hon. Gil Rémillard
Secrétaire gén. assoc., Lise Morency

Secrétariat du Développement
économique
885, av. Grande-Allée est, éd. J, r.c.
Québec, G1A 1A2
*Président du Comité ministériel permanent
  au développement économique,*
  L'hon. Gérard D. Levesque
Secrétaire gén. assoc., Ghislain Fortin

Secrétariat à l'Aménagement et
au Développement régional
875, av. Grande-Allée est, éd. H, 2e ét.
Québec, G1R 4Y8
*Président du Comité ministériel permanent
  de l'aménagement et du développement
  régional,*
  L'hon. Marc-Yvan Côté
Secrétaire gén. assoc., André Trudeau

Secrétariat des Affaires culturelles
et sociales
875, av. Grande-Allée est, éd. H, 2e ét.
Québec, G1R 4Y8
*Président du Comité ministériel permanent
  des affaires culturelles et sociales,*
  L'hon. Claude Ryan
Secrétaire gén. assoc., Pierre Sarault

Secrétariat aux Affaires
intergouvernementales canadiennes
875, av. Grande-Allée est, éd. H, 2e ét.
Québec, G1R 4Y8
*Ministre délégué aux Affaires
  intergouvernementales canadiennes,*
  L'hon. Gil Rémillard
Secrétaire gén. assoc., Diane Wilhelmy

Bureau du Québec à Toronto
20 Queen St. W., Ste. 1004
Box 13, Toronto, ON M5H 3S3
Représentant, Julien Arsenault

Bureau du Québec à Ottawa
Place de Ville, Tower B, 12th Flr.
112 Kent St., Ottawa, ON K1P 5P2
Représentant, Yves Bélanger

Bureau du Québec à Moncton
Place de l'Assomption
770 Main St., Moncton, NB E1C 1E7
Représentant, Robert Keating

Bureau du Québec à Edmonton
Highfield Place Bldg., 10th Flr.
10010-106th St., Edmonton, AB T5J 3L8
Représentant, Gérard Vézina

Secrétariat aux Affaires
autochtones (SAA)
875, av. Grande-Allée est, éd. H, 2e ét.
Québec, G1R 4Y8
Secrétaire gén. assoc., Gilles Jolicoeur

Secrétariat à la Réforme
administrative et
aux Emplois supérieurs
885, av. Grande-Allée est, éd. J, 2e ét.
Québec, G1A 1A2
Secrétaire gén. assoc., Renaud Caron
Secrétaires adj.:
  André Gélinas, Francine Boivin

Secrétariat à la Condition féminine
875, av. Grande-Allée est, éd. H, 2e ét.
Québec, G1R 4Y8
Ministre déléguée à la Condition féminine,
  L'hon. Monique Gagnon-Tremblay
Secrétaire gén. assoc. (p.i.), Ghyslaine Morin

Conseil du statut de la femme
8, rue Cook, bur. 300, Québec, G1R 5J7

The Conseil du statut de la femme (Council on the Status of Women), established in 1973, is an advisory and study body whose mandate is to provide advice to the Minister responsible for the Status of Women on any matter referred to it regarding equality and women's issues.

The Council may also inform women, both groups and individuals, on any question affecting the status of women. It may undertake studies, conduct research, receive suggestions from individual citizens and groups, and make recommendations to the Minister responsible.

The Council is composed of ten members appointed by the Quebec government on the recommendation of representative groups and eight deputy ministers from different departments particularly involved in women's issues.

Présidente, Claire McNicoll

Office des services de garde à l'enfance
100, rue Sherbrooke est, Montréal, H2X 1C3

The Office des services de garde à l'enfance is the bureau responsible for applying *An Act respecting child day care*, which was assented to on Dec. 21, 1979 and came into force on Oct. 16, 1980. The Office is under the jurisdiction of the Minister responsible for the Status of Women.

The Act defines five categories of service: day care centres, stop-over centres, nursery schools, home day care, and school day care.

Under the Act, the Office has a mandate to ensure that high-quality child day care is provided, and to co-ordinate, organize, and develop these services in keeping with other family policies.

The Office provides professional and technical assistance to existing day care services and groups promoting them, and produces and distributes information about day care services.

The Office determines the regulations concerning the licensing and operation of day care services, as well as the conditions concerning subsidies for them and financial aid for parents.

Présidente, Nicole Marcotte
Direction des opérations
Directrice, Rose-Mary Thonney
Administration et Secrétariat général
Directeur, Georges Labrosse

Secrétariat à la Réforme électorale
875, av. Grande-Allée est, éd. H, 2e ét.
Québec, G1R 4Y8
Ministre délégué à la Réforme électorale,
Michel Gratton
Direction générale de l'Administration
Directeur gén., Gilles Regimbal
Ressources humaines
Directeur (p.i.), Paul Blouin

Bureaux de l'Opposition
(Opposition Offices)

PARTI QUÉBECOIS
Assemblée Nationale, Hôtel du Parlement
Québec, G1A 1A4
Chef de l'Opposition officiel,
Guy Chevrette (p.i.)
Directeur de cabinet, Hubert Thibault
Chef du Parti Québécois, Jacques Parizeau

Cabinet du Leader de l'Opposition
Ed. A, chambre 298
Hôtel du Gouvernement, Québec, G1A 1A4
Leader de l'Opposition, François Gendron
Directeur de cabinet, René Blouin

Cabinet du Whip de l'Opposition
Ed. A, chambre 281
Hôtel du Gouvernement, Québec, G1A 1A4
Whip de l'Opposition, Jacques Brassard
Directeur de cabinet, Raymond Brien

Bibliothèque de l'Assemblée nationale
(Legislative Library)

Édifice Pamphile-Le May, Québec, G1A 1A5
(418) 643-4408

The Bibliothèque de l'Assemblée nationale provides library services for the parliamentarians, as well as for all employees of the National Assembly and members of the Press Gallery.

The number of documents kept in the Library, including books, periodicals, microfilms, and microtexts, amounts to some 300,000 physical units. Approximately 50,000 printed documents and microforms are added to this collection every year. About 43,000 of these documents consist of Canadian, American, and foreign government publications.

Directeur, Jacques Prémont
Directeur adj., Gaston Bernier

Protecteur du citoyen
(Ombudsman)

2875, boul. Laurier, 4e ét., Ste-Foy, G1V 2M2
1-800-463-5070

5199, rue Sherbrooke est, bur. 2931
Montréal, H1T 3X1
1-800-361-5804

The office of the provincial Ombudsman was created by statute, S.Q. 1968, Chapter P-32, and the first Ombudsman was sworn in on May 1, 1969.

The Ombudsman is an officer of the National

Assembly whose duty is to uphold the rights of a person (or group of persons) in his or her dealings with the Quebec public administration.

The Ombudsman receives complaints from persons (or groups of persons) who feel they have been wronged by the administration of the Quebec government. If he feels that justice has not been done, appropriate recommendations will be made to correct the situation. Conversely, if the complaint is unjustified, a full explanation will be given to the complainant.

Protecteur du citoyen, Daniel Jacoby
Vice-protecteur, Jacques Meunier
Directeurs d'enquête:
    Michel Daoust, Gérald Fournier
Secrétaire gén. et directeur des
    communications, Paul-Emile Racine
Directeur des services administratifs,
    Paul-H. Desrochers

MINISTÈRE DES AFFAIRES CULTURELLES

(Cultural Affairs)
225, av. Grande-Allée est, Québec, G1R 5G5
General Information: (418) 643-2183
454, place Jacques-Cartier, Montréal, H2Y 3B3
General Information: (514) 873-6190

CABINET DE LA MINISTRE
Ministre, L'hon. Lise Bacon

BUREAU DE LA SOUS-MINISTRE
Sous-ministre, Nicole Malo
Direction des communications
Directrice, Lorraine Malenfant Loiselle
Direction des relations intergouvernementales
Directeur, Pierre-Denis Cantin
Direction de la recherche
Directrice, Marie-Charlotte de Koninck
Service juridique
Directeur, Vacant

Milieux Culturels
Sous-ministre adj., Michèle Courchesne
Direction générale des régions
Directeur gén., Pierre Lafleur
Secrétariat aux équipements et à la coordination
Directeur, Claude Roy

DIRECTIONS RÉGIONALES:
Direction de Montréal
454, place Jacques-Cartier, 2e ét.
Montréal, H2Y 3B3
Directeur rég., Jean-Guy Théorêt
Direction de Québec
225, av. Grande-Allée est, Québec, G1R 5G5
Directrice, Odette Blouin-Cliche
Nouveau Québec et service aux autochtones
225, av. Grande-Allée est, Québec, G1R 5G5
Directeur, Michel Noël

Mauricie—Bois-Francs
100, rue Laviolette, 2e ét.
Trois-Rivières, G9A 5S9
Directeur, Michel Bonneau
Estrie
740, rue Galt ouest, 3e ét.
Sherbrooke, J1H 1Z3
Directrice, Carole G.-Thibault
Outaouais
Ed. Montferrand, 6e ét.
70, rue Hôtel-de-Ville, Hull, J8X 4C2
Directeur, Eric Soucy
Est-du-Québec
337, rue Moreault, 2e ét., Rimouski, G5L 1P4
Directeur, John Michaud
Saguenay—Lac-St-Jean
930, rue Jacques-Cartier est, 1er ét.
Chicoutimi, G7H 2A9
Directrice, Marie-Josée Champagne
Abitibi-Témiscamingue
19, rue Perreault ouest, bur. 450
Rouyn-Noranda, J9X 6N5
Directeur, Guy Lemire
Côte-Nord
625, boul. Laflèche, bur. 500
Baie-Comeau, G5C 1C5
Directeur (p.i.), François Paquette

Direction générale du patrimoine
Directeur gén., Adélard Guillemette
Direction des services centraux
Directeur, Michel Dufresne
Direction du patrimoine — Québec
Directeur, André Couture
Direction du patrimoine — Montréal
Directeur, Robert Fortin
Direction générale des arts et des lettres
Directeur gén., Roland Sasseville
Direction des arts visuels, des musées et des bibliothèques
Directeur, Laurent Bouchard
Direction des arts d'interprétation
Directeur, Pierre Lafleur
Direction des industries culturelles
Directeur, Jean-Pierre Bastien
Direction des services aux artistes
Directrice, Marie-Claire Lévesque

Institutions nationales
Sous-ministre adj., Henri-Paul Chaput
Direction des relations avec les organismes gouvernementaux
Directeur, André Garon

DIRECTION GÉNÉRALE DE L'ADMINISTRATION
Directeur gén., Claude Archambault
Direction des ressources humaines
Directeur, Jean Cossette
Direction des ressources financières et des systèmes de gestion
Directeur, Serge Doyon
Direction des ressources matérielles
Directeur, Michel-A. Rousseau
Direction de la vérification interne
Directeur, Bertrand Gravel

Direction de la comptabilité
Directeur, Othman Mzoughi
Centre de conservation du Québec
476, rue Desrochers, Vanier, G1M 1C2
Directeur, Michel Cauchon

CONSERVATOIRE DE MUSIQUE ET D'ART
DRAMATIQUE DU QUÉBEC
580 Grande-Allée est, bur. 420
Quebec, G1R 2K2
Directeur gén., Pierre Thibault
Direction de l'enseignement
Directeur, Roger Bédard
Direction de l'administration
Directeur, Jean Charron

MUSIQUE
Québec
270, rue St-Amable, Québec, G1R 5G1
Directeur, Wilfrand Guillemette
Montréal
100, rue Notre-Dame est, Montréal, H2Y 1C1
Directeur, Albert Grenier
Rimouski
22, rue Ste-Marie
C.P. 1210, Rimouski, G5L 8M2
Directeur (p.i.), Pierre Normandin
Trois-Rivières
587, rue Radisson, C.P. 1146
Trois-Rivières, G9A 5K8
Directeur, Michel Kozlovsky
Val-d'Or
1220, Septième rue, Val d'Or, J9P 3R7
Directrice (p.i.), Josée Blackburn
Chicoutimi
520, rue Jacques-Cartier est
Chicoutimi, G7H 1Z5
Directeur, Jacques Clément
Hull
430, boul. Alexandre-Taché, Hull, J9A 1M7
Directeur, Yvon Pépin

ART DRAMATIQUE
Québec
31, rue Mont-Carmel, Québec, G1R 4A6
Directeur (p.i.), Jacques Lessard
Montréal
100, rue Notre-Dame est, Montréal, H2Y 1C1
Directeur, Raymond Cloutier

AGENCIES, BOARDS AND COMMISSIONS

Archives nationales du Québec
1210, av. du Séminaire
C.P. 10450, Ste-Foy, G1V 4N1

The Archives of Quebec were created in 1920. Since 1983, they have existed under the provisions of the *Loi sur les archives.*

The principal mandate of the Archives is to preserve important government records, to make them available to the public, and to assist other government agencies and ministries in the management of their archives.

Equally, the Archives play a role in acquiring and in making accessible to the public private archives of special significance.

Through nine regional offices, the Archives make accessible a collection that includes 25 kilometres of printed documents, 620,000 maps and plans, thousands of hours worth of movie and audio film, and close to 10,000 microfiches.

Conservateur en chef, Robert Garon
Direction de Québec
Conservateur adj., Yvan Dussault
Direction de Montréal
1945, rue Mullins, Point-St-Charles
Montréal, H3K 1N9
Conservateur adj., Normand Gouger
Direction des autres régions
Conservateur adj., Jean-Guy Leblanc

Bibliothèque nationale du Québec
1700, rue St-Denis, Montréal, H2X 3K6

The Bibliothèque nationale du Québec was established on Aug. 12, 1967. Its role is to acquire, catalogue, preserve, and make available all documents published in Quebec, as well as those documents published elsewhere that are relevant to Quebec.

To facilitate the acquisition of these documents, the *Loi sur la Bibliothèque du Québec*, R.S.Q., Chapter B-2, stipulates that publishers must deliver, at their own expense, two copies of each document published by them to the National Library within 30 days of its publication. Coinciding with the cataloguing of documents, the Library is engaged in the ongoing publication of a bibliography of Quebec works. The Library also compiles an index to Quebec periodicals, which is published at regular intervals.

The permanent preservation of documents published in Quebec, especially in their original form, is the priority of the Library. To provide access to its collections, and to promote their use, the Library places its reading rooms at the disposal of the public and offers a full range of reference services. In addition, it organizes exhibitions for which catalogues are issued.

Directeur gén., Georges Cartier
Direction du développement et
du traitement des collections
Directeur, Pierre Deslauriers
Direction de la diffusion des
ressources documentaires
Directeur, Gilles-Mathieu Boivin
Direction de l'administration, de la recherche
et de la planification
Directeur, Marcel Fontaine

Commission d'appel de francisation des entreprises
630, boul René-Lévesque ouest, bur. 2540
Montréal, H3J 2S1
Président, Renald Savoie
Secrétaire, Vacant

Commission de la fonction publique du Québec
8, rue Cook, 4ᵉ ét., Québec, G1R 5J8

Since April 1, 1984, under terms of the *Civil Service Act*, the Commission de la fonction publique hears and rules on all appeals made under section 33 by non-union members of the civil service staff with regard to classifications; demotion or removal; and suspension, dismissal, temporary release from duties, or other disciplinary measures.

The Commission also hears and rules on all appeals made by civil servants on promotions or grade advancement examinations (section 35). Moreover, the Commission makes inquiries into compliance with the Act and its Regulations, particularly adherence to the rule of selection according to merit. The Commission also ascertains that civil servants are treated with impartiality and fairness and formulates recommendations to the appropriate authorities.

Président, Jean-Noël Poulin
Commissaires:
Jean-Paul Roberge, Juliette Barcelo
440, boul. René-Lévesque, bur. 1403
Montréal, H2Z 1V7

Commission de protection de la langue française

Tour de la Bourse, 40e ét., C.P. 68
Montréal, H4Z 1A8

Established on Aug. 26, 1977 by Quebec's *Charter of the French Language*, this Commission is responsible for dealing with violations of the Charter, and related matters.

The Commission's role is to remedy situations where violations have occurred, so as to ensure that the basic linguistic rights of the people of Quebec are respected. The goal is to make French the normal and usual language of work, education, communications, commerce, and business in Quebec.

To perform its duties, the Commission conducts inquiries. An individual or a group of citizens may request an inquiry; as well, the Commission may launch an investigation on its own initiative when it has reason to believe that the law has not been respected. Investigation commissioners are responsible for individual cases; they are assisted in their work by inspectors.

Where an offender systematically refuses to remedy a situation that violates the Charter, the case is referred to the Quebec Ministry of Justice. If deemed appropriate, the ministry may institute legal proceedings against the offender.

In 1986, responsibility for this organization shifted from the Ministère des Communautés culturelles et de l'Immigration to the Ministère des Affaires culturelles.

Présidente, Ludmila de Fougerolles
Responsable des services administratifs,
Line Paradis
Directeur des services aux clientèles,
Michel Houle
Directeur des services juridiques,
Joseph G. Turi

Commission de reconnaissance des associations d'artistes

425, boul. de Maisonneuve ouest, 9e ét.
Montréal, H3A 1L6
Président, Denis Hardy

Commission de toponymie du Québec

220, Grande-Allée est, Québec, G1R 2J1
Toponymic Consultations: (418) 643-2817
General Information: (418) 643-9705

The Commission de toponymie was created in 1977 under the *Charter of the French Language.* It replaced the Commission de géographie, which had been set up in 1912. Under its official mandate, the Commission must:

- establish the standards and rules of spelling to be followed in place names;
- catalogue and preserve place names;
- establish and standardize geographical terminology, in co-operation with the Office de la langue française;
- officially register place names;
- publicize the official geographical nomenclature of Quebec; and
- advise the government on any question relating to toponymy submitted to it by the Commission.

To date, the Commission has registered more than 130,000 place names; however, this corpus of official names represents only a fraction of the places in Quebec that could be given a name. Official names are published in the *Gazette officielle du Québec* once a year, and their use from that date onwards is obligatory. In 1987, the Commission published, as it does periodically, the *Répertoire toponymique du Québec, 1987,* which contains all official place names (nearly 100,000 as at Jan. 1, 1987). The Commission also publishes a number of other documents, including *Le toponyme,* a quarterly bulletin available on request.

Président, Henri Dorion
Adj. au président, Jean Poirier
Direction de l'inventaire et du traitement
Directeur, Alain Vallières
Service de l'odonymie
Responsable, Marcel Fourcaudot
Service de la toponymie
Responsable, Denis Tremblay
Service de la normalisation
Responsable, Christian Bonnelly
Direction du secrétariat et de la toponymie officielle
Directeur, Jean-Claude Fortin
Service de l'information
Responsable, Réal Dumoulin
Service de l'implantation
Responsable, Pierre Barabé
Service de l'évaluation
Responsable, Georges Larouche

Commission des biens culturels du Québec

12, rue Ste-Anne, Québec, G1R 3X2

The Cultural Property Commission was created by the *Cultural Property Act,* enacted in July 1972 and amended in 1978 and 1985.

The main objectives of the *Cultural Property Act* are to establish a Cultural Property Commission; to authorize the Minister of Cultural Affairs, after taking the advice of the Commission, to recognize or classify a cultural property; to provide for the regulation of archeological excavation surveys; and to authorize the government to declare as a historic district a territory with a concentration of historic sites or monuments, or a natural district whose setting presents an esthetic, legendary, or scenic interest.

The Cultural Property Commission consists of 12 members, including a chairman and a vice-chairman, appointed by the government. It provides advice to the minister on any question referred to it by him, and on any question relating to the conservation of cultural property.

The Commission may establish committees or sub-committees to study matters within its scope. It may also hold public hearings to hear persons or groups on matters related to cultural property.

Président, Cyril Simard

Conseil de la langue française
800, place d'Youville, 13e ét., Québec, G1R 3P4
1410, rue Stanley, 7e ét., Montréal, H3A 1P8

Established on Aug. 26, 1977 by Quebec's *Charter of the French Language,* the Conseil de la langue française is the administrative body responsible for advising the minister on Quebec policy concerning the French language and on any question relating to the interpretation and application of the Charter.

The Conseil's primary role is to keep a watch on language developments in Quebec in regard to the status and quality of the French language. As well, the Conseil informs the minister of any question pertaining to language that, in its opinion, requires attention or action by the Quebec government. In order to achieve its aims, the Conseil has published more than 150 studies to date in several specific fields such as law, education, immigration, sociolinguistics, and language planning.

The Conseil is composed of 12 members who are appointed by the Quebec government. Except for the chairman and the secretary, each member is chosen after consultation with the representative body of which he or she is a member.

Président, Pierre Martel
Secrétaire du Conseil, Robert L'Heureux
Directions:
Etudes et recherches, Pierre Georgeault
Services administratifs et communications,
Pierre Carrier
Gestion, Charlotte Caron
Communications, Léo Gagné

Institut québécois de recherche sur la culture
14, rue Haldimand, Québec, G1R 4N4
General Information: (418) 643-4695
290, place d'Youville, Montréal, H2Y 2B6

The Institut québécois de recherche sur la culture is a public agency which was established as a corporation within the meaning of the *Civil Code* in legislation enacted by the Quebec National Assembly in June 1979.

The Institut enjoys all the rights and privileges of a corporation of the government, but is not subsidized by the government. It is a research body whose primary object is to contribute to Quebec's cultural development by conducting, encouraging, and supporting research and studies on various cultural phenomena.

In pursuing its objectives, the Institut may, in particular, devise and carry out research plans and programs for a better understanding of cultural change in Quebec; promote co-operation and concerted action by researchers in the cultural field; provide such researchers with information and services useful to their work; hold meetings, conferences, or information sessions; and publish the results of studies and research conducted by the Institut or other agencies pursuing similar ends. It may also assist in the preparation and revision of cultural policies through the results of its work, its forecasts, and its recommendations.

The Minister of Cultural Affairs is responsible for implementing the *Act to establish the Institut québécois de recherche sur la culture.*

P.-D.G., Fernand Dumont

Institut québécois du cinéma
80, rue de Brésoles, Montréal, H2Y 1V5

Established in 1983 under the *Loi sur le cinéma,* the Institut is a meeting-place for all sectors of Quebec's film industry. In permanent contact with the profession, the Institut provides advice to the Minister of Cultural Affairs on devising and implementing policy for the cinema industry.

The Institut determines the direction of the Quebec film industry, advises the minister on objectives of the Société générale des industries culturelles (SOGIC) and approves its aid programs. The Institut also makes recommendations on upcoming governmental regulation. Furthermore, the Institut conducts research and studies in the field of cinema and holds public hearings at least once every two years on subjects prescribed in the *Loi sur le cinéma* in the section entitled "Contrôle et Surveillance du cinéma".

The Institut is dedicated to economic understanding of the film industry, film studies, professional apprenticeship, creation, visibility of the film industry, French-speaking audio-visual practice, and international exchanges.

The membership of the Institut consists of a chairman and 11 directors nominated by the Minister of Cultural Affairs. The intention in selecting members is to achieve representation from each of the following eight groups within the private sector of the cinema industry: directors, producers, technicians, distributors, exhibitors, actors, scriptwriters, and the technical industries.

Président, Claude Fournier
Vice-président, Marc-F. Gélinas

Secrétaire gén., Bernard Boucher
Trésorier, Jean Colbert

Musée d'art contemporain de Montréal
Cité du Havre, Montréal, H3C 3R4

The Musée d'art contemporain de Montréal was established in 1964. It is a national museum by virtue of the law governing national Quebec museums. It is also an associated museum in the context of the Museum Assistance Program of Communications Canada.

The Musée is entirely dedicated to the diffusion and conservation of contemporary art in all its forms. It presents work by locally and internationally acclaimed artists, as well as featuring exhibitions of works selected from its outstanding permanent collection. In addition, performances, lectures, film presentations, and education programs are offered regularly.

Président, J.V. Raymond Cyr
Directeur gén., Marcel Brisebois

Musée de la civilisation
85, rue Dalhousie, C.P. 155, succ. B
Québec, G1K 7A6
Information and tours: (418) 643-2158

A national institution with an international vocation, the Musée de la civilisation is located in the heart of the Vieux-Port de Québec, near Place Royale. With 5,641 m² of display area and a total area of 20,238 m², it is the fourth largest museum in Canada.

As a museum of mankind, it puts special emphasis on ideas and the humanities. Furthermore, the content of its exhibitions is developed around major themes relating to five areas of human behaviour: the body, matter, society, language, and ideas.

A place to relax and enjoy, the Museum is also a place for reflection, learning, and discovery. Offering a look at the past, the Museum allows visitors a better understanding of the present and some possible solutions for the future. The Musée de la civilisation, which presents about a dozen exhibitions a year, is also responsible for the direction and management of the Maison Chevalier (Place Royale).

Président, Roger Décary
Directeur gén., Roland Arpin

Musée du Québec
Parc des Champs-de-Bataille
1, av. Wolfe-Montcalm, Québec, G1R 5H3

The Musée du Québec was created on Dec. 29, 1922, by the Government of Quebec with the coming into force of the *Law dealing with the Museums of the Province of Quebec.* On Nov. 14, 1984, the Museum was declared a "société d'Etat" (Crown corporation) by decree, L.R.Q., Chapter M-44. The Museum is administered by a board of directors consisting of nine members drawn from the public and private sectors.

The Musée's objective is to maintain and promote Quebec art belonging to all periods,

ancient and modern, and to ensure a presence of international art as well. It is active in exhibitions and similar activities. Presently, the Musée's collection comprises approximately 12,000 paintings, sculptures, and other works of art. From June 1986 to May 1987, in excess of 300,000 persons visited the Museum.

Président, Jean-Marie Roy
Directrice gén., Andrée Laliberté-Bourque

Office de la langue française
800, place Victoria, 16e ét., Tour de la Bourse
C.P. 316, Montréal, H4Z 1G8
700, boul. St-Cyrille est, place Hauteville
Québec, G1R 5G7

The Office de la langue française is the administrative body responsible for applying the *Charter of the French Language* adopted by the National Assembly of Quebec on Aug. 26, 1977. Its mandate is to define and conduct Quebec policy on linguistic research and terminology and to see that the French language becomes, as soon as possible, the language of communication, work, commerce, and business in both civil administration and in business firms. The law creating the Office de la langue française was the third linguistic law enacted within ten years.

One of the main tasks of the Office is to make sure that French really becomes the usual and customary language for all commerce and labour dealings. Besides recognizing fundamental rights for all Quebeckers, the *Charter of the French Language* obliges all firms employing more than 50 persons to analyze their linguistic situation and to establish, if needed, a francization program generalizing the use of the French language at all levels of their organization.

Président, Pierre-Etienne Laporte
Cadre-conseil, Luc Sénécal
Directrice de l'administration (p.i.),
Astrid Coulombe
Directeur des services au public,
Jean-Yvon Houle
Directeur du personnel, Luc Couvrette
Directeur de la recherche et
du secrétariat, Gilles Racine
Directeur des productions linguistiques
et terminologiques, Jean-Marie Fortin
Directeur des programmes de
francisation, Solange Chalvin

Office des ressources humaines
1039, rue de la Chevrotière, Québec, G1R 5E9
General Information: (418) 649-3308

Established under the *Loi sur la fonction publique (Civil Service Act,* S.Q. 1983, Chapter 55), the Office des ressources humaines has been in operation since April 1, 1984. By means of competitions, the Office recruits and selects candidates for appointment and promotion in the Quebec civil service, making sure that every qualified person has a reasonable opportunity to apply.

The Office assesses the candidates' experience, general knowledge, and professional skills by such means as written or oral examinations or, on occasion, practical examinations. The Office lists the candidates by order of merit according to their results. This list is taken into account by the departments and government bodies which ultimately appoint the candidates.

The Office is composed of a president and two vice-presidents appointed by the government. Staff for the head and regional offices is appointed and remunerated in accordance with the *Loi sur la fonction publique.*

Président, Jocelyn Jacques
Direction de l'administration et des communications
Directeur, François Giroux
Direction des services juridiques
Directeur, Jean François Duchaine
Carrière et emploi
Vice-président, Jean Mercier
Direction du personnel d'encadrement et professionnel
Directeur, Serge Lemaire
Service de placement
Directeur, Vacant
Direction des bureaux régionaux de l'est
Directeur, Michel Lanouette
Direction des bureaux régionaux de l'ouest
Directeur, Pierre Gagnon
Egalité en emploi et développement
Vice-présidente, Francine Roy
Bureau d'égalité en emploi
Directrice, Murielle Côté
Direction de l'évaluation et de l'aide aux employés
Directrice, Gisèle Tourigny
Direction de la formation
Directeur, André Robert
Direction du développement du personnel d'encadrement
Directeur, Louis St-Pierre
Direction générale de la gestion de l'information
Directeur, Jean Laliberté
Direction de la planification et de la gestion des données
Directeur, Gérard Chouinard
Direction du développement des systèmes
Directrice, Nicole Méthot
Direction du service aux usagers
Directeur, Léo Ferland
Direction générale de la recherche et de la planification
Directeur, Jean Larochelle
Direction des politiques et des programmes
Directeur, André Bazinet
Direction de la recherche, des études et des statistiques
Directeur, Raynald Martel

Régie du cinéma
455, rue Ste-Hélène, Montréal, H2Y 2L3
General Information: (514) 873-2371

The Régie du cinéma, which has replaced the Cinema Supervisory Board, has as its functions:

to classify films and trailers; to issue, renew, suspend, or revoke exhibitor's, distributor's, and video material dealer's licences; to issue filming licences; and to supervise and control the sale, lease, lending, or exchange of video material.

The Régie du cinéma is a three-member board, and is an autonomous body responsible to the Minister for Cultural Affairs.

Président, Claude Benjamin
Secrétaire, Denis Belleville

Société de la Place des Arts de Montréal
1501, rue Jeanne-Mance, Montréal, H2X 1Z9

The board of directors of the Place des Arts is composed of nine members who are appointed by the Quebec government, three of them in consultation with the Montreal Urban Community. It is the purpose of the board to administer, develop, maintain, and operate the Place des Arts, a cultural centre comprised of three theatre halls and a café-théâtre, which together welcome a total of one million spectators each year. The board aims to provide balanced programming in line with the tastes of the general public, while at the same time taking into account the varied nature of the performing arts.

In addition to the many presentations staged by various impresarios, the board itself has been active over the past few years in producing artistic performances and activities which enable it to broaden its cultural policy with two major objectives in mind: to offer reasonably priced performances through various artistic activities and to endeavour, by means of these performances, to broaden the scope of experience for the public in the artistic and cultural spheres.

Présidente, Danièle Touchette Robitaille
Directeur gén., Guy Morin
Secrétaire et adj. au directeur gén., France Fortin

Société du Grand Théâtre de Québec
269, boul. St-Cyrille est, Québec, G1R 2B3

The main function of the Société is "to administer the Grand Théâtre de Québec and to put on performances there." The nine members of the Société, including the president, are appointed by the Lieutenant-Governor in Council for a renewable period of office lasting two years.

The Grand Théâtre is the result of a Centennial project, officially opening its doors on Jan. 16, 1971. The architect is Victor Prus, winner of a national competition launched in 1964 by the Quebec Ministry of Cultural Affairs.

The Grand Théâtre has two main halls: the Louis Fréchette Hall (1,800 seats) and the Octave Crémazie Hall (650 seats). Thanks to this facility, Quebec City has become a centre of cultural activities in all disciplines of the interpretative arts. Space is also reserved for visual art. Performances are geared to people of all ages and backgrounds, in keeping with the management's policy of accessibility for the widest possible audience.

Président, Louis Vézina
Directrice gén., Michelle Mercier

Société générale des industries culturelles (SOGIC)
1755, boul. René-Lévesque est, bur. 200
Montréal, H2K 4P6
20, rue St-Pierre, C.P. 5, succ. B
Québec, G1K 7A1

The Société générale des industries culturelles (SOGIC), created in 1988, is the product of the amalgamation of the Société de développement des industries de la culture et des communications (SOGICC), the Société générale du cinéma du Québec, and the Direction des industries culturelles of the Ministère du Commerce extérieur et du Développement technologique.
The mandate of SOGIC includes three basic elements: aid to the Quebec film industry, financing for cultural and communications companies, and support for these companies to compete in foreign markets.

P.-D.G., Charles Denis
Vice-président, Robert Brisebois
Vice-présidente, Huguette Bailly-Lallouz
Secrétaire, Michel Fortier

MINISTÈRE DES AFFAIRES INTERNATIONALES

(International Affairs)
1225, place Georges V est, Québec, G1R 4Z7
General Information: (418) 643-3044

CABINET DU MINISTRE
Ministre, L'hon. Gil Rémillard

BUREAU DE LA SOUS-MINISTRE
Sous-ministre (p.i.), Diane Wilhelmy
Sous-ministre adj., Denis Ricard
Service de vérification interne
Chef de service, Edouard Lavoie
Commissaire général à la francophonie, Jean-Marc Léger
Relations avec le gouvernement fédéral
Coordonnateur, Vacant
Direction du protocole
Directeur, Raymond Bégin
Direction des communications
Directeur, Charles-Henri Dubé

PLANIFICATION
Directeur gén., Julien Aubert
AFFAIRES INTERNATIONALES
Directeur gén., Pierre Jobin
ADMINISTRATION
Directeur gén., Jacques Laliberté

MINISTÈRE DES AFFAIRES MUNICIPALES

(Municipal Affairs)
20, av. Chauveau, Québec, G1R 4J3

CABINET DU MINISTRE
Ministre, L'hon. Pierre Paradis

BUREAU DU SOUS-MINISTRE
Sous-ministre (p.i.), Florent Gagné
Sous-ministres adj.: Rita Bédard, Florent Gagné, Jacques Fournier

DIRECTION GÉNÉRALE DE L'ADMINISTRATION FINANCIÈRE
Directeur gén., Alphé Poiré
Service des études et programmes
Directeur, Antoine Sylvain
Service de la gestion financière et administrative
Directeur, Jacques Asselin
Service du financement municipal
Directeur, Jean-Pierre Michel
Service de la vérification
Directeur, Benoît Arial

DIRECTION GÉNÉRALE DE L'ÉVALUATION FONCIÈRE
Directeur gén., Réjean Carrier
Service des programmes de compensation
Directeur, Gaston Vachon
Service de l'animation
Directeur, Roger Mayrand

DIRECTION GÉNÉRALE DE LA PRÉVENTION DES INCENDIES
Directeur gén., Gaetan Levasseur
Service de la prévention
Directeur, Jean-Claude Roch
Service de la protection municipale
Directeur, Jean-Guy Delage

DIRECTION GÉNÉRALE DES RELATIONS AVEC LES MUNICIPALITÉS
Directeur gén., Louis Dussault
Service de l'organisation municipale
Directeur, François Gelinas
Service des affaires nordiques et amérindiennes
Directeur, Jean-Guy Blouin
Service des bureaux régionaux
Directeur, André Demers
Service de la formation municipale
Directrice, Lise Monette
Direction des communications
Directeur, Richard Thériault

DIRECTION GÉNÉRALE DE L'URBANISME ET DE L'AMÉNAGEMENT DU TERRITOIRE
Directeur gén., Georges Felli
Directeur du service de l'aide à la planification, rive-sud, Marcel Meunier
Directeur du service de l'aide à la planification, rive-nord, Fernand Martin

Service de l'administration des programmes
d'urbanisme et d'aménagement
Directeur, Robert Aubé
Service des études et projets
Directeur, Jean Rousseau
Service des orientations gouvernementales en
aménagement
Directeur, Pierre Lavergne

DIRECTION GÉNÉRALE DE LA GESTION
Directeur gén., Yvon Verrette
Service des ressources humaines
Directeur, Yves Turenne
Service du budget
Directrice, Raymonde Fiset
Service des systèmes
Directeur, Jacques Leguay
Service des ressources matérielles
Directeur, Pierre Chabot
Direction de la comptabilité
Directeur, Roland Perreault
Direction de la recherche et des politiques
Directeur, Robert Cournoyer
Service juridique
Directeur, Jacques Lanctôt

BUREAUX RÉGIONAUX:
Rimouski
337, rue Moreault, 2e ét., Rimouski, G5L 1P4
Délégué, Jules Coulombe
Saguenay—Lac-St-Jean
555, av. Bégin, 1er ét., Chicoutimi, G7H 4N7
Délégué, André Rochefort
Québec
690, Grande-Allée est, 4e ét., Québec, G1R 2K5
Délégué, Roland Verreault
Trois-Rivières
100, rue Laviolette, bur. 317A
Trois-Rivières, G9A 5S9
Délégué, Normand Papineau
Estrie
740, rue Galt ouest, bur. 401
Sherbrooke, J1H 1Z3
Déléguée, Bernadette Doyon
Montréal
3, place Desjardins, 26e ét., Montréal, H5B 1E3
Délégué, Raymond Lynch
Outaouais
170, rue Hôtel-de-Ville, bur. 6.380
Hull, J8X 4C2
Délégué, Pierre Ricard
Abitibi-Témiscamingue
19, rue Perreault ouest, bur. 460
Rouyn, J9X 6N5
Délégué, Denis Bureau
Côte-Nord
625, boul. Laflèche, bur. 103
Baie-Comeau, G5C 1C5
Délégué, Louis Bélanger

AGENCIES, BOARDS AND COMMISSIONS

Bureau de révision de l'évaluation foncière du Québec
39, rue St-Louis, 4e ét., Québec, G1R 3Z2
3, place Desjardins, Tour nord, 27e ét.
C.P. 125, Montréal, H5B 1E3

The Bureau de révision de l'évaluation foncière
du Québec (Quebec Real Estate Assessment
Review Board) is a body whose function and
characteristics are those of a specialized tribunal.
Its purpose is to hear and proceed with complaints lodged by taxpayers against the real estate
values and the rental values entered on the
assessment rolls prepared by municipal corporations.

The Board is divided into two sections: the
Montreal section, which has jurisdiction in the
same territory as the Court of Appeal sitting at
Montreal, and the Quebec section, which has
jurisdiction in the same territory as the Court of
Appeal sitting at Quebec, pursuant to the *Code of
Civil Procedure.*

The Board is composed of 37 members, the
majority of whom are specialized in a given
profession: law, appraisal, or engineering. The
Act governing the Board provides that its members shall sit in the municipality where the
property of the complainant is located, or within a
radius of 100 km for the hearing of any complaint
relating to a real estate value of less than $250,000
or to a rental value of less than $25,000.

The Board must render a decision within a year
of the filing of a complaint and all the decisions of
the Board can be appealed first to the provincial
court, then to the Quebec Appeal Court, and
finally to the Supreme Court of Canada.

Président, Me Christian Beaudoin

Commission municipale du Québec
20, av. Chauveau, Québec, G1R 4J3

The Quebec Municipal Commission was established in 1932. It is composed of 15 members,
including the chairman and three vice-chairmen.

As agent of the Crown for the province, the
Municipal Commission has administrative and
quasi-judicial powers in matters of: municipal
administration in general; financial administration
of municipalities and works; administration of
municipalities which are placed under its control
by a judgment of the Quebec Superior Court;
property assessment; regrouping of municipalities; and protection of the environment.

In exercising its powers, the Commission acts
as a board of inquiry in matters of municipal
management and, in particular, financial administration. In addition, it receives appeals from
municipal officers or employees not covered by
the *Quebec Labour Code* who have been
removed from office or whose salaries have been
reduced; it hears requests from charitable institutions and non-profit bodies seeking real estate tax
exemptions; and it determines the criteria for
property assessors' permits and issues such
permits.

Président, Juge Richard Beaulieu
Vice-présidents: Me Jean-Charles Lafond,
Me François Mathieu, Jean-Paul Boucher
Membres: Mariette Bécotte, Lucien Caron,
Guy Desbiens, Roland Dion, Claude Gélinas,
Jérémie Giles, Jean-Guy Houde,
Paul Laliberté, Odette Lapalme,

Roger Létourneau, Jean-Marc Rivest,
Marcel Robidas, Louise Sauvé-Cuerrier,
Armand Trottier
Secrétaire, Me Caroline Pouliot

Régie des entreprises de construction du Québec
577, boul. Henri-Bourassa est, 2e ét.
Montréal, H2C 1E2
800, place d'Youville, 16e ét., Québec, G1R 5K7
General Information: (514) 383-0606

The Régie des entreprises de construction was created on June 27, 1975 under the *Act respecting building contractors' vocational qualifications*, R.S.Q., Chapter Q-1.

The Régie consists of nine persons appointed by the government, three of whom (the president, the vice-president, and one member) are appointed for terms of not more than ten years. They exercise all the powers of the Régie and are responsible for its administration. The six other members are experienced contractors appointed for three years. They are chosen from among the persons proposed by the employer associations most representative of the construction industry. They vote on the Régie's constitution, on the Regulations, and on the rates payable for the issue or renewal of licences.

The main functions of the Régie are to supervise the activities of building contractors in Quebec and, in particular, to issue them a licence attesting to their solvency and their competence in three areas: administration, technical operations, and construction site safety.

P.-D.G., Réal Mireault
Vice-président (Québec), Maurice Renaud
Régisseur, Jean-Paul Gagnon
Directeur des affaires juridiques et enquêtes, et secrétaire de la Régie, Jacques Leroux
Communications
Directeur, Pierre Boivin
Qualification
Directeur, Claude Lamarche
Ressources humaines et budgétaires
Directeur, Michel Gélinas
Bureau de Québec
Directeur, Pierre-Paul Morissette

Régie du logement du Québec
1, rue Notre-Dame est, 11e ét.
Montréal, H2Y 1B6

The Régie du logement du Québec was created on Oct. 1, 1980. Its main functions are to inform landlords and tenants of their respective rights and obligations, to promote goodwill between them, and to settle disputes whenever friendly agreements cannot be reached. The Régie offers its services throughout the province via a network of regional offices. Landlords and tenants may use these services with or without help from a lawyer.

The Régie holds the powers of an administrative tribunal. Save for applications of which the sole object is the fixing of rent, where its jurisdiction is exclusive, it is a first-instance court for applications concerning residential leases, specifically for rooms, apartments, low-income housing, mobile homes, and property intended for the installation of mobile homes, along with their services, accessories, and dependencies, even if separate leases are made for the latter.

The Régie also has jurisdiction to hear most applications for damages and lease cancellation. The Régie may hear applications to convert a building into a condominium, to demolish a building, or to sell a building within a unit.

Présidente, Louise Thibault
Vice-présidente, Me Nicole Archambault
Vice-président, Me Rémi Lussier
Direction des communications
Directeur, Benoît de Margerie
Bureau de Laval
1717, boul. St-Martin ouest, 2e ét.
Laval, H7S 1N2
Directrice, Me Ginette Chartrand
Bureau de Longueuil
Edifice Montval, 6e ét.
201, place Charles-Lemoyne
Longueuil, J4K 2T5
Directeur rég., Jean Pierre Prescott
Bureau de Montréal-Centre
Place Dupuis
800, boul. de Maisonneuve est, 12e ét.
Montréal, H2L 4L8
Directeur, Me Jean-Yves Landry
Bureau de Montréal-Est
Village Olympique, bur. 2161
5199, rue Sherbrooke est, Montréal, H1T 3X1
Directeur, Michel Sauvé
Bureau de Montréal-Nord
577, boul. Henri-Bourassa est, bur. 1.05
Montréal, H2C 1E2
Directrice, Me Ginette Chartrand
Bureau de Montréal-Ouest
6767, ch. de la Côte-des-Neiges, 6e ét.
Montréal, H3S 2B5
Directeur, Me Gaston Fréchette
Bureau de Montréal-Sud-Ouest
4475, rue Bannantyne, Verdun, H4G 1E2
Directrice, Me Lucie Landriault

Société d'aménagement de l'Outaouais
Maison du Citoyen
25, rue Laurier, C.P. 1666, Hull, J8X 3Y5

The Société d'aménagement de l'Outaouais is a para-governmental corporation established by an Act of the National Assembly of Quebec on Dec. 23, 1969, S.Q. 1969, Chapter 85. The board of the Société has seven members who are appointed by the Lieutenant-Governor in Council.

The Société has two purposes: to promote the economic expansion of the Outaouais region, and to carry out industrial, commercial, recreational, and tourist projects on its territory.

The Société owns and manages three industrial parks located in Gatineau, Hull, and Aylmer and also owns and operates the Gatineau Airport.

The territory over which the Société has jurisdiction covers 34,260 km² in the Outaouais region and includes Gatineau, Papineau, and

Pontiac counties, and the towns of Hull, Gatineau, Aylmer, Buckingham, Maniwaki, and Thurso.
P.-D.G., Jean-Marie Séguin
Adj. au P.-D.G. et directeur des biens et immeubles, André-Jean Desmarais
Secrétaire gén. et directeur du Service du personnel, Guy Gagnon
Direction des finances
Directeur, François Lacaille
Direction du développement économique
Directeur, Franco Materazzi
Direction du développement touristique
Directeur, Jean-Guy Noël

Société d'habitation du Québec
1054, rue Conroy, Bloc 2
Aile St-Amable, 4e ét., Québec, G1R 5E7

The Société d'habitation du Québec (Quebec Housing Corporation) has the following objectives:
* to inform the minister on the requirements, priorities, and objectives of all housing sectors in Quebec;
* to stimulate the development of public and private initiatives in the field of housing, and co-operation among their proposers;
* to make low-rental housing available to the citizens of Quebec;
* to promote the development and implementation of programs of housing construction, acquisition, development, restoration, and management;
* to facilitate the acquisition of real property by the citizens of Quebec; and
* to promote housing improvement.

To meet these objectives, the Corporation has, since 1967, contributed to the implementation and financing of various programs, including improvement of residential areas, construction and renovation of residential buildings, and ownership assistance programs.
Président du conseil d'administration,
Guy A. Bouchat
P.-D.G., J.-P. Arsenault
Vice-président, Jean-Louis Lapointe
Secrétaire, Jean-Luc Lesage
Adjoint exéc., Jean-Pierre Gagnon
Direction générale de la gestion des programmes
Directeur gén., Paul Angers
Direction générale du financement et de l'administration
Directeur gén., Raymond Baillargeon
Direction des communications
Directeur, André Lachapelle
Direction générale du bâtiment
Directeur gén., Marc Paradis
Bureau de Québec (bâtiment)
Directeur, Claude Desmeules
Bureau de Montréal (bâtiment)
3, place Desjardins, 25e ét., Montréal, H5B 1E3
Directeur, Georges Latendresse
Direction générale de la planification et de la recherche
Directeur gén., Vacant

Société de développement de la Baie James (SDBJ)
C.P. 970, Matagami, J0Y 2A0
Président, Laurent Levasseur
Vice-président exéc., Donald R. Murphy
Trésorier, Claude Hubert
Secrétaire et directeur du contentieux, Me Réal Lavigne
Société de tourisme de la Baie James (Sotour)
C.P. 970, Matagami, J0Y 2A0
Secrétaire, Me Réal Lavigne

MINISTÈRE DE L'AGRICULTURE, DES PÊCHERIES ET DE L'ALIMENTATION

(Agriculture, Fisheries and Food)
200-A, ch. Ste-Foy, Québec, G1R 4X6
General Information: (418) 643-2673

CABINET DU MINISTRE
Ministre, L'hon. Michel Pagé

MINISTRE DÉLÉGUÉ AUX PÊCHES
150, boul. St-Cyrille est, Québec, G1R 4Y3
Ministre, L'hon. Yvon Picotte

BUREAU DES SOUS-MINISTRES
Sous-ministre, Ghislain Leblond
Sous-ministres adj.: André Vézina, Robert Lemieux, Guy Jacob, Yvan Rouleau, Jean-Yves Lavoie
Coordonnateur aux affaires autochtones, Gilles Drolet
Direction des études économiques
Directeur gén., Raymond Cloutier
Coordination scientifique et technique
Directeur, Daniel Chez
Conseil des productions animales du Québec
Secrétaire, Christiane Migret
Conseil des productions végétales du Québec
Secrétaire, Guy Hayart
Conseil des recherches en agro-alimentaire et en pêches du Québec
Secrétaire, Jocelyn Cantin
Conseil des denrées alimentaires du Québec
Secrétaire, Abdesslam Guerch
Comité de références économiques en agriculture du Québec
Secrétaire, Charles White
Conseil en économie et gestion agricoles du Québec
Secrétaire, Charles Lépine
Service d'aide aux organismes et gestion de concours
Directeur, Robert Giasson
Bureau de la répondante à la condition féminine
Responsable, Jocelyne Martell Parisé
Direction de la comptabilité
Directeur, Jacques Mélançon
Direction des approvisionnements et services
Directeur, André Bédard

Direction des ressources financières
Directeur, André Abgral
Service juridique
Directeur, Jean-Paul Dupré
Santé animale
Directeur (p.i.), Denis Sanfaçon
Services des productions animales
1020, rte de l'Eglise, 4ᵉ ét., Ste-Foy, G1V 4P3
Directeur (p.i.), Luc Boutin
Direction des systèmes
Directeur, André Roy
1279, boul. Charest ouest, 6ᵉ ét.
Québec, G1N 4K7
Direction de la vérification interne
Directeur, René Laforte
Direction des ressources humaines
Directeur, Gaston Gaudreau
Direction de la coordination et de l'évaluation
de programmes
Directeur, Jacques Landry
Direction de la gestion et de la conservation
des ressources
Directeur, Gary Coupland
Service du génie
Responsable, Rosemond Caron
Direction des communications
Directrice, Nadine Girardville
Direction de la commercialisation
201, boul. Crémazie, 4ᵉ ét., Montréal, H2M 1L4
Directeur, Yves Proulx
Service des politiques alimentaires
et des relations commerciales
Directeur, Gilles Hains jr.
Direction des marchés extérieurs
Directrice (p.i.), Michelle Lejeune
Direction du développement industriel
Directeur, Gaston Plourde
Direction de l'inspection des produits végétaux
Directeur, Louis Rousseau
Direction de l'inspection des produits carnés
Directeur (p.i.), André Simard
Direction de l'inspection des produits marins
Directeur, Michel Lemay
Direction de l'inspection des aliments à la
consommation
Directeur, Serge Robert
Direction de l'inspection des produits laitiers
Directeur, Gaétan Busque
Direction des laboratoires d'expertises et
d'analyses alimentaires
Directeur, Jacques Boulanger
Direction de la normalisation
Directeur (p.i.), Louis Rousseau
Direction de l'enseignement en agro-alimentaire
1020, rte de l'Eglise, 1ᵉʳ ét., Ste-Foy, G1V 4P3
Directeur, Pascal Van Nieuwenhuyse
*Institut de technologie agro-alimentaire de La
Pocatière*
401, rue Poiré
La Pocatière (Kamouraska), G0R 1Z0
Directeur (p.i.), Jean-Jacques Paradis
*Institut de technologie agro-alimentaire de
St-Hyacinthe*
3230, rue Sicotte, St-Hyacinthe, J2S 2M2
Directeur, Gilles Gauthier

Direction de la recherche agro-alimentaire
2700, rue Einstein, Ste-Foy, G1P 3W8
Directeur, Jean Hébert

DIRECTION GÉNÉRALE DES PÊCHES
MARITIMES
96, montée Sandy Beach, C.P. 1070
Gaspé, G0C 1R0
Direction des services administratifs
Directeur, Jules Poirier
Direction des services aux usagers
Directeur, Jean Carbonneau
Direction de la recherche scientifique et
technique
Directeur, Lucien Poirier

AGENCIES, BOARDS AND COMMISSIONS

MARKETING BOARDS

Marketing boards for agricultural products in Canada are created by a number of different pieces of legislation. National wheat and dairy products plans flow from the *Canadian Wheat Board Act* and the *Canadian Dairy Commission Act* respectively. Egg and poultry boards derive their authority from the *Farm Products Marketing Agencies Act*. As well, many have their own provincial statutes and are normally within the jurisdiction of an umbrella provincial agency. The individual boards are, however, non-governmental and made up largely of elected farmer representatives.

There is also a variety of types. The Economic Council of Canada's study on marketing boards identified five: promotional and developmental boards with little power; selling-desk boards that handle marketing but do not set prices; boards that negotiate prices; boards that set prices; and full-fledged boards that establish quotas. These last are known as supply-management marketing boards. Currently, there are more than 100 active boards in Canada.

RÉGIE DES MARCHÉS AGRICOLES DU
QUÉBEC
201, boul. Crémazie est, Montréal, H2M 1L3

Created by the *Farm Products Marketing Act* (*Loi sur la mise en marché des produits agricoles*), R.S.Q., Chapter M-35, to co-ordinate, supervise, and improve marketing of agricultural farm products, the Quebec Agricultural Marketing Board began operation in 1956.

The general duty of the Board is to promote the orderly, effective, and fair marketing of farm products. For that purpose, it assists in directing farm production. It co-ordinates the various operations of marketing farm products, working with producers, co-operative or professional organizations of farmers, associations of consumers and representatives of industry and commerce, and other persons engaged in marketing farm products.

The Board is composed of not more than seven members, including a chairman and two vice-chairmen, who are appointed by the government for a maximum term of ten years. It has its corporate seat in Montreal and an office in Quebec City.

Président, Gilles Prégent
Vice-présidents: Gilles Le Blanc,
Jean Bertrand, Fernand Beaudet
Secrétaire et conseiller juridique,
Claude Régnier

Centre d'insémination artificielle du Québec (CIAQ) inc.
C.P. 518, St-Hyacinthe, J2S 7B8

Until Aug. 9, 1981, the Centre d'insémination artificielle du Québec (CIAQ) inc. was a division of the Ministère de l'Agriculture, des Pêcheries et de l'Alimentation du Québec. CIAQ became a full subsidiary of the Société québécoise d'initiatives agro-alimentaires (SOQUIA) under legislation passed by the Government of Quebec. It is incorporated under Part 1A of the *Companies Act.*

The primary aim of CIAQ is to encourage the genetic improvement of the Quebec cattle population with the purchase and maximum use of qualified dairy and beef sires. Through CIAQ, artificial insemination is made available to all breeders who wish to develop, at reasonable cost, herds with high genetic potential.

The personnel at CIAQ collect, dilute, put into straws, and freeze the semen of 700 sires housed in its barns. This semen is distributed to all regions of Quebec and also exported to several countries.

Directeur gén., Robert Chicoine

Commission de protection du territoire agricole (CPTAQ)
200A, ch. Ste-Foy, 2e ét., Québec, G1R 4X6

The Commission de protection du territoire agricole, created in 1978, is the body responsible for enforcing the *Act to preserve agricultural land* and the *Act governing the acquisition of farm land by non-residents.*

The purpose of these laws is to preserve for agricultural purposes all lots which, because of their biophysical characteristics and the climatic conditions of the environment, are favourable to agriculture, while at the same time controlling the subdivision of lots and protecting farming districts from intrusion by other land uses.

Président, Pierre-Luc Blain

Commission des courses de chevaux du Québec
51, rue d'Auteuil, Québec, G1R 4C2
Président, Dr. Louis Bernard

Office du crédit agricole
1020, rte de l'Eglise, bur. 500
Ste-Foy, G1V 4P2
General Information: (418) 643-2610

Established in 1936 by the *Farm Credit Act,* R.S.Q., Chapter C-75, the Office du crédit agricole is continued, since August 1988, by the *Act respecting farm financing,* S.Q. 1987, Chapter 86.

The Office is a corporation and a mandatary of the Quebec government. Its powers are the general powers of a corporation and those specific powers defined by the *Act respecting farm financing* and by other Acts administered by the Office.

The Office is comprised of not more than seven members, including a chairman and a vice-chairman. It reports to the Ministre de l'Agriculture, des Pêcheries et de l'Alimentation.

The primary objective of the Office is to further the development of agriculture by making farm financing more readily accessible to family businesses and, in particular, by providing specific measures, including loans and subsidies, to promote the establishment of young farmers so as to ensure the operation of farming businesses in the future. Another objective of the Office is to promote the exploitation of private forests by facilitating access to forestry credit in virtue of the *Act to promote forest credit by private institutions,* R.S.Q., Chapter C-78.1.

Loans approved by authorized lenders within the framework of the Acts administered by the Office are guaranteed by the Fonds d'assurance-prêts agricoles et forestiers, which was established by the *Act on farm and forestry loans insurance,* R.S.Q., Chapter A-29.1.

Président (p.i.), J. Claude Simoneau
Vice-président, J. Claude Simoneau
Secrétaire et conseiller juridique,
Me Charles-Edouard Gagnon
Personnel
Directeur (p.i.), Jean-Denis Riendeau
Direction du financement agricole
Directeur, Jean-Paul Tremblay
Direction du financement forestier
Directeur, Michel Pleau
Service juridique
Directeur, Me Jean-Louis Boucher
Service financier
Directeur, Pierre Simard
Service de la recherche et de la planification
Directeur, Julien Burns
Service de la gestion des systèmes
Directeur, Jean Roberge

Régie des assurances agricoles du Québec
113, rue St-Georges ouest, Lévis, G6V 4L2

The mandate of the Quebec Agricultural Insurance Board is as follows:

• to establish and administer the crop insurance programs that offset severe decreases in yield due to weather, insects, and other effects of nature. The cost of administering these programs is completely subsidized by the Quebec and federal governments, with 50 per cent of the premium paid by the producer and 50 per cent shared equally between the two governments; and

• to administer the income stabilization insurance scheme which offsets large market price decreases, guaranteeing farmers a positive annual income. The administrative costs are completely subsidized by the Quebec government. One third of the premium is paid by the producer and the other two thirds by the Quebec government.

P.-D.G., Michel R. Saint-Pierre
Vice-présidents: Guy Blanchet, Norbert Dubé
Secrétaire, Jean-Marc Lafrance

Société québécoise d'initiatives agro-alimentaires (SOQUIA)
2, parc Samuel-Holland, bur. 284
Québec, G1S 4S5
General Information: (418) 643-1580

SOQUIA is a Crown corporation established by the Quebec government in 1975 to assist in the development of the Quebec food and fish industries.

As shareholders, associated companies in SOQUIA may purchase preferred stocks, grant loans or guarantees to companies of which it is a shareholder, or provide technical advice to partner companies. It may also undertake feasibility and profitability studies concerning new ventures.

SOQUIA's board of directors is composed of executives from the private sector as well as senior civil servants.

Président, Jean Guilbault
Vice-président et directeur gén.,
William Lacoursière
Finance et administration
Directeur, André Cloutier
Services juridiques
Directeur, Denis Héroux

MINISTÈRE DES APPROVISIONNEMENTS ET SERVICES

(Supply and Services)
Complexe G, 7e ét.
1045, rue de la Chevrotière, Québec, G1R 5L4

CABINET DU MINISTRE
Ministre, L'hon. Gilles Rocheleau

CABINET DU SOUS-MINISTRE
Sous-ministre, Jean-Marc Bard
Sous-ministre adj., directeur gén. de la gestion des contrats et services,
Germain Halley
Sous-ministre adj., directeur gén. des services immobiliers et des relations avec les organismes, Jacques Privé

MINISTÈRE
Direction des communications,
Edward Collister
Directeur de l'administration, André Taillon
Ressources humaines
Directeur, André Caron
Ressources financières et matérielles
Directeur, Jean Tremblay
Systèmes de gestion

Directeur, Serge Cloutier
Directeur des contrats, Jacques Lafrance
Services gouvernementaux
Directeur, Richard Dumas

DIRECTION GÉNÉRALE DES APPROVISIONNEMENTS
150, boul. St-Cyrille est, 8e ét.
Québec, G1R 5K4
Directeur gén., Jean-Claude Careau
Directeur des opérations, Paul Plamondon
Gestion des biens
Directeur, Roland Cloutier
Développement
Directeur, Denis Corriveau
Contrôleur des assurances, Pierre Blais

AGENCIES, BOARDS AND COMMISSIONS

Bureau de la protection civile du Québec
1200, rte de l'Eglise, Ste-Foy, G1V 4M1
Directeur gén. (p.i.), Germain Halley
Plans et opérations
Directeur, Laval Côté
Recherche et développement
Directeur, Pierre Brien
Secrétaire, Alain Lauzier
Communications
Directeur, Pierre Doyle
Administration
Directeur, André Parent
Service juridique et programmes d'assistance financière
Directeur, Me Pierre Lavoie

Régie des installations olympiques
4141, av. Pierre-de-Coubertin
Montréal, H1V 3N7
General Information (activities, events, complaints, lost and found): (514) 252-4400

The Régie des installations olympiques is a mandatary corporation of the government of Quebec, incorporated by the Quebec National Assembly under *an Act to incorporate the Régie des installations olympiques,* S.Q. 1975, Chapter 72.

The Régie was subsequently mandated to operate the Olympic installations, the Olympic Village (S.Q. 1976, Chapter 43) and the Centre Paul Sauvé (S.Q. 1978, Chapter 83).

The Régie's revenue is primarily used for its operations. Any excess funds are to be used for the repayment of loans, advances, or other obligations of the Régie concerning the completion of the Olympic installations. The Special Olympic Fund, which was amassed out of a portion of the Quebec tax on tobacco, was created for this repayment. As soon as these loans, advances, and obligations of the Olympic Park are satisfied, the installations of the Olympic Park will become the property of the City of Montreal.

P.-D.G., Jean Deschamps
Directions supérieures:
Affaires juridiques

Secrétaire et vice-présidente, Mireille Zigby
Marketing
Vice-président, Guy Morin
Administration
Trésorier et vice-président, Jean-Pierre Payette
Construction
Vice-président, Serge Talbot
Exploitation
Vice-président, Robert Thériault
DIRECTION DES SERVICES À LA CLIENTÈLE
Stade, Vélodrome, Centre Paul Sauvé et piscines
Directeur, Daniel Legros
Village olympique
Directeur, Guy Lapointe

Société immobilière du Québec
475, rue St-Amable, 7e ét., Québec, G1R 4X9

The Société immobilière du Québec was established by the *Act respecting the Société immobilière du Québec*, R.S.Q., Chapter S-17.1, adopted on Dec. 21, 1983. It is responsible for profitably and efficiently providing government agencies with premises suited to their needs.

To this end, it assumes the powers and obligations of a real estate manager. It is responsible for building, purchasing, renting, and improving buildings required by departments and agencies designated by the government. Like other landlords, it must also administer, maintain, and ensure the preservation of its buildings.

Upon request, the SIQ may also administer real estate owned by its clients and extend the same advantages and services to other public or parapublic agencies.

P.-D.G., Miville Vachon
Secrétaire corporatif et adj. au président, Michel Hébert
Vice-président, construction, Guy Vachon
Vice-président, opérations immobilières, Guy Bisson
Vice-président, affaires immobilières, Michel Salvas
Vice-président, finances et administration, Pierre Prémont
Contrôleur corporatif, Gilles Baribeau

MINISTÈRE DU COMMERCE EXTÉRIEUR ET DU DÉVELOPPEMENT TECHNOLOGIQUE

(Trade and Technological Development)
875, Grande-Allée est, éd. H, 3e ét.
Québec, G1R 4Y8
Place Mercantile, 6e-7e et 10e ét.
770, rue Sherbrooke ouest, Montréal, H3A 1G1

CABINET DU MINISTRE
Ministre, L'hon. Pierre MacDonald

BUREAU DU SOUS-MINISTRE
Sous-ministre, Marcel Bergeron

Sous-ministre assoc. aux relations extra-ministérielles, Florian Rompré
Sous-ministre adj. aux opérations, Pierre Coulombe

DIRECTION GÉNÉRALE DE L'ADMINISTRATION
Directeur gén., Raynald Brûlotte
Direction des communications
Directrice, Janine Beaulieu

DIRECTION GÉNÉRALE DE LA PROSPECTION DES INVESTISSEMENTS
Directeur gén., Paul Lussier
DIRECTION GÉNÉRALE DES PROGRAMMES D'AIDE
Directeur gén., Harold Mailhot
DIRECTION GÉNÉRALE DE LA TECHNOLOGIE
Directeur gén., Jean-E. Bouchard

DIRECTION GÉNÉRALE DES RELATIONS ÉCONOMIQUES AVEC L'EXTÉRIEUR
Directeur gén., François Paradis
Direction de la coopération économique
Directeur, Peter Dunn
Direction de la coordination géographique
Directeur, Claude Beaudry
Direction des études et analyses
Directeur, Gérald Audet

DIRECTION GÉNÉRALE DE LA POLITIQUE COMMERCIALE
Directeur gén., Carl Grenier

DIRECTION GÉNÉRALE DES OPÉRATIONS DE PROMOTION
Directeur gén., Paul-Emile Blouin
Direction des foires et des expositions
Directeur, Michel Dagenais
Direction des missions
Directrice, Micheline Fortin

FOREIGN REPRESENTATIVES:

CANADA
Edmonton
Bureau du Québec
Highfield Place Bldg., 10th Flr., 10010-106th St.
Edmonton, T5J 3L8
Conseiller économique, Bertin Tremblay
Toronto
Bureau du gouvernement du Québec
20 Queen St. W., Ste. 1004, Box 13
Toronto, M5H 3S3
Conseiller économique, Maurice Lalonde

UNITED STATES
Atlanta
Bureau du Québec
Peachtree Ctr. Tower, Ste. 1501
230 Peachtree St. N.W., Atlanta, GA 30303
Directeur, Réginald Bourgeois
Boston
Délégation du Québec
Exchange Pl., 19th Flr.
53 State St., Boston, MA 02109 U.S.A.
Conseiller économique, Yvon Bergeron

Chicago
Délégation du Québec
35 East Wacker Dr., Ste. 2052
Chicago, IL 60601 U.S.A.
Conseiller économique, Pierre Dionne
Los Angeles
Délégation du Québec
700 S. Flower St., Ste. 1520
Los Angeles, CA 90017 U.S.A.
Conseiller économique, Richard Tremblay
New York
Délégation générale du Québec
17 W. 50th St., Rockefeller Ctr.
New York, NY 10020-2201 U.S.A.
Conseiller économique, André Migneault

EUROPE
Dusseldorf
Bureau du Québec, service economique
Königsallee 30, Kö-Center
4000 Dusseldorf 1, Bundesrepublik Deutschland
Directeur, André Sirois
London
Délégation générale du Québec
59 Pall Mall, London SW 1Y 5JH, England
Conseiller économique, Herman Vyncke
Brussels
Délégation générale du Québec
Av. des Arts 46, 7ᵉ ét.
1040 Bruxelles, Belgique
Conseiller économique, Louis Granger
Paris
Délégation générale du Québec
66, rue Pergolèse, 75116 Paris, France
Directeur, Jean-Paul Ruszkowski
Milan
Délégation du Québec
Via Piccinni no. 2, 4o piano
20131 Milano, Italia
Conseiller économique, Vacant
Stockholm
Bureau du Québec
Rema Kontorshotell AB
Hantverkargatan 7, Box 22114
104 22 Stockholm, Sverige
Directeur, Pierre-G. Bélanger

LATIN AMERICA
Bogota
Bureau du Québec
Edificio Profinanzas, Carrera 01
74-08, Piso 5, Oficina 505, Bogota, Colombia
Directrice, Michelle Bussières
Caracas
Bureau du Québec
Edificio ABA, Piso 4, A.P. 2736
Calle Veracruz, Las Mercedes
Caracas 1010A, Venezuela
Directeur, Alain Bardoux
Mexico
Délégation générale du Québec
Avenida Taine 411
Colonia Bosques de Chapultepec
11580 México, D.F.
Conseiller économique, Jean Cogné

ASIA
Hong Kong
Délégation du Québec
Admiralty Ctr., Twr. 1, Ste. 1716
18 Harcourt Rd., Hong Kong
Conseiller économique, Jean-Pierre Guay
Singapore
Bureau du Québec
The Octagon, 105 Cecil St., No. 12-02
Singapore 0106
Directeur, Dominique Bonifacio
Tokyo
Délégation du Québec
Kojimachi Hiraoka Bldg., 5th Flr.
1-3 Kojimachi Chiyoda-Ku, Tokyo 100, Japan
Conseiller économique, Marcel Merlen

MINISTÈRE DES COMMUNAUTÉS CULTURELLES ET DE L'IMMIGRATION

(Cultural Communities and Immigration)
360, rue McGill, Montréal, H2Y 2E9
General Information: (514) 873-2445
Ed. G, Aile Conroy, 2ᵉ ét.
1056, rue Conroy, Québec, G1R 5E6
General Information: (418) 643-1850

CABINET DE LA MINISTRE
Ministre, L'hon. Louise Robic

BUREAU DU SOUS-MINISTRE
Sous-ministre, Norman Riddell
Sous-ministre assoc., Nicole Brodeur
Sous-ministre adj., Laurette C. Robillard

DIRECTIONS FONCTIONNELLES
Direction de l'administration
Directrice, Michelle Rivard
Direction des communications
Directrice (p.i.), Michelle Rivard
Direction des ressources humaines
Directeur, Pierre-Paul Clermont
Direction de la planification et de l'évaluation
Directeur, Paul Simard
Service juridique
Responsable, Me Michel Jarry

DIRECTION GÉNÉRALE DU RECRUTEMENT ET DE LA SÉLECTION
Direction des services aux investisseurs
Directeur (p.i.), Raynald Joubarne
Direction des services de sélection à l'étranger
Directeur, Bernard de Jaham
Division des renseignements aux
candidats à l'immigration
Responsable, Yvon Guérin
Direction des services de sélection au Québec
Directeur, Yvan Turcotte
Responsable, Lucie Boudreau
Direction des étudiants des garants et des travailleurs
Directeur, Marcel Vaillancourt

Division des étudiants
Responsable, Jean-Paul Normand
Division des garants
Responsable, Michel Béliveau
Division des travailleurs
Responsable, Denis Auclair

DIRECTION GÉNÉRALE DES COMMUNAUTÉS
CULTURELLES ET DES SERVICES AUX
IMMIGRANTS
Direction de l'adaptation
Directrice (p.i.), Madeleine Lussier
Service de l'accueil
Responsable, Micheline Brunet
Service d'évaluation et de référence scolaire et
professionnelle
Chef de service, Marcel Bougie
Direction des communautés culturelles
Directrice, Madeleine Lussier
Direction de la formation linguistique
Directeur, Roger Thériault
Secrétariat de l'administration des ententes de
sécurité sociale (SAESS)
Coordonnateur, Yves Chagnon

AGENCIES, BOARDS AND COMMISSIONS

**Conseil des communautés culturelles et de
l'immigration du Québec (CCCI)**
800, place Victoria, 4ᵉ ét.
C.P. 158, succ. Tour de la Bourse
Montréal, H4Z 1C3

The law establishing the Quebec Council on
Cultural Communities and Immigration was
passed Dec. 21, 1984 and took effect on April 1,
1985.

The Council is composed of 15 members
appointed by the government. These include a
president and two vice-presidents: one for cultural community affairs and the other responsible for
immigration.

The Council's purpose is to advise the Minister
of Cultural Communities and Immigration regarding these two areas, and to respond to any
requests from the minister for advice. The Council
may make public its recommendations. Further,
upon request or with the minister's approval, it
may set up special committees to study particular
questions. The Council may consult, carry out or
commission research, solicit opinions, accept
requests, and refer to the minister any matter
concerning cultural communities and immigration that requires the government's attention or
action.

Présidente, J.R. Westmoreland-Traoré
Vice-présidente aux communautés
culturelles, Raymonde Folco
Vice-président à l'immigration,
Raymond Paquin
Secrétaire, Jacques Johnson

MINISTÈRE DES COMMUNICATIONS

(Communications)
1037, rue de la Chevrotière
Ed. G, (Tour), 3ᵉ ét., Québec, G1R 4Y7
General Information: (418) 643-1529

CABINET DU MINISTRE
Ministre, L'hon. Richard D. French

BUREAU DU SOUS-MINISTRE
Sous-ministre, Jacques Pigeon
Direction générale de la coordination et des
politiques
Directeur gén., Pierre Lampron
Direction générale de l'administration
Directeur gén., Eric Martin
Direction du service de la comptabilité
Directeur, Pierre Rompré
Direction des ressources financières
Directeur, Richard Sirois
Direction des ressources matérielles
Directeur, Emile Loranger
Direction de l'évaluation et de la vérification
interne
Directeur, Donald Grenier
Direction des systèmes d'information et de
l'innovation
Directeur, Thong Tran Van
Direction des ressources humaines
Directeur, Jean-Claude Kirouac
Direction des communications
Directeur, Gilles Tremblay

Direction générale des médias
Sous-ministre adj., Claude Beausoleil
Directeur général, François-C. Reny
Direction générale des publications
gouvernementales
Directeur gén., Jean-Paul Gagné
Direction générale des médias,
Directeur gén., Serge Thibaudeau
Direction générale des communications
Directrice gén., Monique L. Bégin

Technologies
Sous-ministre adj., Jean-Pierre Delwasse
Direction générale de l'informatique
Directeur gén., Bernard Beauchemin
Direction générale des télécommunications
Directeur gén., Eric Martin
Direction générale des technologies de
l'information
Directrice gén., Monique Charbonneau

AGENCIES, BOARDS AND COMMISSIONS

Commission d'accès à l'information
900, place d'Youville, bur. 720
Québec, G1R 3P7
General Information: (418) 643-5544

The Commission d'accès à l'information is an
administrative court created in June 1982 by the
Act respecting access to documents held by

public bodies and the protection of personal information, R.S.Q., Chapter A-2.1. The Act established two new rights: access to the documents held by public bodies and access by an individual to personal information kept on him.

An individual wishing to gain access to a document or to personal information kept on him, or to have any corrections made, must submit a request in writing to the person in charge of that particular body. This person has 20 days in which to reply; if the request is denied, in whole or in part, an appeal can be made to the Commission, in writing, within 30 days. The Commission's decisions are executory, but are subject to appeal in provincial court.

Président, Me Jacques O'Bready
Commissaires:
Thérèse Giroux, Carole-Lynne Wallace
Secrétaire et directeur du service
juridique, André Ouimet
Directeur de l'analyse et de l'évaluation,
Clarence Whyte

Régie des télécommunications du Québec
2875, boul. Laurier, bur. 1200
Ste-Foy, G1V 2M2
General Information: (418) 643-5560

The Régie des télécommunications du Québec is responsible for supervising and regulating public communications companies in Quebec. In this capacity, it has exclusive jurisdiction over 18 Quebec telephone firms and pay TV, and it evaluates the educational character of Radio-Québec's programming.

The purpose of the Régie is:

- to make available high-quality telecommunications services throughout the province;
- to ensure that tariffs are fair and reasonable;
- to standardize telecommunications charges throughout the province;
- to balance the interests of users and owners when regulating costs; and
- continuing and expanding telecommunications services to promote local and regional economic development.

The Régie is made up of a president, a vice-president and one full-time member, all appointed for terms of not over five years. As well, up to two part-time members may also be appointed.

Président, André Dufour
Vice-président, Claude Simard, avocat
Régisseurs:
Jean-Marc Demers, avocat
Jean-Claude Duchesne, ing.
J. Ronald Tennet, ing.
Secrétaire de la Régie,
Jean-Guy Paquet, avocat
Directeurs:
Economique et tarification, Louis-Philippe Milot
Ingénierie, Jean-Pierre Gauvreau
Information, Patrick Thériault
Administration et programmation, Pierre Piché

Société de Radio-Télévision du Québec (Radio-Québec)
800, rue Fullum, Montréal, H2K 3L7
General Information: (514) 521-2424

Radio-Québec is a para-governmental organization. Its mandate is to manage an educational and cultural television network throughout the province of Quebec.

P.-D.G., Françoise Bertrand
Administration et technique
Vice-président (p.i.), Alain Dufour
Programmation
Vice-président, Pierre Roy
Direction juridique
Secrétaire gén. et directrice juridique,
Madeleine Leduc
Conseiller juridique, M.-C. Beaudry
Service des relations publiques
Adjoint à la p.-d.g. et chef de service
des relations publiques, André Beaudet
Ressources humaines
Directrice, Carmen Bourque
Direction des acquisitions et des coproductions
Directeur, André de Bellefeuille
Direction des services à la programmation
Directeur, Paul Breton
Direction de la planification de la
programmation
Directeur, Kees Vanderheyden
Direction de la TV éducative formelle (DTEF)
Directeur, André Chamberland
Direction de la réalisation
Directrice, Nicole Le Blanc
Direction du réseau et des aménagements
Directeur, Yvon Malo
Exploitation
Directeur, Vacant
Direction des finances et de l'administration
Directeur (p.i.), Roberto Luca
Marketing
Directeur, Jean-Louis Nadeau
Direction des activités régionales
Directeur, Daniel Beauchesne

CONSEIL DU TRÉSOR

(Treasury Board)
Edifice André Laurendeau
1050, rue St-Augustin, Québec, G1R 5A4

CABINET DU MINISTRE
*Président du Conseil et ministre délégué
à l'Administration,* L'hon. Daniel Johnson

SECRÉTAIRE DU CONSEIL
Secrétaire, Denis Bédard
Greffier, Michel Crevier
Greffier adj. et chef des services
administratifs, Louise Roy
Directeur, Réjean Thellend

Secteur des politiques de gestion
Secrétaire adj., Bruno Grégoire

Direction des politiques de gestion de l'information et des technologies de l'information
Directeur, Martial Lemay
Service de l'analyse des dossiers des technologies de l'information
Chef de service, Guy Ahern
Direction des politiques de gestion des biens et des services
Directeur (p.i.), Paul Périard
Service des études et des analyses
Chef de service (p.i.), Johanne St-Cyr
Direction des politiques de gestion financière et de contrôle des effectifs
Directeur, Marcel Rhéaume
Service des systèmes de gestion budgétaire, financière et comptable
Chef de service, Bernard Gayraud
Secrétariat permanent du comité consultatif en matière de vérification interne
Secrétaire, Michel Racine
Service d'étude et de développement des politiques de gestion
Chef de service, Claude Lamonde
Centre d'information de gestion
Chef de service, Ho Van Hap Guy

Secteur des politiques budgétaires
Secrétaire adj., André Dicaire
Direction de la planification et des systèmes budgétaires
Directeur, Michel Bordeleau
Service des études et des prévisions budgétaires
Chef de service, Paul-Emile Arsenault
Direction des programmes administratifs
Directrice, Louise Pagé
Service des programmes municipaux
Chef de service, François Côté
Service des programmes administratifs
Chef de service, Lucy Wells
Direction des programmes économiques
Directeur, Gilbert Delage
Chef de service, Yves Lessard
Chef de service, Vacant
Direction des programmes sociaux et de santé
Directeur, Léandre Nadeau
Service des programmes sociaux
Chef de service, François Turenne
Service des programmes de santé
Chef de service, Diane Jean
Direction des programmes éducatifs et culturels
Directeur, Alain Bruneau
Service de l'éducation et des affaires culturelles
Chef de service, Bernard Guay
Service de l'enseignement supérieur et des communications
Chef de service, Mario Laliberté

Secteur des politiques de personnel et des relations de travail
Secrétaire assoc., Michel Crête
Directeur, André G. Savard
Direction des politiques de personnel d'encadrement

Directeur, Réjean Villeneuve
Directeur adj., André Leclerc
Direction des conditions de travail et des politiques de personnel
Directeur, Jacques S. Roy
Service des conditions de travail et des régimes collectifs
Chef de service, Jacques Thibault
Service de l'accès à l'égalité
Chef de service, Clémence Veillette
Services des politiques de personnel
Chef de service, Claude Tremblay
Direction des politiques de rémunération et de classification
Directeur, Yvan Cossette
Service de la rémunération
Chef de service, Jean-Pierre Bérubé
Service de la classification
Chef de service, Richard Tanguay
Service d'étude, d'analyse et de comparaison de marché
Chef de service, Vacant

Relations de travail
Secrétaire adj., Gilles Filion
Service juridique
Directeur, Jacques Bergeron
Direction des relations de travail
Directeur, Georges-Noël Fortin
Service des relations de travail (Fonction publique)
Chef de service, Pierre Boudreault
Service de la coordination et des organismes
Chef de service, Jean-Yves Baril
Greffe des tribunaux d'arbitrage (Fonction publique)
Chef de service, Reina Denis

MINISTÈRE DE L'ÉDUCATION

(Education)
1035, rue de la Chevrotière
Québec, G1R 5A5
General Information: (418) 643-7095

CABINET DU MINISTRE
Ministre, L'hon. Claude Ryan

BUREAU DU SOUS-MINISTRE
Sous-ministre, Thomas J. Boudreau
Sous-ministre assoc., catholique, Michel Stein
Sous-ministre assoc., protestant, Ann Schlutz
Secrétaire gén., Jacques Lamarche
Direction de la vérification interne
Directeur, J.M. Verreault
Direction des relations extérieures
Directeur, Roger Haeberlé
Coordination des activités en milieux amérindien et inuit
Directeur, Jean-Paul Olivier
Direction de l'enseignement catholique
Directrice, Micheline Lavallée
Direction de l'enseignement protestant
Directeur, Ross Davidson

Direction de la comptabilité
Directeur, Roger Morin
Service juridique
Directeur, Marcel Blanchet

Secteur des réseaux
Sous-ministre adj., Jean-Claude Rondeau
Direction générale de l'éducation des adultes
Directeur, Valmont Richard
Direction générale de l'enseignement privé
Directeur (p.i.), Pauline C. Lesage
Direction générale des services
administratifs aux réseaux
Directeur gén., Henri Tardif
Direction de la coordination des reseaux
Directrice, Alberte Décarie
Services éducatifs aux anglophones
Directeur, Keith Fitzpatrick

Secteur de la planification et du développement pédagogique
Sous-ministre adj., Jean-Claude Cadieux
Direction générale de la recherche
et du développement
Directeur, Jacques Babin
Direction générale de l'évaluation
et des ressources didactiques
Directeur, Paul Vachon
Direction générale des programmes
Directeur, Maurice Morand
Coordination à la condition féminine
Directrice, Lisette Bédard

Secteur de l'administration
Sous-ministre adj., Michel Paquet
Direction générale des ressources
informationnelles
Directeur, Michel Bédard
Direction des ressources humaines
Directeur, Carole Pelletier
Direction des ressources matérielles
Directeur, Marcel Therrien
Direction générale du financement
Directeur, Rejean Morel
Direction des communications
Directrice, Suzanne Beaulieu
Direction de la formation à distance
Directeur, Ovila Gaudreault

Secteur des relations de travail (réseaux)
Sous-ministre adj., Jean-Guy Gagnon
Direction générale des ressources humaines
(réseaux)
Directeur, Michel Bergeron

AGENCIES, BOARDS AND COMMISSIONS

Commission consultative de l'enseignement privé
1035, de la Chevrotière, éd. G, 11e ét.
Québec, G1R 5A5

The Commission consultative de l'enseignement privé is an advisory body established in March 1969 under the law governing private education, which was adopted in December 1968.

The Commission is composed of nine members appointed for a two-year term by the government on recommendation of the Minister of Education. At least six of the members are appointed after consultation with the groups most representative of the directors, teachers, and parents of pupils in the private-school sector.

The minister must obtain the Commission's advice on all matters required by law: permits, declarations of public interest, recognitions for purposes of grants, revocations, suspensions, or changes in status, etc. The Commission, in turn, must submit an annual report on its activities, including a list of all the requests it has received and all of its recommendations.

Président, Paul-Aimé Paiement
Secrétaire, Jacques Marois

Commission d'appel sur la langue d'enseignement
1035, rue de la Chevrotière, 12e ét.
Québec, G1R 5A5
Président, Jean-Marie Beauchemin

Conseil supérieur de l'éducation
2050, boul. St-Cyrille ouest, 4e ét.
Ste-Foy, G1V 2K8

The Conseil supérieur de l'éducation, a consulting organization working in conjunction with the Minister of Education and the Minister of Higher Education and Science, was created by the legislature in 1964 (R.S.Q., Chapter C-60). The Council exercises its responsibilities in three main areas:

1) it advises the Minister of Education on the Regulations which he must submit to the Council;
2) it provides advice to the ministers on any question they refer to it; and
3) it submits to the Minister of Education an annual report on its activities and on the state of educational needs, which he in turn submits to the National Assembly.

The Council also: solicits opinions, and receives requests or suggestions from the public on educational matters; submits recommendations on any educational concerns to the minister; and enacts Regulations for the Council's internal board, which are in turn submitted to the government for its consideration.

Président, Pierre Lucier
Vice-président, Vacant
Secrétaire, Jean Proulx
Secrétaire conjoint, Alain Durand

MINISTÈRE DE L'ÉNERGIE ET DES RESSOURCES

(Energy and Natural Resources)
200, ch. Ste-Foy, 7e ét., Québec, G1R 4X7
General Information: (418) 643-8060
Fax: (418) 643-0720; Telex: 0512274

BUREAU DE MONTRÉAL
3, place Desjardins
Tour du Nord, bur. 2659, Montréal, H5B 1B3
General Information: (514) 873-6796
Fax: (514) 873-6780

CABINET DU MINISTRE
200, ch. Ste-Foy, 6ᵉ ét., Québec, G1R 4X7
Ministre, L'hon. John Ciaccia

CABINET DU MINISTRE DÉLÉGUÉ AUX FORÊTS
200, ch. Ste-Foy, 6ᵉ ét., Québec, G1R 4X7
Ministre, L'hon. Albert Côté

CABINET DU MINISTRE DÉLÉGUÉ AUX MINES ET AUX AFFAIRES AUTOCHTONES
1620, boul. de l'Entente, bur. 2.04
Québec, G1S 4N6
Ministre, L'hon. Raymond Savoie
Affaires autochtones
875, av. Grande-Allée est, bur. 2.718
Québec, G1R 4Y8

CABINET DU SOUS-MINISTRE
Sous-ministre, Pierre Sarault
Bureau du coordonnateur aux affaires autochtones
Coordonnateur, Bernard Arsenault
Direction de la comptabilité
Directeur, Patrick W. Desbiens
Direction des affaires juridiques
Directeur (p.i.), Jean Giroux
Direction de la vérification interne
5555, Troisième av. ouest, 4ᵉ ét.
Charlesbourg, G1H 6R1
Directeur, Alain Chassé

Administration
Sous-ministre adj., Jean Renaud Poirier
Direction des communications
Directrice (p.i.), Danielle Paré
Direction des sociétés d'Etat et
de la planification
Directrice, Louise Ouellet

DIRECTION GÉNÉRALE DES RESSOURCES HUMAINES ET MATÉRIELLES
Directeur gén., Vacant
Direction des ressources humaines
Directeur, Serge Tourangeau
Direction des ressources matérielles
5555, Troisième av. ouest, 4ᵉ ét.
Charlesbourg, G1H 6R1
Directeur, Jean-Claude Legault

DIRECTION GÉNÉRALE DES RESSOURCES FINANCIÈRES ET INFORMATIONNELLES
Directeur gén., Michel Després
Service de la gestion des documents
Chef, René Fortin
Direction du budget
Directeur, Louis-Gilles Picard
Direction des services et systèmes financiers

Directeur, Marcel Lambert
Direction des technologies de l'information
Directeur, André Belley
Direction de la gestion des ressources informationnelles
Directeur, Pierre Leclerc

Energie
8, rue Cook, Québec, G1R 5H2
Sous-ministre assoc., François Geoffrion
Conseiller spécial, Claude Y. Turgeon
Coordonnateur des relations intergouvernementales, Michel Marcouiller
Conseillers des relations intergouvernementales,
Patrice de la Brosse, Carl Boileau

DIRECTION GÉNÉRALE DE L'ANALYSE ÉCONOMIQUE ET FINANCIÈRE
Directeur gén., J.-P. Pellegrin
Direction des prix et des études financières
Directeur, Roch Veilleux
Direction des politiques et des études économiques
Directeur, Claude Desjarlais
Direction des études structurelles et des informations statistiques
Directeur, Florent Côté
Groupe de l'analyse quantitative
Responsable, Roger Corbeil

DIRECTION GÉNÉRALE DES ÉNERGIES CONVENTIONNELLES
Directeur gén., Vacant
Direction de l'aménagement des forces hydrauliques et de l'exploration
Directrice, Michèle Laberge
Direction de la distribution
Directeur, Jean Servais
Direction des hydrocarbures
Directeur, Pierre Lavallée
Direction de l'électricité
Directeur, Gaby Polisois

DIRECTION GÉNÉRALE DES ÉCONOMIES D'ÉNERGIE ET DU DÉVELOPPEMENT DES ÉNERGIES NOUVELLES
Directeur gén., Denis Baribeau
Bureau de l'efficacité énergétique
425, av. Viger ouest, bur. 600
Montreal, H2Z 1W9
Directeur, Sohel Zariffa
Direction des technologies et des énergies nouvelles
Directeur, Guy Bouchard

Forêts
200, ch. Ste-Foy, Québec, G1R 4X7
Sous-ministre assoc., Gilbert G. Paillé
Secrétariat aux politiques administratives
Secrétaire, Jacques Caron
Service administratif
Chef, Jean-Louis Bussières
Groupe d'implantation du régime forestier

Ingénieur forestier, Emile Ouellet
Direction de la planification
Directeur, Robert Deffrasnes
Direction du développement industriel
Directeur, Jean-Paul Gilbert

Direction générale des opérations régionales
Sous-ministre adj. et directeur gén.,
Bernard Harvey

DIRECTIONS RÉGIONALES:
Bas-St-Laurent—Gaspésie et
Iles-de-la-Madeleine
405, boul. St-Germain ouest
Rimouski, G5L 3N5
Administrateur, Pierre Cornellier
Saguenay—Lac-St-Jean
3950, boul. Harvey, Jonquière, G7X 8L6
Administrateur, Marc-André Turgeon
Québec
1995, boul. Charest ouest, Ste-Foy, G1N 4H9
Administrateur, Yvon Fortin
Trois-Rivières
100, rue Laviolette, 2e ét.
Trois-Rivières, G9A 5S9
Administrateur, Gaston Côté
Estrie
1335, rue King ouest, bur. 300
Sherbrooke, J1J 2B8
Administrateur, Gaétan Côté
Montréal
800, boul. de Maisonneuve est, bur. 1150
Montréal, H2L 4L8
Administrateur, Louis-René Pedneault
Outaouais
170, rue Hôtel-de-Ville, bur. 7340
Hull, J8X 4C2
Administrateur, Jacques Robitaille
Abitibi-Témiscamingue
70, boul. Québec, Rouyn-Noranda, J9X 6R1
Administrateur, Henrico Laberge
Côte-Nord
625, boul. Laflèche, bur. 1.100
Baie-Comeau, G5C 1C5
Administrateur, Roger Lafrance

Direction générale des forêts
Sous-ministre adj. et directeur gén.,
Rémy Girard
Direction de la sylviculture
Directeur, Yvon Martin
50, rue St-Jean, 3e ét., Québec, G1R 1N5
Direction de l'aménagement forestier
Directeur, Gilles Geoffroy
Direction de la forêt privée et des coopératives
forestières
785, av. de Salaberry, 4e ét., Québec, G1R 2T8
Directeur, Fernand Côté
Direction du bois
Directeur, Laurent Marois
Direction de la conservation des forêts
Directeur, Guy Boissinot
5555, Troisième av. ouest, 4e ét.
Charlesbourg, G1H 6R1

Direction de la recherche et du développement
Directeur, Claude Godbout
2700, rue Einstein, bur. B.1.185A
Ste-Foy, G1P 3W8

Mines
1620, boul. de l'Entente, Québec, G1S 4N6
Sous-ministre assoc., Onil Roy
Direction politique et évaluation
Directeur, Gilles Mahoney
Service de la statistique et du secrétariat
des opérations
Chef, Denise Malo

DIRECTION GÉNÉRALE DE L'INDUSTRIE
MINÉRALE
Directeur gén., Yvan Godbout
Direction des redevances et titres miniers
Directeur, Raymond Boutin
Direction de l'analyse économique
et du développement minier
Directeur, Jacques Lebuis

Direction générale de l'exploration géologique
et minérale
Sous-ministre adj. et directeur gén.,
Robert Lamarche
Direction de l'assistance à l'exploration minière
Directeur, André Bissonnette
Direction de la recherche géologique
Directeur, Jean-Louis Caty
Service géologique de Québec
Chef, Jules Cimon

DIVISIONS:
Division de Ste-Anne-des-Monts
10, boul. Ste-Anne ouest, C.P. 697
Ste-Anne-des-Monts, G0E 2G0
Géologue résident et resp., Gilles Duquette
Division de Sherbrooke
740, rue Galt ouest, bur. 112
Sherbrooke, J1H 1Z3
Géologue résident et resp., Serge Lachance
Division de Montréal
2100, rue Drummond, bur. 240
Montréal, H3G 1X1
Géologue résident et resp., Yvon Globensky
Division de Sept-Iles
456, rue Arnaud, bur. 1.04
Sept-Iles, G4R 3B1
Géologue résident et resp., Pierre Marcoux
Service géologique du Nord-Ouest
400, boul. Lamaque, Val-d'Or, J9P 3L4
Chef, Alain Simard
Division de Chibougamau
375, Troisième rue, bur. 2
Chibougamau, G8P 1N4
Géologue résident et resp., André Gobeil
Division de Rouyn-Noranda
Complexe Théberge
19, rue Perreault ouest, bur. 330
Rouyn-Noranda, J9X 6N5
Géologue résident et resp., Maurice Rive
Division de Val-d'Or
874, Troisième av., Val-d'Or, J9P 1T1
Géologue résident et resp., Denis Racicot

DIRECTION GÉNÉRALE DU CENTRE DE
RECHERCHES MINÉRALES
2700, rue Einstein, Ste-Foy, G1P 3W8
Directeur gén., Jacques Saint-Cyr
Direction de l'analyse minérale
Directeur, Marc Pichette
Direction de la recherche métallurgique
Directeur, Alain Claveau

**Terres et direction générale du domaine
territorial**
200, ch. Ste-Foy, Québec, G1R 4X7
Sous-ministre assoc. et directeur gén.,
Antonio Sergi
Direction des relevés techniques
1995, boul Charest ouest, Ste-Foy, G1N 4H9
Directeur, Claude de St-Riquier
Direction des levés fonciers
Directeur, Normand Jobidon
Direction de la gestion du territoire
Directeur (p.i.), Réal Perron
Centre d'information géographique
et foncière
Chef, Pierre Leblanc
1995, boul. Charest ouest, Ste-Foy, G1N 4H9

AGENCIES, BOARDS AND COMMISSIONS

Hydro-Québec
75, boul. René-Lévesque ouest
Montréal, H2Z 1A4
General Information: (514) 289-2211

Hydro-Québec, created in 1944, is a government-owned electrical utility that ensures the
generation, transmission, and distribution of
electricity throughout Quebec. The utility has five
wholly owned subsidiaries, including the Société
d'énergie de la Baie James, Hydro-Québec
International, and Nouveler Inc., a company that
promotes energy conservation and efficiency. It
also holds a 34.2 per cent interest in Churchill
Falls (Labrador) Corp. Ltd.

Ranking among the world's leading electrical
utilities, Hydro-Québec is unique in that 97 per
cent of its production is hydroelectric. Moreover,
its research and scientific personnel are constantly developing and testing new methods and
equipment for the electrical industry.

The utility serves almost 3 million residential,
commercial, and industrial accounts in a
1,554,000 km^2 territory. In 1987, sales of electricity
exceeded 152 billion kWh, of which 28.8 billion
kWh were exported to other provinces and to the
U.S. Hydro-Québec is not only one of Quebec's
major economic forces, it is also Canada's largest
industrial company in terms of net income and
assets. The members of the board of directors are
appointed by the Quebec government.

*Président du conseil d'administration,
et chef de direction,* Richard Drouin
Président et chef de l'exploitation,
Claude Boivin
Secrétaire gén., Jean Bernier
Information et affaires publiques

Vice-président, Marcel Couture
Vérificatrice gén., Rollande Montsion
Planification générale
Vice-président (p.i.), André Délisle
Développement des ressources humaines
Vice-président, Jacques Nadeau
Equipement
Vice-président exéc., Benoit Michel
Personnel de l'exploitation
Vice-président, Michel Blais
Technologie et affaires internationales
et IREQ
Vice-président exéc., Maurice Huppé
Finances et administration
Vice-président exéc., John A. Hanna
Marchés externes
Vice-président exéc., Jacques Guèvremont
Marchés québécois
Vice-président exéc., Jacques Finet
Exploitation régionale
Vice-président exéc., Gilles Béliveau
Production, transport et distribution
Vice-président, Jean-Claude Roy

Hydro-Québec International
800, boul. de Maisonneuve est, 23e ét.
Montréal, H2L 4L8
General Information: (514) 289-6822

Hydro-Québec International is a wholly-owned
subsidiary of Hydro-Québec, the province's electrical utility corporation. Hydro-Québec International exports know-how in the planning, design,
construction, and management of electric-power
systems. It offers foreign organizations producing
and distributing electrical energy an array of
technical resources and the expertise acquired in
the building of large-scale power projects.

President and CEO, Claude Descôteaux
Marketing
Vice-President, Epiphane A. Mawussi
Administration
Vice-President, Michel-André Demers
Studies and Projects
A/Vice-President, Raymond Pronovost

Régie du gaz naturel
(Natural Gas Board)
2100, rue Drummond, bur. 200
Montréal, H3G 1X1

The Régie du gaz naturel is a quasi-judicial and
administrative tribunal whose chief functions are:
• to fix the tariffs proposed by natural gas
  distributors;
• to determine a distributor's rate of return;
• to order a distributor to reimburse any surplus
  earnings to its consumers, where necessary;
  and
• to arbitrate disputes between consumers and
  natural gas distributors.

Président, Bernard Cloutier
Vice-président, Me Guy Leclerc
Régisseurs:
Jean-Louis Bourret, Marc E. LeClerc
Secrétaire, Me Laurette Laurin

Service juridique, Me Pierre Théroux
Service écono-financier, Raymond Cazes

SOQUIP (Société québécoise d'initiatives pétrolières)
1175, rue Lavigerie
C.P. 10650, Ste-Foy, G1V 4P5

SOQUIP is a Quebec Crown corporation established in 1969. Originally, it conducted oil and gas exploration exclusively, but today its activities are more diversified. The Company has formed oil and gas exploration partnerships in various parts of Canada as well as hydrocarbon production partnerships in Quebec and western Canada.

SOQUIP Alberta Inc., a subsidiary, manages the Company's exploration and production activities in western Canada. PAREX, a partnership company with two large private Canadian firms, plays an active role in the exploration for hydrocarbon deposits off the east coast of Canada.

SOQUIP is also involved in natural gas distribution in Quebec.

Président et chef de la direction,
Richard Pouliot
Vice-président, opérations, et secrétaire,
Yves Rheault
Administration et affaires publiques
Vice-président, Pierre Boivin
Développement
Vice-président, Jean A. Guérin
Affaires juridiques et Domaine minier
Directeur, Pierre S. Boivin

Société d'énergie de la Baie James
800, boul. de Maisonneuve est, 19e ét.
Montréal, H2L 4M8
General Information: (514) 289-5925
Vice-président et chef des opérations,
Paul-F. Tremblay

Société de récupération, d'exploitation et de développement forestiers du Québec (REXFOR)
(Quebec Wood Salvage, Logging and Forest Development Company)
1195, rue Lavigerie, Ste-Foy, G1V 4N3

REXFOR is a Quebec government corporation which grew out of the Office de récupération des bois des rivières Manicouagan et aux Outardes, set up in 1961.

REXFOR is active on three levels: evaluating forests and forestry operations, transforming forest resources, and marketing wood products.

Its main role is to stimulate implementation and development within the forest industry, as well as to create jobs. REXFOR is involved either directly as owner and manager of enterprises, or in joint ventures to set up or relaunch companies working in the forestry field.

Président, Robert Darveau
Développement
Vice-président, Jean-Marie Pouliot
Domaine forestier
Vice-président, Jean-Louis Caron

Domaine pâtes et papiers
Vice-président, Maurice Moore
Domaine industriel
Vice-président, Roger Morasse
Finances
Directeur, Paul A. Coulombe
Secrétaire de la société, Guy Veer

Société nationale de l'amiante
850, boul. Ouellet ouest
Thetford Mines, G6G 7A5

The Société nationale de l'amiante (SNA) is a Crown corporation incorporated by a special law passed by the Quebec government. According to its constitution, the objects of the SNA are: to search for, develop, and exploit asbestos deposits; to become involved in the manufacturing of asbestos fibre, or any commercial venture directly or indirectly relating to its processing; and to research and develop new uses or processing methods for asbestos.

P.-D.G., Benoît Cartier
Contrôleur, Mario Simard
CERAM-SNA INC.
4125, rue Garlock, Sherbrooke, J1L 1W9

Société québécoise d'exploration minière (SOQUEM)
Place Belle Cour, bur. 600
2590, boul. Laurier, Ste-Foy, G1V 4M6
General Information: (418) 658-5400

The Société québécoise d'exploration minière (SOQUEM) was established in July 1965 as a government-owned joint-stock company to promote the development of Quebec's natural resources. It was entrusted with the same general duties, privileges, and objectives — including profitability — as private companies engaged in mineral exploration.

According to its charter, SOQUEM conducts mining exploration by all methods and prospects for developing mines, and processes mineral substances. To pursue its objectives, SOQUEM may, according to law, associate or make agreements with any person or company.

SOQUEM's affairs are managed by a board of directors appointed by the government. Its accounting records are audited by the Auditor-General.

P.-D.G., André-F. Laurin
Vice-président, Raymond Raby
Trésorier, Guylaine Caron
Contentieux
Directeur et secrétaire, Robert Desroches
Exploration
Directeur gén., Denis Simoneau
Conseil d'administration
Président, Robert De Coster

MINISTÈRE DE L'ENSEIGNEMENT SUPÉRIEUR ET DE LA SCIENCE

(Higher Education and Science)
1033, rue de la Chevrotière, 16e ét.
Québec, G1R 5K9
General Information: (418) 643-6788
BUREAU DE MONTRÉAL:
454, place Jacques-Cartier, 4e ét.
Montréal, H2Y 3W3
General Information: (514) 873-8066

CABINET DU MINISTRE
Ministre, L'hon. Claude Ryan

BUREAU DU SOUS-MINISTRE
Sous-ministre, Marcel Gilbert
Sous-ministre adj. à l'enseignement supérieur, Vacant
Sous-ministre adj. à la science, Guy Létourneau
Sous-ministre adj. à l'administration et à l'aide financière aux étudiants, Pierre Boisvert

AGENCIES, BOARDS AND COMMISSIONS

Centre québécois de recherche sur les applications pédagogiques de l'ordinateur
2001, boul. St-Laurent, Montréal, H2X 2T3

The Centre québécois de recherche sur les applications pédagogiques de l'ordinateur (APO QUÉBEC) was created by Decree no. 865-85 on May 8, 1985, by the Government of Quebec, under the auspices of the Ministry of Higher Education and Science. It is administered by a board of directors consisting of 13 members drawn from the education and business sectors.

APO QUÉBEC's main goal is to promote research and development in educational computing. Its main functions are: to initiate, carry out or commission, support, and direct research and development; to collect and circulate information; to identify needs and to set priorities in research and development; to encourage industrial and commercial applications of research findings; and to encourage co-operation and exchange among all individuals and centres dealing with educational computing.

P.-D.G., Pierre Bordeleau

Centre québécois de valorisation de la biomasse
3180 ch. Ste-Foy, 2e ét., Ste-Foy, G1X 1R4

The Centre québécois de valorisation de la biomasse was established as a government corporation in May 1985 to promote research and development in the field of biomass utilization. The Centre's goal is to maximize benefits to be gained from biomass on behalf of Quebec society.

The Centre participates with partners in conducting studies and projects to perfect and scale-test methods for assessment of biomass potential. It participates in a dynamic way, carrying out tasks on a contract basis for the most part, in accordance with calls for proposals. The Centre also accepts unsolicited projects.

As a pivotal element promoting excellence in the development and demonstration of new techniques and methods to utilize biomass, the Centre operates in five areas: research, up-scaling, practical applications, the updating of technological data, and co-ordination.

P.-D.G., Marcel Risi

Centre québécois pour l'informatisation de la production
1600, boul. Henri-Bourassa ouest, bur. 408
Montréal, H3M 3E2
General Information: (514) 335-6116

Established on June 6, 1984 by the government of Quebec, the Centre québécois pour l'informatisation de la production (CQIP) is a non-profit corporation under the direct responsibility of the Ministry of Higher Education and Science. CQIP was designed to promote the computerization of production. In March 1988, CQIP's mandate was extended to March 1991.

Since its founding, CQIP has been responsible for creating a favourable environment for the introduction of CIM (computer-integrated manufacturing) and for developing CIM technologies in all areas likely to benefit from them. CQIP has also focused on identifying existing CIM expertise in Quebec (private firms, research centres, specialized manufacturers, consultants, etc.), bringing these specialists together in CIM laboratories, and providing resources to them in the form of clerical and technical assistance.

P.-D.G., Roland Dugré, ing.
Directeur gén. adj., André St-Onge

Conseil de la science et de la technologie
2050, boul. St-Cyrille ouest, 5e ét.
Ste-Foy, G1V 2K8

The Science and Technology Council of Quebec was established in June 1983. The main function of the Council is to advise the Minister of Higher Education and Science on all questions related to scientific and technological development in Quebec. The Council responds to specific requests from the minister but may also forward its recommendations to the minister on any subject of its choice.

The 18 members of the Council are representative of Quebec's scientific community.

Président, Maurice L'Abbé
Secrétaire gén., Camil Guy

Conseil des collèges
900, place d'Youville, 8e ét., Québec, G1R 3P7

The Conseil des collèges is an advisory body, created in 1979, which reports to the Minister of Higher Education and Science. The minister is required to seek the Council's advice on a number of matters affecting education at the college level; for instance, new teaching programs, the establishment of new colleges, and budgets.

The Council may, on its own initiative, carry out research and studies, solicit opinions, and make recommendations to the minister on any question concerning college education.

The Council is composed of two commissions: the Commission on Professional Teaching and the Commission on Appraisement.

Président, Yvon Morin

Conseil des universités
Tour Frontenac, 8e ét.
2700, boul. Laurier, Ste-Foy, G1V 2L8

The Conseil des universités is a provincial government body whose main tasks are to advise the Minister of Higher Education and Science on needs for higher education and university research, and to offer recommendations as to how these needs can be met.

The Council is composed of 17 members drawn from university, business, labour, and government circles. The members are appointed by the government on the recommendation of the Minister of Higher Education and Science.

Président, Jacques L'Ecuyer

Fonds pour la formation de chercheurs et l'aide à la recherche
3700, rue du Campanile, bur. 102
Ste-Foy, G1X 4G6

The corporation Fonds (FCAR) is a funding body which receives financial resources from the Quebec government in order to carry out programs of assistance and support for research and advanced studies.

P.-D.G., Christiane Quérido

Office des professions du Québec
Place Jacques-Cartier
320, rue St-Joseph est, 1er ét.
Québec, G1K 8G5
General Information: (418) 643-6912
Fax: (418) 643-0973

The Office des professions is a regulatory and supervisory body set up under the *Professional Code* in 1973. It is responsible for seeing that each of the 40 professional corporations fulfils its task of protecting the public. In particular, the Office ensures that every corporation adopts and enforces a body of regulations governing the activities of its members. It may even adopt certain important regulations itself with a view to protecting the public if a corporation neglects to do so.

The Office appoints members of the public to the board of directors of each corporation. It acts as advisor to the government. It may suggest the creation of new corporations, the amalgamation or dissolution of existing corporations or amendments to professional laws when the interests of the public so require. The Office informs the public of its rights with respect to professional services.

Président, Me Thomas J. Mulcair

MINISTÈRE DE L'ENVIRONNEMENT
(Environment)
3900, rue Marly, Ste-Foy, G1X 4E4
General Information: (418) 643-6071
Bureau administratif de Montréal
5199, rue Sherbrooke est, bur. 3860
Montréal, H1T 3X9

CABINET DE LA MINISTRE
Ministre, L'hon. Lise Bacon

BUREAU DU SOUS-MINISTRE
Sous-ministre, J.-C. Deschênes
Direction des communications et de l'éducation
Directrice, Marcelle Girard
Bureau de coordination de la stratégie industrielle, Raymond Perrier
Service juridique
Directeur, Robert Bissonet
Direction de la comptabilité
Directeur, Marc Begin

DIRECTION GÉNÉRALE DE L'ADMINISTRATION
Directeur gén., Gaston Couillard
Direction des ressources humaines
Directeur, Jean Boudreau
Direction des ressources matérielles
Directeur, Jean Aumont
Direction des ressources financières
Directeur, Louis-M. Bissonnette
Direction de l'organisation et des systèmes
Directeur, Normand Trempe

Gestion et assainissement atmosphériques et terrestres
Sous-ministre adj., Michel Gagnon
Direction de l'assainissement de l'air
Directeur, Gaston Paulin
2360, ch. Ste-Foy, Ste-Foy, G1V 4H2
Direction de la météorologie
Directeur, Michel G. Ferland
2360, ch. Ste-Foy, Ste-Foy, G1V 4H2
Direction des substances dangereuses
Directeur, Conrad Anctil
Direction de la récupération et du recyclage
Directeur, Alain Sariefy
Direction de la gestion et du contrôle des pesticides
Directeur, Yves L. Pagé

Planification et prévention
Sous-ministre adj., Gérard Divay
Direction des relations intergouvernementales
Directeur, Jean Piette
Coordination des affaires nordiques et amérindiennes
Coordonnateur, Michel Beaulieu
Direction des stratégies et des politiques environnementales
Directeur, Clément Veilleux
Direction des évaluations environnementales
Directeur, Gilles Coulombe

Direction de coordination de la recherche et du développement
Directeur, Henri Saint-Martin
Direction des laboratoires et du Laboratoire de Québec
Directeur, Aristide Bouchard
2700, rue Einstein, Ste-Foy, G1P 3W8
Laboratoire de Montréal
Directeur, Donald Colgan
9312, boul. St-Laurent, Montréal, H2N 1N4
Direction générale des inspections et des enquêtes
Directeur gén., Alain Robert

Gestion et assainissement de l'eau
Sous-ministre adj., Clermont Gignac
Direction générale de l'assainissement des eaux
Directeur gén., Maurice Masse
Direction de l'assainissement urbain
Directeur, Jacques Lapointe
Direction de l'assainissement industriel
Directeur, Robert Tetreault
Direction de l'assainissement agricole
Directeur, Yvon Gosselin
Direction de la qualité du milieu aquatique
Directrice, Denyse Gouin

DIRECTION GÉNÉRALE DES RESSOURCES HYDRIQUES
Directeur gén., André Harvey
Direction du milieu hydrique
Directeur, Pierre Fabi
Direction de l'hydraulique
Directeur, Claude Pesant
Direction des eaux souterraines et de consommation
Directeur, Jean Vachon
Direction du contrôle budgétaire
Directeur, Pierre Gagnon

DIRECTION GÉNÉRALE DE LA CONSERVATION
Directeur gén., Réal P. L'Heureux
Direction de l'aménagement des lacs et des cours d'eau
Directeur, Tony Le Sauteur
Direction du patrimoine écologique
Directeur, Léopold Gaudreau

Opérations
Sous-ministre adj., Bertrand Tétreault
Direction générale des opérations, secteur est
Directeur gén., André Chamberland

DIRECTIONS RÉGIONALES:
Bas-St-Laurent—Gaspésie—Iles-de-la-Madeleine
337, rue Moreault, Rimouski, G5L 1P4
Directeur rég., Mario Fontaine
Saguenay—Lac-St-Jean
3950, boul. Harvey, Jonquière, G7X 8L6
Directeur rég., Raymond Guérin
Québec
917, av. Msgr-Grandin, Québec, G1V 3X8
Directeur, Michel Gauvin

Mauricie—Bois-Francs
100, rue Laviolette, Trois-Rivières, G9A 5S9
Directrice (p.i.), Suzanne Giguère
Estrie
209, rue Belvédère nord, Sherbrooke, J1H 4A7
Directeur, Rolland Mercier
Côte-Nord
818, boul. Laure, Sept-Iles, G4R 1Y8
Directeur, Jean-Marie Boucher

Direction générale des opérations, secteur ouest
Directeur gén., Antonio Flammand

DIRECTIONS RÉGIONALES:
Montréal-Lanaudière
5199, rue Sherbrooke est, bur. 3860
Montréal, H1T 3X9
Directeur, Guy Demers
Laval-Laurentides
4, place Laval, bur. 300, Laval, H7N 5Y3
Directeur, Michel A. Provencher
Montérégie
Imm. Le D'Assigny
201, place Charles-Lemoyne, 2e ét.
Longueuil, J4K 2T5
Directeur, Claude Rouleau
Outaouais
170, rue Hôtel-de-Ville, Hull, J8X 4C2
Directeur rég., Jacques Beaulieu
Abitibi-Témiscamingue et du Nord quebécois
29, rue du Terminus ouest, Noranda, J9X 2P3
Directeur, Noël Savard

Direction générale du programme d'aide à l'amélioration de la gestion des fumiers
Directeur, Guy Audet

AGENCIES, BOARDS AND COMMISSIONS
Bureau d'audiences publiques sur l'environnement
12, rue Ste-Anne, 1er ét., Québec, G1R 3X2
5199, rue Sherbrooke est, bur. 3860
Montréal, H1T 3X9

The Bureau d'audiences publiques sur l'environnement was established by the Quebec *Environmental Quality Act* in December 1978. Its principal function is to hold public hearings, according to the environmental impact assessment and review process, in order to inform the public and advise the Minister of Environment.

Members are appointed by the government for a term not exceeding five years. They have the powers and immunity of commissioners appointed under the *Act respecting public inquiry commissions.*

Président, Victor Goldbloom
Secrétaire, Jean-Paul Sabourin

Comité consultatif de l'environnement Kativik
Administration régionale Kativik
C.P. 9, Kuujjuaq, J0M 1C0

The Kativik Environmental Advisory Committee was established in 1975 under the *James Bay and Northern Quebec Agreement.* It is governed by the *Environment Quality Act* and by the *Northern Quebec Native Claims Settlement Act,* S.C. 1976-1979, Chapter 32. Its role is to advise the different levels of government (federal, provincial, regional, and local) on issues affecting the environment and social milieu of the Kativik region — the region of northern Quebec situated north of the 55th parallel.

The Committee is a body made up of members appointed by the Kativik Regional Government, Canada, and Quebec. It advises the appropriate levels of government in the formulation of laws and regulations relating to the environmental and social protection regime. It also oversees environmental and social impact assessment, and review mechanisms and procedures, and it reviews land use mechanisms for the region.

Président, Jacques Siquère

Comité consultatif pour l'environnement de la Baie-James
3900, rue Marly, Ste-Foy, G1X 4E4

The James Bay Advisory Committee on the Environment (JBACE) was created pursuant to section 22 of the *James Bay and Northern Quebec Agreement.* The JBACE is made up of Crees and representatives from the Quebec and Canadian governments involved in environmental management, natural resource exploitation, community planning, and the administration of social programs. Its mandate is generally to review and oversee the application of the environmental protection regime established by the Agreement. The Committee deals with a large number of issues involving impact assessment, the application of environmental laws and regulations in the North, and the development of policy guidelines in areas such as water treatment, forestry, and the monitoring and development of projects in the James Bay and northern Quebec territory south of the 55th parallel.

The JBACE meets at least quarterly, and operates through a series of sub-committees with mandates in the areas of forestry, environmental regulation, planning of municipal services, ecological monitoring, and the overseeing of environmental impact assessments.

Président, Thomas Coon
Secrétaire, Marc-Alain Côté

Conseil de la conservation et de l'environnement
800, place d'Youville, 19e ét., Québec, G1R 3P4

The Conseil de la conservation et de l'environnement is composed of a president and 10 members appointed by the government on the recommendation of the Minister of Environment. Its principal function is to advise the minister on environmental and conservation questions. It may also, on its own initiative or at the request of interested persons, organizations, or associations, submit advice on any matter it sees fit. To this end, it may consult with interested parties, invite opinions, receive submissions, and carry out any research it feels necessary to carry out its mandate.

The Conseil, created by an act of the Quebec Legislature on Dec. 17, 1987, replaces the Conseil consultatif de l'environnement and the Conseil consultatif sur les réserves écologiques.

Président, Marcel Junius
Secrétaire, Camille Rousseau

Société québécoise d'assainissement des eaux
1055, boul. René-Lévesque est, 10e ét.
Montréal, H2L 4S5

The Société québécoise d'assainissement des eaux (SQAE) was created by Bill 92 on June 18, 1980 by the Government of Quebec, under the auspices of the ministère de l'Environnement. It is administered by a board of directors consisting of seven members drawn from the municipal and business sectors.

The SQAE is a management and financing corporation which, within the scope of the provincial water purification program, acts as an intermediary between the municipalities involved in the program and all parties concerned. Its main functions are: to design, construct, improve, enlarge, and put into operation water purification works which meet the needs of the municipalities; to carry out rehabilitation work on the municipal sewerage systems; and to carry out studies with respect to the rehabilitation of the municipal sewerage systems and other studies in matters of sewerage and water purification.

P.-D.G., Jean-Yves Babin
Gestion de projets
Vice-président, Germain Laberge
Administration et finances
Vice-président, André Thibault
Relations municipales
Vice-président, Jacques Roux

MINISTÈRE DES FINANCES
(Finance)
12, rue St-Louis, Québec, G1R 5L3
General Information: (418) 691-2233
Telex: 051-3771

CABINET DU MINISTRE
Ministre, L'hon. Gérard D. Levesque

CABINET DU MINISTRE DÉLÉGUÉ AUX FINANCES ET À LA PRIVATISATION
Ministre, L'hon. Pierre Fortier

BUREAU DU SOUS-MINISTRE
Sous-ministre, Claude Séguin

Politiques et opérations financières
Sous-ministre adj., Alain Rhéaume
Direction générale des politiques et opérations financières
Directeur gén., Vacant

Direction générale de la gestion de l'encaisse et des emprunts
Directeur gén., Jocelyn Girard
Direction des sociétés d'Etat
Directeur, Daniel Paillé

Financement
Sous-ministre adj., Robert Lacroix
Direction générale des marchés financiers
Directeur gén., François Gagnon

Fiscalité
Sous-ministre adj., André Delisle
Direction des politiques de taxation
Directeur, Marcel Leblanc
Direction de l'analyse et des prévisions fiscales
Directeur, Gilles Godbout
Direction des relations financières intergouvernementales
Directeur (p.i.), Gilles Dufour

RECHERCHE ÉCONOMIQUE
Directeur gén., Jean-Guy Turcotte
Direction de l'analyse et de la prévision économique
Directeur, Abraham Assayag
Direction des politiques économiques
Directeur, Gérard Harvey
Direction des études structurelles
Directeur, Gilles Demers

ADMINISTRATION
Directeur gén., André Montminy
Direction du personnel
Directeur, Yves Sagnon
Direction des communications
Directeur, Marcel Gilbert
Services juridiques
Directeur, Jean Martel

Contrôleur des finances
Bloc 2, partie basse, 2ᵉ ét.
1058, rue Conroy, Québec, G1E 5E6
Contrôleur des finances, Pierre-André Paré
Contrôleur adj. et directeur gén.
des opérations, Roger Couture
Direction des systèmes et méthodes
Directeur, André Blondin
Direction générale de la vérification
Directeur, Gilles Chabot

AGENCIES, BOARDS AND COMMISSIONS

Caisse de dépôt et placement du Québec
1981, av. McGill College, Montréal, H3A 3C7

The Caisse de dépôt et placement du Québec is a public pension and insurance fund management organization created in 1965 by a special act of the National Assembly.

It is administered by a board made up of its general manager, appointed for ten years, the president of the Régie des rentes du Québec (the Quebec Pension Board) and seven other mem-

bers appointed for a three-year term by the government. The board also includes three associate members who sit without voting privileges.

The Caisse is empowered to receive deposits and to manage funds only from those bodies or pension plans authorized by law to make such deposits. At present, funds are deposited by eleven bodies and supplemental pension plans.

The Caisse's investments are many and varied, ranging from bonds and conventional mortgage loans to real estate investments and stocks.

The Caisse's investment policy is based on three major objectives: profitability of funds invested, security of capital, and promotion of economic growth.

P.-D.G., Jean Campeau
Planification et relations avec les déposants
Premier vice-président, Michel Nadeau
Placements à revenu fixe
Premier vice-président, Claude Ferland
Placements à revenu variable
Premier vice-président, Michel Grignon
Affaires juridiques et institutionnelles et placements immeubles
Premier vice-président, Jean-Claude Scraire
Administration et contrôle
Premier vice-président, Vacant

SODIC Québec Inc.
(Société de développement de l'industrie des courses de chevaux du Québec)
500, rue Sherbrooke ouest, 16ᵉ ét.
Montréal, H3A 3G6

SODIC, incorporated under the *Companies Act,* R.S.Q., Chapter 38, in February 1982, is dedicated to the development and promotion of the Quebec horse racing industry. It was first established in December 1975 as a replacement for the Comité de promotion de la race chevaline. SODIC is now a fully owned subsidiary of the Société des loteries et courses du Québec (Loto-Québec), which operates under the authority and the responsibility of the Minister of Finance.

SODIC's budget, a fixed percentage of the pari mutuel betting volume, is distributed to the industry in the form of Supplemental Purse Grants (87 per cent of the budget) and Standardbred Race Track Improvement Grants. SODIC also manages a number of programs which promote and develop the Quebec horse-breeding industry and provide funds for equine research.

Président du conseil d'administration,
Denis Vandry
P.-D.G., Louis Bernard

Société des loteries et courses du Québec (Loto-Québec)
500, rue Sherbrooke ouest, Montréal, H3A 3G6

The Société des loteries et courses du Québec, popularly known as Loto-Québec, is a Crown corporation founded in 1970 for the sole purpose of conducting lotteries in the province. Quebec's Ministry of Finance is the only shareholder.

Loto-Québec's range of products falls into three main categories: conventional lotteries (Mini, Inter, Inter Plus and Provincial); numbers games, using on-line computer terminals (Sélect 42, La Quotidienne daily lottery and Lotto 6/49); and instant lotteries (scratch-card games, of which eight are conducted each year on various themes). Loto-Québec has 750 full-time employees and sells tickets through 14,000 retail merchants throughout the province.

P.-D.G., David Clark
Vice-président, direction générale,
Denis Vandry
Vice-présidente, affaires corporatives,
Me Marguerite Bourgeois
Vice-président, loteries, Claude Trudel
Vice-président, nouveaux marchés et systèmes,
Roger Bertrand

MINISTÈRE DE L'INDUSTRIE, DU COMMERCE ET DE LA TECHNOLOGIE

(Industry, Commerce and Technology)
710, place d'Youville, Québec, G1R 4Y4
General Information: (418) 691-5950
770, rue Sherbrooke ouest, Montréal, H3A 1G1
General Information: (514) 873-3548

CABINET DU MINISTRE
Ministre, L'hon. Pierre MacDonald

CABINET DU MINISTRE DÉLÉGUÉ AUX PETITES ET MOYENNES ENTREPRISES
Ministre, L'hon. Richard French
Placement étudiant du Québec
Directeur, Michel Nadeau

BUREAU DU SOUS-MINISTRE
Sous-ministre, Michel Audet

Administration et planification
Sous-ministre adj., Marcel Pelletier
Secteur des coopératives
Directeur, Marc Jean
Secteur du contrôle
Responsable, André Dallaire
Secteur du développement
Responsable, Willy Bisreth
Direction des relations avec les sociétés d'Etat
Directeur, Michel Leguerrier
Direction des relations extra-ministérielles
Directeur, Michel Gauthier
Direction de la promotion des investissements
Directeur, Jacques Girard
Direction de la vérification interne
Directeur, Simon-Pierre Rainville

Secteur biens d'équipement et de consommation
Sous-ministre adj., Michel La Salle
Centre d'information
Responsable, Pierre Bazinet

Direction des biens d'équipement
Directeur, André P. Caron
Service des équipements de transport
Chef, Denis Carette
Division automobile et pièces
Responsable, Rémy Kelly
Service de la machinerie, de l'usinage et de l'estampage
Chef, Gilles Delisle
Service des produits électriques et électroniques
Chef, Micheline Fortin
Service du logiciel et des équipements bureautiques et informatiques
Chef, Marcel Ruel
Direction des biens de consommation
Directeur, Michel Chevrier
Service des produits du textile et de l'habillement
Chef, Michel Hanson
Service des produits de consommation
Chef, Jean-Luc Dubé
Service des produits du bâtiment
Chef, André Cloutier
Service de l'industrie des boissons alcooliques
Chef, Jacques Ouimet
Bureau de normalisation du Québec
50, rue St-Joseph est, Québec, G1K 3A5
Directeur (p.i.), Philippe Fontaine

Secteur grands projets chimie et métallurgie
Sous-ministre assoc., André Dorr
Bureau des grands projets
Directeur, Vacant
Direction des industries chimiques
Directeur, Pierre Girard
Service des industries chimiques inorganiques
Directeur de service, Roger Marchand
Service des industries biotechnologiques et pharmaceutiques
Directeur de service, Mishèle Bérubé
Groupe des industries pétrochimiques
Chef, Marc St-Onge
Direction des matériaux et métaux
Directeur, Vacant
Service des industries des matériaux
Directeur de service, Pierre Marceau
Service des industries métallurgiques
Directeur de service, Jacques Drolet
Direction de la promotion des produits québécois
Directeur, Paul Déry

Développement régional et services aux entreprises
Sous-ministre adj., Pierre Delisle
Direction de la promotion l'entrepreneurship
Directrice, Brigitte Van-Coillie-Tremblay
Direction générale des services aux entreprises
Directeur gén., Yves Rancourt
Direction des services aux entreprises commerciales
Directeur, Paul Meunier
Direction de l'aide à l'implantation industrielle
Directrice, Francine Dumont

Direction des services aux entreprises industrielles
Directeur, Jacques Quévillon
Direction de programmes aux entrepreneurs
Responsable, H.-Yvon Bédard

DIRECTIONS RÉGIONALES:
01—Bas-St-Laurent—Gaspésie—
Iles-de-la-Madeleine
Les Galeries G.P., 92, Deuxième rue ouest
Rimouski, G5L 8B3
Directeur (p.i.), Réjean Dion
02—Saguenay—Lac-St-Jean
3950, boul. Harvey, r.c., Jonquière, G7X 8L6
Directrice, Hélène Tremblay Corneau
03—Québec
20, rue St-Joseph, bur. 201, Québec, G1R 8G5
Directeur, Yvon Giasson
04—Mauricie—Bois-Francs
Edifice Capitanal, bur. 3.21
100, rue Laviolette, Trois-Rivières, G9A 5S9
Directeur, Paul Clermont
05—Estrie
740, rue Galt ouest, bur. 303
Sherbrooke, J1H 1Z3
Directeur, André Labrie
06a—Montréal-Laval
770, rue Sherbrooke ouest, 7e ét.
Montréal, H3A 1G1
Directeur, Pierre Chamberland
06b—Laurentides-Lanaudière
Edifice administratif
85, rue de Martigny ouest, bur. 3.7
St-Jérôme, J7Y 3R8
Directeur, François Cournoyer
06c—Montérégie
Edifice Montval, bur. 104
201, place Charles-Lemoyne
Longueuil, J4K 2T5
Directeur, Jacques Doyon
07—Outaouais
Place du Centre, Edifice Jos-Montferrand
170, rue Hôtel-de-Ville, 6e ét., Hull, J8X 4C2
Directeur, Pierre Lévesque
08—Abitibi-Témiscamingue
180, boul. Rideau, bur. 1.01
Rouyn-Noranda, J9X 1N9
Directeur, Claude Lecours
09—Côte-Nord/
10—Nouveau-Québec
Centre commercial Laflèche
625, boul. Laflèche, Baie-Comeau, G5C 1C5
Directeur (p.i.), Jacques Tremblay

DIRECTION GÉNÉRALE DE
L'ADMINISTRATION
Directeur gén., Michel Gagnon
Direction de la gestion des ressources humaines
Directeur, Donald Giguère
Direction des communications
Directeur, Yves Durand

DIRECTION GÉNÉRALE DE LA RECHERCHE
ET DE LA PLANIFICATION
Directeur gén., Michel Bussière

Direction de l'analyse économique et des relations internationales
Directeur, Yvon Pomerleau
Direction de l'analyse des politiques et des programmes
Directeur, Jean-Claude Fréchette
Direction des études sectorielles
Directeur, Richard Roy
Direction de la comptabilité
Directeur, Rosaire Plante
Direction des affaires juridiques
Responsable, Paul Carpentier

AGENCIES, BOARDS AND COMMISSIONS

Centre de recherche industrielle du Québec (CRIQ)

333, rue Franquet, C.P. 9038, Ste-Foy, G1V 4C7
8475, rue Christophe-Colomb
C.P. 2000, succ. Youville, Montréal, H2P 2X1
General Information:
Quebec: (418) 659-1550
Montreal: (514) 383-1550

The Centre de recherche industrielle du Québec (CRIQ) is a government corporation whose main role is to contribute to the economic development of Quebec by promoting innovation in Quebec manufacturing firms. CRIQ helps such companies to be competitive and to meet the demands of the market by supplying technical or industrial information. It helps them to solve their production problems and to develop and improve their products and production methods, by providing information, technical assistance, and advice on technology transfer and on research and development.

P.-D.G., Guy Bertrand, ing.

SIDBEC-DOSCO INC.

300, rue Léo-Pariseau, Place du Parc
Montréal, H2W 2S7
General Information: (514) 286-8600
Président et chef de direction,
John Le Boutillier

Société de développement des coopératives (SDC)

430, ch. Ste-Foy, Ste-Foy, G1S 2J5
General Information: (418) 687-9221

The Société de développement des coopératives is a Crown corporation which aims to promote the creation and development of co-operative enterprises. Its main role is to provide co-operatives with supplementary financing, aside from that received from members and financial institutions. As well, the Société may advise co-operatives on matters of financing, while ensuring that they have access to any technical assistance they may require.

With regard to financing, the Société's primary role is to guarantee capital loans. Other forms of financial aid are also available. The Société may take over the interest on certain loans that are granted to co-operatives, or it may guarantee loans in the form of a credit advance.

In summary, the Société helps co-operative organizations to attain more quickly the financial autonomy they need for their development.

P.-D.G., Gérard Barbin

Société de développement industriel du Québec (SDI)
1126, ch. St-Louis, bur. 700, Sillery, G1S 1E5
General Information: (418) 643-5172
Edifice Banque Mercantile
770, rue Sherbrooke ouest, 9ᵉ ét.
Montréal, H3A 1G1
General Information: (514) 873-4375

The Société de développement industriel du Québec (SDI) was established in 1971 to spur economic development in the province of Quebec through financial incentives. Legislative changes in its mandate in 1986 focused SDI's activities on the sound capitalization of small- and medium-sized businesses in Quebec. To achieve this, SDI offers two unique forms of financial assistance — venture loans and the SPEQ, a program allowing individuals to gain a tax deduction while investing in selected Quebec firms — which are designed to allow enterprises to avoid resorting to debt financing.

SDI's programs are designed to stimulate:

• investment for the establishment, expansion, or modernization of manufacturing enterprises;
• research and innovation for the development of new or improved products and technology;
• export to encourage business to sell Quebec-produced goods and services outside the province; and
• establishment of an SPEQ, which entails tax deductions, to stimulate investment in small- and medium-sized enterprises.

Eligible enterprises must operate in the manufacturing or tourist sectors. SDI also manages special assistance programs enacted by the Quebec government.

P.-D.G., Gérald Tremblay

Société des alcools du Québec (SAQ)
905, rue de Lorimier, Montréal, H2K 3V9
2900, rue Einstein, Ste-Foy, G1X 4B3
General Information:
Quebec: (418) 643-4321
Montreal: (514) 873-2020

The Société des alcools du Québec was created by the Quebec government in 1921 as a publicly owned company with an exclusive mandate to import, distribute, and sell alcoholic beverages in Quebec. Originally known as the Commission des liqueurs du Québec (Quebec Liquor Commission), it became the Régie des alcools du Québec (Quebec Liquor Board) in 1961 and the Société des alcools du Québec in 1971 under the *Société des alcools du Québec Act*, R.S.Q., Chapter S-13.1.

The SAQ is managed by a board of directors drawn from Quebec industry, business, and professional circles and is responsible to the Quebec Ministry of Industry, Commerce and Technology for its operations. The sole shareholder is the Quebec Ministry of Finance.

The Société operates some 354 retail stores throughout the province and imports wines and spirits from 42 countries. It has one of the largest distribution centres in Quebec, featuring a warehouse with a storage capacity of 1.5 million cases, a large vat room with a capacity of 2.6 million gallons of wines and spirits imported in bulk, and four bottling lines with a capacity of 3.8 million cases per year.

P.-D.G., Jocelyn Tremblay

Société du parc industriel du centre du Québec (SPICQ)
1000, boul. Arthur-Sicard, Bécancour, G0X 1B0
General Information: (819) 294-6656

SPICQ runs a 3,100-hectare waterfront industrial park, with 2,025 hectares available for industrial purposes. Major highways, a CN rail line, and a heliport are on the site. A 735-kW electricity line feeds the site, as well as a 350-psi natural gas line. Industrial water is also available.

The port facilities offer five wharves totalling 1,525 metres of berthing space that can accommodate ships of any size sailing the St. Lawrence River all year round and 60 hectares of stockpiling area for bulk and general cargo handling. All services related to port and shipping activities are available on port site.

Gen. Manager, Pierre Clouâtre
Director of Marketing, Gilles Julien

Société du parc industriel et commercial aéroportuaire de Mirabel (SPICAM)
Edifice Banque Mercantile
770, rue Sherbrooke ouest, 10ᵉ ét.
Montréal, H3A 1G1

Wholly owned by the Government of Quebec, SPICAM was incorporated in 1976 in accordance with its special Act, S.Q. 1976, Chapter 32. The Ministry of Industry, Commerce and Technology is entrusted with the application of this Act.

Renseignements, Guy M. Lord

Société générale de financement (SGF)
600, rue de la Gauchetière ouest, bur. 1700
Montréal, H3B 4L8
General Information: (514) 876-9290

The Société générale de financement is an industrial development company wholly owned by the Government of Quebec.

The mission of the Société is to promote and carry out, in co-operation with partners, industrial projects in strategic sectors in accordance with the economic development policies of the government of Quebec. Its five major sectors of activity are aluminum, petrochemicals, energy-related products, forest products, and biotechnology.

Its subsidiaries are Dofor inc., Marine Industrie ltée, Ethylec inc., Bio-Méga inc., and Albecour, société en commandite.

The wholly owned subsidiary, Dofor inc., holds

SGF's 28 per cent of Domtar Inc. Ethylec is an equal partner with Union Carbide Canada Ltd. in Petromont, société en commandite, Alcools de Commerce Enrg., and Pipeline Shawinigan Enrg.

SGF also has investments in Novacap inc., Cegelec Industrie inc., and Cegelec Entreprises Inc.

President and CEO, Paul Berthiaume
Exec. Vice-President, Robert Tessier

Société Inter-Port de Québec
1126, ch. St-Louis, bur. 802, Sillery, G1S 1E5
General Information: (418) 643-8713

The Société Inter-Port de Québec is a government-owned corporation created by Quebec legislation in 1974 to co-ordinate and stimulate industrial development and activities in the Quebec metropolitan area. Sixty per cent of the shares are owned by the Quebec government and 40 per cent by the Government of Canada.

The Société has the power to expropriate land within its territory, which covers 38 municipalities. Furthermore, the Société can participate financially in industrial projects in the area.

Directeur gén., Vacant

INSPECTEUR GÉNÉRAL DES INSTITUTIONS FINANCIÈRES

(Financial Institutions)
800, place d'Youville, Québec, G1R 4Y5
800, place Victoria, Montréal, H4Z 1H9

CABINET DU MINISTRE RESPONSABLE
Ministre, L'hon. Pierre Fortier

BUREAU DE L'INSPECTEUR GÉNÉRAL
Inspecteur gén., Jean-Marie Bouchard
Service juridique
Directeur, Richard Boivin

DIRECTION GÉNÉRALE DES ASSURANCES
Surintendant, Guy Monfette
Direction du contrôle des assurances de personnes
Directeur (p.i.), Michel Noreau
Direction du contrôle des assurances générales
Directeur, André Vallière
Direction de la surveillance des pratiques et des intermédiaires
Directeur, Claude Coulombe
Direction de la recherche et de la statistique
Directeur, Raynald Viger

DIRECTION GÉNÉRALE DES INSTITUTIONS DE DÉPÔTS
Surintendant, Fernand Gauthier
Direction des sociétés de fiducie et d'épargne
Directeur (p.i.), Fernand Gauthier
Direction des caisses d'épargne et de crédit
Directeur, Conrad Veillette

Direction de l'information et des études financières
Directeur, Jean-Pierre April

DIRECTION GÉNÉRALE DE L'ADMINISTRATION ET DES ENTREPRISES
Directeur gén., Jacques Cardinal
Direction des ressources humaines
Directrice, Annette Plante
Direction des communications
Directeur, Thomas-Louis Simard
Direction des ressources matérielles et financières
Directeur, Jean-Pierre Marcil
Direction des entreprises
Directeur, Roger Lequy
Direction de l'organisation et de la technologie
Directrice, Christiane Côté

AGENCIES, BOARDS AND COMMISSIONS

Régie de l'assurance-dépôts du Québec
800, place d'Youville, 9ᵉ ét., Québec, G1R 4Y5

The Régie was constituted by the *Deposit Insurance Act,* R.S.Q., Chapter A-26, and started operations in July 1970.

The role of the Régie is to guarantee to every person who makes a deposit of money with a registered institution or a bank, the payment of such deposit at maturity in principal and interest (up to a maximum of $60,000) should the institution be unable to effect repayment at maturity. As a rule, this guarantee does not apply to deposits of money made outside Quebec or payable only outside Quebec, or to deposits of money made or payable in foreign currency.

A registered institution is one which, following compliance with the terms and conditions prescribed by the Regulations of the Régie, has been issued a permit by the Régie. This permit authorizes the institution to solicit or receive deposits of money. Registered institutions, which include savings and credit unions, and trust and loan companies, must display at their entrances and inside their places of business the official registration sign provided by the Régie.

P.-D.G., Jean-Marie Bouchard
Directeur gén. adj., Alfred Vaillancourt

MINISTÈRE DE LA JUSTICE

(Justice)
1200, rte de l'Eglise, Ste-Foy, G1V 4M1

CABINET DU MINISTRE
1200, rte de l'Eglise, 9ᵉ ét., Ste-Foy, G1V 4M1
Ministre de la Justice, Procureur général, ministre du Secrétariat aux affaires intergouvernementales canadiennes,
L'hon. Gil Rémillard
MONTRÉAL
1, rue Notre-Dame est, 11ᵉ ét.
Montréal, H2Y 1B6

CABINET DU SOUS-MINISTRE
Sous-ministre, sous-procureur gén.,
Jacques Chamberland
Avocat(e)s: Julienne Pelletier, Réjean Gauthier,
Jean Latulippe, Nicole Breton
Directeur du bureau, Jean-Pierre Marcotte
Relations intergouvernementales
Coordonnateur, Me Réjean Gauthier
Activités ministérielles en milieu autochtone
Coordonnateur, Jacques L. Auger
Vérification interne
Directeur (p.i.), Gérald White
Direction des communications
Directrice (p.i.), Nicole Legendre
Victimes d'actes criminels
Coordonnatrice, Christine Viens
Comptabilité
Directeur, Pierre Pelletier

Contentieux
Sous-ministre assoc., Jean-K. Samson
Services administratifs
Directeur, Michel Verge
Direction générale du contentieux
Directeur gén. adj., Me Gaétan Lemoyne
Droit administratif, Denis Lemieux
Droit constitutionnel
Directrice adj., Odette Laverdière
Service juridique
Directeur, Jean-C. Dallaire
Service central des réclamations
Chef, Serge Massicotte
Direction des affaires notariales
Directeur, René Côté
300, boul. Jean-Lesage, Québec, G1K 8K6
Directeur adj., Pierre Beaudoin
1, rue Notre-Dame est, Montréal, H2Y 1B6
Services juridiques
300, boul. Jean-Lesage, Québec, G1K 8K6
Directeur (p.i.), Michael Sheehan
Directeur, Jean-Yves Bernard
1, rue Notre-Dame est, Montréal, H2Y 1B6

Affaires criminelles et pénales
Sous-ministre assoc., Me Michel Bouchard
Code de la sécurité routière
Directeur, Louis Dufour
Affaires pénales
Substitut en chef (p.i.), Paul Monty
Crime économique
Substitut en chef, Jean-Paul Roger
Affaires criminelles
Substitut en chef, Jean-François Dionne

Affaires législatives
1200, rte de l'Eglise, Ste-Foy, G1V 4M1
Sous-ministre assoc., Me Roch Rioux
Bureau des règlements
Directeur, Michel Leclerc
Bureau des lois
Directeur, Jean Allaire
Bureau du droit civil
Directeur, André Cossette
Direction de la législation ministérielle
Directrice, Marie-Josée Longtin

Direction de la recherche
Directeur, Denis Carrier
Direction de la refonte des lois et des
règlements
Directeur, Pierre Legendre

Personnel, administration et registraire du Québec
Sous-ministre assoc., Raymond Benoît
Directeur du budget, Claude Lafrance
Ressources matérielles
Directeur, André Drolet
Direction des systèmes d'informatique
Directeur, Simon Cantin
Direction des ressources humaines
Directeur, Albert Thibault
Evaluation et planification
Directeur (p.i.), Fernand Gosselin

Enregistrement
Sous-ministre adj., Clément Ménard
Courtage immobilier
Surintendant, Réal Martel
L'enregistrement, secteur est
Directeur, Gilles Paquet
L'enregistrement, secteur ouest
Directeur, Simon Morency
Direction des enregistrements officiels
Directeur, Jean-Claude Duchesneau
Bureau d'administration de la loi
sur les huissiers
Directeur, Pierre Morin

Services judiciaires
Sous-ministre assoc. (p.i.), Raymond Benoît

COURS DE JUSTICE
(See Judiciary listings)

AGENCIES, BOARDS AND COMMISSIONS

Commission des droits de la personne
(Human Rights Commission)
360, rue St-Jacques ouest, mezz.
Montréal, H2Y 1P5

The Commission des droits de la personne was
established in 1976 under the *Charter of Human
Rights and Freedoms.* Its role is to promote the
principles of basic political, judicial, social, and
economic rights and of equality as included in the
Charter.

The Commission carries out investigations in
cases of discrimination and exploitation; assists
individuals and groups in obtaining hearings; and
works to bring about corrective measures to end
the violation of human rights. The Commission is
involved in education and research, and serves as
a source of information. It makes legislative
recommendations and co-operates with other
human rights organizations as well.

Since June 26, 1985, under Part III of the
Charter, any organization operating in Quebec
can, on a voluntary basis, devise and implement

an affirmative action program. Even if these voluntary programs are not subject to prior approval, the Commission must, whenever required, lend assistance for the devising of such a program.

Furthermore, following a complaint or as part of an investigation on its own initiative, the Commission has the authority to investigate and determine whether an affirmative action program is required.

Thirteen grounds for discrimination are mentioned in the Charter: race, colour, sex, pregnancy, sexual orientation, civil status, age (except as provided by law), religion, political convictions, language, ethnic or national origins, social conditions, and handicaps.

Président, Jacques Lachapelle
Vice-présidente, Sophia Florakas-Petsalis

Commission des services juridiques

(Legal Services Commission)
2, place Desjardins, Tour de l'Est, bur. 1404
C.P. 123, Montréal, H5B 1B3

Legal aid in Quebec is administered by a corporation consisting of 12 members appointed by the government. These persons are chosen from those groups which, because of their activities, are likely to contribute to the study and solution of the legal problems of the underprivileged. The president and vice-president of the Commission must be lawyers.

Official functions of the Commission include the following: the general administration of the budget received from the Ministry of Justice and the Treasury Board; the general orientation of the legal aid network; the promotion of the development of programs of legal information; the undertaking of studies and inquiries designed to plan the development of legal aid; the formation of a review committee to hear applicants who have been denied legal aid; and the establishment of regional corporations designed to provide legal aid.

Président, Yves Lafontaine
Vice-président, Denis Bouchard
Secrétaire, Jacques Lemaître-Auger
Trésorier, René A. Morin, c.a.

Conseil de la magistrature du Québec

1, rue Notre-Dame est, bur. 7.45
Montréal, H2Y 1B6

The Conseil de la magistrature du Québec was established in July 1978 (S.Q. 1978, Chapter 33). Its principal functions are:

a) to organize refresher programs for judges;
b) to adopt and amend, if necessary, a judicial code of ethics;
c) to receive and examine any complaint lodged against a judge appointed by the government of the province of Quebec;
d) to promote the efficiency and standardization of procedure before the courts;
e) to receive suggestions, recommendations, and requests made to it regarding the

administration of justice, to study them, and to make the appropriate recommendations to the Minister of Justice; and
f) to co-operate, in accordance with the law, with any body pursuing similar purposes outside Quebec.

A permanent secretariat has existed since July 1979.

Président, Juge Gaston Rondeau
Secrétaire, Me J.-Pierre Barrette

Fonds d'aide aux recours collectifs

1, rue Notre-Dame est, bur. 7.50
Montréal, H2Y 1B6

Class action is a legal proceeding which allows a person to assert not only his own rights before the courts, but also those of a group of individuals when their claims have enough in common to justify their being grouped together in the same proceeding.

Fonds d'aide aux recours collectifs is a corporation administered by three persons appointed by the government. Its purpose is to ensure the financing of class actions and to disseminate information respecting the exercise of such actions.

The Fund pays the recipient in the manner provided for in the agreement and up to the amount decided upon. Costs covered include:
• the fees of the attorney;
• the fees and costs of experts and advocates-counsel;
• the costs and other court disbursements including notice costs if they are the recipient's responsibility; and
• the other expenses disbursed in the preparation or submission of the class action.

If the Fund refuses the applicant's request for assistance, he may appeal the decision before the Court of Quebec.

Président, Me Allan Zilbert
Directeur gén., Me Jacques A. Dufour

Office de la protection du consommateur

400, boul. Jean-Lesage, bur. 450
Québec, G1K 8W4
General Information: (418) 643-1484
Village olympique
5199, rue Sherbrooke est, Montréal, H1T 3X1
General Information: (514) 873-7771

The Office de la protection du consommateur is established under the *Consumer Protection Act,* S.Q. 1971, Chapter 74.

The main duties of this government body are as follows:
• to supervise the application of this or any other Act under which it is charged with such supervision;
• to receive complaints from consumers;
• to educate and inform the population on matters of consumer protection;
• to carry out studies in co-operation with consumer protection services or bodies;

- to make merchants, manufacturers, and advertisers aware of consumer needs and demand;
- to evaluate goods and services offered to consumers;
- to co-operate with the various departments and bodies of the Quebec government in matters of consumer protection and to co-ordinate the work done by such departments and bodies for such purposes;
- to represent consumers to governmental bodies whose activities affect consumers; and
- to create, by Regulation, consumer protection regional advisory councils for the regions designated by it, and to determine their composition, functions, duties and powers, and their administrative modes and procedures, and to provide compensation to their members.

Président, Gilles Moreau
Vice-président, Vincent Dumas
Direction des ressources et systèmes
Directeur, Gaétan Ste-Marie
Direction des affaires juridiques
Directeur (p.i.), Jacques Vignola
Direction des communications
Directeur (p.i.), V. Dumas
Direction des bureaux régionaux
Directeur, Yvon Bélair
BUREAUX RÉGIONAUX:
Abitibi-Témiscamingue
33, rue Gamble ouest, r.c., Rouyn, J9X 2R3
Responsable rég., Denise Tellier
Bas-St-Laurent
337, rue Moreault, Rimouski, G5L 1P4
Responsable rég., Micheline Côté
Côte-Nord
456, rue Arnaud, Sept-Iles, G4R 3B1
Responsable rég. (p.i.), Léonard Fortin
Estrie
740, rue Galt ouest, bur. 202
Sherbrooke, J1H 1Z3
Responsable rég., Yves Leclairc
Gaspésie—Iles-de-la-Madeleine
Edifice Pierre-Fortin
11, rue de la Cathédrale
C.P. 1418, Gaspé, G0C 1R0
Responsable rég. (p.i.), Robert Bisaillon
Laurentides-Lanaudière
85, rue de Martigny ouest, bur. 1.03
St-Jérôme, J7Y 3R8
Responsable rég., Jean-Jacques Marchand
Mauricie—Bois-Francs
Edifice Capitanal, r.c.
100, rue Laviolette, Trois-Rivières, G9A 5S9
Responsable rég., Jacques Brochu
Montréal
Village olympique, Aile A, bur. 3671
5199, rue Sherbrooke est, Montréal, H1T 3X2
Responsable rég., Richard Farmer
Outaouais
170, rue Hôtel-de-Ville, 6e ét.
Hull, J8X 4C2
Responsable rég., Micheline Gamache
Québec
400, boul. Jean-Lesage, 3e ét.
Québec, G1K 8W4
Responsable rég., Claude Ruel

Rive-Sud—Montérégie
210, place Charles-Lemoyne, bur. 401
Longueuil, J4K 2T5
Responsable rég., Pierre Aubry
Saguenay—Lac-St-Jean
2481, rue St-Dominique, Jonquière, G7X 6K4
Responsable rég., Léonard Fortin

MINISTÈRE DU LOISIR, DE LA CHASSE ET DE LA PÊCHE

(Recreation, Hunting and Fishing)
150, boul. St-Cyrille est, Québec, G1R 4Y3
General Information: (418) 643-3127

CABINET DU MINISTRE
Ministre, L'hon. Yvon Picotte

CABINET DU SOUS-MINISTRE
Sous-ministre, Pierre Bernier
Direction des communications
Directeur, Jean-Philippe Gagnon
Service information et production
Chef de service, Vacant
Service des relations avec les clientèles
Chef de service, Guy Baillargeon
Coordination du développement des initiatives privées
Coordonnateur, P.A. Bélanger
Direction des affaires juridiques
Directeur, Me Michel Lalande
Direction de la comptabilité
Directeur, Hervé Bolduc
Secrétariat et recherche socio-économique
Directeur, André Magny
Analyse et recherche socio-économique
Chef de service, Claudette Blais
Service des infractions
Responsable, Guy Larose
Secrétariat à l'évaluation et à la vérification
Directeur, Byrne Amyot
Service de la vérification interne
Chef de service, Ernest Bruyère
Secrétariat de la conférence nationale du loisir
Coordonnateur, Guy Gauthier

Direction générale de la ressource faunique
Directeur gén., sous-ministre adj.,
Georges Arseneault
Relations avec les autochtones
Coordonnateur, Gilles Lamontagne
Direction de la gestion des espèces et des habitats
Directeur, Daniel Saint-Onge
Faune terrestre (grande faune)
Chef de service (p.i.), Rodrigue Bouchard
Faune terrestre (petite faune)
Chef de service, Normand Traversy
Faune aquatique (eau froide)
Chef de service, Yvon Côté
Faune aquatique (eau fraîche)
Chef de service, Camille Pomerleau
Faune aquatique (aquaculture)
Chef de service, Serge Gonthier

Etudes écologiques
Chef de service, Louis Aubry
Direction de la réglementation, de la tarification et des permis
Directeur, Richard Châtelain
Direction des territoires fauniques
Directeur, P.H. Ouellet
Direction de l'éducation
Directeur, P.E. Ohl

Direction générale du loisir, des sports et des parcs

Directrice gén., sous-ministre adj.,
Gisèle Desrochers
Direction du loisir socio-culturel et des programmes à la jeunesse
Directeur, Emilien Landry
Service de la gestion des subventions
Directeur, Jacques Lévesque
Direction des sports
Directeur, Jean-Guy Tessier
Direction des programmes municipaux
Directeur, Guy Desrosiers
Direction du plein air et des parcs
Directeur, Guy Bussières

DIRECTION GÉNÉRALE DE L'ADMINISTRATION ET DES SERVICES TECHNIQUES
Directeur gén., Marcel Miville Deschène
Direction des ressources humaines
Directeur, Jacques Rivard
Service développement dotation et organisation
Directeur, Jacques Leclerc
Service relations de travail, santé soutien administratif
Chef de service, Michel Julien
Direction des ressources financières
Directeur, Roger Tardif
Service de la programmation et de l'analyse budgétaire
Chef de service, René Billette
Service des opérations budgétaires et des contrats
Chef de service, Emile Bolduc
Direction de l'informatique
Directeur, Jacques Blondeau
Direction des ressources matérielles
Directrice, Marc Gauvin
Service de l'approvisionnement
Chef de service, Jacques Sauvageau
Service gestion des locaux
Chef de service, Gilles D'Amours
Service des télécommunications
Chef de service, Gérard Latulippe
Service developpement des systèmes
Chef de service, Maurice Gagnon
Service soutien interne
Chef de service, Caroll O'Keefe
Direction des services techniques
Directeur, Conrad Bolduc
Service de la construction
Chef de service, Julien Lessard

Direction générale des opérations régionales

Directeur gén., *sous-ministre adj.,*
André Lachance
Directeur gén. adj., Eric-Yves Harvey
DIRECTIONS RÉGIONALES:
Région 01—Bas-St-Laurent—Gaspésie
Directeur, Michel Brouillard
92, Deuxième rue ouest, Rimouski, G5L 8B3
Région 02—Saguenay—Lac-St-Jean
Directeur (p.i.), Luc Berthiaume
3950, boul. Harvey, Jonquière, G7X 8L6
Région 03—Québec
Directeur, Bernard Lavergne
9530, rue de la Faune, C.P. 7200
Charlesbourg, G1G 5H9
Région 04—Trois-Rivières
Directeur, Robert De Nobile
100, rue Laviolette, C.P. 187
Trois-Rivières, G9A 5S9
Région 05—l'Estrie
Directeur, Pierre H. Boisvenu
85, rue Holmes, Sherbrooke, J1E 1S1
Région 06—Montréal
Directeur, André Laforte
6255, Treizième av., Rosemont, H1X 3E6
Région 07—l'Outaouais
Directeur, Pierre Levac
13, rue Buteau, Hull, J8Z 1V4
Région 08—Abitibi-Témiscamingue
Directeur, Jean-Guy Dagré
180, boul. Rideau, Noranda, J9X 1N9
Région 09—Côte-Nord
Directeur, Raynald Girard
818, av. Laure, Sept-Iles, G4R 1Y8
Région 10—Nouveau-Québec
Directeur, Claude Despatie
1995, boul. Charest ouest, Ste-Foy, G1N 4H9

AGENCIES, BOARDS AND COMMISSIONS

Fondation de la faune du Québec
690, Grande-Allée est, 2e ét., Québec, G1R 2K5

Established under the *Act respecting the conservation and development of wildlife,* R.S.Q., Chapter C-61.1, the Fondation de la faune du Québec is a mandatary corporation of the government of Quebec. The Fondation is administered by a board of directors composed of nine members. It held its first meeting in November 1985.

The main functions of the Fondation are: to receive contributions (donations, bequests, etc.); to rent or buy real property; to conclude agreements with individuals or groups; and to promote or aid restoration, development, and upgrading of wildlife and wildlife habitat.
P.-D.G., Michel Damphousse

Régie de la sécurité dans les sports du Québec
Ed. Capitanal, bur. 114, 100, rue Laviolette
Trois-Rivières, G9A 5S9
MONTRÉAL
Village olympique, bur. 3721
5199, rue Sherbrooke est, Montréal, H1T 3X2

The Régie de la sécurité dans les sports du Québec is a government body whose objective is to make the practice of sport as safe as possible for both participants and spectators.

The Régie was created under the *Act respecting safety in sports*, which was assented to in Dec. 21, 1979 and came into force on June 25, 1980.

The Régie promotes the importance of safety in sports to sports circles and to the public through educational and prevention programs. In accomplishing its objective, it works in co-operation with all parties involved in sports — organizations, sports federations, groups, and individuals.

Président, Raymond Bernier
Vice-président, Jean Duquette
Communications
Directrice, Lucie Ranger
Opérations
Directeur, Guy Bigras
Services administratifs
Responsable, Claude Lamarre
Service de la recherche
Responsable, Guy Régnier
Service juridique et Secrétariat
Directrice et secrétaire, Me Diane Bois-Dalpé
Service des sports de combat
Responsable, Mario Latraverse

Société des établissements de plein air du Québec
650, rue Sir-Louis-Jetté, Québec, G1S 2W3
P.-D.G., Michel Noël de Tilly
Secrétaire et directeur des services juridiques,
Yvan Bilodeau
Finances et administration
Vice-président, Claude Tremblay
Comptabilité
Directeur, Roger Labbé
Contrôle
Directeur, Vacant
Parc du Mont-Ste-Anne
Directeur, Claude Beaudoin
C.P. 400, Beaupré, G0A 1E0
Activités fauniques
Vice-président, Langevin Gagnon
Anticosti
Directeur, Armand Leblond
Budget, trésorerie et ressources matérielles
Directeur, Jean Lortie
Développement
Vice-président, Jacques Gariépy
Marketing
Directeur, Normand Bolduc
Personnel
Directeur, Ghislain Bernard

MINISTÈRE DE LA MAIN-D'OEUVRE ET DE LA SÉCURITÉ DU REVENU
(Manpower and Income Security)
425, rue St-Amable, Québec, G1R 4Z1
255, boul. Crémazie est, Montréal, H2M 1L5

CABINET DU MINISTRE
Ministre, L'hon. Andre Bourbeau

CABINET DU SOUS-MINISTRE
Sous-ministre en titre, Jean Pronovost
Secrétariat général
Directeur, Michel Stewart
Direction des affaires extra-ministérielles
Directeur, Jacques Roberge
Vérification
Directeur (p.i.), Réal Beaulieu
Direction des services juridiques
Directeur (p.i.), Luc Crevier

DIRECTION GÉNÉRALE DES POLITIQUES ET DES PROGRAMMES
Directeur gén. (p.i.), Pierre Fontaine
Direction des politiques et des programmes de sécurité du revenu
Directeur, Guy Nolet
Direction des politiques et des programmes du développement de l'employabilité
Directeur, Donald Bouffard
Direction des politiques et des programmes de main-d'oeuvre
Directeur, Claude Pagé
Recherche
Directrice, Monique Frappier
Condition féminine
Directrice, Colette Bétit
Evaluation et statistique
Directeur, Paul Gagnon

Direction générale de la formation professionnelle
Sous-ministre adj., Hermann C. Girand
Direction du soutien à la gestion du réseau
Directeur, Vacant
Direction du développement de programmes
Directeur, Pierre Amyot
Direction de la gestion de programmes et de services
Directeur, Alfred Richard
Service des secteurs d'activités économiques
Directeur, André Lavigne
Service des programmes d'apprentissage et de qualification
Directeur, Jean Beaunoyer
Service d'analyses et projets
Directeur, Denis Jacques
Service des programmes de formation professionnelle
Directeur, Jean-Guy Despres

Direction générale du réseau Travail-Québec
Sous ministre adj., Julien Lemieux
Investigation
Directeur, J.-A. Marcel Lapointe
Recouvrement
Directeur, Gilles Dubé
Qualité des services
Directeur, Yves Traversy
Directeur gén., secteur centre, Robert Lavoie
Directeur gén., secteur ouest, Roger Pelletier
Directeur gén., secteur est, André Laliberté

Direction générale de l'administration

Sous-ministre adj., Serge Rémillard
Ressources humaines
Directeur, Maurice Busque
Ressources financières
Directeur, Alain Deroy
Ressources matérielles
Directeur, Camille Côté
Communications
Directeur, Luc Poirier

DIRECTION GÉNÉRALE DES RESSOURCES INFORMATIONNELLES

Directeur gén., André Gariépy
Direction du soutien de la productivité
Directeur, Claude Carignan
Direction du développement "Refonte"
Directeur, Gilles Héon
Direction du développement "Continuité"
Directeur, André Rivard
Traitement de l'information
Directeur, Michel Langlois

AGENCIES, BOARDS AND COMMISSIONS

Commission des affaires sociales

1020, rte de l'Eglise, 2ᵉ ét., Ste-Foy, G1V 3V9
General Information: (418) 643-3400
440, boul. René-Lévesque ouest
Montréal, H2Z 1V7
General Information: (514) 873-5643

The Social Affairs Commission is the appeal tribunal for all provincial social security legislation in the province of Quebec.

It is composed of a president (judge of the Court of Quebec), 19 lawyers, and 26 assessors who are medical doctors, psychiatrists, or social workers. The Commission hears appeals of decisions rendered by administrative boards dealing with such matters as pensions, welfare, worker's compensation, state-run automobile insurance, social and health services, and the protection of the mentally ill.

Before rendering any decision, the Commission must allow concerned parties to be heard. The Commission may confirm or reverse any decision referred to it. If it reverses a decision, it must render the decision which in its opinion is appropriate. All decisions are final and without appeal.

Président, Gilles Poirier
Vice-présidente, Céline Turcotte
Vice-président, Daniel Harvey
Directrice des opérations, Micheline Leduc
Directeur des opérations, Jean-Guy Blouin
Support Bureau de Montréal
Directeur, Michel Gallay

Commission des normes du travail

400, boul. Jean-Lesage
C.P. 18500, Terminus postal, Québec, G1K 7Z5

The Commission des normes du travail is an agency responsible to the Minister of Manpower and Income Security. It was created pursuant to the *Act respecting labour standards,* S.Q. 1979, Chapter 45, which came into force on April 16, 1980.

Its objective is to protect workers in Quebec, and in particular, workers who are not unionized or governed by a decree; in short, all workers not protected by a labour agreement.

The Commission informs the population about labour standards and supervises their application. Labour standards are established for minimum wage, the work week, annual vacations, paid statutory holidays, special leave, maternity leave, prior notice of lay-off, and certification.

The Commission also offers recourse against illegal dismissal if, for example, an employee has been dismissed for exercising his rights under the *Act respecting labour standards,* or because he has reached the normal retirement age. Another avenue of appeal, recourse against dismissal not made for good and sufficient cause, is offered by the Commission to employees who have had five years of uninterrupted service with one employer.

P.-D.G., Paul-Emile Bergeron
Secrétaire (p.i.), Lucie Paquet
Membres de la Commission:
Paul-Emile Bergeron, Hervé Dickner,
Pearl Castonguay-Dolgin, Jacques Fortin,
Gérald A. Poncton, Jean Renaud,
Yvette St-Onge
Directeur gén. de l'administration,
Michel C. Bilodeau
Directeur gén. de l'application des normes,
Jean-Louis Boulanger
Directeur des affaires juridiques,
Richard Parent
Directeur des communications,
J.-Alphée Gagné
Directeur du secrétariat et
de la recherche (p.i.), Lucie Paquet
Directeur des ressources humaines,
Jacques Dumas
Directeur des systèmes d'information,
Aurélien D'Allaire
Directeur des ressources matérielles,
Jean Rochette
Directeur des finances, Edmour Bergeron
Directrice de la vérification interne,
Francine Martel Vaillancourt
Chef du service du prélèvement (p.i.),
Edmour Bergeron

Office de la sécurité du revenu des chasseurs et piégeurs cris

Tour Frontenac, bur. 703, 2700, boul. Laurier
Ste-Foy, G1V 2L8

The Income Security Board administers a program of guaranteed annual income for Cree hunters and trappers in the James Bay area of Quebec. The program was set up pursuant to section 30 of the *James Bay and Northern Quebec Agreement,* signed in November 1975 between, among others, the Cree and the federal and provincial governments. The program, in operation since 1976, is administered by a board composed of six members, three of them appointed by the Cree Regional Authority and three by the Government of Quebec. The chairmanship and vice-chairmanship alternate annually between the government and the Cree Regional Authority.

Président, Roger Grenier
Secrétaire gén., Monique Caron

Régie des rentes du Québec
2525, boul. Laurier
C.P. 5200, Québec, G1V 2L2

The Régie des rentes du Québec, established in July 1965 by virtue of the *Act respecting the Quebec Pension Plan,* is a Crown agency invested with the general powers of a corporation and the specific powers conferred upon it by law. The mandate of the Régie includes the administration of the *Act respecting the Quebec Pension Plan,* the *Act respecting supplemental pension plans,* and the *Family Allowances Act.*

The Régie is administered by a representative-type board of directors, composed of a president and 11 other members appointed by the Quebec government.

P.-D.G., Claude Legault
Vice-président aux opérations, Vacant
Vice-président aux affaires professionnelles, Vacant
Vice-présidente à l'administration, Nicole René
Secrétaire de la régie, Guy Lachance
Directeur de la recherche, Jacques Gagné
Services professionnels
Directrice, Marie-Claude Lévesque
Régimes de retraite
Directeur, Yves Slater
Coordination et des systèmes corporatifs
Directeur, Lucien Drolet
Relations avec la clientèle
Directeur, Bernard Le May
Opérations centralisées
Directeur, Guy Chaloux
Finances
Directeur, Jacques Dallaire
Ressources humaines
Directeur, Jean-Luc Henry
Communications
Directrice, Micheline Paradis
Systèmes d'information
Directeur, Pierre Guimont
Conseil d'arbitrage
Président, Jean Levesque

MINISTÈRE DU REVENU
(Revenue)
3800, rue Marly, Ste-Foy, G1X 4A5
3, place Desjardins
C.P. 3000, succ. Desjardins, Montréal, H5B 1A4

CABINET DU MINISTRE
Ministre, L'hon. Yves Séguin

BUREAU DU SOUS-MINISTRE
Sous-ministre, Bernard Angers
Sous-ministres adj.: Marcel Robert, Denis Rheault, André St-Jean, Alain Dompierre, Jean-Paul Beaulieu
Directeur, Jacques Fortier
Comptabilité
Comptable, Claude Marceau

SERVICES AU PUBLIC
Directeur gén., Gilles Néron
Services aux clientèles—Québec
Directeur, Maurice Poirier
Services aux clientèles—Montréal
Directrice, Jocelyne Aubin
Communications
Directrice, Michèle LaSanté

CONTENTIEUX
Bureau de Québec, André Rochon
Bureau de Montréal, Yves Ouellet
Bibliothèque du ministère
Responsable, Pierre-Paul Blais
Vérification interne
Directeur, Louis Morissette
PLANIFICATION ET BUDGET
Directeur gén., Bertrand Croteau

RESSOURCES
Directeur gén., Michel Vaillancourt
Pourvoyeuse, Nicole Boily
LÉGISLATION
Directeur gén., André St-Jean
SYSTÈMES D'INFORMATION ET DE GESTION
Directeur gén., Denis Rheault
PERCEPTION
Directeur gén., Gabriel Cayer

OPÉRATIONS
Directeur gén., Alain Dompierre
Coordination
Directeur, Raymond Pilon
Programmes et procédés
Directrice, Suzanne Francoeur
Bureau des opérations—Québec
Directrice, Suzanne M.-Benoit
Bureau des opérations—Montréal
Directeur, Bernard Verroeulst

VÉRIFICATION
Directeur gén., Marcel Robert
Programmes et méthodes
Directeur, Marc Paquet

Bureaux de la vérification:
Québec
Directeur, Gaston L'Anglais
Montréal
Directeur, André Mongrain

Enquêtes spéciales:
Québec et Montréal
Directeur, Alain Dufour
Refonte des systemes
Bertrand Croteau

AGENCIES, BOARDS AND COMMISSIONS

Régie des loteries et courses du Québec

2055, rue Peel, bur. 700, Montréal, H3A 2K9

The Régie des loteries et courses du Québec was created on Dec. 23, 1969 by an *Act respecting lotteries and racing*, which was subsequently amended on Dec. 22, 1978, by an *Act respecting lotteries, racing, publicity contests and amusement machines*. The Act gives the Régie a mandate to supervise, regulate, and control the aforementioned activities.

To do so, the Régie is empowered:

- to deliver licences, to receive duties related to those licences and to refuse to deliver or to suspend or revoke a licence;
- to make rules on procedures, conditions and standards governing the conduct of matters under its jurisdiction and rules of procedure and practice for matters coming before the board; and
- to the exclusion of any tribunal, to hear and decide certain litigations brought before it (decisions are final).

P.-D.G., Marcel R. Savard, f.c.a.
Vice-président, Albert Raymond
Membres: Marie Caron, Gilles Michaud, Jacques Veilleux

MINISTÈRE DE LA SANTÉ ET DES SERVICES SOCIAUX

(Health and Social Services)
1075, ch. Ste-Foy, Québec, G1S 2M1
General Information: (418) 643-3380
6161, rue St-Denis, Montréal, H2S 2R5
General Information: (514) 873-2580

CABINET DE LA MINISTRE

Ministre, L'hon. Thérèse Lavoie-Roux

CABINET DU SOUS-MINISTRE

Sous-ministre, Réjean Cantin
Service juridique
Directeur, Laurence Demers
Condition féminine
Coordonnatrice, Marie Leclerc
Secrétariat à la coordination,
Jean-Claude Beaulieu
Vérification interne, Jean-Marie Lampron
Secrétariat à l'adoptation
Coordonnateur (p.i.), Lucien Leblanc

PLANIFICATION ET ÉVALUATION
Directeur gén., Paul A. Lamarche
1075, ch. Ste-Foy, 2ᵉ ét., Québec, G1S 2M1
Evaluation
Directrice (p.i.), Sylvie Dillard
Planification
Directeur (p.i.), Paul A. Lamarche
Planification stratégique, coordination de la recherche et coopération
Directeur, Simon Caron

Prévention et services communautaires

Sous-ministre adj., Denise Laberge-Ferron
Prévention et protection de santé publique
Directeur (p.i.), Marc Dionne
Programmes communautés, famille et jeunesse
Directrice, Mireille Fillion
Liaisons
Directrice, Louise Milhomme

Recouvrement de la santé

Sous-ministre adj., (p.i.) Raynald Gagnon
Santé physique
Directeur (p.i.), Mario Alberton
Santé mentale
Directeur (p.i.), Claude Voisine
Services professionnels
Directeur, Jacques Nadon
Liaisons
Directeur (p.i.), Jacques Robitaille

Réadaptation et services de longue durée

Sous-ministre adj., Duc Vu
Réadaptation
Directeur, Gratien Audet
Services de longue durée
Directeur (p.i.), René Dionne
Liaisons
Directeur, Jules Côté
Planification budgétaire, Donald Morasse

Relations de travail

Sous-ministre adj., Jean-Yves Légaré
Personnel syndiqué
Directeur, Jean-Jacques Deguire
Professionnels de la santé
Directeur, André Bergevin
Cadres
Directeur, Gaétan Langlois
Main-d'oeuvre et rémunération
Directeur, Albert Melançon

Equipements et services

Sous-ministre adj., Lorain Groleau
Programmation et équipement
Directeur, Fernand Pagé
Construction
Directeur (p.i.), Conrad Dubuc
Ressources matérielles
Directeur, Claude Allard
Communications
Directeur, Benoît Roy
Mesures d'urgence et ambulances
Directeur, Louis-Philippe Langlois

Budget et administration

Sous-ministre adj., André D'Astous
Systèmes d'information
Directeur, Gilles Ampleman
Politiques et systèmes financiers
Directeur, Marc Lecours
Directeur du budget, Guymont Parent
Ententes fédérales-provinciales
Directeur, Pierre Roy
Ressources humaines
Directrice (p.i.), Marthe St-Arneault

AGENCIES, BOARDS AND COMMISSIONS

Comité de la santé mentale du Québec
1075, ch. Ste-Foy, 2ᵉ ét., Québec, G1S 2M1

Created in 1977 by Order-in-Council 2967 of the government of Quebec, the Comité de la santé mentale du Québec assists and co-operates in the planning and evaluation of the general mental health policies of the government of Quebec, as well as of those for which the Ministry of Health and Social Services is specifically responsible.

Recent studies published by the Comité have treated the following areas of research: the concept of mental health, the efficacy of treatments, the protection and the development of the mental health of children, alternative resources in mental health, and a comparative survey of mental health services in France, Great Britain, Italy, and the U.S.

Secrétaire, Pierre Vendette

Comité sur les abus exercés à l'endroit des personnes âgées
1075, ch. Ste-Foy, 3ᵉ ét., Québec, G1S 2M1
Secrétaire, Patricia Caris

Conseil consultatif de pharmacologie
1125, ch. St-Louis, 7ᵉ ét., Sillery, G1S 1E7

The Advisory Council on Pharmacology was created in 1971 by an amendment to the *Quebec Health Insurance Act.*

The Council's main function is to assist the Minister of Health and Social Services in keeping up to date the drug list contemplated in section 4 of the *Quebec Health Insurance Act* and, for this reason, it gives him advice on the therapeutic value of each drug and on the fairness of the price exacted.

The Council also assists the minister in making the list of drugs which may be used in health establishments throughout the province as contemplated in section 150 of the *Health Services and Social Services Act.*

Président, Dr. Jacques Le Lorier
Directeur gén., Pierre Gouin

Conseil d'évaluation des technologies de la santé
800, place Victoria, bur. 42.05
C.P. 215, succ. Tour de la Bourse
Montréal, H4Z 1E3

The Conseil d'évaluation des technologies de la santé was created on Jan. 20, 1988 by Order-in-Council 88-88. Its membership of 12 independent experts was named July 13 the same year.

The mandate of the Conseil is:
- to promote and support the evaluation of new health technologies, to publish the results of evaluations, and to encourage their use in appropriate medical treatments; and
- to advise the minister on the introduction, diffusion, and use of new technologies and, to

this end, to provide data on their effectiveness, safety, cost, and impact on the health care system as a whole.

Président, Dr. Maurice McGregor

Conseil des affaires sociales
1126, ch. St-Louis, Sillery, G1S 1E5

The Conseil des affaires sociales is an advisory and study body created by an act of the National Assembly in 1970.

Whether by request or with the approval of the minister concerned, or on its own initiative, the Council conducts studies in the fields of health, social services and assistance, and social insurance. Depending on the subject, any conclusions or recommendations are submitted to the Minister of Health and Social Services or the Minister of Manpower and Income Security. In carrying out its inquiries, the Council receives and hears requests and suggestions made by individuals or groups with regard to the questions studied.

The Council is composed of a president and 15 members who are appointed by the government on the recommendation of groups which represent the areas of health and social services, as well as family associations, socio-economic groups, trade unions, and university circles.

Présidente, Dr. Madeleine Blanchet
Secrétaire gén., Yvon Leclerc

Conseil québécois de la recherche sociale
1088, rue Raymond-Casgrain, 1ᵉʳ ét.
Québec, G1S 2E4

The Conseil québécois de la recherche sociale was created on July 8, 1979 by Order-in-Council 2207-79. It acts as a funding agency of the Ministère de la Santé et des Services sociaux.

The mandate of the Conseil is:
- to advise the minister on social research, funding in this area, and related questions;
- to improve the quality of research, distribute the results of this research, and apply them to professional practice in social services as well as to government policy; and
- to institute and administer, with the approval of the minister, support programs in social research and to evaluate such programs.

The Conseil administers three funding programs: research funding for the gathering and publishing of research data, bursaries for specific individuals or groups, and study and analysis funding for projects given priority status.

Corporation d'hébergement du Québec
2050, boul. St-Cyrille ouest, 6ᵉ ét.
Ste-Foy, G1V 2K8

The Corporation d'hébergement du Québec was created in September 1974. It is a non-profit corporation constituted under Part III of the *Loi des compagnies du Québec.* The Minister of Health and Social Services appoints the members of the board, whose number currently stands at five.

The Corporation has a dual role: to oversee the construction of health and social service establishments; and to guarantee short and/or long term financing for the construction and/or acquisition of furnishings by such establishments in Quebec.

Président, Reynald Gagnon
Secrétaire, John Gauvreau
Finances
Directeur (p.i.), Jacques Vézina

Fonds de la recherche en santé du Québec
550, rue Sherbrooke ouest, bur. 1950
Montréal, H3A 1B9

The Fonds de la recherche en santé du Québec is a non-profit organization created on Jan. 25, 1984. According to the provisions of its enabling legislation, the Fonds is created as a corporation governed by Part III of the *Loi des compagnies du Québec* and remains under the authority of the Minister of Health and Social Services.

The board of directors is composed of 14 members including a president and a director-general appointed by the government.

Président, Serge Carrière
Directeur gén., Yvon Poirier

MINISTÈRE DE LA SÉCURITÉ PUBLIQUE
(Public Security)
1200, rte de l'Eglise, Ste-Foy, G1V 4T4

CABINET DU MINISTRE
1200, rte de l'Eglise, 3ᵉ ét., Ste-Foy, G1V 4T4

Ministre (p.i.), L'hon. Gil Rémillard

BUREAU DU SOUS-MINISTRE

Sous-ministre, Jacques Beaudoin
Directeur, Charles Côte
Counseillère, Danielle Bellemare
Counseiller, Régis Larrivée

Services correctionnels

Sous-ministre assoc., Normand Carrier
Direction de la détention
Directeur, Marc-André Laliberté
Secteur est
Directeur adj., Gilles Blanchard
Secteur ouest
Directeur adj., Richard Pelletier
Direction des politiques correctionnelles et du développement communautaire
Directeur, Jean-Claude Fortier
Direction de la probation
Directeur, Jean Demers

Sécurité et prévention

Sous-ministre assoc., Serge Roberge
Direction des services de sécurité et de protection
Directeur, Marc Poulin

Direction de la coordination et des services consultatifs
1, rue Notre-Dame est, 9ᵉ ét.
Montréal, H2Y 1B6
Directeur, Gérard Barbeau
Direction de la recherche et du développement
Directeur, Réal Ouellet

Laboratoire de police scientifique
1701, rue Parthenais
C.P. 1500, succ. C, Montréal, H2L 4K6
Directeur (p.i.), Pierre Boulanger

Laboratoire de médecine légale
1701, rue Parthenais
C.P. 1500, succ. C, Montréal, H2L 4K6
Directeur (p.i.), André Lauzon

Institut de police du Québec
350, place d'Youville, Nicolet, J0G 1E0
Directeur, Gilles Bouchard

Service des expertises comptables
1, rue Notre-Dame est, 9ᵉ ét.
Montréal, H2Y 1B6
Directeur, Claude Chamberland

Administration

Sous-ministre assoc., Raymond Conti
Direction de l'organisation et des ressources humaines
Directeur, Réal Bisson
Direction des ressources matérielles et financières
Directeur, Jean-Charles Godbout
Direction des relations de travail
Directeur, Kevin Walsh

SÛRETÉ DU QUÉBEC
1701, rue Parthenais, Montréal, H2L 4K7
Directeur gén., Robert Lavigne
Planification et technologie
Directeur gén. adj., Marc Lizotte
Ressources humaines
Contrôleur gén., Paul Curzi
Ressources financières et matérielles
Responsable (p.i.), Pierre Paul Armand
Enquêtes criminelles et supports techniques
Directeur gén. adj., Robert Therrien

AGENCIES, BOARDS AND COMMISSIONS
Bureau du coroner
Place Belle-Cour, bur. 420
2590, boul. Laurier, Ste-Foy, G1V 4M6

The Bureau du coroner was created March 3, 1986, under the *Loi sur la recherche des causes et circonstances des décès.*

The Coroner has authority to investigate the causes and circumstances of all deaths occurring in Quebec, especially those occurring under mysterious or violent circumstances, and over the transporting of human remains into or out of the province.

To administer the Act and investigate and/or hold inquest into each of 11,500 death notices received annually, the Bureau du coroner has a permanent staff of 54 (inquest coroners, investigating coroners, and administrative staff) in the regions of Quebec, Montreal, and Hull. In addition, there are 100 part-time investigating coroners across the province.

Reports on investigations and inquests are maintained at and issued from the archives of the chief coroner.

Coroner en chef, Dr. Jean Grenier
2, place Desjardins, Tour de l'Est, bur. 1817
C.P. 424, Montréal, H5B 1B5
Coroner en chef adj., Carmen Crepin
Coroner en chef adj., Dr. Paul G. Dionne

Commission de police du Québec
2050, boul. St-Cyrille ouest, 2e ét.
Québec, G1V 2K8

The Commission de police du Québec was constituted by the Government of Quebec in 1968. Its main responsibility is to promote the efficiency of police services in Quebec. It may also, according to by-law, determine the qualifications and training requirements for the police and the characteristics of police equipment.

The Commission may be called upon to conduct inquiries into:
a) the administration or operations of the Sûreté du Québec (Quebec Provincial Police) or of any municipal force, and into the conduct of their members;
b) the adequacy of police services in any municipality; and
c) the dismissal or reduction of salary of a director or any municipal police officer who is not an employee within the meaning of the *Labour Code,* and in these cases, the Commission renders a decision, which is final.

Whenever requested to do so by the government, the Commission shall make an inquiry into organized crime, terrorism, subversion, or any other aspect of crime.

Président, Juge Jean Alarie
Vice-présidents:
Me Claude Brazeau, Me Jean-Guy Gilbert
Secrétaire, Me Louise Cobetto
BUREAU DE MONTRÉAL
Palais de justice, bur. 14.10
10, rue St-Antoine est, Montréal, H2Y 1A2

Commission québécoise des libérations conditionnelles
2055, rue Peel, bur. 600, Montréal, H3A 1V4

The Quebec Parole Commission has jurisdiction over persons held for six months or more in a Quebec detention facility. This jurisdiction includes inmates who, according to a transfer agreement, are serving a sentence of two years or more in a Quebec establishment rather than in a federal penitentiary.

The Commission determines the conditions under which prisoners are granted parole. The intent is not to revise the sentence imposed by the court; rather, it is to allow inmates who are able to reintegrate into society to complete their sentences among their fellow citizens. Any person on parole who does not respect the conditions set down by the Commission may be reincarcerated for the remainder of his or her sentence.

Présidente, Renée Collette
Palais de justice, r.c., bur. 31
300, boul. Jean-Lesage, Québec, G1K 8K6
Secrétaire, Guy Beaulieu

Office de protection du consommateur
400, boul. Jean-Lesage, Québec, G1K 8W4

Président, Gilles Moreau
Vice-présidente, Marie Bédard
5199, rue Sherbrooke est, bur. 2360
Montréal, H1T 3X1
Vice-président, Jacques Vignola

Régie des permis d'alcool du Québec
1281, boul. Charest ouest, Québec, G1N 2C9

The Régie des permis d'alcool du Québec is responsible for the issuing, renewal, suspension, and cancellation of liquor permits in Quebec. The Régie is composed of a chairman, a vice-chairman, and at least four other directors.

The mandate of the Régie is to evaluate the request for a liquor permit as well as the establishment in question. The Régie must also consider, during this evaluation, whether the issuing of a permit is in the public interest and whether it respects the norms of public tranquillity. Public meetings are held in different areas of the province to hear applications and also to hear cases concerning the possible suspension or cancellation of permits when infractions have been committed.

P.-D.G., Ghislain K.-Laflamme
Secrétaire, Carole Robitaille
1, rue Notre-Dame est, Montréal, H2Y 1B6
Vice-président, André Laurence

MINISTÈRE DU TOURISME
(Tourism)
4, place Québec, bur. 403, Québec, G1R 4X3

CABINET DU MINISTRE
2, place Québec, bur. 336, Québec, G1R 2B5
Tour de la Bourse, bur. 316
800, place Victoria, C.P. 83, Montréal, H4Z 1B7
Ministre, L'hon. Michel Gratton

CABINET DU SOUS-MINISTRE
2, place Québec, bur. 336, Québec, G1R 2B5
Sous-ministre, Jacques-Yves Therrien
Sous-ministre adj., Jacques Demers
Direction des communications
2, place Québec, bur. 344, Québec, G1R 2B5
Directrice, Judith Grenon

ADMINISTRATION
Ressources financières
Directeur, Pierre A. Thibaudeau
Ressources matérielles
Directeur, Robert Madore

Ressources humaines
Directeur, Arthur Mercure

DIRECTION GÉNÉRALE DU MARKETING
Directeur gén., Michel Carpentier
Tour de la Bourse, bur. 260
800, place Victoria, C.P. 125
Montréal, H4Z 1C3
Direction analyse et développement
Directeur, Michel Lambert
710, place d'Youville, 3e ét., Québec, G1R 4Y4

DIRECTION GÉNÉRALE DU DÉVELOPPEMENT
Tour de la Bourse, bur. 260
800, place Victoria, C.P. 125
Montréal, H4Z 1C3
Directeur gén., Henri Chapdelaine
Direction des projets spéciaux
Directeur, Claude Tanguay
Direction du crédit touristique
Directeur, Jean Moussette
4, place Québec, bur. 408, Québec, G1R 4X3
Direction hôtellerie
Directeur, Michel-Claude Demers
710, place d'Youville, 3e ét., Québec, G1R 4Y4
Institut de tourisme et d'hôtellerie du Québec
401, rue de Rigaud, Montréal, H2L 4P3
Directeur gén., Pierre D. Brodeur

AGENCIES, BOARDS AND COMMISSIONS

Société du Palais des congrès de Montréal
201, av. Viger ouest, Montréal, H2Z 1X7

The Montreal Convention Centre officially opened on May 27, 1983. Since its opening, the Centre has hosted more than 750 events attracting 2.5 million visitors, of whom more than 300,000 were delegates from outside Quebec. There are now events booked on the Centre's reservation calendar until the year 2000.

Located in the business district and near Old Montreal and the major hotels, the Centre is built astride the Ville-Marie Expressway. With a total of 30 meeting rooms (accommodating from 30 to 1,000) the Centre also includes a Congress Hall with a seating capacity of 5,800 and a 9,500-m^2 Exhibition Hall with a capacity of 520 booths.
Administration et finance
Vice-président, Jean-Guy Sylvain

MINISTÈRE DES TRANSPORTS
(Transport)
Place Hauteville, 29e ét.
700, boul. St-Cyrille est, Québec, G1R 5H1
General Information: (418) 643-6864

CABINET DU MINISTRE
Ministre, L'hon. Marc-Yvan Côté

CABINET DU SOUS-MINISTRE
Sous-ministre, Pierre Michaud

SECRÉTARIAT DU MINISTÈRE
Directeur, Pierre-Emile Tremblay
Comptabilité
Directeur, André Fiset
Contentieux
Directrice, Anne-Marie Bilodeau
Relations extra-ministérielles
Chef, Jean Simon
Archives et messagerie
Chef, Michel Hamel
Service aérien gouvernemental
Chef, Jean-Guy Paquin
Aéroport, Ste-Foy, G2E 3L9
Vérification interne
Chef, Marcel Plante
Enquêtes
Chef, André Lévesque
Recherche
Directeur, Pierre LaFontaine
Programmation
Directeur, Jacques Ménard
Communications
Directeur, Jacques DeRome

Secrétariat à la mise en valeur du St-Laurent
385, av. Grande-Allée est, Québec, G1R 2H8
Directeur, M. Hugues Morrissette

Direction générale du transport des personnes et des marchandises
Sous-ministre adj., Liguori Hinse
Développement du transport terrestre des personnes
Directeur, Yvon Parenteau
Programme d'aide en transport terrestre des personnes
Directeur, Gordon Smith
Expertise technique en transport terrestre des personnes
Directeur, Gilles Lussier
Direction du transport maritime, aérien et ferroviaire
Directeur, Jacques Girard
Direction du transport routier des marchandises
Directeur, Jean Boulet

Direction générale du génie
Sous-ministre adj., Yvan Demers
Direction des sols et matériaux
Directeur, Paul-A. Brochu
200, rue Dorchester sud, r.c.
Québec, G1K 5Z1
Direction des structures
Directeur, Jean Normand
200, rue Dorchester sud, 2e ét.
Québec, G1K 5Z1
Direction de la circulation et des aménagements
Directeur, Jean-Luc Simard
200, rue Dorchester sud, 6e ét.
Québec, G1K 5Z1
Direction des acquisitions
Directeur, Euclide Harel
750, boul. Charest est, 4e ét., Québec, G1K 3J7

Direction générale des opérations
Sous-ministre adj., Claude Lortie
Direction de la construction
Directeur, Roger Fortin
Direction de l'entretien
Directeur, T. Jiona
DIRECTIONS RÉGIONALES:
Région 01—Bas-St-Laurent—
Gaspésie—Iles-de-la-Madeleine
92, Deuxième rue ouest, 1ᵉʳ ét., local 101
Rimouski, G5L 3E6
Directeur rég., Bernard Baribeau
Région 02—Saguenay—Lac-St-Jean
3950, boul. Harvey, Jonquière, G7X 8L6
Directeur rég., Alain Vallières
Région 3-1—Québec
1995, boul. Charest ouest, Ste-Foy, G1N 4H9
Directeur rég., Jean-Guy Tremblay
Région 3-2—Chaudière-Appalaches
1712, 23ᵉ rue nord, Charny, G6W 2N4
Directeur rég., Jacques-A. Charland
Région 04—Mauricie—Bois-Francs
100, rue Laviolette, Trois-Rivières, G9A 5S9
Directeur rég., Guy Bourelle
Région 05—Estrie
3330, rue King ouest, local 170
Sherbrooke, J1L 1C9
Directeur rég., Paul Brodeur
Région 6-1—Drummond-Yamaska
380, boul. St-Joseph ouest, C.P. 668
Drummondville, J2B 6W8
Directeur rég., André Brien
Région 6-2—Montérégie
201, place Charles-Lemoyne, 5ᵉ ét.
Longueuil, J4K 2T5
Directeur rég., Yvon Tourigny
Région 6-3—Montréal
770, boul. Henri-Bourassa ouest
Montréal, H3L 1P5
Directeur rég., Robert Schiettekatte
Région 6-4—Laurentides
85, rue de Martigny ouest, 3ᵉ ét.
C.P. 720, St-Jérôme, J7Y 3R8
Directeur rég., Gilles Plouffe
Région 07—Outaouais
170, rue Hôtel-de-Ville, bur. 5110, Hull, J8X 4C2
Directeur rég., J.P. Tremblay
Région 08—Abitibi-Témiscamingue
392, rue Burke, Rouyn, J9X 3V3
Directeur rég., François Bérard
Région 09—Côté-Nord
440, rue Brochu, Sept-Iles, G4R 2W8
Directeur rég., Michel Labrie

Direction générale de l'administration et de la gestion financière
Sous-ministre adj., Paul Maranda
Direction du contrôle budgétaire
Directeur, André Descotaux
Direction des contrats et approvisionnements
Directeur, Paul-René Roy
Direction des réclamations
Directeur, Noel Ouellet
Direction du personnel
Directeur, Vacant

Direction des systèmes de gestion
Directeur, Daniel Deschênes

AGENCIES, BOARDS AND COMMISSIONS

Commission des transports du Québec
585, boul. Charest est, Québec, G1K 7W5
General Information: (418) 643-5673
505, rue Sherbrooke est, Montréal, H2L 1K2
General Information: (514) 873-6414

Operating according to provisions of the *Transport Act*, the *Trucking Act,* and the *Motor Vehicle Act,* the Commission issues licences and fixes rates and tariffs. It regulates Quebec's transport industry so as to guarantee the public the best transportation services at competitive prices.

Président, Maurice Ferland
Vice-présidents:
Lise Lambert (Québec)
René Vincent (Montréal)
Administrateur, Lise Villeneuve
Secrétaire, Pierre Simard

Régie de l'assurance automobile du Québec
1134, ch. St-Louis, Sillery, G1S 1E5
Insurance and accident reporting, drivers' licences and vehicle registration:
Quebec: (418) 643-5650
Montreal: (514) 873-7620
Toll-free: 1-800-361-7620

The Régie de l'assurance automobile du Québec was created in 1977 to set up and administer a comprehensive, no-fault insurance plan for the compensation of victims of bodily injury sustained in an automobile accident. The plan was established by the *Automobile Insurance Act,* which came into force on March 1, 1978. The Régie is also responsible for issuing drivers' licences and registration certificates, monitoring compulsory liability insurance for property damage, issuing permits for driving schools, and carrying out various safety programs for road users and their vehicles.

The Régie is a corporation within the meaning of the *Civil Code,* vested with the powers and privileges of a Government agent. It is managed by a board of directors composed of eleven members, including a chairman and a vice-chairman. All the members are appointed by the Government and the chairman is also chief executive officer of the Régie. The Minister of Transport is responsible to the National Assembly for the activities of the Régie.

P.-D.G., Jean-P. Vezina
Secrétaire et directeur des services juridiques, Claude Gélinas
Vérification interne
Directeur, Raynald Noël
Communications
Directeur, Pierre Théberge
Code de la sécurité routière
Vice-président, Georges Lalande
Dossier conducteur
Directeur, Dominique Dubuc

Dossier véhicule
Directeur, Bernard Lefrançois
Permis et immatriculation
Directeur, Alain Marcoux
Opérations régionales
Vice-président, Denis L'Homme
Planification
Vice-président, Michel Roy
Etudes et analyses
Directeur, André Viel
Statistique
Directeur, Réal Marshall
Politiques et programmes
Directeur, Jean-Claude Cloutier
Administration et finances
Vice-président, André Thibault
Ressources humaines
Directeur, Léo Martin
Ressources financières et matérielles
Directeur, Roger Croteau
Systèmes d'information
Directeur, Jocelyn Lévesque
Directeur, Martin Breton
Service aux accidentés
Vice-président, Ronald Clark
Services médicaux et de réadaptation
Directeur, Marc Giroux
Programmation et opérations centrales
Directeur, Camille Genest
Indemnisation, centre
Directeur, Jacques Gosselin
Indemnisation, ouest
Directeur, Denis Giguère
Indemnisation, est
Directeur, Normand Bergeron

Société des traversiers du Québec
109, rue Dalhousie, C.P. 36, succ. B
Québec, G1K 7A1

The Société des traversiers du Québec is a joint-stock company incorporated by a special act assented to by the National Assembly of Quebec on June 4, 1971. The company's shares belong to the public domain and are allotted to the Minister of Finance. However, the Minister of Transport is responsible for application of the act.

The company's main purpose is to provide ferry service across rivers and lakes situated in the province of Quebec.

Originally, the company provided transport services between the cities of Quebec and Lévis only. Following rapid expansion, however, the company now owns 12 ferry boats and operates six different routes (Sorel/St-Ignace-de-Loyola; Québec/Lévis; Montmagny/Ile-aux-Grues; St-Joseph-de-la-Rive/Ile-aux-Coudres; Tadoussac/Baie-Ste-Catherine; Matane/Baie-Comeau/Godbout).

P.-D.G., Jean-Yves Gagnon
Vice-président à l'exploitation,
Patrice St-Amant, ing.
Vice-présidente à l'administration et aux finances, Danielle Paradis
Vice-président aux affaires juridiques,
Jocelyn Fortier, avocat

Vice-président aux ressources humaines,
Jules Lapierre

Société du port ferroviaire Baie-Comeau-Hauterive
28, place La Salle, C.P. 135
Baie-Comeau, G4Z 2G9

Président, Jacques Asselin
Vice-président, André Létourneau
Administrateurs: André Legault, Sylva Lord, Jean-Guy Rousseau
Sec.-trésorier, Michel Caron

Société québécoise des transports
1410, rue Stanley, 8e ét., Montréal, H3A 1P8

The goals of the Société are: to promote the setting up, modernization, expansion, development, and consolidation or reorganization of firms in the transportation sector in order to meet Quebec's commercial and industrial needs; to promote the exporting of goods produced in Quebec; to maximize the socio-economic benefits arising from transportation or related activities; and to carry out investment activities in the transportation sector.

P.-D.G., Pierre Michaud

MINISTÈRE DU TRAVAIL
(Labour)
425, rue St-Amable, Québec, G1R 5M3
255, boul. Crémazie, Montréal, H2M 1L5

CABINET DU MINISTRE
425, rue St-Amable, 2e ét., Québec, G1R 5M3
Ministre, L'hon. Yves Séguin

CABINET DU SOUS-MINISTRE
Sous-ministre, Robert Diamant
Secrétariat et vérification interne
Secrétaire, Jean Larivière
Direction de la planification et de l'évaluation
Directeur (p.i.), Louis J. Lemieux
Service juridique
Directeur (p.i.), Luc Crevier
Affaires extra-ministérielles
Directeur, Jacques Roberge

Relations du travail
Sous-ministre adj., Raymond Désilets
Directeur gén., Gilles Michaud
Commissaire gén. du travail, Robert Lovac
Médiation préventive
Directeur, Yves Dulude
Commissaire de la construction, Gilles Gaul
Direction des décrets
Directeur (p.i.), Eugène Cantin
Direction de l'arbitrage
Directrice, Micheline Maheux
Direction de la conciliation
Directeur (p.i.), Jean Des Trois Maisons
Direction de la médiation, secteurs
public et parapublic

Directeur (p.i.), Normand Gauthier
Direction de l'arbitrage médical
Directeur, Jean R. Lemieux
Direction des enquêtes spéciales
Directeur, Maurice Sarrazin

Recherche, normalisation et administration
Sous-ministre adj., Vacant
Centre de recherche et de statistiques
sur le marché du travail
Directeur, Louis J. Lemieux
Direction générale de la normalisation
Directeur gén., Gérard Pedneault
Direction générale de l'administration
Directeur gén., Guy Picard

Inspection
Sous-ministre adj., Marius Dupuis
Comité aviseur
Président (p.i.), Jacques Tremblay
Direction des politiques et des programmes
Directeur, François Delorme
Direction générale des bureaux régionaux
de l'inspection
Directeur gén., Roger Morin
Direction de la coordination administrative
et technique
Directeur est, Eugène Arrelle
Directeur ouest, Rémi Sauvé

AGENCIES, BOARDS AND COMMISSIONS

Commission de la construction du Québec
3530, rue Jean-Talon ouest
Montréal, H3R 2G3
825, rue Ste-Thérèse, Quebec, G1N 1S6

The Commission de la construction du Québec is a quasi-governmental body whose mandate it is to promote favourable working conditions in the construction industry, working closely with management, labour, and government representatives to attain this goal.

The *Act on labour relations, professional training and manpower management in the construction industry* created the Commission de la construction du Québec on Jan. 1, 1987 in order that it might:
• oversee the application of collective agreements and decrees;
• verify and control the application of the Act and Regulations;
• ensure the competence of those employed in the construction trades;
• organize and oversee union certification votes;
• oversee the application of measures and programs related to professional training;
• manage the complementary fringe benefits plan;
• maintain an audit service to control and verify the collection of dues and contributions established by the Act; and
• structure and manage any indemnity fund that ensures the payment of wages and fringe benefits.

The Commission has 13 regional offices across the province of Quebec that deal directly with the 100,000 workers and the 20,000 employers of the Quebec construction industry.

P.-D.G., Alcide Fournier
Membres du conseil d'administration:
Michel Dion, Roméo Julien, Armand Houle,
Clément Tremblay, Donald Fortin, Yves Paré,
Maurice Pouliot, Jean Lavallée,
Raymond H. Richard, Jacques Henry,
Hermann C. Girard, Michel Gauthier
Secrétaire, Hugues Ferron

Commission de la santé et de la sécurité du travail
1, parc Samuel-Holland, Québec, G1S 4E1
General Information: (418) 643-6319
1199, rue de Bleury, C.P. 6056, succ. A
Montréal, H3C 4E1
General Information: (514) 873-7545

The Commission de la santé et de la sécurité du travail (CSST) administers the government's occupational health and safety plan. Its mandate is to develop, propose, and implement policies on the health and safety of workers so as to ensure better working conditions.

In order to carry out this mandate, the CSST establishes standards of workplace health and safety, and inspects and prosecutes in support of these standards. As well, it supports the development and application of prevention programs, participation mechanisms, training, health services, and information services.

The Commission also operates an accident fund financed by employer assessments. These assessments finance a reserve fund set up to cover future benefit payments on accident claims as well as current benefit payments and administration expenses. Inspection costs are reimbursed by the Quebec government.

The CSST also compensates crime victims and persons who incur injury while performing acts of good citizenship. The sums paid out are reimbursed by the Quebec government.

The various mandates of the Commission are governed by the following laws:
• *Act respecting occupational health and safety*, R.S.Q., Chapter S-2.1
• *Workmen's Compensation Act*, R.S.Q., Chapter A-3
• *Act respecting industrial accidents and occupational diseases*, R.S.Q., Chapter A-3.001
• *Crime Victims Compensation Act*, R.S.Q., Chapter I-6
• *Act to promote good citizenship*, R.S.Q., Chapter C-20
• *Act respecting indemnities for victims of asbestosis and silicosis in mines and quarries*, R.S.Q., Chapter I-7
• *Government Employees Compensation Act*, R.S.C. 1970, Chapter G-8.

P.-D.G., Monique Jérôme-Forget
Administration
Vice-président, Pierre Shedleur

Vice-président adj., Paule-Emile Boucher
Opérations
Vice-président, Gilles Taillon
Relations avec les bénéficiaires
Vice-présidente, Lise Thibault
Services
Vice-président, Yves Tardif
Secrétariat
Secrétaire gén., Pierre Lafrance
Services juridiques
Directeur, Serge Lafontaine
Indemnisation des victimes d'actes criminels
(IVAC)
Directrice, Rolande Couture
Ressources humaines
Directeur, Donald Brisson
Communications
Directrice, Louise Champoux-Paillé
Services médicaux
Directrice, Dr. Louise Mercier
Services financiers
Directeur, Robert Talbot
Programmation budgétaire
Directeur, Gilles Beauchesne
Systèmes
Directeur, Gérard P. Bélanger
Vérification interne
Directeur, Serge Filion
Ressources matérielles
Directeur, Jean-Guy Désilets
Réseau-Ouest
Directrice, Diane Gaudet
Réseau-Montréal
Directeur, Jean-Pierre Arsenault
Réseau-Est
Directeur, Normand Cloutier
DIRECTIONS RÉGIONALES:
Abitibi-Témiscamingue
33, rue Gamble ouest, Rouyn, J9X 2R3
Jean-Guy Dugré
Bas-Saint-Laurent
180, rue des Gouverneurs, Rimouski, G5L 8G1
Paule-André Lavoie
Côte-Nord
690, boul. Laure, bur. 20, Sept-Iles, G4R 4N8
Jean-Marie Boudreault
Estrie
1335, rue King ouest, Sherbrooke, J1J 2B8
Jean-Charles Guindon
Gaspésie—Iles-de-la-Madeleine
144, boul. Gaspé, C.P. 5000, Gaspé, G0C 1R0
Rolland Auger
Ile-de-Montréal
1, place Desjardins, Tour de Sud, 31e ét.
C.P. 3, succ. Desjardins, Montréal, H5B 1H1
Jules Roireau
Lanaudière
432, rue de Lanaudière, Joliette, J6E 7X1
Marcel Laferrière
Laurentides
1000, rue Labelle, St-Jérôme, J7Z 5N6
Jean-François Couillard
Laval
1700, boul. Laval, Laval, H7S 2G6
Yves Saint-Marie

Mauricie—Bois-Francs
1055, boul. des Forges, 2e ét.
Trois-Rivières, G8Z 4J9
Jean-Pierre Arsenault

Montérégie
25, boul. Lafayette, bur. 500
Longueuil, J4K 5B7
Maurice Nantel

Nouveau-Québec
C.P. 690, Radisson, J0Y 2X0
Jean-Guy Dugré

Outaouais
15, rue Gamelin, Hull, J8Y 6N5
Pierre Roy

Québec
1, parc Samuel-Holland, bur. 340
Québec, G1S 4R7
Jean-Guy Lockquell

Saguenay—Lac-St-Jean
901, boul. Talbot, Chicoutimi, G7H 6P8
Serge Gauthier

Conseil consultatif du travail et de la main-d'oeuvre
800, Place Victoria, bur. 2026
C.P. 87, Tour de la Bourse, Montréal, H4Z 1B7
425, rue St-Amable, Québec, G1R 5M3

The Conseil consultatif du travail et de la main-d'oeuvre is an advisory council established in December 1968.

The CCTM answers any questions submitted to it by the Minister of Labour and the Minister of Manpower and Income Security. It also conducts studies in the field of labour and manpower, or may cause such studies and research to be carried out on its behalf. It may invite opinions and suggestions from the public on any current or future studies. Its recommendations are submitted to both ministers.

Since 1969, the Conseil has formed many special committees for the study of such topics as arbitration, Labour Code amendments, international labour standards, health and safety, and others. It also publishes an annual report and an annual list of recognized arbitrators in Quebec.

Président, Raymond Parent
Secrétaire, Romuald Dufour

Conseil des services essentiels
5199, rue Sherbrooke est
Montréal, H1T 3X1
690, av. Grande-Allée est, Québec, G1R 2K5

Présidente, Madeleine Lemieux

Institut de recherche et d'information sur la rémunération
500, rue Sherbrooke ouest, bur. 1220
Montréal, H3A 3C6

P.-D.G., Jean-Louis Hérivault
Vice-présidente, Hélène Wavroch

Régie des entreprises de construction du Québec
577, boul. Henri-Bourassa est
Montréal, H2C 1E2
800, place d'Youville, 16ᵉ ét.
Québec, G1R 5K7

Président, Réal Mireault
Vice-président, Clément Côté

INDEPENDENT AGENCIES, BOARDS, COMMISSIONS AND CROWN CORPORATIONS

Commission administrative des régimes de retraite et d'assurances
2875, boul. Laurier, 2ᵉ ét., Ste-Foy, G1V 4J8

The Commission was established under the *Loi sur le régime de retraite des employés du gouvernement et des organismes publics,* ratified on Dec. 22, 1973. The purpose of the Commission is to administer the Government and Public Employees Retirement Plan, the Teachers' Pension Plan, and the Civil Service Superannuation Plan, as well as all insurance and pension plans whose administration is conferred upon it by law or by the government.

Since its creation, the Commission, which now has a staff of approximately 375, has been given the administration of 15 pension plans and three life insurance plans. Over 450,000 employees currently contribute to the pension plans and about 72,000 persons receive benefits.

Assisted by a 15-member Pension Committee, the Commission advises organizations on the administration of certain insurance plans, acts as payments agent for certain pension plans, and advises the provincial Treasury Board on all benefits received by employees of the public and para-public sectors in Quebec.
Ministre délégué à l'administration et président du Conseil du Trésor, L'hon. Daniel Johnson

Président, Michel Sanschagrin
Vice-président, opérations, Jean-Yves Uhel
Vice-président, l'administration, Guy Morneau
Secrétaire de la commission, Henri Ouellet

Commission des valeurs mobilières du Québec
Tour de la Bourse, 17ᵉ ét., 800, square Victoria
C.P. 246, Montréal, H4Z 1G3

The Commission des valeurs mobilières du Québec is an agency responsible for the control and surveillance of trading in securities. Its role is to promote the development of an efficient securities market, to protect investors against dishonest and fraudulent practices, to regulate disclosure of information to shareholders and to the public by issuers of securities to the public, and to promote competition in the securities market. It also provides a framework for the registration of securities dealers, investment councils and salesmen, and self-regulatory bodies.

The Commission is composed of three full-time members, including the president, and not more than four part-time members appointed by the government. There is also a staff of about 100 people. The Commission's files on issuers, consisting of prospectuses, proxy statements, annual reports, insider reports, etc., are available to the public.

The Commission has delegated to three divisional directors most of the powers in the *Securities Act.* The "Directeur de l'information" is responsible for corporate finance, continuous disclosure, and take-over bids. The "Directeur de l'encadrement du marché" is responsible for: the registration of advisors, dealers, and their representatives; the inspection of registrants; and self-regulatory bodies. Finally, the "Directeur des affaires juridiques" is responsible for investigations and legal proceedings.

Président, Paul Guy
Vice-présidents:
Paul Fortugno, Maurice Cusson
Membres: Gérard M. Beaulieu, Roland Côté, Michel Le Rouzès, Marcellin Tremblay
Secrétaire, Louise leBel-Chevalier
Directeur de l'information, Jean Paré
Directeur de l'encadrement du marché, Pierre Lizé
Directeur des affaires juridiques, Jacques Labelle
Directeur de l'administration, Raymond Hardy
Chef du service de conseil juridique, Antoni Dandonneau

Office de planification et de développement du Québec
Edifice G, Aile St-Amable, 3ᵉ ét.
1060, rue Conroy, Québec, G1R 5E6

Established in 1968 by the *Loi sur l'Office de planification et de développement du Québec,* the OPDQ operates primarily as the provincial government's representative in co-ordinating regional economic initiatives.

The OPDQ maintains offices in each of the 16 regions of Quebec and is closely involved with:
• organization of regional socio-economic summits;
• follow-up of government commitments made at these summits;
• co-ordination of government actions in the regions through the Conférence administrative régionale (CAR); and
• collection of regional economic data.

The OPDQ manages the Fonds de développement régional (FDR) which helps with the financing of projects favouring regional economic development. It also has available the Programme expérimental de création d'emplois communautaires (PECEC) which aims at creating jobs through subsidizing the establishment or expansion of businesses.

P.-D.G., Jacques Gagnon
Développement
Directeurs gén. adj. (développement):
Jacques Vézeau, secteur est
Pierre Deland, secteur ouest
Directeur de l'administration et des ressources humaines, Marc Delaunay
Secrétariat et communications
Secrétaire, Claude P. Côté

Direction régionale de la Gaspésie
488, rue de l'Hôtel-de-Ville, C.P. 1360
Chandler, G0C 1K0
Directeur rég. (p.i.), Jean-Yves Joannette

Direction régionale du Bas-St-Laurent
337, rue Moreault, Rimouski, G5L 1P4
Directeur rég., Bernard Dusseault

Direction régionale du Saguenay—Lac St-Jean
3950, boul. Harvey, Jonquière, G7X 8L6
Directeur rég., Pierre Gauthier

Direction régionale de Québec
Edifice G, Aile St-Amable, 1er ét.
1060, rue Conroy, Québec, G1R 5E6
Directeur rég., Laurent Boucher

Direction régionale de la Mauricie—Bois-Francs
100, rue Laviolette, 4e ét.
Trois-Rivières, G9A 5S9
Directeur rég., Robert Gauthier

Direction régionale de l'Estrie
740, rue Galt ouest, bur. 314
Sherbrooke, J1H 1Z3
Directeur rég., J.P. Gendron

Direction régionale de Montréal
440, boul. René-Lévesque ouest, 8e ét.
Montréal, H2Z 1V7
Directeur rég., Bryant McDonough

Direction régionale de Lanaudière
656, rue de Lanaudière, Joliette, J6E 3M7
Directeur rég., Gérald Durocher

Direction régionale des Laurentides
85, boul. de Martigny ouest, 2e ét.
St-Jérôme, J7Y 3R8
Directeur rég., Paul-Emile Vallée

Direction régionale de Montérégie
Edifice du Métro, local 285
100, place Charles-Lemoyne
Longueuil, J4K 2T4
Directeur rég., André Labbé

Direction régionale de l'Outaouais
170, rue Hôtel-de-Ville, bur. 7.120
Hull, J8X 4C2
Directrice rég., Diane Pintal

Direction régionale de l'Abitibi-Témiscamingue
180, boul. Rideau, Rouyn-Noranda, J9X 1N9
Directeur rég. (p.i.), Robert Sauvé

Direction régionale de la Côte-Nord
625, boul. Laflèche, bur. 352
Hauterive, G5C 1C5
Directeur rég., Florent Gagné

Direction régionale du Nord-du-Québec
Edifice G, Aile St-Amable, 3e ét.
1060, rue Conroy, Québec, G1R 5E6
Directeur rég., Jacques Meunier

Régie de l'assurance-maladie du Québec
1125, ch. St-Louis, Sillery, G1K 7T3

The Régie de l'assurance-maladie du Québec, which was established by the *Quebec Health Insurance Board Act* in June 1969, is a corporation within the meaning of the *Quebec Civil Code*. It has the general powers of a corporation and the special powers granted to it by the *Quebec Health Insurance Board Act*.

The Régie administers the Quebec Health Insurance Plan, which comprises a complete range of health-care programs, a prescription drug program for the elderly and people on welfare, and special programs providing functional aids and services to various categories of disabled persons. In addition, the Régie administers a series of programs on behalf of other government departments.

The president of the Régie de l'assurance-maladie is appointed for a period not exceeding ten years. He is assisted by a vice-president and 12 representatives, from the public and private sectors, health organizations, and government bodies, who are given a three-year mandate.

P.-D.G., Dr. J.-Auguste Mockle
Direction développement administratif
des programmes
Directeur, Dominique Carmichael
Directeur gén. adj. à l'administration des programmes, André Roy
Direction contrôle des programmes
Directeur, Paul-Emile Lafrance
Direction ressources humaines
Directeur, Marc St-Pierre
Direction ressources matérielles et financières
Directeur, Henri Roberge
Direction des systèmes
Directeur, Denis Forcier
Contentieux et secrétariat
Secrétaire et directeur, Denis Morency
Direction planification stratégique
Directeur, Pierre Houde

JUDICIARY AND JUDICIAL OFFICERS

La Cour supérieure
(Superior Court)

DISTRICT D'APPEL DE MONTRÉAL
Palais de Justice
10, rue St-Antoine est, Montréal, H2Y 1A2
General Inquiries: (514) 393-2327

Juge en chef: L'hon. Alan B. Gold
Juge en chef adjoint:
  L'hon. Lawrence A. Poitras

Juges:
L'hon. Maurice Archambault
L'hon. Guy Arseneault
L'hon. François Auclair
L'hon. Alphonse Barbeau
L'hon. Jules Beauregard
L'hon. François Bélanger
L'hon. Marcel Belleville
L'hon. Claude Benoît
L'hon. Anthime Bergeron
L'hon. Jean-Paul Bergeron
L'hon. André G. Biron
L'hon. Ivan Bisaillon
L'hon. John Bishop
L'hon. Jules Blanchet
L'hon. Jean-Guy Boilard
L'hon. Pierre Boudreault
L'hon. Bernard de L. Bourgeois
L'hon. Jean-Marie Brassard
L'hon. André Brossard
L'hon. Jean-Jude Chabot
L'hon. Vital Cliche
L'hon. Réjane L. Colas
L'hon. Michel Côté
L'hon. Jean Crépeau
L'hon. Jean-Jacques Crôteau
L'hon. Louis de Blois
L'hon. Jules Deschênes*
L'hon. André Deslongchamps
L'hon. Kevin Downs
L'hon. Jacques Ducros
L'hon. Jacques Dugas
L'hon. Roland Durand
L'hon. Denis Durocher
L'hon. Jean Filiatreault
L'hon. Bernard Flynn
L'hon. Yves Forest*
L'hon. André Forget
L'hon. Jean Frappier
L'hon. Raynald Fréchette
L'hon. John H. Gomery
L'hon. Bernard Gratton
L'hon. Benjamin J. Greenberg
L'hon. Claude Guérin

L'hon. A. Derek Guthrie
L'hon. Irving J. Halperin
L'hon. John R. Hannan
L'hon. René Hurtubise
L'hon. Yvon Jasmin
L'hon. W. Austin Johnson
L'hon. Paul Jolin
L'hon. Claire Barrette Joncas
L'hon. James T. Kennedy
L'hon. Maurice E. Lagacé
L'hon. Ruston B. Lamb
L'hon. Hélène LeBel
L'hon. Jean Legault
L'hon. Jean-Louis Léger
L'hon. Lyse Lemieux
L'hon. Anatole Lesyk
L'hon. Denis Lévesque
L'hon. Yvan A. Macerola
L'hon. Kenneth C. Mackay
L'hon. Jean Marquis
L'hon. J. Fraser Martin
L'hon. Paul A. Martineau
L'hon. Israel S. Mass
L'hon. Yves Mayrand
L'hon. Victor Melançon
L'hon. Maurice Mercure
L'hon. Perry Meyer
L'hon. Pierre A. Michaud
L'hon. Jean-Claude Nolin
L'hon. Luc Parent
L'hon. Réjean F. Paul
L'hon. Charles A. Phelan
L'hon. Ginette Piché
L'hon. Pierre Pinard
L'hon. Jean Provost
L'hon. Paul Reeves
L'hon. Gilles-Y. Renaud
L'hon. Jean-Guy Riopel
L'hon. Gontran Rouleau
L'hon. Jeannine M. Rousseau
L'hon. Thérèse Rousseau-Houle
L'hon. Gerald J. Ryan
L'hon. André Savoie
L'hon. Henry Steinberg
L'hon. Louis S. Tannenbaum
L'hon. Pierre Tessier
L'hon. François Tremblay
L'hon. Paul Trudeau
L'hon. Clément Trudel
L'hon. Gérard Turmel
L'hon. Jacques Vaillancourt
L'hon. Pierre Viau
L'hon. Jeanne L. Warren
L'hon. Dionysia Zerbisias
L'hon. Jerry Zigman

---

* Supernumerary

DISTRICT D'APPEL DE QUÉBEC
Palais de Justice
300, boul. Jean-Lesage, Québec, G1K 8K6
General Inquiries: (418) 649-3501

Juge en chef associé: L'hon. Pierre Côté

Juges:
L'hon. Jules Allard
L'hon. Paul-Etienne Bernier
L'hon. Jean Bienvenue
L'hon. Jacques Blanchard
L'hon. Gérald Boisvert
L'hon. Jacques Delisle
L'hon. Gaston Desjardins
L'hon. André Desmeules
L'hon. René-W. Dionne
L'hon. Louis Doiron
L'hon. Jacques Dufour
L'hon. Yvan Gagnon
L'hon. André Gervais
L'hon. Ross Goodwin
L'hon. Ovide Laflamme
L'hon. Robert-B. Lafrenière
L'hon. Henri LaRue
L'hon. Gérard Lebel
L'hon. Robert Lesage
L'hon. René Letarte
L'hon. Vincent Masson
L'hon. Ivan Mignault
L'hon. Jean Moisan
L'hon. Jacques Philippon
L'hon. Jean Richard
L'hon. Claude Rioux
L'hon. Gabriel Roberge
L'hon. François Tremblay
L'hon. André Trotier
L'hon. Hubert Walters

ALMA
Palais de Justice
725, boul. Harvey ouest, G8P 1P5
Juge: L'hon. Gaston Harvey

AMOS
Palais de Justice
891, Troisième rue ouest, J9T 2T4
Juges:
L'hon. Charles-N. Barbès,
L'hon. Jacques Viens

BAIE-COMEAU & MINGAN
Palais de Justice
71, rue Mance, Baie-Comeau, G4Z 1N2
Juge: L'hon. Paul A. Corriveau

CHICOUTIMI
Palais de Justice
227, rue Racine est, G7H 5C5
Juges:
L'hon. Pierre Bergeron,
L'hon. Marcel Simard

GRANBY
Palais de Justice, 77, rue Principale, J2G 9B3
Juge: L'hon. Thomas Toth

HULL
Palais de Justice, 17, rue Laurier, J8X 4C1
Juges:
L'hon. Bernard de L. Bourgeois,
L'hon. François Chevalier,
L'hon. Jean R. Dagenais,
L'hon. Orville Frenette,
L'hon. Louis-P. Landry, L'hon. Charles B. Major

RIMOUSKI
Palais de Justice
183, av. de la Cathédrale, C.P. 800, G5L 5J1
Juge: L'hon. Claude Jourdain

ROUYN
Palais de Justice
2, av. du Palais, Rouyn, Abitibi, J9X 2N9
Juge: L'hon. Camille L. Bergeron

SHAWINIGAN
Palais de Justice, 212, Sixième rue, G9N 8B6
Juge: L'hon. Gilles Gauthier

SHERBROOKE
375, rue King ouest, J1H 6B9
Juges:
L'hon. Pierre Boily, L'hon. Carrier Fortin,
L'hon. Louis-Philippe Galipeau,
L'hon. Paul M. Gervais,
L'hon. Jean-L. Peloquin,
L'hon. Georges Savoie

TROIS-RIVIÈRES
Palais de Justice, 250, rue Laviolette, G9A 1T9
Juges:
L'hon. Jacques Lacoursière,
L'hon. Raymond Landry, L'hon. Roger Laroche,
L'hon. Guy Lebrun, L'hon. Robert Legris

VAL-D'OR
Palais de Justice, 900, Septième rue, J9P 4P8
Juge: L'hon. Claude Larouche

La Cour d'appel
(Court of Appeal)

Montréal—Palais de Justice
1, rue Notre-Dame est, H2Y 1B6
General Inquiries: (514) 393-2022

Québec—Palais de Justice
300, boul. Jean-Lesage, G1K 8K6
General Inquiries: (418) 649-3401

Juge en chef: L'hon. Claude Bisson
Juges:
L'hon. Fred Kaufman
L'hon. André Dubé
L'hon. Yves Bernier
L'hon. Rodolphe Paré
L'hon. Amédée Monet
L'hon. Marc Beauregard
L'hon. Gérald McCarthy
L'hon. Maurice Jacques

L'hon. Albert Malouf
L'hon. Marcel Nichols
L'hon. Claude Vallerand
L'hon. William S. Tyndale
L'hon. Roger Chouinard
L'hon. Melvin L. Rothman
L'hon. Louis LeBel
L'hon. Paul-Arthur Gendreau
L'hon. Louise Mailhot
L'hon. Christine Tourigny
L'hon. Charles D. Gonthier

Cour du Québec
(Court of Quebec)

Palais de Justice, 1, rue Notre-Dame est
Montréal, H2Y 1B6

Juge en chef: Albert Gobeil

DIVISION RÉGIONALE DE MONTRÉAL
Palais de Justice, 1, rue Notre-Dame est
Montréal, H2Y 1B6

Juge en chef assoc.: Louis Vaillancourt

Chambre civile

Juge en chef adjoint: Paul Mailloux
Juge en chef adjointe: Huguette St-Louis
Juge coordonnateur: Marc E. Cordeau
Juges: Paul Beaudry, René Beaulac,
   Gilles Bélanger, Rodolphe Bilodeau,
   Guy Boissonneault, Roland Bourret,
   Simon Brossard, Charles Cimon,
   Michael J.P. Cuddihy, Michel Desmarais,
   Jacques Désormeau, Jean Dionne,
   Claude-René Dumais, Pierre Durand,
   Yvette Dussault-Mailloux, Gilles Filion,
   André Forget, Roy Fournier,
   François M. Gagnon, Robert Hamel,
   Marie-Claire Kirkland, Paule Lafontaine,
   Jean-Louis Lamoureux, Huguette Marleau,
   Joseph A. Mendelson, Jean-Paul Noel,
   Raymond Pagé, Claude Pothier,
   Conrad Prénouveau, Adolphe Prévost,
   André Quesnel, Louis Guy Robichaud,
   Roland Robillard, Gaston Rondeau,
   Robert Sauvé, Bernard Tellier,
   Jacques Tisseur, Gilles Trudel, Pierre Verdy,
   François Wilhelmy

DRUMMONDVILLE
1680, boul. St-Joseph, J2C 2G3
Juge: Jacques Biron

GRANBY
77, rue Principale, J2G 9B3
Juges: Guy Genest, Bernard Légaré,
   Claude Léveillé

HULL
17, rue Laurier, J8X 4C1
Juge coordonnateur: Gérard Charron

Juges: Edgar Allard, Jules Barrière,
   Bernard Dagenais, Jean-Pierre Plouffe,
   Jérôme Somers, Pierre Taché

JOLIETTE
450, rue St-Louis, J6E 2Y9
Juges: Jean-Pierre Bourduas,
   Monique Sylvestre

ST-HYACINTHE
1550, rue Dessaulles, J2S 2S8
Juges: Michel Dumaine, Denis Robert

ST-JEAN
109, rue St-Charles, J3B 2C2
Judges: Yvan Mayrand, Jacques Rancourt

ST-JÉRÔME
400, rue Laviolette, J7Y 2T5
Juge coordonnateur: André Surprenant
Juges: Denis Charette, Jean-Claude Paquin,
   André Soumis

SHERBROOKE
375, rue King ouest, J1H 6B9
Juge coordonnateur: Louis D. Bouchard
Juges: Jean-Guy Blanchette, Jacques Pagé,
   Yvon Roberge, Jean Rouillard

TROIS-RIVIÈRES
250, rue Laviolette, G9A 1T9
Juge: Yves Gabias

VALLEYFIELD
180, rue Salaberry ouest, J6T 2J2
Juges: Raphael Barrette, Raymond Boyer,
   Pierre Laberge

Chambre criminelle et pénale

Juge en chef adjoint: Jean-Pierre Bonin
Juge coordonnateur: Yves Lagacé

Juges: John D'Arcy Asselin,
   Marcel J. Beauchemin, Bernard Bilodeau,
   Pierre Brassard, André Chaloux, Bruno Cyr,
   Jean-Paul Dansereau, H. Rosaire Desbiens,
   Monique-P. Dubreuil, André Duranleau,
   Jean-B. Falardeau, Guy Fortier,
   Gérard Girouard, Bernard Grenier,
   Guy Guérin, Maurice Johnson,
   Claude Joncas, Marc Lamarre,
   Jacques Lessard, Jean Longtin,
   Claude Millette, Gilbert Morier,
   Albert Ouellette, Céline Pelletier,
   Gérard Rouleau, Hugues Saint-Germain,
   Roger Savard, Benjamin Schecter,
   Jean Sirois, Joseph Tarasofsky,
   Luc Trudel, Roger Vincent

DIVISION STATUTAIRE
Juges: Louise Bourdeau, Aldéric Deschamps,
   Jean-Charles Hamelin, Robert Iuticone,
   Cyrille Morand

JOLIETTE
450, rue St-Louis, J6E 2Y9
Juges: André Daviault, André Joly,
Marc Vanasse

LONGUEUIL
1111, boul. Jacques-Cartier est, J4M 2J6
Juge coordonnateur: Rhéal Brunet
Juges: Paul-A. Bélanger, Denys Dionne,
Ronald Dudemaine, Lucien Roy,
Robert Sansfaçon

MONTRÉAL
a/s Régie de la sécurité dans les sports
5199, rue Sherbrooke est, bur. 3721, H1T 3X2
Juge: Raymond Bernier

ST-JÉRÔME
400, rue Laviolette, J7Y 2T6
Juge coordonnateur: Stephen Cuddihy
Juges: François Beaudoin, Jacques Coderre,
Roger Lagarde, Claude Lamoureux

SHERBROOKE
375, rue King ouest, J1H 6B9
Juge coordonnateur: Gérald-E. Desmarais
Juges: Michel Côté, Gabriel Lassonde

Chambre de la jeunesse
410, rue de Bellechasse est
Montréal, H2S 1X3

Juge en chef adjoint: Michel Jasmin
Juge coordonnateur: Oscar D'Amours

Juges: Jean-Pierre Barrette,
Rolland Beauchemin, Gérard Beaudry,
Nicole Bernier, Barrie H. Brown,
Basil Danchyshyn, Elaine Demers,
Ginette Durand-Brault, André Fauteux,
Jean-Claude Gagnon, François J. Godbout,
Normand Lafond, Pierre Lavery,
Guy Lévesque, Gilles L. Ouellet,
André Saint-Cyr, Jean-Paul St-Louis

GRANBY
77, rue Principale, J2G 9B3
Juge: Gilles Therriault

HULL
17, rue Laurier, 3ᵉ ét., J8X 4C1
Juges: Maurice Chevalier, Lionel Mougeot

JOLIETTE
435, rue Baby, J6E 2W3
Juge: Paul Grégoire

LAVAL
1750, boul. de la Concorde est, H7G 2E7
Juge: Jacques Lamarche

LONGUEUIL
1111, boul. Jacques-Cartier est, J4M 2J6
Juge coordonnateur: Pierre G. Dorion
Juges: Henri Choinière, Claude Crête

ST-HYACINTHE
1150, rue Ste-Anne, J2S 5G9
Juge: Constant Cordeau

ST-JÉRÔME
85, rue de Martigny ouest, J7Y 3R8
Juge: Andrée Ruffo

SHERBROOKE
375, rue King ouest, J1H 6B9
Juges: Lise Dubé, Michel Durand

VALLEYFIELD
180, rue Salaberry ouest, J6T 2J2
Juge: Mireille Allaire

Chambre de l'expropriation

Vice-président/Juge: Léon Nichols
Juges: Jean-Pierre Lortie, René Roy

DIVISION RÉGIONALE DE QUÉBEC
Palais de Justice
300, boul. Jean-Lesage, Québec, G1K 8K6

Juge en chef assoc.: Yvon Mercier

Chambre Civile
Juge en chef adjoint: Gill Fortier

Juges: Denys Aubé, Jean Beaulieu,
Gérald Bossé, Raymond Boucher,
André Cartier, Georges Chassé,
Pierre Choquette, Yvon Coté,
Bertrand Gagnon, André Gobeil,
Denis Gobeil, Robert Langevin,
Michel Lemieux, Alexandre-J. Lesage,
André Lévesque, André Marceau,
Gaston Michaud, Bernard Pinard,
Guy Pinsonnault, Louis Rémillard,
Michael Sheehan, André Verge,
Michel Simard, Jean-Marc Tremblay

ALMA
725, rue Harvey ouest, G8B 1P5
Juge: Maurice Abud

AMOS
891, Troisième rue ouest, J9T 2T4
Juge coordonnateur: Gaston Labrèche
Juge: Serge Boisvert

ARTHABASKA
800, boul. Bois-Francs sud, G6P 5W5
Juge: Claude Pinard

BAIE-COMEAU
71, av. Mance, G4Z 1N2
Juge: Sarto Cloutier

CHICOUTIMI
227, rue Racine est, G7H 5C5
Juge coordonnateur: Lucien Tremblay
Juges: Jean-Paul Aubin,
Louis-Charles Fournier, Glaude Gagnon,
Jean Simard, Guy Tremblay

JONQUIÈRE
3950, boul. Harvey, C.P. 608, G7X 6K0
Juge: Jean-Yves Tremblay

MATANE
382, rue St-Jérôme, G4W 3B3
Juge coordonnateur: Charles-B. Quimper

NEW CARLISLE
C.P. 84, G0C 1Z0
Juge: Jean Bécu

PERCÉ
Rue Principale, C.P. 39, G0C 2L0
Juge: Jean-Marc Roy

RIMOUSKI
183, rue de la Cathédrale, G5L 5J1
Juges: Marc Gagnon, Raoul Poirier

ROBERVAL
750, boul. St-Joseph, G8H 2L5
Juge: Claude Vaillancourt

ROUYN
2, rue du Palais, J9X 2N9
Juge coordonnateur: Jean-Charles Coutu
Juge: Paul J. Bélanger

ST-JOSEPH-DE-BEAUCE
795, av. du Palais, C.P. 820, G0S 2V0
Juge: Marcel Blais

SEPT-ÎLES
425, boul. Laure, G4R 1X6
Juge: Bernard Lemieux

SHAWINIGAN
212, Sixième rue, G9N 8B6
Juge coordonnateur: Rosaire Lajoie

THETFORD-MINES
693, rue St-Alphonse, G6G 5T6
Juge: James W. Johnson

TROIS-RIVIÈRES
250, rue Laviolette, G9A 1T9
Juges: Jean-Marie Châteauneuf,
   Serge Gagnon, Pierre Trudel

VAL-D'OR
900, Septième rue, J9P 3P8
Juges: Denis Lavergne, Miville St-Pierre

Chambre criminelle et penale
Juge en chef adjoint: Remi Bouchard

Juges: Michel Babin, André Bilodeau,
   Gilles Carle, Louis Carrier, Marc Choquette,
   Anatole Corriveau, Jean Drouin,
   Marc-André Drouin, Laurent Dubé,
   Mark Dubé, Marc DuFour, Jean-L. Dutil,
   Louis Fortin, Gilles La Haye, Denis Lanctot,
   Roch LeFrançois, Marcisse Proulx,
   Yvon Sirois, Pierre Verdon

RIVIÈRE-DU-LOUP
33, rue de la Cour, G5R 1J1
Juge: Jean-Paul Bérubé

ST-JOSEPH-DE-BEAUCE
795, av. du Palais, G9X 2V0
Juge: Charles Cliche

TROIS-RIVIÈRES
250, rue Laviolette, G9A 1T9
Juges: René Crochetière, Maurice Langlois

Chambre de la jeunesse
Juge en chef adjoint: François Godbout

Juges: Andrée Bergeron, Jean-Paul Boutet,
   Marguerite Choquette,
   Louise Galipeault-Moisan, Rodolphe Roy,
   André Sirois

AMOS
891, Troisième rue ouest, J9T 2T4

BAIE-COMEAU
71, av. Mance, G4Z 1N2
Juge: Claude Tremblay

CHICOUTIMI
227, rue Racine est, G7H 5C5
Juges: Bernard Gagnon, Romuald Roy

NEW CARLISLE
C.P. 637, G0C 1Z0
Juge: Jean Arsenault

RIVIÈRE-DU-LOUP
204, rue Lafontaine, C.P. 218, G5R 3Y8
Juge: Bertrand LaForest

ROUYN
2, rue du Palais, J9X 2N9
Juge: Gilles Gendron

TROIS-RIVIÈRES
878, rue de Tonnancourt, G9A 4P8
Juge: Pierre Houde

Chambre de l'expropriation
930, ch. Ste-Foy, Québec, G1S 2L4

Président/Juge: Guy Dorion
Président adjoint/Juge: Jean-Marie Dussault

District Court Officers

C: Clerk   Except where otherwise shown,
   holds two offices: Clerk of the Crown and
   Clerk of the Peace.
D: Deputy
P: Prothonotary
S: Sheriff

ABITIBI
891, Troisième rue, Amos, J9T 2T4
C/P/S: Cécile Brunet

ALMA
725, rue Harvey ouest, #RC31, G8B 1P5
C/P/S: Germain Naud

ARTHABASKA
800, boul. Bois-Franc sud, G6P 5W5
C/P/S: Yvon Corriveau

BEAUCE
795, av. du Palais, St-Joseph, G0S 2V0
C/P/S: Jean-Claude Morin

BEAUHARNOIS
180, rue Salaberry, Valleyfield, J6T 2J2
C/P/S: André Ménard

BEDFORD
920, rue Principale, Cowansville, J2K 1K2
C/P/S: Francine Nadeau
77, rue Principale, Granby, J2C 9B3
C/P/S: Aimé Beaudry

BONAVENTURE
Rue Principale, C.P. 517
New Carlisle, G0C 1Z0
C/P/S: Jean-Léon Roy

CHARLEVOIX
30, ch. de la Vallée, La Malbaie, G0T 1J0
C/P/S: Pierre Gaudreault

CHICOUTIMI
202, rue Jacques-Cartier est, G7H 5C5
C/P/S: Jean-Claude Basque

DRUMMOND
1680, boul. St-Joseph
Drummondville, J2C 2G3
C/P/S: Marie Laforce-Shooner

FRONTENAC
693, rue St-Alphonse ouest, C.P. 579
Thetford-Mines, G6G 5T6
C/P/S: Robert Chartrand

GASPÉ
Rue Principale, C.P. 188, Percé, G0C 2L0
C/P/S: Jean Bourget

HAUTERIVE
71, av. Mance, Baie-Comeau, G4Z 1N2
C/P/S: Romain Desrosiers

HULL
17, rue Laurier, J8X 4C1
C/P/S: Pierre-Yves Lefebvre

IBERVILLE
109, rue St-Charles
St-Jean-d'Iberville, J3B 2C2
C/P/S: André Beauchamp

JOLIETTE
450, rue St-Louis, J6E 2Y9
C: Michel Boudrias
P: Gilles E. Pelletier
S: Suzanne Piché

KAMOURASKA
33, rue de la Cour, Rivière-du-Loup, G5R 3Y8
C/P: Ubald Savard
S: Jean-Charles Fraser

LABELLE
645, rue de la Madone, Mont-Laurier, J9L 1T1
C/P/S: Raymond Fortin

LONGUEUIL
201, place Charles-Lemoyne, bur. 2.10
J4K 2T5
C/P/S: Raymond Gallant

MÉGANTIC
5527, rue Frontenac, Lac Mégantic, G6B 1H6
C/P/S: Harold Bruneau

MINGAN
425, boul. Laure, Sept-Iles, G4R 1X6
C/P/S: Yvan Vigneault

MONTMAGNY
25, rue du Palais, G5V 1P6
C/P: André Gagné
S: Gemma Nicole

MONTRÉAL
1, rue Notre-Dame est, H2Y 1B6
C/P: Lorraine L. Landry
S: Paul St-Martin

PONTIAC
159, av. John, Campbell's Bay, J0X 1K0
C/P/S: Gilbert Blanchet

QUÉBEC
300, boul. Jean-Lesage, G1K 8K6
C/P/S: Pierre Coté

RICHELIEU
46, rue Charlotte, Sorel, J3P 6N5
C/P/S: Pierre Lafrenière

RIMOUSKI
183, av. de la Cathédrale, G5L 7C9
C/P/S: Louis-G. Chassé

ROBERVAL
725, boul. St-Joseph, G8H 2L5
C/P/S: Gerald Taillon

ROUYN-NORANDA
2, av. du Palais, Rouyn, J9X 2N9
C/P/S: Denis Gendron

ST-FRANÇOIS
191, av. du Palais, Sherbrooke, J1H 4R1
C/P: Benoît Bachand
S: Jean-François Bilodeau

ST-HYACINTHE
1550, rue Dessaulles, J2S 2S8
C/P/S: Alain Larocque

ST-MAURICE
212, Sixième rue, Shawinigan, G9N 8B6
C/S/P: Michel-Noël Tremblay

TÉMISCAMINGUE
8, St-Gabriel, Ville-Marie, J0Z 3W0
C/P/S: Albert Boucher

TERREBONNE
100, rue Laviolette, St-Jérôme, J7Y 2T6
OP: Gilles Caron
OS: Michel Rouleau

TROIS-RIVIÈRES
250, rue Laviolette, G9A 1T9
C/P/S: Daniel Kimpton, J.P. Cossette

Registrars in Bankruptcy

City or Town	Registrars
Arthabaska	Nicole Simoneau
Baie-Comeau	Romain Desrosiers
	Carol-Ann Croteau
Chicoutimi	Jean-Claude Basque
	Céline Claveau
Cowansville	Francine Nadeau
	Aimé Beaudry

City or Town	Registrars
Drummondville	Marie Laforce-Shooner
Hull	Michel Martin
Joliette	Danielle Michaud
Montréal	Pierre Pellerin
	Lise Hamel
New Carlisle	Normand Martel
Québec	André Lessard
Percé	Jocelyne Côté
Rimouski	Louis-Georges Chassé
Rivière-du-Loup	Ubald Savard
Roberval	Gérald Taillon
Rouyn	Richard Laflamme
St-Jean-d'Iberville	André Beauchamp
St-Jérôme	Chantal Flamand
St-Joseph-de-Beauce	Jean-Claude Morin
Sept-Iles	Yvan Vigneault
Sherbrooke	Guy Daigle
Thetford Mines	Robert Chartrand
	Daniel Kimpton
	Jean-Paul Cossette
Trois-Rivières	Gérald Bernier
Val-d'Or	Jean-Gilles Racicot
Valleyfield	Claude Rostan

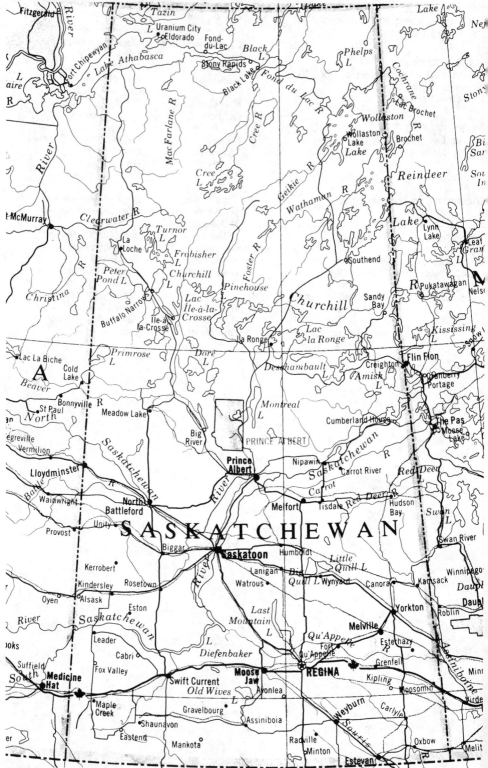

This map is based on information taken from map MCR 4032. © Her Majesty in Right of Canada with permission of Energy, Mines and Resources.

PROVINCE OF SASKATCHEWAN

Prairie Lily
(*Lilium philadelphicum andinum*)

Entered Confederation: Sept. 4, 1905
Capital: Regina
Motto: Multis E Gentibus Vires
(from many peoples, strength)
Flower: Western Red Lily
Area: 670,700 km²
  percentage of Canada's total area: 6.5
  LAND: 652,330 km²
  FRESHWATER: 81,630 km²
Elevation:
  HIGHEST POINT: Cypress Hills (1,392 m)
  LOWEST POINT: Lake Athabasca shoreline
  (64.9 m)
Population (April 1988): 1,011,000
  five-year change: +2.4%

  per square kilometre: 1.5
  percentage of Canada's total
    population: 3.9
  URBAN: 61%
  RURAL: 39%
Gross domestic product, 1987: $17.3 billion

Government Finance:
  REVENUE, 1986/87 est.: $4.3 billion
  EXPENDITURE, 1986/87 est.: $4.8 billion
  DEBT PER CAPITA (March 1987): $468
Personal income per capita, 1987: $15,766
Unemployment rate, 1988
  (annual average): 7.5%

HISTORY

The area now known under Confederation as the province of Saskatchewan (named after the Indian word for "swift flowing river", Kisiskatchewan) was first granted to the Hudson's Bay Company. It was surrendered back to the British Crown by the *Rupert's Land Act* of 1868. In 1870, the territory was transferred to the newly-formed Dominion of Canada. In 1875, provision was made for a resident governor and for members to be elected to the territorial council. The year 1897 saw the emergence of responsible government with an elected legislative assembly.

In 1905, Saskatchewan became a province of Canada with Regina as its capital. The Hon. Amadée Emmanuel Forget was Saskatchewan's first Lieutenant-Governor and the Hon. Walter Scott its first premier. The present premier is the Hon. Grant Devine.

THE LAND

The province of Saskatchewan is located in the centre of the three prairie provinces, bounded by Manitoba to the east, Alberta to the west, the Northwest Territories to the north, and the states of Montana and North Dakota on the international boundary to the south. The province extends 1,224 km north to south and has an average width of 539 km.

Most of the northern third of the province is underlain by Precambrian rock formation, typical of the Canadian Shield of which it is a part. Saskatchewan encompasses innumerable lakes and rivers, large areas of muskeg and swamp, extensive forest growth, and scattered outcroppings of rock. The southern two-thirds of the province is a relatively level plain broken by ridges and valleys which are the result of glacial erosion. This portion accounts for most of the settled area.

There are three major river systems crossing the province, all emptying into Hudson Bay. They are the Assiniboine, North and South Saskatchewan, and Churchill rivers.

Saskatchewan's climate is dry and this factor contributes to the extremes in temperature between summer and winter. Temperatures can vary from 38°C in the summer to −45°C in the winter. The average frost-free period ranges from 135 days in the southwest to less than 105 days in the north. Total precipitation varies from 28 to 38 cm on the open plains. Average snowfall in Regina is 127 cm.

THE PEOPLE

It is believed that the first people in Saskatchewan were Paleo-Indians who crossed from Asia to North America 20-30,000 years ago. Foraging throughout the country, they segregated into several tribal groups. In the north, the main tribes were the Chipewyan and Blackfoot. In the prairies and the buffalo plains were the Assiniboine and the Cree, the latter being the dominant tribe.

As the European explorers and the fur-trading companies moved west, settlements were established. Among the first to settle were the Métis people of mixed Indian and European blood. With the arrival of the railroad in the province, a flow of new immigrants began.

The population of Saskatchewan is made up of approximately one million people of various origins, divided almost evenly between urban and rural residents. In ethnic terms, the province is primarily made up of persons of British extraction followed by those of German, Ukrainian, Scandinavian, French, Native Indian, Dutch, Polish, Russian, and non-European descent. The principal religious denominations are United Church, Roman Catholic, Anglican, Lutheran, Greek Catholic, Greek Orthodox, and Presbyterian.

At present, Saskatchewan is experiencing a large out-migration. In 1988, 16,000 people were estimated to have left.

Saskatchewan has 12 cities, 144 towns, 325 villages, and 299 rural municipalities. Regina and Saskatoon, the largest cities, are about equal in size, amounting to about a third of the province's population. Regina is the seat of the provincial government, training centre for the Royal Canadian Mounted Police, and home of the University of Regina. Saskatoon is the site of the University of Saskatchewan.

THE ECONOMY

Saskatchewan's economy operates on a balanced mix of resources: agriculture, minerals, energy, and forestry. The provincial gross domestic product for 1987 was $17.3 billion. Provincial estimates indicate agriculture accounted for $2.0 billion; minerals, $1.6 billion; construction, $792 million; forestry, $42 million; and manufacturing, $1.1 billion.

Agriculture. Almost half of Canada's cultivated farm land is located in Saskatchewan, with 46 per cent of the total land area used for agricultural purposes. The province produces about 60 per cent of all the wheat grown in Canada. It also produces most of the country's oats, barley, rye, flaxseed, and canola. In the 1986/87 crop year, the harvest of these grains reached 25.8 million tonnes. The 1987 harvest represented a 26 per cent yield increase from 1985. Agriculture accounted for an estimated 11.8 per cent of the province's gross domestic product and 19.5 per cent of its employment.

In 1988, agricultural production is estimated to have fallen by 37 per cent. The drought caused producers to abandon large amounts of planted acreage, and wheat yields were drastically reduced. However, since the 1988 grain crop was of high quality and exports of livestock increased significantly, the effect of the production decline was less severe than expected.

Mining. Saskatchewan's major mineral resources include potash, petroleum, uranium, coal, sodium sulphate, natural gas, copper, zinc, gold, silver, salt, and gravel. More than 40 per cent of the world's recoverable potash reserves — enough to last 3,000 years — is tapped by nine mines in the province which supply 25 per cent of the world demand.

Saskatchewan is the second largest Canadian crude oil producer, with 11 per cent of the country's reserves. A $600-million heavy oil upgrader is under construction in Regina. It's estimated there are 700 million m³ of potentially recoverable heavy oil in the province.

Saskatchewan has about 50 per cent of Canada's recoverable uranium resources. The uranium ore is of extremely high grade, particularly in the recently found Cigar Lake deposit which contains 145 million kg of uranium metal in ore over 50 times richer than that mined in other parts of the country. The Key Lake mine, which opened in 1983, is the world's largest uranium producer. As for gold, the Star Lake gold mine was officially opened in 1987.

Saskatchewan has an inventory of $9 billion in major projects planned or under way for the next five years. These projects include expansion of the pulp and paper industry, development of the fertilizer industry, expansions in the food processing sector, and a broad range of capital construction in educational and health institutions, the oil and mineral sectors, and in other areas of the economy.

In 1988, Saskatchewan experienced an estimated 4.8 per cent decline in provincial output. In comparison, estimates placed the 1987 real growth rate at 3.4 per cent, compared with 3.8 per cent growth for the national average.

The 1988 average unemployment figure continued to be the second lowest among the provinces. Employment growth, which Saskatchewan had not experienced in two years, took place in 1988 and is expected to continue. The areas that will be most affected by this growth will be agriculture, manufacturing, and construction.

Information provided by Government of Saskatchewan Information Services and the Saskatchewan Bureau of Statistics.

GOVERNMENT OF SASKATCHEWAN

Seat of Government:
Legislative Bldg., Regina, S4S 0B3

Lieutenant-Governor:
The Hon. Sylvia O. Fedoruk, O.C., S.O.M.
Government House, 4607 Dewdney Ave.
Regina, S4P 3V7

EXECUTIVE COUNCIL

(In order of precedence, as of Jan. 1, 1989)

Premier, President of the Executive Council, Minister of Agriculture,
The Hon. Grant Devine
Deputy Premier, Provincial Secretary,
The Hon. Eric Berntson
Minister of Trade and Investment, Minister of Justice, Attorney General,
The Hon. Robert Andrew
Minister of Finance, Minister of Telephones,
The Hon. J. Gary Lane
Minister of Public Participation,
The Hon. Graham Taylor
Minister of Economic Development and Tourism, Minister responsible for Northern Affairs,
The Hon. Joan H. Duncan
Minister of Rural Development,
The Hon. Neal Hardy
Minister of Health,
The Hon. George McLeod
Minister of Energy and Mines,
The Hon. Patricia Smith
Minister of Education,
The Hon. Lorne Hepworth
Minister of Parks, Recreation and Culture,
The Hon. Colin Maxwell
Minister of Highways and Transportation,
The Hon. Grant Hodgins
Minister of Human Resources, Labour and Employment, Minister of Social Services, Minister responsible for the Indian and Native Affairs Secretariat,
The Hon. Grant Schmidt
Minister of Urban Affairs,
The Hon. Jack Klein
Minister of Science and Technology, Minister of Consumer and Commercial Affairs,
The Hon. Ray Meiklejohn
Minister of the Environment and Public Safety,
The Hon. Herb Swan

CABINET COMMITTEES

Cabinet Planning and Priorities
Chairman, The Hon. Grant Devine
Treasury Board
Chairman, The Hon. Gary Lane
Legislative Review
Chairman, The Hon. Grant Schmidt
Regulations Review
Chairman, The Hon. Herb Swan

LEGISLATIVE ASSEMBLY

21st Legislature, 3rd Session
Date of last election: Oct. 20, 1986
   (Maximum duration five years)
Majority party: Progressive Conservative
Total number of seats: 64
Party standings:
   Progressive Conservatives: 37
   New Democrats: 26
   Vacant: 1

Officers

Speaker, The Hon. A.B. Tusa
Clerk of the Assembly, Gordon Barnhart
Deputy Clerk, Gwenn Ronyk
Legislative Counsel and Law Clerk,
   Robert Cosman
Sergeant-at-Arms: W. Goodhand

Salaries, Indemnities and Allowances

MEMBERS: $37,028 Member's Annual Indemnity, plus annual expense allowance of $7,322.
PREMIER: $52,300, plus Member's Indemnity, annual expense allowance and sessional allowance.
LEADER OF THE OPPOSITION PARTY: $36,610, plus Member's Indemnity, plus annual expense allowance and sessional allowance, and office allowance of $100,000 per annum.
MINISTERS: $36,610, plus Member's Indemnity, annual expense allowance and sessional allowance.

For further information regarding any aspect of the Government of Saskatchewan, contact:
Saskatchewan Provincial Inquiry Centre
217 Walter Scott Bldg., 3085 Albert St., Regina, S4S 0B1
(306) 787-6291

SPEAKER: $20,920, plus Member's Indemnity, annual expense allowance and sessional allowance.
DEPUTY SPEAKER: $7,845, plus Member's Indemnity, annual expense allowance and sessional allowance.

Members

Constituency	Member and Affiliation
Arm River	Gerald S. Muirhead (PC)
Assiniboia/ Gravelbourg	Vacant
Athabasca	F.J. Thompson (NDP)
Bengough/Milestone	Bob Pickering (PC)
Biggar	Harry Baker (PC)
Canora	Lorne Kopelchuk (PC)
Cumberland	Keith Goulet (NDP)
Cut Knife/ Lloydminster	M.A. Hopfner (PC)
Estevan	The Hon. D. Grant Devine (PC)
Humboldt	Eric Upshall (NDP)
Indian Head/ Wolseley	The Hon. Graham Taylor (PC)
Kelsey/Tisdale	The Hon. Neal H. Hardy (PC)
Kelvington/Wadena	Sherwin Petersen (PC)
Kindersley	The Hon. Robert L. Andrew (PC)
Kinistino	Joe Saxinger (PC)
Last Mountain/ Touchwood	The Hon. A.B. Tusa (PC)
Maple Creek	The Hon. Joan H. Duncan (PC)
Meadow Lake	The Hon. George M. McLeod (PC)
Melfort	The Hon. Grant Hodgins (PC)
Melville	The Hon. Grant Schmidt (PC)
Moose Jaw North	Glenn Hagel (NDP)
Moose Jaw South	Lorne Calvert (NDP)
Moosomin	Dan Toth (PC)
Morse	Harold Martens (PC)
Nipawin	Lloyd Sauder (PC)
Pelly	Rod Gardner (PC)
Prince Albert	Myron Kowalsky (NDP)
Prince Albert/Duck Lake	Eldon Lautermilch (NDP)
Qu'Appelle/ Lumsden	The Hon. J. Gary Lane (PC)
Quill Lakes	Murray Koskie (NDP)
Redberry	John Gerich (PC)
Regina Centre	E.B. (Ned) Shillington (NDP)
Regina Elphinstone	Dwain Lingenfelter (NDP)
Regina Lakeview	Louise Simard (NDP)
Regina North	Kim Trew (NDP)
Regina North East	E.L. Tchorzewski (NDP)
Regina North West	John Soloman (NDP)
Regina Rosemont	Bob Lyons (NDP)
Regina South	The Hon. Jack Klein (PC)
Regina Victoria	Harry Van Mulligan (NDP)
Regina Wascana	Beattie Martin (PC)
Rosetown/Elrose	The Hon. Herb J. Swan (PC)
Rosthern	Bill Neudorf (PC)
Saltcoats	W.R. Johnson (PC)
Saskatoon Centre	Anne Smart (NDP)
Saskatoon Eastview	Bob Pringle (NDP)
Saskatoon Fairview	Bob Mitchell (NDP)
Saskatoon Mayfair	The Hon. Ray Meiklejohn (PC)
Saskatoon Nutana	Pat Atkinson (NDP)
Saskatoon Riversdale	Roy Romanow (NDP)
Saskatoon South	Herbert Rolfes (NDP)
Saskatoon Sutherland	Mark Koenker (NDP)
Saskatoon University	Peter Prebble (NDP)
Saskatoon Westmount	John Brockelbank (NDP)
Shaunavon	Ted Gleim (PC)
Shellbrook/Torch River	Lloyd J. Muller (PC)
Souris/Cannington	The Hon. Eric A. Berntson (PC)
Swift Current	The Hon. Patricia A. Smith (PC)
The Battlefords	Doug Anguish (NDP)
Thunder Creek	Rick Swenson (PC)
Turtleford	The Hon. Colin Maxwell (PC)
Weyburn	The Hon. Lorne H. Hepworth (PC)
Wilkie	John Britton (PC)
Yorkton	Lorne A. McLaren (PC)

NDP — New Democrat
PC — Progressive Conservative

Office of the Premier

Legislative Bldg., Regina, S4S 0B3

Premier and President of the Executive Council, The Hon. Grant Devine

Deputy Minister's Office
Deputy Minister to the Premier, Larry Martin

Cabinet Secretariat
Cabinet Secretary, Larry Martin
Asst. Cabinet Secretary, Lynn Minja
Clerk of the Executive Council, Ron Hewitt

ELECTORAL OFFICE
Rm. 301, 2222-13th Ave., Regina, S4P 1V9
Chief Electoral Officer, Keith Lampard

Policy Secretariat
Assoc. Deputy Minister, Ron Hewitt

Intergovernmental Affairs
Assoc. Deputy Minister, André Dimitrijevic
Federal-Provincial Affairs
Director, Vacant
Constitutional and International Affairs
Director, Don Carroll
Protocol Office
Chief, Michael Jackson

Ottawa Office
Royal Bank Centre, Ste. 512, 90 Sparks St.
Ottawa, K1P 5H4
Director, Vacant

Public Affairs
Exec. Director, Vacant

Principal Secretary's Office
Principal Secretary, Craig Dutton

Offices of the Official Opposition

265 Legislative Bldg., Regina, S4S 0B3

Leader of the Opposition, Roy J. Romanow
Chief of Staff, Garry Aldridge
Research Director, Craig Dotson
Administration Director, Sandra Morgan

Legislative Library

234 Legislative Bldg., Regina, S4S 0B3
(306) 787-2276; Fax: (306) 787-1772

The Legislative Library serves the Members of the Legislative Assembly. The emphasis in its collection is on government documents, books, pamphlets, and periodicals dealing with law, Canadian public affairs, economics, history, the political and social sciences generally, and materials relating to Saskatchewan. The resources of the Library are also made available, with certain restrictions, to individuals pursuing specialized research projects, and to the general public.

Legislative Librarian, Marian Powell

Office of the Ombudsman

2310 Scarth St., Regina, S4P 3V7
(306) 787-6211

The *Ombudsman Act,* passed by the Province of Saskatchewan in 1972, makes the Ombudsman accountable directly to the Legislature, ensures that information received is kept in confidence, and provides the Ombudsman with authority to recommend solutions. Citizen complaints of unjust treatment dealt out by a department or agency of the government are investigated. However, the Ombudsman does not investigate federal or municipal governments, consumer problems, or cases where the court has already made a decision.

Ombudsman, Gerald P. McLellan
Solicitor to the Ombudsman, Gordon K. Mayer
Asst. to the Ombudsman, Earl A. McKeen
Saskatoon Office:
206 S. 4th Ave., Saskatoon, S7K 2H6
Asst. to the Ombudsman, G.R. Thomson
(306) 933-5500

DEPARTMENT OF AGRICULTURE

Walter Scott Bldg., Regina, S4S 0B1

MINISTER'S OFFICE
Legislative Bldg., Regina, S4S 0B3
Minister, The Hon. Grant Devine

DEPUTY MINISTER'S OFFICE
Dep. Minister, John L. (Jack) Drew
Asst. Dep. Minister, Stuart L. Kramer
Asst. Dep. Minister, Les Bowd

COMMUNICATIONS BRANCH
Director, Harvey Johnson
ADMINISTRATIVE SERVICES
Director, Wesley Mazer
Admin. Officer, Ross Johnson
Accountant, K.T. Petruic
Systems Co-ordinator, Duane Klippenstine
Legislative Co-ordinator
and Agrologist, Mike McAvoy

HUMAN RESOURCES BRANCH
Director, Carl Folk
Asst. Director, Erna Stinnen
Personnel Administrator, Violet Woloschuk
ECONOMICS BRANCH
Director, Doug Lisle
Agriculture Development Fund (ADF)
Manager, John Taylor
*Agricultural Development and
Diversification Secretariat*
Exec. Director, David Sim

LIVESTOCK BRANCH
Director, Vacant
Protection and Diversification Section
Administrator, Roger Fry
Production and Development Section
Administrator, Robert J. Ford
SOILS AND CROPS BRANCH
Director, John Buchan

VETERINARY BRANCH
Provincial Veterinary Laboratory
Regina, S4S 0B1
Director, Dr. Peter Rempel
SASKATCHEWAN FARM PURCHASE
PROGRAM
Manager, Ed Reimer
Northern Farms Unit
A/Co-ordinator, Mike McAvoy

AGENCIES, BOARDS, COMMISSIONS AND CROWN CORPORATIONS

MARKETING BOARDS

Marketing boards for agricultural products in Canada are created by a number of different pieces of legislation. National wheat and dairy products plans flow from the *Canadian Wheat Board Act* and the *Canadian Dairy Commission Act* respectively. Egg and poultry boards derive their authority from the *Farm Products Marketing Agencies Act.* As well, many have their own provincial statutes and are normally within the jurisdiction of an umbrella provincial agency. The individual boards are, however, non-governmental and made up largely of elected farmer representatives.

There is also a variety of types. The Economic Council of Canada's study on marketing boards identified five: promotional and developmental boards with little power; selling-desk boards that handle marketing but do not set prices; boards that negotiate prices; boards that set prices; and full-fledged boards that establish quotas. These last are known as supply-management marketing boards. Currently, there are more than 100 active boards in Canada.

SASKATCHEWAN NATURAL PRODUCTS MARKETING COUNCIL
Rm. 329, Walter Scott Bldg.
3085 Albert St., Regina, S4S 0B1

The Natural Products Marketing Council oversees the activities of seven producer marketing boards and one commission established under the *Natural Products Marketing Act*. The Council represents Saskatchewan's position in the development of marketing plans at the national level, examines marketing problems for all agricultural products and advises the Minister of Agriculture on problems related to marketing agencies. The Council acts as an appeal body in disputes between producers and marketing agencies. Also, the Council conducts or supervises votes on producer marketing plans and approves all regulations of producer boards and commissions under its jurisdiction.
Vice-Chairman, Blair Backman
Secretary, Roy White

BROILER HATCHING EGG MARKETING BOARD
18, 909 Grey St., Regina, S4T 5H1

This producer-financed and operated marketing board was created to provide for the orderly marketing of broiler chicken hatching eggs in Saskatchewan. Maintaining stable prices, relative to costs, and ensuring adequate supplies to meet demand are major areas of effort.
Chairman, Gerry Leduc
Sec.-Manager, D.H. Conrad

MILK CONTROL BOARD
620, 2045 Broad St., Regina, S4P 1Y4

The Saskatchewan Milk Control Board was established in 1935 under *An Act respecting the production, supply, distribution and sale of milk*, R.S.S. 1978, Chapter M-15. Its principal purpose is to establish and administer regulations relative to the production, supply, distribution and sale of milk in Saskatchewan. In the establishment of these regulations, the Board is concerned primarily with the interests of the public and the continuity and quality of supply. The Board also administers the Saskatchewan Market Share Quota Program, a joint federal-provincial undertaking.
Chairman, Stan Barber
Admin. Officer, J. Frass

SASKATCHEWAN BEEF STABILIZATION BOARD
309 Hoffer Dr., Regina, S4N 6E2

The Saskatchewan Beef Stabilization Board administers a voluntary stabilization plan for slaughter-beef that is designed to assist producers in overcoming the problems of unstable prices. Two programs are available.

The Cow Calf to Finish Market Insurance program is available to producers who own and operate a cow herd. Protection is provided at 100 per cent of cash costs and 50 per cent of non-cash costs for raising the calf and finishing it for slaughter. Maximum coverage is 200 slaughter animals per individual operator per year. A producer levy of 2 to 6 per cent of market value is charged with the provincial government matching this contribution.

The Feeder to Finish Market Insurance program is available to any resident of Saskatchewan or any organization which is owned (at least 51 per cent) by Saskatchewan residents. Protection is provided at 100 per cent of cash costs and 50 per cent of non-cash costs for purchasing the feeder animal and finishing it for slaughter. A producer levy of 1 to 3 per cent of market value is matched by the provincial government for the stabilization fund.

The Saskatchewan Beef Stabilization Board is a ten-member producer board which administers the programs with the provincial re-imbursing the Board for costs of administering the stabilization programs.
Chairman, Boyd Anderson
Gen. Manager, Jim Stalwick

SASKATCHEWAN CHICKEN MARKETING BOARD
1810-9th Ave. N., Box 1637
Regina, S4P 3C4

The Chicken Marketing Board was formed in 1965. Its five members are elected by the registered broiler, roaster and cornish hen growers of the province. These growers provide funding for the Board through a deduction from the growers' flock proceeds.

The objectives of the Saskatchewan Chicken Marketing Plan are to regulate the production and marketing of chicken and chicken products in an orderly manner; to maintain a stable chicken price that relates to the cost of production; to fulfil consumer demand year-round; and to work with other groups having similar objectives in other areas of Canada.

The Board has the power to regulate provincial supplies of broiler and roaster chicken and cornish hen, within the general confines of the provincial production allotment issued to Saskatchewan by the Canadian Chicken Marketing Agency. The Board also has the power to set grower prices for the above types of chicken after consultation and usually negotiation with the processors.
Chairman, Charles Stueck
Sec.-Manager, G.J. Novak

SASKATCHEWAN COMMERCIAL EGG PRODUCERS MARKETING BOARD
Box 1637, Regina, S4P 3C4

The Saskatchewan Commercial Egg Producers Marketing Board was founded in 1968 and is governed by the *Natural Products Marketing Act* and the Canadian Egg Marketing Agency.

The Board of Directors is composed of six registered producers, who represent the registered producers of the province in any decisions concerning the Board.

The purpose of the Board is to distribute the provincial quota, as allocated by the Canadian Egg Marketing Agency, throughout the province. It directs the advertising and sales promotion of able egg products in Saskatchewan. The Board provides information and inspection services for the registered producers of the province in order to control any potential disease and to monitor the quality of the product. It also assists the producers in the removal of surplus eggs from the province.

Chairman, Ted Wiens
Manager, Dave Mackie

SASKATCHEWAN PORK PRODUCERS MARKETING BOARD
2nd Flr., 502-45th St. W.
Saskatoon, S7L 6H2

The Saskatchewan Pork Producers Marketing Board was established in 1972 as the Saskatchewan Hog Marketing Commission pursuant to the province's *Natural Products Marketing Act*. This appointed commission was replaced, following a plebiscite in 1984, by a producer-elected board.

The Board is responsible for the sale of all market hogs in the province of Saskatchewan with the objective of maximizing overall return to producers of hogs. Live hogs are sold domestically and are also exported to the U.S. Chilled and fresh pork carcasses are cut and sold, through the Board's Provisions Department, to domestic, U.S., and offshore customers.

Other activities of the Board include operation of a cull sow and boar marketing program. These animals are sold both live and in carcass and cut form. Much of this product is processed at Moose Jaw Packers, a small Saskatchewan meat packing plant partially owned by the Board.

The Board also operates 16 hog assembly points throughout the province and underwrites an "in transit" hog insurance program for producers.

The Board funds swine-related research projects and maintains liason with research organizations, other provincial boards and commissions, as well as with provincial and federal agricultural agencies.

The Saskatchewan Pork Producers Marketing Board is an active member of the Canadian Pork Council, a producer-owned national organization involved in pork promotion at the consumer level.

Chairman, Richard Wright
Gen. Manager, J.B. Morris

SASKATCHEWAN PULSE CROP DEVELOPMENT BOARD

The Saskatchewan Pulse Crop Development Board is a producer-controlled body incorporated under special regulations contained in the *Natural Products Marketing Act*. Its purpose is to develop the pulse crop industry in Saskatchewan. Funding is provided by a levy assessed against producers of pulse crops on the basis of the monetary value of the pulses they sell.

Chairman, Ron McKinnon
Abernethy, S0A 0A0
Administrator, Don Jacques
Box 516, Regina, S4P 3A2

SASKATCHEWAN TURKEY PRODUCERS' MARKETING BOARD
502-45th St. W., Saskatoon, S7L 6H2

The Board was established under the *Natural Products Marketing Act* in 1967. It is directed and totally financed by turkey producers.

The objectives of the Board are:
- to use the powers provided under the marketing plan to regulate the production and marketing of turkey and turkey products and to maintain a fair, stabilized price throughout the province;
- to provide for the initiation, support, or conduct of studies and research in connection with production and marketing of turkey and turkey products, and including studies and research dealing with consumer demands;
- to provide for the initiation, support, or conduct of promotional activities dealing with production and marketing of turkeys and turkey products; and
- to work and co-operate with the federal and provincial marketing bodies having similar objectives.

Chairman, Dennis Billo
Sec.-Manager, Fred Longstaff

SASKATCHEWAN VEGETABLE MARKETING AND DEVELOPMENT BOARD
Box 159, Outlook, S0L 2N0

The general purpose and intent of the Board is to provide for the effective development of the Saskatchewan vegetable industry and the promotion, control and regulation by the Board of the marketing of the regulated product within the province. The Board's main emphasis has been on supplying information to growers and acting as a development agency.

Chairman, William Childerhose

SHEEP AND WOOL MARKETING COMMISSION
2910-11th St. W., Saskatoon, S7K 2H6
Vice-Chairman, Larry Sothmann
Gen. Manager, Jim Koal

Agricultural Credit Corp. of Saskatchewan
250 Central Ave. N., Box 820
Swift Current, S9H 3W8
General Inquiry: (306) 778-8455

The Agricultural Credit Corporation of Saskatchewan, was established as a Crown corporation in 1973 under the *Agricultural Incentives Act,* and continued under the *Agricultural Credit Corporation of Saskatchewan Act,* R.S.S. 1978, Chapter A-8.1.

The Corporation's major objectives are to provide developing farmers or potential farmers with an opportunity to establish profitable farm units through livestock and irrigation enterprises, and to encourage diversification of Saskatchewan's agricultural industry as a means of adding stability to the provincial economy.

The Agricultural Credit Corp. provides low interest loans to farmers who wish to begin or expand a livestock or irrigation enterprise. Persons who are eligible to receive assistance must reside in Saskatchewan during the term of the loan and must intend to make farming their principal occupation.

Loan funds obtained under the program may be used for purchasing breeding stock, purchasing materials for construction or renovation of buildings and other improvements, such as fencing or water supply, and for purchasing equipment for livestock production or irrigation.

Minister responsible, The Hon. Grant Devine

Chairman, Mr. Lynn Biggart
President, Norm Ballagh
Vice President (Administration), M.L. Machin
Vice President (Lending), Denis Cote
Special Loans Manager, Rick Lillejord
Loan Administration, Bob Shoemaker
Accounting Manager, Vacant
Information System Manager, Vacant
Administration Manager, Don Schepens
Finance Director, Barry Miller
Research Manager, Margot Sommerville
Regional Managers:
Lyle Ballard
110 Souris Ave., Box 2003, Weyburn, S4H 2Z9
Dennis Lafreniere
350 Cheadle St. W., Swift Current, S9H 4G3
Don Pierce
1107-99th St., Box 1480, Tisdale, S0E 1T0
Joe Rakochy
3130-8th St. E., Saskatoon, S7H 0W2
R.I. Foreman
Provincial Office Bldg., 1146-102nd St.
North Battleford, S9A 3G7

Saskatchewan Crop Insurance Corp.
484 Prince William Dr.
Box 3000, Melville, S0A 2P0
General Inquiries: (306) 728-7200

The Saskatchewan Crop Insurance Corp. was established by Order-in-Council 544/74 on March 29, 1974 to provide such services and facilities as may be required of the Corporation by the Saskatchewan Crop Insurance Board in the exercise of the powers and the carrying out of the duties of the Board under the *Saskatchewan Crop Insurance Act,* R.S.S. 1978, Chapter S-12, as amended.

Effective July 1, 1984, the *Crop Insurance Act*

S.S. 1983-84, Chapter C-47.2 was proclaimed, amalgamating the Saskatchewan Crop Insurance Board and the Saskatchewan Crop Insurance Corp. Board of Directors. This gives the Corporation Board decision-making powers for both policy and administrative matters.

The Canada-Saskatchewan Crop Insurance Program makes comprehensive all-risk crop insurance available to all farmers in the province on a voluntary basis. This is an effort to reduce instability of farm income due to variability in crop yields resulting from natural hazards.

Chairman, William Farley
President, Henry Zilm
Administration Services Division
Vice-President, J.C. Walters
Admin. Officer, Chris S. Wass
Field Operations Division
Vice-President, Earl Silcox
Manager, Ron Osika
Marketing Manager, Harvey Rothecker
Human Resources Manager, John Persson
Research Manager, Henry Schappert
Financial Manager, Walter Charabin
Accounting Supervisor, Lawrence Matwijeczko

Saskatchewan Grain Car Corp.
Walter Scott Bldg., 3085 Albert St.
Regina, S4S 0B1

The Saskatchewan Grain Car Corporation owns and manages 1,000 grain hopper cars on behalf of the Saskatchewan government under the *Saskatchewan Grain Car Corporation Act, 1980.*

The cars are operated under an agreement with Canadian National Railway, Canadian Pacific Rail, and the Canadian Wheat Board. The cars, acquired in 1981, are for the movement of wheat, oats, barley, rye, flaxseed, and rapeseed, which are transported at statutory rates within the Western Division of the Canadian Wheat Board.

The Saskatchewan Grain Car Corp. monitors the use of the cars from its head office in Melville, Saskatchewan.

Chairman, The Hon. Grant Devine
A/Gen. Manager, Stuart L. Kramer
Fleet Sup't, Don Shawaga

Saskatchewan Lands Allocation Appeal Board
Walter Scott Bldg., 3085 Albert St.
Regina, S4S 0B1

The Saskatchewan Lands Allocation Appeal Board was established under the provincial *Lands Act* to hear appeals regarding the allocation or termination of agricultural leases on provincial land.

The Board consists of at least five members, one of whom is designated chairman and one vice-chairman. Three members of the Board constitute a quorum.

Chairman, Hugh McLaughlin, Q.C.
1136 Riverview Cres., Swift Current, S9H 1V9
Secretary, Dennis Wickenheiser

DEPARTMENT OF CONSUMER AND COMMERCIAL AFFAIRS

1871 Smith St., Regina, S4P 3V7
General Inquiry: (306) 787-5550

MINISTER'S OFFICE
Legislative Bldg., Regina, S4S 0B3
Minister, The Hon. Ray Meiklejohn

DEPUTY MINISTER'S OFFICE
Dep. Minister, Ronald Kesslar
Administration and Human Resources Branch
Director, Al Dwyer
Education and Communications Branch
Director, Gillian McCreary
Corporations Branch Director, Phil Flory
Licensing and Investigation Branch
Sup't of Insurance, O.A. MacGillivray
Dep. Sup't, John Page
Agricultural Implements Board
Officer-in-charge, Noela Bamfordt
Policy and Planning Branch
Director, Ron Zukowsky

REGIONAL OFFICE:
122-3rd Ave. N., Saskatoon, S7K 2H6
Licensing and Investigations
A/Consumer Services Officer in Charge,
Alice Christie

DEPARTMENT OF ECONOMIC DEVELOPMENT AND TOURISM

Ramada Renaissance, 1919 Saskatchewan Dr.
Regina, S4P 3V7
Telex: 071-2675
Business Information: (306) 787-2207
Tourism Saskatchewan; (306) 787-2300
Toll-Free (Canada and USA): 1-800-667-7191
(within Saskatchewan): 1-800-667-7538
Venture Capital Program: 787-2252
(Toll-Free): 1-800-667-7530
General Inquiries: (306) 787-2300

MINISTER'S OFFICE
Rm. 348, Legislative Bldg., Regina, S4S 0B3
Minister, The Hon. Joan Duncan

DEPUTY MINISTER'S OFFICE
7th Flr., 1919-11th Ave., Regina, S4P 3V7
Dep. Minister, Dr. David Rothwell
Asst. Dep. Ministers:
Ken McNabb, Robert Volk
Administration
Director, Harvey Murchison

BUSINESS SERVICES DIVISION
Regional Services Branch
Director, Lyle Pederson
BUSINESS RESOURCE CENTRES:
Regina
1870 Albert St., Regina, S4P 3V7
Manager, Ken Adie

Estevan
1322-3rd St., Estevan, S4A 0S2
Manager, Ken Morine
Moose Jaw
Rm. 102, 111 Fairford St. E.
Moose Jaw, S6H 7X5
Manager, Grant McWilliams
North Battleford
1281-100th St., North Battleford, S9A 0V6
Consultant, Jan Swanson
Prince Albert
Main Flr., McIntosh Mall
800 Central Ave., Prince Albert, S6V 6G1
Manager, Wayne Phillip
Saskatoon
311-21st St. E., Saskatoon, S7K 2H6
Manager, Raj Manek
Swift Current
350 Cheadle St. W.
Swift Current, S9H 4G3
Manager, Bruce Wallace
Yorkton
7-1st Ave. N., Yorkton, S3N 1J3
Manager, Mark Litowitz
La Ronge
Box 5000, La Ronge, S0J 1L0
Manager, Jim Bogard
Buffalo Narrows/Meadow Lake
Box 249, Buffalo Narrows, S0M 0J0
Consultant, Stuart McDonald
Creighton
Box 28, Creighton, S0P 0A0
Consultant, Dennis Strom

INDUSTRIAL DEVELOPMENT BRANCH
Director, Bryce Baron
Development Co-ordinators:
Del Bain, Mel Brough, Lorne Bryden
Program Manager, Vacant
Research Officer, Russ Paul
Program Manager, Ian Sinclair
Development Co-ordinator, Terry Field
Policy Development Branch
Director, David McQuinn
Business Librarian, Rochelle Smith
Program Management Branch
Director, Roy Hynd
Venture Capital Branch
Director, Jim Zatulsky
Co-operatives Branch
A/Director, Vern Kaisler
Tourism Development Branch
Director, Tom Young
Saskatoon Regional Office
Manager, Ian McGilp
Tourism Marketing Branch
Director, Dave Livingstone
Business Travel Manager, Vacant
Leisure Travel
A/Manager, Vacant
Corporate Affairs Branch
Director, Leona Gorr
Creative Services Manager, Neil Sawatzky
Advertising Manager, Lorraine Garratt

DEPARTMENT OF EDUCATION
2220 College Ave., Regina, S4P 3V7

MINISTER'S OFFICE
Rm. 361, Legislative Bldg., Regina, S4S 0B3
Minister, The Hon. Lorne Hepworth

DEPUTY MINISTER'S OFFICE
Dep. Minister, Lawrie McFarlane

Skill Training and Apprenticeship Division
Asst. Dep. Minister, Elizabeth Crosthwaite
Training Division
Exec. Director, Vacant
Regional Colleges Director, Jake Kutarna
Institute Affairs Director, John Biss
Training Programs Co-ordination
Director, Lorne Sparling
Apprenticeship and Trade Certification
Director, Dan Roberts
Literacy Council Director, Richard Bonokoski

PLANNING AND INFORMATION
SERVICES DIVISION
Exec. Director, Donna Krawetz
Information Resources Management
Director, Greg Thomas
Policy and Planning Director, Rita Archer

FINANCE AND OPERATIONS DIVISION
Exec. Director, Mike Benson
Student Financial Assistance
Director, Deb Achen
Financial Planning Branch
Director, Robin Johnson
Administration and Resources Distribution
Director, Don Trew
School Facilities Planning
Director, I. Brunas
Board and Teacher Services
Director, Gene Hodgson
Communications Branch Director, Vacant
School Grants
A/Director, Gerry Sing Chin

PROVINCIAL LIBRARY
Provincial Librarian, Karen Adams
Professional Services Director, Joy Campbell
Technical Services Director, Gloria Materi
Bureau of Statistics
Director, Ron McMahon

Regional Services and Field Support Division
Assoc. Dep. Minister, Lorne Glauser
Principal of Correspondence School,
Steve Senyk

R.J.D. Williams School for the Deaf
221 Cumberland Ave. N.
Saskatoon, S7N 1M3
A/Principal, Bill Lockert

REGIONAL DIRECTORS OF EDUCATION
Art Scherr
Box 2003, 110 Souris Ave., Weyburn, S4H 2Z9

Brian Keegan
350 Cheadle St. W., Swift Current, S9H 4G3
Dr. Don Drozda
1855 Victoria Ave., Regina, S4P 3V5
Glen Penner
3130-8th St. E., Saskatoon, S7H 0W2
Harley Sundbo
105 Crawford Ave. E., Melfort, S0E 1A0
Ernie Cychmistruk
1192-102nd St.
North Battleford, S9A 1E8
Northern Division
Box 5000, La Ronge, S0J 1L0
Exec. Director, Ray McKay
University Affairs
Director, Dianne Anderson
Human Resources Division
Exec. Director, Brenda Beug

Curriculum and Instruction Division
Asst. Dep. Minister, Marine Perran
OFFICIAL MINORITY LANGUAGE OFFICE
Exec. Director, Victor Tetreault
French Curriculum Development Branch
Director, Stan Frey
French Minority Education
Director, Andre Moquin
Federal/Provincial Programs
A/Director, Valerie Deane

CURRICULUM AND INSTRUCTION DIVISION
Exec. Director, Fred Renihan
Community Education Director, Saul Arbess
Math and Science Director, Barry Mitschke
Social Science and Resource Centre Services
Director, Ivan Yackel
Humanities Director, Sandra Klenz
Special Education Director, Bob Livingston
Saskatchewan School
Improvement Program Co-ordinators:
Garth Findahl, Linda Pusch
Evaluation and Student Services
Director, Susan Winter

AGENCIES, BOARDS AND COMMISSIONS

Saskatchewan Educational Boundaries Commission
2220 College Ave., Regina, S4P 3V7

The Commission consists of five members and is constituted under the terms of *The Education Act.*

The Commission functions as an advisory body to the Minister of Education in matters dealing with the alterations of the boundaries of school divisions.

Chairman, William Werezak
Secretary, Ronald F. Thomas

Teachers' Superannuation Commission
3rd Flr., 1870 Albert St., Regina, S4P 3V7

The Commission is a seven-member board constituted under the provisions of the *Teachers'*

Superannuation Act, R.S.S. 1978, Chapter T-9, which came into force on July 1, 1930.

The Commission is responsible for administering the *Teachers' Superannuation Act* and *Teachers' Life Insurance (Government Contributory) Act,* R.S.S. 1978, Chapter T-8. This includes the administration of a pension plan for the 12,000 teachers in Saskatchewan and a group life insurance and accidental death and dismemberment insurance for the teachers. The superannuation fund contains approximately $500 million and the value of the life insurance in force is approximately one billion dollars.

Chairman, John Chyzowski
Exec. Secretary, Arleen Schultz
Manager, Sandi Kullman

DEPARTMENT OF ENERGY AND MINES

1914 Hamilton St., Regina, S4P 4V4
General Inquiries: (306) 787-2526

MINISTER'S OFFICE
Legislative Bldg., Regina, S4S 0B3
Minister, The Hon. Patricia Smith

DEPUTY MINISTER'S OFFICE
Dep. Minister, John Reid

Finance and Administration Division

Asst. Dep. Minister, Ray Clayton
Personnel and Administration Branch
Director, Janis Rathwell
Systems Services Branch
Director, Adeline Skwara
Mineral Revenues Branch
Director, Steve Zurawski

Resource Policy and Economics Division

Asst. Dep. Minister, Pat Youzwa
Policy Analysis Branch
A/Director, Jane Forster
Energy Technology Branch
Director, Dan McFadyen
Fiscal Management Branch
Director, Robert Lee

GEOLOGY AND MINES DIVISION
Exec. Director, Dr. L.S. Beck
Mines Branch Director, Phil Reeves
Mineral Development Branch
Director, Tom Sibbald
Precambrian Geology Branch
Director, Bob Macdonald
Sedimentary Geodata Branch
Director, Paul Guliov
Petroleum Geology Branch
Director, Doug Paterson
Support Services Branch
Director, Charlie Harper

Subsurface Geological Laboratory
201 Dewdney Ave. E., Regina, S4N 4G3
Supervisor, Don Forsberg
FIELD OFFICE:
La Ronge/Creighton
Box 5000, La Ronge, S0J 1L0
Geologist, Dr. A.J. Gracie
Geologist, Pam Schuiam

PETROLEUM AND NATURAL GAS DIVISION
Exec. Director, Bruce Wilson
Petroleum Development Branch
Director, J. Gossard
Engineering Services Branch
Director, M. Sereda
Economic and Fiscal Analysis
Director, Dale Fletcher
Geology and Petroleum Lands Branch
Director, G. Hutch
Petroleum Statistics Branch
Director, J. Dang
FIELD OFFICES:
Kindersley
Box 850, Kindersley, S0L 1S0
Petroleum Development Officer, W. Mahaffey
Estevan
1219 Fifth St., Estevan, S4V 0Z1
Petroleum Development Officer, J. Wysminity
Swift Current
Provincial Bldg., 2nd Flr.
350 Cheadle St. W., Swift Current, S9H 4G3
Petroleum Development Officer, R. Dafoe
Lloydminster
4815-50th Ave., Lloydminster, S9V 0M8
Petroleum Development Officer, B. Mathieson

DEPARTMENT OF THE ENVIRONMENT AND PUBLIC SAFETY

3085 Albert St., Regina, S4S 0B1
General Inquiries: (306) 787-6113

MINISTER'S OFFICE
Rm. 302, Legislative Bldg., Regina, S4S 0B3
Minister, The Hon. Herb Swan

DEPUTY MINISTER'S OFFICE
Dep. Minister, P.S. vanEs

ADMINISTRATION AND COMMUNICATIONS BRANCH
Director, R.P. Knoll
Financial Services Manager, R.D. Gilmour
Human Resources Manager, S.G. Bellamy
Systems Services Manager, G.C. Strasser
Information Services Manager, D.A. Cairns

Environmental Protection Division

Asst. Dep. Minister, R.R. Sentis
Environmental Assessment Branch
Director, Vacant

Water Quality Branch
Director, D.A. Fast
Asst. Director, D.D. Nargang
Standards and Approvals Section
Manager, D.D. Nargang
Municipal Assessment and
Certification Section
Manager, B.W. Ganong
Water Quality Management Section
Manager, R.G. Ruggles
Air and Land Protection Branch
Director, L.J. Lechner
Air Quality Section Manager, Vacant
Waste Management Section
Manager, B.J. Ryma
Chemical Management Section
Manager, V.S. Chang
Mines Pollution Control Branch
Box 3003, Prince Albert, S6V 4V1
Director, R.G. Barsi
Uranium Mines Section
Manager, P.A. Courtney
Technical Services Section
Manager, C.L. Potter
Potash/Coal Section
Manager, J.C. Hayward

PUBLIC SAFETY DIVISION
1870 Albert St., Regina, S4P 3V7
A/Exec. Director, N. Surtees
Boiler and Pressure Vessel Safety Branch
Chief Inspector, N. Surtees
Fire Commissioner's Branch
Fire Commissioner, A.S. Bartlett
Building Standards Branch
Chief Inspector, L.G. Harmsworth
EMERGENCY MEASURES ORGANIZATION
2151 Scarth St., Regina, S4P 3V7
Exec. Director, M.G. Hegan
Director, A.T. Auser

DEPARTMENT OF FINANCE
2350 Albert St., Regina, S4P 4A6
(unless otherwise indicated)
General Inquiry: (306) 787-6768
Fax: (306) 787-6055

MINISTER'S OFFICE
Legislative Bldg., Regina, S4S 0B3
Minister, The Hon. J. Gary Lane, Q.C.

DEPUTY MINISTER'S OFFICE
Dep. Minister, Art Wakabayashi

Investment and Financial Services Division
Asst. Dep. Minister, W. Davern Jones
Finance and Administration Branch
Director, Don Baldwin
Cash and Debt Management Branch
Director, Dennis Polowyk
Investments Branch Director, Vacant

TAXATION AND ECONOMIC POLICY DIVISION
Exec. Director, John Wright
Revenue and Economic Policy
Director, Jim Marshall
Taxation Policy Director, Kirk McGregor

Treasury Board Division
Assoc. Dep. Minister, Keith Laxdal
Personnel Policy Secretariat
Exec. Director, B. Woulds

PROVINCIAL COMPTROLLER'S DIVISION
Provincial Comptroller, Gerry Kraus
Financial Management Branch
A/Director, Terry Paton
Central Accounting Branch
Director, Peter Knecht
Systems Management Branch
Director, M. Robinson

ADMINISTRATION DIVISION
Exec. Director, Bill Van Sickle
Human Resources Branch
Director, Jim Graham
Support Services Branch
Director, Sharon Bierd
Financial Services Branch
Director, Bill Hoover

REVENUE DIVISION
Exec. Director, Len Rog
Revenue Operations Branch
Director, Russ Moore
Audit Branch Director, Walter Biech

AGENCIES, BOARDS AND COMMISSIONS

Municipal Financing Corp. of Saskatchewan
c/o Crown Management Board
300, 2400 College Ave., Regina, S4P 1C8

The Municipal Financing Corp. of Saskatchewan, established in 1970, assists in making capital funds available for the financing of local improvements, schools, hospitals, and other municipal projects. The Corporation purchases a portion of the authorized debentures sold each year by Saskatchewan local authorities.

Chairman, The Hon. J. Gary Lane, Q.C.
Gen. Manager, W. Davern Jones

Public Employees Benefits Agency
4th Flr., 2350 Albert St., Regina, S4P 4A6
Inquiries: (306) 787-2992

The Public Employees Benefits Agency was established in 1982. Activities of the Agency include administration of group dental, group life, group long-term disability and pension plans for employees of the government of Saskatchewan and some Crown corporations.
Exec. Director, Brian Smith

Saskatchewan Pension Plan
5th Flr., 2350 Albert St., Regina, S4P 4A6

The Saskatchewan Pension Plan (SPP) is a voluntary money-accumulation plan that gives Saskatchewan residents a unique opportunity to save for their retirement. The plan is regulated by the *Saskatchewan Pension Act, 1987* and is administered by a board of trustees.

A unique feature of the plan is that the amount of annual contributions is not based on employment earnings. Thus, the SPP allows people to contribute to a pension plan who might not otherwise qualify for enrolment in the Canada Pension Plan or private pension plans. It is also of particular interest to those who wish to supplement their pensions, such as part-time workers whose contributions to CPP or other private plans are low, and who therefore will receive a small pension.

In addition, the government of Saskatchewan will match contributions of people with little or no income who might not be able to afford a substantial contribution on their own. Money paid into the plan cannot exceed $600 per year. Depending on the member's income, the government may make up to $300 in matching contributions.

More than 40,000 Saskatchewan residents now belong to the plan. Women account for 80 per cent of membership, and half describe themselves as homemakers.

Chairperson and Gen. Manager,
Theresa A. Holizki

DEPARTMENT OF HEALTH
T.C. Douglas Bldg.
3475 Albert St., Regina, S4S 6X6
General Inquiries: (306) 787-3168

MINISTER'S OFFICE
Rm. 334, Legislative Bldg., Regina, S4S 0B3
Minister, The Hon. George McLeod

DEPUTY MINISTER'S OFFICE
Dep. Minister, Stan Sojonky
Departmental Solicitor, Gerald Tegart

Assoc. Dep. Ministers:
G.H. Loewen, David Babiuk, Michael Shaw

HEALTH PROMOTION BRANCH
Director, Loretta Eberts
Health Educator, Joanna Alexander
Resource Centre Co-ordinator, Lynn Kozun
ADMINISTRATIVE SERVICES BRANCH
Exec. Director, Kathy Langlois
HUMAN RESOURCES AND PAY
NEGOTIATIONS BRANCH
Exec. Director, Lucille Bechard

STRATEGIC PLANNING AND EVALUATION
BRANCH
Exec. Director, Glenda Yeates

Economics and Evaluation
A/Manager, M. Gormley
Planning and Advisory Services
Manager, Vacant
Vital Statistics Division
Inquiries: (306) 787-3092
Director, W. Berg

PROVINCIAL LABORATORY AND
COMMUNICABLE DISEASE CONTROL
Exec. Director, Dr. Roy West
Microbiology and Communicable
Disease Control
Director, Dr. Greg Horsman

MENTAL HEALTH SERVICES BRANCH
Inquiries: (306) 787-3286
Exec. Director, John Labatt
Assoc. Exec. Director, Dr. John W. Elias
Administrative and Project Co-ordinator,
Sadhna Kaushik
Asst. Exec. Director, Boris Titus
NGO Services Co-ordinator, Sharon Ratcliffe
Director of Child and Youth Services, Vacant
Director of Rehabilitative and
Residential Services, Fred Harshman
Sr. Policy and Program Analyst, Dr. K. Silzer
Accountant, Elaine Dykstra

COMMUNITY HEALTH SERVICES BRANCH
3475 Albert St., Regina S4S 6X6
Inquiry: (306) 787-1501
Exec. Director, S.J. Malach
Asst. Exec. Director, Administration
J. Dvernichuk
Assoc. Exec. Director, Vacant
Medical Consultant, Vacant
Accountant, J. Culig
Systems Co-ordinator, Vacant
Public Health Inspection
Director, L. Corkery
Dental Health Education
Director, Lou Karpinski
Public Health Inspection (Food and Milk)
Consultant, Yvonne Schiller
Public Health Inspection (Environment)
Consultant, Vacant
Public Health Nursing Director, M. Dirk
Chiropody Director, Dr. S. Ritchie
Regina Clinic
6th Flr., London Life Bldg.
1855 Victoria Ave., Regina, S4P 3T2
Community Therapy Director, D. Bjore
Speech and Language Pathology
Director, Kelly Richter
Provincial Nutritionist, Karen Cooper
Saskatchewan Aids to Independent Living
Director, R. Wallace
Co-ordinator, K. Hopkin
Saskatchewan Hearing Aid Plan
Director, Louise Watley

Regina Clinic
3rd Flr., Gordon Bldg.
2180-12th Ave., Regina, S4P 0M5
Inquiry: (306) 787-3116

Clinic Supervisor, Celeste Heaney
Admin. Supervisor, Vacant

Saskatoon Clinic
Sturdy-Stone Clinic
122 Third Ave. N., Saskatoon, S7K 2H6
Inquiry: (306) 933-5694
Clinic Supervisor, B. Angelstad
Office Manager, Tarrie MacDuff

SASKATCHEWAN HOSPITAL SERVICES
BRANCH
Exec. Director, Neil Gardner
Assoc. Exec. Director, John Borody
Hospital Standards and Ambulance Services
Director, Vacant
Hospital Services Director, Vacant
Finance and Administration
Director, Duncan Fisher
Program Development and Construction
Director, Bill Barry
Systems and Data Processing
Director, L.G. MacNeill
Benefits Director, Doreen Aaron
Strategic Planning
Director, W.A. Dorsett

SASKATCHEWAN PRESCRIPTION DRUG PLAN
Inquiries: (306) 787-3317
Exec. Director, R.J. (Ron) Waschuk
Professional Services Division
Director, T. Quinn
Drug Cost Control Unit, J.W. Campbell
Formulary and Research Unit, Vacant
Pharmacy Claims Division
A/Director, P. Suwala
Administration Division
Director, C. Woloshyn

CONTINUING CARE
Exec. Director, George Peters
Special Care Homes Division
Director, Vacant
Home Care Division
Director, Lois Borden
NORTHERN HEALTH SERVICES BRANCH
Exec. Director, Dr. Gary Plant
Asst. Exec. Director, Thom Carnahan

AGENCIES, BOARDS AND COMMISSIONS

Medical Care Insurance Branch
3475 Albert St., Regina, S4S 6X6
General Inquiries: (306) 787-3475

The Saskatchewan Medical Care Insurance Commission is responsible for administering the Medical Care Insurance Plan. The Commission has seven to 11 members and is responsible to the Minister of Health.

The Medical Care Insurance Plan, inaugurated on July 1, 1962 under the *Saskatchewan Medical Care Insurance Act,* R.S.S. 1978, Chapter S-29, provides insurance coverage to Saskatchewan residents for a wide range of services provided by physicians, chiropractors and optometrists. The Plan is financed through the Medical Care Insurance Fund. This fund is in turn supported by an appropriation made by the Legislative Assembly from the Consolidated Fund to which contributions are made by the federal government under the *Federal-Provincial Fiscal Arrangements and Established Programs Financing Act,* 1977. No premiums are levied.

Newcomers to the province are generally eligible for benefits from the first day of the third month following the date they establish residence in the province. Eligibility is solely dependent upon registration. All beneficiaries under the plan receive the same coverage regardless of age or state of health.
Exec. Director, Lawrence Krahn
Assoc. Exec. Director, Bryan Middlemiss
Medical Consultants: Dr. J.P. Barschel
Dr. J.M.R. Garson, Dr. P.D. Palko
Automated Data Systems
Director, Peter Jmaeff
Receiving, Records and Inquiries
Director, R.G. Crawford
Claims Processing and Assessment
Director, R.S. Herauf
Administrative Services Director, J. Fazakas
Supplementary Health Benefits
Director, K. Scobie
Program Analysis and Review
Director, Verlin Gwin
Verification and Audit Director, D. Trew

Saskatchewan Health Research Board
5, 3002 Louise St., Saskatoon, S7J 3L8

The Saskatchewan Health Research Board administers *The Health Research Act* passed in 1979. The Board administers the Health Research Fund and is empowered to assist and stimulate research in the healing arts and health sciences.

The Board provides both personnel awards and research grants. Personnel awards consist of postdoctoral fellowships. The research grants are divided into bio-medical and socio-health categories. All awards are aimed at augmenting the number and quality of health researchers in Saskatchewan.

Awards are granted through annual competitions. Details may be obtained directly from the Board. The Board consists of 12 members plus administrative staff. Annual Board expenditures are about $1 million.
Chairman, Dr. B. Robertson
Exec. Director, Steven Lewis

DEPARTMENT OF HIGHWAYS AND TRANSPORTATION
1855 Victoria Ave., Regina, S4P 3V5
General Inquiries: (306) 787-4800

MINISTER'S OFFICE
315 Legislative Bldg., Regina, S4S 0B3
Minister, The Hon. Grant Hodgins

DEPUTY MINISTER'S OFFICE
Dep. Minister, Jack Sutherland
Communications Branch
Director, Mike Woods

SUPPORT SERVICES DIVISION
Exec. Director, Paul Fitzel
Financial Services Branch
Director, Colleen Laing
Management Services Branch
Director, Dennis Domoney
Human Resource Branch
Director, Steve Pillipow
Safety Supervisor, Morley Yarotsky
Property Services Branch
Director, Art Lowey

**TRANSPORTATION PLANNING AND
RESEARCH DIVISION**
Exec. Director, Phil Pearson
Planning Support Branch
Director, Roger P. Couturier
Transportation Policy Branch
Director, Neil Petrovitch
Transportation Systems Branch
Director, Bernie Churko
Capital Program Planning Branch
Director, Masood Hassan
Technical Research Branch
Director, Andy Horosko

ENGINEERING DIVISION
Exec. Director, Don Metz
Geotechnical and Materials Branch
1610 Park St., Regina, S4N 2G1
Director, Allan Widger
Surfacing Branch Director, Garry Heiman
Maintenance Branch Director, Barry Martin
Highway Permit Clerk, Martin Kubik
Equipment Branch
Director, John Palaschuk
Design and Traffic Safety Branch
Director, Al Popoff

OPERATIONS DIVISION
Exec. Director, Myron Herasymuik
Bridge Branch Director, Lorne Hamblin
Operations Branch Director, Bob Cocks
Works Branch
A/Director, Dave Silzer
DISTRICT OFFICES:
Regina District
2402-2nd Ave., Regina, S4R 1A6
District Engineer, Ray Gerbrandt
Swift Current District
350 Cheadle St. W., Box 490
Swift Current, S9H 4G3
District Engineer, Norm Woodcock
Yorkton District
41 Broadway W., Yorkton, S3N 3T9
District Engineer, John Dunlop
North Battleford District
1146-102nd St.
North Battleford, S9A 1E9
District Engineer, Ed Bobick

Saskatoon District
3130-8th St. E., Saskatoon, S7K 2H6
District Engineer, Marcel Coquet
Prince Albert District
Box 3003, 365-36th St. W.
Prince Albert, S6V 6G1
District Engineer, R. Stu Armstrong

**TRANSPORTATION PLANNING AND
RESEARCH DIVISION**
Exec. Director, Bill McLaren
Board Affairs and Support Services Branch
Administrator, Phyllis Glowatsky
Motor Carrier Regulation Branch
Director, Ron Blackburn
Transportation Legislation and Safety Branch
Director, Dave Stewart
Transport Compliance Branch
Director/Chief Traffic Officer, Barry Weafer

AGENCIES, BOARDS AND COMMISSIONS

Highway Traffic Board
2260-11th Ave., Regina, S4P 3V7

The Highway Traffic Board is established under the *Highway Traffic Act,* S.S. 1986, Chapter H-3.1. It is composed of 14 members appointed by the Lieutenant-Governor in Council.

The Board is responsible for the granting of business licences (operating authority certificates) to for-hire truck and bus operators in the province, for both intra-provincial and extra-provincial transportation. The Board also sets out the terms and conditions under which licensed carriers may operate.

The Board will be administering several standards as part of the new National Safety Code for truck and bus transportation in Canada.

The Highway Traffic Board is responsible for developing motor vehicle registration fees for the provincial government, as well as outlining the different uses for each of the 15 vehicle registration classes.

The Board also administers off-highway vehicle legislation (snowmobiles and all-terrain vehicles have separate Acts), legislation relating to traffic rules, and dangerous goods transportation requirements. It also acts as an appeal body for certain decisions made by Saskatchewan Government Insurance regarding suspension of a driver's licence.

Chairman, Bill McLaren
Administrator, Phyllis Glowatsky

DEPARTMENT OF HUMAN RESOURCES, LABOUR AND EMPLOYMENT
1870 Albert St., Regina, S4P 3V7
(except where otherwise indicated)

MINISTER'S OFFICE
Rm. 340, Legislative Bldg., Regina, S4S 0B3
Minister, The Hon. Grant Schmidt

DEPUTY MINISTER'S OFFICE
Dep. Minister, Gerry Meier

ADMINISTRATION SERVICES BRANCH
Inquiry: (306) 787-2413
Director, P.J. More
Asst. Director, Vacant
Systems Manager, Brian Schwab
COMMUNICATIONS BRANCH
Director, Nancy Consaul

Human Resources and Employment

Asst. Dep. Minister, Vacant
Human Resources
Personnel Consultant, Louise Sawyer
Personnel Asst., Karen Kurtz

EMPLOYMENT EQUITY
Co-ordinator, Natalia Carroll
Employment Unit for Persons
with Physical Disabilities
Manager, Judy Ryan

EMPLOYMENT OPPORTUNITIES BRANCH
3rd Flr., 1914 Hamilton St., Regina, S4P 4V4
Exec. Director, Anne McFarlane
Policy and Research Unit
Manager, Bill Warriner
Youth Services Unit Manager, Rick Pawliw
Major Projects Employment Co-ordinator,
Peter Suderman

Labour

Asst. Dep. Minister, Judy Moore

LABOUR RELATIONS BRANCH
Inquiry: (306) 787-2391
Exec. Director, Dave Argue
Conciliation Services
A/Director, Mike Grainger
Labour Relations Officer, Laura Scott
Office of the Worker's Advocate
Inquiry: (306) 787-2456
Labour Policy and Research
Director, Lorraine Nicol

LABOUR STANDARDS BRANCH
Inquiry: (306) 787-2438/2486
Director, Lionel McNabb
A/Director, Vacant
Asst. Director, Eric Greene

OCCUPATIONAL HEALTH AND SAFETY
BRANCH
Inquiry: (306) 787-4496
Exec. Director, John Alderman
A/Asst. Director, George Scattergood
Workplace Safety Unit
Manager, Herb Schmunk

Asst. Manager, Bob Ross
Medical Unit
Sr. Toxicologist, Dr. Fayek Kelada
Hygiene Unit
A/Manager, Herb Wooley
Mines Safety Unit
A/Manager, Phil Rosen
Radiation Safety Unit
Radiation Health Physicist, Dr. Denis Brown
Support Services Section
A/Manager, Bob Armstrong
Farm Safety Unit Manager, Barry Armstrong
Information and Resource Unit
Manager, Glen Brooman

Library Information: (306) 787-2422

PENSIONS BRANCH
Inquiry: (306) 787-7650
Sup't, J. Mans Crozier

SENIORS' DIRECTORATE
2151 Scarth St., Regina, S4P 3Z3
Inquiry: (306) 787-7478
Director, Harold Danchilla
Policy and Co-ordination Manager, Vacant
Seniors' Programs Manager, Del Fuchs
Inquiry: (306) 787-2682
Saskatchewan Income Plan
Inquiry: (306) 787-4104
Grants for Seniors Services
Inquiry: (306) 787-5016

WOMEN'S DIRECTORATE
1914 Hamilton St., Regina, S4P 4V4
Inquiry: (306) 787-2329
Director, Joan Greaves

AGENCIES, BOARDS AND COMMISSIONS

Labour Relations Board
652, 1914 Hamilton St., Regina, S4P 4V4
Inquiry: (306) 787-2406

The main provisions of the *Trade Union Act,*
R.S.S. 1978, Chapter T-17, are administered by
the Labour Relations Board. The board is empowered to issue orders that:
- certify unions as bargaining representatives for
  appropriate units of employees;
- require persons to refrain from unfair labour
  practices; and
- reinstate employees discharged contrary to the
  Trade Union Act.

Also, the board may act as an arbitration board
and determine any dispute referred to it by
employers and trade unions.

Chairman, Dennis P. Ball
Vice-Chairman, John Hobbs
Board Secretary, Sandra Leflar

Minimum Wage Board
1870 Albert St., Regina, S4P 3V7
Inquiry: (306) 787-2438

The Minimum Wage Board, subject to the approval of the Lieutenant-Governor in Council, may issue orders with respect to certain labour standards. The Board may determine the minimum wage, the minimum meal break period, the maximum charge by employers for meals or lodgings provided, require an employer to repair and launder uniforms, fix the minimum age at which persons may be employed, require that female employees be provided with free transportation to their residence after completion of work shifts during certain hours of the day, fix the period in any day within which the hours of work of employees shall be confined, require a detailed pay statement to be presented to employees, and provide for a rest period.

The minimum wage regulations do not apply to employees working in undertakings in which only members of the employer's family are employed, to agricultural workers, persons employed in sheltered workshops or work activity centres for the physically handicapped, or employees employed exclusively as domestic workers in private homes except where a wage subsidy is given to the employer from public funds.

Chairperson, Mary T. Rocan

Workers' Compensation Board
1840 Lorne St., Regina, S4P 2L8
General Inquiry: (306) 787-4370

The *Workers' Compensation Act, 1979,* is a provincial statute providing financial protection along with other services to workers and their dependants in cases of injury or death arising out of and in the course of employment.

The Act is based on the principles of collective liability and no-fault protection. Employers collectively pay the cost of compensation for injuries occurring in their category of industry. The compensation which a worker is entitled to under the Act takes the place of the right of action against the employer.

The scope of coverage under the Act is very broad. Virtually all workers are covered with the exception of those enumerated in the Act and its Regulations.

The Workers' Compensation Board established by the Act is responsible for its administration. Its three members, a chairman and two board members, are appointed by the Lieutenant-Governor in Council. Two senior vice-presidents and a staff of over 250 carry out the daily work of the Board.

Chairman, Garnet Garven
Board Members:
G. Leonard Larson, Philip J. Leduc
Sr. Vice-President (Adjudication),
J.A. McLean
Sr. Vice-President (Administration),
K.L. Brown

DEPARTMENT OF JUSTICE
1874 Scarth St., Regina, S4P 3V7
(except where otherwise indicated)
General Inquiries: (306) 787-5480

MINISTER OF JUSTICE AND ATTORNEY GENERAL'S OFFICE
Legislative Bldg., Regina, S4S 0B3
Attorney Gen. and Minister of
Justice, The Hon. Robert Andrew

DEPUTY MINISTER OF JUSTICE AND DEPUTY ATTORNEY GENERAL'S OFFICE
Dep. Minister of Justice and
Dep. Attorney Gen., Brian Barrington-Foote

Corrections and Justice Services
Asst. Dep. Minister, Terry Thompson

COURT SERVICES
Exec. Director, Gary Brandt
Administrative Support
A/Director, Brent Brownlee
Court Operations
A/Director, Barb Hookenson
Sheriff Services Director, Brent Prenevost
Court Operations
Asst. Director, Les Ell
Registrar of Courts
Court House, Regina, S4P 3V7
Registrar of Courts, Fred Newis
Maintenance Enforcement Office
Director, Maurice Herauf

CORRECTIONS DIVISION
Inquiries: (306) 787-3490
Exec. Director, Dick Till
Institutional Operations
A/Director, L. Wilson
Community Facilities
Director, Peter Guenther
Community Operations
A/Director, T. Lang
Community Participation
Director, Cathy Joyner

PROPERTY REGISTRATION BRANCH
Director and Master of Titles, Ray Petrich
Personal Property Registry
3rd Flr., 1874 Scarth St., Regina, S4P 3S5
A/Registrar, Eva Winter

Administration Division
Asst. Dep. Minister, James Benning
Administrative Services Branch
A/Director, Twila Meredith
Sytems Branch Director, Garry Spencer
Human Resources Branch
Director, Barry Sockett
Communications Branch Director, Vacant

POLICING BRANCH
Director, John Baker
Security Guards and Private Detectives
Registrar, Ms. Pat Styles
Chief Provincial Firearms Officer, Al Terry

PUBLIC TRUSTEE
Public Trustee, Mary Ellen Wellsch
Dep. Public Trustee, Armand Bachelu
CORONERS BRANCH
Chief Coroner, Dr. O. Diane Stephenson
Admin. Officer, Murray Selinger

CIVIL LAW DIVISION
Exec. Director, Darryl Bogdasavich, Q.C.
Co-ordinator of Litigation,
Don McKillop, Q.C.
Solicitors: Wayne Mulholland, Lian Schwann
Co-ordinator of General Legal Services,
Larry Anderson
Solicitors: Dale Beck, Gary Moran,
Heather Sinclair, Linda Zarzeczny,
Tony Koschinsky, Merv Woods
Co-ordinator of General Services,
Gerald Tegart
Solicitors: Damon Bailey,
Leta Brierley, Barry Hornsberger,
Garry Moran, Mona Nasser

PUBLIC LAW AND POLICY
Exec. Director, Robert Richards
Constitutional Branch
Solicitors: R. Macnab, George Peacock,
Andrea Seale, Ken Tyler, Gale Welsh
Policy, Planning and Evaluation
Director, Betty Ann Pottruff
Crown Solicitor, Carol Snell
Research Officers: Shaukat Nasim, Jan Turner
Legislative Services
Co-ordinator, Doug Moen
Solicitors: Susan Amrud, Madeleine Hollman,
Sam McCullough, D. McGovern
Legislative Drafting
Co-ordinator, Ian Brown
Crown Solicitors: K. Chutskoff,
Garnet Holtzman, Q.C., Jane Sather

PUBLIC PROSECUTIONS DIVISION
10th Flr., 1874 Scarth St.
Regina, S4P 3V7
Exec. Director, Ellen Gunn, Q.C.
Appeals Director, Murray Brown
Sr. Appellate Counsel,
Kenneth W. MacKay, Q.C.
Gen. Counsel (Criminal), Serge Kujawa, Q.C.
Director of Prosecutors,
Richard Quinney, Q.C.
Sr. Crown Prosecutor, Doug Britton

AGENCIES, BOARDS AND COMMISSIONS

Farm Land Security Board
207, 3988 Albert St., Regina, S4P 4V4

The Farm Land Security Board was established in December 1984 under the *Farm Land Security Act*, R.S.S., Chapter F-8.01, to protect agricultural land from being foreclosed on in debt recovery. The Board is currently made up of eleven members, three of whom hear any case.

The Board automatically stays proceedings against the farmer in question for 120 days while a hearing can take place. The Board attempts to mediate between the farmer and the financial institution and, in the event that this is of no avail, the Board's report on the farm's viability is given primary consideration by the courts.

Chairman, David Angell
Gen. Manager, Fred Switzer
Inquiry: (306) 787-5147

Law Reform Commission of Saskatchewan
Sturdy-Stone Ctr.
122-3rd Ave. N., Saskatoon, S7K 2H6

The Law Reform Commission of Saskatchewan was created by a special Act of the Legislative Assembly. The Commission is charged with keeping under review all the law of the province to facilitate its systematic development and reform, including codification, elimination of anomalies, repeal of obsolete and unnecessary enactments, reduction in number of separate enactments and, generally, simplification and modernization of the law. Recommendations for new legislation are made to the Minister of Justice after an opportunity has been given to the public to comment on them.

Chairman, Dale G. Linn
Commissioners:
Madame Justice Marjorie A. Gerwing,
Gordon J. Kuski, Q.C.
Director of Research, K.P.R. Hodges
Legal Research Officer, Michael J.W. Finley

Provincial Mediation Board/Rentalsman
5th Flr., 2103-11th Ave., Regina, S4P 3V7
General Inquiry:
(Mediation Board) (306) 787-5408/5387
(Rentalsman) (306) 787-2699

The Provincial Mediation Board is empowered to confer with and advise debtors and creditors in mediating the settlement of disputes of debt-related problems without recourse to legal proceedings. The Board also administers Part X of the *Bankruptcy Act* "Orderly Payment of Debts", which provides a legal remedy for debt problems.

The Board has some responsibilities under the *Landlord and Tenant Act,* R.S.S. 1978, Chapter L-6, and attends to the disposition of security deposits and rent review applications under the *Residential Tenancies Act,* R.S.S. 1978, Chapter R-22.

The office of the Rentalsman is responsible for all other aspects of the *Residential Tenancies Act.* The purpose of the Act is to maintain well-balanced relations between landlords and tenants, provide a third-party mediation service and issue judgments on landlord/tenant disputes.

Rentalsman/Chairman, E.R. Madill
Sr. Board Member and
Sr. Dep. Rentalsman, Ken McKenzie
Mediation Board Member and
Dep. Rentalsman, Mary Cherneskey

Public and Private Rights Board
11th Flr., 1874 Scarth St., Regina, S4P 3V7

The Public and Private Rights Board is constituted under the *Expropriation Procedure Act,* R.S.S. 1978, Chapter E-16.

The Board is empowered to review the route, situation or design of any public improvement where land is, or may be, expropriated by a provincial expropriation authority. The Board is also empowered to review the amount of compensation offered for expropriated land. The Board can conduct a review by means of a public hearing or a private inquiry or both. After reviewing the matters in question the Board attempts to arrange a settlement between the expropriating authority and the landowner.

Chairman, Pauline A. Duncan
Director, Glen T. Hamilton

Rent Appeal Commission
224-4th Ave. S., Saskatoon, S7K 2H6

The Rent Appeal Commission was established under the provisions of the *Residential Tenancies Act.*

The purpose of the Commission is to adjudicate and issue compliance orders on appeals heard by the Commission from tenants or landlords who feel they have been aggrieved by an order issued by the Office of the Rentalsman. Commission orders may be appealed within thirty days of the issuance of an order to the Saskatchewan Court of Appeal on a matter of law or jurisdiction. Members of the Commission are appointed by the Lieutenant-Governor in Council.

Chairman, John Milani
Secretary to the Commission,
Jane Vibert

Saskatchewan Criminal Injuries Compensation Board
10th Flr., Provincial Bldg.
122-3rd Ave. N., Saskatoon, S7K 2H6

The Criminal Injuries Compensation Board was established on Sept. 1, 1967, by the *Criminal Injuries Compensation Act,* R.S.S. 1978, Chapter C-47, under the jurisdiction of the Department of Justice. This agency is financed by a cost-sharing program between the provincial and federal governments. The Board consists of three members, who consider applications for compensation filed by the victims of violent crime.

The program provides for payment of compensation to persons who have been injured and to dependents of persons who have been killed in Saskatchewan, as the result of such criminal offences as assault, murder, rape, criminal negligence, robbery, impaired driving, or various other acts of a similar nature. Compensation is awarded for expenses actually and reasonably incurred, lost income, and pain and suffering. The financial need of the applicant is also considered by the Board.

The purpose of the program is to compensate victims for those pecuniary losses not covered by other social programs and insurance plans. The magnitude of the award is not comparable to amounts recovered from civil suits.

Chairman, Morris Cherneskey, Q.C.
Vice-Chairman, Leona Hazelwanter
Member, Eileen Bateman
Secretary, Lorna Johnson

Saskatchewan Farm Ownership Board
3130-8th St. E., Saskatoon, S7K 2H6

The Saskatchewan Farm Ownership Act, R.S.S. 1978, Chapter S-17, effective May 6, 1980, allows acquisitions of agricultural land not exceeding 4 hectares, by non-resident individuals and corporations not primarily involved in agricultural production. Special exemption is provided for acquisition of agricultural land by non-resident relatives of one-time Saskatchewan farmers. The Act also provides that a non-eligible person or corporation may apply for an exemption which, if granted, will allow an acquisition exceeding 4 hectares, subject to any terms and conditions considered advisable.

The Farm Ownership Board, appointed by the Lieutenant-Governor in Council, is responsible for the administration of the Act. This responsibility includes deciding policy under the Act, making decisions regarding applications for exemption, issuing orders for divestment of landholdings acquired in contravention of the Act, initiating investigations of land transfers and recommending prosecutions for violations of the Act.

Part VI of the *Saskatchewan Farm Security Act,* proclaimed in the fall of 1988, replaced the provisions of the *Saskatchewan Farm Ownership Act.* Though a major portion of the old Act was retained, the following changes should be noted:

- A special exemption for acquisitions of agricultural lands will be provided for non-resident relatives of past or present Saskatchewan residents; and
- Canadian residents will be allowed to have or acquire agricultural land in an amount not to exceed 129 hectares or two quarter sections, whichever is the greater.

Chairman, J.A. Brown
Director, Ed Rasmussen

Saskatchewan Human Rights Commission
Canterbury Towers, #802
224-4th Ave. S., Saskatoon, S7K 2H6
General Inquiry: (306) 933-5952
Superphone: (306) 373-2119

The Saskatchewan Human Rights Commission, established in November 1972, is the agency responsible for the administration of the *Saskatchewan Human Rights Code.* The Code prohibits discrimination in employment, housing, public accommodation, education and civil liberties because of a person's race, creed, religion, colour, sex, marital status, age (18-64), physical disability, nationality, ancestry or place of origin.

Persons who believe they have been discriminated against may file complaints with the Saskatchewan Human Rights Commission. Investigators are assigned to investigate these complaints. There is no charge for this service.

The Commission is also responsible for approving and monitoring affirmative action programs. These are special programs designed to eliminate the disadvantages suffered by any group of individuals protected under the Code. Commission staff will also conduct educational programs upon request.

Chief Commissioner, Ronald Kruzeniski, Q.C.
Exec. Director, K.C. Jamont

Regional Office:
1819 Cornwall St., Regina, S4P 3V7
Inquiry/Superphone: (306) 787-2530

Saskatchewan Police Commission
5th Flr., 2350 Albert St.
Regina, S4P 4A6
General Inquiry: (306) 787-6518

The Saskatchewan Police Commission promotes the preservation of peace and the prevention of crime, the efficiency of police services, and the improvement of police relations with the communities in the province. The Commission is authorized to make regulations on various matters that will upgrade police services generally through training and standardization. The Commission can inquire into the conduct of or the performance of duty by a member of a municipal police force or the RCMP. Citizens' complaints made directly to the Commission office will be investigated by the Commission's own investigator. The Commission also operates the Saskatchewan Police College where recruit and in-service training programs are conducted on a year-round basis for all municipal police personnel in the province.

Chairman, Donald K. MacPherson, Q.C.
Vice-Chairman, Jacelyn A. Ryan
Member, Richard J.N. Gamble
Exec. Director, Robert J. Mills
Commission Officer, Gary F. Treble

Saskatchewan Securities Commission
8th Flr., T-D Bank Bldg.
1914 Hamilton St., Regina, S4P 3V7

The Securities Commission is a regulatory body created under the authority of *The Securities Act, 1988,* to oversee and regulate the securities industry. This includes approval of securities prospectuses and registration of sales people (stock brokers) as well as enforcement and investigation of aspects of the industry.

Chairman, W.M. Wheatley
Registrar, Barbara Shourounis
Dep. Registrar, Ian McIntosh

Surface Rights Board of Arbitration
2350 Albert St., 5th Flr., Regina, S4P 4A6

The Board was appointed pursuant to the authority contained in and to meet the requirements of the *Surface Rights Acquisition and Compensation Act,* R.S.S. 1978, Chapter S-65, and amendments. The Board's purpose is to administer the Act which is designed:

- to provide for a comprehensive procedure for acquiring surface rights;
- to provide for payment of just and equitable compensation for the acquisition of surface rights;
- to provide for the maintenance and reclamation of the surface of land acquired in connection with surface rights acquired under the Act; and
- to investigate matters in dispute or complained of, interview persons deemed necessary, inspect any land or other property that is involved relevant to the dispute in order to effect settlement.

The Board assists in arriving at fair and equitable agreements between landowners and mineral operators when part of the surface holding is taken for mineral operation. The Board is required under the Act to hold hearings as and when the occasions arise for the purpose of receiving representations as to compensation for surface rights which is under dispute, to deal with applications made for immediate right of entry, and to formulate and issue orders pursuant to such hearings.

Chairman, Leonard Dahl

NORTHERN AFFAIRS SECRETARIAT
Box 5000, La Ronge, S0J 1L0

MINISTER'S OFFICE
Rm. 348, Legislative Bldg., Regina, S4S 0B3

Minister, The Hon. Joan Duncan

SECRETARY'S OFFICE
5th Flr., 2350 Albert St., Regina, S4P 4A6

Secretary, Walter Keyes
Asst. Secretary, Alison Stickland

Northern Office
Box 5000, La Ronge, S0J 1L0
Manager, B. Goffin
Research Officer, Carol Rowlett

Northern Development Advisory Council
Box 5000, La Ronge, S0J 1L0

Chairman, Bill Klassen
Manager, Elmer Morin
Research Officer, Richard Turkheim

DEPARTMENT OF PARKS, RECREATION AND CULTURE

3211 Albert St., Regina, S4S 5W6
General Inquiries: (306) 787-2700
Fax: (306) 787-8441

MINISTER'S OFFICE
Rm. 346, Legislative Bldg., Regina, S4S 0B3
Minister, The Hon. Colin Maxwell

DEPUTY MINISTER'S OFFICE
Dep. Minister, Douglas Cressman

Culture and Sport Division

Asst. Dep. Minister, Keith Rogers
1942 Hamilton St., Regina, S4P 3V7
Arts and Multicultural Branch
Director, Paul Fudge
Arts Manager, Valerie Creighton
Multicultural Manager, Armand Martin
Zone Arts and Multicultural Manager,
Rod Hardie

HERITAGE BRANCH
Director, W. Dean Clark
Saskatchewan Museum of Natural History
Manager, Ron Borden
Heritage Resources
Manager, Dr. Brian E. Spurling
Museum Consultant, Susan Birley

SPORT AND RECREATION BRANCH
Director, Bill Werry
Sport Manager, Emile St-Amand
Recreation Manager, Gene Lambert
Zone Sport and Recreation Manager,
Bruce Medhurst

Renewable Resources Division

Asst. Dep. Minister, Alan Appleby
Integrated Resource Policy
Manager, G.W. Pepper

FORESTRY BRANCH
McIntosh Mall, 800 Central Ave.
Prince Albert, S6V 6G1
Exec. Director, Paul Brett
Forest Inventory, Larry Stanley
Timber Management, Jamie Benson
Regional Operations, Murray Little
Silviculture, Vic Begrand
Administration, Felix Casavant

FISHERIES BRANCH
Director, Paul Naftel
Biological and Data Services
15 Innovation Blvd., Saskatoon, S4N 2X8
Manager, Bill Sawchyn
Fish Enhancement
Box 3003, Prince Albert, S6V 6G1
Sup't, Vacant

WILDLIFE BRANCH
Director, Dennis Sherratt
Region Supervisor, Dave Phillips
Sup't of Wildlife, Hugh Hunt
Habitat Supervisor, Syd Barber
Landowner Assistance Supervisor,
Cam Scheelhaase

RESOURCE LANDS BRANCH
Director, Doug Mazur
Land Administration (North)
McIntosh Mall, 800 Central Ave.
Prince Albert, S6V 6G1
Supervisor, Larry Oberik

PARKS BRANCH
A/Director, Ken Lozinsky
Regional Parks Manager, Clark Gabel
Park Visitor Programs Manager, Sharon Wood
Park Planning Manager, David Powell
Park Programs Manager, Bob Herbison

OPERATIONS DIVISION
Exec. Director, Ross MacLennan
Saskatoon Region
122-3rd Ave. N., Saskatoon, S7K 2H6
Reg. Director, Pat Nelson
Swift Current Region
350 Cheadle St. W., Swift Current, S9H 4G3
Reg. Director, Dave Noble
Melville Region
117-3rd Ave., Melville, S0A 2P0
Reg. Director, Dick Hutchinson
Regina Region
3211 Albert St., Regina, S4S 5W6
Reg. Director, Terry Swystun
Northern Field Services
McIntosh Mall, 800 Central Ave.
Prince Albert, S6V 6G1
Director, Glen Rolles
Forest Fire Management
Operations Head, Glen Conacher
Meadow Lake Region
Box 580, Meadow Lake, S0M 1V0
Reg. Director, Merv Swanson
Prince Albert Region
McIntosh Mall, 800 Central Ave.
Prince Albert, S6V 6G1
Reg. Director, Gus MacAuley
Hudson Bay Region
Natural Resources Bldg.
Hudson Bay, S0E 0Y0
Reg. Director, Ken Murray
La Ronge Region
Box 5000, La Ronge, S0J 1L0
Reg. Director, Ross Duncan

Support Services Division

Asst. Dep. Minister, Dick Bailey
Human Resources Branch
Director, Ron Wight
Staff Development Manager, Pat Brown
Personnel Services Manager, Lynn Jacobson
Communications Branch
Director, Nolan Matthies

Contract Services Director, Shelly Vandermey
Management Services Director, Bill Marr

AGENCIES, BOARDS AND COMMISSIONS

New Careers Corp.
1260-8th Ave., Regina, S4P 3V7

The New Careers Corporation was established in May 1984 to provide training and employment for individuals in receipt of provincial financial assistance. The Corporation, which is essentially a construction company, contracts primarily with the Department of Parks, Recreation and Culture to construct recreational projects in provincial parks. Trainees spend approximately 18 months in the program gaining work experience and/or institutional upgrading to enable them to obtain full-time employment. Eighty-five per cent of trainees completing career plans find full-time employment.

Chairperson, Ted Brady
CEO, Brian Woodcock
Manager, Terry Lyons
Meadow Lake Project Sup't, Gordon Wykes
Lake Diefenbaker Project
Sup't, Lee Anderson
Regina Project Sup't, Gifford Brass
Saskatoon Project Sup't, Jack Yerex
Duck Mountain Project Sup't, David Fraser
Training and Placement
Co-ordinator, Henry Joerissen
Recruitment and Counselling
Co-ordinator, Jim Dean

Saskatchewan Arts Board
2550 Broad St., Regina, S4P 3V7

The Saskatchewan Arts Board was established in 1949 by an Act of the Legislative Assembly "to make available to the people of Saskatchewan, opportunities to engage in any one or more of the following activities: drama, the visual arts, music, literature, crafts, and other arts . . . and to promote the maintenance and development of high standards of such activities."

The Arts Board is an arm's-length agency of the province, funded by the provincial government through an annual grant. It is composed of fifteen members appointed by Order-in-Council. These volunteers, from all parts of the province (but representing no specific geographic or artistic area) meet frequently to formulate policy and to help establish priorities on the cultural needs of the people of Saskatchewan. As well, there is a full-time professional staff who provide consultative and other arts-related services.

It is the Board's purpose to serve all the province and all the disciplines of the arts. To achieve these goals, work is done in many areas: programming, funding, counselling and communications, among others. Two of the most widely-known of the Board's ongoing projects are the School of the Arts and the Permanent Collection of art and crafts by provincial artists.

Chairperson, Joan Bissett
Exec. Director, Wayne Cunningham

Saskatchewan Centre of the Arts
200 Lakeshore Dr., Regina, S4P 3V7
General Inquiries: (306) 584-5050

The Saskatchewan Centre of the Arts has the facilities to accommodate more than 2,000 delegates for meetings, is fully equipped to provide in-house catering for conventions, banquets and trade shows, and has dining facilities for groups from 30 to 1,200. The aims and objectives of the Centre are:

- to enhance the quality of life of the people of Saskatchewan by attracting as many as possible to participate in a broad range of entertainment and other activities at the Centre;
- to provide facilities for entertainment and educational and cultural facilities, and generally to cater to the public in respect of those facilities; and
- to promote the development of its facilities as a centre for entertainment, exhibition and the promotion and presentation of dramatic, musical and artistic works in the province.

Chairperson, Joan Bissett
Exec. Director, George C. Haynes
Sales and Marketing Director, Dennis Perko
Convention and Catering Director, Wilf Baker
Theatre Director, Eleanor Hollihn

Saskatchewan Heritage Advisory Board
Box 1044, Hudson Bay, S0E 0Y0

The Saskatchewan Heritage Advisory Board is appointed by the minister under the provisions of *The Heritage Property Act*. The Board advises the Minister of Culture and Recreation on matters related to the conservation, protection and preservation of heritage property in the province.

Chairperson, Hugh MacKie

Saskatchewan Heritage Property Review Board
1942 Hamilton St., Regina, S4P 3V7

The Heritage Property Act provides for the conservation, protection and preservation of heritage property, which is any property, whether natural or man-made, that is of interest for its architectural, historical, cultural, environmental, aesthetic or scientific value. This includes sites where architectural, historical, cultural or scientific property is or may reasonably be expected to be found. Under the powers of the Act, local governments and the provincial government may designate heritage properties. The Act provides an avenue for appeal for anyone adversely affected by the implementation of the legislation in the form of the Saskatchewan Heritage Property Review Board.

The Board consists of three to seven members appointed by the Lieutenant-Governor in Council. The term of office is for three years with members eligible for one further three-year term. Expenses are met out of funds appropriated by the Legislative Assembly.

Under the Act, the Board holds public hearings on matters properly referred to it that relate to the conservation, protection and preservation of heritage property in the province. The Board reports its findings to the appropriate bodies which may then take such actions as are provided for under the legislation.

Chairperson, Dave Hyndman

Saskatchewan Multicultural Advisory Council
1942 Hamilton St., Regina, S4P 3V7

The *Saskatchewan Multicultural Act,* R.S.S. 1978, Chapter S-31, was passed in 1974. The Act provided a framework for provincial government policy on the "preservation and development" of multiculturalism in Saskatchewan. It also established the legislative authority for the granting of provincial funds to groups and individuals in the province who had a specific interest in multiculturalism.

Under the provisions of the Act, the Lieutenant-Governor in Council appoints five to fifteen members to the Saskatchewan Multicultural Advisory Council, with terms of service of two to four years.

The functions of the Council can be divided into two general categories:

• to advise the Minister of Parks, Recreation and Culture in respect to grant applications made under the Act; and
• to provide the Government of Saskatchewan, through the Minister of Parks, Recreation and Culture, with advice on a wide range of issues pertaining to multiculturalism.

Chairperson, Ernie Epp

Saskatchewan Western Development Museums
Box 1910, 2935 Melville St.
Saskatoon, S7K 3S5
General Inquiry: (306) 934-1400

The Saskatchewan Western Development Museums exist by virtue of an Act of the Legislative Assembly of Saskatchewan (the *Western Development Museum Act,* R.S.S. 1978, Chapter W-12) which established a board of directors charged with the duties of:

a) procuring tools, machinery, implements, engines, devices and other goods and chattels of historic value and importance connected with the economic and cultural development of western Canada;
b) collecting, arranging, cataloguing, reconditioning, preserving and exhibiting these items to the public;
c) stimulating interest in the history of the economic and cultural development of western Canada; and
d) co-operating with organizations having similar objectives.

The Saskatchewan Western Development Museums comprise four branches, each with its own distinct theme: Moose Jaw — The Story of Transportation; North Battleford — The Story of Agriculture; Saskatoon — The Story of Western Development; Yorkton — The Story of the People.

The Museum is organized on a headquarters/branch system, whereby core staff located at a provincial service centre in Saskatoon provide service to branch museums.

Chairperson, Peter Kilburn
Exec. Director, David Richeson

SASKATCHEWAN PROPERTY MANAGEMENT CORP.
2045 Broad St., Regina, S4P 3V7
(except where otherwise indicated)

MINISTER'S OFFICE
Rm. 303, Legislative Bldg., Regina, S4S 0B1
Minister, The Hon. Graham Taylor

PRESIDENT'S OFFICE
President, Otto Cutts
Executive Support Director, Sue McLaughlin
External Relations Manager, Joe Donlevy

Corporate Affairs Division
Vice-President, Jim Penrod
Public Affairs Director, Vacant
Corporate Planning Director, Rae Reid

Security Division
Asst. Vice-President, Harry Stienwand
Physical Security Unit
Director, Doug Olafson
Awareness and Crime Prevention
Director, Patrick Shaw
Investigations Director, Doug Porter

FINANCE AND ADMINISTRATION
Exec. Director, Shirley Raab
Controller, Norm Drummond
Support Services Director, Mike Lynden
Financial Planning Director, Les Handford
Treasury Management
Director, Paul McIntyre

HUMAN RESOURCES DIVISION
Exec. Director, Jim Penrod
Human Resources and Management
Director, Barrie Hilsen
Human Resource Development
Director, D. McLaughlin
Compensation/Labour Relations
Manager, Tom Langstaff

Facility Planning and Management
Vice-President, Brian Eger
Client Services Director, Doug Kozak
Capital Projects Director, David Thom
Capital Financing and Forecasting
Director, Bev Bradshaw
Technical Development and Support
Director, Clive Rodham
Furniture Branch
110 Henderson Dr., Regina, S4P 3V7
Director, Bruce Murray

Realty Division
Vice-President, Ken Rankin
Realty Services Branch
Director, Alf Bernstein
Divisional Services Branch
Director, Deborah Johnson
Accommodation Services
Director, Greg Osicki
Research Director, Dale Minion

Information Systems Division
Vice-President, Al Moffat
Technical Services Director, Andy Jani
Telecommunications
Director, Darryl Williams
Policy and Planning Director, Chris Hecht
Buy Saskatchewan Agency
1919 Saskatchewan Dr., Regina, S4P 3V7
Gen. Manager, Tom Douglas
Central Survey and Mapping
Gen. Manager, John Turnbull

Procurement
A/Vice President, Ian Laidlaw
Supply Agency
110 Henderson Dr., Regina, S4P 3V7
Director, Bob Cade

Operations and Services
Vice-President, Ian Laidlaw
Commercial Enterprises
Gen. Manager, Rick Sinotte
Central Vehicle Agency
Vehicle Services Director, Al Nordin
Aviation Services Director, Rick Sinotte

QUEEN'S PRINTER
A/Queen's Printer, Bill Matthew
Mail Services Director, Ken Zasibida
Photographic Services
Director, Ray Christensen
Gazette Editor, Dianna Bereti

PROPERTY MANAGEMENT BRANCH
North Battleford Region
Reg. Director, Bill Bunko
Prince Albert Region
Reg. Director, Ray Fieber
Saskatoon Region
Reg. Director, Maurice Arsenault
Yorkton Region
Reg. Director, Ray Fieber
Moose Jaw Region
A/Reg. Director, Garth Rusconi
Legislative Region
Reg. Director, Lorne Fries
Regina City Region
Reg. Director, Gerry Murray

PROVINCIAL AUDITOR
Chateau Tower
1500, 1920 Broad St., Regina, S4P 3V7
General Inquiry: (306) 787-6398

Provincial Auditor, W.G. Lutz
Asst. Provincial Auditor, G.F. Wendel
Dep. Provincial Auditors:
B.R. Atkinson, J.A. Hunt, M.A. Heffernan
Professional Development
Director, Bob Black
Computer Auditing Director, Patricia Hall
Audit Managers: Mobasher Ahmad,
Ray Bohn, Rick Ellis, Andrew Martens,
Edward Montgomery, Judy Ferguson,
Philip Creaser, Glen Nyhus,
Lloyd Orrange, Karim Pradhan

DEPARTMENT OF THE PROVINCIAL SECRETARY
10th Flr., 1919 Saskatchewan Dr.
Regina, S4P 3V7

MINISTER'S OFFICE
Rm 322, Legislative Bldg., Regina, S4S 0B3
Minister, The Hon. Eric Berntson

DEPUTY PROVINCIAL SECRETARY'S OFFICE
Dep. Provincial Secretary, Bill Clarke
Program Advisory Branch
Project Co-ordinator, Robert Hersche
Project Analyst, Diane Tucker
Provincial Inquiry Centre
Director, R.G. (Bob) Leonard

AGENCIES, BOARDS AND COMMISSIONS

Agricultural Development Corp. of Saskatchewan (Agdevco)
Trade and Convention Centre
11th Flr., 1919 Saskatchewan Dr.
Regina, S4P 3V7
Inquiries: (306) 787-5035

The Corporation's primary purpose is to develop, process, diversify and upgrade agriculture in Saskatchewan, as well as market specialized crops, such as lentils, canary seed, mustard seed, faba beans, and peas. Agdevco is also involved in the marketing of purebred livestock, semen and embryo transplants.

The Corporation also serves as a government vehicle in the management and implementation of national and international aid and commercial projects as well as countertrade.

Chairman, The Hon. Eric Berntson
President, B. Hanson
Corporate Vice-President, Barry Ambrosia
Trade and Countertrade
Vice-President, Tim Marshall

Crown Management Board of Saskatchewan
300, 2400 College Ave., Regina, S4P 1C8
Inquiries: (306) 787-6851

The Crown Management Board of Saskatchewan (CMB) is a provincial Crown corporation, without share capital, operating under the authority of *The Crown Corporations Act, 1978*. The Corporation is responsible for administering provincial government policy as it relates to those Crown corporations under its purview with particular emphasis on business efficiency and effective management.

For administrative purposes, CMB has grouped the corporations into three sectors: resource; utilities; and financial services. The corporations provide a wide variety of services and sell various commodities in both domestic and international markets.

Minister responsible, Hon. Eric Berntson

Chairman of the Board, Wolfgang Wolff
President, Bill Gibson
Sr. Vice-President, Ron Rogers
Corporate Planning
Vice-President, S.D. Elbaum
Accounting Services Director, G.A. Mrazek
Gen. Counsel, T.A. Leier
Secretary to the Board, D.A. Marce
Project Director, I.A. Ellis
Project Director, D.G. Hughes
Pension and Benefits Director, H.E. McEwen
Project Director, Bob McKenzie

Future Corp.
1919 Saskatchewan Dr., Regina, S4P 3V7
Minister responsible, The Hon. Eric Berntson

President, Cliff Wright
Gen. Manager, Richard Letilley

Saskatchewan Power Corp.
2025 Victoria Ave., Regina, S4P 0S1
Telex: 071-2287
General Inquiries: (306) 566-2121

SaskPower is a publicly owned utility which was established by an Act of the Legislature in 1949 to provide electricity and natural gas to the residents of Saskatchewan.

In June 1988, a subsidiary company, Provincial Gas Ltd., was formed to serve customers with natural gas, and another subsidiary, TransGas, was formed to transport natural gas. A holding company, Saskatchewan Energy Corp., co-ordinates the business of Provincial Gas and Trans-Gas.

SaskPower continues to provide electricity to consumers from thermal and hydro stations. The major fuel source is lignite coal mined in southern Saskatchewan. Electricity is imported also from Manitoba and North Dakota. A new coal-fired station is under construction in southwestern Saskatchewan.

In 1987, SaskPower served 401,660 customers with 10.8 billion kWh of electricity.

The forerunner of the Corporation was the Saskatchewan Power Commission, which was formed in 1929. The Commission was authorized to regulate and operate the utility industry, co-operating with the privately and municipally owned utility companies. When the Commission unified the system by purchasing the privately owned utility companies, and their holdings, the *Power Corporation Act* came into force in 1950, establishing the Saskatchewan Power Corp.

In the early 1950s, the Corporation embarked on a massive rural electrification program and also expanded its service to include natural gas.

A transmission grid connects SaskPower's generating plants. Interties exist with Manitoba and North Dakota, and an interconnection is being planned to Alberta. This will be the final link to complete a North American electrical network.

Minister responsible, The Hon. Eric Berntson

Chairman of the Board, Don Stankov
President and CEO, George D. Hill, Q.C.
Exec. Vice-President, F.R. Bates
Sr. Vice-President (Finance), H. Jim
Sr. Vice-President (Operations),
R.G. Lawrence
Sr. Vice-President (Corporate Affairs),
L.S. Portigal
Manager, Internal Audit, R.A. Bruce

Electrical and Elevator Safety Branch
Chief Inspector, J.C. Chin

Gas Safety Branch
Chief Inspector, R.R. Ross

North-Sask Electric Ltd.
Box 284, La Ronge, S0J 1L0
Manager, W.C. McLachlan

Saskatchewan Energy Corp.
President, O.W. Hanson

TransGas Limited
President, V. Nelson

Provincial Gas
President, G.R. Labas

Souris Basin Development Authority
814-4th St., Estevan, S4A 0V9
Inquiries: (306) 634-4791

The Souris Basin Development Authority was created by Order-in-Council 270/86 on March 6, 1986. The Authority is a Crown corporation charged with co-ordinating the planning and approvals for and the construction of the Rafferty and Alameda dams on the Souris River system near Estevan. It is directly in charge of overseeing the land acquisition, design and construction of the dam as the agent of a number of other Saskatchewan government agencies, notably the Saskatchewan Power Corp. and the Saskatchewan Water Corp.

When completed, the dams and accompanying reservoirs will provide irrigation, flood control, wildlife enhancement and recreational facilities. Estimated cost is $120 million. As some of the benefit from the flood control is intended for the State of North Dakota, the U.S. is a partner in the project.

Chairman, The Hon. Eric Berntson
CEO, George D. Hill, Q.C.
Planning and Operations
Director, George N. Hood

DEPARTMENT OF PUBLIC PARTICIPATION
Rm. 331, Walter Scott Bldg.
3085 Albert St., Regina, S4S 0B1

MINISTER'S OFFICE
Minister, The Hon. Graham Taylor

DEPUTY MINISTER'S OFFICE
Dep. Minister, Dr. Graham Parsons
Asst. Dep. Minister, Dennis Wieler
Asst. Dep. Minister, Ken Brehm

DEPARTMENT OF RURAL DEVELOPMENT
3085 Albert St., Regina, S4S 0B1
(except where otherwise indicated)

MINISTER'S OFFICE
Rm. 204, Legislative Bldg., Regina, S4S 0B3
Minister, The Hon. Neal Hardy

DEPUTY MINISTER'S OFFICE
Dep. Minister, Bill Reader
Executive Officers:
Transportation Services, Ernest Anderson
Development Services, Dennis Webster
Management Services, Larry Chaykowski
Administrative Services Manager, Ron Sitter
Community Planning and Development Services
Director, Lloyd Talbot
Asst. Director, Garry Parker
Sr. Planner (Regina), Terry Crowe
Sr. Planner, Trent Good
122-3rd Ave. N., Saskatoon, S7K 2H6
Rural Services Division
Director, Doug McNair
Manager, Bob Mason
Road Services Director, Larry Johnson
Bridge and Ferry Services
Director, L. Mouland
Municipal Finance and Advisory Services
Director, Ken Engel
Communications Director, Bonnie Nixon
Planning Director, Walter Antonio
Drafting Services Manager, Fred Blondeau
Information Services
Manager, Brad Champagen
Extension Service Branch
Director, Sandy Lauder
Agricultural Engineering
Supervisor, Martin Wrubleski
Lands Branch Director, John Babcock

AGENCIES, BOARDS AND COMMISSIONS

Rural Board of Examiners
3085 Albert St., Regina, S4S 0B1
  The Board issues certificates of qualification to administrators of rural municipalities and to other such persons who qualify for such offices.
Chairman, Ken Engel
Secretary to the Board, Margaret Neal

DEPARTMENT OF SCIENCE AND TECHNOLOGY
15 Innovation Blvd., Saskatoon, S7N 2X8
1919 Saskatchewan Dr., Regina, S4P 3V7

MINISTER'S OFFICE
307 Legislative Bldg., Regina, S4S 0B3
Minister, The Hon. Ray Meiklejohn

DEPUTY MINISTER'S OFFICE
Dep. Minister, Harley D. Olsen
Administration Division
A/Director, Irene Ositis-Schmeiser

TECHNOLOGY DEVELOPMENT DIVISION
Exec. Director, Vacant
Policy and Planning Director, Wayne McElree
Advanced Technology Director, Peter McNeil
Communications Director, Dona Miller

DEPARTMENT OF SOCIAL SERVICES
1920 Broad St., Regina, S4P 3V6
General Inquiries: (306) 787-3494

MINISTER'S OFFICE
340 Legislative Bldg., Regina, S4S 0B3
Minister, The Hon. Grant Schmidt

DEPUTY MINISTER'S OFFICE
Dep. Minister, Henry Kutarna
Asst. Dep. Minister, Dr. Allan Hansen
Asst. Dep. Minister, Ray Barnard

POLICY AND PROGRAM SERVICES DIVISION
Exec. Director, Lorelle Schoenfeld
Federal Provincial Arrangements
Director, Don Fairbairn
Human Resources Branch
Director, Sharon Roulston
INCOME SECURITY DIVISION
Exec. Director, Vacant

FAMILY SUPPORT DIVISION
Child Protection, Adoption, Foster Care
Exec. Director, Dan Perrins
Non-governmental Organization
Services Branch
Director, Gloria Tillus
Child Day Care Branch
Director, Donna Young

YOUNG OFFENDERS PROGRAM DIVISION
Exec. Director, Lorne Koback
COMMUNITY LIVING DIVISION
110 Ominica St. W., Moose Jaw, S6H 6V2
Exec. Director, Dr. Allan Hansen

SUPPORT SERVICES DIVISION
Accounting, Assets, Procurement Systems
Exec. Director, Vacant

AGENCIES, BOARDS AND COMMISSIONS

Saskatchewan Legal Aid Commission
820-410 22nd St. E., Saskatoon, S7K 2H6
General Inquiries: (306) 933-5300
Toll-Free Inquiries: 1-800-667-3764

The objectives of the *The Legal Aid Act* are to provide legal services to persons and organizations in respect of civil and criminal matters where such persons and organizations are financially unable to secure such services from their own resources and where such services are not fee generating services.

Chairman, Donald R. Morgan
Gen. Counsel, H.P. Pick, Q.C.

DEPARTMENT OF TRADE AND INVESTMENT
1919 Saskatchewan Dr., Regina, S4P 3V7
Inquiries: (306) 787-2232

MINISTER'S OFFICE
Rm. 355, Legislative Bldg., Regina, S4S 0B3
Minister, The Hon. Robert Andrew

DEPUTY MINISTER'S OFFICE
Dep. Minister, Don Wright

Trade Division

Asst. Dep. Minister, Paul Haddow
Trade Promotions Director, Gerry Adamson
Trade Policy Director, Bob Perrin
Public and Corporate Affairs
Director, Harvey Linnen
Trade Development Director, Paul Osborne

Office of the Agent-Gen. for Saskatchewan
16 Berkeley St., London
W1X 5AE England
Agent-Gen., Paul Rousseau

Investment Division and Administration

Asst. Dep. Minister, Garth Gish
Investment Strategy and Policy
Director, Vacant
Investment Development Director, Vacant
Administration Director, Terry Tarowski

DEPARTMENT OF URBAN AFFAIRS
2151 Scarth St., Regina, S4P 3V7
Fax: (306) 787-8748
General Inquiries: (306) 787-2635

MINISTER'S OFFICE
Rm. 345, Legislative Bldg., Regina, S4S 0B3
Minister, The Hon. Jack Klein

DEPUTY MINISTER'S OFFICE
Dep. Minister, D.M. Innes
Asst. Dep. Minister, Keith Schneider
Administrative Services Branch
Director, Don Harazny

MUNICIPAL FINANCE BRANCH
Exec. Director, Ron Davis
NORTHERN MUNICIPAL SERVICES BRANCH
Box 5000, La Ronge, S0J 1L0
Director, Gerry Stinson
COMMUNITY PLANNING SERVICES BRANCH
Exec. Director, Dr. Henry McCutcheon

AGENCIES, BOARDS AND COMMISSIONS

Board of Examiners (Urban)
2151 Scarth St., Regina, S4P 3V7

The Board issues certificates of qualification to clerks and treasurers of urban municipalities and to other such persons who qualify for such offices.

Chairman, Keith Schneider
Secretary, Linda Barnes

INDEPENDENT AGENCIES, BOARDS AND COMMISSIONS

CAMECO
8th Flr., 122-3rd Ave. N.
Saskatoon, S7K 2H6
Fax: (306) 933-7460
General Inquiries: (306) 933-5000

In 1988, the provincially owned Saskatchewan Mining and Development Corp. and federally owned Eldorado Nuclear Ltd. were merged to form CAMECO. Over the course of the next months, CAMECO will be privatized through a series of stock offerings.

Among CAMECO's holdings are properties formerly held by SMDC: 50 per cent of the Key Lake uranium mine, 20 of the Cluff Lake uranium mine, and 50 per cent of the Star Lake gold mine.

Chairman, President and CEO, W.A. Gatenby
Vice-Chairman, R.E. Lloyd
Sr. Vice-President (Operations), B. Michel
Vice-President (Finance), T.J. Gorman

Vice-President (Marketing), S.J. Bonny
Vice-President (Corporate Affairs), A.E. Hillier
Vice-President (Exploration), Dr. G.D. Pollock
Administration and Northern Affairs
Vice-President, D.G. Somers
Systems Manager and Corporate Audit
Manager, S.K.M. Qadri
Corporate Affairs Manager, R.M. Mirwald
Marketing Manager, Gordon T. Leaist
Corporate Development Manager, A.J. Webb
New Projects
Exploration Manager, J. Bloemraad
Central Canada
Exploration Manager, K. Downes
Uranium and Support Services
Exploration Manager, L. Homeniuk

Indian and Native Affairs Secretariat
3rd Flr., Saskatchewan Pl.
1870 Albert St., Regina, S4P 4B7
General Inquiry: (306) 787-6268
Minister responsible, The Hon. Grant Schmidt
Secretary, Joe Leask
Funding and Liaison Director, Lorri Lampard
Economic Development
Asst. Secretary, Al Higgs
Native Economic Development
Director, Eugene Larocque
Policy Analyst, Arlene Goulet
Indian Economic Development
Director, John Reid
Policy Analyst, Doreen Bradshaw
Lands and Constitutional Affairs
Asst. Secretary, Bill Calder
Lands and Resources
Director, Doug Drummond
Policy Analyst, Marian Dinwoodie
Crown Solicitor, Ray Petrich

Potash Corp. of Saskatchewan
122-1st Ave. S., Saskatoon, S7K 7G3
General Inquiry: (306) 933-8500

The Potash Corp. of Saskatchewan (PCS) was created by an Order-in-Council on Feb. 4, 1975 and continues to operate under the *Potash Corporation of Saskatchewan Act, 1976,* R.S.S. 1978, Chapter P-17.

PCS has become the largest single producer and exporter of potash in the western world and operates two wholly-owned subsidiaries, PCS Mining and PCS Sales.

PCS Mining's production comes from five geographically distinct operations in Saskatchewan. PCS Sales sells in the North American marketplace, and is responsible for the efficient movement of product to market. The head office of the Corporation has overall responsibility for policy, planning, objectives and results.

Chairman, Paul Schoenhals
President and CEO, Charles E. Childers

Vice-President, Corporate Affairs and
Human Resources, John Gugulyn
Vice-President and Gen. Counsel,
John Hampton
Vice-President (Finance), Barry Humphreys
Vice-President (Technical Services),
Rick Lacroix
PCS Mining
122 First Ave. S., Saskatoon, S7K 7G3
President, Jim Bubnick
PCS Sales
122 First Ave. S., Saskatoon, S7K 7G3
President, Bill Doyle
Exec. Vice-President, Doug Logsdail
Director of Sales, Sid Blair

Saskatchewan Alcohol and Drug Abuse Commission (SADAC)
3475 Albert St., Regina, S4S 6X6
General Inquiries: (306) 787-4085

The Saskatchewan Alcohol and Drug Abuse Commission was established by and operates under the authority of the *Alcohol and Drug Abuse Commission Act,* R.S.S. 1978, Chapter A-18.

The purpose of the Commission is to counteract the incidence and prevalence of alcohol and other drug abuse in Saskatchewan. To accomplish this, the Commission has the following objectives:

- to promote greater community awareness of the dimensions of the problem with a view to community action, and to foster and maintain healthy attitudes and behaviour patterns of the general population so as to reduce the risk of problems with alcohol and other drug use;
- to provide early intervention to identify and rectify irresponsible use and abuse of alcohol and other drugs by the population at risk so as to reduce the social and emotional costs of current behaviour and promote healthier lifestyles;
- to assist, through community-based programs and co-operation with the social and legal systems, alcoholic and other chemically-dependent persons, their families and associates to cease current problematic behaviour and avoid recurrence of such behaviour; and
- to increase awareness of the resources and alternatives available in Saskatchewan to deal with the problems relating to alcohol and/or other drug use, abuse and dependency.

The Commission provides prevention, intervention and treatment services throughout the province with the major treatment facilities being in Saskatoon and Regina. The Commission also funds 23 different allied agencies to provide additional services throughout the province of Saskatchewan.

Minister-in-charge,
The Hon. George McLeod
A/Chairman, T.M. Gusway
Exec. Director, Danni Boyd
A/Assoc. Exec. Director, Neil Yeates

Medical Director, Dr. Dmytro Cipywnyk
503 Canterbury Towers
224-4th Ave. S., Saskatoon, S7K 2H6

PROVINCIAL SERVICES
Administration Division
Director, Gordon Leach
Prevention and Training Division
Director, Allan Walker
Evaluation and Research Division
Director, Bob Markosky

REGIONAL SERVICES
Northern Division
Box 5000, La Ronge, S0J 1L0
Director, John Kreiser
Central Division
503 Canterbury Twrs.
224-4th Ave. S., Saskatoon, S7K 2H6
Director, Lynn Tait
Southern Division
2140 Hamilton St., Regina, S4P 3V7
Director, Lyell Armitage

Saskatchewan Archives Board

University of Regina, Regina, S4S 0A2
General Inquiries: (306) 787-4068

Established in 1945, the Saskatchewan Archives Board is a joint government-university body responsible for acquiring, preserving and making publicly accessible, documents bearing on the history of Saskatchewan.

The *Archives Act,* R.S.S. 1978, Chapter A-26, regulates the disposition of the official records of all provincial government departments, boards, commissions and Crown corporations. A substantial portion of the Archives' holdings consists of such records, along with the private papers of politicians and community leaders as well as the records of churches, co-operatives, voluntary associations, businesses, unions, and political parties. Through its two offices, the Archives Board conducts an active program to preserve historical records in all documentary media. In addition to its textual records, the Archives holds extensive collections of historical photographs, oral histories, broadcast archives, maps, motion picture films, newspapers and architectural drawings.

The Archives Board publishes the journal *Saskatchewan History* three times a year together with Saskatchewan Archives Reference Series, special historical directories and guides.

Chairman, Dr. B. Zagorin
Provincial Archivist, Trevor J.D. Powell

Saskatchewan Assessment Management Agency

2161 Scarth St., Regina, S4P 2H8
The Saskatchewan Assessment Management

Agency is responsible for the real property assessment function in the province. The Agency provides valuations for tax base purposes to all Saskatchewan municipalities except the cities of Regina, Saskatoon, Moose Jaw, and Prince Albert. These cities provide their own valuations using assessment standards and manuals developed by the Agency. The Agency's head office is located in Regina, with regional offices in Saskatoon, Weyburn, Yorkton, Melfort, North Battleford, and Swift Current.

The Agency is governed by a seven-member board of directors. Two members are appointed by the Saskatchewan Urban Municipalities Assn., two by the Saskatchewan Assn. of Rural Municipalities, one by the Saskatchewan School Trustees Assn., and one by the government. The chairman is appointed by the government after consultation with SUMA and SARM. Funding for the agency is provided by an annual government grant with the balance shared equally between the government and the municipalities.

The board of directors sets assessment policy for the province. However, any change to policy that requires legislative amendment must be passed by the government.

Minister responsible, The Hon. Jack Klein
Chairman of the Board, Arthur H. Hosie
Exec. Director, Don W. Bennett
Asst. Exec. Director, J.D. Robinson
Director of Operations, G.P. Krismer
Director of Policy and Research, Donald Koop

Saskatchewan Computer Utility Corp. (SaskComp)

1801 Hamilton St., Regina, S4P 3V7

SaskComp is a computer service corporation serving the government of Saskatchewan, the universities of Saskatchewan and Regina, provincial Crown corporations, and private sector customers. Its services include the provision of systems analysis and planning, program development, and equipment selection and installation.

Chairman, Gavin Koyl
President, Gerald Thom
Vice-President (Customer Services), D. Poulin
Vice-President (Administration), T. Dagg
Vice-President (Computer Operations), G. Fiske
Vice-President (Corporate Development), B. Nell
Controller, Kent Fitch
Facilities Development Manager, I. Volk
Saskatoon Regional Ctr.
4600 SEDCO Ctr., 15 Innovation Blvd.
Saskatoon, S7N 2X8
Saskatoon Operations Manager, A. Borycki

Saskatchewan Development Fund Corp.

Box 765, Regina, S4P 3A8
General Inquiries: (306) 787-1645

The Saskatchewan Development Fund Corporation has three to six members responsible to the minister in charge. The Corporation is responsible for administering the Saskatchewan Development fund.

The Saskatchewan Development Fund was created under the *Saskatchewan Development Act,* R.S.S. 1978, Chapter S-14. It is an open-end investment trust which provides the residents of the province with an opportunity to put a portion of their savings into a low-risk investment for both income and long-term growth. The intention is to give preference to Saskatchewan-based investments, however, the Fund is permitted to acquire securities of companies located in other parts of Canada if these securities provide good opportunities for income and growth.

Chairman, Vacant
Board Members:
The Hon. J. Gary Lane, Q.C.
Howard Walrod, Terry Eddy, Nap Boutin,
Al McDougall, Dale Duckworth
Gen. Manager, William B. Gibson
Secretary to the Board, Ian Disbery

Saskatchewan Economic Development Corp. (SEDCO)
1106 Winnipeg St.
Box 5024, Regina, S4P 3W2

The Saskatchewan Economic Development Corporation is a provincial Crown corporation established by the *Industrial Development Act,* R.S.S. 1978, Chapter I-4, passed by the Legislative Assembly in 1963.

SEDCO's objective is to facilitate industrial development in Saskatchewan by providing financial and property services to viable industrial companies.

SEDCO's services and programs are flexible and can be arranged in various combinations to accommodate the variety of complex financial and property needs of each individual client — situations which sometimes prevent other institutions from accepting the project.

SEDCO is also responsible for the development of a number of specialized industrial parks, including Holiday Park Industrial Centre, Agri-Place Industrial Centre and Innovation Place. All parks are located in Saskatoon, with Holiday Park specializing in high tech/low industrial firms and AgriPlace in agriculture-related businesses. Innovation Place, Western Canada's most advanced research park, is located next to the University of Saskatchewan.

Minister-in-charge, The Hon. Joan Duncan
Chairman of the Board, Larry A. Kyle, Q.C.
President, Douglas S. Price
Corporate Affairs Director, Mel Hinds
Communications Officer, Vacant
Finance and Administration
Vice-President, Leo P. Larsen
Loans and Investment

Vice-President, Dennis Frohlick
Properties
Vice-President, Gerald Offet
Regina Office
1106 Winnipeg St., Regina, S4P 3W2
Branch Manager, Roland W. Duplessis
Properties Manager, John Leslie
Saskatoon Office
15 Innovation Blvd., Innovation Place
Saskatoon, S7N 2X8
Branch Manager, Norm Klatt
Properties Manager, Doug Tastad

Saskatchewan Forest Products Corp.
550-1st Ave. E., Prince Albert, S6V 2A5
Telex: 074-29121
General Inquiries: (306) 953-3838

Saskatchewan Forest Products Corp., a Crown corporation of the Province of Saskatchewan, conducts logging operations for a plywood plant, two sawmills and a wood preserving plant. It produces plywood, dimension lumber and treated products including poles, pilings, posts, lumber and plywood.

The Corporation was founded in 1949 through Order-in-Council 1899/49. Northern Forest Operations Ltd., a wholly owned subsidiary, was acquired in 1984.

Minister responsible,
The Hon. George McLeod
Chairman, Pat Hill
Gen. Manager, D. Barclay
Controller, Fred J. Hachey
Lumber Division
Carrot River Sawmill
Box 669, Carrot River, S0E 0L0
Manager, Roland St. Louis
Marketing, Henry Peters
Plywood Division
Box 40, Hudson Bay, S0E 0Y0
Sales, Eric Hedlund
8872 Finch Court, Burnaby, BC, V5A 4K6
Treated Wood Division
A/Manager, Ken Wall

Saskatchewan Government Insurance (SGI)
2260-11th Ave., Regina, S4P 0J9
General Inquiries: (306) 565-1200
Fax: (306) 525-5455

Established in 1945, SGI operates as a general insurance company in the property/casualty market. The Corporation offers home, tenant, farm, commercial and auto extension coverage to the public through independent agents throughout Saskatchewan.

SGI is the largest insurer in Saskatchewan and one of the leading property/casualty insurers in Canada. Head office is in Regina, but the corporation also operates claims branches in 12 other major centres in Saskatchewan.

On behalf of the provincial government, SGI administers the Saskatchewan Auto Fund (SAF), a driver and vehicle licensing system. The SAF, by authority of the *Automobile Accident Insurance Act,* R.S.S. 1978, Chapter A-35, provides compulsory universal insurance to all Saskatchewan motorists when they purchase a licence and vehicle registration. Coverages include third party liability, bodily injury coverage, and collision and comprehensive (fire and theft) on the vehicle. Additional coverage is available through SGI or private insurers.

The Saskatchewan Auto Fund became a separate legal entity distinct from the competitive business through legislation passed in November 1983. The SAF operates on a break-even basis, with surpluses and deficits from any given year retained in a rate stabilization reserve and carried forward into future years.

Chairman, A.W. Wagar
President, A. Wilde
Vice-President (Motor Vehicle Division),
G. Gibson
Vice-President (Underwriting Operations),
R. Warren
Vice-President (Claims Operations), L. Fogg
Vice-President (Finance), J. Hilsden
Vice-President (Systems), A. Cockman
Vice-President (Human Resources and
Corporate Relations), D. Kopp
Corporate Counsel, Ken Lerner

Saskatchewan Government Printing Co.

2005-8th Ave., Regina S4R 7B2
General Office: (306) 787-9393

The Saskatchewan Government Printing Company is a Crown corporation established in 1945. The Corporation operates a general job printing and book binding business.

Chairman, The Hon. Graham D. Taylor
Comptroller, P.L. Lang
Plant Sup't, P.J. Schwartz
Production Control Supervisor, L.J. Harrison

Saskatchewan Housing Corp.

800 North Canadian Oils Bldg.
2500 Victoria Ave., Regina, S4P 3V7
General Inquiries: (306) 787-4177

The Saskatchewan Housing Corporation, established in 1973 through the *Saskatchewan Housing Corporation Act,* R.S.S. 1978, Chapter S-24, provides a wide range of housing programs directed to limited and moderate income families, senior citizens and the disabled. Assistance is provided to help provincial homeowners completing repairs to their principal residence.

Chairman, The Hon. Jack Klein

President, Larry Little
Exec. Vice-President and
Secretary to the Board, Larry Boys
Program Operations
Vice-President, Ron Styles
Strategic Planning and Communications
Exec. Director, Larry Dybvig
Property Management and Field Services
Exec. Director, Ron Sotski
Field Services Director, Larry Evans

Saskatchewan Liquor Board

Box 5054, Regina, S4P 3M3
General Inquiries: (306) 787-4213

The Saskatchewan Liquor Board, an agency of government, controls, distributes and sells liquor pursuant to the *Liquor Act.*

Liquor, wine and import beer are distributed to liquor stores and special vendor agencies from a central warehouse located in Regina. Domestic beer is controlled and distributed to Board stores, special vendors and licensees through the Saskatchewan Brewer's Assn. warehouses located through the province.

Purchasing of products is handled through the Board's Products and Distribution Branch, which deals with principals in Canada and abroad. The Board is the only legal importer of liquor into the province.

Special Occasion Permits, allowing individuals and organizations to serve and sell liquor in public places are issued by the Board.

The licensing and supervision of beverage rooms, dining rooms, clubs, cocktail lounges, etc., under the *Liquor Licensing Act* is handled through the Board's Liquor Licensing Branch.

Chairman, H.E. (Ted) Urness
Product and Distribution
Director, K.G. Thomas
Liquor Licensing Director, E.C. Holzer
Finance and Retail Operations
Director, A.A. Dennett

Saskatchewan Municipal Board

4th Flr., 2151 Scarth St.
Regina, S4P 2H8

The Municipal Board was created in 1988 under the authority of the *Municipal Board Act,* S.S. 1988-89, Chapter 23.2. It replaces the Local Government Board, the Provincial Planning Appeals Board, and the Saskatchewan Assessment Appeals Board.

The new Board's powers are largely a unification of those of the three predecessor boards. It will advise on and approve debt financing by local municipalities; review and approve local financial matters arising from provincial statutory requirements; consider boundary change applications; and supervise local governments that are experiencing financial crises.

Minister responsible, The Hon. Jack Klein
A/Chairman of the Board, B.G. McNamee
A/Vice-Chairman, J.S. Pass
Saskatchewan Municipal Board and
the Local Government Committee
Secretary, M. Saucier
Municipal Boundary Committee and
the Planning Appeals Committee
Secretary, B. Fry
Assessment Appeals Committee
Secretary, K. Mackie

Saskatchewan Public Service Commission

3211 Albert St., Regina, S4S 5W6
Employment Inquiries: (306) 787-7575

The Saskatchewan Public Service Commission operates by authority of the Public Service Act, R.S.S. 1978, Chapter P-42, and serves as the central personnel agency for the Government of Saskatchewan.

The Commission is structured into five divisions: Employment Services; Employee Relations and Compensation: Classification Services; Staff Development; and Administrative and Information Services.

The principal services performed by the Commission include: recruitment for and staffing of all permanent positions within the classified service; negotiation and administration of classification and compensation plans; provision of human resource information regarding public service employees; and development of human resource policies and procedures within the public service.

The Commission also provides advice on human resource matters to departments in the public service and publishes the PS Post, a provincial government employee newsletter.
Minister responsible,
The Hon. Lorne H. Hepworth

Chairman, John D. McPhail

Employment Services Division
Exec. Director, Ray Smith
In-Scope Staffing Manager, Vacant
Management Staffing Manager, Dawn Davis
Executive Resourcing Manager, Karen Aulie

Employee Relations and Compensation Division
Exec. Director, Mike Russell
Compensation Director, Dave Atkinson

Classification Division
Director, Will Loewen

Staff Development Division
Exec. Director, Jim McKinlay
Director, Ruth Warick

Administrative and
Information Services Division
Director, Mary Kutarna
Human Resources Information: (306) 787-5628
A/Manager, Ken Hack
Communication Manager, Gabriele Burmeister

Saskatchewan Research Council

15 Innovation Blvd., Saskatoon, S7N 2X8
Telex: 074 2484; Fax: (306) 933-7446
General Inquiries: (306) 933-5400

The SRC's objectives are to promote the implementation of technology in Saskatchewan; to aid in the development of Saskatchewan's renewable, non-renewable and energy resources, and to further the protection and enhancement of the Saskatchewan environment.
Minister responsible,
The Hon. Ray Meiklejohn
307 Legislative Bldg., Regina, S4S 0B3

Chairman, Gordon Birney
102, 308-4th Ave. N., Saskatoon, S7K 2L7
President, Jim Hutch
Energy and Minerals Branch
Vice-President, Dr. Earl St. Denis
Administration and Financial Services
Vice-President, George A. MacKay
Technology Transfer and
Business Development
Vice-President, Ravi Maithel
Canadian Centre for Advanced Instrumentation
Vice-President, Ravi Maithel
Environment Division
Principle Research Scientist,
Dr. John Maybank
Petroleum Division
Director, Jim Hutchinson
515 Henderson Dr., Regina, S4N 5X1
Technology Services Division
Director, Dave Grier
Product Development Division
Director, Gord Pierce
Analytical Services Chemical Lab
Manager, Gene Smithson
Bovine Blood Typing Laboratory
Manager, Dr. Gerry Kraay
Communications
Manager, Katherine Lawrence
Human Resources Manager, Jim Sanderson
Controller, Ron McGrath

Saskatchewan Telecommunications (SaskTel)

2121 Saskatchewan Dr., Regina, S4P 3Y2
General Inquiries: (306) (306) 777-3737

SaskTel is a provincial Crown corporation responsible for the provision of local and long distance telephone service as well as related data and image telecommunications services within the province. Similar services, on a national and international level, are offered through the corporation's membership in Telecom Canada. SaskTel has over 700,000 telephones serving the province's one million residents.

SaskTel's 3,400 km fibre optic network, completed in 1984, was the world's first commercial fibre optics system. The new network is the basis for an all-digital broadband communications network.

The corporation's workforce consists of approximately 4,400 people located in Regina (head office) and Saskatoon, as well as almost 60 other communities throughout the province.

Chairman of the Board, Garth Kennedy
President and CEO, James A. Coombs
Vice-President (Engineering), W.B. Lambert
Vice-President (Operations South),
G.A. Spencer
Vice-President (Operations North),
D.R. Carlin
Vice-President (Finance and
Corporate Development), R.E. Bason
Vice-President (Human Resources,
Supplies and Services), B.E. Roberts
Vice-President (Corporate Affairs),
H.J. Osborne
Vice-President and Corporate Counsel,
John C. Meldrum
Vice-President, Business Development
C.J. Elmer

SaskTel International
President, W.A. (Bill) Bruce

Saskatchewan Transportation Co.

2041 Hamilton St., Regina, S4P 2E2
General Inquiries: (306) 787-3340

The Saskatchewan Transportation Company is a provincial Crown corporation, established by Order-in-Council 168/46, Jan. 29, 1946, for the purpose of providing an efficient and reliable passenger and parcel express motor coach service to as many of the communities of Saskatchewan as is economically possible. These services are extended beyond the boundaries of Saskatchewan through inter-line arrangements with other motor coach companies.

In addition to the passenger and parcel express service, the Company provides charters for Saskatchewan residents requiring group travel service.

President, D. Castle
Vice-President (Operations), D. Lowry
Vice-President (Administration and Finance),
D. Sentes
Sales/Traffic Manager, G.G. Beattie
Equipment Manager, Les Wills
Controller, R. Weir

Saskatchewan Water Corp.

Victoria Place, 111 Fairford St. E.
Moose Jaw, S6H 7X9

On July 1, 1984, the Government of Saskatchewan created the Saskatchewan Water Corp. The Corporation was given responsibility for water management issues and funding programs previously housed in several other government agencies and departments, including the Municipal Water Assistance Board and the Saskatchewan Water Supply Board.
Minister responsible, The Hon. H.J. Swan

President, V.C. Fowke
Vice-President (Operations), A.M. Veroba
Vice-President (Resource Management),
D.L. MacLeod
Vice-President (Finance and Administration),
R.W. Phillips

JUDICIARY AND JUDICIAL OFFICERS

Court of Appeal

Court House, 2425 Victoria Ave.
Regina, S4P 3V7
General Inquiries: (306) 787-5382

Chief Justice of Saskatchewan:
The Hon. E.D. Bayda

Judges:
The Hon. Mr. Justice W.J. Vancise
The Hon. Mr. Justice C.F. Tallis
The Hon. Mr. Justice S.J. Cameron
The Hon. Mr. Justice R.N. Hall*
The Hon. Madam Justice M.A. Gerwing
The Hon. Mr. Justice T.C. Wakeling
The Hon. Mr. Justice N.W. Sherstobitoff

Court of Queen's Bench

Court House, 2425 Victoria Ave.
Regina, S4P 3V7
General Inquiries: (306) 787-5380

Chief Justice:
The Hon. Madam Justice M.J. Batten

Judges:
The Hon. Mr. Justice G.H.M. Armstrong
 (Regina)
The Hon. Mr. Justice R.L. Barclay (Regina)
The Hon. Mr. Justice P.J. Dielschneider
 (Humboldt)
The Hon. Mr. Justice C.L.B. Estey (Saskatoon)
The Hon. Mr. Justice G.M. Forbes (Regina)*

* Supernumerary

The Hon. Mr. Justice T.L. Geatros (Melville)
The Hon. Mr. Justice W.F. Gerein (Saskatoon)
The Hon. Mr. Justice I. Goldenberg (Saskatoon)
The Hon. Mr. Justice I. Grotsky (Saskatoon)
The Hon. Mr. Justice K.R. Halvorson (Regina)
The Hon. Mr. Justice P. Hrabinsky (Saskatoon)
The Hon. Mr. Justice W.N. Lawton (Estevan)
The Hon. Mr. Justice R.A. MacLean
  (Moose Jaw)
The Hon. Mr. Justice K.R. MacLeod (Regina)
The Hon. Mr. Justice E.C. Malone (Regina)
The Hon. Mr. Justice W.R. Matheson (Regina)
The Hon. Mr. Justice G.A. Maurice (Regina)
The Hon. Mr. Justice J.G. McIntyre (Regina)
The Hon. Mr. Justice I.D. McLellan
  (Swift Current)
The Hon. Mr. Justice J.D. Milliken
  (Prince Albert)
The Hon. Mr. Justice B. Moore (Swift Current)*
The Hon. Mr. Justice G.E. Noble (Saskatoon)
The Hon. Mr. Justice H.A. Osborn
  (Yorkton)
The Hon. Mr. Justice E.A. Scheibel (Regina)
The Hon. Mr. Justice A.L. Sirois (Saskatoon)
The Hon. Mr. Justice S.J. Walker (Saskatoon)
The Hon. Madam Justice M.A. Wedge
  (Saskatoon)
The Hon. Mr. Justice C.R. Wimmer
  (Battleford)
The Hon. Mr. Justice D.H. Wright (Saskatoon)

Unified Family Court

224 S. 4th Ave., Saskatoon, S7K 2H6
General Inquiries: (306) 933-5174

Judges:
The Hon. Mr. Justice F.G. Dickson
The Hon. Madam Justice M.Y. Carter
The Hon. Mr. Justice J.S. Gagné

Judicial Officers

*(If a position is not designated, the offical is
sheriff, court clerk and local registrar.)*

ASSINIBOIA
Court House, S0H 0B0
M. Smith

BATTLEFORD
Court House, 291 W. 23rd St.
Box 340, S0M 0E0
Sheriff: D.I. Dament
Local Registrar: G.E. Curry

ESTEVAN
Court House, Box 697, S4A 2A6
P. Boxrud

GRAVELBOURG
Court House, Box 179, S0H 1X0
D. Green

HUMBOLDT
Court House, Box 490, S0K 2A0
Sheriff: G. Laing
Deputy Local Registrar: E. Lange

KERROBERT
Court House, Box 228, S0L 1R0
Sheriff: D.I. Dament
Deputy Sheriff, Deputy Local Registrar:
  H. McGinnis

MELFORT
Court House, Box 850, S0E 1A0
M.A. McNaughton

MELVILLE
Court House, 256 W. 2nd Ave.
Box 1659, S0A 2P0
Deputy Sheriff, Local Registrar: D. Kraushaar

MOOSE JAW
Court House, 110 W. Ominica St., S6H 4P1
D. Paquin

MOOSOMIN
Court House, S0G 3N0
Deputy Sheriff, Local Registrar: D. Raab

PRINCE ALBERT
Court House
Central Ave. & E. 19th St., S6V 4W7
M.A. McNaughton

REGINA
Court House, 2425 Victoria Ave., S4P 3V7
Sheriff: W. Siemens
Registrar of Courts: F.C. Newis
Local Registrar: G. Ullman

SASKATOON
Court House, 520 E. Spadina Cres., S7K 2H6
Sheriff: G. Laing
Unified Family Court: D. Scott
Local Registrar: D. Berezowsky

SHAUNAVON
Court House, Box 159, S0N 2M0
Deputy Sheriff, Deputy Local Registrar:
  J. Krause

SWIFT CURRENT
Court House, 121 W. Lorne St., S9H 0J4
M. Melinchuk

---

* Supernumerary

WEYBURN
Court House, 301 Prairie Ave., S4H 0L4
W. Dammann

WYNYARD
Court House, Box 369, S0A 4T0
Deputy Sheriff, Deputy Local Registrar:
  G. Fewster

YORKTON
Court House, 29 E. Darlington St., S3N 0C2
Sheriff, Local Registrar: S. Urbanoski

Registrar in Bankruptcy

Court House, Regina, S4P 3V7
General Inquiries: (306) 787-8982

Registrar: F.C. Newis

OFFICIAL ADMINISTRATORS:
*Assiniboia, Gravelbourg, Moose Jaw, Weyburn,
  Wynyard*
Co-operative Trust Co. of Canada
Ste. 200, 1960 Albert St., Regina, S4P 4A3

Battleford, Estevan, Kerrobert, Swift Current
Montreal Trust Co., 1908-11th Ave.
Box 4500, Regina, S4P 3W7

Humboldt, Melfort, Prince Albert
Co-operative Trust Co. of Canada
333 N. 3rd Ave., Saskatoon, S7K 2M2

*Melville, Moosomin, Regina, Saskatoon,
  Shaunavon, Yorkton*
Guaranty Trust Co. of Canada
2020-11th Ave., Regina, S4P 0J3

Provincial Court

Provincial Court, 1815 Smith St.
Regina, S4P 3V7
General Inquiries: (306) 787-5250

Chief Judge: B.P. Carey
Judges:
His Hon. Judge R.H. Allan (Regina)
His Hon. Judge K.A. Andrychuck (Yorkton)
His Hon. Judge J.R.O. Archambeault
  (Prince Albert)
His Hon. Judge D.M. Arnot (North Battleford)
His Hon. Judge K.E. Bellerose (Regina)
His Hon. Judge E.S. Bobowski (Yorkton)
His Hon. Judge H.J. Boyce (Regina)
His Hon. Judge A.R. Chorneyko (Wynyard)

His Hon. Judge R.N. Conroy (Saskatoon)
His Hon. Judge L.P. Deshaye (North Battleford)
His Hon. Judge E.C. Diehl (Melfort)
His Hon. Judge C.R. Fafard
  (Box 5000, La Ronge, S0J 1L0)
His Hon. Judge D.E. Fenwick (Regina)
His Hon. Judge T.W. Ferris (Prince Albert)
His Hon. Judge G.K. Fielding (Swift Current)
His Hon. Judge Finley (Saskatoon)
His Hon. Judge J.J. Flynn (Regina)
His Hon. Judge H.W. Goliath (Prince Albert)
His Hon. Judge W.V. Goliath (Prince Albert)
His Hon. Judge E.R. Gosselin (Saskatoon)
His Hon. Judge B.D. Henning (Regina)
His Hon. Judge H.M. Ketcheson (Regina)
His Hon. Judge G.C. King (Moose Jaw)
His Hon. Judge R.J. Kucey (Saskatoon)
His Hon. Judge R.E. Lee (Estevan)
His Hon. Judge E.A. Lewchuck (Regina)
Her Hon. Judge P.M.B. Linn (Saskatoon)
His Hon. Judge A.C. McMurdo (Saskatoon)
His Hon. Judge W.L. Meagher (Regina)
His Hon. Judge G.R. Moxley
  (Box 5000, La Ronge, S0J 1L0)
His Hon. Judge A.J. Muir (Moose Jaw)
His Hon. Judge R.J. Neville (Weyburn)
His Hon. Judge J.B.J. Nutting (Saskatoon)
His Hon. Judge D. Orr
  (Box 849, Meadow Lake, S0M 1V0)
His Hon. Judge H.D. Parker (Regina)
His Hon. Judge R.A. Rathgeber (Melville)
His Hon. Judge G.T. Seniuk (Saskatoon)
His Hon. Judge G.B. Shaner (Swift Current)
His Hon. Judge L.J. Smith (Regina)
His Hon. Judge R.J. Smith (Melfort)
His Hon. Judge W.B. Tennant (Kerrobert)
His Hon. Judge P.G. Trudelle (Regina)
His Hon. Judge K. Young
  (4950-50th St., Lloydminster, S9V 0X9)

Land Registration Officials

Master of Titles: Raymond Petrich
1874 Scarth St., 10th Flr., Regina, S4P 3V7
General Inquiries: (306) 787-5508

Location	Registrar
Battleford	E.C. Fuchs
Humboldt	S. McNabb
Moose Jaw	A. Rollie
Prince Albert	R. Heebner
Regina	Barry Dauncey
Saskatoon	A. Goertzen
Swift Current	R. Karpinski
Yorkton	R. Wilhelm

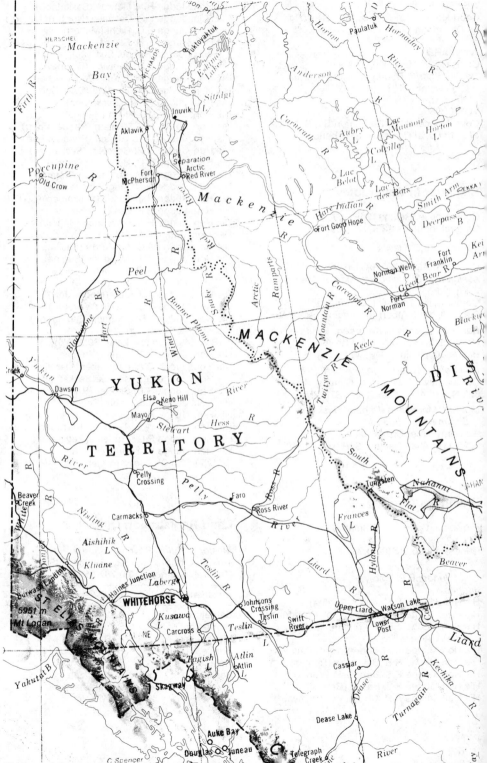

This map is based on information taken from map MCR 4032. © Her Majesty in Right of Canada with permission of Energy, Mines and Resources.

YUKON TERRITORY

Fireweed
(Epilobium augustifolium)

Organized: June 13, 1898
Capital: Whitehorse
Motto: None
Flower: Fireweed
Area: 483,450 km²
   percentage of Canada's total area: 4.8
   LAND: 478,970 km²
   FRESHWATER: 4,480 km²
Elevation:
   HIGHEST POINT: Mount Logan (5,951 km)
   LOWEST POINT: arctic shore at sea level
Population (1988): 28,484
   five-year change: +2.1%

   per square kilometre: 0.04
   percentage of Canada's total
     population: 0.1
   URBAN: 65%
   RURAL: 35%

Government Finance:
   REVENUE, 1988/89 est.: $57.2 million
   EXPENDITURE, 1988/89 est.: $304.5 million
   DEBT PER CAPITA (March 1987): $2,583
Unemployment rate (March 1988): 15%
Consumer prices, March 1988
   vs. year earlier: +3.2%

HISTORY

Archaeological discoveries of prehistoric sites near Old Crow revealed that the first traces of modern man in Canada precede the arrival of Europeans by approximately 30,000 years.

European discovery of Yukon came in 1825 when explorer Sir John Franklin, searching for the Northwest Passage, arrived at what is now called Herschel Island off the northernmost tip of Yukon.

Franklin's news of fur trading in the territory prompted the Hudson's Bay Company to renew explorations in the vast wilderness. In 1847, the Hudson's Bay Company established a trading post at Fort Yukon on the Yukon River. When the boundary between the U.S. and Canada was drawn, Fort Yukon became part of Alaska.

Fur traders were the first to come, but soon to follow were the gold seekers who began entering the Yukon River valley in the 1860s. In 1896, a discovery on Rabbit Creek, a tiny tributary on the Klondike River, sparked the mad gold rush of 1898. Tens of thousands of people from many countries stormed the Chilkoot and White Passes to reach the gold-rich fields of the Klondike. The ensuing boom put Dawson City on the map and, for a few brief years, the city experienced one of the most colourful episodes in modern history.

With the arrival of the Second World War, the face of Yukon changed. One of the era's greatest engineering feats was undertaken by the United States Army with the construction of the Alaska Highway in 1942. In just eight months, 2,438 km of highway was built over muskeg and mountains, from Mile 0 at Dawson Creek, B.C. to Fairbanks, Alaska. For the first time, there was an overland corridor connecting Alaska with the rest of Canada and the lower 48 states.

Subsequently, mines and transportation systems were established and the population grew, contributing to a more stable economy in the territory.

THE LAND

With 483,450 km² within its borders, Yukon is larger than all of Canada's Maritime provinces combined, or contains over half of the land mass of neighbouring British Columbia.

The territory is located in the extreme northwestern corner of Canada and is home of the country's most westerly community. Yukon is bordered on the north by the Arctic Ocean, on the south by British Columbia, on the east by the Northwest Territories, and on the west by the state of Alaska.

Nestled in the extreme southwest corner of the territory is Kluane (kloo-ah-nee) National Park, which measures 13,600 km² and boasts Canada's highest peak and the largest non-polar icefields in North America. Mount Logan towers to 5,951 m and is surrounded by the spectacular St. Elias mountain range.

Yukon is known for its beautiful scenery — a vast and pristine wilderness which includes thousands of square kilometres of forests, mountains, tundra, rivers, and lakes. The largest body of water in Yukon is Kluane Lake which covers 244.8 km². Other major lakes in the territory include: Leberge, Bennett, Marsh, Teslin, Tagish, Frances, Simpson, Frenchman, Aishihik (ay-she-ak), and Dezadeash (dez-a-dee-ash).

The Yukon River, North America's fifth largest, courses through the central region of the territory. The Yukon River is born at the north end of Marsh Lake, just a few kilometres south of Yukon's capital city of Whitehorse, and empties into the Bering Sea nearly 3,200 km from its headwaters. Other major Yukon rivers include the Pelly, the Stewart, the Donjek, the White, the Firth, the Teslin, and the Liard. The Yukon River basin makes up one of the largest on the North American continent.

Yukon's only island, Herschel, consists of a speck of land, barren of trees, located off the north coast in the Beaufort Sea. The Yukon's first territorial park has been designated for Herschel, which served as a major Arctic whaling centre in the 1890s.

A few of the geographical oddities in the territory include the craggy peaks in Kluane National Park; one of the smallest deserts in the world near the community of Carcross, 72 km southwest of Whitehorse; and the mountains and valleys on the Klondike which were formed by natural erosion, having been missed by glaciation during the last ice age.

THE PEOPLE

The population of Yukon decreased as the economy faltered in the early 1980s but has since begun to climb close to the record levels experienced during the Klondike Gold Rush. In 1986, Yukon halted its downward trend with a population growth of 4 per cent. By March 1988, the population was growing at an annual rate of 5.2 per cent.

Among Yukoners, 43.6 per cent of the population is of British ancestry. The next largest group are the native Indians. Under the Yukon Indian land claim currently being negotiated, the distinction made by the *Indian Act* between status and non-status will become redundant. Therefore, the

Yukon Indian population makes up close to 20 per cent of the total population.

Grouped under the Athapascan family of North American Indians, the Yukon native Indian population, from north to south, includes Vunta-Kut-chin, Han, Tutchone, Kaska, Tagish and Southern Tutchone, whereas the Tlingit share customs and language with their relatives of the coastal Alaskan panhandle.

Of the two official languages, English is the prevailing tongue by far, at 91.9 per cent. Less than one tenth of one per cent speak only French, and 7.9 per cent are bilingual. Only 0.2 per cent of the population speak neither English nor French.

The largest community in Yukon is Whitehorse, with a population of approximately 19,824, followed by Dawson City (1,611), Watson Lake (1,659), and Faro (1,299). The most westerly settlement in Canada, Beaver Creek, is on the Yukon-Alaskan border.

THE ECONOMY

A combination of strong world metal prices, steady tourism growth, and government expenditures on local economic initiatives has spurred an economic recovery from the recession of the early 1980s. Much of the optimism for Yukon's economy hinges on the upswing in the mineral industry. Strong prices for gold and the reopening of the large lead-zinc open pit mine at Faro in 1986 have boosted revenues considerably. The mine directly employs just over 500 people, and the ripple effect has been felt in all other sectors. Two small scale gold mines, Canamax near Ross River and Mount Skukum near Whitehorse, have started year round production while placer mining for gold still attracts a large interest during the summer.

Strong world metal prices also boosted mineral exploration in the Yukon during 1987. It is predicted that 1988 will also be a strong year.

Preliminary estimates indicate that $439.9 million worth of metals was produced in the Yukon in 1987. Of this, zinc accounted for $196.8 million; lead, $106.0 million; gold, $97.2 million; and silver, $39.7 million.

Tourism continued to be a significant contributor to the Yukon's economy. A study of 1987 tourist travel indicated that visitors to the Yukon spent $37 million directly in the territory and that the total value was considerably higher.

Retail trade during the first quarter of 1988 was $31.8 million compared with $29.6 million during the same period in 1986. The change represented a 7.5 per cent increase.

The 1987 unemployment rate in the Yukon fluctuated from a high of 16 per cent in April to a low of nine per cent in August, while the labour force grew from 12,613 in March 1986 to 13,458 in March 1987.

Information provided by the Public Affairs Bureau, Yukon Executive Council Office. Updating and population data courtesy of Statistics Canada.

GOVERNMENT OF THE YUKON TERRITORY

Seat of Government:
Box 2703, Whitehorse, Y1A 2C6

THE YUKON ACT

The Yukon Act provides for the Yukon Territory to be administered by a Commissioner appointed by the Governor in Council in Ottawa.

Changes announced in October 1979, however, provide for a further measure of responsible government by the elected members of the Yukon Legislative Assembly. Former Progressive Conservative Indian Affairs and Northern Development Minister Jake Epp permitted the establishment of a wholly elected executive council (cabinet) to oversee the local matters of the territory.

Approval of all territorial legislation still requires the signature of the federally appointed Commissioner, but the role of the Commissioner has been altered and the person holding the post is no longer required to be involved in the day-to-day activities of the Yukon government.

The Legislative Assembly has power to make Acts dealing with the imposition of local taxes, the establishment of territorial offices, municipal institutions, election of members of the assembly, the licensing of businesses, the incorporation of companies, the administration of justice, education, the preservation of wildlife, and generally all matters of a local nature.

The Northern Affairs Branch of the Department of Indian Affairs and Northern Development has legislative and administrative control of all renewable and non-renewable resources, including Crown land.

Minister responsible: Hon. Pierre H. Cadieux, Minister of Indian Affairs and Northern Development

OFFICE OF THE COMMISSIONER

Box 2703, Whitehorse, Y1A 2C6
Commissioner of Yukon, J. Kenneth McKinnon

EXECUTIVE COUNCIL (CABINET)

Government Leader, Minister of Health and Human Resources, Minister responsible for the Yukon Development Corporation, Minister of the Executive Council Office,
The Hon. Tony Penikett
Government House Leader, Minister of Education, Minister of Economic Development: Mines and Small Business,
The Hon. Piers McDonald
Minister of Justice, Minister responsible for the Women's Directorate, for the Public Service Commission, and for the Workers' Compensation Board,
The Hon. Margaret Joe
Minister of Tourism, Minister of Renewable Resources, Minister responsible for the Yukon Liquor Corporation,
The Hon. Art Webster
Minister of Community and Transportation Services, Minister of Government Services, Minister responsible for the Yukon Housing Corporation,
The Hon. Maurice Byblow

EXECUTIVE COUNCIL OFFICE
Deputy Minister, Eloise Spitzer
Asst. Deputy Minister, Bill Oppen

INTERNAL AUDIT
Director, Ben Anderson
Auditors: Stewart Rae, Dale Emery

POLICY AND INTERGOVERNMENTAL RELATIONS
Director, Jim Beebe
Policy and Intergovernmental Officers:
Debra McNevin, Brenda Riis, Linda Martin

LAND CLAIMS SECRETARIAT
Chief Negotiator, Barry Stuart

PUBLIC AFFAIRS BUREAU
Chief Information Officer, Dennis Senger
Sr. Information Officer, Liz McKee
Information Officers: Ken Sillak, Ron Billingham

FEDERAL RELATIONS OFFICE — OTTAWA
350 Sparks St., Ste. 707, Ottawa, K1R 7S8
Director, John Lawson
Secretary, Debbie Kelly

BUREAU OF STATISTICS
Director, Glenn Grant
Statistics Officer, Paul Harris
Survey Officer, Dianne Oppen

For further information regarding any aspect of the Government of Yukon, contact:
Yukon Government Inquiry Centre
Box 2703, Whitehorse, Y1A 2C6
(403) 667-5811

LEGISLATIVE ASSEMBLY

27th Legislature, 1st Session
Date of last election: Feb. 20, 1989
Number of seats: 16
Party standings:
New Democrats: 9
Conservatives: 7
Vacant: 0

Salaries, Indemnities and Allowances

MEMBERS: $26,613 Member's Indemnity, plus
$13,307 for an out-of-town Member or $11,619
for an in-town Member (tax-free expense
allowance).
MINISTERS WITH PORTFOLIO: $22,260 salary,
plus Member's Indemnity and expense allowance.
GOVERNMENT LEADER: $30,496 salary, plus
Member's Indemnity and expense allowance.
OPPOSITION LEADER: $22,260 salary, plus Mem-
ber's Indemnity and expense allowance.
THIRD PARTY LEADER: $4,452 salary, plus
Member's Indemnity and expense allowance.
SPEAKER: $7,420 salary, plus Member's Indem-
nity and expense allowance.
DEPUTY SPEAKER: $5,565 salary, plus Member's
indemnity and expense allowance.

Officers

Speaker, The Hon. Sam Johnston
Clerk of the Legislative Assembly and
Deputy Minister, Patrick Michael
Clerk Asst., Administrative, Jane Steele
Clerk Asst., Legislative, Missy Follwell
Sergeant-at-Arms: Frank Ursich

Members

Constituency	Member and Affiliation
Campbell	Sam Johnston (NDP)
Faro	The Hon. Maurice Byblow (NDP)
Hootalinqua	Willard Phelps (PC)
Klondike	The Hon. Art Webster (NDP)
Kluane	Bill Brewster (PC)
Mayo	The Hon. Piers McDonald (NDP)
Old Crow	Norma Kassi (NDP)
Tatchun	Danny Joe (NDP)
Watson Lake	John Devries (NDP)
Whitehorse North Centre	The Hon. Margaret Joe (NDP)
Whitehorse/Porter Creek East	Dan Lang (PC)

Constituency	Member and Affiliation
Whitehorse/Porter Creek West	Alan Nordling (PC)
Whitehorse/ Riverdale North	Doug Phillips (PC)
Whitehorse/ Riverdale South	Bea Firth (PC)
Whitehorse South Centre	Joyce Hayden (NDP)
Whitehorse West	The Hon. Tony Penikett (NDP)

Lib — Liberal
NDP — New Democrat
PC — Progressive Conservative

Government Leader's Office

Government Leader, The Hon. Tony Penikett
Principal Secretary, John Walsh
Exec. Assistant, Lesley McCullough
Communications Advisor, Catherine Holt

Offices of the Official Opposition

Box 2703, Whitehorse, Y1A 2C6

Leader of the Official Opposition,
Willard Phelps

DEPARTMENT OF COMMUNITY AND TRANSPORTATION SERVICES

Box 2703, Whitehorse, Y1A 2C6

MINISTER'S OFFICE
Minister, The Hon. Maurice Byblow

DEPUTY MINISTER'S OFFICE
A/Dep. Minister, Roger Graham
Departmental Executive Services
A/Head, Peble Sutton

A/Asst. Dep. Minister, Municipal and
Community Affairs Division, Terry Sewell

FINANCE AND ADMINISTRATION
Director, Virginia Labelle
Financial Operations Manager, Brian Kembel
Policy and Planning
A/Policy Analyst, Norman Marcy
Personnel and Administration
Manager, Irene Davie
COMMUNICATIONS
Director, Ronald Robbins

COMMUNITY SERVICES
Director, Rick Butler
Municipal Administration
Manager, Mickey Fisher

Municipal Advisors:
Led Chasse, Dale Kozmeniuk
Local Employment Opportunities Program
Project Manager, Mike Ivens

PROTECTIVE SERVICES
Manager and Fire Marshal, Larry Hipperson
Chief Building Inspector, Bryant Yeomans
Gas/Plumbing Inspector, Roy Jackson
Chief Electrical Inspector, Vern Toews
Chief Boiler and Elevator Inspector,
David Tessier
A/Dep. Fire Marshal, Jim Smith
Property Assessments and Taxation
Manager, Mel Smith
Taxation Administrator, Max Wismark

Arts, Sport and Recreation
Manager, Peter Milner
Arts Consultant, Laurel Parry
Sports/Fitness Consultant, Tom O'Hara
Community Relations
Consultant, Peter Menzies

LANDS BRANCH
Lands Director, Chris Cuddy
Lands Manager, Perry Savoie
Lands Disposal Officer, E. Elrose
Land Use Officer, Bruce Gilroy
Land Development
Co-ordinator, Lyle Henderson
Land Planning Advisor, Dy Robb
MUNICIPAL ENGINEERING BRANCH
Director, Vacant
Municipal Services Officer, Ray Gosse
Utility Systems Advisor, Reinhart Trautman

Transportation Division
Asst. Dep. Minister, John Cormie
Program Analyst, Kathleen Lewis

TRANSPORTATION MAINTENANCE BRANCH
Director, Ray Magnuson
Western Area Transportation
Sup't, Colin Yeulet
Eastern Area Transportation
Highway Sup't, Gordon Eftoda
Northern Area Transportation
Sup't, Alva Close
Box 219, Dawson City, Y0B 1G0
Mechanical
Operations Manager, R.B. Arnold
Workshop Sup'ts:
Robert Magnuson, Robert Frederickson
TRANSPORTATION CAPITAL DEVELOPMENT
Director, Turgut Ersoy
TRANSPORTATION ENGINEERING
Director, Robin Walsh
Airports
Manager, Nate Casselman
Transport Services
Manager, Bob Iwanicki
Regulatory Programs
Co-ordinator, Lynn Alcock

Motor Vehicles
Dep. Registrar, Fred Jennex
Supervisor, Sandra Florence
Weigh Stations and Enforcement
Chief, Bill Blinston

AGENCIES, BOARDS AND COMMISSIONS

Motor Transport Board
Box 2703, Whitehorse, Y1A 2C6
General Inquiries: (403) 667-5782

The Motor Transport Board regulates the motor transport industry through a certificate and permit system. The Board has a mandate to receive public complaints, investigate those complaints, and cause deficiencies to be corrected. Moreover, the Board may, on its own initiative, inquire into, hear, and determine any matter respecting the provision of transport services to the public.
Chairman, Jim Yamada
Vice-Chairman, Art Christensen
Members:
Byrun Shandler, Jean Murphy, Dan Finch

DEPARTMENT OF ECONOMIC DEVELOPMENT: MINES AND SMALL BUSINESS
211 Main St., Ste. 400, Box 2703
Whitehorse, Y1A 2C6

MINISTER'S OFFICE
Minister, The Hon. Peirs McDonald

DEPUTY MINISTER'S OFFICE
Dep. Minister, Shakir Alwarid
Asst. Dep. Minister, Vacant
Administration Director, Dorothy Deagle

Economic Policy Planning and Research
Asst. Dep. Minister, Catharine Read
PLANNING AND RESEARCH
Director, Nick Poushinsky
Econometrician, Sam Patayanikorn
Economist, Vacant
A/Sr. Planner, Ray Famega
Resources and Community Development
Chief, Rick McDougall
ENERGY AND MINES
Director, John Maissan
Chief Mining Development Officer, Rod Hill
Mining Development Officer, David Downing
Energy Policy Analyst, Robert Collins
Major Projects Manager, Vacant
Energy Programs Officer, Florent Leveille

BUSINESS DEVELOPMENT OFFICE
211 Main St., Ste. 400, Whitehorse, Y1A 2B2
General Inquiries: (403) 667-3011
Director, Bob Snyder
Financial Programs Manager, Bert Perry

Small Business Manager, Mike Kinney
Community Development Officer, Vacant
Renewable Resources Sub-Agreement
Co-ordinator, Darwin Wreggitt
Business Development Officers:
Guy Cocouyt, Marcia Gaudet
Financial Program Co-ordinator, John Snider
Tourism Sub-Agreement
A/Co-ordinator, Vacant

DEPARTMENT OF EDUCATION

Box 2703, Whitehorse, Y1A 2C6
General Inquiries: (403) 667-5141

MINISTER'S OFFICE
Minister, The Hon. Piers McDonald

DEPUTY MINISTER'S OFFICE
Dep. Minister, Dan Odin
Policy, Planning and Evaluation
Director, Kirk Cameron
Asst. Dep. Minister, Doug Courtice
FINANCE AND ADMINISTRATION
Director, Margaret Noble
Finance and Personnel
Manager, George Gartner
Financial Officer, Judy Vondette
School Services Supervisor, Dwayne Wheeler

PUBLIC SCHOOLS
Reg. Sup't (Area 1), John Davis
Director of Curriculum and
Support Services, Helen Weigel
Reg. Sup't (Area 2), W. Seipp
Reg. Sup't, (Area 3), Robert Smith
Sr. Consultant, William A. Ferguson
Primary Consultant, Jeanette McCrie
Native Curriculum Development
Co-ordinator, Elsie Netro
Educational Computing Consultant, Ian Jukes
Assessment and Counselling
Co-ordinator, Dave Martin
Special Education
Co-ordinator, Peggy McFarlane
Learning Resource Centre
Co-ordinator, Audrey Hiscock
Native Language Director, J. Ritter
French Language Centre
Co-ordinator, Bertrand Lacroix

Advanced Education, Manpower and Immigration
Asst. Dep. Minister, Tom Lownie

HUMAN RESOURCES AND CAREER
DEVELOPMENT
Director, Ken Smith
Secretariat Officer, Marcie Johnsrude
Industrial Training
Manager, John Gryba
Officer, Sheila Parkin
Consultants: Walter Brennan, Norm Ingram

PROGRAM RESEARCH AND PLANNING
Director, Lois Hawkins
Student Financial Services
Officer, Marjorie Wearmouth
Employment Development
Manager, Ross Knox
Yukon College
Box 2799, Whitehorse Y1A 5K4
President, Lynn Ogden
Manager of Finance, Eric Hodges
Registrar, Doug Graham

LIBRARY AND ARCHIVES
Director, Miriam McTiernan
Private and Corporate Records
Asst. Territorial Archivist, D. Chisholm
Government Records Archivist, Doug Whyte
Archives Librarian, Eileen Edmunds
Public Services Librarian, Marg Donnelly
Whitehorse Public Library
Supervisor, Leona Etmanski
Technical Services Librarian, Jos Carver
Audio-Visual Unit
Public Programs Librarian, Mary Raines

DEPARTMENT OF FINANCE

Box 2703, Whitehorse, Y1A 2C6
General Inquiries: (403) 667-5343

MINISTER'S OFFICE
Minister, The Hon. Piers McDonald

DEPUTY MINISTER'S OFFICE
A/Dep. Minister, Charles Sanderson
Departmental Administrator, Bill Curtis

Financial Operations and Revenue Services
Asst. Dep. Minister, Ray Hayes
Financial Systems Director, Medric Tremblay
ACCOUNTING SERVICES
Director, Dave Hrycan
Accounts Payable Supervisor, Allan Brooks
Payroll Supervisor, Norma Armstrong
Accounts Receivable
Supervisor, Karen Mason
REVENUE SERVICES
Director, Linda Engels

Budgets and Fiscal Relations
A/Asst. Dep. Minister, Marc Tremblay
Budgets Director, Connie Zatorski
Fiscal Relations Director, Marc Tremblay
Management Board Secretariat
Secretary, Florian Lemphers

DEPARTMENT OF GOVERNMENT SERVICES

Box 2703, Whitehorse, Y1A 2C6

MINISTER'S OFFICE
Minister, The Hon. Maurice Byblow

DEPUTY MINISTER'S OFFICE
Dep. Minister, Frank Fingland
Asst. Dep. Minister, Property Management, George Salmins
Policy Planning Analyst, John Ferbey
Administration Director, Val Mather

SUPPLY AND SERVICES
Director, Sam Cawley
Purchasing Manager, George Kirk
Warehouse Manager, Ralph Simpson
Asset Control, Jana Bidrman
Transportation/Communication Manager, Ray Pilloud
Business Incentive Office
Supervisor, Brian Werlin
Contract Administrator, Dave Parfitt
Queen's Printer
Printing Services Manager, Trevor Sellars
Records Management
Records Manager, T. Edwards

SYSTEMS AND COMPUTING SERVICES
Director, Peter Laight
Data Processing Manager, Blaine McFarlane
Technical Services
A/Manager, Tom McIlwain
Systems Development
Project Manager, Max Mehlis
Processing Services Manager, Paul Dubord
Information Resource Centre
Manager, Bob Aitken

PROPERTY MANAGEMENT
Property Administration
Manager, Mike Bartsch
BUILDING DEVELOPMENT AND
MAINTENANCE
Director, Doug Campbell
Building Development Manager, Vern Mueller

DEPARTMENT OF HEALTH AND HUMAN RESOURCES
Box 2703, Whitehorse, Y1A 2C6

MINISTER'S OFFICE
Minister, The Hon. Tony Penikett

DEPUTY MINISTER'S OFFICE
Dep. Minister, Jim Davie
Policy and Administration
Director, Duncan Sinclair

Health Services

Asst. Dep. Minister, Dr. Brian Wheatley
General Inquiries: (403) 667-5209
Health Director, Alan Davidson
Operations and Programs
Manager, Louise Tait
Vital Statistics
Dep. Registrar, Arleen Kovac

HUMAN RESOURCES
General Inquiries: (403) 667-5674
Community and Family Services Branch
Director, Maxine Kehoe
Regional Services (North)
Supervisor, Ron Gartshore
Regional Services (South)
Supervisor, Sharon Hume
Placement/Support Services
A/Supervisor, Reita Morgan
Family and Children's Services
Supervisor, Elaine Schroeder
Social Services Branch
Director, Kathy Kinchen
Social Assistance and Senior Services
Supervisor, Janice Hogg
Yukon Opportunity Plan
Co-ordinator, Ernie Fechner
Juvenile Justice Director, Bonnie Clark
Admission and Assessment Centre
305 Lambert St., Whitehorse, Y1A 1Z5
Residential Rehabilitation
Manager, Michael McCann
Alcohol and Drug Services
6118-6th Ave., Ste. 5, Whitehorse, Y1A 1M9
Co-ordinator, Paul MacDonald
General Inquiries: (403) 667-5777
Vocational Rehabilitation Services
Co-ordinator, Marg Render
Communication Disorders Clinic
4110-4th Ave., 2nd Flr., Whitehorse, Y1A 4N7
Speech/Language Pathologists:
Noreen Allen, Anne Caulfield

DEPARTMENT OF JUSTICE
Box 2703, Whitehorse, Y1A 2C6

MINISTER'S OFFICE
Minister, The Hon. Margaret Joe

DEPUTY MINISTER'S OFFICE
Dep. Minister, W.E. Byers, Q.C.
Policy and Planning Director, Jo Thomson
Legislative Counsel, Sydney Horton
LEGAL SERVICES
Director, Gordon Michener, Q.C.
Solicitors: Robert Francis, Thomas Ullyett, Penelope Gawn, Jack Westerberg
Registrar of Land Titles, Dianne Gau
Public Administrator/Chief Coroner, Joan Veinott
FINANCE AND ADMINISTRATION
Director, Rick Curial
Legal Aid Officer, Catherine Buckler

COURT SERVICES/TERRITORIAL
COURT/SUPREME COURT
(See judiciary listings)

CORRECTIONS
Whitehorse Correctional Centre
Director, Duane Nethery

Dep. Director, William Milner
Technical Services Operations
Dep. Director, R.W. Daniels
Adult Probation Services
Sr. Probation Officer, W.P. Sim

CONSUMER, CORPORATE AND LABOUR AFFAIRS

General Inquiries: (403) 667-5256
A/Director, Vicki Hancock
Consumer Services Manager, Vicki Hancock
Consumer Relations Officer, Elsie Bagan
Business and Professional Licences,
Carol Cameron
Consumer Relations Officer, Sharon Hanley

CORPORATE AFFAIRS
Administrator, Malcolm Florence
Societies, Co-operative Assns.
Clerks: Heather Bojsza, Lydia Silich
Securities Clerk, Dorothy Jack
Personal Property Security Clerk,
Kathy Shewchuk

LABOUR SERVICES
Administrator, Noreen McGowan
Labour Services Officers: Bonnitta Ritchie,
Catherine Simpson, Richard Roberts
Occupational Health and Industrial Safety
Chief Officer, Richard Rovere
Officer, R. Zral

AGENCIES, BOARDS AND COMMISSIONS

Yukon Legal Services Society
The Law Centre, 2134-2nd Ave.
Whitehorse, Y1A 5H6

In 1987, responsibility for the delivery of legal aid in Yukon was transferred from the Government of Yukon, Department of Justice, to the Yukon Legal Services Society, which is governed by an eight-member board of directors. The legislative mandate for the legal aid program is contained in the *Legal Services Society Act* and associated Regulations.

Chairperson, Bonnitta Ritchie
Exec. Director, Catharine Buckler

Yukon Medical Council
Box 2703, Whitehorse, Y1A 2C6

The Yukon Medical Council's powers are described in and are pursuant to subsection 8(1) of the *Yukon Medical Profession Act.*

The Council has powers and performs duties as are given or imposed by the Act with respect to regulation of the professional activities of persons who practise medicine in Yukon. It is empowered to make recommendations to the Executive Council to amend and make such regulations as are necessary to carry out the intent of this Act but that are not in conflict therewith.

The Council's primary activity is to review and grant licences to medical practitioners who wish to practice in Yukon. All complaints against a practitioner are lodged with the Council and appropriate action is taken.

The Council's overall objective is to ensure that the highest possible medical standards are maintained and that the public is protected.
Contact person, Vicki Hancock

Yukon Utilities Board
Box 2703, Whitehorse, Y1A 2C6

The Yukon Utilities Board was established to regulate the operation of public utilities in Yukon. The Board regularly reviews rate adjustment proposals submitted by the Yukon Electrical Co. Ltd. and the Northern Canada Power Commission, on behalf of Yukon consumers. Beyond rate matters, the Board has broad powers to hear and determine any matter respecting production and transmission on any significant proposed energy project. Public hearings may be called to assist the Board in these deliberations.
Exec. Secretary, Audrey Wipp

PUBLIC SERVICE COMMISSION
Box 2703, Whitehorse, Y1A 2C6

MINISTER'S OFFICE

Minister, The Hon. Margaret Joe
Public Service Commissioner, J.N. Besier
Systems and Administration
Director, Jeff Frketich
Recruitment and Training Branch
Director, P.I. Malloch
Labour Relations Branch
Director, Pat Cumming
Compensation and Classification Branch
Director, Don Trochim
Employee Records and Pension Unit
Manager, Terry Kinney
Staff Training and Development Unit
Manager, Stan Boychuk
Positive Programs Director, Dorothy Thorsen

DEPARTMENT OF RENEWABLE RESOURCES
Box 2703, Whitehorse, Y1A 2C6

MINISTER'S OFFICE
Minister, The Hon. Art Webster

DEPUTY MINISTER'S OFFICE
Dep. Minister, Bill Klassen

POLICY AND PLANNING BRANCH
Director, Tim McTiernan
Program Manager, Mark Hoffman
Information and Education Officer, Jack Schick
Policy Analysis and Devolution
Manager, Stephen Fuller

Resources Regulations Officer, Steve Smyth
ADMINISTRATION
Director, Stan Marinoske
AGRICULTURE
Director, Dave Beckman

PARKS, RESOURCES AND REGIONAL
PLANNING
Director, Dave Reynolds
Regional Planning Chief, Yvonne Harris
Parks and Resources Chief, Kees Ruurs
Parks Resources Planning
Sr. Planner, Finlay McRae
Operations and Development
Sup'ts: Peter Frankish, Ray Wotton,
Rodger Vizbar
FISH AND WILDLIFE
Director, Hugh Monaghan
Field Services Chief, Russ Fillmore
WILDLIFE MANAGEMENT BRANCH
Habitat Management and Research
Supervisor, Manfred Hoefs

DEPARTMENT OF TOURISM
Box 2703, Whitehorse, Y1A 2C6

MINISTER'S OFFICE
Minister, The Hon. Art Webster
Dep. Minister, George Tawse-Smith

MARKETING
Director, Klaus Roth
Policy Analyst, George Sinfield
Information Services Chief, Dave Austin
Industry Liaison Officer, John Kostelnik
Publicity Officer, Kevin Shackell
DEVELOPMENT
Director, John Spicer
Development Officer, Robert Clark
HERITAGE BRANCH
Director, Vacant
Historic Sites Co-ordinator, Vacant
Museums Advisor, Ed Krahn
Art Gallery Curator, Ruth McCullough
Native Heritage Advisor, Louise Profeit-Leblanc

INDEPENDENT AGENCIES, BOARDS AND COMMISSIONS

Women's Directorate
Box 2703, Whitehorse, Y1A 2C6
(403) 667-3030; Telex: 036-8-260

The Women's Directorate was established by the Government of Yukon in 1985 as a free-standing central agency reporting directly to the Minister responsible for the Status of Women. Its goal is to promote economic, social, and legal equality for women.

In order to fulfil its mandate, the Directorate: analyzes and evaluates existing and proposed legislation, policies, and programs for their impact on women; assists government departments in developing and co-ordinating policy and program initiatives to benefit women; identifies women's issues and priorities; and informs the public about such issues. Through consultation with women, women's groups, and government representatives, priorities have been identified, including education and training opportunities for women, the development of a positive employment program to provide equal opportunities for women in the public service, and promotion of the participation of Yukon women on government boards and committees.

The staff consists of a director, a policy analyst, and an administrative support person.
Minister, The Hon. Margaret Joe
Director, Bobbi Smith
Policy Analyst, Pat Byers

Yukon Development Corp.
Financial Plaza, Box 2703
Whitehorse, Y1A 2C6
Minister responsible, The Hon. Tony Penikett
Exec. Director, Shakir Alwarid
Admin. Officer, Valerie Williamson
A/Corporate Treasurer, Ross Perkin
Gen. Counsel, Eric Woodhouse

Yukon Energy Corp.
Financial Plaza, Box 2703
Whitehorse, Y1A 2C6
Minister responsible, The Hon. Tony Penikett

Yukon Housing Corp.
Box 2703, Whitehorse, Y1A 2C6
Minister responsible, The Hon. Maurice Byblow
Board Chairperson, Art Stephenson
President, Maurice Albert
Secretary, Roxane Davidson
Manager, Carl Rumscheidt
Finance and Administration
Manager, Mariette Nygren
Program Administrators:
Ron Brown, David Hedmann
Construction and Maintenance
Manager, Vacant
Home Improvement Program Officer,
Joann Brown

Yukon Liquor Corp.
Marwell Area, Box 2703, Whitehorse, Y1A 2C6
Telex: 036-8-336

The Yukon Liquor Corp., established in April

1977, regulates the importing, distribution, and retailing of all alcoholic beverages within Yukon. It ensures that the requirements of the *Liquor Act*, the attendant Regulations, and the goals and objectives of the Corporation are upheld. It is also responsible for the issuance, cancellation, and suspension of liquor licences, enforcement of the Act, inspections, and all other matters relevant to controlling the sale of liquor.

The board of directors which makes up the Liquor Board has gradually assumed all of the legislated responsibilities, and also has become involved in the gradual evolution of required by-laws, policies, and orders. This discretionary board, appointed by the Commissioner of the Executive Council, functions with full authority as outlined in the *Liquor Act*.

Minister responsible, The Hon. Art Webster
Gen. Manager, Andy Vantell
Finance and Administration
Manager, Joanne Ambrose
Store and Warehouse Operations
Manager, Bob Morris

Yukon Workers' Compensation Board
4114-4th Ave., Ste. 300, Whitehorse, Y1A 4N7

The Workers' Compensation Board was established in October 1978 by Order-in-Council 1978/201 to administer the *Workers' Compensation Act* on behalf of the Commissioner of Yukon.

The Compensation Fund is provided by contributions from employers, who are assessed and levied a percentage of payroll. Capitalized reserves are maintained, sufficient to pay all compensation in future years for all accidents or injuries that occurred during the period of assessment.

When a worker suffers injury or death by accident arising out of and in the course of employment, compensation is paid for wage loss up to the maximum allowable rate. At the time of injury, or any time thereafter during the disability, the Board may provide such medical aid as is deemed necessary.

Minister responsible, The Hon. Margaret Joe

Chairperson, John Wright
Exec. Director, Brian Booth
Director of Claims, Dorothy Drummond
Director of Assessments, Dale Schmekel
Assessment Auditor, Rick Hoenisch

FEDERAL GOVERNMENT DIRECTORY

Canada Mortgage and Housing Corp.
3106-3rd Ave., Ste. 402, Whitehorse, Y1A 5G1
Manager, Dave Kingsley

Canada Post
2 Range Rd., Whitehorse, Y1A 2B0
Postmaster, Ken Strachan

Canadian Broadcasting Corp.
3103-3rd Ave., Whitehorse, Y1A 1E5
Area Manager, Jim Boyles

Department of Communications
4133-4th Ave., Ste. 201, Whitehorse, Y1A 1H8
Regulations Branch
Dist. Manager, Diane Larsen

Department of Employment and Immigration
101 Federal Bldg., Whitehorse, Y1A 2B5
Canada Employment Centre
Territorial Manager, Ken Yendall
Asst. Manager, Brian Gillen
Canada Immigration Centre
A/Manager, Harry Bil

Department of Energy, Mines and Resources
204 Range Rd., Whitehorse, Y1A 3V1
A/Reg. Surveyor, Doug Culham

Conservation and Renewable Energy Office
2078-2nd Ave., Whitehorse, Y1A 1B1
Director, Jerry Bartram

Department of the Environment

Environmental Protection Service
204 Range Rd., Ste. 201, Whitehorse, Y1A 3V1
A/Chief, George MacKenzie-Grieve

Canadian Wildlife Service
204 Range Rd., Ste. 202, Whitehorse, Y1A 3V2
Biologists:
Jim Hawkins, Wendy Nixon, Don Russell

Water Survey of Canada
Box 4117, Whitehorse, Y1A 2C6
Officer-in-Charge, Jim McFarland

Atmospheric Environment Service
Operations Bldg., Rm. 205, Whitehorse Airport
Whitehorse, Y1A 3E4
Officer-in-Charge, Tim Goos

Parks Canada
Bldg. 204, Range Rd., Whitehorse, Y1A 3V1
Historic Sites Division
Area Sup't, Bob Lewis
Kluane National Park
Haines Junction, Y0B 1L0
Sup't, Doug Stewart
Dawson Historic Sites
Sup't, Al Fisk
Box 390, Dawson City, Y0B 1G0

Department of Fisheries and Oceans
122 Industrial Rd., Whitehorse, Y1A 2T9
Dist. Supervisor, Gordon Zealand

Department of Health and Welfare
Medical Services
2 Hospital Rd., Whitehorse, Y1A 3H2
Reg. Director, John Mar
Program Medical Officer, Dr. George Walker

Department of Indian Affairs and Northern Development

INDIAN AND INUIT AFFAIRS PROGRAM
Box 4100, Whitehorse, Y1A 3S9
Reg. Director, Dr. E.R. Daniels
Sr. Land Claims Advisor, Vic Carson
Finance and Administration
A/Director, Dave Steele
Indian Services Director, A. McDiarmid
Communication Services Director, Craig Yeo
Engineering and Architecture
Director, Dale Ostopowich
Transfer Payments
Reg. Manager, Shari Borgford
Capital Management and Band Support
Reg. Manager, Doug Beaumont
Social Development Director, William Brinley
Education
A/Director, Barb Fred
Economic Development
A/Director, Wilf Attwood
Alternative Funding Arrangements
Reg. Manager, R. Smoler
Lands, Revenues and Trusts
Director, P. Garrett
Administration
Contracts and Administration
A/Chief, D. Velder

NORTHERN AFFAIRS PROGRAM
Bldg. 200, Range Rd., Whitehorse, Y1A 3V1
Switchboard: (403) 667-3100
Director Gen., A.E. Ganske
Economic Development
Director, Ron Chambers
Finance and Administration
Director, J. McLachlan
Personnel Services Director, M.R. Freibergs
Communications Services Director, Craig Yeo
Engineering and Architecture
Reg. Manager, Dale Ostopowich
Renewable Resources Director, Lois Craig
Forest Resources
Reg. Manager, Norman Denmark
Water Resources
Reg. Manager, Jack Nickel
Land Resources
Reg. Manager, Angus Robertson
Mineral Resources Director, A.C. Ogilvy
Geology
A/Reg. Manager, Steve Morison
Mineral Development
Reg. Manager, Al Waroway
Mining Safety
Reg. Manager, Naresh Prasad
Mineral Rights
Reg. Manager, B.R. Baxter

Northern Land Use Planning
Director, B. Chambers

Department of Industry, Science and Technology
108 Lambert St., Ste. 301, Whitehorse, Y1A 1Z2
Director, L. Bagnell

Department of Justice
204 Lambert St., Whitehorse, Y1A 1Z4
Director, Thomas A. Dohm

Department of Labour
212 Main St., Ste. 212
Bag 2737, Whitehorse, Y1A 1E5
Labour Affairs Officer, F. Bachmier

Department of National Defence
Canadian Forces Detachment
Federal Bldg., Rm. 241, Whitehorse, Y1A 2B5
Commanding Officer Canadian Forces,
Maj. W.J. Schneider

Department of National Revenue
Federal Bldg., Rm. 116, Whitehorse, Y1A 2B5
Customs Operations
Area Chief, Terry E. Ruttan

Department of Public Works
201 Range Rd., Whitehorse, Y1A 3A4
Sr. Departmental Representative and Reg.
Manager, Transportation, John C. Hudson
Regional Property Manager, J. Wallace

Department of Supply and Services
307 Jarvis St., Ste. 102, Whitehorse, Y1A 1Z4
Contracting Officer, Michael Shaw

Department of Transport
Telecommunications and Electronics Branch
Operations Bldg., Rm. 215, Whitehorse Airport
Whitehorse, Y1A 3E4
Electronic Centre Manager, D. Herman
Airports and Properties Branch
Whitehorse Airport, Whitehorse, Y1A 3E4
Airport Manager, Dave Devlin

Public Service Commission
Yukon District Office
4114-4th Ave., Ste. 302, Whitehorse, Y1A 4N7
A/Director, Adeline Webber

Royal Canadian Mounted Police
"M" Division
4100-4th Ave., Whitehorse, Y1A 1H5
Commanding Officer, Chief Supt. A.J. Toews

JUDICIARY AND JUDICIAL OFFICERS

Court of Appeal

2134-2nd Ave., Whitehorse, Y1A 5H6
General Inquiries: (403) 667-3524

The Judges of the Court of Appeal are:
(a) the Chief Justice of British Columbia;
(b) the Justices of Appeal of British Columbia; and
(c) the Judges of the Supreme Courts of the Yukon and Northwest Territories.

Chief Justice: The Hon. Allan McEachern

Justices of Appeal:
The Hon. Harry C.B. Maddison (Whitehorse)
The Hon. M.M. de Weerdt
The Hon. T.D. Marshall
The Hon. Nathaniel T. Nemetz
The Hon. John David Taggart
The Hon. Peter Donald Seaton
The Hon. A. Brian Carrothers
The Hon. Ernest Edward Hinkson
The Hon. William Alastair Craig
The Hon. John Somerset Aikins*
The Hon. John Douglas Lambert
The Hon. James Allen Macdonald*
The Hon. Richard Philip Anderson*
The Hon. Henry Ernest Hutcheon*
The Hon. Alan Brock Macfarlane
The Hon. William Arthur Esson
The Hon. Wilfred John Wallace
The Hon. Charles Conrad Locke
The Hon. J. Edward Richard
The Hon. Mary Frances Southin
The Hon. Samuel Martin Toy

Supreme Court and Court Officials

2134-2nd Ave., Whitehorse, Y1A 5H6
General Inquiries: (403) 667-3524
Chief Justice: The Hon. H.C.B. Maddison

Ex-officio Judge:
The Hon. Justice M.M de Weerdt

Deputy Judges:
The Hon. Justice S.M. Toy (B.C.)
The Hon. Justice L.G. McKenzie (B.C.)
The Hon. Justice A.G. MacKinnon (B.C.)
The Hon. Justice P.D. Dohm (B.C.)
The Hon. Justice R.P. Kerans (Alta.)
The Hon. Justice W.A. Stevenson (Alta.)
The Hon. Justice C.G. Yanosik (Alta.)
The Hon. Justice A.H.J. Wachowich (Alta.)
The Hon. Justice J.B. Dea (Alta.)
The Hon. Justice P.C.G. Power (Alta.)

The Hon. Justice W.J. Girgulis (Alta.)
The Hon. Justice C.F. Tallis (Sask.)
The Hon. Justice M. Nichols (Que.)
The Hon. Justice V. Masson (Que.)
The Hon. Justice W.D. Griffiths (Ont.)
The Hon. Justice S. Borins (Ont.)
The Hon. Justice K.E. Meredith (B.C.)
The Hon. Justice J.C. Bouck (B.C.)
The Hon. Justice P.N. Proudfoot (B.C.)
The Hon. Justice M.R. Taylor (B.C.)
The Hon. Justice D.B. Hinds (B.C.)
The Hon. Justice T.H. Miller (Alta.)
The Hon. Justice D.C. McDonald (Alta.)
The Hon. Justice J.B. Feehan (Alta.)
The Hon. Justice J.D. Bracco (Alta.)
The Hon. Justice M.M. Hetherington (Alta.)
The Hon. Justice E. Lomas (Alta.)
The Hon. Justice E.D. Bayda (Sask.)
The Hon. Justice C. Bisson (Que.)
The Hon. Justice C.R. Vallerand (Que.)
The Hon. Justice P. Meyer (Que.)
The Hon. Justice A.R. Lutz (Alta.)
The Hon. Justice G.H.F. Moore (Ont.)
The Hon. Justice J.D. Bernstein (Ont.)
The Hon. Justice G.J. Kroft (Man.)

Clerk: Sheila J. Lycan
Sheriff: Brian Pope

Territorial Court and Court Officials

The Law Courts
2134-2nd Ave., Whitehorse, Y1A 5H6
General Inquiries: (403) 667-3524

Chief Judge: Vacant
Judges: Heino Lilles, Vacant
Deputy Judges: Charles C. Barnett,
    William J. Diebolt, Jane Godfrey,
    Robert Halifax, Ralph E. Hudson, Keith Libby,
    N. Jack McGiven, Nancy Morrison,
    Dwayne W. Rowe, T. Shupe, J. Woodrow,
    D. Waurynchuck, D. Luther, P. Hyde,
    G. Lynch-Staunton, C. Scott, S. Enderton

Clerk: James R. Simpson
Sheriff: Brian Pope

Yukon Land Registry

2134-2nd Ave., Whitehorse, Y1A 5H6
General Inquiries: (403) 667-5441

Registrar: Dianne Gau
Dep. Registrar: Sigrid Fischbuch

---

* Supernumerary

INTERGOVERNMENTAL AGENCIES

NOTE: The responsibilities of the organizations listed in this section cross federal-provincial and/or provincial jurisdictions. Because they are operated for — and/or funded by — two or more governments, they fall within the category of "intergovernmental agencies".

Atlantic Lottery Corporation Inc. 18-1
Atlantic Provinces Special Education Authority 18-1
   Atlantic Provinces Resource Centre for the Hearing Handicapped 18-2
   Atlantic Provinces Resource Centre for the Visually Impaired 18-2
Canadian Council of Resource and Environment Ministers 18-2
Canadian Heritage Rivers Board 18-2
Canadian Intergovernmental Conference Secretariat 18-3
The Council of Maritime Premiers 18-3
   Atlantic Coastal Resource Information Centre 18-3
   Land Registration and Information Service 18-3
   Maritime Municipal Training and Development Board 18-3
   Maritime Provinces Education Foundation 18-3
   Maritime Provinces Higher Education Commission 18-3
   Maritime Remote Sensing Committee (MRSC) 18-3
   Maritime Resource Management Service (MRMS) 18-3
Council of Ministers of Education 18-3
Indian Commission of Ontario 18-4
Intergovernmental Committee on Urban and Regional Research 18-4
Interprovincial Lottery Corp. 18-4
Interprovincial Sport and Recreation Council 18-4
Lake of the Woods Control Board 18-4
Prairie Agricultural Machinery Institute 18-5
Prairie Provinces Water Board 18-5
Western Canada Lottery Corp. 18-5

18

ATLANTIC LOTTERY CORP.

Box 5500, Moncton, NB E1C 8W6
General Inquiries: (506) 853-5800

An interprovincial agreement was signed on Aug. 27, 1976 by the four Atlantic provinces, confirming their decision to establish jointly an Atlantic lottery and to create a Crown corporation to manage and operate the lottery. Lotteries currently administered include the Auto Plus, Pik 4, TAG, Provincial, Lotto 6/49, and instant games.

Board of Directors:
Chairman, Ian D. MacBain
   N.B. Dept. of Finance
Vice-Chairman, Douglas Tobin
   N.S. Management Board
Directors:
Douglas B. Boylan
   Chairman, P.E.I. Royal Commission on Land
Gilbert Gill, Nfld. Dept. of Finance
Ernest MacKinnon
   Dep. Minister, N.B. Management Board
Louis Stephen, N.S. Dept. of Housing
Lewis White, Nfld. Treasury Board
Philip MacDougall, P.E.I. Dept. of Finance

ADMINISTRATION
Gen. Manager, Cluny Macpherson
Marketing and Sales Director, Bert McWade
Marketing Manager, Susan Jones
Sales Manager, Bob Scott
Public Relations Manager, Lea Bryden
Information Systems Director, Jim Bursey
Human Resources Manager, Pierre Battah
Comptroller, Doug Milton
Internal Auditor, Vacant
Administration Manager, Cathy Pickard

ATLANTIC PROVINCES SPECIAL EDUCATION AUTHORITY

Trade Mart Bldg.
Box 578, Halifax, NS B3J 2S9
General Inquiry: (902) 424-7765

The Atlantic Provinces Special Education Authority is an interprovincial co-operative agency established in 1975 by joint agreement among the ministers of education of New Brunswick, Nova Scotia, P.E.I., and Newfoundland. The agreement was based upon a study and recommendations made by a committee chaired by Dr. David Kendall of the University of British Columbia. The study was initiated at the request of the ministers of education of the four provinces.

The agreement provides for the creation of the Atlantic Provinces Special Education Authority and authorizes it to provide educational services, programs, and opportunities for persons under the age of 21 years with impairments of vision and hearing who are residents of Atlantic Canada. The agreement is the only one of its kind in Canada.

The Authority is comprised of 12 members, consisting of the deputy ministers of education of the four Atlantic provinces, plus two members from each province who are appointed by Order-in-Council.

Superintendent, Arnold G. Jones
Finance and Administration
Director, Barbara R. Hood
Programs and Services
Consultant, Avery Bain
Staff Training and Development
Consultant, Ruth Kimmins

The Atlantic Provinces Resource Centre for the Hearing Handicapped
Box 308, Amherst, NS B4H 3Z6
Director, Phyllis Cameron

The Atlantic Provinces Resource Centre for the Visually Impaired
5940 South St., Halifax, NS B3H 1S6
Director, Daniel Harmer

CANADIAN COUNCIL OF RESOURCE AND ENVIRONMENT MINISTERS

4905 Dufferin St., Downsview, ON M3H 5T4

The Canadian Council of Resource and Environment Ministers is an intergovernmental agency established as the result of a recommendation of the national "Resources for Tomorrow" conference held in 1961.

The Council was initially intended to focus on natural renewable resources. However, in view of the close relationship between renewable resources and protection of the environment, its membership since 1971 has been composed of federal and provincial ministers of natural resources and environment.

The role of the Council has been defined as providing "a forum for stimulating development of compatible and co-operative natural resources and environmental management policies and programs through exchange of information, consultation, and debate." In recent years, the Council's activities have been focused largely on environmental issues.

One important aspect of the Council is that it was conceived as and has remained a forum in which all member governments enjoy equal status. In this regard, it is supported by a permanent secretariat which is independent from any one government. The presidency and other official posts are rotated annually.

Exec. Director, G.A. Henderson

CANADIAN HERITAGE RIVERS BOARD

c/o National Parks Branch
Canadian Parks Service, Environment Canada
Ottawa, ON K1A 0H3

The membership of the Canadian Heritage Rivers Board comprises one representative from the Canadian Parks Service of Environment Canada, one from the federal Department of Indian Affairs and Northern Development, and one from each of the provincial and territorial jurisdictions that have chosen to participate in the Canadian Heritage Rivers System (CHRS).

The CHRS is a co-operative program established in 1984 by the federal government; the provinces of Newfoundland, Nova Scotia, New Brunswick, Quebec, Ontario, Manitoba, and Saskatchewan; and the Northwest Territories and Yukon. Its objectives are to give national recognition to important rivers and to ensure long-term conservation management.

The Board's main function is to make recommendations on the designation of rivers to the federal Minister of Environment and to the minister of the nominating government. Rivers are nominated for inclusion in the System on the basis of their natural, historical or recreational value. Designation as a Canadian Heritage River occurs after a management plan has been lodged with the Board. To date, 15 rivers have been nominated to the System, of which six have been formally designated: the Alsek River (Yukon), Bloodvein River (Manitoba), Clearwater River (Saskatchewan), French River (Ontario), Mattawa River (Ontario), and South Nahanni River (N.W.T.).

The Board also promotes a public awareness of the CHRS, encourages the nomination of rivers by groups or individuals, and monitors the status of designated rivers.

Chairman, J. Archibald, Exec. Director, N.B. 5
Dept. of Tourism, Recreation and Heritage
MEMBERS:
Don G. Hustins, Director, Parks Division,
Nfld. Dept. of Culture, Recreation and Youth
D. Murray, Director, Parks Division, P.E.I.
Dept. of Tourism and Parks
Barry Diamond, Director, Parks and Recreation
N.S. Dept. of Lands and Forests
Guy Bussière, Director of Planning, Parks
Branch, Que. Min. of Recreation, Hunting
and Fishing
Norm Richards, Director, Parks and
Recreational Areas Branch, Ont. Min. of
Natural Resources
Derek Doyle, Asst. Dep. Minister, Manitoba
Dept. of Natural Resources
Alan Appleby, Asst. Dep. Minister, Sask. Dept.
of Parks, Recreation and Culture
Finlay McRae, Sr. Planner, Yukon Dept. of
Renewable Resources
Alan Vaughan, Asst. Dep. Minister, N.W.T. Dept.
of Economic Development and Tourism
Claude Bugslag, Northern Land Use Planning
Directorate, Northern Affairs Program, Dept.
of Indian Affairs and Northern Development
I. Rutherford, Director Gen., National Parks
Branch, Canadian Parks Service,
Environment Canada
A/Secretary, M.W. Porter
Canadian Heritage Rivers Board Secretariat

Asst. Secretary, D. Gibson
Canadian Heritage Rivers Board Secretariat

CANADIAN INTERGOVERNMENTAL CONFERENCE SECRETARIAT

110 O'Connor St., 10th Flr.
Box 488, Stn. A, Ottawa, ON K1N 8V5

The Canadian Intergovernmental Conference Secretariat was created in May 1973, by the federal and provincial governments to serve federal-provincial and interprovincial meetings of first ministers, ministers, and senior officials held throughout Canada. It is funded and staffed by both the federal and provincial governments.

The services of CICS are provided to all delegations under the direction of the chairman of each conference. They include liaison on conference arrangements with each delegation; the translation, printing, and distribution of documents; simultaneous interpretation; media relations; the preparation of a summary of proceedings; and other measures required for the proper administration of a conference and its records. Over 20 intergovernmental subject matter areas, at ministerial and senior officials' levels, currently receive CICS services.

The CICS acts as the permanent secretariat for federal-provincial First Ministers' Conferences and provides administrative support to the Annual Premiers' Meetings. It also acts as the permanent secretariat of the ongoing Canadian constitutional review.

The CICS maintains a document archives for the use of governments, and is a principal source of unclassified intergovernmental conference documentation for university and municipal libraries in Canada.

Secretary, Stuart MacKinnon
Asst. Secretary, Andre S. Millar
Conference Services Manager, Robert Pelley
Conference Officers:
Eric Burkle, Pierrette Guenette,
Pierre-Luc Perrier, Claude Sirard
Asst. Conference Officers:
Gaétane Sirois, Laurie Webber
Financial and Administrative Services
Chief, Marcel Renaud
Personnel Officer, Lise Yelle-Lafrance
Intergovernmental Document Centre
Manager, Lyse Couchman
Co-ordinator, Carol Bourgeois
Translation Services Chief, Michel Parent

COUNCIL OF MARITIME PREMIERS

5161 George St., Ste. 1006
Box 2044, Halifax, NS B3J 2Z1
General Inquiries: (902) 424-7590

The Council of Maritime Premiers was formed in 1971 through Acts passed in the legislatures of New Brunswick, Nova Scotia, and P.E.I. The premiers meet at least four times a year to discuss matters of mutual concern, such as economic development, energy, education, and transportation. A secretariat provides continuity and co-ordinates the Council's activities.

Secretary to Council, Emery M. Fanjoy
Asst. Secretary, Wendy J. Paquette

Atlantic Coastal Resource Information Centre
Box 310, Amherst, NS B4H 3Z5
General Inquiries: (902) 667-7231
Director, Michael J.A. Butler
ACRIC Library
Chief Librarian, Margaret Campbell

Land Registration and Information Service
Box 6000, Fredericton, NB E3B 5H1
General Inquiries: (506) 453-2112
CEO, Larry Simpson
Administration and Computer Services
Director, Robert Simmonds

Maritime Municipal Training and Development Board
6209 University Ave., Halifax, NS B3H 3J5
General Inquiries: (902) 425-6487
Exec. Director, A. Donald Smeltzer

Maritime Provinces Education Foundation
Box 2044, Halifax, NS B3J 2Z1
Secretary, Wendy J. Paquette

Maritime Provinces Higher Education Commission
King's Place
Box 6000, Fredericton, NB E3B 5H1
Chairman, Timothy Andrew
Financial Planning Director, Larry H. Durling
Research and Academic Planning
Director, Dr. John Keyston

Maritime Remote Sensing Committee (MRSC)
Box 2254, Halifax, NS B3J 3C8
Co-ordinator, Brent Rowley
Maritime Remote Sensing Information Centre
Box 310, Amherst, NS B4H 3Z5
Librarian, Margaret Campbell

Maritime Resource Management Service Inc. (MRMS)
Box 310, Amherst, NS B4H 3Z5
General Inquiries: (902) 667-7231
President, Jim Stanley
Chief Librarian, Margaret Campbell

COUNCIL OF MINISTERS OF EDUCATION

252 Bloor St. W., Ste. 5-200
Toronto, ON M5S 1V5

The Council of Ministers of Education is a national organization founded in 1967 following agreement by the ten provincial governments. The Council serves as a forum and regular meeting-place for the provincial and territorial ministers of Education, their deputy ministers, and committees of senior officials. Its main work is information-sharing and co-operation among the provinces and territories in educational projects at all levels. The Council also facilitates interprovincial consultation on education-related matters that involve the federal government.

Chairman, The Hon. Lyn McLeod
   Ont. Min. of Colleges and Universities
Director Gen., Dr. Francis R. Whyte

INDIAN COMMISSION OF ONTARIO

236 Avenue Rd., 3rd Flr., Toronto, ON M5R 2J4
(416) 973-6390; Fax: (416) 973-4596

The Indian Commission of Ontario is a neutral, independent mechanism which was created in 1978 by the governments of Canada and Ontario and the First Nations in Ontario to assist them primarily through conciliation and mediation to identify, clarify, negotiate, and resolve issues of mutual concern.

Commissioner, Roberta Jamieson

INTERGOVERNMENTAL COMMITTEE ON URBAN AND REGIONAL RESEARCH

150 Eglinton Ave. E., Ste. 301
Toronto, ON M4P 1E8

The Intergovernmental Committee on Urban and Regional Research was formed upon recommendation of the 1967 Federal-Provincial Conference on Housing and Urban Development. The federal, provincial, and territorial governments are represented on the Committee.

ICURR operates an intergovernmental information exchange service in the fields of housing, urban and regional research, regional or economic development, municipal management and planning, environment, transportation, energy, and recreation. The service is available to employees of federal, provincial, and territorial ministries or departments, as well as subscribing municipal governments and consultants.

Chairman, D.M. Innes, Dep. Minister,
   Sask. Dept. of Urban Affairs
Exec. Director, Ken Bauman
Asst. Exec. Director, Alida Flinn
Information Co-ordinator, O. Monica Hope
Information Officers:
Victoria Gregor, Wayne Berry

INTERPROVINCIAL LOTTERY CORP.

101 Bloor St. W., Ste. 203
Toronto, ON M5S 1P7
General Inquiries: (416) 968-7769

The Interprovincial Lottery Corporation, a non-profit organization, was incorporated on Aug. 16, 1976 by the four western provinces and Ontario. In September 1978, Quebec joined the organization, followed by the Atlantic provinces in January 1979.

The Corporation administers the nationwide games known as the Provincial and Lotto 6/49. The four regional marketing organizations — the Western Canada Lottery Corp., Ontario Lottery Corp., Loto-Québec, and Atlantic Lottery Corp. — are responsible for sales, distribution, and marketing in their own regions. Profits from the two nationwide lotteries remain in the region where the tickets were sold.

A board of 21 directors is appointed by the ten provinces to direct the affairs of the Corporation.

Chairman, M.H. Smith
Vice-Chairmen: Marguerite Bourgeois,
W.G.D. Stothers, J.L. Burnett, I.D. MacBain
President, Cluny Macpherson
Vice-Presidents: Len Gzebb, Guy Simonis,
David Clark, Adam Hawkins
Sec.-Treasurer, Chris French

INTERPROVINCIAL SPORT AND RECREATION COUNCIL

Recreation Development Division
Alberta Recreation and Parks
Standard Life Ctr., 16th Flr.
10405 Jasper Ave., Edmonton, AB T5J 3N4

The Interprovincial Sport and Recreation Council serves at the behest of the provincial/territorial ministers responsible for recreation and sport. It provides a forum for exchange among provinces and territories, and a framework for the co-ordination, development, and implementation of sport and recreation programs of national interest.

Chairman, Bob Hillier
First Vice-Chairman, Don Leclair
Second Vice-Chairman, Dennis Adams
Administration
Vice-Chairman, Bill Werry

LAKE OF THE WOODS CONTROL BOARD

Place Vincent Massey, 11e ét.
351, boul. St-Joseph, Hull (Québec) J8Y 3Z5

The Lake of the Woods Control Board is an interjurisdictional board consisting of four members, each with an alternate, who represent Canada (one member), Ontario (two members), and Manitoba (one member). Each member serves as chairman one year in every four. Established in 1921, the Board is responsible for the control of certain water levels and flows in northwestern Ontario. Specifically, the Board regulates the levels of Lake of the Woods and Lac Seul and the flows in the Winnipeg and English rivers upstream of their junction. At times, it also controls the diversion of water from Lake St.

Joseph into Lac Seul. The authority of the Board is defined by concurrent Canada-Ontario-Manitoba legislation and is further mandated by a Canada-United States treaty, necessary since the Lake of the Woods is an international boundary water.

The operational arm of the Board is the Lake of the Woods Secretariat, an autonomous unit which reports to the Board but is housed in the offices of the Inland Waters Directorate, Environment Canada. Costs of the Secretariat and Board operations are shared by the governments.

Members:
D.R. Kimmett, Environment Canada
R.M. Odell, Ont. Min. of Natural Resources
J.E. Eaton, Ontario Hydro
V.M. Austford, Man. Dept. of Natural Resources

PRAIRIE AGRICULTURAL MACHINERY INSTITUTE

Box 1900, Humboldt, SK S0K 2A0
Inquiries: (306) 682-2555; Fax: (306) 682-5080

The Prairie Agricultural Machinery Institute is a co-operative undertaking by Alberta, Manitoba, and Saskatchewan. To meet its objectives of evaluating existing agricultural machinery and developing new and improved machinery, the Institute operates facilities at Portage la Prairie, Man. and Humboldt, Sask. Programs of evaluation, research, and development are conducted relevant to machinery used by prairie farmers.

Evaluation of the functional performance of current production machines in typical prairie operating conditions is a major part of the Institute's work. The results are published in report form and are available by subscription from the Institute.

Minister responsible, The Hon. Grant Devine
    Premier and Sask. Minister of Agriculture
Director and Business Manager, Barry Broad
Humboldt, Sask. Station
Sr. Engineer, J. Wasserman
Portage la Prairie, Man. Station
Box 1060, Portage la Prairie, MB R1N 3C5
Sr. Engineer, Mitchel Omichinski

PRAIRIE PROVINCES WATER BOARD

Rm. 306, Motherwell Bldg.
1901 Victoria Ave., Regina, SK S4P 3R4
(306) 522-6671

The Prairie Provinces Water Board administers the Master Agreement on Apportionment signed on Oct. 30, 1969. This Agreement provides an apportionment formula for interprovincial waters flowing from west to east, and gives recognition to the problems of water quality and to integrated development of the water resources of interprovincial streams.

The Board was formed on July 28, 1948 and consists of two representatives for Canada, and one each for the provinces of Alberta, Saskatchewan, and Manitoba. Operation of the current Board is based on the Master Agreement on Apportionment. The Board is financed on the basis of one-half by Canada and one-sixth by each of the three provinces. The Board operates through a Secretariat located in Regina.

Chairman, Ms. L. Goulet
c/o Environment Canada, Ottawa, ON K1A 0E7
Secretary, G.W. Dunn
Rm. 306, 1901 Victoria Ave.
Regina, SK S4P 3R4

WESTERN CANADA LOTTERY CORP.

125 Garry St., Winnipeg, MB R3C 4J1

The Western Canada Lottery Corporation was formed by the governments of Manitoba, Saskatchewan, and Alberta, in association with Yukon and the Northwest Territories, to operate government-sponsored lotteries in western Canada. Currently, these include Western Express, Provincial, Lotto 6/49, Lotto 6/36, and instant games.

Chairman, J. Burnett
Gen. Manager, Len Gzebb
Information Systems Director, Paul Sawyer
Finance and Administration
Director, Dave Loeb
Marketing Director, Richard Cone

His Worship, Mayor John L. Murphy of St. John's. 1988 was the 100th anniversary of the incorporation of the City of St. John's.
Photo courtesy of the Mayor's Office.

MUNICIPAL GOVERNMENTS

Alberta
Forms of Local Government 19-1
Municipalities and Counties 19-2

British Columbia
Municipal Government 19-6
Municipalities 19-7

Manitoba
Municipal Government 19-10
Municipalities 19-11

New Brunswick
Municipal Government 19-13
Municipalities 19-14

Newfoundland
Municipal Organization 19-15
Municipalities 19-16

Northwest Territories
Municipal Government 19-18
Municipalities 19-18

Nova Scotia
Municipal Government 19-19
Municipalities 19-20

Ontario
Municipal Government 19-21
Glossary of Terms 19-21
Municipalities 19-22

Prince Edward Island
Municipal Government 19-29
Municipalities 19-29

Quebec
Forms of Municipal Government 19-30
Municipalities 19-31

Saskatchewan
Forms of Municipal Government 19-40
Municipalities 19-40

Yukon Territory
Classes of Local Government 19-43
Municipalities 19-43

19

ALBERTA

Forms of Local Government

The *Municipal Government Act* provides that the Lieutenant-Governor in Council by order create and alter the status of municipalities under the following circumstances:

(a) A village may be created or a summer village raised to the status of a village where a petition signed by a majority of the residents who would be electors requests it. The village must contain at least 75 dwellings inhabited for the previous six months. The petition must also be accompanied by a map showing the proposed boundaries of the village.

A village as a corporate entity is managed by three councillors elected for a three-year term who must designate one member as mayor and the council may by by-law provide for a five-member council if it has a population of 250 or more persons.

(b) A village may become a town by way of a resolution by the village council and a request for the change in status to the Minister if it has over 1,000 inhabitants.

A town council consists of the elected positions of a mayor and six councillors for a three-year term.

(c) A town may gain city status by the same procedure of resolution and request as required for a change from village to town if it has over 10,000 inhabitants.

A city council consists of the elected positions of a mayor and six councillors for a three-year term and the council by a by-law may increase its number to any even number not exceeding twenty.

(d) Summer resort areas may be given local government in much the same way as a village, except the requirement for a summer village is not less than 50 separate buildings, each of which has been occupied as a dwelling at any time during the six month period preceding receipt of petition, in which case it will be officially incorporated as a summer village.

The reason for this differentiation is that a summer village, due to its predominantly summer-time use, must hold elections and an annual meeting, etc., during summer months.

A good number of urban municipalities do not fit the above population standards for their groups for the reason that the rules governing incorporation have changed over the years and the provincial government is loath to change the status of any municipality until it is requested to do so by the people concerned.

The *New Towns Act* provides for an interim method of administration by an appointed board of administrators and more ready access to the money required for capital expenditures by loans from the province. Areas experiencing unusual residential growth, such as brought about by the opening of a large new natural resource-based industry, and requiring immediate management expertise and money for the provision of local government-type services are eligible. The "new town" may be an established town or village or an entirely new development.

The *Municipal and School Administration Act* provides for the merging of the municipal administration of a city or town and school district administration under one elected council as an alternative to the usual two separate autonomous bodies. This type of county government has not been as readily accepted in urban municipalities as has its counterpart in rural municipalities.

The remainder of the province is divided into large rural-type units made up of municipal districts, counties, improvement districts, and the special areas.

The *County Act* provides for an alternative form of combined municipal and school administrations in rural areas, similar to that provided for in urban areas by the *Municipal and School Administration Act*. The council may consist of up to eleven members elected for three-year terms and it must appoint one of its members as reeve.

Improvement districts are administrative units in areas that have not reached a sufficient stage of development to warrant local self-government. Five of the nineteen units are reserved to the federal government as National Parks. The others are managed by the Department of Municipal Affairs, as set forth in the *Improvement Districts Act*.

There are three areas on the eastern boundary of the province designated as Special Areas 2, 3, and 4. These areas, created in the 1930s of former municipal and improvement districts due to severe drought conditions, are managed by an appointed board under the overall jurisdiction of the Department of Municipal Affairs, as provided for by the *Special Areas Act*.

Municipal Elections

The *Local Authorities Election Act* provides for the election of all forms of local government in Alberta.

Alberta has a three-year term for its councils and boards. There is no rotation among them. They are elected concurrently and serve for the full three-year term.

Municipalities and Counties

(Generally, only municipalities with more than 1,000 population are included. Population figures given are from Alberta Municipal Affairs Official Population List 1988.)

A: Administrator   Cl: Clerk   Co: Commissioner   D: Director   Ma: Mayor   Mg: Manager
R: Reeve   S: Secretary   T: Treasurer

CITIES
(Address of officials: City Hall)

Airdrie   10,957
Ma—Grant McLean
Mg/S—Deryl Kloster
T—Bob Ferguson
Box 3400, T4B 2B6

Calgary   657,118
Ma—Ralph Klein
Co—George Cornish
T—Al Habstritt
Cl—Joyce Woodward
Box 2100, Stn. M, T2P 2M5

Camrose   12,968
Ma—Dr. Walter Siwak
Mg—Donald Saunders

T—Robert McKenzie
Cl—Roy Mackwood
5204-50th Ave., T4V 0S8

Drumheller   6,366
Ma—William Doucette
Mg—Raymond Romanetz
T—Keith Peers
Cl—Donald Guidolin
Box 430, T0J 0Y0

Edmonton 576,249
Ma—Terry Cavanagh
Mg—C. Armstrong
T—J.K. McAully
Cl—Ulli S. Watkiss
1 Sir Winston Churchill Sq.
T5J 2R7

Fort McMurray 34,949
Ma—Charles Knight
Co—Brian MacRae
T—Vacant
Cl—Gerald Bussières
9909 Franklin Ave.
T9H 2K4

Fort Saskatchewan 11,983
Ma—Pryce Alderson
Co—Glenn Pitman
T—Louise Weklych
Cl—Laurine Gunness
10005-102nd St.
T8L 2C5

Grande Prairie 26,648
Ma—Dwight Logan
Mg—Kelly Daniels
T—E. Douglas Anderson
Cl—Letitia Saunders
9902-101st St., T8V 2P5

Leduc 13,126
Ma—Oscar Klak
Mg—Earl Wedel
Cl—Marvin Littman
1 Alexandra Park, T9E 4C4

Lethbridge 60,610
Ma—David Carpenter
Mg—Bob Bartlett
T—Ramsay Vickers
Cl—John Gerla
910 S. 4th Ave., T1J 0P6

Lloydminster 10,201
Ma—Patricia Gulak
Co—Roger Brekko
D—Donald Newlin
T—Nancy Huston
Cl—Tom Lysyk
5011-49th Ave., S9V 0T8

Medicine Hat 42,290
Ma—Ted Grimm
Co—R.L. Ardiel
Cl—L.P. Godin
580-1st St. S.E., T1A 8E6

Red Deer 54,839
Ma—Robert McGhee
Co—Michael Day
T—Alan Wilcock
Cl—Charlie Sevcik
Box 5008, T4N 3T4

St. Albert 38,318
Ma—Richard Fowler
Mg—Don Corrigan
T—Norbert Van Wyk
Cl—Fiona Daniel
5 St. Anne St., T8N 3Z9

Spruce Grove 11,918
Ma—George Cuff
Mg—Gary Swinamer
T—Randy Dubord
S—Diane Roy
410 King St., T7X 2Z1

Wetaskiwin 10,103
Ma—Leavert Johnson
Mg—John Van Doesburg
T—George Balash
Cl—Darryl Rubis
Box 6266, T9A 2E9

TOWNS

Athabasca 1,975
Ma—A.J. Schinkinger
Mg—Cliff Sawatzky
T—Brian Pysyk
Box 450, T0G 0B0

Barrhead 3,991
Ma—William Stutchbury
Mg—Norm Crawford
T—Mark Power
S—Wes Romanchuk
Box 189, T0G 0E0

Bassano 1,186
Ma—Janet Shydlowski
A—D. Gerry Neighbour
Box 299, T0J 0B0

Beaumont 4,189
Ma—Chris Calvert
Mg—Gordon Stewart
S/T—John T. Davey
Box 330, T0C 0H0

Beaverlodge 1,808
Ma—Gordon Astle
Mg/S—Fay Nichol
T—Ivan Hegland
Box 30, T0H 0C0

Black Diamond 1,436
Ma—Daniel Reid
A—Dianne Kreh
Box 10, T0L 0H0

Blackfalds 1,688
Ma—Wayne Tutty
A—James Rogers
Box 220, T0M 0J0

Bon Accord 1,355
Ma—Lee Danchuk
A—Mina Storry
Box 100, T0A 0K0

Bonnyville 5,575
Ma—Walter Ogrodiuk
Mg—Bill Newell
S—Olga Cross
Box 308, T0A 0L0

Bow Island 1,566
Ma—Glen Olmsted
A—Kenneth J. Hollinger
Box 100, T0K 0G0

Brooks 9,464
Ma—Eric Fleury
Mg—J. Neil Brodie
S/T—Kevin Bridges
Box 880, T0J 0J0

Bruderheim 1,176
Ma—Metro Kalyn
Mg—Debbie From
Box 280, T9B 0S0

Calmar 1,160
Ma—Louise Rumbles
A—Vacant
Box 750, T0C 0V0

Canmore 4,419
Ma—Paula Andrews
Mg—Frank Kosa
S—Marion Buckley
Box 460, T0L 0M0

Cardston 3,497
Ma—Larry Fisk
A—Keith Bevans
Box 280, T0K 0K0

Carstairs 1,498
Ma—Harvey Bazinet
A—Daphne Turner
Box 370, T0M 0N0

Castor 1,030
Ma—F. Kenneth Wetter
A—Michael Yakielashek
Box 479, T0C 0X0

Claresholm 3,382
Ma—Ernie Patterson
S/T—Larry Flexhaug
Box 1000, T0L 0T0

Coaldale 4,964
Ma—William Holmes
Mg—Earl McIlroy
Box 970, T0K 0L0

Cochrane 4,337
Ma—Wally Lepp
Mg—Martin Schmitke
T—Mona Sylvester
Box 10, T0L 0W0

Cold Lake 3,445
Ma—Warren Johnston
A—Myron Goyan
Box 98, T0A 0V0

Coronation 1,310
Ma—J.V. (Jack) Noonan
A—LaReata Workman
Box 219, T0C 1C0

Crossfield 1,472
Ma—Bert Curtiss
Mg—Wayne Ryder
Box 500, T0M 0S0

**The Municipality of
Crowsnest Pass** 6,912
Ma—J. Wayne Terriff
A—John Kapalka
T—Neil Thompson
Box 370, Coleman T0K 0M0

Devon 3,752
Ma—Dale Fisher
Mg—Alfred Weinhandl
S/T—Bill Johnston
Box 400, T0C 1E0

Didsbury 3,184
Ma—Donald Watt
A—E. Michael Storey
Box 790, T0M 0W0

Drayton Valley 5,290
Ma—W.R. Mayhew
Mg—Manny Deol
T—Janice Melynk
S—Robin Wenbourne
Box 837, T0E 0M0

Edson 7,323
Ma—Jerry Doyle
Mg—Dwight Stanford
S/T—Joan Parker
Box 1388, T0E 0P0

Elk Point 1,391
Ma—Bruce Kleeberger
A—L. Patrick Vincent
Box 448, T0A 1A0

Fairview 3,281
Ma—Jim Reynolds
Mg—Don Howden
T—Olga Frank
Box 730, T0H 1L0

Falher 1,178
Ma—Roland Turcotte
A—Gerard Nicolet
Box 155, T0H 1M0

Fort Macleod 3,123
Ma—Wesley Olmstead
Mg—Louis Damphousse
A—Lane McLaren
Box 1420, T0L 0Z0

Fox Creek 2,068
Ma—Bernard Hornby
Mg—Bruce Moltzan
T—Vacant
Box 149, T0H 1P0

Gibbons 2,491
Ma—W.H. Nimmo
A—Maisie Metrunec
Box 68, T0A 1N0

Grand Centre 3,655
Ma—Ray Coates
Mg—Raymond Coad
A—Frances Jordan
Box 70, T0A 1T0

Grande Cache 3,646
Ma—Walter Silvestri
A—Duane Dukart
Box 300, T0E 0Y0

Grimshaw 2,625
Ma—Helena Anderson
Mg—Raymond Rondeau
T—Dianne Hoover
S—Jenny Alcock
Box 377, T0H 1W0

Hanna 3,017
Ma—Gordon Hunter
A—Alec Simpson
Box 430, T0J 1P0

High Level 3,004
Ma—R.E. Walter
Mg—John Ludwig
S/T—Niven Parliament
Box 485, T0H 1Z0

High Prairie 2,817
Ma—Don Lorencz
A—Vacant
Box 179, T0G 1E0

High River 5,096
Ma—Douglas McDougall
A—J. Albert Barrie
T—Leif Pedersen
S—Vacant
Bag 10, T0L 1B0

Hinton 8,846
Ma—Jean Maurer
Mg—Ken Ball
S—Gerald Repecka
Box 818, T0E 1B0

Innisfail 5,535
Ma—Douglas Fee
Mg—Dale Mather
S/T—Barbara Scott
Box 220, T0M 1A0

Killam 1,032
Ma—Jack Warner
A—Vera Engel
Box 189, T0B 2L0

Lac la Biche 2,553
Ma—Mychail Onischuk
T—Colleen Kunz
S—Richard Persson
Box 387, T0A 2C0

Lacombe 6,110
Ma—Donald Thorne
Mg—Robert Jenkins
Box 310, T0C 1S0

Lamont 1,505
Ma—Steve Andrais
Mg—Mary Fedun
Box 330, T0B 2R0

Magrath 1,637
Ma—Forrest Balderson
Mg—Rodney Bly
Box 520, T0K 1J0

Manning 1,144
Ma—Delphine Harbourne
S/T—Lorraine Lovlin
Box 125, T0H 2M0

Mayerthorpe 1,414
Ma—Sylvia Krikun
S/T—Ed Mitchell
Box 420, T0E 1N0

McLennan 1,021
Ma—Lawrence Meardi
Mg/S/T—Laurent Lamoureux
Box 356, T0H 2L0

Millet 1,540
Ma—Vernon Somers
A—Shirley Melnikel
Box 270, T0C 1Z0

Morinville 5,409
Ma—Ross Quinn
Mg—A.M. Gibeault
S/T—H.E. Chalifoux
Box 420, T0G 1P0

Nanton 1,564
Ma—Patricia DuBois
A—Karen Kitchen (acting)
Box 609, T0L 1R0

Okotoks 5,666
Ma—William Wylie
Co—Richard Scotnicki
S—Greg Schneider
Box 220, T0L 1T0

Olds 5,005
Ma—Robert Armstrong
Mg—Ron Hilton
S/T—Howard J. Fenske
Box 189, T0M 1P0

Oyen 1,010
Ma—Douglas Lehman
A—John Lijdsman
Box 360, T0J 2J0

Peace River 6,355
Ma—Michael Procter
Mg—J.W.D. McLeod
S/T—Gordon Lundy
Box 125, T0H 2X0

Penhold 1,495
Ma—Ben Berndt
A—Gwen Robinson
Box 10, T0M 1R0

Picture Butte 1,554
Ma—Richard Casson
S/T—Janet Dickout
Box 670, T0K 1V0

Pincher Creek 3,800
Ma—Juan Teran
Mg—Monte Christensen
T—Malcolm Weisgerber
Box 159, T0K 1W0

Ponoka 5,473
Ma—Norm Nelson
Mg—John West
T—Myra J. Raugust
Box 1029, T0C 2H0

Provost 1,725
Ma—Ken Knox
A—Mrs. Lynda Berry
Box 449, T0B 3S0

Rainbow Lake 1,146
Ma—John Scott
Mg/S—Doreen Bello
Box 149, T0H 2Y0

Raymond 2,957
Ma—Robert Holt
A—Brad Watson
Box 629, T0K 2S0

Redcliff 3,834
Ma—Art Dirkson
Mg—H.W. Beach
T—R. Giesbrecht
Box 40, T0J 2P0

Redwater 2,024
Ma—Brian Brigden
Mg—Keith Miller
Box 397, T0A 2W0

Rimbey 1,748
Ma—Vicki Christensen
Mg—Vacant
S/T—Susan Shigehiro
Box 350, T0C 2J0

Rocky Mountain House 5,261
Ma—David Soppit
TM—Patrick Lyster
Box 1509, T0M 1T0

St. Paul 5,128
Ma—Paul Langevin
S/T—Wayne Horner
Box 1480, T0A 3A0

Sexsmith 1,256
Ma—Walter Paszkowski
Mg—Len Imrie
Box 420, T0H 3C0

Slave Lake 5,611
Ma—Bill Pearson
Mg—Bernie Kreiner
S/T—I. Edward Procyshyn
Box 1030, T0G 2A0

Smoky Lake 1,045
Ma—Ernie Brousseau
S/T—Elmer Oshann
Box 460, T0A 3C0

Spirit River 1,086
Ma—Verna Block
S/T—Elsie L. Hoffarth
Box 130, T0H 3G0

Stettler 5,147
Ma—Robert Stewart
Mg—D.H. Gilliland
S/T—Robert Stoutenberg
Box 280, T0C 2L0

Stony Plain 6,062
Ma—Reg Kotch
Mg—John Cosgrove
S/T—Richard Mah
Box 810, T0E 2G0

Strathmore 3,544
Ma—Wally Freeman
Mg—Doug Plamping
T—Phyllis Allen
S—Carol Engel
Box 359, T0J 3H0

Sundre 1,732
Ma—Robert McIntyre
A—Harvey Doering
Box 420, T0M 1X0

Swan Hills 2,407
Ma—Margaret Hanson
A—John Crisp
S/T—Lolita Teske
Box 149, T0G 2C0

Sylvan Lake 3,937
Ma—Ted Iverson
A—Rick Grimson
Box 70, T0M 1Z0

Taber 6,382
Ma—Paul Primeau (acting)
Mg—John Maddison
A—Clarence Schile
Box 2229, T0K 2G0

Three Hills 3,324
Ma—Daniel Shea
Mg—Brian J. Torpy
T—Terry Nash
Box 610, T0M 2A0

Tofield 1,483
Ma—Charles Sears
A—Lori Pilon
Box 30, T0B 4J0

Turner Valley 1,298
Ma—Victoria A. Prohaszka
A—Laurie Turner
Box 330, T0L 2A0

Two Hills 1,141
Ma—Steve Shybunka
A—M.D. Pawliuk
T—E. Pawliuk
S—M.E. Wysocki
Box 630, T0B 4K0

Valleyview 2,218
Ma—Peter Gilchrist
Mg/T—Doug Topinka
S—Joyce Craig
Box 270, T0H 3N0

Vegreville 5,276
Ma—Kathleen McKenzie
A—Richard Binnendyk
Box 640, T0B 4L0

Vermilion 4,259
Ma—Dave Hughes
Mg—Cliff Magnusson
T—Robert Watt
Box 328, T0B 4M0

Viking 1,160
Ma—W.R. Taylor
A—Lydia Hanson
Box 369, T0B 4N0

Vulcan 1,422
Ma—J. David Mitchell
A—Sandy Tetachuk
Box 360, T0L 2B0

Wainwright 4,665
Ma—Adam Coleman
A—Ernest N. Bouchard
Box 160, T0B 4P0

Wembley 1,227
Ma—Ken Reber
A—Karen Steinke
S—Ruth Breitkreutz
Box 89, T0H 3S0

Westlock 4,463
Ma—Kathleen Vaughan
Mg—Ron Campbell
T—Shelly Rettman
S/T—Sharon Smith
Box 2220, T0G 2L0

Whitecourt 6,126
Ma—Helmut Kreiner
Mg—W.L. Winger
Box 509, T0E 2L0

VILLAGES

Coalhurst 1,289
Ma—David Veres
A—Marge Williams
Box 456, T0L 0V0

COUNTIES

Athabasca 5,979
R—Albert Zachoda

A—Jim Woodward
Box 540, T0G 0B0

Barrhead 5,728
R—Lawrence Miller
M—Allan Charles
Box 820, T0G 0E0

Beaver 5,400
R—Gordon Maxwell
A—Ron Pepper
Box 140, Ryley, T0B 4A0

Camrose 7,475
R—Robert Prestage
A—W.R. Gartner
5402-48A Ave., T4V 0L3

Flagstaff 4,406
R—Paul Schorak
Mg—Everett Mayne
Box 358, Sedgewick, T0B 4C0

Forty Mile 3,335
R—Edward Torsher
A—Gordon Nicoll
Box 160, Foremost, T0K 0X0

Grande Prairie 12,042
R—Jim Tissington
A—Ron Pfau
8611-108th St., T8V 4C5

Lac Ste. Anne 7,765
R—Terry Nelson
Co—Arnold Koberstein
Box 219, Sangudo, T0E 2A0

Lacombe 8,911
R—Larry Waud
Co—Roy Robbins
S/T—Edwin Koberstein
Box 1330, T0C 1S0

Lamont 4,287
R—Edward Stelmach
Mg—David Petroski
Box 150, T0B 2R0

Leduc 11,278
R—Norman Bittner
Mg—Larry R. Majeski
4301-50th St., T9E 2X3

Lethbridge 8,266
R—Roelof Heinen
Mg—Sheldon Steinke
905 S. 4th Ave., T1J 4E4

Minburn 3,894
R—Gordon Miller
Mg—Larry Powley
Box 550, Vegreville, T0B 4L0

Mountain View 8,886
R—Sydney Vollmin
Co—Herman Epp
Box 100, Didsbury, T0M 0W0

Newell 6,143
R—Ford Workes
A—D.N. James
Box 130, Brooks
T0J 0J0

Paintearth 2,439
R—Alastair McRae
S/T—Lloyd Brattly
Box 509, Castor, T0C 0X0

Parkland 20,926
R—Ron Pollock
Co—Jim Simpson
Bag 250, Stony Plain
T0E 2G0

Ponoka 7,739
R—D. Vern Dick
A—Charlie Cutforth
Box 1830, T0C 2H0

Red Deer 13,911
R—Elmer Stoyberg
Co—Robert Stonehouse
Box 920, T4N 5H3

St. Paul 6,595
R—Robert Bouchard
Co—Robert Krawchuk
Box 368, T0A 3A0

Smoky Lake 2,789
R—Alex Makowichuk
Mg—Cary Smigerowsky
Box 310, T0A 3C0

Stettler 5,179
R—Bill Muhlbach
A—Nick Fakas
Box 1270, T0C 2L0

Strathcona 49,802
R—Iris Evans
Co—Eric McGhan
T—Dennis Pommen
S—Gordon Harris
2001 Sherwood Dr.
Sherwood Park, T8A 3W7

Thorhild 3,094
R—Nick Lazowski
S/T—Vacant
Box 10, T0A 3J0

Two Hills 3,086
R—Walter Verenka
A—Gary Popowich
Box 490, T0B 4K0

Vermilion River 8,112
R—Clarance Goldsmith
A—John Scott
Box 69, Kitscoty, T0B 2P0

Vulcan 3,656
R—Alan H. Ingraham
A—Thomas Roberts
Box 180, T0L 2B0

Warner 3,579
R—Henry Schoorl
A—Bert Nilsson
Box 90, T0K 2L0

Wetaskiwin 9,521
R—Clayton Monaghan
A/S/T—John McGowan
5109-51st St., T9A 2G5

Wheatland 5,407
R—Ray Zachariassen
S/T—John Montgomery
Box 90, Strathmore, T0J 3H0

MUNICIPAL DISTRICTS

Acadia 618
R—Bruce Dillabough
S/T—Murray Peers
Box 30, Acadia Valley
T0J 0A0

Bighorn 1,138
R—Gordon Stehr
Mg—Bertram Dyck
S—Merceil Ahearn
Box 310, Exshaw, T0L 2C0

Bonnyville 10,384
R—William Drake
Mg—R.A. Doonanco
Box 1010, T9N 2J7

Cardston 4,419
R—Broyce Jacobs
A—M. Vern Quinton
Box 580, T0K 0K0

Clearwater 9,848
R—Tyrone Lund
Mg—Larry Goodhope
Prov. Bldg., Box 550
Rocky Mt. House, T0M 1T0

Cypress 4,795
R—Jack Osadczuk
Mg—Lutz Perschon
T—Cheryl Friedt
S—Keith Bender
General Delivery
Dunmore, T0J 1A0

Fairview 1,903
R—Walter Doll
S/T—Lyle McKen
Box 189, T0H 1L0

Foothills 9,398
R—Fred Ball
S/T—Harry Riva Cambrin
Box 160, High River
T0L 1B0

Kneehill 4,996
R—Otto Hoff
A—John Jeffrey
Box 400, Three Hills
T0M 2A0

Peace 1,527
R—Starr Bulmer
A—Joyce Sydnes
Box 34, Berwyn, T0H 0E0

Pincher Creek 3,093
R—Tom Ferguson
A—Kenneth Phillips
Box 279, T0K 1W0

Provost 2,725
R—Norman Larson
S/T—Linda McDonald
Box 300, T0B 3S0

Rocky View 17,484
R—Larry Konschuk
Mg—Dale Clark
S—Valerie Schmaltz
T—Peter Kivisto
Box 3009, Stn. B
Calgary, T2M 4L6

Smoky River 2,853
R—Andre Bremont
A—Lucien Turcotte
Box 210, Falher, T0H 1M0

Spirit River 848
R—Frank Zahara
A—Wayne Heyland
Box 389, T0H 3G0

Starland 2,120
R—Almond Garry
A—Ross Rawlusyk
Box 249, Morrin, T0J 2B0

Sturgeon 14,019
R—Clayton Crozier

A—Gilbert Boddez
T—Case Van Herk
S—Larry Kirkpatrick
9601-100th St.
Morinville, T0G 1P0

Taber 5,284
R—Benjamin Friesen
A—Alan Shaw
Box 2230, T0K 2G0

Wainwright 3,937
R—James Christensen
A—Edith Thoreson
Box 670, T0B 4P0

Westlock 6,992
R—Peter Stasiuk
A—Wyatt Glebe
Box 219, T0G 2L0

Willow Creek 4,733
R—John Zoeteman
A—Ruben Hartfelder
Box 550, Claresholm, T0L 0T0

INDIANS
Living on reserves:
population 28,612
(June 3/86)

SUMMARY OF 1988 TOTALS

16 Cities
(incl. Alberta portion of Lloydminster) 1,578,643
108 Towns
(excl. Banff, Jasper, and Waterton).... 309,217
172 Villages (incl. 50 Summer Villages). 48,700

Total Urban 1,936,560

30 Counties 249,630
22 Municipal Districts 118,562
19 Improvement Districts
(incl. 5 National Parks)............ 73,222
3 Special Areas 6,010

Total Rural..................... 447,424

Total Urban and Rural
(excl. Indians on Reserves)........ 2,383,984

BRITISH COLUMBIA

Municipal Government

There are six forms of local government in British Columbia. Municipalities are in four categories — villages, towns, cities, and districts (see section 20 of the *Municipal Act*). Villages have a population of 2,500 persons or less; towns, between 2,500 and 5,000; and cities, more than 5,000. District municipalities cover an area of more than 800 hectares with an average population density of less than five persons per hectare.

Notwithstanding the Act, some cities have populations of less than 5,000 people. These cities were in existence before the Act was amended to create the present classifications. Many district municipalities have grown to average population densities greater than five persons per hectare. There is no section in the Act which stipulates a change in status with a change in population.

Generally, villages and towns have fewer responsibilities than cities and districts and do not have as many sources of revenue as the larger municipalities. Municipalities, regardless of classification, assume policing costs when their populations exceed 5,000.

As of January 1989, there were 47 villages, 13 towns, 37 cities, and 47 districts, excluding the City of Vancouver, which is governed by the *Vancouver Charter* rather than the *Municipal Act*.

All municipalities are governed by a council consisting of a mayor and aldermen. Villages have four aldermen, and cities, districts and towns may have four, six, eight or ten aldermen.

Improvement districts have been organized in non-municipal areas to provide specific services. The majority are water improvement districts but some provide fire protection and street lighting. The powers of these districts are exercised by elected trustees (section 828, *Municipal Act*).

Regional districts were created in the mid-1960s. All lands within the province, except for the sparsely populated north-western region adjacent to the boundary of Alaska, are organized into 29 regional districts. Included within the boundaries of a regional district are all municipalities and all lands formerly known as "unorganized" territories, i.e., those areas without municipal status which were formerly under the direct jurisdiction of the provincial government. Those parts of a regional district which are not municipalities are divided into "electoral areas" each of which elects one or more persons, depending upon population, to the board of the regional district. Municipalities are represented on the board by one or more appointed members of council, the number depending upon population.

Essentially, regional districts are federations of municipalities and electoral areas, and have two principal purposes. First, they are the vehicle created to allow the constituent members to provide services jointly which they could not provide individually. Second, they provide a form of local government for electoral areas.

Regional hospital districts, which have the same boundaries and board as the regional district, are required to plan for hospitals. Apart from the statutory requirements of administration and land-use, a region acquires such functions as its members agree that it should have. Consequently, some regional districts have many functions and others have only a few (see *Annual Report*, Ministry of Municipal Affairs).

Regional districts do not tax citizens directly. When the annual budget has been set, the regional board sends a requisition to each member municipality for the municipal share of the budget and to the provincial government for the electoral area's share.

Municipalities

(Generally, municipalities with a population less than 1,000 are not included. Population figures are from the Municipal and Regional District Directory—March 1989.)

A: Administrator   Ch: Chairman   Cl: Clerk   Ma: Mayor   Mg: Manager   S: Secretary   T: Treasurer

CITIES

Armstrong   2,706
Ma—William Hornby
Cl/T—Barry Gagnon
Box 40, V0E 1B0

Castlegar   6,385
Ma—Audrey Moore
A/T—David Gairns
460 Columbia Ave.
V1N 1G7

Colwood   11,432
Ma—Harry Chow
Cl/A—Barry Bennett
3300 Wishart Rd.
Victoria, V9C 1R1

Courtenay   9,631
Ma—George Cochrane
Cl/A—John E. Wilson
750 Cliffe Ave., V9N 2J7

Cranbrook   15,915
Ma—Richard Jensen
Cl/A—Tim Wood
40 S. 10th Ave., V1C 2M8

Dawson Creek   10,544
Ma—Bob Trail
A—Harald Hansen
Box 150, V1G 4G4

Duncan   4,225
Ma—Michael Coleman
Cl/A—Paul Douville
Box 820, V9L 3Y2

Enderby   1,849
Ma—Terry Fergus
Cl/A—Ron A. Fried
Box 68, V0E 1V0

Fernie   5,188
Ma—Garnet Shatosky
A/T—Colin Dean
Box 190, V0B 1M0

Fort St. John   13,355
Ma—Pat Walsh
Mg—Stan Kary
10631-100th St., V1J 3Z5

Grand Forks   3,282
Ma—Yasushi Sugimoto
Cl/A—Walter Slater
Box 220, V0H 1H0

Kamloops   61,773
Ma—Philip Gaglardi
Cl—Ron Kask
7 W. Victoria St., V2C 1A2

Kelowna   61,932
Ma—James Stuart
A—Ron Born
1435 Water St., V1Y 1J4

Kimberley   6,732
Ma—Jim Ogilvie
A—Robert West-Sells
340 Spokane St., V1A 2E8

Langley   16,557
Ma—Joe Lopushinsky
Cl/A—Bob Wilson
5549-204th St., V3A 1Z4

Merritt   6,180
Ma—Robert Baird
Cl/A—George Sawada
Box 189, V0K 2B0

Nanaimo   49,029
Ma—Frank Ney
A—Gerald Berry
455 Wallace St., V9R 5J6

Nelson   8,113
Ma—Gerald Rotering
Cl/A—Douglas Ormond
502 Vernon St., V1L 4E8

New Westminster   39,972
Ma—Elizabeth Toporowski
A—Douglas Manning
511 Royal Ave., V3L 1H9

North Vancouver   35,959
Ma—Jack Loucks
A—G.H. Brewer
141 W. 14th St., V7M 1H9

Parksville   5,828
Ma—Paul Reitsma
A—Grant McRadu
Box 1390, V0R 2S0

Penticton   23,600
Ma—Dorothy Whittaker
A—George Paul
171 Main St., V2A 5A9

Port Alberni   18,241
Ma—Gillian Trumper
Mg—Donovan Walker
4850 Argyle St., V9Y 1V8

Port Coquitlam   29,115
Ma—Len Traboulay
A—Bryan Kirk
2272 McAllister Ave.
V3C 2A8

Port Moody   15,754
Ma—David Driscoll
A—Leslie Harrington
2425 St. John's St.
V3H 3E1

Prince George   67,621
Ma—John Backhouse
Mg—Chester Jeffery
1100 Patricia Blvd.
V2L 3V9

Prince Rupert   15,755
Ma—Peter Lester
A—William Smith
424 W. 3rd Ave., V8J 1L7

Quesnel   8,358
Ma—Michael Pearce
Cl/A—Al Miller
405 Barlow Ave., V2J 2C3

Revelstoke   8,281
Ma—Geoffrey Battersby
Cl/A—Robert Carter
Box 170, V0E 2S0

Rossland   3,472
Ma—Donald Camozzi
A—Andre Carrel
Box 1179, V0G 1Y0

Terrace   10,532
Ma—Jack Talstra
Cl/A—Robert Hallsor
3215 Eby St., V8G 2X8

Trail   7,951
    Ma—Albert Marcolin
    Mg—Ken Wiesner
    1394 Pine Ave., V1R 4E6
Vancouver   432,385
    Ma—Gordon Campbell
    Mg—Fritz Bowers
    453 W. 12th Ave., V5Y 1V4
Vernon   20,245
    Ma—Mrs. Anne Clarke
    A—Jim Alveberg
    3400-30th St., V1T 5E6
Victoria   66,303
    Ma—Gretchen Brewin
    Mg—Colin Crisp
    1 Centennial Sq., V8W 1P6
White Rock   14,387
    Ma—Gordon Hogg
    Cl/A—Wayne Baldwin
    City Hall, V4B 5C6
Williams Lake   10,280
    Ma—Ray Woods
    Cl/A—Reginald Mitchell
    450 Mart St., V2G 1N3

DISTRICTS

Abbotsford   14,841
    Ma—George Ferguson
    Cl/A—Dennis Donald
    34194 Marshall Rd.
    V2S 5E4
Burnaby   145,161
    Ma—William Copeland
    Mg—Mel Shelley
    4949 Canada Way, V5G 1M2
Campbell River   17,223
    Ma—Robert Ostler
    A—Lorne Anderson
    301 St. Ann's Rd., V9W 4C7
Central Saanich   12,413
    Ma—Ron Cullis
    Cl/A—Gay Wheeler
    Box 26, Saanichton, V0S 1M0
Chetwynd   2,774
    Ma—Charles Lasser
    Cl/A—J.A. (Andy) Teslyk
    Box 357, V0C 1J0
Chilliwack   42,176
    Ma—John Les
    Cl—Ted Tisdale
    8550 S. Young Rd.
    V2P 4P1
Coldstream   6,872
    Ma—Ernie Palfery
    Cl/A—Harry Ellens
    9901 Kalamalka Rd.
    Vernon, V1B 1L6
Coquitlam   69,291
    Ma—Louis Sekora
    A—James Tonn
    1111 Brunette Ave., V3K 1E8
Delta   79,789
    Ma—Doug Husband
    A—Dr. Robert Collier
    4450 Clarence Taylor Cres.
    V4K 3E2
Elkford   3,187
    Ma—John White
    Cl/A—James Montain
    Box 340, V0B 1H0

Esquimalt   15,972
    Ma—Ronald Warder
    Cl/A—Sandy Gray
    1229 Esquimalt Rd.
    Victoria, V9A 3P1
Houston   3,905
    Ma—Tom Euverman
    Cl/A—Wayne Thiessen
    Box 370, V0J 1Z0
Hudson's Hope   1,158
    Ma—Lester Braaten
    Cl/T—Mrs. Fay Lavallée
    Box 330, V0C 1V0
Invermere   1,998
    Ma—Allan Chabot
    Cl—Bill Lindsay
    Box 339, V0A 1K0
Kent   4,085
    Ma—Michael Dunn
    Cl/T—Ross Conlin
    Box 70, Agassiz, V0M 1A0
Kitimat   11,196
    Ma—Richard Wozney
    Mg—David Morris
    270 City Centre, V8C 2H7
Langley   53,900
    Ma—John Beales
    A—James Godfrey
    4914-221st St., V3A 3Z8
Logan Lake   2,001
    Ma—Ove Christensen
    Cl/T—T.C. Day
    Box 190, V0K 1W0
Mackenzie   5,542
    Ma—William Whalley
    Cl—Don De Gagne
    Box 340, V0J 2C0
Maple Ridge   36,035
    Ma—Bill Hartley
    A—Jerry Sulina
    11995 Haney Place
    V2X 6G2
Matsqui   51,497
    Ma—Dave Kandal
    Cl/A—Hedda Cochran
    #200, 32315 S. Fraser Way
    Clearbrook, V2T 1W7
Metchosin   3,676
    Ma—Herman Volk
    Cl/T—Bruce Woodbury
    4450 Happy Valley Rd.
    R.R. 1, Victoria, V8X 3W9
Mission   21,985
    Ma—Sophie Weremchuk
    A—Norman Cook
    Box 20, V2V 4L9
North Cowichan   18,674
    Ma—H. Rex Hollett
    A—John Berikoff
    Box 278, Duncan, V9L 3X4
North Saanich   7,247
    Ma—Linda Michaluk
    A—Ron O'Genski
    Box 2639, Sidney, V8L 4C1
North Vancouver   68,821
    Ma—Marilyn Baker
    A—Melville Palmer
    Box 86218, V7L 4K1
Oak Bay   17,065
    Ma—Susan Brice
    A—Larry Pollock
    2167 Oak Bay Ave.
    Victoria, V8R 1G2

Peachland   2,988
    Ma—George Waldo
    Cl—Harry Lever
    Box 390, V0H 1X0
Pitt Meadows   8,085
    Ma—Bud Tiedman
    A—Joseph Antalek
    Box 160, V0M 1P0
Port Hardy   5,389
    Ma—Al Huddleston
    Cl—James Gustafson
    Box 68, V0N 2P0
Powell River   12,440
    Ma—Don Lockstead
    Cl/A—Mr. V.H. Petersen
    6910 Duncan St., V8A 1V4
Richmond   108,492
    Ma—Gilbert Blair
    A—G. Laubenstein
    6911 No. 3 Rd., V6Y 2C1
Saanich   82,940
    Ma—Howard Sturrock
    A—Bob Sharp
    770 Vernon Ave.
    Victoria, V8X 2W7
Salmon Arm   11,333
    Ma—Dick Smith
    A—Wayne Buchanan
    Box 40, V0E 2T0
Sechelt   4,814
    Ma—Thomas Meredith
    A—Malcolm Shanks
    Box 129, V0N 3A0
Spallumcheen   4,310
    Ma—Harold Norris
    Cl/T—Robert Graham
    Box 100, Armstrong
    V0E 1B0
Sparwood   4,540
    Ma—Toto Miller
    A—Loretta Montemurro
    Box 520, V0B 2G0
Squamish   10,419
    Ma—Phil Turner
    Cl/A—Bill Bloxham
    Box 310, V0N 3G0
Summerland   7,755
    Ma—Robert Shewfelt
    A—George Redlich
    Box 159, V0H 1Z0
Surrey   181,683
    Ma—Robert Bose
    Mg—Michael Jones
    14245-56th Ave., V3W 1J2
Tumbler Ridge   4,387
    Ma—Mike Caisley
    Cl—Robert Miles
    Box 100, V0C 2W0
Vanderhoof   3,505
    Ma—Leonard Fox
    Cl/A—Brian Ritchie
    Box 900, V0J 3A0
West Vancouver   37,514
    Ma—Don Lanskail
    Mg—Terry Lester
    750-17th St., V7V 3T3
Whistler   2,002
    Ma—Drew Meredith
    A—Peter Kent
    Box 35, V0N 1B0

REGIONAL DISTRICTS

(Population figures are from the 1986 Census)

Alberni-Clayoquot 30,092
 Ch—Hans Irg
 S—Allan Kilpatrick
 4586 Victoria Quay
 Port Alberni, V9Y 8G3

Bulkley-Nechako 37,093
 Ch—Gordon McFee
 S—Gary McIntyre
 Box 820, Burns Lake
 V0J 1E0

Capital 261,993
 Ch—Susan Brice
 S—W.M. Jordan
 Box 1000, Victoria
 V8W 2S6

Cariboo 59,009
 Ch—Darlyne Brecknock
 A—Alan Kuroyama
 525 Borland St.
 Williams Lake, V2G 1R9

Central Coast 3,105
 Ch—Brian Roe
 S—Carol Winkler
 Box 10, Hagensborg
 V0T 1H0

Central Fraser Valley 135,951
 Ch—George Peary
 S—John Spanier
 26982 Fraser Hwy.
 Aldergrove, V0X 1A0

Central Kootenay 48,541
 Ch—George Cady
 A—Reid Henderson
 601 Vernon St.
 Nelson, V1L 4E9

Central Okanagan 89,047
 Ch—James Stuart
 S—A.T. Harrison
 540 Groves Ave.
 Kelowna, V1Y 4Y7

Columbia-Shuswap 39,680
 Ch—George Abbott
 S—E.L. Lalonde
 Box 978, Salmon Arm
 V0E 2T0

Comox-Strathcona 70,281
 Ch—Keith Hudson
 S—W.B. d'Easum
 Box 3370, Courtenay
 V9N 5N5

Cowichan Valley 51,990
 Ch—Earle Darling
 S—Frank Raimondo
 137 Evans St.
 Duncan, V9L 1P5

Dewdney-Alouette 68,942
 Ch—Lloyd McKimmon
 S—John Gairns
 32386 Fletcher Ave.
 Mission, V2V 5T1

East Kootenay 52,540
 Ch—Brian Adams
 S—W.C. McNamar
 19 S. 24th Ave.
 Cranbrook, V1C 3H8

Fort Nelson-Liard N/A
 Ch—Frank Parker
 S—Patricia Bailey
 Bag 399
 Fort Nelson, V0C 1R0

Fraser-Cheam 57,316
 Ch—Lloyd Forman
 S—Robert Moore
 8430 Cessna Dr.
 Chilliwack, V2P 7K4

Fraser-Fort George 88,543
 Ch—Colin Kinsley
 S—D.N. Wilson
 987-4th Ave.
 Prince George, V2L 3H7

Greater Vancouver 1,256,075
 Ch—G.J. Blair
 S—J. McLean
 4330 Kingsway
 Burnaby, V5H 4G8

Kitimat-Stikine 39,123
 Ch—Jack Talstra
 S—Bob Marcellin
 #300, 4545 Lazelle Ave.
 Terrace, V8G 1S6

Kootenay-Boundary 30,032
 Ch—D. Swanson
 S—Larry Robinson
 1159 Pine Ave.
 Trail, V1R 4E2

Mount Waddington 14,765
 Ch—Stan McLennan
 S—William Shepard
 Box 729, Port McNeill
 V0N 2R0

Nanaimo 81,365
 Ch—Ian Terry
 S—Gordon Summers
 Box 40, Lantzville
 V0R 2H0

North Okanagan 54,367
 Ch—Earl Shipmaker
 S—Peter Mackiewich
 2903-35th Ave.
 Vernon, V1T 2S7

Okanagan-Similkameen 58,549
 Ch—E. Jean Lamb
 S—Vanessa Sutton
 101 Martin St.
 Penticton, V2A 5J9

Peace River N/A
 Ch—Ben Knutson
 A—Moray Stewart
 Box 810, Dawson Creek
 V1G 4H8

Powell River 18,190
 Ch—Don Silvester
 S—Glen Calvert
 5776 Marine Ave.
 Powell River, V8A 2M4

Skeena-Queen Charlotte 22,752
 Ch—Peter Lester
 S—Bryce Barnewell
 115 W. 1st Ave.
 Prince Rupert, V8J 4K8

Squamish-Lillooet 17,737
 Ch—R. Dan Cumming
 S/T—Ivan Knowles
 Box 219, Pemberton
 V0N 2L0

Sunshine Coast 16,547
 Ch—Mrs. Peggy Connor
 S—Larry Jardine
 Box 800, Sechelt, V0N 3A0

Thompson-Nicola 96,930
 Ch—Jack F. Lapin
 S—Eric Shishido
 2079 Falcon Rd.
 Kamloops, V2C 4J2

TOWNS

Comox 6,873
 Ma—George Piercey
 Cl—Ronald G. Kew
 1809 Beaufort Ave.
 V9N 4B8

Creston 4,098
 Ma—Mrs. Lela Irvine
 Cl/A—William Hutchinson
 904 Vancouver St.
 V0B 1G0

Fort Nelson 3,729
 Ma—Frank Parker
 A—Colin Griffith
 V0C 1R0

Gibsons 2,675
 Ma—Diane Strom
 Cl/A—Lorraine Goddard
 Box 340, V0N 1V0

Golden 3,584
 Ma—James Doyle
 Cl/T—Philip Taylor
 Box 350, V0A 1H0

Hope 3,046
 Ma—C. Keith Gardner
 A—Hedley Crowther
 Box 609, V0X 1L0

Ladysmith 4,393
 Ma—G.R. (Rollie) Rose
 Cl—Ed Gilman
 Box 220, V0R 2E0

Osoyoos 2,956
 Ma—Michael Radi
 Cl/A—Lockie Miles
 Box 3010, V0H 1V0

Port McNeill 2,559
 Ma—Gerry Furney
 Cl/A—Mrs. Margaret McKee
 Box 728, V0N 2R0

Princeton 2,910
 Ma—Gloria Stout
 A—Gordon Sanderson
 Box 670, V0X 1W0

Qualicum Beach 3,410
 Ma—Arthur Skipsey
 Cl/A—Leo Klees
 Box 130, V0R 2T0

Sidney 8,982
 Ma—Mrs. Norma Sealey
 Cl/A—Geoffrey Logan
 2440 Sidney Ave., V8L 1Y7

Smithers 4,713
 Ma—Brian Northup
 Cl/A—Eric McMurran
 Box 879, V0J 2N0

VILLAGES

Ashcroft 1,914
 Ma—Mervin Pears
 Cl/A—Gordon Berdan
 Box 129, V0K 1A0

Burns Lake 2,126
 Ma—William Gilgan
 Cl/A—James Pierce
 Box 570, V0J 1E0

Cache Creek 1,147
 Ma—Bernard Roy
 Cl/T—Mrs. June Gibbons
 Box 7, V0K 1H0

Chase 1,933	**Lillooet** 1,758	**100 Mile House** 1,692
Ma—Charles Marshall	Ma—Joyce Harder	Ma—Donna Barnett
Cl/T—Mrs. Agnes Sweet	Cl/T—Robert Watson	Cl—Ron Haggstrom
Box 440, V0E 1M0	Box 610, V0K 1V0	Box 340, V0K 2E0
Cumberland 1,853	**Lions Bay** 1,152	**Port Alice** 1,387
Ma—William Moncrief	Ma—Gordon Prescott	Ma—Mrs. Clare Whitehead
Cl/A—Norman Paulson	Cl/T—Mrs. Bernice Pullen	Cl/T—Jane Kennedy
Box 340, V0R 1S0	Box 141, V0N 2E0	Box 130, V0N 2N0
Fort St. James 1,983	**Lumby** 1,181	**Salmo** 1,014
Ma—Sandra Kovacs	Ma—David Simpson	Ma—Merle Hanson
Cl/A—Vacant	Cl/A—Leonard Anderson	Cl/T—Bryan Snelgrove
Postal Drawer 640, V0J 1P0	Box 430, V0E 2G0	Box 1000, V0G 1Z0
Fraser Lake 1,182	**Masset** 1,529	**Tahsis** 1,445
Ma—Colin Seeley	Ma—F. Gordon Feyer	Ma—Tom McCrae
Cl/A—Angus Davis	Cl/A—Alfred Brockley	T—Laura Fenton
Box 430, V0J 1S0	Box 68, V0T 1M0	Box 519, V0P 1X0
Fruitvale 1,932	**Montrose** 1,183	**Ucluelet** 1,512
Ma—Edward Lawton	Ma—George Klit	Ma—Erik Larsen
Cl—Karen Skinner	Cl/T—Gerry Henke	Cl/A—Murray Henderson
Box 430, V0G 1L0	Box 510, V0G 1P0	Box 999, V0R 3A0
Gold River 1,879	**Nakusp** 1,410	**Valemount** 1,161
Ma—Anne Fiddick	Ma—Mrs. Rosemarie Johnson	Ma—Norman McNee
Cl/T—Dick Hildebrandt	Cl/A—Cornie Froese	Cl—Bill Sparks
Box 610, V0P 1G0	Box 280, V0G 1R0	Box 168, V0E 2Z0
Lake Cowichan 2,170	**Oliver** 1,963	**Warfield** 1,840
Ma—Donald Gordon	Ma—Hartmut Buckendahl	Ma—William Trewhella
Cl/T—Mrs. Pat Akerley	Cl/A—Ray Martineau	Cl/T—Shirley Tognotti
Box 860, V0R 2G0	Box 638, V0H 1T0	555 Schofield Hwy.
		Trail, V1R 2G7

SUMMARY OF 1986 TOTALS

38 Cities.	1,116,477
47 Districts	1,194,950
13 Towns	53,283
46 Villages	50,408
Total Urban (Census)	2,285,004
Total Rural (Census)	598,363
Total Urban and Rural (excl. Indians on Reserves).	2,883,367

INDIANS

Living on reserves:
population 40,655
(June 3/86)

MANITOBA

Municipal Government

The basic requirements for any locality to be incorporated are as follows:

Village
(a) population of more than 750 inhabitants;
(b) municipal taxable assessment of not less than $750,000;
(c) contains residences of the inhabitants that, in the opinion of the minister, certified by him in writing, are sufficiently close together to form a village.

Town
(a) population of more than 1,500 inhabitants;
(b) municipal taxable assessment of not less than $1.5 million;
(c) contains residences of the inhabitants that, in the opinion of the minister, certified by him in writing, are sufficiently close together to form a town.

City
A city is created by regulation under *The Municipal Act.*

Local Government District
A local government district is created by regulation under *The Local Government Districts Act.*

Municipality
A municipality is created under the *Municipal Act.*

There are 105 rural municipalities, 39 villages, 35 towns, 5 cities and 17 local government districts in Manitoba. This makes a total of 201 local government units.

The *Municipal Act,* in addition to setting the minimum requirements for incorporation, also sets out the necessary administrative procedures.

All municipal units, including local government districts, have elected councils.

Municipalities

(Generally, only municipalities with more than 1,000 population are included. Population figures given are from the 1989 Manitoba Municipal Officials Directory.)

A: Administrator   Cl: Clerk   Ma: Mayor   R: Reeve   RA: Resident Administrator   S/T: Secretary-Treasurer

CITIES

Brandon   38,708
Ma—Kenneth Burgess
Cl—Ian Ford
Box 960, R7A 6A2
Flin Flon   7,243
Ma—Gordon R. Mitchell
S/T—Kenneth W. Shoemaker
Box 100, R8A 1M6
Portage la Prairie   13,198
Ma—William McMillan
Cl—H. Roberts
T—W. Preisentanz
Box 490, R1N 3C1
Thompson   14,701
Ma—Donald MacLean
Cl—Eric McCormick
226 Mystery Lake Rd.
R8N 1S6
Winnipeg   594,551
Ma—William Norrie

Cl—Mr. R.B. Hayes
510 Main St., R3B 1B9

TOWNS

Altona   2,958
Ma—Art K. Dyck
S/T—Jake Sawatzky
Box 1630, R0G 0B0
Beauséjour   2,547
Ma—Donald Mazur
S/T—Henry P. Colmer
Box 1028, R0E 0C0
Boissevain   1,572
Ma—Jack D. Houston
S/T—Gerald May
Box 490, R0K 0E0
Carberry   1,544
Ma—Art Sear
S/T—Mr. E.J.W. McCallum
Box 130, R0K 0H0
Carman   2,500
Ma—Robert S. McKenzie
S/T—Bruce Lyle
Box 160, R0G 0J0
Dauphin   8,875
Ma—Martin Bidzinski
S/T—Alex Dmitruk
21-2nd Ave. N.W., R7N 1H1
Deloraine   1,134
Ma—Lloyd Bolduc
S/T—Mr. R.H. Amey
102 S. Broadway St.
R0M 0M0
Gimli   1,681
Ma—Ted K. Arnason
S/T—Mrs. Doris Lloyd
Box 88, R0C 1B0
Killarney   2,318
Ma—Roy A. Pugh
S/T—Dennis Higginson
Box 10, R0K 1G0

Leaf Rapids   1,950
Ma—Calvin H. Boyd
Mg—Mr. M.P. Riddell
Box 340, R0B 1W0
Melita   1,239
Ma—Ken D. Carels
S/T—Clifford E. Hicks
Box 364, R0M 1L0
Minnedosa   2,520
Ma—Beth Gordon
S/T—Mr. J.K. Wishart
Box 426, R0J 1E0
Morden   5,004
Ma—A.R. (Max) Friesen
S/T—Abe Bergmann
Box 2440, R0G 1J0
Morris   1,613
Ma—Dale Hoffman
S/T—Robert Eslinger
Box 28, R0G 1K0
Neepawa   3,314
Ma—Homer Gill
S/T—Vacant
Box 339, R0J 1H0
Rivers   1,157
Ma—Leroy Stevenson
S/T—Mrs. Jeanne Kozak
Box 520, R0K 1X0
Roblin   1,913
Ma—Lawrence Boguski
S/T—Douglas Frost-Hunt
Box 730, R0L 1P0
Russell   1,669
Ma—William Russell
S/T—Mr. G.W. Brad
Box 10, R0J 1W0
Selkirk   10,013
Ma—Bud Oliver
S/T—Mr. K.R. Conrad
200 Eaton Ave., R1A 0W6
Snow Lake   1,837
Ma—W.J. (Jack) Forsyth
S/T—E.C. (Chuck) Dunning
Box 40, R0B 1M0
Souris   1,751
Ma—Clare Somersall
S/T—Lionel E. Dane
Box 518, R0K 2C0
Steinbach   7,473
Ma—Ernie A. Friesen
S/T—Jack Kehler
Box 1090, R0A 2A0
Stonewall   2,349
Ma—David Lethbridge
S/T—Jerome Mauws
Box 250, R0C 2Z0
Swan River   3,946
Ma—Fred Sigurdson
S/T—Harry Showdra
Box 879, R0L 1Z0
The Pas   6,283
Ma—Bruce Unfried
S/T—A. (Tony) Moule
Box 870, R9A 1K8

Virden   3,054
Ma—Richard J. Plaiser
S/T—Donald Reid
Box 310, R0M 2C0
Winkler   5,926
Ma—Henry F. Wiebe
S/T—Harold Fast
Box 1055, R0G 2X0

VILLAGES

Arborg   1,018
Ma—Bert Kindzierski
S/T—Jack Douglas
Box 159, R0C 0A0
Lac du Bonnet   1,021
Ma—Glen E. Hirst
S/T—Edmond Beaudette
Box 339, R0E 1A0
Niverville   1,452
Ma—Gilbert L. Wiebe
S/T—G. Jim Buys
Box 267, R0A 1E0
Ste. Anne   1,402
Ma—Paul Blanchette
S/T—J. Guy Levesque
Box 220, R0A 1R0
Ste. Rose du Lac   1,036
Ma—Rene L. Maillard
S/T—Marlene M. Bouchard
Box 445, R0L 1S0

RURAL MUNICIPALITIES

Argyle   1,452
R—John E. Thomas
S/T—Mrs. Anna Nordman
Box 40, Baldur, R0K 0B0
Bifrost   2,728
R—David Gislason
S/T—L. Grant Thorsteinson
Box 70, Arborg, R0C 0A0
Birtle   1,015
R—Jack F. Stewart
S/T—Frank R. Stevenson
Box 70, R0M 0C0
Brokenhead   3,163
R—William Kozyra
S/T—Wayne Omichinski
Box 490
Beauséjour, R0E 0C0
Cartier   2,924
R—Earl V. Fossay
S/T—Mr. A.C. Carrière
Box 117, Elie, R0H 0H0
Coldwell   1,475
R—Marvin Desjarlais
S/T—Mrs. Winnie Johnson
Box 90, Lundar, R0C 1Y0
Cornwallis   4,243
R—Mr. P.W. Evans
S/T—Daryl Check
Box 338, Brandon, R7A 5Z2

Dauphin   2,854
R—Mr. R.D. Secord
S/T—Duncan MacLure
Box 574, R7N 2V4

De Salaberry   2,851
R—Fernand Berard
S/T—Ron Musick
Box 40
St. Pierre Jolys, R0A 1V0

Dufferin   2,622
R—William K. Roth
S/T—Mrs. Linda Colpitts
Box 100, Carman, R0G 0J0

East St. Paul   4,385
R—Donald J. Melynk
S/T—Maynard Olson
3021 Birds Hill Rd.
Birds Hill, R0E 0H0

Elton   1,363
R—Dennis H. Heeney
S/T—Kathleen E.I. Dobbyn
Forrest, R0K 0W0

Eriksdale   1,045
R—Gordon K. Smith
S/T—H.K. Rutherford
Box 10, R0C 0W0

Franklin   1,835
R—Archie J. Hunter
S/T—Anthony Hudyma
Dominion City, R0A 0H0

Gilbert Plains   1,270
R—Morris Mazurkewich
S/T—Mrs. Joan Priest
Box 220, R0L 0X0

Gimli   2,458
R—Raymond Sigurdson
S/T—Chris C. Fulsher
Box 1246, R0C 1B0

Grandview   1,202
R—Mr. G.A. Winfield
S/T—Mrs. Joan Scott
Box 340, R0L 0Y0

Grey   2,195
R—Marcel Painchaud
S/T—Ronald Hayward
34 N. Main St.
Elm Creek, R0G 0N0

Hanover   8,003
R—Aron C.S. Friesen
S/T—Charles Teetaert
Box 1720
Steinbach, R0A 2A0

Harrison   1,027
R—Ernest Malchuk
S/T—Mrs. Shelley Glenn
Box 220, Newdale, R0J 1J0

La Broquerie   1,774
R—John M. Gresbrecht
S/T—Laurent Tétrault
Box 130, R0A 0W0

Lac du Bonnet   2,189
R—C.L. (Leo) Drabyk
S/T—Bev Niesteter
Box 100, R0E 1A0

Lansdowne   1,071
R—Valdine H. Smith
S/T—Walter W. Boughton
Box 141, Arden, R0J 0B0

Lorne   2,316
R—Lorne Sierens
S/T—Mrs. Margaret Lussier
Somerset, R0G 2L0

Louise   1,261
R—Roy M. McLaren

S/T—Robert Potter
Box 310
Crystal City, R0K 0N0

Macdonald   3,583
R—Victor Baleja
S/T—Lorne Erb
Box 100, Sanford, R0G 2J0

Miniota   1,123
R—Mr. J.N. Hanlin
S/T—Mrs. S.D. Richardson
Box 70, R0M 1M0

Minitonas   1,298
R—Sam Kublick
S/T—Brent Fowler
Box 9, R0L 1G0

Montcalm   1,706
R—Albert St. Hilaire
S/T—Yves Sabourin
Box 300, Letellier, R0G 1C0

Morris   2,937
R—Dan Thiessen
S/T—Grant MacAulay
Box 518, R0G 1K0

North Cypress   2,201
R—C. Hunter Witherspoon
S/T—E.J.W. McCallum
Box 130, Carberry, R0K 0H0

North Norfolk   3,090
R—James A. Duncan
S/T—Richard Locke
Box 190, MacGregor
R0H 0R0

Oakland   1,039
R—David B. Inkster
S/T—Doug Boake
Box 28, Nesbitt, R0K 1P0

Ochre River   1,032
R—Bernard Kardoes
S/T—Mrs. Ilene Mayne
Box 40, R0L 1K0

Pembina   2,124
R—Dave Harms
S/T—Richard J. Moore
Box 189, Manitou, R0G 1G0

Pipestone   1,987
R—Mr. J.R. Guthrie
S/T—Wm. M. Busby
Box 99, Reston, R0M 1X0

Portage la Prairie   7,233
R—James A. Knight
S/T—Harold Lamb
35 S. Tupper St., R1N 1W7

Rhineland   4,321
R—Jacob H. Schroeder
Cl—Jake Bergen
Box 270, Altona, R0G 0B0

Ritchot   4,588
R—John S. Wallace
S/T—Joseph Brodeur
352 Main St.
St. Adolphe, R0A 1S0

Roblin   1,011
R—Brian Gibson
S/T—Colleen Mullin
Box 9, Cartwright, R0K 0L0

Rockwood   6,923
R—Leon Vandekerckhove
S/T—Mrs. Janis Gluchi
Box 902, Stonewall, R0C 2Z0

Roland   1,014
R—John A. Bartley
S/T—Mrs. Dianne R. Toews
Box 119, R0G 1T0

Rosedale   1,791
R—Arnold M. Birch
S/T—Harold McConnell
Box 100, Neepawa, R0J 1H0

Rosser   1,300
R—Alan Beachell
S/T—Mrs. Betty Lindsay
R0H 1E0

St. Andrews   8,755
R—Peter Ducheck
S/T—Mr. R. Leslie Price
Clandeboye, R0C 0P0

Ste. Anne   3,369
R—Francis H. Benoit
S/T—Mrs. Alice De Bates
Box 40, R0A 1R0

St. Clements   6,922
R—Ronald Wm. Fewchuk
S/T—Adam C. Kulikowski
Box 2, East Selkirk, R0E 0M0

St. Laurent   1,119
R—Henri L'Heureux
S/T—Mrs. Lisa Wurm
R0C 2S0

Ste. Rose   1,127
R—Andre Saquet
S/T—Mrs. Michelle Denys
Box 30, R0L 1S0

Shell River   1,222
R—Albert Nabe
S/T—Charles Filewich
Box 998, Roblin, R0L 1P0

Siglunes   1,540
R—Lorne Park
S/T—Mel Bullerwell
Box 370, Ashern, R0C 0E0

South Norfolk   1,197
R—Robert F. Culbert
S/T—James Archer
Box 30, Treherne R0G 2V0

Springfield   9,836
R—John Nicol
S/T—Eric Towler
628 Main St.
Oakbank, R0E 1J0

Stanley   4,623
R—Melvin Hoeppner
S/T—Monty Foussard
Box 1327
Morden, R0G 1J0

Strathclair   1,216
R—Arnold Pirie
S/T—Jo-Ann McKerchar
Box 160, R0J 2C0

Swan River   3,227
R—William P. Galloway
S/T—Winnifred E. Pico
Box 610, R0L 1Z0

Taché   6,679
R—Marcel Roch
S/T—Emile J. Laurin
Box 100, Lorette, R0A 0Y0

Thompson   1,293
R—Donald J. Alexander
S/T—Mrs. Linda Bayliss
Box 190, Miami, R0G 1H0

Turtle Mountain   1,285
R—Ivan Lawson
S/T—Dennis Higginson
Box 160, Killarney, R0K 1G0

Victoria   1,453
R—Edward L. Budz
S/T—Yvon P.L. Bruneau
Box 40, Holland, R0G 0X0

Wallace	2,070

Wallace 2,070
R—Keith Kinnaird
S/T—Don Stephenson
Box 2200
Virden, R0M 2C0

West St. Paul 3,138
R—Mrs. Linda McDonald
S/T—Melvin E. Didyk
3550 Main St., R.R. 1B
Winnipeg, R3C 4A3

Westbourne 2,006
R—Mr. H.R. Bjarnarson
S/T—Mrs. Patricia Pugh
Box 150, Gladstone, R0J 0T0

Whitehead 1,440
R—Clarence K. Williamson
S/T—W.J. (Jim) Dane
Box 107, Alexander, R0K 0A0

Whitemouth 1,820
R—Donald J. Steiner
S/T—Edna Kozyra
Box 248, R0E 2G0

Woodlands 3,188
R—Edward Peltz
S/T—Mrs. Irene Johnson
R0C 3H0

Woodworth 1,154
R—Robert B. Hunter
S/T—Elgin R. Routledge
Kenton, R0M 0Z0

SUMMARY OF 1988 TOTALS

5 Cities	668,401
35 Towns	93,524
Total Urban (1986 Census)	766,851
105 Rural Municipalities	205,971
Total Rural (1986 Census)	296,165
Total Urban and Rural (excl. Indians on Reserves)	1,063,016

LOCAL GOVERNMENT DISTRICTS

Alexander 2,163
R—Richard Lowing
RA—Roger A. Bouvier
Box 40
St. Georges, R0E 1V0

Alonsa 2,330
R—Bjarni Sigurdson
RA—William Hildebrand
Box 127, R0H 0A0

Armstrong 2,039
R—Peter Masniuk
RA—Don Rybachuk
Box 69, Inwood, R0C 1P0

Churchill 1,217
Ma—Mark A. Ingebrigtson
RA—Conrad Nicholson
Box 459, Churchill, R0B 0E0

Consol 3,107
R—William Kaplanchuk
RA—Mrs. Leona Hrabarchuk
Box 578, The Pas, R9A 1K6

Fisher 2,256
R—Bert J. Vandersteen
RA—Mrs. Linda Podaima
Box 280
Fisher Branch, R0C 0Z0

Gillam 1,909
Ma—Wayne Wittmeir
RA—Hilda Green
Box 100, R0B 0L0

Grahamdale 2,207
R—Colin Brown
RA—Ardene Franz
Box 160
Moosehorn, R0C 2E0

Lynn Lake 1,665
Ma—Stan W. Geddes
RA—Abe H. Enns
Box 100, R0B 0W0

Mountain 2,345
R—Peter L. Reimer
RA—Norman Bruce
Box 389
Swan River, R0L 1Z0

Park 1,395
R—Russell Novalkowski
RA—Sylvester Yakielashek
Box 190, Onanole, R0J 1N0

Pinawa 2,078
Ma—Marvin Ryz
RA—Gary Hanna
Box 100, R0E 1L0

Piney 1,781
R—William Tkachuk
RA—Reynald Preteau
Box 48, Vassar, R0A 2J0

Reynolds 1,175
R—Elden R. Loeppky
RA—Richard Andries
Hadashville, R0E 0X0

Stuartburn 1,629
R—Ed Dolynchuk
RA—Mrs. Judy Reimer
Box 59, Vita, R0A 2K0

INDIANS

Living on reserves:
population 35,919
(June 1/86)

NEW BRUNSWICK

Municipal Government

The Province of New Brunswick comprises 117 incorporated municipalities, being:

	Population
6 Cities	211,824
27 Towns	120,323
84 Villages	99,089
TOTAL	431,236

In addition, there are 350 unincorporated local service districts with a population of approximately 280,000. Particular services are under the direct jurisdiction of the Department of Municipal Affairs and Environment, which in each case acts in consultation with the district's elected advisory committee.

Municipal organization in the province is subject to the *Municipalities Act*, which permits the establishment of the four types of organiza-tions noted above. For incorporation as a city, an area must have a concentrated population of at least 10,000. For a town, the minimum population must be 1,500. There is no minimum population requirement for a village; incorporation, however, is dependent on the results of a feasibility study and the recommendation of the Minister.

Municipal councils consist of a mayor and a number of councillors which is determined through by-law (no fewer than two councillors in the case of a village). Municipalities may be divided into wards, on which basis councillors are elected. Electoral terms are three years in length.

The New Brunswick approach to real property assessment and taxation is unique (although Prince Edward Island's system is similar). Assessment is the responsibility of the province, the base being true market value. The provincial government levies a provincial tax of $1.50 per $100 valuation on properties classified as residential, and a provincial rate of $2.25 per $100 valuation on properties classified as non-residential. It also determines the rate of tax applicable to particular areas in respect of any supplementary school program. The basic elementary and secondary school program is financed from the province's general revenues. Municipal councils determine the rate of tax required for their purposes, and although they have the option to collect this tax, in practice, collection of all real property taxes is vested in the province.

Municipalities

(Generally, only municipalities with more than 1,000 population are included. Population figures given have been updated by the Department of Municipal Affairs and Environment.)

A: Administrator   Cl: Clerk   Ma: Mayor   Mg: Manager   T: Treasurer

CITIES

Bathurst 14,683
Ma—Douglas Williamson
Cl—Louise Wafer
P.O. Drawer D, E2A 3Z1
Campbellton 9,073
Ma—Bruce MacIntosh
Cl—Jacques Jobin
Box 100, E3N 3G1
Edmundston 11,497
Ma—J. Pius Bard
A—Eloi Duguay
7 Canada Rd., E3V 1T7
Fredericton 44,722
Ma—Brad Woodside
Cl—Donna Lavigne
Box 130, E3B 4Y7
Moncton 55,468
Ma—Léopold Belliveau
T—H. Thomas Eno
774 Main St., E1C 1E8
Saint John 76,381
Ma—Elsie Wayne
Cl—Mary Munford
Box 1971, Market Square
E2L 4L1

TOWNS

Beresford 3,851
Ma—Réal Boudreau
A/Cl—Norval Godin
C.P. 600, E0B 1H0
Buctouche 2,420
Ma—André Goguen
Cl—Thérèse Langis
C.P. 370, E0A 1G0
Caraquet 4,493
Ma—Germain Blanchard
Cl—Mme G. LeBlanc
C.P. 420, E0B 1K0
Chatham 6,219
Ma—Rupert Bernard
Cl—James F. Lamkey
Box 309, E1N 3A7
Dalhousie 5,363
Ma—Sandy MacLean
A/Cl—Michael Allain
Box 250, E0K 1B0
Dieppe 9,084
Ma—William Malenfant
Cl—Rolande Gallant
333 Acadia Ave., E1A 1G9
Grand Bay 3,319
Ma—Edward Kelly
Cl—Mrs. Sandra M. Gautreau
Box 180, E0G 1W0

Grand Falls 6,209
Ma—Ronald Ouellette
A/Cl—Joseph Côté
Box 800, E0J 1M0
Lamèque 1,806
Ma—Jean-Charles Chiasson
A/Cl—Henri-Paul Guignard
C.P. 58, E0B 1V0
Nackawic 1,288
Ma—Steven Paul Hawkes
Mg/Cl—Mr. Leslie Kelly
Box 638, E0H 1P0
Newcastle 5,804
Ma—Peter B. Murphy
T/Cl—W.R. Dickison
Box 332, E1V 3M4
Oromocto 9,794
Ma—W.R. (Bill) Duffie
T/Cl—D.B. Wall
137 MacDonald Ave.
E2V 1A6
Quispamsis 7,185
Ma—Emil T. Olsen
Cl—Catherine Snow
Box 459, E0G 2W0
Richibucto 1,609
Ma—Paul-Emile LeBlanc
T/Cl—Ray J. Belliveau
C.P. 337, E0A 2M0
Riverview 15,638
Ma—Wm. David Richardson
Cl—Denis Caron
30 Honour House Ct.
E1B 3Y9
Rothesay 1,605
Ma—Donald O. Horne
T/Cl—L. Marjorie Seely
Box 10, E0G 2W0
Sackville 5,470
Ma—William R. Campbell
A/Cl—Allan G. Mitchell
Box 660, E0A 3C0
St. Andrews 1,612
Ma—Mr. Beverly Lawrence
Mg—A. Keith Robicheau
Box 160, E0G 2X0
St. George 1,305
Ma—Vance Craig
Mg—Ross Norman
Box 148, E0G 2Y0
St. Leonard 1,512
Ma—Roland Dubé
Cl—Paulette Laviolette
Box 390, E0L 1M0
St. Stephen 5,032
Ma—Mrs. A. (Billy) MacCready
Cl—Mrs. Ruth Walker
34 Milltown Blvd., E3L 1G3

Shediac 4,370
Ma—Michel C. Léger
Mg/Cl—Armand Bannister
C.P. 969, E0A 3G0
Shippagan 2,801
Ma—Jean-Camille DeGrâce
Cl—Eloi Haché
C.P. 280, E0B 2P0
Sussex 4,114
Ma—J. Bennett Macaulay
Cl—Paul Maguire
Box 1057, E0E 1P0
Tracadie 2,444
Ma—Raymond A. Losier
Cl—J. Ken Ferguson
C.P. 720, E0C 2B0
Woodstock 4,549
Ma—Harold W. Culbert
Cl—Ken Harding
Box 1059, E0J 2B0

VILLAGES

Atholville 1,501
Ma—J. Raymond Lagacé
Cl—Mme Jeannette Gould
C.P. 10, E0K 1A0
Balmoral 1,969
Ma—Hébert D. Arseneault
Cl—Mme Hélène Cyr
C.P. 60, E0B 1C0
Bas-Caraquet 1,913
Ma—Théophane Noël
A—Richard Frigault
C.P. 60, E0B 1E0
Bertrand 1,279
Ma—Onil Thériault
A—M.J. Léonel Thériault
C.P. 119, E0B 1J0
Blacks Harbour 1,224
Ma—Kenneth W. Hooper
Cl—Deanna Hunter
Box 90, E0G 1H0
Cap-Pelé 2,261
Ma—Léon Richard
Cl—André Sonier
C.P. 159, E0A 1J0
Charlo 1,602
M—Jacques J. Allard
Cl—Adolphe Goulette
Box 62, E0B 1M0
Chipman 1,760
Ma—William W. Davidson
Cl—Brenda Barton
Box 149, E0E 1C0
Doaktown 999
Ma—Benson Parker

Cl—Marilyn Price
Box 97, E0C 1G0
Dorchester   1,198
Ma—E. Ross Monk
Cl—Shirley Trenholm
Box 80, E0A 1M0
Douglastown   1,133
Ma—Ronald S. Kierstead
Cl—Mrs. Ann Rousselle
Box 250, E0C 1H0
East Riverside-Kingshurst 1,031
Ma—John Brittain
Cl—Joan Fitzgerald
2055 Rothesay Rd.
Renforth, E2H 2K2
Eel River Crossing   1,479
Ma—Elie Allard
Cl—Lise B. Cayouette
Box 159, E0B 1P0
Fairvale   4,660
Ma—Jordan W. Miller
Cl—Mrs. Sandra Shields
Box 538, E0G 2W0
Gondola Point   3,596
Ma—James F. Watt
Cl—Wanda Ball
Box 579, E0G 2W0
Hampton   3,405
Ma—William F. Bell
Cl—Stephanie Whalen
Box 118, E0G 1Z0
Hillsborough   1,214
Ma—Eric K. Steeves
Cl—Danny Jonah
Box 100, E0A 1X0
Jacquet River   954
Ma—Francis C. Firlotte
Cl—Donald C. McAlister
Box 99, E0B 1T0
Kedgwick   1,129
Ma—Gilles Girard
Cl—Joanne Normand
E0K 1C0
LeGoulet   1,136
Ma—Bail Roussel
T/Cl—Berthe Savoie
C.P. 300, E0B 1W0
McAdam   1,658
Ma—Ralph H. Annis
Cl—Ann Donahue
Box 299, E0H 1K0

Minto   3,197
Ma—Andrea A. Barnett
Cl—Mrs. Rose Collette
Box 7, E0E 1J0
Néguac   1,754
Ma—Emilien LeBreton
Cl—George R. Savoie
C.P. 106, E0C 1S0
Nelson-Miramichi   1,407
Ma—Vincent McCarthy
Cl—Cathy Goguen
P.O. Drawer 40, E0C 1T0
Nigadoo   974
Ma—Donald McGinn
Cl—M. Serge Boudreau
C.P. 190, E0B 2A0
Norton   1,442
Ma—Juliana Booth
Cl—Mrs. Susan E. Keirstead
Box 240, E0G 2N0
Perth-Andover   1,889
Ma—Burpee Wagner
A/Cl—Murray Watters
Box 219, E0J 1V0
Petit-Rocher   1,924
Ma—Gérald Mallais
Cl—Guy Clavett
C.P. 270, E0B 2E0
Petitcodiac   1,355
Ma—Curtis T. Rogers
Cl—Pam Cochrane
E0A 2H0
Plaster Rock   1,232
Ma—Laura R. Reynolds
Cl—Barbara Wishart
Box 129, E0J 1W0
Pointe-Verte   1,257
Ma—Jean B. Roy
Cl—Donald Hammond
C.P. 89, E0B 2H0
Renforth   1,452
Ma—Malcolm Barry
Cl—Miss J. Fitzgerald
2055 Rothesay Rd.
Saint John, E2H 2K2
Rivière Verte   978
Ma—Will Beaulieu
Cl—Mme Evelyn Therrien
C.P. 100, E0L 1E0
Rogersville   1,273
Ma—Roger L. Richard

Cl—Gérald Fournier
C.P. 70, E0A 2T0
St-Antoine   1,328
Ma—Jean-Claude Cormier
Cl—M. Léger
C.P. 180, E0A 2X0
St-Basile   3,306
Ma—Albert W. Martin
Cl—Doreen Banville
C.P. 261, E0L 1H0
St-Jacques   2,310
Ma—Isidore Boucher
Cl—Pauline Grondin
C.P. 150, E0L 1K0
St-Louis-de-Kent   1,101
Ma—Louis J. Arsenault
Cl—Kenneth Johnson
C.P. 220, E0A 2Z0
St-Quentin   2,264
Ma—Félix J. Dubé
Cl—Roger Cyr
Box 489, E0K 1J0
Ste-Anne-de-Madawaska 1,294
Ma—Gérald R. Martin
Cl—Joyce Roy
C.P. 99, E0L 1G0
Ste-Marie/St-Raphael   1,259
Ma—Maurice Paulin
Cl—Norma Aubut
C.P. 91, St-Raphaël-
sur-Mer, E0B 2N0
Salisbury   1,742
Ma—Ronald E. Tait
Cl—Mrs. Carol Wortman
Box 270, E0A 3E0
Sheila   1,265
Ma—Allan D. Sonier
Cl—Cécile Rousselle
C.P. 429, E0C 1Z0
Sussex Corner   1,295
Ma—William B. Stewart
Cl—Mrs. Ruth Lambe
E0E 1R0
Tide Head   1,085
Ma—Marcus Dickson
(Deputy Mayor)
Cl—Christine Babcock
Box 60, E0K 1K0
Westfield   1,113
Ma—R. Kevin Thorne
Cl—Susan Chase
R.R. 2, E0G 3J0

NEWFOUNDLAND

Municipal Organization

Origin and Growth. In comparison with Canada as a whole, local government in Newfoundland had a relatively late start; it began in 1888 with the incorporation of the Town of St. John's. Although St. John's was granted a city charter in 1921, there were no additional municipal incorporations until the Town of Windsor was established in 1938. At the time of Confederation, there were only nineteen municipalities in the province.

The *Local Government Act* of 1949 was the first successful municipal Act of general application. It set the pattern for a series of succeeding local government Acts culminating in a new *Municipalities Act*, which arose out of the recommendations of the Whalen Royal Commission on Municipal Government. This latter Act, which was proclaimed on April 1, 1980, provides for a complete consolidation and revision of municipal legislation, including provisions for regional government and for greater local autonomy. Also proclaimed on April 1, 1980 was a *Municipal Grants Act* providing for a new system of provincial operating grants to municipalities. The *Municipalities Act* and the *Municipal Grants Act* are designed to meet the legislative and fiscal needs of municipalities for the foreseeable future.

Structure. There are presently 314 municipal organizations in the province, consisting of the cities of St. John's and Corner Brook, which were incorporated under separate Acts, and towns and communities incorporated under the provisions of the *Municipalities Act*. There is also one metropolitan area created by special act. It provides municipal supervision and services on the outskirts of the City of St. John's. The number of municipalities in the various categories are:

    3 Cities
  169 Towns (1 inactive)
  141 Communities (4 inactive)
    1 Metropolitan Area
  146 Local Service Districts

With the enactment of the *Municipalities Act*, revised procedures were prescribed for the establishment of new towns, the amalgamation and annexation of existing towns, the alteration of town boundaries, and the creation of regional governments. Any request for action in any of these areas must now be preceded by a feasibility report prepared by a Commissioner appointed by the Minister of Municipal Affairs. The Lieutenant-Governor in Council, upon the recommendations of the Minister, is empowered to take any action arising out of the recommendations contained in the feasibility report.

The *Municipalities Act* also provides for a reduction in the number of types of municipal organizations. The three cities, which operate under special Acts, have a number of distinct powers, but all other forms of municipal organizations have basically the same duties and responsibilities, including identical powers of taxation. Towns and community councils may now impose only a real property tax, a business tax, water and sewer taxes, and a poll tax. In addition, service levies and local improvement assessments may be imposed to recover the cost of municipal capital works. Municipalities incorporated under the *Municipalities Act* are also authorized to provide such services as road construction and maintenance, water and sewer, garbage disposal, fire protection, parks and recreation, and may exercise control over such matters as buildings, sanitation, shop closing, and animals at large. The *Municipalities Act* also contains a provision for the establishment of regional governments. No regional government has yet been established in the province.

Elections and Appointments. Towns may have appointed or elected councils. Elected councils serve for a term of four years and are scheduled to be elected on the same day. The day set for the general municipal elections is the second Tuesday in November. By-elections are held in the interim, as are elections of councillors for new municipalities.

Elections are conducted under the *Municipalities Act,* which contains new provisions permitting voting by proxy and the holding of advance polls. The *City of St. John's Act* provides for the election of a mayor and eight councillors, with the mayor elected by a separate ballot. A similar provision is contained in the *City of Corner Brook Act* for the election of a mayor and six councillors. Town councils may consist of not fewer than five and not more than ten persons; most councils have seven members. Community councils, which consist of five persons, have the same powers as town councils except in the matter of election procedures. Councils are elected by secret ballot at annual meetings of the community held between Jan. 1 and March 31 of each year, provided that the council has been two years in office. The *Municipalities Act* also grants community councils the right to conduct elections in the same manner as town councils, with certain limitations.

Local Service Districts. In addition to providing for the establishment and operation of municipalities, the *Municipalities Act* also provides for the creation of quasi-municipal bodies known as local service districts. These bodies, which operate in accordance with ministerial regulations, are intended to provide limited services in areas not ordinarily considered viable for the establishment of municipal entities. While local service districts now function as independent bodies, it is intended that they will come under the jurisdiction of regional governments when such governments are established in Newfoundland.

Municipalities

(Generally, municipalities are not listed unless they have a population of at least 1,000. Population figures are from the 1986 Census.)

Cl: Clerk   Ma: Mayor   Mg: Manager

CITIES

Corner Brook   22,719
  Ma—Raymond A. Pollott
  Cl—K. Furlong
  Mg—C. Keeping
  City Hall, A2H 6E1
Mount Pearl   20,293
  Ma—Harvey Hodder

Mg—Brian A. McArthur
Box 130, A1N 2C2
St. John's   96,216
  Ma—John L. Murphy
  Cl—R. Greene
  Mg—F. Power
  City Hall, A1C 5M2

METROPOLITAN AREA

**St. John's Metropolitan
Area**   6,254
  Chairman—John R. O'Dea
  Cl—N.D. Caines
  Mg—Vacant
  Box 8897, Stn. A
  St. John's, A1B 3T2

TOWNS

Arnold's Cove   1,117
Cl—W. Slade
Box 70, A0B 1A0

Badger   1,151
Cl—P. Hurley
Box 130, A0H 1A0

**Badger's Quay-Valleyfield-
Pool's Island**   1,589
Cl/Mg—D. Hounsell
Box 64, A0G 1B0

Baie Verte   2,049
Cl—R. Burton
Mg—N.R. Genge
Box 218, A0K 1B0

Bay Bulls   1,114
Cl—A. Mulcahy
Box 70, A0A 1C0

Bay Roberts   4,446
Cl—D. Earle
Mg—E. Fradsham
Box 114, A0A 1G0

Bishop's Falls   4,213
Cl—J.M. Budgell
Mg—R. Hancock
Box 310, A0H 1C0

Bonavista   4,605
Cl—D. Hiscock
Mg—C. Rolls
Box 279, A0C 1B0

Botwood   3,916
Cl—A. Rowsell
Mg—R.C. LeDrew
Box 490, A0H 1E0

Buchans   1,281
Cl—M. Hamilton
Box 190, A0H 1G0

Burgeo   2,582
Cl—S. Cossar
Mg—D.G. Kendell
Box 220, A0M 1A0

Burin   2,892
Cl—H. Fizzard
Box 370, A0E 1E0

Burnt Islands   1,042
Cl—E. Keeping
Box 39, A0M 1B0

Carbonear   5,337
Cl/Mg—J. Walsh
Box 999, A0A 1T0

Carmanville   987
Cl—M. Sheppard
Box 239, A0G 1N0

Catalina   1,211
Cl—D. Freake
Box 2, A0C 1J0

Channel-Port aux Basques 5,901
Cl—M. Kettle
Mg—R. Mauger
Box 70, A0M 1C0

Clarenville   2,967
Cl—E. Blackmore
Mg—A.E. Adams
Box 66, A0E 1J0

Clarke's Beach   1,189
Cl—J. Wilcox
Box 159, A0A 1W0

Conception Bay South   15,531
Ma—Fred R. Coates
Cl—M.A. Harvey
Mg—E. Snow
Box 280, A0A 2Y0

Deer Lake   4,233
Cl—M. Hayden
Mg—W. Dominie
Box 940, A0K 2E0

Dunville   1,833
Cl—W.T. Woodman
Box 190, A0B 1S0

Durrell   1,060
Cl/Mg—D. Burton
A0G 1Y0

Englee   1,012
Cl—E.M. Randell
Box 69, A0K 2J0

Fogo   1,153
Cl—B. Pomeroy
Box 57, A0G 2B0

Fortune   2,370
Cl—C. Piercey
Mg—J. Thornhill
Box 159, A0E 1P0

Freshwater (Placentia Bay) 1,219
Cl—F. Smith
Box 190, A0B 1W0

Gambo   2,723
Cl—E. Barkhouse
Box 250, A0G 1T0

Gander   10,207
Ma—Douglas B. Sheppard
Cl—G. Lewis
Mg—L. Holloway
Box 280, A1V 1W6

Glenwood   1,038
Cl—R. Brown
Box 130, A0G 2K0

Glovertown   2,184
Cl—E. Briffett
Mg—L.D. Sparkes
Box 224, A0G 2L0

Goulds   4,688
Cl—J. Pike
Box 130, A0A 2K0

Grand Bank   3,732
Cl—C. Brooks
Mg—G. King
Box 640, A0E 1W0

Grand Falls   9,121
Ma—Paul Hennessey
Cl—D. Shapleigh
Box 439, A2A 2J8

**Halfway Point-Benoit's
Cove-John's Beach-
Frenchman's Cove**   2,182
Cl—M. Evoy
A0L 1A0

Happy Valley-Goose Bay   7,248
Ma—Henry F. Shouse
Cl—V. Sheppard
Mg—A.J.F. Durno
Box 40, Stn. B, A0P 1E0

Harbour Breton   2,432
Cl—B. Strickland
Mg—A. Godwin
Box 130, A0H 1P0

Harbour Grace   3,053
Cl/Mg—L. Forward
Box 399, A0A 2M0

**Harbour Main-Chapel Cove-
Lakeview**   1,293
Cl—A. Dalton
Box 40, A0A 2P0

Hare Bay   1,436
Cl/Mg—G.R. Collins
Box 130, A0G 2P0

Holyrood   2,118
Cl—E. Devereaux
Box 100, A0A 2R0

Isle aux Morts   1,203
Cl—F. Barnes
Box 176, A0M 1J0

**Joe Batt's Arm-Barr'd
Islands-Shoal Bay**   1,232
Cl—P. Anthony
Box 28, A0G 2X0

Kippens   1,556
Cl—N. Childs
2 Juniper Ave., A2N 3H8

La Scie   1,429
Cl—V. Short
Box 130, A0K 3M0

Labrador City   8,664
Ma—Alex Snow
Cl—G. Marche
Mg—C. Vincent
Box 280, A2V 2K5

Lawn   1,015
Cl—R.M. Bennett
Mg—D.J. Drake
Box 29, A0E 2A0

Lewisporte   3,978
Cl—H. Combden
Mg—R. Moyles
Box 219, A0G 3A0

**Logy Bay-Middle Cove-
Outer Cove**   1,163
Cl—B. Power
Site 81, Box 75, S.S. 3
St. John's, A1C 5H4

Marystown   6,660
Cl—D. Kelly
Mg—J. Mayo
Box 1118, A0E 2M0

**Milltown-Head of Bay
d'Espoir**   1,276
Cl—A. Strickland
Mg—C. Brushett
Box 70, A0H 1W0

Musgrave Harbour   1,527
Cl—E. Rumbolt
Box 159, A0G 3J0

Nain   1,018
Cl—N. Maggo
Mg—V. Williams
Box 59, A0P 1L0

**Norman's Cove-
Long Cove**   1,107
Cl—S. Smith
Box 70, A0B 2T0

Norris Arm   1,127
Cl—B. Peyton
Mg—B. Saunders
Box 70, A0G 3M0

Paradise   3,346
Cl/Mg—P.J. Martin
Box 100, A0A 2E0

Pasadena   3,268
Cl—Elizabeth Fisher
Mg—Ian Fremantle
Box 149, A0L 1K0

Peterview   1,130
Cl/Mg—V. Samson
Box 10, A0H 1Y0

Petty Harbour-Maddox Cove 974
Cl—G. Walsh
Box 52, A0A 3H0

Placentia 2,016
Cl—J.M. Kelly
Box 99, A0B 2Y0

Port aux Choix 1,291
Cl/Mg—M. Kelly
Box 89, A0K 4C0

Portugal Cove 2,497
Cl—S. Critch
Box 144, A0A 3K0

Pouch Cove 1,576
Cl—A. Walsh
Box 59, A0A 3L0

Ramea 1,380
Cl/Mg—W. Cutler Jr.
Box 69, A0M 1N0

Robert's Arm 1,111
Cl—A. Payne
Box 10, A0J 1R0

Roddickton 1,223
Cl—M. Cassell
Mg—A.A. Locke
Box 10, A0K 4P0

Rose Blanche-
Harbour Le Cou 967
Cl—L. Fudge
Box 159, A0M 1P0

St. Alban's 1,780
Cl—G. Tremblett
Box 10, A0H 2E0

St. Anthony 3,182
Cl—P. Troy
Mg—J. Parsons
Box 128, A0K 4S0

St. George's 1,852
Cl—N. Chubb
Box 250, A0N 1Z0

St. Lawrence 1,841
Cl—G. Quirke
Mg—L. Slaney
Box 128, A0E 2V0

St. Phillips 1,604
Cl—L. Tucker
Box 35, Site 3, R.R. 1
Paradise, A0A 2E0

Shoal Harbour 1,049
Cl—M. Blackmore
Box 179, A0C 2L0

Spaniard's Bay 2,190
Cl—W. Smith
Box 190, A0A 3X0

Springdale 3,555
Cl—H. Tizzard
Mg—E. Taylor
Box 57, A0J 1T0

Stephenville 7,994
Ma—Kevin Walsh
Cl—E.J. White
Box 420, A2N 2Z5

Stephenville Crossing 2,252
Cl/Mg—N. Dallard
Box 68, A0N 2C0

Summerford 1,169
Cl—V. Anstey
Box 59, A0G 4E0

Torbay 3,730
Cl—M. Thorne
Mg—G. Hayes
Box 190, A0A 3Z0

Trepassey 1,460
Cl/Mg—Y. Power
Box 129, A0A 4B0

Triton 1,253
Cl—A. Fudge
Box 10, A0J 1V0

Twillingate 1,506
Cl/Mg—W.R. Hull
Box 220, A0G 4M0

Upper Island Cove 2,055
Cl/Mg—B. Drover
Box 149, A0A 4E0

Victoria 1,895
Cl—S. Snooks
Box 130, A0A 4G0

Wabana 4,057
Cl—D.C. Butler
Mg—Vacant
Box 1229, A0A 4H0

Wabush 2,637
Cl—C.A. Morris
Mg—K.E. Warren
Box 190, A0R 1B0

Wedgewood Park 1,385
Cl/Mg—J. Murphy
A1A 2M8

Wesleyville 1,208
Cl/Mg—L. Davis Jr.
Box 143, A0G 4R0

Whitbourne 1,151
Cl/Mg—W. Lynch
Box 119, A0B 3K0

Windsor 5,545
Cl—K. Antle
Mg—R. Pitcher
Box 220, A0H 2H0

Witless Bay 1,022
Cl—J. Yard
Box 147, A0A 4K0

SUMMARY OF 1988 TOTALS

3 Cities 139,228
168 Towns 294,536

Total Urban (1986 Census) 334,732
Total Rural (1986 Census) 233,617
Total Urban and Rural 568,349

NORTHWEST TERRITORIES

Municipal Government

Municipal government affairs are administered by the Department of Municipal and Community Affairs within the Government of the Northwest Territories.

The municipalities in the N.W.T. consist of one city, five towns, two villages, and 36 hamlets located in five regions — Baffin, Fort Smith, Inuvik, Keewatin, and Kitikmeot.

In addition, there are eight settlements which have elected councils. Most operate independently. All are funded by the Government of the N.W.T.

There are also 11 smaller communities and several mining settlements which do not have any form of municipal government.

Municipalities

(Population figures are based on the 1986 Census.)

A: Administrator   Ma: Mayor   SAO: Senior Administrative Officer   ST: Secretary-Treasurer

BAFFIN REGION

TOWN

Iqaluit 2,947
Ma—Yvon Blanchette
SAO—Kathryn Garven
Box 460, X0A 0H0

FORT SMITH REGION

CITY

Yellowknife 11,753
Ma—Patricia McMahon
ST—Douglas Lagore
Box 580, X1A 2N4

TOWNS

Fort Smith 2,460
Ma—Dennis Bevington
SAO—Steven Conway
Box 147, X0E 0P0

Hay River   2,964
Ma—Walter Kudelik
Postal Bag 5000, X0E 0R0

VILLAGE

Fort Simpson   987
Ma—Gerry Antoine
SAO—J. Curt Svendsen
Box 438, X0E 0N0

INUVIK REGION

TOWN

Inuvik   3,389
Ma—John Hill
SAO—Diane Cheyney
Box 1160, X0E 0T0

SUMMARY OF 1986 TOTALS

Total Urban (Census) 24,209

Total Rural (Census) 28,029

Total Urban and Rural
(excl. Indians on Reserves). 52,238

VILLAGE

Norman Wells   627
Ma—William Byrne
SAO—Roy Scott
Box 5, X0E 0V0

NOVA SCOTIA

Municipal Government

The term "municipality" in Nova Scotia has two distinct meanings. In one sense it means all local governments, as is usual elsewhere in Canada. In the other sense, it means a municipality incorporated pursuant to the *Municipal Act*, and is often referred to as a rural municipality.

All of Nova Scotia is organized into cities, towns, or rural municipalities. The province is geographically divided into 18 counties. Twelve of these counties constitute separate municipalities. The remaining six counties are each divided into two districts, and each of these districts constitutes a separate municipality. There are thus 24 rural municipalities constituted under the *Municipal Act*.

In addition to the rural municipalities, there are three cities incorporated under their respective city charters and 39 towns incorporated pursuant to the *Towns Act*. While located within the boundaries of a rural municipality, the towns and cities are politically and administratively separate from and independent of the rural municipality, except with respect to joint expenditures.

There are, as well, a number of independent or semi-independent boards and commissions, established either by provincial legislation or by municipal by-law, which provide various municipal services. Within a rural municipality, these organizations include:

1) Village commissions, incorporated under the *Village Service Act* for the purpose of providing municipal services to more densely populated areas of the rural municipality within their jurisdiction. There are currently 26 incorporated villages in Nova Scotia.
2) Local service commissions, incorporated by special Acts of the legislature, generally for purposes of providing street lighting, fire protection, electric and water supply.
3) Rural fire districts, incorporated under the *Rural Fire District Act* to provide fire protection within a designated area of a rural municipality. There are currently nine rural fire districts.

Village commissioners, local commissions, rural fire districts, and some other special purpose bodies are authorized to levy taxes in addition to those levied by the rural municipality itself. In most cases, these taxes are collected by the rural municipality. None of these special purpose bodies may be established in a town or a city.

In a number of cases, commissions and other special purpose bodies have been established in cities, towns, and rural municipalities for such purposes as operating municipal facilities, for example a hospital, parking lot, utility, cemetery or rink, for implementing municipal programs such as parks and recreation, or for operating a joint municipal facility such as a courthouse. Generally, these organizations do not have power to levy taxes, and are financed directly by the municipal unit. It is estimated that there are more than 700 such special purpose bodies in the province.

The basic element of municipal finance is the property tax, together with a number of its variants such as the occupancy tax. Also important to municipal governments are grants from the provincial and federal governments.

Further details concerning the municipalities and many of the other organizations that provide municipal services, including school boards, are contained in the Department's *Annual Report of Municipal Statistics*.

Municipalities

(Generally, only municipalities with more than 1,000 population are included. Population figures given are from the 1986 Census.)

A: Administrator   CAO: Chief Administrative Officer   Cl: Clerk-Treasurer   Ma: Mayor   Mg: Manager

CITIES

Dartmouth   65,243
Ma—Dr. John Savage
Cl—B. Smith
A—J. Burke
Box 817, B2Y 3Z3

Halifax   113,577
Ma—Ronald Wallace
Cl—E.A. Kerr
Mg—P. Calda
Box 1749, B3J 3A5

Sydney   28,115
Ma—Manning MacDonald
Cl—Paul Roach
Mg—Daniel R. MacLeod
Box 730, B1P 6H7

TOWNS

Amherst   9,671
Ma—Walter Purdy
CAO—Fred Haines
Box 516, B4H 4A1

Antigonish   5,291
Cl—Stanley MacLellan
274 Main St., B2G 2C4

Bedford   8,010
CAO—D. English
1496 Bedford Hwy.
Ste. 400, B4A 1E5

Berwick   2,085
Cl—H.E. Jones
Box 130, B0P 1E0

Bridgetown   1,118
Cl—W. Hamilton
Box 609, B0S 1C0

Bridgewater   6,617
Mg—Mike Garrah
Box 9, B4V 2W7

Canso   1,285
Cl—M. MacDougall
Box 189, B0H 1H0

Clark's Harbour   1,098
Cl—Linda Symonds
Box 160, B0W 1P0

Digby   2,525
Cl—J. Wheelhouse
Box 579, B0V 1A0

Dominion   2,754
Cl—Cecelia MacIntyre
128 Commercial St.
B0A 1E0

Glace Bay   20,467
Ma—Donald MacInnis
Cl—Al McDermid
McKeen St., B1A 5B9

Hantsport   1,357
Cl—J.D. McGinn
Box 399, B0P 1P0

Kentville   5,208
Cl—D.P. Hardy
Box 218, B4N 3W4

Liverpool   3,295
Cl—Shirley Nixon
Box 550, B0T 1K0

Louisbourg   1,355
Cl—E. MacPherson
Box 88, B0A 1M0

Lunenburg   2,972
Cl—James Wentzell
Box 129, B0J 2C0

Mahone Bay   1,093
Cl—Kyle Hiltz
Box 239, B0J 2E0

Middleton   1,772
Cl—E.L. Bennett
Box 340, B0S 1P0

Mulgrave   1,051
CAO—David Smith
Box 129, B0E 2G0

New Glasgow   10,022
Ma—Jack MacLean
Cl—J. Langille
Box 7, B2H 5E1

New Waterford   8,326
Ma—Gerard Marsh
Cl—Bernie White
3371 Plummer Ave., B1H 1Y8

North Sydney   7,472
Cl—Angus Fleming
Box 370, B2A 3M4

Oxford   1,376
Cl—Harris M. McCormack
Box 388, B0M 1P0

Parrsboro   1,729
Cl—Ashley Brown
Box 400, B0M 1S0

Pictou   4,413
Cl—D.L. Steele
Box 640, B0K 1H0

Port Hawkesbury   3,869
Cl—C.J. MacDonald
Box 10, B0E 2V0

Shelburne   2,312
Cl—Wilmot Hardy
Box 670, B0T 1W0

Springhill   4,712
Cl—D.E. Maddison
Box 1000, B0M 1X0

Stellarton   5,259
Cl—A.A. Pearson
Box 2200, B0K 1S0

Stewiacke   1,265
Cl—Lillian Smith
Box 8, B0N 2J0

Sydney Mines   8,063
Cl—Lois Gordon
Box 100, B1V 2L5

Trenton   3,083
Cl—C. Robin Campbell
Box 328, B0K 1X0

Truro   12,124
Ma—Douglas Carter
Cl—David G. Gilroy
Box 427, B2N 5C5

Westville   4,271
Cl—Gary Rankin
Box 923, B0K 2A0

Windsor   3,665
Cl—L.A. Armstrong
Box 158, B0N 2T0

Wolfville   3,277
Cl—Roy Thomson
Box 418, B0P 1X0

Yarmouth   7,617
Cl—Katheryn Moses
403 Main St., B5A 1G3

RURAL MUNICIPALITIES

Annapolis County   20,068
Cl—Ronald Grant
Box 100, Annapolis Royal
B0S 1A0

Antigonish County   13,485
Cl—Alan Bond
Box 598, Antigonish
B2G 2H5

Argyle District   9,055
Cl—J.P. Doucet
Box 10, Tusket
B0W 3M0

Barrington District   7,824
Cl—J.R. Fry
Box 100, Barrington
B0W 1E0

Cape Breton County   47,073
Cl—Jerry Ryan
865 Grand Lake Rd.
Sydney, B1P 6W2

Chester District   10,605
Cl—Barry Lenihan
Box 369, Chester, B0J 1J0

Clare District   9,740
Cl—Delphis J. Comeau
Box 458, Little Brook
B0W 1Z0

Colchester County   31,704
Cl—Leon Colburne
Box 697, Truro, B2N 5E7

Cumberland County   17,331
Cl—Arnold Harrison
Box 428, Amherst, B4H 3Z5

Digby District   9,587
Cl—William L. MacMillan
Box 429, Digby, B0V 1A0

Guysborough District   7,294
Cl—Ioan Astle
Box 79, Guysborough
B0H 1N0

Halifax County   119,588
CAO—K.R. Meech
Box 300, Armdale, B3L 4K3

Hants, East District   18,181
Cl—N.D. Glover
Box 190, Shubenacadie
B0N 2H0

Hants, West District   13,345
Cl—Roy Haley
Box 344, Windsor, B0N 2T0

Inverness County   18,077
Cl—A.A. Murray
Box 179, Port Hood
B0E 2W0

Kings County   42,732
CAO—R.G. Ramsey
Box 100, Kentville, B4N 3W3

Lunenburg District   25,196
  CI—D.E. Steele
  Box 200, Bridgewater
  B4V 2W8

Pictou County   22,724
  CAO—Clyde Purvis
  Box 910, Pictou, B0K 1H0

Queens County   9,830
  CI—L.D. Robertson
  Box 1264, Liverpool
  B0T 1K0

Richmond County   11,841
  CAO—Louis A. Digout
  Box 120, Arichat, B0E 1A0

St. Mary's District   3,091
  CI—Helen MacDonald
  Box 276, Sherbrooke
  B0J 3C0

Shelburne District   5,365
  CI—Alan Merritt
  Box 280, Shelburne
  B0T 1W0

Victoria County   8,704
  CI—M.S. MacEachern
  Box 370, Baddeck, B0E 1B0

Yarmouth County   10,401
  CI—W. Scott
  Box 152, Yarmouth
  B5A 4B2

SUMMARY OF 1986 TOTALS

3 Cities. 206,935
39 Towns 173,400

Total Urban (Census) 471,127
Total Rural (Census) 402,049

Total Urban and Rural
(excl. Indians on Reserves). 873,176

INDIANS

Living on reserves:
  population 4,878
  (June 1/86)

ONTARIO

Municipal Government

The legislative framework for the Ontario municipal government system is provided in the Ontario *Municipal Act*, R.S.O., 1980, Chapter 302 and subsequent amendments. This Act sets the basic structure by which the network and inter-relationships of the municipal level of government are established and maintained in Ontario.

The Act provides for a change in status of municipalities as population or local conditions warrant. On application, the Ontario Municipal Board may erect the improvement district, village, town, separated town, or township to a higher status (including city status). In 1982, a new procedure was established for local negotiation of boundary changes and related issues under the *Municipal Boundary Negotiations Act, 1981*.

Representation on the councils of each of the municipal levels in Ontario is established by the *Municipal Act* which provides directions based on municipal status and population and in legislation for restructured areas (see below). The *Municipal Elections Act* outlines the procedures for the conduct of municipal elections. Municipal councils, school board members, and some public utilities and hydro-electric commissions are elected for a three-year term.

A reform of local government in Ontario took place in the late 1960's and early 1970's with the creation of regional governments. During the early to mid-1960's, there was increasing pressure on many areas of the province from urban, commercial, and industrial developments. Accordingly, a program to strengthen local government through the development of regional government and other restructured areas was supported by the Ontario government. This resulted in the formation of twelve regional governments, one restructured county (Oxford), two amalga-mated cities, an amalgamated town, and three large municipalities in the Parry Sound District.

The Regional Municipalities in the province of Ontario with their date of formation are: the Municipality of Metropolitan Toronto (1954), Ottawa-Carleton (1969), Niagara (1970), York (1971), District Municipality of Muskoka (1971), Sudbury (1973), Waterloo (1973), Durham (1974), Halton (1974), Hamilton-Wentworth (1974), Peel (1974), and Haldimand-Norfolk (1974).

The individual Acts which establish these regional municipalities retain specific differences to meet local conditions, with the upper tier regional council generally having authority over capital borrowing, social services, police, arterial roads, water, sewers, planning, and conservation. Area municipalities, the lower tier units, are usually responsible for parks and recreation, local roads, collection of garbage, water, tax collection, and fire protection.

As of Jan. 1, 1989, there were 39 upper tier municipalities in Ontario — 12 regional municipalities or equivalents and 27 counties, and 800 local municipalities — 49 cities, 1 borough, 4 separated towns, 146 towns, 119 villages, 477 townships, and 4 improvement districts.

Glossary of Terms

Borough: A municipal corporation with the legal status of township but resembling a city. The urban municipalities surrounding the City of Toronto became boroughs in the federated system of the Municipality of Metropolitan Toronto. However, in the past several years, four boroughs (North York, Scarborough, Etobicoke, and York) have been granted city status. East York is the only remaining borough in Ontario.

Chief Administrative Officer: Most cities and many towns, townships, counties, and regional municipalities have an appointed, permanent official normally called the chief administrative officer. The title of this official may vary from one municipality to another, for example, 'Manager', 'Clerk-Administrator', 'Clerk-Comptroller', etc. All such officers are appointed to this position by by-law, and many hold other offices within the municipal corporation. The responsibilities of the chief administrative officer include making recommendations to standing committees and co-ordinating the administration of those policies, reviewing and making recommendations on the administrative procedures of municipal departments, and dealing with local boards, operations and other municipalities. He acts as a consultant to the mayor and council, reviews all estimates with department heads and interprets the policies of council to department heads.

City: An incorporated urban municipality in Ontario, generally with a population of more than 15,000.

County: A territorial division of the province of Ontario which forms an administrative, judicial, and political unit. Each county is an incorporated municipality and is a federation of the towns, villages, and townships situated within its borders.

Head of Council: The chairman of a regional municipality or equivalent; the warden of a county; the mayor of a city or town; the reeve of a village or township; or the chairman of an improvement district.

Improvement District: In places where there has been sudden growth and where no basic community existed before an industry such as a mine or pulp and paper plant moved in, an improvement district provides municipal organization. A board of trustees (usually 3 members) manages the municipality until the resident ratepayers want to establish a village, a town, or township. Improve-

ment districts are located in the districts of Northern Ontario and have a population of not less than 50 persons.

Police Village: A small built-up area within an organized township wherein the electors elect three trustees to administer certain statutory powers pertaining to the police village.

Separated Towns: These towns are separated from the county in which they are situated and are considered to have the same status as cities. In Ontario, there are four separated towns: Gananoque, Prescott, St. Mary's, and Smiths Falls.

Town: An incorporated urban municipality with a population usually between 2,000 and 15,000.

Township: The original designation given to the large municipal bodies created within the counties of the province of Ontario. Most rural areas in Southern Ontario are township municipalities of up to 250 km^2. Most have a population between 500 and 5,000.

Unorganized Territories: Those settlements in Northern Ontario not served by a municipal government. These communities are served directly by the provincial government and are geographically situated in districts. In some unorganized territories there is a Local Roads Board which administers the maintenance of local roads in their area. Several communities have a Local Services Board, established under legislation to provide urban services to small communities.

Village: The least populous of urban incorporated municipalities within the province of Ontario, often with a population of 1,000 or less.

Source: Ontario Ministry of Municipal Affairs. Provincial-Municipal Affairs Secretariat.

Municipalities

(Municipalities with populations of less than 2,000 are generally not included. Population figures are from the Ministry of Municipal Affairs 1988 list.)

A: Administrator   CAO: Chief Administrative Officer   Ch: Chairman   Cl: Clerk   Ma: Mayor   R: Reeve
W: Warden

METROPOLITAN MUNICIPALITY

Metropolitan Toronto   2,133,559
Ch—Alan Tonks
CAO—Dale Richmond
Cl—Daniel Crombie
100 Queen St. W.
Toronto, M5H 2N1

REGIONAL MUNICIPALITIES

Durham   347,837
Ch—Garry Herrema
CAO—Donald Evans

Cl—Cecil Lundy
Box 623, Whitby, L1N 6A3
Haldimand-Norfolk   89,225
Ch—Keith Richardson
CAO—Charles Douglas
Cl—Mary Lou Johnston
70 Town Centre Dr.
Townsend, N0A 1S0
Halton   281,668
Ch—Peter Pomeroy
CAO—John Fleming
Cl—David Varley
Box 7000, Oakville
L6J 6E1
Hamilton-Wentworth   429,466
Ch—Reg Whynott

CAO—Wm. Carson
Cl—Patrice N. Johnson
Box 910
Hamilton, L8N 3V9
Niagara   365,197
Ch—Wilbert Dick
CAO—M.H. Boggs
Cl—Allan Pierson
Box 1042
Thorold, L2V 4T7
Ottawa-Carleton   623,135
Ch—Andrew S. Haydon
CAO—Ronald S. Clark
Cl—Gail Brown
222 Queen St.
Ottawa, K1P 5Z3

Peel   608,327
  Ch—Frank Bean
  CAO—Richard Frost
  Cl—Deborah Trouten
  10 Peel Centre Dr.
  Brampton, L6T 4B9
Sudbury   151,314
  Ch—Tom Davies
  CAO—Herb Akehurst
  Cl—Paul Philion
  Postal Bag 3700
  Stn. A, P3A 5W5
Waterloo   342,030
  Ch—Kenneth Seiling
  CAO—Robert Richardson
  Cl—Mrs. Evelyn Stettner
  20 Erb St. W.
  Waterloo, N2J 4G7
York   409,292
  Ch—Eldred King
  CAO—Bob Forhan
  Cl—Robert Vernon
  Box 147, Newmarket
  L3Y 4W9

DISTRICT MUNICIPALITY

Muskoka   39,958
  Ch—Allen Sander
  CAO/Cl—Bill Calvert
  Box 1720, Bracebridge
  P0B 1C0

COUNTIES

Brant   102,085
  W—Warne Emmott
  Cl—Dan Ciona
  Box 160, Burford, N0E 1A0
Bruce   57,119
  W—Bradley Davis
  CAO—Wayne Jamieson
  Cl—Bettyanne Bray
  Box 70, Walkerton
  N0G 2V0
Dufferin   34,452
  W—Ernie Staveley
  CAO/Cl—Scott Wilson
  51 Zina St.
  Orangeville, L9W 1E5
Elgin   69,174
  W—Albert Ford
  Cl—George Leverton
  450 Sunset Dr.
  St. Thomas, N5R 5V1
Essex   314,952
  W—Carl Gibb
  CAO/Cl—John Curran
  360 Fairview Ave. W.
  Essex, N8M 1Y6
Frontenac   119,332
  W—Stan Johnston
  CAO—Steven G. Silver
  Cl—Mrs. Sylvia Coburn
  Court House
  Kingston, K7L 2N4
Grey   75,157
  W—Delton Becker
  CAO—H. Lorne Floto
  595-9th Ave. E.
  Owen Sound, N4K 3E3

Haliburton   11,945
  W—Keith Tallman
  Cl—Gary McKnight
  Box 399, Minden, K0M 2K0
Hastings   106,240
  W—Harry Danford
  CAO/Cl—William Bouma
  Postal Bag 4400
  Belleville, K8N 3A9
Huron   55,589
  W—David W. Johnston
  CAO/Cl—Bill G. Hanly
  Court House Sq.
  Goderich, N7A 1M2
Kent   105,176
  W—Paul Reno
  CAO/Cl—Robert Foulds
  Box 1230, Chatham
  N7M 5L8
Lambton   119,528
  W—Larry O'Neill
  CAO/Cl—H. Wayne Kloske
  Box 3000, Wyoming
  N0N 1T0
Lanark   49,483
  W—John A. Chaplin
  CAO/Cl—Keith Coulthart
  Box 37, Perth, K7H 3E2
Leeds and Grenville*   83,166
  W—Betty Weedmark
  CAO/Cl—George Brown
  Box 729, Brockville, K6V 5V8
Lennox and Addington   32,998
  W—Harold J. Kring
  CAO/Cl—Larry Keach
  Postal Bag 1000
  Napanee, K7R 3S9
Middlesex   344,586
  W—Charles Corbett
  CAO—Ron Eddy
  399 Ridout St. N.
  London, N6A 2P1
Northumberland   67,232
  W—Roger E. Wilson
  CAO/Cl—Peter Cramp
  860 William St.
  Cobourg, K9A 3A9
Oxford   84,008
  W—Ernie Hardeman
  Cl—J. Harold Walls
  Box 397, Woodstock   N4S 7Y3
Perth   66,226
  W—Ivan Norris
  Cl—James Bell
  1 Huron St.
  Stratford, N5A 5S4
Peterborough   105,493
  W—Donald Boa
  CAO/Cl—Doug Armstrong
  470 Water St., K9H 3M3
Prescott and Russell*   59,138
  W—Gaston Patenaude
  CAO/Cl—Raymond Ouimet
  Box 304, L'Orignal, K0B 1K0
Prince Edward   21,793
  W—Eleanor Lindsay
  CAO—Donald Ward
  Box 1550, K0K 2T0
Renfrew   85,953
  W—Eric Ashick
  CAO—Michael Johnson
  169 William St.
  Pembroke, K8A 1N7

Simcoe   241,694
  W—Harry Adams
  CAO—Duncan Green
  Cl—Al F. Pelletier
  Admin. Centre
  Midhurst, L0L 1X0
Stormont, Dundas and
  Glengarry*   101,978
  W—Stewart Hart
  CAO—Raymond Lapointe
  20 Pitt St., Cornwall, K6J 3P2
Victoria   55,132
  W—Dennis Sweeting
  CAO—Claire McKay
  Box 9000, Lindsay
  K9V 5R8
Wellington   143,778
  W—John C. Green
  Cl—James Andrews
  74 Woolwich St.
  Guelph, N1H 3T9

*United Counties

NORTHERN DISTRICTS

Algoma 117,339
Cochrane 84,846
Kenora 35,150
Manitoulin 6,771
Nipissing 74,599
Parry Sound 30,138
Rainy River 18,981
Sudbury 17,363
Thunder Bay 140,951
Timiskaming 35,741

CITIES

Barrie   49,818
  Ma—Mrs. Janice Laking
  CAO—Ben Straughan
  Cl—Richard Bates
  Box 400, L4M 4T5
Belleville   35,326
  Ma—George A. Zegouras
  CAO—Clifford J. Belch
  Cl—William Moreton
  169 Front St., K8N 2Y8
Brampton   192,045
  Ma—Kenneth Whillans
  CAO—Al Solski
  Cl—Leonard Mikulich
  150 Central Park Dr.
  L6T 2T9
Brantford   75,465
  Ma—Mrs. Karen George
  CAO—Geoffrey R. Wilson
  Cl—Wilf A. Coulson
  100 Wellington Sq., N3T 2M3
Brockville   20,607
  Ma—Stephen Clark
  CAO—Doug G. Ellis
  Cl—A. John Miles
  1 King St. E., K6V 3P5
Burlington   118,546
  Ma—Roly Bird
  CAO—Michael Fenn
  Cl—Helen Macrae
  Box 5013, L7R 3Z6

Cambridge 80,657
Ma—Mrs. Jane Brewer
CAO—Don Smith
Cl—James Anderson
Box 669, N1R 5W8

Chatham 41,840
Ma—William Erickson
CAO—Hugh J. Thomas
Cl—Brian Knott
Box 640, N7M 5K8

Cornwall 45,529
Ma—Phil Poirier
CAO—Hugh John Cook
Cl—Richard Allaire
360 Pitt St., K6H 5T9

Etobicoke 293,433
Ma—G. Bruce Sinclair
CAO—David G. Deaves
Cl—Ronald S. Gillespie
399 The West Mall, M9C 2Y2

Gloucester 93,121
Ma—Harry Allen
CAO—David O'Brien
Cl—Fred Meldrum
Box 8333, K1G 3V5

Guelph 80,786
Ma—John Counsell
CAO—Milton Sather
Cl—Mrs. Lois A. Giles
59 Carden St., N1H 3A1

Hamilton 307,160
Ma—Robert Morrow
CAO—Lou Sage
Cl—Edward Simpson
71 Main St. W., L8N 3T4

Kanata 30,295
Ma—Des Adam
CAO—Brian Switzer
Cl—Maureen Meikle
150 Katimavik Rd.
Ste. 200, K2L 2N3

Kingston 57,382
Ma—Mrs. Helen Cooper
CAO—Robert Hamilton
Cl—Mrs. Marion Rogers
216 Ontario St., K7L 2Z3

Kitchener 152,771
Ma—Dominic Cardillo
CAO—Tom McKay
Cl—Robert Pritchard
Box 1118, N2G 4G7

London 281,745
Ma—Thomas Gosnell
CAO—Maurice Engels
Cl—Kenneth Sadler
Box 5035, N6A 4L9

Mississauga 385,156
Ma—Mrs. Hazel McCallion
CAO—Douglas Lychak
Cl—Terence Julian
300 City Centre Dr.
L5B 3C1

Nanticoke 20,441
Ma—Orval Shortt
Cl—David Kilpatrick
230 Main St.
Port Dover, N0A 1N0

Nepean 97,883
Ma—Ben Franklin
CAO—Merv Beckstead
Cl—David Hobbs
101 Centrepointe Dr.
K2G 5K7

Niagara Falls 70,540
Ma—William Smeaton
CAO—Jack Collinson
Cl—Paul Brennan
Box 1023, L2E 6X5

North Bay 51,313
Ma—Stan D. Lawlor
CAO—Morley Daiter
Cl—Robert Barton
200 McIntyre St. E., P1B 8H8

North York 544,560
Ma—Mel Lastman
Cl—Blair MacLeod
5100 Yonge St., M2N 5V7

Orillia 23,893
Ma—John Palmer
Cl—Bruce D. Bayne
Box 340, L3V 6J1

Oshawa 120,904
Ma—Allan Pilkey
Cl—Robert Henderson
50 Centre St. S., L1H 3Z7

Ottawa 303,747
Ma—James Durrell
CAO—Alcide DeGagné
Cl—John R. Cyr
111 Sussex Dr., K1N 5A1

Owen Sound 19,913
Ma—Ovid Jackson
Cl—Glen E. Henry
808-2nd Ave. E., N4K 2H4

Pembroke 13,595
Ma—Terry McCann
Cl—K. June Nighbor
Box 277, K8A 6X3

Peterborough 62,005
Ma—Mrs. Sylvia Sutherland
CAO—David Hall
Cl—David W. Oakes
500 George St. N., K9H 3R9

Port Colborne 17,893
Ma—Bob Saracino
CAO/Cl—L.C. (Len) Hunt
239 King St., L3K 4G8

St. Catharines 120,567
Ma—Joseph McCaffery
CAO—Larry Tufford
Cl—Thomas Derreck
Box 3012, L2R 7C2

St. Thomas 28,405
Ma—Mrs. Janet Golding
CAO—Robert A. Barrett
Cl—Peter Leack
Box 520, N5P 3V7

Sarnia 46,448
Ma—Mike Bradley
CAO—John C. Robertson
Cl—Ann M. Tuplin
Box 3018, N7T 7N2

Sault Ste. Marie 78,568
Ma—Joseph Fratesi
CAO—Allan Jackson
Cl—Wm. G. Lindsay
Box 580, P6A 5N1

Scarborough 470,406
Ma—Joyce Trimmer
CAO—Jack J. Poots
Cl—John W. Nigh
150 Borough Dr., M1P 4N7

Stoney Creek 45,329
Ma—Stanley Napper
CAO—Raymond G. Waters
Cl—Joseph A. Brezina
Box 9940, L8G 4N9

Stratford 26,078
Ma—Dave Hunt
CAO/Cl—Ron Schulthies
1 Wellington St., N5A 2L1

Sudbury 89,698
Ma—Peter Wong
CAO—William Rice
Cl—Ellen Kerr
Bag 5000, P3A 5P3

Thorold 16,589
Ma—William Longo
CAO/Cl—Kenneth Todd
Box 1044, L2V 4A7

Thunder Bay 109,269
Ma—Jack Masters
CAO—Paul Harper
Cl—Harry Kirk
500 Donald St. E.
P7E 5V3

Timmins 46,065
Ma—Dennis Welin
CAO—Ray Canie
Cl—Grant Chevrette
220 Algonquin Blvd. E.
P4N 1B3

Toronto 597,126
Ma—Art Eggleton
CAO—Arthur Stevenson
Cl—Roy V. Henderson
100 Queen St. W.
M5H 2N2

Trenton 14,765
Ma—Neil Robertson
CAO—Brian Fagan
Cl—David Emmons
Box 490, K8V 5R6

Vanier 18,190
Ma—Mrs. Gisèle Lalonde
Cl—René L. Doré
300 White Fathers Ave.
K1L 7L5

Waterloo 67,435
Ma—Brian Turnbull
CAO—Robert Bryon
Cl—Ron Keeling
Box 337, N2J 4A8

Welland 44,569
Ma—Roland Hardy
Cl—David Barrett
411 East Main St., L3B 3X4

Windsor 190,198
Ma—John Millson
CAO—Hillary G. Payne
Cl—Thomas Lynd
Box 1607, N9A 6S1

Woodstock 26,295
Ma—Joe Pember
CAO—Vacant
Cl—John McGinnis
Box 40, N4S 7W5

York 131,537
Ma—Fergy Brown
Cl—Carlyle Rodrigo
2700 Eglinton Ave. W.
Toronto, M6M 1V1

BOROUGH OF METRO TORONTO

East York 96,497
Ma—David J. Johnson
Cl—William Alexander Jr.
550 Mortimer Ave.
Toronto, M4J 2H2

TOWNS

Ajax   45,046
  Ma—James Witty
  Cl—Albert Hodges
  65 Harwood Ave. S.
  L1S 2H9

Alexandria   3,229
  Ma—Jean Paul Touchette
  Cl—Leo Poirier
  Box 700, K0C 1A0

Alliston   4,885
  Ma—Rick Milne
  Cl—Brian Gauley
  Box 910, L0M 1A0

Almonte   4,026
  Ma—Mrs. Dorothy Finner
  Cl—J. Des Houston
  Box 400, K0A 1A0

Amherstburg   8,211
  Ma—William Gibb
  Cl—Thomas C. Kilgallin
  Box 159, N9V 2Z3

Ancaster   19,728
  Ma—Robert E. Wade
  Cl—Lloyd Hayden
  300 Wilson St. E., L9G 2B9

Arnprior   6,002
  Ma—Thomas E. Sullivan
  Cl—Gary M. Buffam
  Box 130, K7S 3H4

Aurora   24,545
  Ma—John G. West
  Cl—Mrs. Colleen Gowan
  50 Wellington St. W.
  L4G 3L8

Aylmer   5,457
  Ma—Donald H. Pearson
  Cl—Phyllis Ketchabaw
  46 Talbot St. W., N5H 1J7

Belle River   3,764
  Ma—Richard Tighe
  Cl—Henry Sipila
  499 Notre Dame St.
  N0R 1A0

Blenheim   4,336
  Ma—Peter Shillington
  Cl—Mrs. Elinor Mifflin
  Box 399, N0P 1A0

Blind River   3,263
  Ma—Robert Gallagher
  Cl—Ken Corbière
  Box 640, P0R 1B0

Bracebridge   9,968
  Ma—James D. Lang
  Cl—Kenneth Veitch
  Box 360, P0B 1C0

Bradford   10,188
  Ma—Wm. dePeuter
  Cl—Patrick Storey
  Box 160, L3Z 2A8

Brighton   3,686
  Ma—Wm. Pettingill
  Cl—Shirley Patterson
  Box 189, K0K 1H0

Caledon   31,126
  Ma—Emil Kolb
  Cl—Gary Boyce
  Box 1000
  Caledon East, L0N 1E0

Campbellford   3,408
  Ma—Hector MacMillan
  Cl—Martin De Rond
  Box 1056, K0L 1L0

Capreol   3,531
  Ma—Frank Mazzuca
  Cl—Edgar Bérubé
  Box 700, P0M 1H0

Carleton Place   6,634
  Ma—Mrs. Melba Barker
  Cl—W. Keith Morris
  175 Bridge St., K7C 2V8

Clearwater   24,429
  Ma—James Mason
  Cl—Mrs. Edith A. Jolly
  2109 London Rd. N7T 7H2

Clinton   3,091
  Ma—John Cochrane
  Cl—Mrs. Marie Jefferson
  Box 400, N0M 1L0

Cobourg   13,210
  Ma—Angus Read
  Cl—Bryan Baxter
  55 King St. W., K9A 2M2

Cochrane   4,370
  Ma—David S. Hughes
  Cl—Pierre Demers
  Box 490, P0L 1C0

Collingwood   12,196
  Ma—Joseph B. Sheffer
  Cl—Carmen Morrison
  Box 157, L9Y 3Z5

Deep River   4,166
  Ma—Lyall Smith
  Cl—Larry H. Simons
  Box 400, K0J 1P0

Dresden   2,546
  Ma—Anthony Stranak
  Cl—James L. Babcock
  Box 730, N0P 1M0

Dryden   6,219
  Ma—Thomas S. Jones
  Cl—Bruce Hoffstrom
  30 Van Horne Ave.
  P8N 2A7

Dundas   20,640
  Ma—John Addison
  Cl—Rob Gerrie
  60 Main St., L9H 2P8

Dunnville   11,323
  Ma—Bernie Corbett
  Cl—Ronald T. Sparks
  Box 187, N1A 2X5

Durham   2,487
  Ma—Floyd Lawrence
  Cl—Mrs. Judith Gray
  Box 639, N0G 1R0

East Gwillimbury   16,513
  Ma—Robert Featherstonhaugh
  Cl—John F. Hopkins
  18066 Leslie St.
  Sharon, L0G 1V0

Elliot Lake   16,229
  Ma—George Farkouh
  Cl—Larry Burling
  45 Hillside Dr. N., P5A 1X5

Espanola   5,358
  Ma—Kenneth Buck
  Cl—Merwyn Sheppard
  Box 638, P0P 1C0

Essex   6,252
  Ma—James MacPherson
  Cl—Wayne Miller
  33 Talbot St. S., N8M 1A8

Exeter   3,767
  Ma—Bruce Shaw
  Cl—Mrs. Elizabeth Bell
  Box 759, N0M 1S0

Fergus   6,757
  Ma—William Beirnes
  Cl—George Woods
  Box 10, N1M 2W7

Flamborough   27,116
  Ma—C. James Robb
  Cl—Mrs. M. Jane Lee
  Box 50, Waterdown
  L0R 2H0

Forest   2,555
  Ma—Gordon Minielly
  Cl—Henry Maas
  Box 610, N0N 1J0

Fort Erie   23,486
  Ma—John T. Teal
  Cl—Carolyn Booth
  200 Jarvis St., L2A 2S6

Fort Frances   8,589
  Ma—Richard Lyons
  Cl—Glenn W. Treftlin
  Box 38, P9A 3M5

Georgina   22,587
  Ma—Robert Johnston
  Cl—Larry Simpson
  Civic Centre Rd., R.R. 2
  Keswick, L4P 3E9

Geraldton   2,528
  Ma—Malcolm Power
  Cl—Roy Sinclair
  Box 70, P0T 1M0

Goderich   7,384
  Ma—Eileen Palmer
  Cl—Larry J. McCabe
  57 West St., N7A 2K5

Gravenhurst   8,624
  Ma—Gord Adams
  Cl—John R. McColl
  Box 1360, P0C 1G0

Grimsby   16,996
  Ma—Ronald W. Book
  Cl—Ronald Bracher
  Box 159, L3M 4G3

Haileybury   4,744
  Ma—Thomas Despres
  Cl—Daniel Gatien
  Postal Bag D, P0J 1K0

Haldimand   18,211
  Ma—Edith Fuller
  Cl—Mrs. Janis Lankester
  Box 400, Cayuga, N0A 1E0

Halton Hills   34,189
  Ma—Russel Miller
  Cl—Dan Costea
  Box 128, Georgetown
  L7G 4T1

Hanover   6,327
  Ma—Ernest Duncan
  Cl—Gerald B. Kueneman
  451-10th Ave., N4N 2P1

Harrow   2,395
  Ma—Peter Timmins
  Cl—Jerome Marion
  Box 129, N0R 1G0

Hawkesbury   9,400
  Ma—Yves Drouin
  Cl—Jacques Poulin
  600 Higginson St.
  K6A 1H1

Hearst   5,239
  Ma—Giles Gagnon
  Cl—Louis Corbeil
  Postal Bag 5000, P0L 1N0

Huntsville   12,320
Ma—Terry Clarke
Cl—Edward H. Hares
Box 2700, P0A 1K0

Ingersoll   8,253
Ma—Douglas Harris
Cl—Gerald Staples
Box 340, N5C 3V3

Iroquois Falls   5,895
Ma—Rene Boucher
Cl—John Buchan
Box 230, P0K 1G0

Jaffray and Melick   3,651
Ma—Edward G. Alcock
Cl—Gordon R. Meads
R.R. 2, 243 Rabbit Lake Rd.
Kenora, P9N 3W8

Kapuskasing   10,830
Ma—Theodore Jewell
Cl—John Langsford
88 Riverside Dr., P5N 1B3

Keewatin   1,974
Ma—Donald Parfitt
Cl—Warren Spencer
Box 139, P0X 1C0

Kemptville   2,491
Ma—Mrs. Jean Somerville
Cl—Melvin R. McIntyre
Box 130, K0G 1J0

Kenora   9,373
Ma—Kelvin Winkler
Cl—Mrs. Janice Tivy
Box 1110, P9N 3X7

Kincardine   5,734
Ma—Mrs. Donna Wilson
Cl—Ronald R. Shaw
707 Queen St., N2Z 1Z9

Kingsville   5,332
Ma—James Gaffan
Cl—Stan Brophy
41 Division St. S.
N9Y 1P4

Kirkland Lake   11,300
Ma—Joe Mavrinac
Cl—J. Bev Bennetts
Box 757, P2N 3K3

Leamington   12,764
Ma—Bruce E. Crozier
Cl—Brian R. Sweet
38 Erie St. N., N8H 2Z3

Lincoln   14,335
Ma—Ray A. Konkle
Cl—Michael F. Duc
Box 1030, Beamsville
L0R 1B0

Lindsay   15,265
Ma—Lorne Chester
Cl—William B. Bates
180 Kent St. W., K9V 2Y6

Listowel   5,083
Ma—Bert Johnson
Cl—Hartley Fischer
330 Wallace Ave. N.
N4W 1L3

Longlac   2,133
Ma—Ronald Beaulieu
Cl—Mrs. Jane Jantunen
Box 640, P0T 2A0

Marathon   4,140
Ma—Mrs. Wendy Bell
Cl—Raymond Mitchell
Box 190, P0T 2E0

Markham   129,501
Ma—Anthony Roman
Cl—Gary Roseblade
8911 Woodbine Ave.
L3R 1A1

Mattawa   2,491
Ma—Mrs. Colette Wilson
Cl—Wayne Belter
Box 390, P0H 1V0

Meaford   4,283
Ma—Gordon Crapper
Cl—Graham Shaw
Box 758, N0H 1Y0

Midland   12,171
Ma—E.F. Ted Symons
Cl—Fred Flood
575 Dominion Ave. W.
L4R 1R2

Milton   30,529
Ma—Gordon Krantz
Cl—William Roberts
Box 1005, L9T 4B6

Mitchell   3,078
Ma—Harold Jordan
Cl—Donald Eplett
169 St. David St.
N0K 1N0

Mount Forest   3,713
Ma—Alex Watson
Cl—E.C. "Al" Brubacher
Box 188, N0G 2L0

Napanee   4,604
Ma—Chris Seeley
Cl—Jack C. McNamee
Box 97, K7R 3L4

New Liskeard   5,159
Ma—Charles Caldwell
Cl—Kenneth Boal
Box 730, Whitewood
P0J 1P0

Newcastle   37,769
Ma—Mrs. Marie Hubbard
Cl—Mrs. Patti Barrie
40 Temperance St.
Bowmanville, L1C 3A6

Newmarket   37,277
Ma—Raymond J. Twinney
Cl—Robert M. Prentice
Box 328, L3Y 4X7

Niagara-on-the-Lake   12,050
Ma—Stan Ignatczyk
Cl—Robert Howse
Box 100, Virgil, L0S 1T0

Nickel Centre   11,063
Ma—Stan Hayduk
Cl—Maureen Cleroux
190 Church St.
Garson, P0M 1V0

Oakville   98,404
Ma—Mrs. Ann Mulvale
Cl—Donald W. Brown
Box 310, L6J 5A6

Onaping Falls   5,153
Ma—Robert Parker
Cl—Richard Demers
Box 400, Dowling, P0M 1R0

Orangeville   15,293
Ma—Gordon Courtney
Cl—William C. Norris
87 Broadway, L9W 1K1

Palmerston   2,085
Ma—A. Keith Askett
Cl—Larry C. Adams
Box 190, N0G 2P0

Paris   7,907
Ma—Jack L. Bawcutt
Cl—Peter H. Dearling
66 Grand River St. N.
N3L 2M2

Parry Sound   5,895
Ma—Roy O'Halloran
Cl—W. Ed Ewing
52 Seguin St., P2A 1B4

Pelham   12,430
Ma—Mrs. Mardi Collins
Cl—Murray Hackett
Box 400, Fonthill, L0S 1E0

Penetanguishene   5,533
Ma—Robert Sullivan
Cl—Yvon Gagné
Box 580, L0K 1P0

Perth   5,463
Ma—Lowell C. Yorke
Cl—Thomas Kent
80 Gore St. E., K7H 1H9

Petrolia   4,168
Ma—Marcel Beaubien
Cl—Brad Loosley
Box 1270, N0N 1R0

Pickering   56,132
Ma—Wayne Arthurs
Cl—Bruce Taylor
1710 Kingston Rd.
L1V 1C7

Picton   4,049
Ma—Albert Piroth
Cl—Sterling Johnston
Box 1670, K0K 2T0

Port Elgin   5,909
Ma—Fred Wuerth
Cl—Doug Court
Box 550, N0H 2C0

Port Hope   10,243
Ma—Donald Chalmers
Cl—F. Neill Wakely
Box 117, L1A 3V9

Rayside-Balfour   13,702
Ma—Lionel E. Lalonde
Cl—Raymond G. Poulin
Box 639, Chelmsford
P0M 1L0

Renfrew   7,914
Ma—Mrs. Audrey Green
Cl—Trip Kennedy
Bag 2000, K7V 4G7

Richmond Hill   57,082
Ma—William F. Bell
Cl—Robert Douglas
10266 Yonge St., L4C 4Y5

Ridgetown   3,152
Ma—Russel MacMillan
Cl—Gerald P. Secord
Box 550, N0P 2C0

Rockland   5,119
Ma—Jean-Marc Lalonde
Cl—Jean-Pierre Pitre
Box 909, K0A 3A0

Seaforth   2,100
Ma—Mrs. Hazel Hildebrand
Cl—James Crocker
Box 610, N0K 1W0

Shelburne   3,123
Ma—Mrs. Irene Davis
Cl—Wallace Rintoul
Box 69, L0N 1S0

Simcoe   14,197
Ma—James Earl
Cl—Mrs. Lori Heinbuch
Box 545, N3Y 4N5

Sioux Lookout   3,027
Ma—Terrence Jewell
Cl—Phillip Salem
Box 158, P0V 2T0

Smooth Rock Falls   2,052
Ma—Roger Duguay
Cl—Mrs. Helen Valiquette
Box 249, P0L 2B0

Southampton   2,695
Ma—Douglas Kreutzweiser
Cl—Wray R. Smith
Box 340, N0H 2L0

Stayner   3,045
Ma—Bruce Parton
Cl—Pearson Spellman
Box 200, L0M 1S0

Strathroy   9,186
Ma—Dick Nywening
Cl—Arden Royce
52 Frank St., N7G 2R4

Sturgeon Falls   5,770
Ma—Michel De Caen
Cl—Guy Savage
Box 270, P0H 2G0

Tecumseh   8,873
Ma—Harold Downs
Cl—Leo Lessard
917 Lesperance Rd.
N8N 1W9

Tilbury   4,186
Ma—Charles Carrick
Cl—Robert Bourassa
Box 1299, N0P 2L0

Tillsonburg   10,621
Ma—Mrs. Jean Ferrie
Cl—Ken Holland
200 Broadway, Ste. 204
N4G 5A7

Valley East   19,119
Ma—John Robert
Cl—Roland Chenier
Box 430, Val Caron
P0M 3A0

Vaughan   88,475
Ma—Mrs. Lorna Jackson
Cl—Bob Panizza
2141 Major Mackenzie Dr.
Maple, L6A 1T1

Walden   9,048
Ma—Charles White
Cl—Alex J. Sedunow
Box 910, Lively, P0M 2E0

Walkerton   4,687
Ma—James Bolden
Cl—Richard Radford
Box 68, N0G 2V0

Wallaceburg   11,462
Ma—Gary O'Flynn
Cl—Sheldon Parsons
786 Dufferin Ave.
N8A 2V3

Wasaga Beach   4,807
Ma—Walter Borthwick
Cl—Eric Collingwood
Box 110, L0L 2P0

Westminster   6,062
Ma—A. David Murray
Cl—John Trudgen
Box 1270
Lambeth, N0L 1S0

Whitby   49,948
Ma—Robert Attersley
Cl—Donald McKay
575 Rossland Rd. E.
L1N 2M8

Whitchurch-Stouffville   16,705
Ma—Mrs. Fran Sainsbury
Cl—Mrs. Patricia G. Oakes
Box 419, Stouffville
L4A 7Z6

Wiarton   2,080
Ma—Barney McKillop
Cl—Ronald G. Brown
Box 310, N0H 2T0

Wingham   2,970
Ma—Ian Moreland
Cl—J. Byron Adams
Box 90, N0G 2W0

SEPARATED TOWNS

Gananoque   4,866
Ma—Frederick Delaney
Cl—Gary W. Drysdale
Box 100, K7G 2T6

Prescott   4,413
Ma—Mrs. Sandra S. Lawn
Cl—Arie Hoogenboom
Box 160, K0E 1T0

St. Mary's   4,923
Ma—Gerald Teahen
Cl—Kenneth Storey
Box 998, N0M 2V0

Smiths Falls   9,047
Ma—Laurence S. Lee
Cl—W. Murray Metcalfe
Box 695, K7A 4T6

VILLAGES

Arthur   1,967
R—Mrs. Doreen Hostrawser
Cl—Marlene Ternan
Box 490, N0G 1A0

Bancroft   2,248
R—Lloyd Churchill
Cl—Dean F. Patterson
Box 790, K0L 1C0

Beeton   2,189
R—Garry Burton
Cl—Ruth Shaw
Box 130, L0G 1A0

Casselman   2,021
R—Conrad Lamadeleine
Cl—Gilles Lortie
Box 710, K0A 1M0

Elora   2,991
R—Mrs. Mary Dunlop
Cl—Kenneth Miller
Box 508, N0B 1S0

Erin   2,308
R—Terry Mundell
Cl—Patricia McDermott
Box 149, N0B 1T0

Frankford   2,020
R—Earl E. Hewison
Cl—Wayne B. Tod
Box 388, K0K 2C0

L'Orignal   1,970
R—Claude Laflamme
Cl—Mrs. Diane Lalonde
Box 271, K0B 1K0

Lakefield   2,359
R—Bill Bullied
Cl—Rosemary Rutledge
Box 400, K0L 2H0

Morrisburg   2,237
R—William Dillabough
Cl—Cheryl Tynski
Box 737, K0C 1X0

Petawawa   5,189
R—Mike Habec
Cl—Robert Rantz
Box 69, K8H 2X1

Point Edward   2,216
R—William E. Boyd
Cl—Joe Simon
36 St. Clair St., N7V 4G8

Rockcliffe Park   2,295
Ma—Patrick Murray
Cl—Murray MacLean
350 Springfield Rd.
Ottawa, K1M 0K7

St. Clair Beach   3,367
R—Fred Cada
Cl—Andre Barrette
13677 St. Gregory's Rd.
Windsor, N8N 3E4

Tottenham   2,856
R—Mrs. Joan Sutherland
Cl—Sterling Zeran
Box 310, L0G 1W0

Winchester   2,167
R—Larry Gray
Cl—William Appleby
Box 489, K0C 2K0

TOWNSHIPS
(Population over 5,000)

Ameliasburgh   5,005
R—William Bonter
Cl—Mrs. Doreen Kendall
General Delivery, K0K 1A0

Anderdon   4,992
R—Gregory Stewart
Cl—David Mailloux
Box 362, Amherstburg
N9V 2Y9

Augusta   6,811
R—Ed Coons
Cl—Ray Gilmour
R.R. 2 Prescott K0E 1T0

Blandford-Blenheim   6,457
Ma—Edward Down
Cl—Keith Reibling
Box 100, Drumbo N0J 1G0

Brantford   6,445
R—Steve Comisky
Cl—David A. Kelman
Box 1295, N3T 5T6

Brock   10,082
Ma—Donald C. Hadden
Cl—George Graham
Box 10, Cannington
L0E 1E0

Burford   5,497
R—Randy Covey
Cl—Bettyanne Cadman
Box 249, N0E 1A0

Cambridge   5,249
R—Denis Pomainville
Cl—Roger Brunette
R.R. 3 Casselman
K0A 1M0

Caradoc   5,458
R—John Groenewegen
Cl—Mrs. Marion Loker
Box 190, Mt. Brydges
N0L 1W0

Charlottenburgh   7,004
R—Mrs. Carol-Ann Ross
Cl—Marcel Lapierre
Box 40, Williamstown
K0C 2J0

Chatham   6,369
R—Hector Van Damme
Cl—Nelson J. Praill
785 St. Clair St. Ext.
N7M 5J7

Clarence   7,885
R—Raymond Bouvier
Cl—Richard Lalonde
Box 70, Clarence Creek
K0A 1N0

Cornwall   5,770
R—John R. Moss
Cl—Bernard Chisholm
R.R. 1, Long Sault
K0C 1P0

Cumberland   30,164
Ma—Peter D. Clark
Cl—Mrs. Carmelle Bédard
Box 15, R.R. 3
Navan, K4B 1J1

Delhi   14,539
Ma—Gordon Lee
Cl—Vacant
Box 182, N4B 2W9

East Zorra-Tavistock   6,878
Ma—Mrs. Nell Hostetler
Cl—John Killing
Box 100, Hickson, N0J 1L0

Elizabethtown   6,711
R—Carl W. Jowett
Cl—Stephen McDonald
R.R. 2, Addison K0E 1A0

Emily   5,350
R—Stanley Smith
Cl—Mrs. Linda O'Neill
R.R. 4 Omemee K0L 2W0

Erin   6,606
R—Duncan Armstrong
Cl—R. Murray Clarke
Box 250, Hillsburgh
N0B 1Z0

Ernestown   11,108
R—Ian Wilson
Cl—Michael Wade
Box 57, Odessa
K0H 2H0

Essa   12,828
R—Charlie Pridham
Cl—Mrs. Brenda Sigouin
Box 10, Angus, L0M 1B0

Fenelon   5,141
R—David A. Murray
Cl—Rhona Woodcock
Cameron, K0M 1G0

Georgian Bay   1,890
Ma—Mrs. Doris Donnelly
Cl—Tina Agnello
R.R. 1, Port Severn
L0K 1S0

Glanbrook   9,493
Ma—Mrs. Helen Bell
Cl—Craig Switzer
Box 130, Mount Hope
L0R 1W0

Gosfield South   7,362
R—Ron DiMenna
Cl—Dan M. DiGiovanni
2021 Division Rd. N.
Kingsville, N9Y 2Y9

Goulbourn   13,099
Ma—Anton Wytenburg
Cl—Moira A. Winch
Box 189, Stittsville
K0A 3G0

Hamilton   8,085
R—John Avery
Cl—Mrs. Grace Bastin
R.R. 4 Cobourg, K9A 4J7

Harwich   6,089
R—John Jenner
Cl—W. Michael Phipps
Box 89, Blenheim
N0P 1A0

Innisfil   14,529
R—Grant Andrade
Cl—Richard Groh
Box 5000, Stroud
L0L 2M0

King   16,607
Ma—Mrs. Margaret Britnell
Cl—Cameron Duncan
R.R. 2 King City
L0G 1K0

Kingston   32,774
R—Mrs. Isabel Turner
Cl—Doug Gordon
Postal Bag 3400
Kingston, K7L 5L8

Lake of Bays   2,305
Ma—Malcolm D. Scott
Cl—Mrs. Faye Tibbel
General Delivery
Dwight, P0A 1H0

Lobo   5,056
Ma—Jamie Bycraft
Cl—Mrs. Sharon A. McMillan
R.R. 2 Ilderton, N0M 2A0

London   5,626
R—Alan Johnson
Cl—Albert Bannister
15 Medway Rd.
Arva, N0M 1C0

Maidstone   8,850
R—Kirk Walstedt
Cl—Annette Drouillard
R.R. 3 Essex, N8M 2X7

Malahide   5,182
R—Emil Neukamm
Cl—Randall Millard
87 John St. S.
Aylmer West, N5H 2C3

Mariposa   5,771
R—Edward Starr
Cl—Mrs. Sandra Lloyd
Box 70, Oakwood
K0M 2M0

Mersea   8,464
R—Clair Cowan
Cl—Lynn Foster
38 Erie St. N.
Leamington, N8H 2Z3

Moore   9,867
R—Charles S. Nisbet
Cl—Ron Whitman
Box 40, Brigden
N0N 1B0

Murray   5,958
R—Fred G. Jones
Cl—Gayle P. Bates
R.R. 1
Trenton, K8V 5P4

Norfolk   10,514
Ma—Clarence Abbott
Cl—Robert Loncke
Box 128, Langton
N0E 1G0

North Dorchester   7,201
R—William Irwin
Cl—Clyde Walton
Box 209, Dorchester
N0L 1G0

North Dumphries   5,486
Ma—Joe Martens
Cl—Marvin Bosetti
R.R. 4, Cambridge
N1R 5S5

Norwich   9,453
Ma—John Heleniak
Cl—Robert Watkins
Box 100, Otterville
N0J 1R0

Orillia   7,238
R—Jack A. Fountain
Cl—James Mather
R.R. 4, Box 159, L3V 6J3

Oro   7,789
R—Robert Drury
Cl—Robert Small
R.R. 1, Oro Station
L0L 2E0

Osgoode   11,670
Ma—Albert Bouwers
Cl—Wayne Robinson
Box 130, Metcalfe
K0A 2P0

Petawawa   7,905
R—Denis Carmody
Cl—Mitchell Stillman
680 Hwy. #17 W.
Pembroke, K8A 7H5

Pittsburgh   10,848
R—Barry F. Gordon
Cl—Mrs. Beulah Webb
Box 966, Kingston
K7L 4X8

Raleigh   5,596
R—Thomas S. Suitor
Cl—S.E. (Stu) Cuthbert
R.R. 5 Merlin, N0P 1W0

Rideau   10,370
Ma—R. Glenn Brooks
Cl—Georgina Heggart
Box 310, North Gower
K0A 2T0

Russell   8,518
R—Gaston Patenaude
Cl—Jean Guy Bourdeau
Box 570, Embrun
K0A 1W0

Sandwich South   4,943
R—Allan Parr
Cl—Mrs. Evelyn Oliver
3455 N. Talbot Rd.
Oldcastle, N0R 1L0

Sandwich West   14,629
R—Vince Marcotte
Cl—Ken Antaya
5950 Malden Rd.
Windsor, N9H 1S4

Scugog 15,675
Ma—Howard Hall
Cl—Earl Cuddie
Box 209, Port Perry
L0B 1N0
Sidney 15,791
R—Tom Nobles
Cl—E. Hugh Lyons
R.R. 5 Belleville
K8N 4Z5
Smith 8,002
R—Donald Boa
Cl—Derick Holyoake
Box 270, Bridgenorth
K0L 1B0
South West Oxford 8,067
Ma—Ernie Hardeman
Cl—Mrs. Helen Prouse
R.R. 1, Mount Elgin
N0J 1N0
Tay 5,943
R—Bruce Tinney
Cl—Brian D. Hopkins
Box 100, Victoria Harbour
L0K 2A0

Tecumseth 7,370
R—James Heath
Cl—Linda Duczak
Box 220, Beeton, L0G 1A0
Thurlow 6,864
R—George Beer
Cl—James R. Pine
Box 128, Cannifton
K0K 1K0
Tiny 7,393
R—Anthony Lancia
Cl—Guy Maurice
Perkinsfield, L0L 2J0
Uxbridge 12,281
Ma—Gerri-Lynn O'Connor
Cl—Walter Taylor
Box 190, L0C 1K0
Vespra 6,502
R—Harry B. Adams
Cl—Julian Tofts
Midhurst, L0L 1X0
Wainfleet 5,809
Ma—Stan Pettit
Cl—Albert Guiler
Box 38, L0S 1V0

Wellesley 7,500
Ma—Albert Erb
Cl—Gordon Ludington
Box 40, Linwood
N0B 2A0
West Carleton 12,301
Ma—Eric Craig
Cl—Bruce Leclaire
Box 410, Carp, K0A 1L0
West Lincoln 9,933
Ma—Mrs. Joan Packham
Cl—Salter Hayden
Box 400, Smithville
L0R 2A0
Wilmot 11,423
Ma—Lynn Myers
Cl—Jerry Langner
Box 599, New Hamburg
N0B 2G0
Woolwich 16,758
Ma—Robert Waters
Cl—Kris Fletcher
Box 158, Elmira, N3B 2Z6
Yarmouth 7,781
R—Bill Martyn
Cl—Ken Sloan
1229 Talbot St.
St. Thomas, N5P 1G8
Zorra 7,984
Ma—Wallis W. Hammond
Cl—Wayne Johnson
Box 306, Ingersoll, N5C 3K5

INDIANS

Living on reserves:
population 34,783
(June 1/86)

SUMMARY OF 1986 TOTALS

49 Cities	5,831,697
147 Towns	1,560,894
Total Urban (Census)	7,469,420
Total Rural (Census)	1,632,274
Total Urban and Rural (excl. Indians on Reserves)	9,101,694

PRINCE EDWARD ISLAND

Municipal Government

In Prince Edward Island there are:

1 City
8 Towns
79 Communities

The city of Charlottetown and the town of Summerside operate under individual acts of incorporation. Charlottetown is governed by a council composed of a mayor and ten aldermen, while Summerside has a mayor and six councillors. Elections for the entire council are held triennially in November.

Seven towns and 79 communities operate under the provision of the *Municipalities Act*. All are governed by a council. In the case of the towns, the head of council is a mayor, while in the communities the head is a chairman. The entire council is elected for a three-year term with elections held every third November.

Municipalities

(Municipalities with a population of less than 1,000 are generally not included in this list. Population figures given are from the 1986 Census.)

A: Administrator   Ma: Mayor

CITY

Charlottetown 15,572
Ma—John E. Ready
A—Harry Gaudet
Box 98, C1A 7K2

TOWNS

Alberton 1,085
A—Susan Wallace
Main St., C0B 1B0
Georgetown 725
A—Albert E. Hobbs
Box 89, C0A 1L0

Kensington 1,091
A—T.J. Stewart
Box 418, C0B 1M0
Montague 1,981
A—Karen Bethune
Box 546, C0A 1R0

Parkdale   2,047
  A—Arnold Llewellyn
  20 Linden Ave., C1A 5Y8
Souris   1,364
  A—Mildred Ehler
  75 Main St., C0A 2B0
Summerside   7,917
  Ma—Basil Stewart
  A—Michael Ryan
  Box 1510, C1N 4K4

COMMUNITIES
Afton   N/A
  A—Joseph Clow
  R.R. 2 Cornwall, C0A 1H0
Belfast   N/A
  A—Janice MacDonald
  C0A 1A0
Bunbury   1,046
  A—Carole Ferguson
  Box 1237, Charlottetown
  C1A 7M8

Cornwall   1,884
  A—Richard Montigny
  Box 183, C0A 1H0
Crossroads   1,751
  A—David Madren
  Box 2347, Charlottetown
  C1A 7N7
East Royalty   2,026
  A—Deena Robb
  1 Avonlea Dr.
  Charlottetown, C1C 1C8
Eastern Kings   N/A
  A—Mrs. Rufus Sweeny
  Elmira P.O., C0A 1K0
Hillsborough Park   977
  A—Nancy Coughlin
  Box 788, Charlottetown
  C1A 7L9
Malpeque Bay   N/A
  A—Mrs. Justin MacLellan
  R.R. 5, Kensington
  C0B 1M0
Miltonvale Park   1,073
  A—Judy K. MacDonald
  Box 38, R.R. 2, Winsloe
  C0A 2H0

North River   1,716
  A—Eldon Sentner
  Site 11, Box 2, R.R. 4
  Cornwall, C0A 1H0
O'Leary   819
  A—Beverley Coughlin
  Box 130, C0B 1V0
St. Eleanors   3,679
  A—Judie Goulden
  1 West Dr., C1N 4E5
Sherwood   5,719
  A—Joseph Coady
  31 Gordon Dr., C1A 6B8
Southport   1,313
  A—Carol Lowther
  Box 2404, Charlottetown
  C1A 8C1
Tignish   953
  A—Karen Buote
  Box 57, C0B 2B0
West Royalty   2,059
  A—Roderick Beck
  Box 365, Charlottetown
  C1A 7K7
Wilmot   1,700
  A—Susan Jeffery
  110 Gillespie Ave., C1N 4P5
Winsloe   1,118
  A—Betty Pryor
  Box 121, C0A 2H0

SUMMARY OF 1986 TOTALS

1 City	15,572
8 Towns	16,717
Total Urban (Census)	48,289
Total Rural (Census)	78,353
Total Urban and Rural (excl. Indians on Reserves)	126,646

INDIANS
Living on reserves:
  population 365
  (June 1/86)

QUEBEC

Forms of Municipal Government

Quebec municipalities are governed by two general laws, the *Municipal Code,* (R.S.Q. 1977, Chapter C-27.1) for the rural municipalities, and the *Cities and Towns Act* (R.S.Q. 1977, c. C-19) for urban municipalities. The cities of Montreal and Quebec are not, however, generally subject to this legislation but are governed by special charters. In addition, following the James Bay and Northern Quebec agreements with the native peoples, special legislation provides for the creation of Cree, Naskapi and northern villages, and the Kativik Regional Administration.

At the beginning of 1988, there were 1,506 local municipalities in Quebec, including 2 cities, 254 towns, 214 villages, 433 parishes, 112 townships, 12 united townships, 458 municipalities without designation, 8 Cree villages, 1 Naskapi village, and 12 northern villages. All local municipalities, except the 9 Cree and Naskapi villages, were included in one of the 99 "regional" municipalities covering the whole inhabited territory of the province. These included 95 regional county municipalities, 2 urban communities, 1 regional community, and the Kativik Regional Administration.

In 1979, the *Act respecting land use planning and development* (S.Q. 1979, c. 51) provided for the bringing together of rural and urban municipalities in a unified regional structure — the regional county municipality — for land use planning and development purposes. The council of a regional county municipality is composed of the mayors of all the member municipalities, with additional representatives for some of the larger municipalities, as provided in the letters patent establishing each regional municipality.

Another type of regional or second-tier institution has been in place since 1970. It consists of the two urban communities in the Montreal and the Quebec metropolitan areas respectively, and the regional community in the Hull-Gatineau metropolitan area. Each community has been established by a specific act and has somewhat different powers, although all three have responsibility for public transport, sewage treatment, solid waste disposal, property assessment, and planning. The Montreal Urban Community exercises additional powers with respect to air and water pollution, regional parks, and police.

Further information is published in the *Répertoire des municipalités du Québec 1988* (Government of Quebec, 1988).

Municipalities

(Municipalities with a population of less than 2,000 are generally not included. Population figures given are from the Ministry of Municipal Affairs' 1989 list.)

DG: directeur/trice général/e (city manager)   G: greffier (clerk/registrar)   Ma: maire/esse (mayor)
S: secretaire-trésorier/ère (secretary-treasurer)   T: trésorier/ère (treasurer)

CITÉS (cities)

Côte-St-Luc 28,582
Ma—Bernard Lang
DG—James Butler
5801, boul. Cavendish
H4W 3C3

Dorval 17,354
Ma—Peter Yeomans
DG—Pierre Larivée
60, av. Martin, H9S 3R4

VILLES (towns/cities)

Acton Vale 4,333
Ma—Gaston Giguère
S—Fernand Ménard
C.P. 640, J0H 1A0

Alma 25,923
Ma—Nicol Tremblay
DG—Gaetan Tremblay
140, rue St-Joseph sud
G8B 3R1

Amos 13,502
Ma—Jean-Paul Veilleux
DG—André Talbot
182, Première rue est
J9T 2G1

Amqui 4,338
Ma—Gaetan Archambault
G—Mario Lavoie
C.P. 784, G0J 1B0

Anjou 36,916
Ma—Richard Quirion
DG—Claude Denault
7701, boul. Louis-H.-
Lafontaine, H1K 4B9

Arthabaska 7,244
Ma—Pierre Roux
DG—Fernand Daigle
841, boul. Bois-Francs sud
G6P 5W3

Asbestos 6,961
Ma—André Bachand
DG—Yvon Hamel
C.P. 88, J1T 3M9

Aylmer 28,976
Ma—Constance Provost
DG—Denis Hubert
115, rue Principale
J9H 3M2

Baie-Comeau 26,244
Ma—Roger Thériault
DG—Paul Bourassa
19, av. Marquette, G4Z 1K5

Baie-d'Urfé 3,571
Ma—Anne Myles
DG—Richard White
20410, ch. Lakeshore
H9X 1P7

Baie-St-Paul 3,925
Ma—Jacynthe B.-Simard
DG—Gilles Bard
C.P. 969, G0A 1B0

Beaconsfield 19,301
Ma—Patricia M.-Rustad
DG—Georges Kromery
303, boul. Beaconsfield
H9W 4A7

Beauceville 4,129
Ma—J. Raymond Mathieu
DG—Hilaire Turmel
C.P. 579, G0S 1A0

Beauharnois 6,519
Ma—Claude Haineault
DG—Maurice Hews
103, rue St-Laurent
J6N 1V8

Beauport 62,869
Ma—Jacques Langlois
DG—Andre Letendre
C.P. 5187, G1E 6P4

Beaupré 2,725
Ma—Lucien Gauthier
S—Jean Paul Paré
C.P. 310, G0A 1E0

Bécancour 10,472
Ma—Jean-Guy Dubois
DG—M. Camirand
1295, rue Nicolas-Perrot
G0X 1B0

Bedford 2,733
Ma—Marcel Bechard
S—Bertrand Déry
C.P. 420, J0J 1A0

Beloeil 17,958
Ma—Julien Bussière
DG—Robert Weemaes
C.P. 210, J3G 4S9

Berthierville 3,805
Ma—Bernard Grégoire
DG—Pierre-Y. Laporte
C.P. 269, J0K 1A0

Black Lake 4,824
Ma—Georges-H. Cloutier
S—Réjean Martin
C.P. 310, G0N 1A0

Blainville 16,175
Ma—Paul Mercier
DG—Jacques Brault
1000, rue de la Mairie
J7C 3B5

Bois-des-Filion 4,935
Ma—Pierre Paquin
DG—Paul G. Brunet
60, 36e av. sud, J6Z 2G6

Boisbriand 14,360
Ma—Michel Gagné
DG—Clement Sauriol
940, Grande Allée
J7G 2J7

Boucherville 31,116
Ma—Hugues Aubertin
DG—Ronald Beaupré
500, rue de la Rivière-
aux-Pins, J4B 2Z7

Bromont 2,838
Ma—Pierre Bellefleur

G—Pierre Simoneau
89, boul. Bromont, J0E 1L0

Bromptonville 2,979
Ma—Clément Nault
DG—Michel Dupont
C.P. 610, J0B 1H0

Brossard 57,441
Ma—Georgette Lepage
DG—Richard Labrecque
3200, boul. Lapinière
J4Z 2B4

Buckingham 8,820
Ma—Reginald Scullion
DG—Michel Merleau
515, rue Charles, J8L 2K4

Cabano 3,284
Ma—Paulette G.-Bourgoin
DG—Jean-L. Ouellet
C.P. 188, G0L 1E0

Candiac 9,096
Ma—Claude Hébert
DG—Claude Donaldson
9, boul. Montcalm nord
Bur. 430, J5R 3L5

Cap-Chat 3,217
Ma—Augustin St-Laurent
G—Claudette Lemieux-Soucy
C.P. 279, G0J 1E0

Cap-de-la-Madeleine 32,800
Ma—Jean-Claude Beaumier
DG—Ronald Marcoux
C.P. 220, G8T 7W4

Cap-Rouge 12,101
Ma—André Juneau
DG—Louis Beaupré
4473, rue St-Félix, G1Y 3A6

Carignan 4,784
Ma—Paul-André Perreault
G—Andrée Daigle
1523, ch. de Chambly
J3L 3P9

Carleton 2,663
Ma—Denis Henry
S—André Allard
C.P. 237, G0C 1J0

Causapscal 2,339
Ma—Jean-Marie Abud
G—Victor Tremblay
1, rue St-Jacques nord
G0J 1J0

Chambly 12,869
Ma—Georges Flores
DG—Michel Lavoie
1, place de la Mairie
J3L 4X1

Chandler 3,715
Ma—Jean Paquin
DG—Paul Becu
C.P. 459, G0C 1K0

Chapais 2,875
Ma—Jacques Bérubé
S—Daniel Dufour
C.P. 380, G0W 1H0

Charlemagne 5,331
Ma—Jacques Laurin
G—Leo M. Lepage
29, rue St-Paul, J5Z 3C8

Charlesbourg 68,996
Ma—Ralph Mercier
DG—André Doré
160, 76ᵉ rue est
G1H 7H5

Charny 9,123
Ma—Marc Lavallée
DG—René Roy
5333, rue de la Symphonie
G6X 3B6

Château-Richer 3,802
Ma—Léo Laplante
S—François Gravel
8006, av. Royale
G0A 1N0

Châteauguay 37,865
Ma—Jean-Bosco Bourcier
DG—Jean-C. Boucher
5, boul. Youville
J6J 2P8

Chibougamau 9,922
Ma—Ronald Blackburn
DG—Gerald Fournier
650, Troisième rue
G8P 1P1

Chicoutimi 61,083
Ma—Ulric Blackburn
DG—Marcel Demers
C.P. 129, G7H 5B8

Clermont 3,426
Ma—Mathias Dufour
S—Guy-R. Savard
C.P. 760, G0T 1C0

Coaticook 6,440
Ma—André Langevin
DG—Roma Fluet
150, rue Child, J1A 2B3

Cowansville 11,643
Ma—Jacques Charbonneau
DG—Georges H. Bernier
220, place Municipale
J2K 1T4

Dégelis 3,528
Ma—Emilien Nadeau
DG—Jean-C. Dumont
C.P. 130, G0L 1H0

Delson 4,997
Ma—Georges Gagné
G—Nicole Perron
C.P. 40, J0L 1G0

Deux-Montagnes 10,531
Ma—Jean-Guy Bergeron
G—Luc Amireault
C.P. 55, J7R 4K1

Disraeli 3,004
Ma—André Rodrigue
DG—Emile Chamma
C.P. 2050, G0N 1E0

Dolbeau 8,554
Ma—Henri-Paul Brassard
DG—Gaston Blouin
1100, boul. Wallberg
G8L 1G7

Dollard-des-Ormeaux 43,089
Ma—Edward Janiszewski
DG—Wesley Lancaster
12001, boul. de Salaberry
H9B 2A7

Donnacona 5,435
Ma—Denis Denis
DG—Bernard Naud
138, av. Pleau, G0A 1T0

Dorion 5,469
Ma—André Bourbonnais
DG—André Chartrand
C.P. 70, J7V 5V8

Drummondville 36,020
Ma—Francine Ruest-Jutras
DG—Gerald Lapierre (p.i.)
C.P. 398, J2B 1G8

Dunham 3,108
Ma—Pierre Bernier
G—Pierre Loiselle
C.P. 70, J0E 1M0

East Angus 3,701
Ma—Roland Brousseau
S—Michel Roy
C.P. 400, J0B 1R0

Farnham 6,102
Ma—Jules Belisle
DG—Gilles Biron
477, rue de l'Hôtel-de-Ville
J2N 2H3

Fermont 3,592
Ma—Maurice Bérubé
DG—Paul Fillion
C.P. 520, G0G 1J0

Forestville 3,955
Ma—Gilbert Tremblay
DG—Raymond Joncas
C.P. 70, G0T 1E0

Gaspé 17,350
Ma—Robert Pidgeon
DG—Henri Bernier
C.P. 618, G0C 1R0

Gatineau 77,694
Ma—Robert Labine
DG—Claude Doucet (p.i.)
144, boul. de l'Hôpital
J8T 7S7

Granby 38,508
Ma—Mario Girard
DG—Robert Duval
87, rue Principale
J2G 2T8

Grand-Mère 14,582
Ma—Jacques Marchand
DG—Réal Beauchamp
C.P. 350, G9T 5L1

Grande-Rivière 4,413
Ma—Edmond Sirois
DG—John Carbery
C.P. 188, G0C 1V0

Greenfield Park 18,290
Ma—Stephen Olynyk
DG—Allen Mainville
156, boul. Churchill
J4V 2M3

Hampstead 7,451
Ma—Irving Adessky
DG—Wm. Remington
5569, ch. Queen Mary
H3X 1W5

Hudson 4,426
Ma—Taylor Bradbury
S—Louise Villandre
C.P. 550, J0P 1H0

Hull 58,722
Ma—Michel Legère
DG—J. Aime Desjardins
C.P. 1970, succ. B
J8X 3Y9

Huntingdon 2,919
Ma—Gérald Brisebois
G—Richard Alary
C.P. 898, J0S 1H0

Iberville 8,547
Ma—Luc Gauthier
DG—André L. Fréchette
855, Première rue, J2X 3C7

Joliette 16,845
Ma—Jacques Martin
DG—Jean Tremblay
614, boul. Manseau
J6E 6J3

Jonquière 58,467
Ma—Gilles Marceau
DG—Jean-M. Gagnon
C.P. 2000, G7X 7W7

Kirkland 13,376
Ma—Sam L. Elkas
DG—David Johnstone
17000, boul. Hymus
H9J 2W2

La Baie 20,753
Ma—Claude Richard
DG—Marc Potvin
200, rue Victoria, G7B 3M4

Lac-Brome 4,466
Ma—Gilles Descelles
DG—Raymond Poitras
C.P. 60, Knowlton, J0E 1V0

Lac-Etchemin 2,666
Ma—Pierre Pouliot
DG—Marcel Lachance
C.P. 370, G0R 1S0

Lac-Mégantic 5,732
Ma—Jean-Guy Cloutier
DG—Robert Charland
Bur. 200, G6B 1H6

Lachenaie 10,177
Ma—Marcel Therrien
DG—Denis Leclerc
3355, boul. St-Charles
J6W 3T8

Lachine 34,906
Ma—Guy Descary
DG—Robert Bourgeois
1800, boul. St-Joseph
H8S 2N4

Lachute 11,586
Ma—Kenneth Billingham
DG—Jean-Marc Lalande
380, rue Principale
J8H 1Y2

La Malbaie 3,948
Ma—Jules Maltais
DG—Otis Serge
280, rue Nairn, G5A 1L9

L'Ancienne-Lorette 13,747
Ma—Emile Loranger
DG—Michel Dagenais
1575, rue Turmel, G2E 3J5

La Pocatière 4,816
Ma—Louis-Joseph Gosselin
DG—Michel Beauchemin
C.P. 668, G0R 1Z0

La Prairie 11,072
Ma—Jean-Guy Tessier
DG—Roger Bérubé
600, boul. Ste-Elizabeth
J5R 1V1

LaSalle 75,621
Ma—Michel Leduc
DG—Robert Barbeau
55, av. Dupras, H8R 4A8

La Sarre 8,622
Ma—Paul-A. St-Pierre
DG—François Casaubon
6, Quatrième av. est
J9Z 1J9

L'Assomption 5,280
Ma—René Langlais
DG—Yves Landry
399, rue Dorval, J0K 1G0

La Tuque 10,723
Ma—André Duchesneau
DG—André L'Esperance
558, rue Commerciale
G9X 3A9

Laurentides 2,018
Ma—Normand Choquette
S—Jean-G. Champoux
C.P. 128, J0R 1C0

Lauzon 13,620
Ma—Jean-Marc Lessard
DG—Michel Bernier
10, rue Giguère, G6V 1N6

Laval 284,164
Ma—Claude Lefebvre
DG—Claude Asselin
1, place du Souvenir
Chomedey, H7V 1W7

Lebel-sur-Quévillon 3,465
Ma—Denis Lévesque
DG—Jean-Y. Truchon
C.P. 430, J0Y 1X0

Le Gardeur 9,230
Ma—Gilles Foisy
DG—Michel Gobeil
1, montée des Arsenaux
J5Z 2C1

Lemoyne 5,634
Ma—Louise Gravel
S—André Bellefeuille
2205, rue St-Georges
J4R 1V7

Lennoxville 3,898
Ma—Duncan Bruce
S—Jacques Gagnon
150, rue Queen, J1M 1J6

L'Epiphanie 2,846
Ma—Donald Bricault
G—Louis Bilodeau
C.P. 190, J0K 1J0

Léry 2,316
Ma—John Goodfellow
S—Hélène Boudreau
1, rue Hôtel-de-Ville
J6N 1E8

Lévis 18,310
Ma—Vincent Chagnon
DG—Michel Thibault
225, côté du Passage
G6V 5T4

L'Ile-Perrot 6,586
Ma—Pierre Bleau
DG—Yvon Veillette
110, boul. Perrot, J7V 3G1

Longueuil 125,441
Ma—Roger Ferland
DG—Jean Verdy
C.P. 5000, J4K 4Y7

Loretteville 14,335
Ma—Denis Giguère
DG—Gilles Martel
305, rue Racine, G2B 1E7

Lorraine 7,334
Ma—Laurent Belley
DG—Roger Lepage

33, boul. de Gaulle
J6Z 3W9

Louiseville 8,062
Ma—Sylvain Desaulniers
DG—Ghislain Lessard
C.P. 38, J5V 2L6

Magog 13,530
Ma—Paul-René Gilbert
DG—Yves Langlois
C.P. 249, J1X 1Y4

Malartic 4,474
Ma—Jacques Plante
DG—Réjean Hamel
C.P. 3090, J0Y 1Z0

Maniwaki 5,168
Ma—Gabriel Lefebvre
DG—Daniel Mayrand
186, rue Principale sud
J9E 1Z9

Maple Grove 2,127
Ma—Jacques Gendron
S—Dina Larouche
149, rue St-Laurent
J6N 1K2

Marieville 4,913
Ma—Armand Gladu
DG—Claude Rondeau
C.P. 980, J0L 1J0

Mascouche 21,285
Ma—Bernard Patenaude
G—Jacques Lacroix
3034, boul. Ste-Marie
J7K 1P1

Masson 4,842
Ma—Robert Rochon
S—Pierre Hayes
57, ch. de Montréal-est
J0X 2H0

Matagami 2,738
Ma—Robert Labelle
DG—Jean-Robert Gagnon
C.P. 160, J0Y 2A0

Matane 13,243
Ma—Maurice Gauthier
DG—Denis Paquet
230, av. St-Jérôme
G4W 3A2

Mercier 7,264
Ma—Jocelyn Lazure
G—Chantal Bergeron
64, boul. St-Jean-
Baptiste est, J6R 2L3

Métabetchouan 3,285
Ma—Marcel Duchesne
DG—Laurent Rheault
C.P. 367, G0W 2A0

Mirabel 13,875
Ma—Hubert Meilleur
DG—Yves Lacroix
C.P. 60, Ste-Monique
J0N 1R0

Mistassini 6,734
Ma—Jean-Marc Gendron
DG—Melville Morissette
C.P. 219, G0W 2C0

Mont-Joli 6,670
Ma—Jean-Louis Desrosiers
DG—Gilles Thibault
40, av. L'Hôtel-de-Ville
G5H 1W8

Mont-Laurier 7,937
Ma—Jean-Claude Lebel
DG—Vianney Landreville
485, rue Mercier, J9L 3N8

Montmagny 11,958
Ma—Gilbert Normand
G—Louise Bherer
134, rue St-Jean-Baptiste est
G5V 1K6

Montréal 1,015,420
Ma—Jean Doré
G—Leon Laberge
275, rue Notre-Dame est
H2Y 1C6

Montréal-Est 3,592
Ma—Yvon Labrosse
DG—Réjean Guillette
11370, rue Notre-Dame est
H1B 2W6

Montréal-Nord 90,303
Ma—Yves Ryan
DG—Jean-G. Themens
4242, pl. de L'Hôtel de Ville
H1H 1S5

Montréal-Ouest 5,200
Ma—Roy D. Locke
DG—Ron Fitzgibbon
50, av. Westminster sud
H4X 1Y7

Mont-Royal 18,350
Ma—Vera Danyluk
DG—John Warren
90, av. Roosevelt, H3R 1Z5

Mont-St-Hilaire 10,588
Ma—Honorius Charbonneau
DG—Laurent Olivier
100, rue du Centre-Civique
J3H 3M8

Murdochville 2,302
Ma—Bertrand St-Pierre
DG—Daniel Bujold
C.P. 1120, G0E 1W0

New Richmond 4,100
Ma—Jean-Marie Jobin
DG—Denis Gagnon
145, boul. Perron est
G0C 2B0

Nicolet 5,065
Ma—Clément Dubois
DG—Frank Vallée
C.P. 670, J0G 1E0

Normandin 4,069
Ma—Yvette Nadeau
G—Florian Girard
C.P. 520, G0W 2E0

Notre-Dame-du-Lac 2,239
Ma—Réal Voisine
DG—Yves Rousseau
C.P. 158, G0L 1X0

Otterburn Park 4,571
Ma—Marcel Lacoste
S—Henri Pagé
472, av. Prince-Edward
J3H 1W4

Outremont 23,080
Ma—Jérôme Choquette
DG—J. Victor Mainville
510, av. Davaar
H2V 2B9

Percé 4,686
Ma—Yvon Gaudreault
S—Bruno Cloutier
C.P. 99, G0C 2L0

Pierrefonds 39,605
Ma—Cyril McDonald
DG—Gerard Le Page
C.P. 2500, H9H 4N2

Pincourt   9,121
Ma—Michel Kandyba
DG—Guy-Armand Paquette
919, ch. Duhamel
J7V 4G8
Plessisville   7,042
Ma—Madeleine Dusseault
DG—Jean Marcoux
1700, rue St-Calixte
G6L 1R3
Pohénégamook   3,526
Ma—André Senechal
DG—Alain Gagné
C.P. 159, G0L 1J0
Pointe-Claire   26,026
Ma—Malcolm Knox
DG—Tom Buffitt
451, boul. St-Jean
H9R 3J3
Port-Cartier   6,858
Ma—Anthony Detroio
DG—Bernard Otis
40, av. Parent, G5B 2G5
Princeville   3,905
Ma—Jean-Maurice Talbot
S—Fernand Poiré
C.P. 370, G0P 1E0
Québec   164,580
Ma—Jean Pelletier
DG—Jacques Perreault
C.P. 700, G1R 4S9
Repentigny   40,778
Ma—Jacques Dupuis
DG—Louis W. Le Page
435, boul. d'Iberville
J6A 2B6
Richelieu   2,020
Ma—Pierre Lareau
S—Claire Côte
1030, Deuxième rue
J3L 3Y1
Richmond   3,260
Ma—Marc-André Martel
S—Gilles Ducharme
745, rue Gouin, J0B 2H0
Rigaud   2,203
Ma—Jean Goupil
S—Marielle D'Aoust
C.P. 460, J0P 1P0
Rimouski   29,672
Ma—Philippe Michaud
DG—Claude Sirois
C.P. 710, G5L 7C7
Rivière-du-Loup   13,321
Ma—Jean-Léon Marquis
G—Georges Deschênes
C.P. 37, G5R 3Y7
Roberval   11,448
Ma—André-Guy Laroche
DG—Jeannot Gagnon
851, boul. St-Joseph
G8H 2L6
Rock Forest   12,210
Ma—Gaétan Lavallée
DG—Jean Rouillard
C.P. 1830, J1N 1C3
Rosemère   8,673
Ma—Pierre Robitaille
DG—Guy Robitaille
100, rue Charbonneau
J7A 3W1
Rouyn-Noranda   26,189
Ma—Jacques Bibeau

DG—Denis Charron
C.P. 220, J9X 5C3
Roxboro   6,138
Ma—William G. Boll
DG—David Johnstone
13, rue Centre-Commercial
H8Y 2N9
Ste-Adèle   4,272
Ma—Daniel J. Dubé
DG—Denis Lemay
C.P. 1108, J0R 1L0
**Ste-Agathe-des-
Monts**   5,254
Ma—Marc Cloutier
G—Marcelle Pellerin
C.P. 40, J8C 1M9
Ste-Anne-de-Beaupré   3,162
Ma—Jean Boisvert
S—Michel Jean
9336, av. Royale, G0A 3C0
Ste-Anne-de-Bellevue   4,140
Ma—René Martin
DG—G. Lafrenière
C.P. 40, H9X 1M2
Ste-Anne-des-Monts   5,993
Ma—Regis Vallée
DG—Georges-E. L'Italien
C.P. 458, G0E 2G0
Ste-Anne-des-Plaines   8,931
Ma—Jean-Marc Nepveu
DG—Serge Lepage
139, boul. Ste-Anne
J0N 1H0
St-Antoine   7,691
Ma—Normand Plouffe
DG—Serge Forget
854, boul. St-Antoine
J7Z 3C5
St-Basile-le-Grand   8,852
Ma—Bernard Gagnon
DG—Cecile Cleroux
204, rue Principale
J0L 1S0
St-Bruno-de-Montarville   23,103
Ma—Marcel Dulude
G—Hélène Drapeau
1585, boul. Montarville
J3V 3T8
Ste-Catherine   7,020
Ma—Raymond Bellavance
DG—Pierre Beaudry
5465, boul. Marie-Victorin
J0L 1E0
St-Césaire   2,960
Ma—Carol Wagner
S—Pierre Despars
C.P. 570, J0L 1T0
St-Constant   12,508
Ma—Jacques Perreault
DG—Gerald Lamoureux
C.P. 130, J0L 1X0
**St-David-de-
l'Auberivière**   5,769
Ma—André Carrier
DG—Germain Lavoie
784, rue Commerciale
G6W 1E9
St-Eustache   32,226
Ma—Jean Prevost
DG—Ronald Biard
145, rue St-Louis, J7R 1X9
St-Félicien   9,324
Ma—Benoît Laprise

DG—Christian Perron
C.P. 7000, G8K 2R5
Ste-Foy   69,615
Ma—Andrée P. Boucher
DG—Gilles Bertrand
1000, rte de l'Eglise
G1V 4E1
St-Gabriel   2,929
Ma—Maurice Roberge
DG—Robert Desrosiers
C.P. 750, J0K 2N0
Ste-Geneviève   2,588
Ma—Jacques Cardinal
G—Luc Tremblay
15736-A, rue Pierrefonds
H9H 2X2
St-Georges   11,723
Ma—Alain Gilbert
DG—Michel Lambert
11700, boul. Lacroix
G5Y 1L3
St-Georges-Ouest   6,352
Ma—Richard Busque
DG—Laurent Nadeau
1500, Sixième av., G5Y 3W1
St-Hubert   66,218
Ma—Pierre Girard
DG—Yvan Grenier
5900, boul. Cousineau
J3Y 7K8
St-Hyacinthe   38,603
Ma—Clément Rhéaume
DG—Alain Rivard
C.P. 10, J2S 5B2
St-Jean-Chrysostome   8,797
Ma—Arthur Roberge
DG—J. Leblanc
959, rue de l'Hôtel-de-Ville
G6Z 2N8
St-Jean-sur-Richelieu   34,745
Ma—Delbert Deschambault
DG—Edouard Bonaldo
C.P. 1025, J3B 7B2
St-Jérôme   23,316
Ma—Jean-Claude Hébert
DG—Normand Verville
280, rue Labelle
J7Z 5L1
St-Joseph-de-Beauce   3,183
Ma—Hermann Cloutier
S—Jacques Giguère
C.P. 88, G0S 2V0
St-Joseph-de-Sorel   2,272
Ma—Olivar Gravel
S—Jean-G. Trépanier
700, rue Montcalm
J3R 1C9
St-Jovite   3,744
Ma—Bernard Forget
S—Jacques St-Louis
C.P. 159, J0T 2H0
Ste-Julie   15,502
Ma—Maurice Savaria
DG—Pierre Bernardin
C.P. 60, J0L 2C0
St-Lambert   20,030
Ma—Eric Sharp
DG—Paul-H. Savard
55, rue Argyle, J4P 2H3
St-Laurent   67,002
Ma—Marcel Laurin
DG—Pierre Lebeau
777, boul. Laurentien
H4M 2M7

St-Léonard   75,947
　Ma—Raymond Rénaud
　DG—Pierre Santamaria
　8400, boul. Lacordaire
　H1R 3B1

St-Luc   10,951
　Ma—Gilles Dolbec
　DG—Jean-P. Bruneau
　C.P. 90, J0J 2A0

Ste-Marie   9,536
　Ma—Pierre-M. Vachon
　DG—Gilles Fortin
　C.P. 1750, G6E 3C7

Ste-Marthe-sur-le-Lac   6,143
　Ma—Michel Leroux
　DG—Eugene McClish
　3000, ch. Oka, J0N 1P0

St-Nicolas   6,123
　Ma—Yvan Canac-Marquis
　G—Yvon Lemay
　1365, rte Marie-Victorin
　G0S 2Z0

St-Pamphile   3,224
　Ma—Réal Laverdière
　S—Richard Pelletier
　C.P. 638, G0R 3X0

St-Pascal   2,718
　Ma—Ernest Ouellet
　DG—Jacques Tanguay
　C.P. 250, G0L 3Y0

St-Pierre   4,944
　Ma—Yvon Boyer
　DG—Gerard Goyette
　69, Cinquième av., H8R 1P1

St-Raymond   3,422
　Ma—Richard Corriveau
　S—Réjeanne Julien
　C.P. 1538, G0A 4G0

St-Rédempteur   5,033
　Ma—Claude Boiteau
　DG—Michel Hamel
　95, 19e rue, G0S 3B0

St-Rémi   5,288
　Ma—Charles Verge
　DG—Fernand Wells
　C.P. 578, J0L 2L0

St-Romuald   9,953
　Ma—Denis Grenier
　DG—Sabin Tremblay
　C.P. 2007, G6W 5M3

Ste-Thérèse   19,336
　Ma—Elie Fallu
　DG—Claude Dagenais
　C.P. 100, J7E 4H7

St-Tite   2,831
　Ma—Maurice Roberge
　DG—Pierre-A. Desaulniers
　540, rue Notre-Dame
　G0X 3H0

Salaberry-de-Valleyfield   27,849
　Ma—Gaétan Rousse
　DG—Robert Cyr
　61, rue Ste-Cécile
　J6T 1L8

Senneterre   4,017
　Ma—Gerard Lafontaine
　DG—Yvon Boucher
　C.P. 789, J0Y 2M0

Sept-Îles   25,637
　Ma—Jean-Marc Dion
　DG—Marcel Blouin
　546, av. Dequen, G4R 2R4

Shawinigan   21,470
　Ma—Roland Desaulniers

　DG—Claude Paille
　C.P. 400, G9N 6V3

Shawinigan-Sud   11,412
　Ma—Claude Pinard
　DG—Charles Mills
　1550, 118e rue, G9P 3G8

Sherbrooke   74,438
　Ma—Jean-Paul Pelletier
　DG—Roch Letourneau
　C.P. 610, J1H 5C1

Sillery   12,784
　Ma—Margaret Delisle
　DG—Claude Delisle
　C.P. 215, G1T 1Z2

Sorel   19,522
　Ma—Marcel Gauthier
　DG—Georges Zakaib
　C.P. 368, J3P 7K1

Témiscaming   2,546
　Ma—Roger Labrosse
　S—Richard Shank
　451, rue Kipawa, J0Z 3R0

Terrebonne   33,310
　Ma—Irenée Forget
　DG—Charles Dubuc
　775, St-Jean-Baptiste
　J6W 1B5

Thetford Mines   18,561
　Ma—Henri Therrien
　DG—Yvan Faucher
　C.P. 489, G6G 5T3

Thurso   2,578
　Ma—Desmond Murphy
　S—Mario Boyer
　161, rue Galipeau
　J0X 3B0

Tracy   12,546
　Ma—Emile Parent
　DG—Menard Anctil
　3025, boul. de la Mairie
　J3R 1C2

Trois-Pistoles   4,290
　Ma—Jean-Marc D'Amours
　DG—Gabriel Desjardins
　C.P. 550, G0L 4K0

Trois-Rivières   50,122
　Ma—Gilles Beaudoin
　DG—Jean-Luc Julien
　C.P. 368, G9A 5H3

Trois-Rivières-Ouest   15,538
　Ma—Jean-Charles Charest
　DG—Roland Lottinville
　500, côte Richelieu
　G9A 2Z1

Val-Bélair   13,105
　Ma—Claude Beaudoin
　DG—Gaétan Thellend
　1105, av. de l'Eglise nord
　G3K 1X5

Val-d'Or   22,252
　Ma—André Pelletier
　DG—Guy Faucher
　C.P. 400, J9P 4P4

Valcourt   2,501
　Ma—Camille Rouillard
　G—Manon Beauchemin
　C.P. 340, J0E 2L0

Vanier   10,208
　Ma—Robert Cardinal
　DG—Gaétan Binet
　233, boul. Pierre-Bertrand
　G1M 2C7

Varennes   10,489
　Ma—Jean Robert

　DG—Luce Doucet
　C.P. 800, J0L 2P0

Vaudreuil   8,253
　Ma—Réjean Boyer
　DG—Jean-Yves Truchon
　2, rue Dutrisac, J7V 7E6

Verdun   60,246
　Ma—Raymond Savard
　DG—Jean-P. Hébert
　4555, av. Verdun, H4G 1M4

Victoriaville   22,500
　Ma—Denis St-Pierre
　DG—Albert R. Audet
　C.P. 370, G6P 6T2

Ville-Marie   2,621
　Ma—Jacques Leblanc
　S—Denise Ringuette (p.i.)
　C.P. 730, J0Z 3W0

Warwick   2,807
　Ma—Gérard Laroche
　S—Jacques Hamel
　C.P. 70, J0A 1M0

Waterloo   4,265
　Ma—André Belanger
　G—René Bellefeuille
　417, rue de la Cour
　J0E 2N0

Westmount   20,011
　Ma—May Cutler
　DG—Peter Patenaude
　4333, rue Sherbrooke ouest
　H3Z 1E2

Windsor   4,850
　Ma—Adrien Peloquin
　G—Joseph Plante
　22, rue St-Georges, J1S 1J3

VILLAGES

Bernierville   2,032
　Ma—Bernard Larochelle
　S—Sylvie Tardif
　C.P. 340, St-Ferdinand
　G0N 1N0

Brownsburg   2,679
　Ma—Bernard Dumas
　S—Marc Carrière
　C.P. 40, J0V 1A0

Chute-aux-Outardes   2,219
　Ma—Yoland Gagné
　S—Gilles Lavoie
　C.P. 219, G0H 1C0

Ferme-Neuve   2,172
　Ma—Carol Lafontaine
　S—Claude Campeau
　C.P. 370, J0W 1C0

Lafontaine   5,344
　Ma—Raymond Laroche
　S—Fernand Campbell
　70, 106e av., J7Y 1G5

L'Annonciation   2,318
　Ma—Jocelyn Séguin
　S—Lise Cadieux
　C.P. 398, J0T 1T0

Lavaltrie   2,690
　Ma—Gérard Lavallée
　S—Réjean Nantais
　C.P. 90, J0K 1H0

McMasterville   3,665
　Ma—Ferdinand Borremans
　S—Jeannette Lemaire
　300, rue Caron, J3G 1S5

Melocheville   2,050
Ma—Jean-Paul Roy
S—Normand Charette
380, boul. Edgar-Hébert
J0S 1J0

Mont-Rolland   2,123
Ma—Gilles Legault
S—Jacques Dupras
C.P. 280, J0R 1G0

Napierville   2,551
Ma—Michel Charbonneau
S—Michel Duval
C.P. 1120, J0J 1L0

Pointe-Calumet   3,450
Ma—André Soucy
S—Pierre-Yves Vermette
861, boul. de la Chapelle
J0N 1G0

Pont-Rouge   3,694
Ma—Marcel Bédard
S—Marc-A. Trudel
C.P. 1240, G0A 2X0

Price   2,081
Ma—Claude Dupont
S—Louise Furlong
18, rue Fournier, G0J 1Z0

Rawdon   3,032
Ma—Michel Lane
S—Jean-Guy Charest
C.P. 550, J0K 1S0

Rimouski-Est   2,354
Ma—Gilbert St-Laurent
S—Denis Ouellet
540, rue St-Germain est
G5L 1E9

St-Boniface-de-
Shawinigan   3,294
Ma—Hilarion Gelinas
S—Jacques Caron
140, rue Guimont, G0X 2L0

St-Emile   5,521
Ma—Rénaud Auclair
S—Jean Savard
C.P. 9, G0A 3N0

St-Georges   3,653
Ma—Guy Gelinas
S—Jean Bilodeau
505, 105e av., G9T 3H3

St-Jacques   2,153
Ma—François Migue
S—Gilles Sincerny
16, rue Maréchal, J0K 2R0

St-Jean-de-Boischatel   3,662
Ma—Jacques Couture
S—Michel Lefebvre
C.P. 158, Boischatel
G0A 1H0

St-Marc-des-Carrières   2,084
Ma—Guy Denis
S—Jean-P. Julien
965, boul. Bona-Dussault
G0A 4B0

St-Prime   2,499
Ma—Bertrand Grenier
S—Regis Girard
599, rue Principale
G0W 2W0

Ste-Rosalie   3,225
Ma—Leon Plante
S—Diane Beauregard
C.P. 30, J0H 1X0

St-Sauveur-des-Monts   2,435
Ma—Georges Filion

S—Normand Patrice
C.P. 130, J0R 1R0

St-Timothée   2,073
Ma—Jean-N. Tessier
S—Jean-L. Sicotte
C.P. 69, J0S 1X0

St-Zotique   2,025
Ma—Yvon Leroux
S—Louise Viau-Perron
C.P. 150, J0P 1Z0

Val-David   2,497
Ma—Réal Tessier
S—André Desjardins
C.P. 220, J0T 2N0

PAROISSES (parishes)

Baie-St-Paul   2,139
Ma—Jean-René Fortin
S—Roland Lepage
C.P. 220, G0A 1B0

Bellefeuille   7,697
Ma—Gilles Bouchard
S—Claudette Pion-Moreau
999, rue de l'Eglise
J0R 1A0

L'Ange-Gardien   2,412
Ma—Raymond Gariepy
S—Jacques Villeneuve
6405, av. Royale, G0A 2K0

La Plaine   5,996
Ma—Michel Monette
S—Marc Vallières
C.P. 90, J0N 1B0

L'Assomption   3,617
Ma—Jean-Guy Masse
S—Jean-D. Savoie
1059, boul. L'Ange-
Gardien nord, J0K 1G0

L'Epiphanie   2,152
Ma—Pierre Goyette
S—Nicole Renaud
48, rue Leblanc, J0K 1J0

Notre-Dame-de-L'Île-
Perrot   3,880
Ma—Marcel Lalonde
S—Serge Jolin
21, rue de l'Eglise, J7V 5V6

Notre-Dame-des-
Prairies   5,809
Ma—François Arnault
S—Yves Poirier
225, boul. Antonio-Barette
J6E 1E7

Notre-Dame-du-Mont-
Carmel   4,054
Ma—Pierre Bouchard
S—Jean Lachance
3860, rue de l'Hôtel-de-
Ville, G0X 3J0

Oka   2,104
Ma—Yvan Patry
S—Jean-Pierre Quevillon
C.P. 38, J0N 1E0

Plessisville   2,723
Ma—Gerard Dubois
S—Jacques Leclerc
C.P. 245, G6L 2Y7

St-Alexis-des-Monts   2,604
Ma—Jean-Paul Plante
S—Gilles Frappier
C.P. 300, J0K 1V0

St-Ambroise-de-Kildare   2,731
Ma—Gilles Courchesne
S—Yvon Dûcharme
C.P. 57, J0K 1C0

St-Anaclet-de-Lessard   2,483
Ma—Robert Ross
S—Danielle Albert
C.P. 99, G0K 1H0

St-André-d'Acton   2,063
Ma—Marcel Chagnon
S—Marthe Gauthier
C.P. 309, J0H 1A0

St-Anicet   2,104
Ma—René Brisebois
S—C. Genier-Leblanc
335, av. Jules-Léger
J0S 1M0

Ste-Anne-de-Sorel   2,662
Ma—Rejane T.-Salvail
S—Peter S. White
1685, ch. du Chenal-du-Moine
J3P 5N3

St-Antoine-de-Lavaltrie   2,630
Ma—Jacques Auclair
S—Yvon Mousseau
C.P. 300, J0K 1H0

St-Antonin   3,203
Ma—Claude Bélanger
S—Gina Dionne
C.P. 340, G0L 2J0

St-Athanase   5,715
Ma—Réal Oligny
S—C. Bergeron-Laurin
90, rte 104
D'Iberville, J2X 1H1

St-Augustin-de-
Desmaures   9,013
Ma—Denis Côté
S—Daniel Martineau
200, rte de Fossambault
G3A 2E3

St-Benoît-Joseph-Labré   2,102
Ma—Jean-Marc Paquet
S—Thérèse Côté-Gagne
C.P. 1030, Amqui
G0J 1B0

St-Colomban   2,684
Ma—François Lemay
S—Gerard Gagné
325, montée de l'Eglise
J0R 1N0

St-Damien-de-Buckland   2,260
Ma—Paul Veilleux
S—Jacques Thibault
C.P. 40, G0R 2Y0

St-Dunstan-du-Lac-
Beauport   3,713
Ma—Michel Giroux
S—Henri Zicat
C.P. 159, Lac-Beauport
G0A 2C0

St-Elie d'Orford   3,700
Ma—Richard Gingras
S—Pierre Auger
161, ch. St-Roch, J0B 2S0

St-Etienne-des-Grès   3,303
Ma—Jules Bellemare
S—Pierre St-Onge
1260, rue St-Alphonse
G0X 2P0

St-Fabien   2,024
Ma—François Beauchesne
S—Murielle Cloutier
C.P. 70, G0L 2Z0

St-Félix-de-Valois   3,054
Ma—Germain Aubin
S—Gaston Charette
600, ch. Joliette, J0K 2M0
St-Gabriel-de-Brandon   2,042
Ma—Jacques Sarrazin
S—André Comtois
C.P. 929, J0K 2N0
Ste-Geneviève-de-
Berthier   2,079
Ma—André Perrault
S—Thérèse Lavallée
400, rang Rivière-Bayonne sud
Berthier, J0K 1A0
St-Georges-Est   2,418
Ma—Mario Veilleux
S—Yvon Gilbert
11785, Première av.
G5Y 2C7
St-Gérard-Majella   2,514
Ma—Jacques Raynault
S—Diane Rassette
2680, rte 343, J0K 3P0
Ste-Hélène-de-
Breakeyville   2,385
Ma—Gilles Boutin
S—Jean-Guy Brassard
67, rue Ste-Hélène
Breakeyville, G0S 1E0
St-Hippolyte   3,626
Ma—Georges Loulou
DG—Rosaire Sénécal
2253, ch. les Hauteurs
J0R 1P0
St-Isidore   2,262
Ma—Bernard Dubuc
S—Daniel Vinet
671, rue St-Régis, J0L 2A0
St-Jean-Baptiste   2,711
Ma—Richard Turcotte
S—Denis Meunier
C.P. 300, J0L 2B0
St-Jean-Baptiste-
de-Nicolet   2,443
Ma—Jean-Jacques Duval
S—Sylvie Provencher
C.P. 790, Nicolet
J0G 1E0
St-Jean-de-Matha   2,926
Ma—Muguette Perreault
S—Jean-M. Gadoury
C.P. 60, J0K 2S0
St-Joseph-du-Lac   2,691
Ma—Paul-Yvon Lauzon
S—Fernand Larocque
1110, ch. Principale
J0N 1M0
Ste-Julienne   4,972
Ma—Eugène Marsan
S—Jimmy Laveaux
C.P. 250, J0K 2T0
Ste-Justine   2,035
Ma—Raymond Marceau
S—Gilles Vézina
C.P. 10, G0R 1Y0
St-Lambert-de-Lauzon   3,611
Ma—Joseph Stella
S—Magdalen Blanchet
C.P. 160, G0S 2W0
St-Lazare   5,064
Ma—Jerry Weiner
S—Gaétan Prévost
C.P. 360, J0P 1V0

St-Lin   5,398
Ma—André Auger
S—Linda Duquette
C.P. 220, Laurentides
J0R 1C0
St-Louis-de-France   5,579
Ma—André Levasseur
S—Gilles Toupin
100, rue de la Mairie
G8W 1S1
Ste-Madeleine-de-
Rigaud   2,800
Ma—Jean-Guy Faubert
S—Jean-D. Séguin
C.P. 580, J0P 1P0
St-Malachie-d'Ormstown   2,041
Ma—Harold Merson
S—Jean-C. Marcil
C.P. 279, Ormstown
J0S 1K0
Ste-Marie-de-Monnoir   2,235
Ma—Lise Rainville
S—Francine Guertin
C.P. 1396, J0L 1J0
St-Martin   2,445
Ma—Jean-Marc Paquet
S—Carmelle Veilleux
C.P. 99, G0M 1B0
Ste-Martine   2,186
Ma—Léo Myre
S—C. Dubuc-Lefebvre
C.P. 430, J0S 1V0
St-Mathias-sur-
Richelieu   3,065
Ma—Jean Vézina
S—Normande Vigeant
C.P. 90, J0L 2G0
St-Maurice   2,157
Ma—Onil Gagnon
S—Gisele Lefebvre
C.P. 9, G0X 2X0
St-Patrice-de-la-
Rivière-du-Loup   3,021
Ma—Marc Pelletier
S—Adryen Sénéchal
252, rue Fraser
Rivière-du-Loup, G5R 3Y4
St-Paul-d'Abbotsford   2,666
Ma—Martial Gousy
S—Josée Parent
926, rue Principale est
J0E 1A0
St-Philippe   3,357
Ma—Carol Dupuis
S—Alfred Trudeau
C.P. 30, J0L 2K0
St-Pie   2,234
Ma—Maurice St-Pierre
S—Cecile Charron
C.P. 519, J0H 1W0
St-Pierre-de-Sorel   5,098
Ma—Réjean Auger
S—Raymond Fortier
1275, ch. des Patriotes
J3P 2N4
St-Raphaël-de-l'Île-
Bizard   8,535
Ma—Jacques Denis
S—Gaston Ladouceur
350, rue de l'Église
H9C 1G9
St-Raymond   4,416
Ma—André Girard

S—Guy Alain
111, rte des Pionniers
G0A 4G0
St-Roch-de-l'Achigan   3,535
Ma—Marcel Henri
S—Philippe Riopelle
C.P. 480, J0K 3H0
St-Thomas   2,689
Ma—René Vincent
S—Roger Drainville
C.P. 390, J0K 3L0
St-Thomas-d'Aquin   3,004
Ma—Jean Overbeek
S—Murielle Archambault
105, rue Prévert, J0H 2A0
St-Timothée   5,381
Ma—Rolland Latreille
S—André Halle
C.P. 219, J0S 1X0
Ste-Victoire-
d'Arthabaska   6,038
Ma—Henri Normand
S—André Allard
50, La Grande Ligne
Victoriaville, G6P 6R9
Ste-Victoire-de-Sorel   2,150
Ma—Joseph-A. Papillon
S—Michel St-Martin
510, ch. Ste-Victoire
J0G 1T0

CANTONS (townships)

Ascot   8,854
Ma—Robert Pouliot
S—Diane Groleau
1955, rue Belvedère sud
Bur. 100, J1H 5Y3
Chatham   3,587
Ma—Claude Ouellette
S—Christiane Lalonde
C.P. 51, St-Philippe
J0V 2A0
Granby   8,145
Ma—Louis Choinière
S—Real Paré
C.P. 579, J2G 8E9
Hinchinbrook   2,225
Ma—Roland Greenbank
S—Eveline Brunet
1056, ch. Brook
Athelstan, J0S 1A0
Hull, partie-ouest   3,908
Ma—Judith Grant
DG—Gilles-A. Dupont
Old Chelsea, J0X 2N0
Magog   3,631
Ma—Rosaire Fillion
S—Jean-P. Asselin
R.R. 2, J1X 3W3
Rawdon   2,641
Ma—Réjean Neveu
S—Ginette Filion
C.P. 730, J0K 1S0
Shefford   3,278
Ma—Rolland Ostiguy
S—Maurice Campbell
415, rue Court, Waterloo
J0E 2N0
Shipton   3,089
Ma—Marcel Grenier
S—Michel Lecours
C.P. 209, Danville, J0A 1A0

Stoke 2,142
Ma—Monique Demers
S—Diane Roy-Dubois
C.P. 81, J0B 3G0
Stoneham-et-Tewkesbury (CU) 3,743
Ma—Rodrigue Harvey
S—Irma Johnston
545, Première av.
Stoneham, G0A 4P0
Thetford, partie sud 3,189
Ma—Lorenzo St-Cyr
S—André Bourret
2093, rue Notre-Dame nord
G6G 2Y9
Tremblay 3,292
Ma—Noël Tremblay
S—Laurent Riverin
1215, rte Martel, G7H 5B2
Warwick 2,002
Ma—André Laroche
S—Michel Fournier
281A, rue St-Louis ouest
J0A 1M0

(CU) Canton-uni (United township)

MUNICIPALITIES WITH NO DESIGNATION

Ascot-Corner 2,179
Ma—Jacques Langlois
S—Suzanne B.-Jacques
C.P. 29, J0B 1A0
Baie-James 2,869
Ma—Laurent Levasseur
DG—Claude Hubert
C.P. 500, Matagami
J0Y 2A0
Bernières 6,110
Ma—Raynald Breton
S—Roger Noël
1240, ch. Filteau, G7A 1A5
Bonaventure 2,995
Ma—Réal Grant
S—Andre Mimeault
C.P. 428, G0C 1E0
Brigham 2,115
Ma—Normand Sirois
S—Jacqueline Giroux
116, av. des Cèdres
J0E 1J0
Cantley 3,550
Ma—Bernard Bouthilette
S—Anne-Marie Paul
C.P. 552, J0X 1L0
Cap-St-Ignace 3,207
Ma—Léandre Boutin
S—Donald Bernier
C.P. 190, G0R 1H0
Cap-Santé 2,438
Ma—Roger Dusseault
S—Jacques Blais
194, rte 138, G0A 1L0
Caplan 2,076
Ma—Doris Boissonnault
S—Argee Garant
C.P. 360, G0C 1H0
Contrecoeur 5,553
Ma—Roch Bernier

S—Yves Beaulieu
440, rue Ducharme
J0L 1C0
Coteau-du-Lac 3,537
Ma—Henri-Paul Desforges
S—Guy Lauzon
C.P. 240, J0P 1B0
Côte-Nord-du-Golfe-St-Laurent 5,315
Admin.—Richmond Monger
Chevery, G0G 1G0
Delisle 4,054
Ma—Gerald Fleury
S—Florent Côté
C.P. 158, G0W 1L0
Des Ruisseaux 3,889
Ma—Marcel Cyr
S—Normand Bélanger
C.P. 211, J9L 3G6
Evain 3,019
Ma—Paul-Arthur Dickey
DG—Noel Lanouette
C.P. 330, J0Z 1Y0
Fatima 3,216
Ma—Marc-Edouard Nadeau
DG—Donald Longuepée
C.P. 610, G0B 1G0
Fleurimont 12,000
Ma—Julien Ducharme
S—Roger Caron
1735, ch. Galvin, J1G 3E7
Grande-Île 3,401
Ma—Serge Deslières
S—Alain Gagnon
1155, boul. Mgr Langlois
J6S 1B9
Grantham-Ouest 5,432
Ma—Pierre Lemaire
S—Gilles Raiche
2345, rue St-Pierre
Drummondville, J2C 5A7
Haute-Mauricie 2,311
Ma—Réjean Gaudreault
DG—Yves Tousignant
1544, boul. Ducharme
Boîte groupe 231, G9X 3N8
Havre-aux-Maisons 2,348
Ma—Jean-Guy Hubert
S—Jean Richard
C.P. 128, G0B 1K0
Havre-St-Pierre 3,344
Ma—Robert Michaud
DG—André Cyr
1081, rue de la Digue
G0G 1P0
Hébertville 2,452
Ma—Jacques Dallaire
S—Sabin Larouche
C.P. 10, G0W 1S0
Labelle 2,134
Ma—Robert Nantel
S—Jean-G. Rousseau
C.P. 390, J0T 1H0
L'Acadie 4,449
Ma—Benoît Lucier
S—Denis L'Heureux
181, ch. du Clocher
J0J 1H0
Lac-à-la-Tortue 2,644
Ma—Jacques Longpré
S—Liliane Lacroix-Garceau
C.P. 129, G0X 1L0

Lac-St-Charles 6,484
Ma—Donald Brisson
S—Raymond Brassard
510, rue Delage, G0A 2H0
L'Ange-Gardien 2,121
Ma—Pierre Champagne
S—Normand Vachon
R.R. 1 Buckingham
J8L 2W7
La Pêche 5,394
Ma—Hervé Leblanc
S—Jacques Seguin
C.P. 70, Ste-Cécile-de-Masham, J0X 2W0
Laterrière 4,154
Ma—Paul-D. Gagnon
S—Normand Girard
C.P. 69, G0V 1K0
Le Bic 3,086
Ma—Valois Doucet
S—Camille Roussel
C.P. 99, G0L 1B0
Les Cèdres 3,321
Ma—Armand Levac
DG—Normand Meilleur
C.P. 240, J0P 1L0
Les Escoumins 2,340
Ma—Emerentienne B.-Maltais
S—Micheline Savard
2, rue de la Rivière
G0T 1K0
L'Etang-du-Nord 3,062
Ma—Napoléon Cormier
S—Elphege Leblanc
C.P. 29, G0B 1E0
L'Ile-du-Havre-Aubert 2,792
Ma—Renald Briant
S—Jean-Yves Lebreux
C.P. 36, G0B 1J0
Maria 2,461
Ma—Marc Gagné
S—Gilbert Leblanc
C.P. 218, G0C 1Y0
Newport 2,419
Ma—Gaston Fullum
S—G. Walter Smith
C.P. 7, G0C 2A0
Nouvelle 2,137
Ma—Renald Plourde
DG—Pierre Lavoie
C.P. 68, G0C 2E0
Paspébiac 3,070
Ma—Levis Loisel
S—Jean-Guy Duguay
C.P. 130, G0C 2K0
Pintendre 4,001
Ma—Roger Lachance
S—Herve Tremblay
344, Dixième av., G0R 2K0
Pointe-au-Pere 3,685
Ma—Benoît Martin
S—Ginette Ouellet
315, av. Dionne, G0K 1G0
Pointe-du-Lac 5,527
Ma—Jean Simard
DG—Yves Marchand
C.P. 339, G0X 1Z0
Pontiac 3,955
Ma—Marcel Lavigne
S—Germain Clairoux
R.R. 1, Luskville
J0X 2G0

Prévost 5,229
Ma—Claude Hotte
DG—Real Martin
2870, boul. du Curé-Labelle
J0R 1T0

Rivière-Malbaie 2,127
Ma—Gaston Lavoie
S—Daniel Lavoie
400, ch. de la Vallée
La Malbaie
G5A 1B9

Sacré-Coeur 2,121
Ma—Hélène Dufour
S—Sarto Simard
C.P. 159
G0T 1Y0

St-Agapit 2,943
Ma—Marcel Côté
S—Denis Pelletier
1247, rue Principale
G0S 1Z0

St-Amable 4,531
Ma—René-Guy Gemme
S—Michel Martel
C.P. 308
J0L 1N0

St-Ambroise 3,655
Ma—Jean Halley
S—Jean-Rock Claveau
C.P. 190, G0V 1R0

St-Apollinaire 3,090
Ma—Benoît Côté
S—Yvon Demers
94, rue Principale, G0S 2E0

Ste-Brigitte-de-Laval 2,388
Ma—Gabriel Lalonde
S—Jacques Vallée
1, rue Auclair, G0A 3K0

St-Bruno 2,590
Ma—Clément Lajoie
S—Claude Moisan
C.P. 39, G0W 2L0

St-Calixte 3,183
Ma—Alphonse Lavoie
S—Denis Malouin
6230, rue Hôtel-de-Ville
J0K 1Z0

**Ste-Catherine-
Jacques-Cartier** 3,586
Ma—Paul-Guy Boucher
S—Marcel Grenier
C.P. 250, G0A 3M0

St-Charles-Borromée 8,469
Ma—André Henault
S—François Theriault
525, rue Visitation
J6E 4P2

St-Charles-de-Drummond 3,868
Ma—Bernard Boudreau
S—Gilles Proulx
1250, rue Proulx
Drummondville-nord
J2C 5A2

Ste-Claire 3,009
Ma—Gérard Fournier
S—Serge Gagnon
55, rue de la Fabrique
G0R 2V0

St-Cyrille-de-Wendover 3,561
Ma—Jean-Paul Turcotte
S—Mario Picotin
4215, rue Principale
J0C 1H0

St-Dominique 2,041
Ma—Germain Lagace
S—Agnes Archambault
467, rue Deslandes
J0H 1L0

St-Donat 2,627
Ma—André Picard
S—Jules St-Georges
C.P. 460, J0T 2C0

St-Etienne-de-Lauzon 5,785
Ma—Normand Henri
S—Richard Demers
1, place Chamberland
G0S 2L0

St-Fulgence 2,160
Ma—Pascal Boulianne
S—Gilles Tremblay
C.P. 70
G0V 1S0

St-Gabriel-de-Valcartier 2,717
Ma—Brent Montgomery
S—Joan Sheehan
1743, boul. Valcartier
G0A 4S0

St-Henri 3,950
Ma—Réjean Brochu
S—Jacques Risler
C.P. 158
G0R 3E0

St-Honoré 3,643
Ma—Jean-Guy Tremblay
S—Hugues Blackburn
3611, boul. Martel
G0V 1L0

St-Jean-de-Dieu 2,063
Ma—Lucien Belzile
S—Normand Morency
32, rue Principale sud
G0L 3M0

St-Jean-Port-Joli 3,395
Ma—Marc-Arthur Deschênes
S—Mario Caron
7, av. de Gaspé est
G0R 3G0

**Ste-Marthe-Cap-de-
la-Madeleine** 5,109
Ma—Lucien Chausse
S—Marcel Milot
C.P. 158
G8T 7W2

St-Michel-des-Saints 2,021
Ma—Jean-Louis Bellerose
S—Victorien Laforest
390, rue Mattawin
J0K 3B0

St-Nazaire 2,025
Ma—Jean-Paul Bouchard
S—Roger Bouchard
C.P. 130, St-Nazaire-de-
Chicoutimi, G0W 2V0

St-Nicéphore 6,537
Ma—Jean Charpentier
S—Jean-Guy Ayotte
C.P. 1123, J2A 2G2

St-Paul 3,388
Ma—Denis Desrochers
S—Richard Morasse
18, boul. Brassard
J0K 3E0

Ste-Perpétue 2,226
Ma—Gilles Caron
S—Michel Bernier
C.P. 308, G0R 3Z0

St-Prosper 3,646
Ma—Marcel Tanguay
S—Pierre Beaudoin
2025, 29e rue, G0M 1Y0

Ste-Sophie 6,304
Ma—Arnold Greene
S—Yves Desrosiers
C.P. 69, J0R 1S0

Sayabec 2,308
Ma—Jean-Marie Leclerc
S—Jean-Paul Paquet
C.P. 39, G0J 3K0

Shannon 3,311
Ma—Maureen Maher
S—Dale Feeney
75, ch. de Gosford
G0A 4N0

Shipshaw 2,803
Ma—Réjean Bergeron
S—Martine Gagnon
3760, rue St-Léonard
G0V 1V0

Sullivan 2,276
Ma—Robert Veillet
S—Michel Leduc
C.P. 40, J0Y 2N0

Val-des-Monts 4,353
Ma—Jean-Claude Charette
S—Jacques Cousineau
1, boul. du Carrefour
J0X 3J0

Verchères 4,530
Ma—Marc St-Cerny
S—Philippe Collette
581, boul. Marie-Victorin
J0L 2R0

Wickham 2,156
Ma—Omer Blanchard
S—Réal Dulmaine
C.P. 9, J0C 1S0

Yamachiche 2,740
Ma—André Chaine
S—Paul Desaulniers
951, rue Ste-Anne
G0X 3L0

COMMUNAUTÉS (regional governments)

Administration régionale Kativik
Prés.—Tikile Kleist
DG—W. Makiuk
C.P. 9, Kuujjuaq, J0M 1C0

**Communauté régionale de
l'Outaouais**
Prés.—Gaetan Cousineau
DG—P. Ménard
C.P. 2210, succ. B
Hull, J8X 4C8

**Communauté urbaine de
Montréal**
Prés.—Michel Hamelin
DG—C. Cormier
C.P. 129, Montréal
H5B 1E6

**Communauté urbaine de
Québec**
Prés.—Michel Rivard
DG—M. Bergeron
399, rue St-Joseph est
Québec, G1K 8E2

SUMMARY OF 1986 TOTALS

256 Cités and villes 4,926,467

Total Urban (Census) 5,088,995

557 Paroisses and cantons 748,780

Total Rural (Census) 1,443,466

Total Urban and Rural
(excl. Indians on Reserves) 6,532,461

INDIANS

Living on reserves:
population 32,102
(June 1/86)

SASKATCHEWAN

Forms of Municipal Government

Cities: Towns can be formed into cities when the population reaches 5,000. There are 12 cities in Saskatchewan, including the City of Lloydminster situated on the Alberta-Saskatchewan border. Cities are governed by an elected council consisting of a mayor and an even number of aldermen. Seven cities have six aldermen, one has eight, and three have ten. Mayors and aldermen are elected at large, except in the cases of Prince Albert, Regina, and Saskatoon, where aldermen are elected by wards. Regular elections for the whole council are held every three years, the next being in October 1991.

Towns: Villages can be formed into towns when the population reaches 500. There are 144 towns in the province, as well as two Northern Towns (Creighton and La Ronge). Towns are governed by a mayor and six aldermen who are elected at large. Regular elections for the whole council are held every three years. The next elections are slated for October 1991.

Villages: Organized hamlets can be formed into villages when their population reaches 100 and they contain 50 or more dwelling units or business premises. There are currently 363 villages in the province, of which 38 are resort villages. The assessment requirement does not apply to resort villages, and population includes the non-residents who are owners of assessable land, together with their dependents residing with them. Villages are governed by a mayor and either two or four aldermen who are elected at large.

Regular elections for the whole council are held every three years, the next being in October 1991.

Rural Municipalities: There are 299 rural municipalities in the province. The usual area of a rural municipality is nine townships. Rural municipalities are governed by a reeve, who is elected at large, and a councillor elected in each division. Terms of office are for two years, with councillors for the odd-numbered divisions and the reeve being elected one year, and the councillors for the even-numbered divisions being elected the following year.

Northern Villages: A northern hamlet may be formed into a northern village if the taxable assessment is at least $200,000, or the population is at least 200, or the population is at least 100 with a taxable assessment of $100,000 or more, on a 1947 base year for assessments. Northern villages are governed by a mayor and council of four or six members. Elections are held every three years. There are 12 northern villages in Saskatchewan.

Northern Hamlets: A northern settlement can be formed into a northern hamlet if the taxable assessment is at least $100,000 or the population is at least 100, or the population is at least 50 and the taxable assessment is $50,000 or more, on a 1947 base year for assessments. Northern hamlets are governed by a mayor and a council of two or four members. Elections are held every three years. There are 13 northern hamlets in Saskatchewan.

There are 12 cities, 144 towns, 2 northern towns, 325 villages, 38 resort villages, 12 northern villages, 13 northern hamlets, and 299 rural municipalities in the province of Saskatchewan.

Municipalities

(Municipalities with populations of less than 1,000 are generally not listed. Population figures are from the 1986 Census.)

A: Administrator   Cl: Clerk   Ma: Mayor

CITIES

Estevan Ma—John Empey Cl—M. Hoste 1102-4th St., S4A 0W7	10,161	**Lloydminster (Sask.)** Ma—Patricia Gulak Cl—T. Lysyk 5011-49th Ave., S9V 0T8	7,155	**Melfort** Ma—Carol Carson Cl—Arnold Lang Box 2230, S0E 1A0	6,078

Melville 5,123
Ma—Donald Abel
Cl—J. Sedlovitch
Box 1240, S0A 2P0

Moose Jaw 35,073
Ma—Stan Montgomery
Cl—George Stratton
228 N. Main St., S6H 3J8

North Battleford 14,876
Ma—Glenn Hornick
Cl—J.B. Jansen
Box 460, S9A 2Y6

Prince Albert 33,686
Ma—Gordon Kirkby
Cl—T.M. Topping
1084 Central Ave.
S6V 7P3

Regina 175,064
Ma—Doug Archer
Cl—George R. Day
Box 1790, S4P 3C8

Saskatoon 177,641
Ma—Henry Dayday
Cl—J. Kolynchuk
City Hall, S7K 0J5

Swift Current 15,666
Ma—L.A. Stein
Cl—D. Cox
Box 340, S9H 3W1

Weyburn 10,153
Ma—Ron Barber
Cl—F. Martyn
Box 370, S4H 2K6

Yorkton 15,574
Ma—Ed Magis
Cl—Wayne Jensen
Box 400, S3N 2W3

TOWNS

Assiniboia 3,001
A—Huguette Lutz
Box 670, S0H 0B0

Battleford 3,833
A—G. Gelech
Box 40, S0M 0E0

Biggar 2,626
A—R.G. Tyler
Box 489, S0K 0M0

Birch Hills 947
Cl—Lois Cockwill
Box 206, S0J 0G0

Canora 2,602
A—P.N. Dergousoff
Box 717, S0A 0L0

Carlyle 1,172
A—Norman Riddell
Box 10, S0C 0R0

Carnduff 1,090
A—D.H. Preston
Box 100, S0C 0S0

Carrot River 1,101
A—D. Touet
Box 147, S0E 0L0

Churchbridge 1,035
A—B. Leier
Box 256, S0A 0M0

Coronach 1,006
A—Harold Siggelkow
Box 90, S0H 0Z0

Creighton 1,620
A—T. Wheeler
Box 100, S0P 0A0

Dalmeny 1,328
A—Beverly Dobson
Box 400, S0K 1E0

Davidson 1,183
A—G. Edom
Box 340, S0G 1A0

Delisle 986
A—Walt French
Box 40, S0L 0P0

Esterhazy 3,083
A—P. Woznesensky
Box 490, S0A 0X0

Eston 1,383
A—H. Cowan
Box 757, S0L 1A0

Foam Lake 1,535
A—G.E. Kreuger
Box 57, S0A 1A0

Fort Qu'Appelle 1,915
A—H. Taylor
Box 309, S0G 1S0

Gravelbourg 1,305
A—E. Karlson
Box 359, S0H 1X0

Grenfell 1,274
A—K. Levesque
Box 1120, S0G 2B0

Gull Lake 1,164
A—A. Funk
Box 150, S0N 1A0

Herbert 964
A—W. Struck
Box 370, S0H 2A0

Hudson Bay 2,133
A—R. Dolezsar
Box 730, S0E 0Y0

Humboldt 5,089
A—W.L. Herman
Box 640, S0K 2A0

Indian Head 1,886
A—L. Natyshak
Box 460, S0G 2K0

Kamsack 2,565
A—Lawrence Skoretz
Box 729, S0A 1S0

Kelvington 1,084
A—B. Kossmann
Box 10, S0A 1W0

Kerrobert 1,288
A—Wayne Zerff
Box 558, S0L 1R0

Kindersley 4,912
A—John Couldwell
Box 1269, S0L 1S0

Kipling 1,033
A—Bevin Keith
Box 299, S0G 2S0

La Ronge 2,696
A—G. Roeland
Box 568, S0J 1L0

Langenburg 1,371
Cl—D. Petz
Box 400, S0A 2A0

Langham 1,193
A—G.H. Gray
Box 289,
S0K 2L0

Lanigan 1,698
A—Jack Dvernichuk
Box 280, S0K 2M0

Lashburn 873
A—Barbara Fitch
Box 328, S0M 1H0

Leader 1,130
A—Jim Toye
Box 39, S0N 1H0

Lumsden 1,369
A—Charlotte Klempp
Box 160, S0G 3C0

Macklin 1,131
A—D. Bryden
Box 69, S0L 2C0

Maidstone 1,112
A—A. Larson
Box 208, S0M 1M0

Maple Creek 2,452
A—Tim Leson
Box 428, S0N 1N0

Martensville 2,760
A—Phillip Ratzlaff
Drawer 970, S0K 2T0

Meadow Lake 3,976
A—H. Hillestad
Box 610, S0M 1V0

Moosomin 2,557
A—B. Wilson
Box 730, S0G 3N0

Nipawin 4,588
A—Peter Cannon
Box 2134, S0E 1E0

Outlook 2,137
A—L. Zarubiak
Box 518, S0L 2N0

Oxbow 1,229
A—Lorna Wolk
Box 149, S0C 2B0

Pilot Butte 1,387
A—Karen Byrd (acting)
Box 253, S0G 3Z0

Porcupine Plain 918
Cl—B. Warsylewicz
Box 310, S0E 1H0

Preeceville 1,272
A—I.K. Britton
Box 560, S0A 3B0

Radville 960
Cl—L. Fisher
Box 339, S0C 2G0

Rosetown 2,663
A—G.W. Crowder
Box 398, S0L 2V0

Rosthern 1,594
A—J. Weninger
Box 416, S0K 3R0

Shaunavon 2,153
A—J. Janeson
Box 820, S0N 2M0

Shellbrook 1,238
A—Kenneth Danger
Box 40, S0J 2E0

Spiritwood 1,025
A—Lesley Greve
Box 460, S0J 2M0

Tisdale 3,184
A—M. Vey
Box 1090, S0E 1T0

Unity 2,471
Cl—Wm. Barry Thomson
Box 1030,
S0K 4L0

Wadena 1,602
A—B. Sych
Box 730, S0A 4J0

Wakaw 1,010
A—Steve Hryniuk
Box 669, S0K 4P0

Warman   2,455
A—Courtney Skrupski
Box 340, S0K 4S0
Watrous   1,953
Cl—Ian R. Cole
Box 730, S0K 4T0
Watson   964
A—Lorne Negraeff
Box 276, S0K 4V0
Whitewood   1,107
A—Patricia Henry
Box 129, S0G 5C0
Wilkie   1,526
Cl—Jim Puffalt
Box 580, S0K 4W0
Wynyard   2,079
A—R. Bunko
Box 220, S0A 4T0

RURAL MUNICIPALITIES

Bayne   1,089
A—B.M. Alexander
Box 130, Bruno, S0K 0S0
Beaver River   1,231
A—Debra Johnson
Box 129, Pierceland
S0M 2K0
Biggar   1,122
A—Ray Gaudet
Box 280, S0K 0M0
Bjorkdale   1,387
A—S.H. Abbs
Box 10, Crooked River
S0E 0R0
Blucher   1,383
A—R. Thurmeier
Box 100, Bradwell
S0K 0P0
Britannia   1,453
A—B. Mills-Midgley
Box 661, Lloydminster
S9V 0Y7
Buckland   3,460
A—C.L. Marshall
99 E. River St.
Prince Albert, S6V 0A1
Cana   1,235
A—J.B. Chesney
Box 550, Melville, S0A 2P0
Canwood   1,968
A—Grant Doupe
Box 10, S0J 0K0
Churchbridge   1,100
A—Casmer P. Chyz
Box 211, S0A 0M0
Clayton   1,138
A—Doug Ferder
Box 220, Hyas, S0A 1K0
Corman Park   6,488
A—F.J. Sutter
111 Pinehouse Dr.
Saskatoon, S7K 5W1
Edenwold   1,992
A—Donna Strudwick
Box 10, Balgonie, S0G 0E0
Estevan   1,270
A—Dale Malmgren
1329-4th St., S4A 0X1
Excelsior   1,003
A—K.C. Merrells
Rush Lake, S0H 3S0

Fertile Belt   1,149
A—J.V. Jacob
Box 190, Stockholm
S0A 3Y0
Flett's Springs   1,027
A—C.W. Tetarenko
Box 69, Pathlow
S0K 3B0
Foam Lake   1,036
A—R.G. Kostiuk
Box 490, S0A 1A0
Frenchman Butte   1,537
A—Isabelle Jasper
Box 180, Paradise Hill
S0M 2G0
Hazel Dell   1,070
A—U. McLaughlin
Box 87, Okla, S0A 2X0
Hudson Bay   2,100
A—Linda Purves
Box 520, S0E 0Y0
Humboldt   1,232
A—Fred W. Saliken
Box 420, S0K 2A0
Kindersley   1,230
A—D.C. Empey
Box 1210, S0L 1S0
Kinistino   1,086
A—L.W. Edeen
Box 310, S0J 1H0
Laird   1,214
A—L.A. Ratzlaff
Box 160, Waldheim
S0K 4R0
Lajord   1,104
A—R. Heise
Box 36, S0G 2V0
Langenburg   960
A—William Erhardt
S0A 2A0
Leask   1,027
A—R. Poole
Box 190, S0J 1M0
Longlaketon   1,072
A—E. Eggleton
Box 100, Earl Grey
S0G 1J0
Loon Lake   942
A—Diane Zureski
Box 40, S0M 1L0
Lumsden   1,216
A—J.E. Spicer
Box 160, S0G 3C0
Maple Creek   1,276
A—Pamela Urton
Box 188, S0N 1N0
Meadowlake   2,503
A—D. Wilkinson
Box 668, S0M 1V0
Moose Jaw   2,146
A—J. Nichols
170 W. Fairford St.
S6H 1V3
Moose Range   1,612
A—Rick Colborn
Box 699, Carrot River
S0E 0L0
Nipawin   1,547
A—Eunice Rudy
Box 250, Codette, S0E 0P0
North Battleford   1,075
A—B. Kosolofski
1131-100th St., S9A 0V3

Orkney   2,094
A—J. Gazdewich
26 N. 5th Ave., Yorkton
S3N 0Y8
Paddockwood   1,117
A—Carole Moritz
Box 187, S0J 1Z0
Ponass Lake   997
A—Bonnie Lengyel
Box 98, Rose Valley
S0E 1M0
Porcupine   1,559
A—E.F. Poniatowski
Box 190, Porcupine
Plain, S0E 1H0
Preeceville   1,548
A—Lynn Kardynal
Box 439, S0A 3B0
Prince Albert   3,500
A—P.G. Brown
99 E. River St., S6V 0A1
Rosthern   1,920
A—J. Spriggs
Box 126, S0K 3R0
St. Louis   1,393
A—L.G. Gareau
Hoey, S0J 1E0
St. Peter   1,298
A—J. Verhelst
Annaheim, S0K 0G0
Saltcoats   1,005
A—Ronald Risling
Box 150, S0A 3R0
Sasman   1,372
A—J. Little
Box 130, Kuroki, S0A 1Y0
Shellbrook   1,956
A—K. Danger
Box 40, S0J 2E0
Sherwood   1,218
A—M.P. Schneider
1840 Cornwall St.
Regina, S4P 2K2
Sliding Hills   957
A—Marianne Cooper
Box 70, Mikado, S0A 2R0
South Qu'Appelle   1,167
A—Sandra Ostapowich
Box 66, Qu'Appelle
S0G 4A0
Spiritwood   1,793
A—Gloria Teer
Box 340, S0J 2M0
Star City   1,161
A—A. Campbell
Box 370, S0E 1P0
Swift Current   1,801
A—Dave Dmytruk
Box 1210, S9H 3X4
Tisdale   1,351
A—T. Hvidston
Box 128, S0E 1T0
Torch River   2,292
A—Jacques Bertrand
Box 40, White Fox
S0J 3B0
Vanscoy   2,215
A—W.R. Keeler
Box 187, S0L 3J0
Wallace   1,138
A—J. Gazdewich
26 N. 5th Ave., Yorkton
S3N 0Y8

Weyburn	1,080	**Willow Creek**	1,184	**Wilton**	1,910

Weyburn 1,080
A—L.E. Muma
23-6th St. N.E., S4H 1A7

Willow Creek 1,184
A—H.L. Ross
Box 458, Star City, S0E 1P0

Wilton 1,910
A—P. Pylatuk
Box 40, Marshall, S0M 1R0

SUMMARY OF 1986 TOTALS

12 Cities 506,250
144 Towns 166,106

Total Urban (1986 Census) 620,198

Total Rural (1986 Census) 389,415

Total Urban and Rural
(excl. Indians on Reserves) 1,009,613

INDIANS

Living on reserves:
population 27,938
(June 1/86)

YUKON TERRITORY

Classes of Local Government

New municipal legislation has been developed in Yukon, offering greater flexibility, a broader range of powers and more responsibility to Yukon communities. Under the new legislation the previous form of local government — local improvement districts — has been phased out.

The various classes of municipalities (established on the basis of population) include the following: city, town, and village. An additional new category is also provided for: that of hamlet. A hamlet will consist of an elected body of an advisory nature only, with very limited powers.

Municipalities

(Population figures are from the 1986 Census.)

Ma: Mayor   Mg: Manager

CITY

Whitehorse 14,814
Ma—Don Branigan
Mg—Rice Walt
Y1A 2B0

SUMMARY OF 1986 TOTALS

Total Urban (Census) 15,199

Total Rural (Census) 8,305

Total Urban and Rural
(excl. Indians on Reserves) 23,504

TOWNS

Dawson 882
Mg—Alana Tunnicliffe
Y0B 1G0

Faro 391
Mg—D. Power
Y0B 1K0
Watson Lake 814
Mg—Bill Forsythe
Y0A 1C0

VILLAGES

Carmacks 276
Mg—Isabelle Zimmer
Y0B 1C0
Haines Junction 334
Mg—J. Feenstra
Y0B 1L0
Mayo 306
Mg—B. Graham
Y0B 1M0
Teslin 175
Mg—Sharon Sterritt
Y0A 1B0

INDEX

NOTE: Our listings are indexed by the key word of the title and / or by subject. Titles are inverted where necessary so that the key or *most informative* word is the one which designates the entry. For example, Canadian National Institute for the Blind becomes "Blind, Canadian National Institute for the". Cross-references are used where there is more than one possible key word within a title.

All government bodies, including departments, boards and commissions, have been indexed under key-word headings, rather than under "Canada" or the name of the particular province or territory. Included are many subject entries which, together, offer a nationwide guide to government services. For example, under "Day Care Services" or "Student Aid", readers will find the federal, provincial and territorial government bodies which provide such services.

Acronyms — e.g., ACTRA, CRTC — appear at the beginning of the alphabetical listing for each letter. Proper names contained within the name of an organization, such as C.D. Howe Research Institute, are entered by the first name or initial(s) in the body of the listings.

A

ABN Bank Cda., 13-10
ACCESS Network, 17-52
ACTRA, 11-16
ACTRA Fraternal Benefit Soc., 8-231
ACUC, 8-337
ADDICS, 8-270
AIDS assns., 8-266
ALAS, 8-184
ANZ Bank Cda., 13-10
ASSITEJ Cda., 8-342
A.Y., 8-352
Aboriginal peoples (*see also* Eskimo; Indian; Inuit; Métis; Native Peoples)
· Constitutional Affairs, Office of, 16-12
Abortion
· assns., 8-198, -199
· legislation, 1-1, -2
Academic pubns., 8-169—172
Acadia University, 7-12
Acadien, Le Village Historique/Acadian Historical Village, N.B., 17-161
Accountants assns., 8-177—178
Accreditation Bd., Private Colleges, Alta., 17-16
Acid Rain
· Cdn. Coalition on, 8-201
· description, 3-10
Acoustical Assn. Ont., 8-202
Actors
· ACTRA, 8-231, 11-16
· Equity Assn., Cdn., 11-17
· Fund of Cda. Inc., 8-192
· Lab. Theatre, 8-342
Actuaries, Cdn. Inst. of, 8-244
Acupuncture Fdn. of Cda., 8-270
Adam Mickiewicz Fdn., 8-223
Addiction
· Fdn., Cdn. 8-271
· Research Fdn., 8-261
Admail, 9-10
Admissions & Transfer, Alta. Council on, 17-16
Advanced
· Education
· · and Job Training, Dept. of, N.S., 17-217
· · and Training, Dept. of, N.B., 17-149

· Policy Advisory Cttee., Alta., 17-16
· Studies, Dept. of Career Dev't and, Nfld., 17-175
· Systems Fdn., B.C., 17-66
· Technology Assn., Cdn., 8-243
Advertising
· assns., 8-178—179
· BBM Bur. of Measurement, 8-179
· industry, foreign take-overs, 1-2
· pubns., 8-120
· tobacco, 1-2
Aeronautics & Space Inst., Cdn., 8-187
Aerospace
· assns., 8-187
· and Electronic Communications Employees Assn. (RCA-SPAR), 11-16
· pubn., 8-121
Affaires
· culturelles et sociales, Secrétariat des, Qué., 17-333
· intergouvernementales cdne, secrétariat aux, Qué., 17-333
· sociales
· · Comm. des (Qué.), 17-372
· · Cons. des, 17-375
Affirmative Action Advisory Cttee., N.W.T., 17-206
African
· Literature Assn., 8-207
· Studies, Cdn. Assn. of, 8-251
· Violet Soc. of Cda., 8-240
Agency/corporation, Crown, defined, 16-28
Aging (*see also* Senior Citizens)
· Council on
· · Alta., 8-307
· · Cda., National Advisory, 16-81
Agribition, Cdn. Western, 8-225
Agricole
· Office du crédit, 17-346
· Régie
· · des assurances agricoles du Qué., 17-346
· · des marchés agricoles du Qué., 17-345
Agricultural
· Chemical Producers' Assn., Cdn., 8-195
· Credit Corp.,
· · Man., 17-110
· · Sask., 17-399

· Development Corp.,
· · Alta., 17-20
· · Sask., (Agdevco), 17-416
· Exchange Assn., Int'l, 8-354
· Land
· · Commn., B.C., 17-71
· · Protection Commn., Que., (*Comm. de protection du territoire agricole*) 17-346
· Licensing & Registration Review Bd., Ont., 17-256
· Machinery Inst., Prairie, 18-5
· products
· · Bd., Cda., 16-35
· · mktg.: Alta., 17-19; Nfld., 17-189; Que., 17-345
· regions, 4-3—4
· Rehabilitation & Dev't Directorate (ARDA), Ont., 17-256
· Research Inst. of Ont., 17-256
· societies, 8-179—182
· · Advisory Bd., Man., 17-110
· Stabilization Board, 16-35
· statistics, 4-4—6
· subsidies, 1-4
· training schools, 7-10
· Winter Fair Assn., Royal, 8-225
· Wool Growers Ltd., Cdn. Co-op., 8-180

Agriculture
· assns., 8-179—182
· Canada, 14-7—8
· Cdn. commn.
· · dairy, 16-35
· · grain, 16-35
· Credit Corp., Farm, 16-36
· depts. of
· · Alta., 17-17
· · B.C., 17-68
· · Cda., 16-32—38
· · Man., 17-107
· · N.B., 17-150
· · Nfld., 17-188
· · N.S., 17-218
· · Ont., 17-254
· · P.E.I., 17-316
· · Que., 17-344
· · Sask., 17-397
· exhibitions, 8-225
· federations, 8-180, -181
· gov't legislation & programs, 4-2
· industry, 4-2—7

Agriculture (cont'd)
· Livestock Feed Bd., 16-37
· Nat'l Farm Products Mktg. Coun., 16-37
· Prairie
· · aid for, 1-3
· · Farm Rehabilitation Admin. (PFRA), 16-38
· Press Assn., Cdn. Farm, 8-295
· pubns., 8-165—167
· Research Inst., Alta., 17-20
· scientific developments, 4-2—3
· trade & revenues, 4-2

Agro-alimentaires, Soc. qué. d'initiatives, 17-347

Agrologists Assn., Cdn. Consulting, 8-180

Agronomes du Qué., Ordre des, 8-181

Aid
· foreign, 16-189—191
· to prairie farmers, 1-3

Air
· Cadet League of Cda., 8-275
· Cda., 1-1, -3, 10-16
· Crew Assn. Cda., 11-15
· Forces Benevolent Fund, Royal Cdn., 8-194
· Navigation System, 10-16
· traffic control, 10-15
· · assn., 11-18
· transport assns., 8-187, -346

Air Conditioning
· assns., 8-182, -275
· pubns., 8-120

Aircraft
· assns., 8-187
· Operations Group, 11-15

Airline
· companies, in Cda., 10-16—17
· deregulation, 10-14
· Dispatchers Assn., Cdn., 11-17
· Pilots' Assn., Cdn., 11-17
· services, commercial, 10-16

Airports, 10-15
· Mgmt. Conf. of Ont., 8-187

Akaitcho Hall Advisory Bd., 17-204

Alarm & Security Assn., Cdn., 8-304

Alberta
· agriculture, 4-3
· Chamber of Commerce, 8-191
· coat of arms, 17-11
· colleges, 7-45—47
· economy, 14-16, 17-12
· education in, 7-4, -7, -8, -45—47
· forestry, 4-9
· geography, 3-5, 17-11
· government of, 17-13—55
· history, 17-11
· income statistics, 5-10
· judiciary & officers, 17-56—59
· labour legislation, 11-3, -6
· libraries & archives, 8-7—20
· local government, 19-1—2
· minimum wage rate, 11-4
· motor vehicle & traffic regulations, 10-8
· municipal elections, 19-2
· municipalities & counties, 19-2—6
· museums, 8-278, -279
· newspapers, 9-13—16
· population, 5-2, 17-11, -12

· radio stations, 9-45, -52—53
· schools of nursing (hospital-based), 7-46
· Stock Exchange, 13-30—32
· superintendent of insurance, 13-20
· technical institutes, 7-46
· television stations, 9-57
· universities,
· · Alberta, The Univ. of, 7-12—13
· · Athabasca Univ., 7-13—14
· · Calgary, Univ. of, 7-16
· · Camrose Lutheran College, 7-17
· · Lethbridge, Univ. of, 7-22
· vital statistics, 17-38
· vocational centres, 7-46—47

Alcohol & Drug
· Abuse Commn.
· · Alta., 17-52
· · Sask., (SADAC), 17-420
· Concerns Inc., 8-308
· Co-ordinating Coun., N.W.T., 17-204
· Dependency
· · Commn. of Nfld. & Labrador, 17-191
· · Info. & Counselling Services (Man.) (ADDICS) Inc., 8-270

Alcoholics Anonymous, 8-270—271

Alcoholism
· & Drug
· · Addiction Research Fdn., 17-272
· · Dependency Commn., N.B., 17-163
· Fdn. of Man., 17-127

Alcool(s)
· Rég. des permis, Qué., 17-377
· Soc. des, du Qué., 17-365

Alcuin Soc., 8-293

Algonquin, Forestry Auth., Ont., 17-293

Allergy assns., 8-266

Almanacs & directories pubns., 8-148

Alternative & Independent Schools, Ont. Assn. of, 8-216

Aluminum, Brick & Glass Workers Int'l Union, 11-9

Aluminium, Féd. des syndicats du secteur de l', 11-21

Alumni Assn. of the London School of Economics, Cdn., 8-215

Alzheimer assns., 8-266—267

Ambassadors
· Canadian, 16-148—158
· foreign, 16-158—163

Aménagement de l'Outaouais, Soc. d', Qué., 17-343

American
· Bureau of Shipping, 8-308
· Fed. of Grain Millers, 11-9
· Fed. of Musicians of the U.S.A. & Cda., 11-9
· Guild of Variety Artists, 11-9
· Marketing Assn., 8-260
· Soc. for Information Science (ASIS), 8-243
· States, Org. of, 16-186
· Water Works Assn., 8-348

Amiante, Soc. nat. de l', 17-357

Amish Church, Old Order, 6-11

Amnesty International, 8-198

Amphibian & Reptile Conservation Soc., Cdn., 8-349

Amputee sports assns., 8-314

Amusements Regulations Bd., N.S., 17-222

Amyotrophic Lateral Sclerosis Soc. of Cda., 8-267

Anaesthetists' Soc., Cdn., 8-263

Anatomists, Cdn. Assn. of, 8-263

Ancient Free & Accepted Masons, 8-231

Anglers & Hunters, Ont. Fed. of, 8-298

Anglican
· Church of Cda., 6-3—4
· pubns., 8-168
· Youth Ministry, 8-352

Anik satellites, 9-2, -4

Animals
· assns., 8-182—183, -242—243, -349
· · humane societies, 8-242—243
· · protection, 8-242—243
· · science, 8-182, -183
· · wild, 8-349
· pubns., 8-148
· · horses, 8-157—158
· · S.P.C.A., 8-242—43
· Welfare, Int'l Fund for, 8-183

Anthem, national, 2-2

Anthropology
· Sociology and, Assn., Cdn., 8-252
· pubns., 8-169, -170

Anthroposophical Soc. in Cda., 8-251

Antiochian Orthodox Christian Church, 6-11

Antiquarian Booksellers Assn. of Cda., 8-183

Antique(s)
· assns., 8-183—184
· dealers, 8-183
· Locomotive Soc., Vintage, 8-239
· pubns., 8-148

Apostolic Church
· in Cda., 6-4
· of Pentecost of Cda. Inc., 6-4

Appalachian region, 3-6

Applications pédagogiques de l'ordinateur (APO QUÉBEC), Centre qué. de recherche sur les, 17-358

Appraisals assns., 8-295

Apprenticeship
· Bd., B.C. Provincial, 17-67
· and Trade Certification Bd., N.W.T., 17-204
· and Trades Qualification Bd., Man., 17-133

Approvisionnements et Services, Min. de, 17-347

Aquariums, Cdn. Assn. of Zoological Parks and, 8-182

Aquatic Fed. of Cda., 8-316

Arab assns., 8-223

Arabian Horse Registry, Cdn., 8-182

Arabic pubns., 9-40

Arbitration
· assns., 8-248—249
· Centre, B.C. Int'l Commercial, 17-72

Arbitrators' Inst. of Cda. Inc., 8-248

Archaeological Soc.,
· Man., 8-238
· Ont., 8-252

Archery assns., 8-316
Architectural
· Glass & Metal Contractors Assn.,
   8-205
· Metal Assn., 8-205
· Woodwork Manufacturers Assn. of
   Cda., 8-205
Architecture
· assns., 8-184
· pubns., 8-120
Archives
· Bd., Sask., 17-421
· of Cda., National, 16-45
· Nationales du Qué., 17-336
· of N.S., Public, 17-240
· of Ont., 17-270
· Public, Dept. of Community &
   Cultural Affairs, P.E.I., 17-318
Archivistes du Qué., Assoc. des,
   8-253
Archivists
· Cdn., Assn. of, 8-253
· Group, Toronto Area, 8-255
· heritage & historical assns.,
   8-237—239
Arctic (see also Northwest
   Territories; Yukon)
· Archipelago, 3-8
· Cdn. Armed Forces base, 1-1
· coastal area, 3-9
· College Bd. of Governors, N.W.T.,
   17-204—205
· Inst. of North America, 8-184
· pubn., 8-169
· Resources Cttee., Cdn., 8-184
· Universities for Northern Studies,
   Assn. of Cdn., 8-184
· Winter Games Corp., 8-233
Armed Forces, Cdn., 16-179—183
· air, 16-180
· Arctic base, 1-1
· communications, 16-181
· · and Electronics Assn., 8-218
· naval, 16-179
· in other countries, 16-181—182
· training & education, 16-182—183
Armenian pubn., 9-40
Army
· Benevolent Fund, 16-126
· Cadet League of Cda., The, 8-352
· Navy & Air Force Veterans in Cda.,
   8-275
Arpenteurs-géomètres du Qué.,
   Ordre des, 8-340
Art (Visual Arts)
· assns., 8-184—185
· Fdn., Alta., 17-26
· Museum Directors Org., Cdn.,
   8-279
· Oil & Colour Chemists' Assn.,
   8-196
· pubns., 8-148—149, -170
· Therapy Inst.,
· · Toronto, 8-184
· · Vancouver, 8-274
· Universities Art Assn. of Cda.,
   8-252
Art Galleries
· assns., 8-278—279
· Edmonton, 8-110
· of Greater Victoria, 8-105
· National Gallery of Cda., 16-48

· of N.S., 17-232
· of Ont., 17-270

Art Metropole, 8-105

Arthritis Soc., 8-267

Artificial
· Breeders Assn., P.E.I., 8-257
· Insemination Centre of Que.,
   17-346
Artists/Artistes
· American Guild of Variety, 11-9
· assns., 8-184
· · books, 8-207
· Comm. de reconnaissance des
   associations d', 17-337
· Union, 11-28
Arts (see also Crafts; Culture;
   Dance; Music; Museums;
   Theatres)
· Advisory Council, N.W.T., 17-205
· assns., 8-185
· Boards,
· · B.C., 17-88
· · Sask., 17-414
· Cda. Council, 16-41
· Canadian
· · Broadcasting Corp. (CBC),
   9-5—8, 16-41
· · Conference of the, 8-185
· · Eskimo Arts Council, 16-86
· Centre
· · Nat'l: Corp., 16-45; Orchestra,
   8-281
· · Sask., 17-414
· Communications Dept., Museums
   & Heritage Br., 16-40
· Council,
· · Man., 17-117
· · Ont., 17-271
· Finnish Cdn. Art Soc., 8-184
· folk, assns., 8-185
· Fusion: The Ont. Clay & Glass
   Assn., 8-207
· Literary, Alta. Foundation for the,
   17-27
· Metal Arts Guild, 8-248
· Museum of Civilization, Cdn.,
   16-49
· Nat'l
· · Film Bd., 16-46
· · Gallery of Cda., 16-48
· Native Dev't in the Performing &
   Visual Arts, Assn. for, 8-283
· Oil & Colour Chemists' Assn.,
   8-196
· Performing, Alta. Foundation for
   the, 17-28
· pubns., 8-148—149
· and Sciences, Cdn. Academy of
   Recording, 8-280

Asia Pacific Fdn. of Cda., 8-229

Asphalt, technical
· Assn., Cdn., 8-205
· Roofing Technical Committee,
   8-205

Assembly of First Nations, 8-283

Assessment
· Appeal Boards
· · Alta., 17-42
· · B.C., 17-76
· Authority
· · B.C., 17-77
· · Sask., 17-410

· Equalization Bd., Alta., 17-42—43
· Municipal
· · Man., 17-135
· · Nfld., 17-187
· · N.S., 17-230
· · Que., Dir. gén. de l'evaluation
   foncière, Min. des Affaires
   municipales, 17-341
· Review Bds.
· · Ont., 17-254
· · Que., 17-342
Assessors of Ont., Inst. of
   Municipal, 8-296
Associated Gospel Churches of
   Cda., 6-4
Associations & societies,
   8-177—354
Assurance, Régie de l',
· -dépôts du Qué., 17-366
· maladie du Qué., 17-384
Asteroids, 2-12
Asthma Soc. of Cda., 8-267
Astronomical
· observatories, 2-19
· societies, 2-19
· · The Canadian, 2-20
· · Royal, Soc. of Cda., 2-20
Astronomy, 2-10—22
· events of the months, 2-17—19
· National Research Council, Assoc.
   Cttee. on, 2-19
Athabasca Univ., 7-13—14
Athletic
· assns., 8-312—339
· · education, 8-314
· · therapists, 8-313
Atlantic
· Building Supply Dealers Assn.,
   8-205
· Canada
· · Assn. of Free Will Baptists, 6-4
· · Opportunities Agency, 16-128
· · Plus Assn., 8-293
· coastal
· · area, 3-9
· · Resource Information Centre,
   18-3
· Communication & Technical
   Workers' Union, 11-17
· Council of Cda., The, 8-246
· Filmmakers' Co-operative Ltd.,
   8-197
· fisheries, 4-12
· · assns., 8-227
· Lottery Corp. Inc., 18-1
· Masonry Assn., 8-205
· Newspapers Assn., Community,
   8-294
· Oil Workers, 11-17
· pubns., 8-148, -154, -155
· Universities, Assn. of, 8-214
Atlantic Provinces
· Art Gallery Assn., 8-279
· Chamber of Commerce, 8-191
· Council on the Sciences, 8-217
· Economic Council, 8-210
· Hatchery Fed., 8-293
· library assns., 8-253
· Nursery Trades Assn., 8-285
· Resource Centre
· · hearing handicapped, 18-2
· · visually impaired, 18-2
· Special Education Authority, 18-1

Atomic Energy
- Control Bd., 16-61—62
- Energy Mines & Resources Dept., Energy Sector, 16-60—61
- Int'l, Agency, 16-185
- N.B. Power, 17-166
- Ontario
- - Energy: Bd., 17-275; Corp., 17-275
- - Hydro, 17-276
- - Min. of Energy, 17-275

Attorney General (see also Justice, depts.)
- depts.
- - Alta., 17-21
- - B.C., 17-71
- - Man., 17-112
- - N.S., 17-219
- - Ont., 17-258

Audio Visual Assn. of Cda. (NAVAC), Nat'l, 8-212

Audit Bureau of Circulation, 8-178

Auditing Fdn., Cdn. Comprehensive, 8-301

Auditor(s)
- Certification Bd., B.C., 17-76—77
- Internal, Inst. of, 8-178
- Provincial
- - Man., 17-105
- - Ont., 17-295
- - Sask., 17-416

Auditor General
- federal, 16-26, -38
- depts. of,
- - N.B., 17-151
- - N.S., 17-220
- - P.E.I., 17-324
- Nfld., 17-175

Australia-New Zealand Assn., 8-223

Auteur(s)
- recherchistes, documentalistes et compositeurs, Soc. des, 11-26
- Soc. cdne-française de protection du droit d', 8-206

Authors Assn., Cdn. 8-352

Autism Soc. Cda., 8-234

Autistic Citizens, Ont. Soc. for, 8-237

Auto Pact, Cda.-U.S., 14-23

Auto Workers Union (CAW), Cdn., 1-2, -3, 11-18

Autochtones, Secrétariat aux affaires (SAA), Qué. 17-333

Automatic Merchandising Assn., Cdn., 8-189

Automobile
- Aerospace & Agricultural Implement Workers
- - of America, Int'l Union, 11-12
- - Union of Cda., Nat'l, 11-23
- assns., 8-185—187, -297, -316
- - antique, 8-183
- industry, Cdn., 14-11
- Sport Clubs, Cdn., 8-316

Automobile Insurance
- Alta., Auto Insce. Bd., 17-25
- B.C., Insce. Corp. of B.C., 17-85
- Man., Autopac, Man. Public Insce. Corp., 17-140
- N.B., Public Utilities Bd., 17-163
- N.S., Dept. of Consumer Affairs, Insurance Div., 17-222

- Ont.
- - Bd., 17-279
- - Motor Vehicle Accident Claims, Min. of Financial Institutions, 17-279
- Qué.,
- - Dir. gén. des assurances, Inspecteur gén. des institutions financières, 17-366
- - Régie de l'assurance automobile, 17-379
- Sask., Sask. Gov't Insce. (SGI), 17-422
- superintendents of insce., 13-20

Automotive
- accessories
- - assns., 8-186
- - pubns., 8-121
- assns., 8-185—187
- - pubns., 8-121, -149
- Publisher's Assn., Cdn. Auto Traders, 8-294
- Transportation Service Superintendents Assn., 8-346

Aviation (see also Air)
- Aerospace, Defence & Industrial Benefits Br., Dept. of Industry, Science & Technology, 16-89
- assns., 8-187—188
- civil, 10-14—17
- - administration & policy, 10-14—15
- - Licensing, Legislation & Enforcement, 10-15
- exhibitions, 8-225
- Hall of Fame, Cda.'s, 8-279
- museums, 8-279
- Nat'l
- - Museum of Science & Technology, Nat'l Aviation Museum, 16-50
- - Research Coun., Nat'l Aeronautical Establishment, 16-139
- Ont., Min. of Natural Resources, Aviation & Fire Mgmt. Centre, 17-293
- pubns., 8-121, -149, -163
- Qué., Min. des transports, Dir. du transport maritime, aérien et ferroviaire, 17-378
- Safety, 10-15
- - Bd., Cdn., 16-121—122
- Supply & Services Cda., Aerospace, Marine & Electronics Systems Dir., 16-115

Avro Arrow, 1-1

Award Cttee., Commissioner's, N.W.T., 17-205

B

BBM Bureau of Measurement, 8-179

BOMI Cda., 8-296

BT Bank of Cda., 13-10

B'nai Brith
- Canada, 8-198
- Hillel Fdn., 8-309
- League for Human Rights of, 8-199

- Women of Cda., 8-350
- Youth Org., 8-352—353

Badminton assns., 8-317

Baha'i
- Faith in Cda., The, 6-5
- Studies, Assn. for, 8-299

Baie James
- Comité consultatif pour l'environnement de la, 17-361
- Soc.
- - de développement de la, 17-344
- - d'énergie de la, 17-357

Bakery
- Confectionery & Tobacco Workers' Int'l Union, 11-10
- Council of Cda., 8-227

Baking pubns., 8-131

Ball hockey assns., 8-317

Ballet (see also Dance)
- companies & societies, 8-203—204

Banca
- Commerciale Italiana of Cda., 13-11
- Nazionale del Lavoro of Cda., 13-13

Banco Central of Cda., 13-11

Band Assn. (Ont.) Inc., Cdn., 8-280

Bank
- Act, 13-6
- of America Cda., 13-10
- of Boston Cda., 13-10
- of Canada, 13-3—5, 16-74
- chartered banks, 13-6—8, -8—14
- - domestic, 13-8—10
- - foreign, 13-10—14
- - rates, 13-7
- of Commerce, Cdn. Imp., 13-9
- of Credit & Commerce Cda., 13-11
- Hapoalim (Cda.), 13-12
- Inspector General of, see Superintendent of Financial Institutions, 13-2—3
- Leumi le-Israel, 13-12
- of Montreal, 13-8
- of Nova Scotia/Scotiabank, 13-8
- rate, 13-4
- of Tokyo Cda., 13-14

Bankers assns., 8-225, -226

Banking
- Alta., Treasury Dept., 17-51
- B.C., Supt. of Financial Institutions, 17-76
- Cda. Deposit Insurance Corp., 16-74
- and finance industry, 14-13—14
- Man.,
- - Agricultural Credit Corp., 17-110
- - Finance, Dept. of, 17-125
- - Man. Development Corp., 17-132
- N.S. Trusts & Debt Mgmt., Dept. of Finance, 17-224
- Que., Inspecteur gén. des Institutions financières, 17-361
- regulation of, 13-2—3
- Supt. of Financial Institutions, 16-73—74

Bankruptcy, 13-34
- administrators, Ont., 17-311
- registrars
- - B.C., 17-101
- - Nfld., 17-195
- - N.W.T., 17-211
- - N.S., 17-245
- - Que., 17-391
- - Sask., 17-427

Banque Nationale de Paris, 13-13

Banting Research Fdn., 8-261

Baptist(s)
· assns., 8-299
· Atlantic Cda. Assn. of Free Will, 6-4
· Fed., Cdn., 6-6
· North American, Conference, 6-11
· pubns., 8-168

Bar Assn., Cdn., 8-250

Barber(s)
· pubns., 8-144
· Shop Quartet Singing in America (SPEBSQSA), Soc. for the Preservation & Encouragement of, 8-282

Barbering Bd. of Examiners, Man., 17-133

Barclays Bank of Cda., 13-10

Baseball assns., 8-317—318

Basketball assns., 8-318

Bata Shoe Museum Fdn., 8-229

Baton Twirling Fed., Cdn., 8-297

Battlefields Commn., Nat'l, 16-68

Beauticians pubns., 8-144

Beauty Assn., Allied, 8-307

Beaverbrook Cdn. Fdn., 8-192

Beef
· Commn., Man., 17-108
· Stabilization Bd., Sask., 17-398

Beekeepers assns., 8-181

Beetz, Mr. Justice Jean, 1-3

Belarusen Autocephalous Orthodox Church, 6-12

Bertram (H.G.) Fdn., 8-192

Better Business Bureau, 8-189—190
· Directory & Consumer Guide, 8-148

Beverages
· assns., 8-227-229
· pubns., 8-131, -154

Biathlon Cda., 8-332

Bible
· Colleges
· · Assn. of Cdn., 8-217
· · Cdn., 6-16—17
· Holiness Movement, 6-5
· Hour, Cda.'s Nat'l, 8-299
· institutes, 6-16—17
· Soc., Cdn., 8-299

Biblical Studies, Cdn. Soc. of, 8-217

Bibliographical Soc. of Cda., 8-251

Bibliothécaires du Qué., Assoc. des, 8-253

Bibliothèque
· de l'Assemblée nationale, 17-334
· nationale du Qué., 17-336

Bickell (J.P.) Fdn., 8-192

Bicycling Assn. of B.C., 8-321

Biens culturels du Qué., Comm. des, 17-337

Big Brothers assns., 8-309

Big Sisters assns., 8-309

Bilingual legislation, 1-1, -2

Bilingualism
· Cda., Official Languages Br., Treasury Bd., 16-124
· Commissioner of Official Languages, 16-134—135
· Man., Dept. of Culture, Heritage & Recreation, 17-116

· Ont., Languages of Instruction Commn. of Ont., 17-274
· Sask., Official Minority Language Office, Dept. of Education, 17-402

Billiards & Snooker Referees' Assn., Cdn., 8-297

Biochemical Soc., Cdn., 8-305

Biological Coun. of Cda., 8-305

Biomass
· Centre qué. de valorisation de la, 17-358
· Energy Institute, The, 8-219

Birks Family Fdn., The, 8-192

Birth Control (see also Family Planning)
· Calgary, assn., 8-286

Birth rates, 5-5

Birthright, 8-286

Biscuit Mfrs., Assn. of Cdn., 8-227

Bishop's University, 7-14

Bissonnette, André, 1-1

Black
· Cultural Research Soc. of Alta., 8-208
· History Soc., Ont., 8-238
· pubns., 9-40
· Theatre Cda., 8-342

Black holes, 2-14

Black Powder, B.C., 8-331

Black Watch Inc., The Toronto, 8-276

Blainey, Justine, 1-1

Blind
· assns., see handicapped, 8-234—237
· and Deaf Schools, 7-8—9
· sports assns., 8-315

Blue Cross Plans, Cdn. Coun. of, 8-271

Blueberry Co-op Assn., B.C., 8-180

Boating
· Allied, Assn. of Cda., 8-258
· Fed., Cdn., 8-297
· and Yachting, pubns., 8-149—150

Bobsleigh & Luge assns., 8-318

Body Building assns., 8-318

Boiler
· and Machinery Underwriters' Assn., Cdn., 8-244
· Soc., Cdn., 8-258

Boilermakers, Iron Ship Builders, Blacksmiths, Forgers & Helpers, Int'l Brotherhood of, 11-11

Bond yield averages & conventional mortgage rates, 13-35

Book(s)
· Children's Book Centre, 8-294
· Export of Cdn., Assn. for the, 8-294
· Information Centre, Cdn., 8-294
· and Periodical Development Council, 8-294
· pubns., 8-121—122
· publishers, assns. & societies, 8-293—295

Bookbinders & Book Artists Guild, Cdn., 8-207

Booksellers assns., 8-183, -294, -295

Boreal Inst. for Northern Studies, 8-184

Botanical
· Assn., Cdn., 8-305
· Gardens, Royal Ont., 17-272

Bouchard, Lucien, 1-2

Boulangerie du Qué., Conseil de la, 8-228

Boundary Commns.
· B.C.-Alberta, 17-75
· B.C.-Yukon-N.W.T., 17-75
· Int'l, 16-185
· Sask. Educational, 17-402

Bourassa, Robert, 1-4

Bowling, assns., 8-318—319, -328
· Lawn, 8-328

Boxing
· assns., 8-319
· Authority, N.S., 17-235

Boy Scouts of Cda., 8-353

Boys' Brigade in Cda., 8-353

Boys & Girls Clubs
· of Cda., 8-353
· of Ont., 8-353

Brandon University, 7-14

Brazil-Cda. Chamber of Commerce, 8-229

Breeders, Western Ont., 8-257

Brethren in Christ Church, 6-5

Brewers Assn. of Cda., 8-227

Brewery
· and General Workers, Local 325, Cdn. Union of, 11-24
· Malt & Soft Drink Workers, Local 304, 11-24

Brewing & Malting Barley Research Inst., 8-301

Bricklayers
· and Allied Craftsmen, Int'l Union of, 11-12
· Masons Ind. Union of Cda., 11-17

Bridal pubns., 8-164

Bridge, Structural & Ornamental Iron Workers, Int'l Assn. of, 11-10

British Columbia
· agriculture, 4-4, 17-62
· Chamber of Commerce, 8-191
· coat of arms, 17-61
· community colleges, 7-47
· courts, 17-95—99
· economy, 14-16—17, 17-62
· education, 7-4, -7, -8, -47
· Ferry Corp., 17-95
· fishing, 17-62
· forestry, 4-7, -9, 17-62
· geography, 3-5—6, 17-61
· government, 17-63—96
· Heritage Trust, 17-88
· income statistics, 5-10
· judicial officers, 17-97—101
· labour legislation, 11-3, -6
· libraries & archives, 8-20—28
· manufacturing, 17-62
· minimum wage rate, 11-4
· mining, 17-62
· motor vehicle & traffic regulations, 10-8
· municipal government, 19-6
· municipalities, 19-7—10
· newspapers, 9-16—20
· Nurses' Union, 11-17
· population, 5-2, 17-61
· radio stations, 9-46, -53

B.C. (cont'd)
· Rail Ltd., 17-95—96
· superintendent of insurance, 13-20
· television stations, 9-58
· universities & colleges,
· · B.C., Univ. of, 7-14—15
· · Royal Roads Military College,
  7-35
· · Simon Fraser Univ., 7-38
· · Trinity Western Univ., 7-41
· · Victoria, Univ. of, 7-41
British Columbia & Yukon
· Building Trades Council, 8-203
· Chamber of Mines, 8-276
· Newspapers Assn., Community,
  8-294

British Israel World Fed., 8-299

Broadcast
· assns. & societies, 8-188—189
· Employees
· · and Technicians (NABET), Nat'l
  Assn. of, 11-23
· · Union, Radio-Québec Television,
  11-27
Broadcasting (see also Radio;
  Telecommunications;
  Television)
· Act, 9-7
· assns., 8-188—189
· native, 8-188, -189
· CRTC, 9-2, 16-43—45
· in Cda, 9-5—8
· Cdn. Broadcasting Corp. (CBC),
  1-1, 7-5, 9-5—8, 16-41—43
· Policy, Task Force on, 9-8
· pubns., 8-122
· Que., (Radio-Québec), 17-351
· services in remote communities,
  9-8

Brock University, 7-15—16

Broilers (See Poultry)

Broomball assns., 8-319—320

Brotherhood of
· Locomotive Engineers, Int'l 11-11
· Maintenance of Way Employees,
  11-10
· Railway Carmen of the U.S. &
  Cda., Cdn. Div., 11-10

Bruce Trail Clubs
· Bruce Trail Assn., 8-284
· Dufferin Hi-Land, 8-284

Buckwheat statistics, 4-7

Buddhist Churches of Cda., 6-5

Budget, federal, 1-1, Manitoba, 1-1

Building(s)
· Construction Wages Bd., 17-135
· Corp., B.C., 17-79
· Inspectors' Assn. of B.C., 8-203
· Maintenance Contractors Assn. of
  Cda., 8-307
· Materials Retailers Assn. of Que.,
  8-205
· owners & managers assns., 8-296
· pubns., 8-126, -157
· Standards Bd., Man., 17-133
  .Trades Coun.
· · B.C. & Yukon, 8-203
· · and Construction:
    Man.-Winnipeg, 8-249; Ont.,
    8-249

Bus industry, 10-7, -10
· assn., 8-346
· legislation, 10-5—6
· structure, 10-10

Business (see also Industrial)
· and the Arts in Cda., Coun. for,
  8-185
· assns., 8-189—191
· Communicators, Int'l Assn. of,
  8-352
· Council
· · of B.C., 8-257
· · of Cda., Int'l, 8-190
· · on Nat'l Issues, 8-189
· · N.W.T., 17-206
· Development
· · Bank, Federal, 16-91—92
· · Centre, 8-189
· Forms Assn., Cdn., 8-293
· Health Research Inst., Cdn., 8-301
· Loan Fund Advisory Bd., N.W.T.,
  17-209
· media, NEWS Business, 8-295
· performances & prospects in Cda.,
  14-1—6
· Professional Advertising Assn.,
  8-179
· pubns., 8-120—148
· · business, 8-122—125
· · consumer, see Finance, 8-153
· Telecommunications Alliance,
  Cdn., 8-341

Business Regulations
· Alta., Dept. of Consumer &
  Corporate Affairs, 17-25
· B.C., Dept. of Finance & Corporate
  Relations, 17-75
· Canada,
· · Consumer & Corporate Affairs,
  16-51—52
· · Industry, Science & Technology,
  Dept. of, 16-87—92
· · Revenue Cda., Taxation,
  16-104—106
· Man., Dept. of Co-operative,
  Consumer & Corporate Affairs,
  17-115
· N.B., Corporate & Trust Affairs Br.,
  Justice Dept., 17-155
· Ont., Commercial Standards
  Program, Min. of Consumer &
  Commercial Relations, 17-265
· P.E.I., Corporations Div., Justice
  Dept., 17-320
· Que.,
· · Min. de l'Industrie, du Commerce
  et de la Technologie, 17-363
· · Min. du Revenu, 17-373
· Sask., Dept. of Consumer &
  Commercial Affairs, 17-401

Byelorussian
· assns., 8-223
· pubn., 9-40

C

C.A. Pippy Park Commn., Nfld.,
  17-188

CAA, 8-186

CABNL, see Les Editions l'image de
  l'art, 8-110

CAMECO, 17-419

CANDU Industries, Org. of, 8-220

CARES, 8-187

CARFAC, see Cdn. Artists
  Representation, 8-184

CASARA, 8-187

CAW, 1-2, -3, 11-18

CBC (See Canadian Broadcasting
  Corp.)

CCAB Inc., 8-179

CCMC Music Gallery, 8-280

C.D. Howe Institute, 8-210

CEGEP, 7-7, -50—52
· Teachers, Fed. of, 11-20

CEREP Inc., 8-210

CGIT — see Nat'l CGIT Assn., 8-354

CGRSA, 8-188

CIDA — Cdn. International
  Development Agency, 7-5,
  16-132—134, -190—191

CISTI, 16-140

CJRT-FM Inc., 17-270

CLC, 11-7—8

CM: A Reviewing Journal of Cdn.
  Materials for Young People,
  8-122

CMA (see also Municipal chapter,
  19-1—43), 5-3

CNCP Telecommunications, 9-2

CNTU, see Confederation of Nat'l
  Trade Unions, 11-9

CPP—Cda. Pension Plan, 11-5

CRTC, 1-3, 9-2, -7—8, 16-43—45

CSIS, 16-110—111

Cabinet(s)
· committee system, 16-10—11
· committees, 16-19—20
· federal, 15-2—3, -11—12, 16-9—12
· · ministers, 16-19
· provincial (See Executive
  Councils)

Cable
· Telecommunications Assn., Ont.,
  8-188
· Television, 1-3, 9-6, -7, -8
· · Assn., Cdn., 8-188
· · and the CRTC, 1-3
· · companies, 9-6, -61—68

Cadet
· leagues, 8-275, -352
· movement in Cda., 16-182

Cairns Group, 1-4

Caisse(s)
· de dépôt et placement du Qué.,
  17-362
· populaires, La Féd. des
· · Acadiennes, 8-226
· · Fonds de Sécurité des caisses
    populaires, 17-116
· · Man., 8-226
· · Ont., 8-226

Calendar, 2-20
· perpetual, see inside back cover

Calgary
· Chamber of Commerce, 8-191
· Communities, Fed. of, 8-200
· libraries & archives, 8-8—11
· music, assns., 8-280
· newspapers, 9-13
· Olympics, 1-1
· pubn., 8-151
· radio stations, 9-45, -52
· Stampede, Exhibition &, 8-225
· television stations, 9-57
· Tourist & Convention Bur., 8-344
· Univ. of, 7-16

Cameron, Michelle, 1-3

Camping
· assns., 8-297
· pubns., 8-150

Camrose Lutheran College, 7-17

Canada
· Act, text of, 15-16—17
· area, land & freshwater, 3-9
· by-election, 1-2
· -China Trade Council, 8-229
· climate, 3-10—12
· coastal waters, 3-9
· coat of arms, 2-2
· Council, 16-41
· Deposit Insurance Corp., 16-74
· Development Investment Corp.,
   16-129
· dimensions, 3-1
· economy, 14-1—25
· election, 1-3, -4
· emblems of, 2-3
· federal state, 15-3—9
· flag, 2-3
· Games Park Commn., Nfld.,
   17-178
· geographical structure, 3-1
· geology, 3-6—8
· · map, 3-8
· Great Seal, 2-2
· holidays & anniversaries, 2-8
· income statistics, 5-10
· inland waters, 3-8, -9
· islands, 3-9
· -Japan Trade Council, 8-229
· judiciary, 12-6—7, 16-146—148
· Lands Co.
· · Mirabel, 16-129
· · Le Vieux Port de Montréal,
   16-129
· minimum wage rates, 11-4
· Mortgage & Housing Corp.,
   16-129—130
· mountains, 3-7
· national anthem, 2-2
· Pension Plan, 11-5
· permanent missions abroad,
   16-185—186
· political regions, 3-4—6
· population, 5-1—14
· Post Corp., 9-9—11, 16-131
· rivers, 3-8—9
· soils & vegetation, 3-12—13
· superintendent of insurance, 13-20
· system of gov't, 15-1—13
· vital statistics, 5-4, -5, -6, -7, -8
· · comparison of Cda. with other
   countries, 5-8
· West Fdn., 8-283

Canadian
· Airlines Int'l, 10-16, -17
· Bar Assn., 8-250
· Broadcasting Corp. (CBC), 7-5,
   9-5—8, 16-41—43
· Clubs, Assn. of, 8-287
· National Railways, 10-2—3, -4,
   16-122
· Radio-television &
   Telecommunications Commn.
   (CRTC), 9-2, -7-8, 16-43—45
· Shield, 3-6
· Studies, The Assn. for, 8-251

Canadienne-française de l'Ont.,
   L'Assoc., 8-207

Canaryseed statistics, 4-7
Canative Housing Corp., 8-283
Cancer
· Inst.
· · of Cda., Nat'l, 8-270
· · Ont., 17-284
· Research Soc., 8-262
· Soc., Cdn., 8-267
· Treatment & Research Fdn.,
· · Man., 17-128
· · Ont., 17-284
Canoeing assns., 8-320
Canola
· Coun. of Cda., 8-181
· Growers Assn.,
· · Alta., 8-180
· · Sask., 8-181
· pubn., 8-166
Canon Law Soc., Cdn., 8-250
Cape Breton
· Development Corp., 16-128—129
· pubn., 8-151
· Tourist Assn., 8-345
· University College of, 7-17
Capital Commn.
· Nat'l, 16-138
· Prov., B.C., 17-89
Caravan, Metro Toronto Int'l, 8-208
Carbonization Research Assn.,
   Cdn., 8-301
Cardiologie de Qué., Inst. de, 8-265
Cardiovascular Soc., Cdn., 8-267
CARE Cda., 8-192
Care Facilities, 8-191
Care-Ring Ont., 8-310
Career(s)
· assns., 8-216—217
· Colleges, Assn. of Cdn., 8-214
· Development & Advanced Studies,
   Dept., Nfld., 17-175
Caribbean Cultural Cttee., 8-208
Cariboo Lumber Mfrs.' Assn., 8-351
Caribou Management Bds., 16-86,
   -87
Carleton University, 7-17—18
Carpenters & Joiners of America,
   United Brotherhood of, 11-14
Carpet Inst., Cdn., 8-258
Cartographic Assn., Cdn., 8-252
Casting Fed., Cdn., 8-297
Cathay, Int'l Commercial Bank of,
   13-12
Catholic(s)
· Charities of the Archdiocese of
   Toronto, 8-193
· Children's Aid Soc. of Metro
   Toronto, 8-310
· Church Extension Soc. of Cda.,
   8-193
· churches
· · Polish Nat'l, 6-13
· · Roman Catholic, 6-14
· and Divorced, Cdn. Assn. of
   Separated, 8-309
· Family Services
· · Soc., 8-310
· · of Toronto, 8-310
· Health Assn. of Cda., 8-272
· Historical Assn., Cdn., 8-299
· Occasional Teachers' Assn., Ont.,
   11-24
· Org. for Dev't & Peace, Cdn.,
   8-246

· Parent-Teacher Assns. of Ont.,
   Fed. of, 8-215
· pubns., 8-168, -169
· religion, assns., 8-299, -300
· School Trustees Assn.
· · Alta., 8-213
· · Cdn., 8-214
· Teachers,
· · Fed. of English Speaking, 8-213
· · Provincial Assn. of, 11-25
· Women's League of Cda., 8-350
· Youth Org., 8-354
Cattle
· assns., 8-255, -256, -257
· Commn., Alta., 17-19
· pubns., 8-165, -166, -167
· statistics, 4-4—5
Caulking Contractors Assn., 8-203
Celestial Events, 2-17—19
Cell Biology, Cdn. Soc. for, 8-305
Cement, Lime, Gypsum & Allied
   Division, Int'l Brotherhood of
   Boilermakers, Iron Ship
   Builders, Blacksmiths, Forgers
   & Helpers, 11-11
Cemeteries (See Funeral)
Censorship (of Films)
· Alta., Motion Picture Censor Bd,
   17-28
· B.C., Film Classification Div, 17-91
· Man., Film Classification Bd.,
   17-117
· N.B., Film Classification Bd.,
   17-162
· N.S., Amusements Regulation Div.,
   17-222
· Ont., Theatres Br., 17-267
· Qué., Régie du cinéma, 17-340
Census
· data, 5-1—12
· metropolitan areas (see also
   Municipal Governments
   chapter, 19-1—43), 5-3
Centennial Centre Corp., Man.,
   17-117
Centraide-Québec, 8-310
Ceramic(s)
· pubn., 8-125
· Soc., Cdn., 8-207
Ceramists Cda., 8-207
Cercle Molière, Le, 8-342
Cerebral Palsy
· Adult Cerebral Palsy Inst. of Metro
   Toronto, 8-234
· assns., 8-234, -236, -267—268,
   -315
· Children's Rehabilitation &
   Cerebral Palsy Assn., 8-269
· Fdn. Inc. (Grotto), 8-236
· Sports assns., 8-315
Certified General Accountants
· assns., 8-177
· Research Fdn., Cdn., 8-177
Chambers of Commerce & Boards
   of Trade, 8-191—192, -230
Champlain Soc., 8-238
Charitable organizations & assns.,
   8-183, 192—195
Charlottetown
· Area Development Corp., P.E.I.,
   17-322
· Festival, 8-342

Charolais Assn., Cdn., 8-256

Charter of Rights & Freedoms, Cdn., 12-4—5, 15-17—19

Chartered banks, 13-6—14
· domestic, 13-8—10
· foreign, 13-10—14
· rates, 13-7

Chartered Secretaries & Administrators in Cda., Inst. of, 8-190

Chase Manhattan Bank of Cda., 13-11

Chemical
· assns. & societies, 8-195—196
· Bank of Cda., 13-11
· Engineering
· · Cdn. Soc. for, 8-221
· · pubn., 8-169
· fertilizer, 8-195, -196
· Process Industries, assns., 8-195—196
· pubns., 8-125
· scientific assns., 8-305, -306
· Workers Union, Energy and, 11-19

Chemists
· Cdn. Assn. of Textile Colourists and, 8-341
· Clinical, Cdn. Soc. of, 8-306

Cheshire Homes Fdn. (Cda.) Inc., 8-193

Chess assns., 8-239

Chicken (See Poultry)

Chief Electoral Officer, 16-27

Chiefs of Ont. Joint Indian Assn., 8-283

Child
· & Family Service, Jewish, 8-310
· Find Ontario, 8-196
· Health, Cdn. Inst. of, 8-271

Child care
· assns., 8-196—197
· pubn., 8-129

Child Welfare
· Alta, Child Protection Services, 17-46
· B.C., Family & Children's Services Div., 17-90
· Man., Child & Family Services Div., 17-115
· Nfld., Child Welfare, 17-190
· N.S., Family & Children's Services, 17-220
· Ont.
· · Child & Family Services Review Bd., 17-264
· · Min. of Community & Social Services, 17-263
· P.E.I., Dept. of Health & Social Services, 17-319
· Sask., Community Health Services Br., Dept. of Health, 17-405
· Yukon, Dept. of Health & Human Resources, 17-435

Children
· assns., 8-196—197
· · charitable, 8-193, -194
· Crippled, B.C. Lions Soc. for, 8-235
· Education, Ont. Assn. for Early Childhood, 8-211
· and the Law, Cdn. Fdn. for, 8-250
· Visually Impaired, Ont. Fdn. for, 8-237

Children's
· Apparel Mfrs. Assn., 8-341
· Authors, Illustrators & Performers (CANSCAIP), Cdn. Soc. of, 8-352
· Broadcast Institute, 8-188
· Mental Health Centres, Ont. Assn. of, 8-274
· pubns., 8-150—151
· Rehabilitation & Cerebral Palsy Assn., 8-269

Chimistes du Qué., Ordre des, 8-196

Chinchilla Breeders of Cda., Nat'l, 8-233

Chinese
· assns., 8-223
· pubns., 9-40

Chiropractic
· assns., 8-264
· Education, The Coun. on, 8-217
· Examining Bd., Cdn., 8-264

Choral assns., 8-279—283

Christian(s)
· Blind Mission Int'l, 8-236
· charities, 8-193
· Children's Fund of Cda., 8-193
· Church (Disciples of Christ), 6-7
· Farmers Fed. of Alta., 8-181
· holidays, 2-9
· and Jews, Cdn. Coun. of, 6-2—3
· Labour Assn. of Cda., 11-19
· and Missionary Alliance in Cda., The, 6-6
· pubns., 8-168
· Reformed
· · Church in North America, The, 6-7
· · World Relief Cttee. of Cda., 8-193
· Science, 6-8
· Service Brigade, 8-193
· Studies, Inst. for, 8-217

Chromosphere, 2-11

Church(es)
· Army in Cda., 8-310
· in Canada, 6-3—16
· Cdn. Coun. of, 6-3
· of Christ in Cda., 6-8
· Community, Universal Fellowship of Metropolitan, 6-16
· Council on Justice & Corrections, 8-251
· of God, 6-8
· of Jesus Christ of Latter-day Saints (Mormons), 6-8
· Library Assn., 8-254
· of the Nazarene, 6-8
· statistics
· · churches by denomination, 6-2
· · clergy, 6-2
· · membership, 6-2

Churchill Falls (Lab.) Corp. Ltd., 1-2, 17-192

Cinema/Cinéma
· assns., 8-197—198
· Inst. québécois du, 17-338
· pubns., 8-153
· Rég. du, 17-340
· Television & Radio Artists (ACTRA), Alliance of Cdn., 11-16
· and Television General Union—NFB Section, 11-28

Circulation Mgrs.' Assn., Cdn., 8-295

Citibank Cda., 13-11

Cities, see Municipalities, 19-1—43

Citizens
· Coalition, Nat'l, 8-291
· for Public Justice, 8-290
· rights, 12-3—6
· Safety Coun., Metro., 8-304

Citizenship
· Cda., Secretary of State Dept., 16-108
· Coun. of Man., 8-277
· Fed., Cdn., 8-310
· Ont.
· · Advisory Coun. on Multiculturalism and, 17-261
· · Min. of, 17-261
· Qué., Min. des Communautés culturelles et de l'Immigration, 17-349

City
· clerks, see Municipalities, 19-1—43
· pubns., 8-151—152

Civil Liberties (see also Human Rights)
· assns., 8-198—199

Civil Rights, pubns., 8-142

Civil Service
· Commn.,
· · Man., 17-139
· · N.B., 17-164
· · N.S., 17-234
· · Ont., 17-291
· · P.E.I., 17-322
· · Que., 17-336
· pubn, 8-142
· Superannuation Bd., Man., 17-138

Classical Assn. of Cda., 8-252

Classification Research Group, Cdn., 8-253

Clay Brick Assn. of Cda., 8-205

Clean Environment Commn., Man., 17-124

Cleaners assns., 8-307, -308

Cleft Lip & Palate Family Assn., Cdn., 8-268

Climate
· of Cda., 3-10—12
· temperature & precipitation data for various districts, 3-11—12

Clinical Research Soc. of Toronto, 8-301

Clothing (see also Textiles)
· industry assns., 8-341—342
· manufacturers, 8-341, -342
· pubns., 8-145
· and Textile Workers Union, Amalgamated, 11-9
· Workers Inc., Nat'l Fed. of, 11-21

Clubs (See Fraternal & Social)

Coaching Assn. of Cda., 8-313

Coal, 4-19—20
· Assn. of Cda., 8-277
· Ltd., New Brunswick, 17-164—165
· Research & Technology, Office of, Alta., 17-34

Coast
· Fdn. Soc., 8-193
· Guard, Cdn., 10-13, 16-120

Coastal Waters & Islands of Cda., 3-9

Coat of arms
· national, 2-2
· provincial, *see* individual entries

Cod War, 1-2

Coffee Coun. of Cda., 8-228

Collective Agreement Bd., Man.,
  17-119

Colleges/Collèges (*see also*
  Universities)
· agricultural, 7-10
· of Applied Arts & Technology of
  Ont.,
· · Assn. of, 8-217
· · Council of Regents for, 17-262
· assns., 8-211—218
· Athletic Assn.,
· · Cdn., 8-314
· · Ont., (OCAA), 8-314
· Bd. of Governors, Arctic, N.W.T.,
  17-204
· Cdn. Bible, Assn. of, 8-217
· Cdn. Career, Assn. of, 8-214
· Community, 7-10—11, -45—54
· Cons. des, Qué., 17-358
· dominicain, 7-19
· d'enseignement général et
  professionnel (CEGEP), 7-7,
  -50—52
· military, 7-34, -35, -53, 16-183
· du Qué., Assoc. des, 8-213
· Relations Commn., Ont., 17-262
· United World, 8-213
· and Universities, Ont. Ministry of,
  17-262
· and University
· · Libraries, Cdn. Assn. of, 8-253
· · Professionals, Fed. of, 11-20

Colombo Plan, 16-185

Color, Cdn. Soc. for, 8-195

Combined Training Assn. Inc., Cdn.,
  8-312

Comerica Bank Cda., 13-11

Comets, 2-13

Commerce (*see also* Trade &
  Commerce)
· extérieur et du Développement
  technologique, Min. du, Qué.,
  17-348
· Féd. du, 11-21
· et de la Technologie, Min. de
  l'Industrie, du, 17-363
· and Technology, N.B. Dept of,
  17-151

Commercial
· Appeals Commn., B.C., 17-93
· Arbitration Centre, B.C. Int'l, 17-72
· Corp., Cdn., 16-132
· Registration Appeal Trib., Ont.,
  17-266
· Travellers' Assn. of Cda., 8-345
· Workers Union, United Food and,
  1-2

Commissioner
· for Federal Judicial Affairs, 16-94
· Fire, Cda., 16-96
· of Official Languages, 16-134

Commissioner's Award Cttee.,
  N.W.T., 17-205

Commissionnaires, Corps of,
· B.C., 8-275
· Cdn., 8-276

Commodity exchange, 13-33

Commonwealth
· Cda.'s role in, 16-188
· Games Assn. of Cda., 8-233
· of Nations, 16-186
· Secretariat, 16-188
· Soc., Royal, 8-287
· War Graves Commn. (Cda.),
  16-127, -189

Communautés culturelles et de
  l'Immigration
· Min. des, Qué., 17-349
· du Qué. (CCCI), Cons. des, 17-350

Communication(s)
· and Allied Workers, Cdn. Assn. of,
  11-18
· assns., 8-252, -284
· Cdn.
· · Broadcasting Corp. (CBC), 7-5,
  9-5—8, 16-41—43
· · Radio-television &
  Telecommunications Commn.
  (CRTC), 9-2, -7—8, 16-43—45
· computer
· · Inst., 8-341
· · Man-Computer Comm. Soc.,
  Cdn., 8-200
· cross-cultural, centre, 8-277
· depts.,
· · Alta., Dept. of Technology,
  Research &
  Telecommunications, 17-48
· · Cda., 16-38—51
· · Nfld., Dept of Consumer Affairs
  & Communications, 17-176
· · N.S., Dept. of Transportation &
  Communications, 17-232
· · N.W.T., Dept. of Culture &
  Communications, 17-201
· · Ont., Min. of Culture &
  Communications, 17-269
· · Que., Min. des Communications,
  17-350
· Educational
· · Authority (TVOntario), Ont.,
  17-271
· · Corp., Alta., 17-52
· and Electrical Workers of Cda.,
  11-19
· · Féd. nationale des, 11-21
· Man. Telephone System, 17-140
· military
· · Armed Forces, and Electronics
  Assn., 8-218
· · Cdn. Forces Communication
  Command, 16-181
· Nat'l Film Bd., 16-46
· N.S., Bd. of Commrs. of Public
  Utilities, 17-233
· pubns., 8-169
· · broadcasting, 8-122
· · telecommunications, 8-145
· radio, 9-2
· Sask. Telecommunications
  (SaskTel), 17-424
· Workers,
· · of America—Printing, Publishing
  & Media Workers Sector,
  11-10
· · Cdn. Union of, 11-28
· · Nat'l Fed. of, 11-21

CommuniCAtion, 8-123

Communist Party of Cda., 8-290

Community(ies)
· Arts Council of Vancouver, 8-185
· Assn. for Riding for the Disabled,
  8-316
· Colleges, 7-10—11, -45—54
· · Trustees' Assn., Sask., 8-215
· and Cultural Affairs, Dept. of,
  P.E.I., 17-318
· Economic Development Fund,
  Man., 17-138
· Information Centre
· · of Metro. Toronto, 8-310
· · in Ont., Assn. of, 8-309
· Newspapers Assn., Cdn., 8-295
· Services
· · Council (Nfld. & Labrador), 8-200
· · Man. Dept. of, 17-114
· and Social Services, Ministry of,
  Ont., 17-263
· and Transportation Serv., Dept. of,
  Yukon, 17-432
· Yukon, Assn. of, 8-278

Community Planning
· Alta. Planning Bd, Municipal
  Affairs Dept., 17-42
· assns., 8-199—200
· B.C., Min. of Municipal Affairs,
  Recreation & Culture, 17-87
· Canada,
· · Cda. Mortgage & Housing Corp.,
  16-129—130
· · Indian Affairs & Northern Dev't
  Dept., 16-82—87
· Man., Interdepartmental Planning
  Bd, 17-136
· N.B., Municipal Affairs &
  Environment Dept., 17-158
· Nfld., Municipal Affairs Dept.,
  17-187
· N.W.T., Dept. of Municipal &
  Community Affairs, 17-203
· N.S., Community Planning,
  Municipal Affairs Dept., 17-230
· Ont., Community Planning, Min. of
  Municipal Affairs, 17-292
· P.E.I., Planning Services, Dept. of
  Community & Cultural Affairs,
  17-318
· Que., Min. des Affaires
  municipales, Dir. gén. de
  l'urbanisme et de
  l'aménagement du territoire,
  17-341
· Sask., Community Planning
  Services Br., Dept. of Urban
  Affairs, 17-419
· Yukon, Dept. of Community &
  Transportation Services, 17-432

Community Services
· Alta., Dept. of Social Services,
  17-46
· B.C., Min. of Social Services &
  Housing, 17-90
· Man., Community Services Dept.,
  17-114
· N.B., Local Gov't Services Div.,
  Municipal Affairs & Environment
  Dept., 17-158
· Nfld., Social Services Dept.,
  17-190
· N.W.T., Social Services Dept.,
  17-204

Community Services (cont'd)
· N.S., Dept. of, 17-214
· Ont., Min. of Community & Social
  Services, 17-263
· P.E.I., Community & Cultural
  Affairs Dept., 17-318
· Que., Min. de la Santé et des
  Services sociaux, 17-374
· Sask., Dept. of Social Services,
  17-418
· Yukon, Dept. of Community &
  Transportation Services, 17-432

Compassion of Cda., 8-193

Competition Tribunal, 16-52

Composers assns., 8-280, -281

Compressed Gas
· Assn. Inc., 8-220
· Bd. of Examiners for, N.B., 17-156

Comptroller, Office of the, N.B.,
  17-164

Computer(s)
· -Assisted Manufacturing Centre,
  Que., 17-358
· assns., 8-200—201
· communications, 9-5
· · Institute, 8-200
· Health, Cdn. Org. for
  Advancement of Computers in,
  8-260
· pubns., 8-126, -152, -170
· Services Ltd., Nfld. & Lab., 17-192
· Utility Corp. (SaskComp), Sask.,
  17-421

Concept Party of Alta., Western
  Cda., 8-292

Concordia University, 7-18

Concrete assns., 8-203, -204, -205

Condominium assns., 8-211, -295

Confectionery Manufacturers Assn.
  of Cda, 8-228

Confederation, 15-1, -3—4, -13—14

Confederation/Confédération
· of Cdn. Unions (CCU), 11-9
· générale de la publicité, 8-179
· of National Trade Unions (CNTU),
  11-9
· of Resident & Ratepayer Assns.
  (CORRA), 8-200

Conference
· Bd. of Cda., 8-211
· of the Congregational Christian
  Churches in Ont., 6-8
· of Mennonites of Cda., 8-300

Congregational Christian Churches
  in Ont., Conf. of, 6-8

Conseils scolaires de l'Ontario,
  Assoc. française des, 8-213

Conservation
· Alta., Environment Coun. of, 17-35
· Amalgamated Consv. Soc., 8-201
· amphibian & reptile, soc., 8-349
· assns., 8-201—202
· B.C., Min. of Environment, 17-75
· Cda., Dept. of the Environment,
  16-65—68
· Districts Commn., Man., 17-137
· Employees' Union, Quebec
  Wildlife, 11-27
· Institute, Cdn., 16-40
· Land, and Reclamation Council,
  Alta., 17-35

· Man., Dept. of Environment &
  Workplace Safety & Health,
  17-123
· Nat'l
· · Gallery of Cda., Restoration &
  Conservation Lab., 16-48
· · Museum of Natural Sciences,
  16-48—49
· N.B., Dept. of Municipal Affairs &
  Environment, 17-158
· Nfld., Wildlife Div., Dept. of
  Culture, Recreation & Youth,
  17-177
· N.W.T., Denendeh Conservation
  Board, 17-205
· N.S., Policy & Program Dev't,
  Dept. of Lands & Forests,
  17-229
· Ontario, Conservation Authorities
  & Water Mgmt., Min. of Natural
  Resources, 17-293
· organizations, int'l, 16-185
· P.E.I., Dept. of Community &
  Cultural Affairs, 17-318
· pubns., 8-158—159
· Que.,
· · Fdn. de la faune du Québec,
  17-370
· · Min. du Loisir, de la Chasse et
  de la Pêche, 17-369
· Review Bd., Ont., 17-270
· Sask., Renewable Resources Div.,
  Dept. of Parks, Recreation &
  Culture, 17-413

Conservatoire de musique et d'art
  dramatique du Québec, 17-336

Conservators, Cdn. Assn. of Prof.,
  8-238

Consommateur, Office de la
  protection du, 17-368

Constables
· for the Gov't of Que., Union of
  Special, 11-27
· of the Quebec Dept. of Transport,
  Brotherhood of, 11-22

Constitution(al), 15-1—26
· Act, 1982, text of, 15-17—26
· Affairs, Office of Aboriginal, 16-12
  .Amendment
· · 1987 (Meech Lake Accord), 1-2,
  15-5, -24—26
· · procedures, 15-5, -20—21
· Cda., Secretary of State Dept.,
  16-107—110
· Conference, 15-20, -26
· Nat'l
· · Archives of Cda., 16-45
· · Library of Cda., 16-47—48
· Royal Proclamation, text of, 15-16

Construction
· Alta.,
· · Bur. of Statistics, Treasury Dept.,
  17-51
· · Planning & Research Services
  Br., Dept. of Labour, 17-39
· assns., 8-202—205
· · home builders, 8-242
· B.C.,
· · Central Statistics Bureau, Min. of
  Finance & Corporate
  Relations, 17-75
· · Min. of Social Services &
  Housing, 17-90

· Cda.,
· · Inst. for Scientific & Technical
  Information, Nat'l Research
  Coun. of Cda., 16-140
· · Mortgage & Housing Corp.,
  16-129—130
· Industry Panel, N.S., 17-228
· Labour Relations, assns., 8-248,
  -249
· Management Bureau Ltd., 8-248
· materials assns., 8-205—206
· N.B., Dept. of
· · Supply & Services, 17-160
· · Transportation, 17-162
· Nfld., Dept. of Public Works &
  Services, 17-187
· N.S., Dept. of Labour, 17-227
· Ont.,
· · Construction Health & Safety Br.,
  Min. of Labour, 17-288
· · Min. of Housing, 17-284
· pubns., 8-120, -126—127
· Que.,
· · construction du Qué.: Comm. de
  la, 17-381, Régie des
  entreprises de, 17-343
· · Min. de la Main-d'oeuvre et de la
  Sécurité du revenu, 17-371
· Safety Assn. of Ont., 8-304
· Statistics Cda., 16-142—145
· steel (*See* Steel)
· Trades Council, Man.-Winnipeg
  Building and, 8-249
· wages boards, Man., 17-135

Consular
· Assistance, 16-176
· Corps Assn. of Toronto, 8-210

Consulates & Trade Commissions in
  Cda., 16-163—174

Consulting Engineers, assns., 8-220

Consumer
· Affairs, Dept. of,
· · Nfld., 17-176
· · N.S., 17-222
· assns., 8-206
· and Corporate Affairs,
· · Alta., 17-25
· · Cda., 16-51—52
· · Man., 17-115
· Electronics Marketers of Cda.,
  8-219
· Health Org. of Cda., 8-272
· magazines, 8-148—165
· Ont., and Commercial Relations,
  Min. of, 17-265
· Price Index (CPI), 14-6—7
· Sask., and Commercial Affairs,
  Dept. of, 17-401

Consumer Protection
· Alta., Consumer & Corporate
  Affairs Dept., 17-25
· B.C., Min. of Labour & Consumer
  Services, 17-84
· Canada, Bureau of Consumer
  Affairs, Consumer & Corporate
  Affairs Dept., 16-52
· Man., Consumer's Bur., 17-115
· N.B., Dept. of Justice, Consumer
  Affairs Br., 17-155
· Nfld., Dept. of Consumer Affairs &
  Communications, 17-176
· N.S., Dept. of Consumer Affairs,
  17-222

Consumer Protection (cont'd)
· Ont., Min. of Consumer &
  Commercial Relations, 17-265
· P.E.I., Dept. of Justice, Consumer
  Servs. Br., 17-320
· Que., Consumer Protection Bur.,
  17-368
· Sask., Consumer & Commercial
  Affairs Dept., 17-401

Continuing Education (See Adult
  Education; Colleges; Education;
  Universities)

Conventions
· assns., 8-344, -345, -346
· pubns., 8-127—128

Co-operative(s) (see also specific
  categories)
· Alta., Consumer & Corporate
  Affairs Dept., 17-25
· assns., 8-206
· B.C., Min. of Finance & Corporate
  Relations, 17-75
· Canada
· · Cda. Mortgage & Housing Corp.,
    16-129—130
· · Corporations Br., Consumer &
    Corporate Affairs Cda., 16-52
· · Indian Affairs & Northern Dev't
    Dept., Education & Social
    Development Branches, 16-83
· Consumer and Corporate Affairs,
  Dept. of, Man., 17-115
· Loans
· · Bd. of Ont., 17-256
· · and Loans Guarantee Bd., The,
    Man., 17-115
· N.S., Registrar of Joint Stock Cos.,
  Dept. of Attorney General,
  17-219
· Ont., Credit Unions &
  Co-operatives Br., Min. of
  Financial Institutions, 17-278
· Promotion Bd., Man., 17-115
· Sask., Co-operatives Br., Dept. of
  Economic Development &
  Tourism, 17-401
· Soc. de développement des
  co-opératives (SDC), 17-364

Copper & Brass Dev't Assn., Cdn.,
  8-277

Copyright assns. & societies, 8-206,
  -280

Cordilleran region, 3-7—8

Corona, 2-11

Coroners
· Alta., Medical Examiner/Fatality
  Inquiries, Dept. of Attorney
  General, 17-23
· B.C.,
· · Min. of Attorney General, 17-71
· · Service, 17-92
· Man. Dept. of the Attorney
  General, 17-112
· N.B., Dept. of Justice, 17-155
· Nfld., Dept. of Justice, 17-184
· N.W.T., Dept. of Justice, 17-203
· N.S., Dept. of Attorney General,
  17-219
· Ont., Chief Coroner's Office,
  17-297
· P.E.I., Dept. of Justice, 17-320
· Que., Bureau du coroner, 17-376

· Sask., Dept. of Justice, Chief
  Coroner, 17-410
· Yukon, Justice Dept., Chief
  Coroner, 17-435

Corporation Securities Registration,
  N.B. 17-162

Corps Assn., Cdn., 8-276

Correctional
· Investigator, 16-12
· Services
· · of Cda., The, 12-12—13,
    16-111—112
· · Ont., Ministry of, 17-268

Corrections & Criminology, Ont.
  Assn. of, 8-251

Corrugated
· Case Assn., Cdn., 8-286
· Steel Pipe Inst., 8-259

Cosmetic
· pubns., 8-128
· Toiletry & Fragrance Assn., Cdn.,
  8-303

Cost Reduction, Cdn. Inst. of, 8-258

COSTI-IIAS Immigrant Services,
  8-309

Côté, Michel, 1-1

Cottagers' Assns., Fed. of Ont.,
  8-242

Couchiching Inst. on Public Affairs,
  8-212

Counties, see Municipal Gov'ts,
  19-1—43

Country (See Agricultural;
  Agriculture; Farm; Rural)

Courses de chevaux du Qué.
· · Comm. des, 17-346
· · Soc. de développement de
    l'industrie des, (SODIC),
    17-362

Court(s), 12-6—7
· adult, 12-11
· of Cda.
· · Court Martial Appeal, 12-7,
    16-146—147
· · Federal, 12-7, 16-146
· · Supreme, 12-7, 16-146
· provincial, see 17-1
· of Revision, B.C., 17-78

Crafts
· assns., 8-206—207
· pubns., 8-156

Cranberry Mktg. Bd., B.C., 17-69

Creamerymen's Assn., Ont., 8-209

Credit/Crédit
· assns., 8-225—226
· Commercial de France, 13-11
· Co-operative Credit Soc., Cdn.,
  13-15
· Corp. of Sask., Agricultural,
  17-399
· Counselling Services, Ont. Assn.
  of, 8-311
· Lyonnais Cda., 13-11
· pubns., 8-130
· Suisse Cda., 13-11

Credit Union(s), including caisse
  populaire federations, 13-14—15
· Centrals, prov., 8-226
· Province House, Ltd., N.S., 17-239
· Stabilization Fund, Man., 17-116

Cricket Assn., Cdn., 8-320—321

Crime
· adult offenders & convictions,
  12-11

· and delinquency, 12-10—13
· Statistics for Cda., 12-11

Crime Compensation (see also
  Criminal)
· Alta., Crimes Comp. Bd., 17-23
· B.C. Criminal Injury Section, 17-93
· Man., Criminal Injuries Comp. Bd.,
  17-113
· Nfld. Crimes Compensation Bd.,
  17-185
· N.S., Criminal Injuries
  Compensation Bd., 17-219
· Ont., Criminal Injuries
  Compensation Bd., 17-260
· Qué., Comm. de la santé et de la
  sécurité du travail, 17-381
· Sask. Criminal Injuries
  Compensation Bd., 17-411
· Yukon, Worker's Compensation
  Bd., 17-438

Criminal
· Code of Cda., 12-2—3
· Lawyers Assn., 8-251

Criminology, Comparative, Int'l
  Centre for, 8-302

Crippled children (See Children)

Crisis Intervention
· and Public Information Soc. of
  Victoria, 8-310
· and Suicide Prevention Centre for
  Greater Vancouver, 8-310

Croat, Serb, Macedonian &
  Slovenian, pubns., 9-40

Crombie, David, 1-1

Crop Insurance
· Alta. Hail & Crop., 17-21
· B.C., Dept. of Agriculture, 17-69
· Man., Corp., 17-111
· N.B. Commn., 17-151
· N.S., 17-219
· Ont., Arbitration Bd., 17-256;
  Commn., 17-256
· P.E.I., 17-324
· Que., 17-346
· Sask., 17-400

Crop Introduction & Expansion
  Program, Ont., 17-257

Crops
· field, statistics, 4-4
· horticultural, 4-6
· pubns., 8-165, -166

Cross Cultural Communications
  Centre, 8-277

Cross-Cda. Writers Workshop, 8-352

Crossroads Int'l, Cdn., 8-246

Crown
· Attorneys, Man. Assn. of, 11-23
· in Canada, 15-10, 16-5
· corporation, defined, 16-28
· Mgmt. Bd. of Sask., 17-416

Crown Lands
· Alta., Public Lands Div., Dept. of
  Forestry, Lands & Wildlife,
  17-37
· B.C., Min. of Crown Lands, 17-73
· Manitoba, Lands Br., Dept. of
  Natural Resources, 17-137
· N.B., Crown Lands Br., Dept. of
  Natural Resources & Energy,
  17-159
· Nfld., Crown Lands Br., Dept. of
  Environment & Lands, 17-181
· N.S., Dept. of Lands & Forests,
  17-229

Crown Lands (cont'd)
· Ont., Min. of Natural Resources, 17-292
· Qué., Dir. gén. du domaine territorial, Min. de l'Énergie et des Ressources, 17-356
· Sask., Resource Lands Br., Dept. of Parks, Recreation & Culture, 17-413

Cruise missile Conversion Project, 8-290

Cryonics Soc. of Cda., 8-260

Cultural
· assns. (see also ethnic assns.), 8-207—208
· Heritage, Alta.
· · Coun., 17-27
· · Fdn., 17-27
· Jewish Community Centres, Cdn. Coun. of Y's and, 8-297
· Property
· · Commn., Que., 17-337
· · Export Review Board, Cdn., 16-43
· pubns., 8-170

Culture
· Alta., and Multiculturalism, Dept. of, 17-26
· B.C., Min. of Municipal Affairs, Recreation and, 17-87
· Man., Heritage & Recreation, Dept. of, 17-116
· N.B., Cultural Development, Dept. of Tourism, Recreation & Heritage, 17-161
· Nfld., Recreation & Youth, Dept. of, 17-177
· N.W.T., and Communications, Dept. of, 17-201
· N.S., Tourism and, Dept. of, 17-232
· Ont., and Communications, Min. of, 17-269
· P.E.I. Dept. of Community & Cultural Affairs, 17-318
· Qué., Min. des Affaires culturelles, 17-335
· Sask., Recreation, Parks and, 17-413

Culturel franco-manitobain, Le Centre, 17-117

Culturelles
· Min. des Affaires, 17-335
· Soc. gén. des industries, (SOGIC), 17-341

Curling
· assns., 8-321
· pubn., 8-160

Current Account Balance, 14-21—22

Custodians and Maintenance Assn. of Waterloo County Board of Education, 11-19

Customs
· Brokers, Cdn. Assn. of, 8-189
· and Excise, 16-103—104
· Information for Cdn. Residents, 16-177—178

Cutting Horse Assn., Cdn., 8-183

Cycling
· assns., 8-321—322
· pubns., 8-149

Cystic Fibrosis Fdn., Cdn., 8-268

Cytology, Int'l Academy of, 8-262

Czech, pubns., 9-43

D

Dai-Ichi Kangyo Bank, 13-11

Dairy
· assns., 8-208—209
· Bd., Man., 17-111
· Commns.,
· · Cdn., 16-35
· · N.S., 17-218
· Control Bd., Alta., 17-19
· councils, 8-208, -209
· Employees & Driver Salesmen, Alta. Brotherhood of, 11-15
· and Food Industries Supply Assn., Cdn., 8-228
· N.B., Farm Prods. Mktg. Commn., 17-150
· Products, Domestic Disappearance of Specified, 4-5
· pubns., 8-128, -165, -166, -167

Dairying (see also Agriculture Departments)
· Dept. of Reg'l Industrial Expansion, Service Industries & Consumer Goods, Food Products, 16-90
· statistics, 4-5—6

Daiwa Bank Cda., 13-11

Dalhousie University, 7-19

Dance
· assns., 8-209
· pubns., 8-152

Dangerous Goods, Transport of, 10-2

Danish pubn., 9-40

Darts assns., 8-322

Data Processing
· Mgmt. Assn. of Cda., 8-200
· pubns., 8-126

Date Line, Int'l, 2-21

Day Care Services
· Advocacy Assn., Cdn., 8-196
· Alta., Child Care Programs, Dept. of Social Services, 17-46
· B.C., Min. of Social Services & Housing, 17-90
· Man., Child Day Care Br., Dept. of Community Services, 17-115
· Nfld., Day Care & Homemaker Services, Dept. of Social Services, 17-191
· N.W.T., Dept. of Social Services, 17-204
· N.S., Day Care Services, Dept. of Community Services, 17-220
· Ont., Min. of Community & Social Services, 17-263
· P.E.I., Dept. of Health & Social Services, 17-318
· Que., Off. des services de garde à l'enfance, 17-334
· Sask., Day Care Br., Dept. of Social Services, 17-418
· Yukon Dept. of Health & Human Resources, 17-435

Daylight Saving Time, 1-1, 2-22

De Havilland Moth Club of Cda., 8-187

Deaf
· schools for the, 7-8—9
· assns., see Handicapped, 8-234—237
· Sports Fed., Cdn., 8-315

Death rates, 5-6

Debating assns., 8-249

Debt financing, 13-35

Decoupeurs' Guild of Ont., 8-207

Deeds (See Land Titles)

Defence
· Armed Forces, Cdn. 16-179—183
· Construction (1951) Ltd., 16-99
· Environmental Medicine, and Civil Inst. of, 8-302
· National, Dept., 16-97—100, -179
· · schools, 7-6
· Permanent Joint Board on, 16-72

Delinquency
· crime and, 12-10—13
· juvenile, 12-11—12

Demography (see also Vital Statistics)
· age distribution, 5-7
· language, 5-8—9
· marital status, 5-8
· sex, 5-7
· statistics, 5-4—9

Dene Nation, 8-283
· Denendeh Conservation Bd., N.W.T., 17-205
· land claims settlements, 1-2, -3

Dental
· assns., 8-209—210
· Education, Cdn. Fund for, 8-212
· Health Workers Bd., Man., 17-127
· pubns., 8-128
· Research, Cdn. Assn. for, 8-301

Dentistry
· Academy of, 8-209
· Assn. of Cdn. Faculties of, 8-217

Departmental Crown corp., defined, 16-28

Deportation of Turkish refugees, 1-1

Deposit Insurance Corp.
· of B.C., Credit Union, 17-78
· Cda., 13-3, 16-74

Dépôt et placement du Qué., Caisse de, 17-362

Deregulation
· air transportation, 10-14
· financial institutions, 13-2
· transportation, 10-1—2, -6, -14

Dermatological Assn., Cdn., 8-264

Design, assns.
· industrial, 8-243
· interior, 8-245—46

Detroit Cda., Nat'l Bank of, 13-12

Deutsche Bank (Cda.), 13-11

Development
· Agency (CIDA), Cdn. Int'l, 7-5, 16-132—134, -190—191
· Agency, P.E.I., 17-324
· Corp.,
· · Eastern Ont., 17-287
· · Lower Churchill, 17-192
· · Man., 17-132
· · N.B., Regional, 17-167
· · Nfld. & Labrador, 17-180
· · Northern Ont., 17-287
· · Ont., 17-276
· · Yukon, 17-437

Development (cont'd)
· depts.,
· · B.C., Min. of Regional, 17-90
· · Nfld., and Tourism, 17-178
· · N.S., Small Business, 17-230
· · Yukon, 17-433
· economic, assns., 8-243
· through Education, Cdn. Org. for,
    8-216
· Fund Corp., Sask., 17-421
· industrial, assns., 8-243
· Inst., Prof., 8-258
· Research Centre, Int'l, 7-5, 16-137,
    -190
· Summerside Waterfront, Corp.,
    17-326
· urban, assns., 8-200

Développement
· économique, Secrétariat du,
    17-333
· en économique, Centre de
    recherche et, 8-211
· industriel du Qué., Soc. de, 17-365
· Office de planification et de, du
    Qué., 17-383
· régional, Secrétariat de
    l'aménagement et au, Qué.,
    17-333

Diabetes/Diabète
· Cdn. Diabetes Assn., 8-268
· du Qué., Assoc. du, 8-267

Die Casters Assn., Cdn., 8-259

Dietetic Assn.
· Cdn., 8-264
· Ont., 8-265

Diététique du Qué., Assoc. des
    techniciennes et techniciens en,
    11-16

Diététistes du Qué.,
· Corp. prof. des, 8-265
· Syndicat prof. des, 11-28

Dietitians' & Nutritionists' Assn.,
    B.C., 8-262

Digital Network, Integrated Service,
    9-4

Dimensions, Cda.'s physical, 3-1

Diplomatic representatives
· Canadian, 16-148—158
· foreign, 16-158—163

Direct
· Mktg. Assn., Cdn., 8-260
· Sellers Assn., 8-303

Directors Guild of Cda., 8-198

Dirigeants d'entreprise, Centre des,
    8-258

Disabled
· assns., see Handicapped,
    8-234—237
· Cdn. Fed. of Sports Orgs. for the,
    8-315
· Persons, Advisory Council for,
    Ont., 17-252
· Persons, Office for, Ont., 17-252
· Premier's Coun. on the Status of,
    N.B., 17-148
· Skiing, Cdn. Assn. for, 8-314

Disaster
· Assistance Bd., Man., 17-126
· Services Div., Alta. Public Safety
    Services, 17-53

Discovery Fdn./Discovery
    Enterprises, B.C., 17-67

Discrimination (see also Human
    Rights)
· legislation prohibiting, in
    employment, 11-6—7

Disease Control, B.C. Centre for,
    17-82

Distillers, Assn. of Cdn., 8-227

Distillery, Wine, and Allied Workers
    Int'l Union, 11-10

Diving assns., 8-322

Documentation, Int'l Fed. for, 8-243

Dominicain, Collège, 7-19

Donations & Public Affairs Research
    (IDPAR), Inst. of, 8-302

Donner Cdn. Fdn., 8-193

Drainage Tribunal, Ont., 17-257

Drama assns., 8-342—344

Dresdner Bank Cda., 13-11

Drinking/Driving Countermeasures,
    Ont., 17-260

Driver Control Bd., Alta., 17-48

Drivers' Licences, 10-8—9
· Alta., Motor Vehicle Div., Dept. of
    Solicitor General, 17-47
· B.C., Motor Vehicle Dept., Min. of
    Solicitor General, 17-91
· Man.,
· · Driver & Vehicle Licensing Div.,
    Dept. of Highways &
    Transportation, 17-130
· · Drivers' Licence Suspension
    Appeal Bd., 17-130
· N.B.,
· · License Suspension Appeal Bd.,
    17-162
· · Motor Vehicle Br., Dept. of
    Transportation, 17-162
· Nfld., Dept. of Transportation,
    17-191
· N.W.T., Motor Vehicles Div., Dept.
    of Transportation, 17-204
· N.S., Registry of Motor Vehicles,
    Dept. of Transportation, 17-233
· Ont., Min. of Transportation &
    Communications, 17-300
· P.E.I., Dept. of Transportation &
    Public Works, 17-321
· Que., Régie de l'assurance
    automobile du, 17-379
· Sask.,
· · Highway Traffic Bd., Dept. of
    Highways & Transportation,
    17-406
· · Sask. Gov't Insce. (SGI), 17-422
· Yukon, Dept. of Community &
    Transportation Services, 17-432

Droits de la personne (Qué.),
    Comm. des, 12-6, 17-367

Drug (see also Addiction; Alcohol;
    Alcoholism; Pharmaceutical)
· Abuse, Coun. on, 8-272
· Dependency N.S., Commn. on,
    17-235
· Manufacturers Assn.,
    NonPrescription, of Cda., 8-195
· Wholesale Drug Assn., Cdn., 8-348
· Standards & Therapeutics Cttee.,
    Man., 17-127

Drugs (see also Addiction; Alcohol;
    Alcoholism)
· Alta., Dept. Health, 17-37

· B.C., Alcohol & Drug Programs,
    Min. of Labour & Consumer
    Services, 17-84
· Cda., Dept. of Health & Welfare
· · Drugs Directorate, 16-80
· · Health Protection Br., 16-79—80
· Man., Alcoholism Fdn., 17-127
· N.B., Dept. of Health & Community
    Services, 17-154
· Nfld., Dept. of Health, 17-183
· N.W.T., Alcohol, Drug &
    Community Mental Health
    Services, Dept. of Social
    Services, 17-204
· Ont., Alcoholism & Drug Addiction
    Research Fdn., 17-283
· Parents Against, 8-311
· pubns., 8-142
· Que., Min. de la Santé et des
    Services sociaux, 17-374
· Sask. Alcohol & Drug Abuse
    Commn. (SADAC), 17-420
· Yukon, Alcohol & Drug Services,
    Dept. of Health & Human
    Resources, 17-435

Dry Cleaners assns., 8-308

Ducks Unlimited, 8-349

Dutch
· Cdn. Assn. of Greater Toronto,
    8-223
· pubns., 9-41

Duty, Customs information,
    16-177—178

Dying with Dignity, 8-260

E

Early Childhood Education Ont.,
    Assn. for, 8-211

Earth Movers of Ont., Associated,
    8-203

Earthquake, 1-4

East Indian, pubn., 9-41

Easter Seal Soc. Ont., 8-236

Eastern Ont. Development Corp.,
    17-286

Eating Disorder Info. Centre, Nat'l,
    8-272

Eaton Fdn., 8-193

Eaux, Soc. qué. d'assainissement
    des, 17-361

Ecology assns., see Conservation &
    Environment, 8-201—202

Economic(s)
· assns., 8-210—211
· Co-operation & Development, Org.
    for, 16-186
· Council
· · Atlantic Provinces, 8-210
· · of Cda., 16-135
· · of Nfld. & Labrador, 17-179
· Development
· · Advisory Board, Native, 16-92
· · assns., 8-243
· · Commns., N.B. Regional, 17-152
· · Corp. (SEDCO), Sask., 17-422
· · and Tourism, Dept. of, N.W.T.,
    17-202
· · and Tourism, Dept. of, Sask.,
    17-401
· · and Trade, Dept. of, Alta., 17-28
· · Diversification, Dept. of Western,
    16-128

Economic (cont'd)
· Education, Cdn. Fdn. for, 8-217
· European Communities, 16-185
· Journal, Cdn. Home, 8-128
· pubns., 8-169
· summit, 1-2

Economic & Social Research
· Alta., Dept. of Economic
  Development & Trade, 17-28
· Bank of Cda., 13-3—5, 16-74
· B.C., Central Statistics Bureau,
  Min. of Finance & Corporate
  Relations, 17-76
· Canada,
· · Cda. Mortgage & Housing Corp.,
  16-129—130
· · Economic Coun. of Cda., 16-135
· · Health & Welfare Cda., 16-77—82
· · Indian & Northern Affairs Dept.,
  Natural Resources &
  Economic Development Br.,
  16-83
· Institute of Social & Economic
  Research, 8-113
· Man.,
· · Bureau of Statistics, 17-121
· · Strategic Planning & Economic
  Dev't, Dept. of Industry, Trade
  & Technology, 17-132
· Nat'l Archives of Cda., 16-45
· N.B.,
· · Dept. of Commerce &
  Technology, 17-151
· · Dept. of Health & Community
  Services, 17-154
· Nfld.,
· · Economic Research & Analysis,
  Dept. of Dev't & Tourism,
  17-179
· · Inst. of Social & Economic
  Research, Memorial
  University of, 7-27
· N.S.,
· · Dept. of Community Services,
  17-220
· · Dept. of Industry, Trade &
  Technology, 17-227
· Ont.,
· · Min. of Community and Social
  Services, 17-263
· · Min. of Treasury and Economics,
  17-302
· Que.,
· · Min. de l'Industrie et du
  Commerce, 17-363
· · Min. de la Main-d'oeuvre et de la
  Sécurité du revenu, 17-371
· Sask., Economic Development &
  Tourism Dept., 17-401
· Social Sciences & Humanities
  Research Coun., 16-50
· Statistics Cda., 16-142—145
· Transport Cda., Policy &
  Co-ordination, 16-118

Economists', Sociologists' &
  Statisticians' Assn., 11-19

Economy, Cdn., 14-1—25
· Summary of Economic
  Performance — 1988, 14-1—3
· Prospects for 1989, 14-3—6

Ecumenical Councils, 6-2—3

Editors/ Éditeurs
· Canadiens, Assoc. des, 8-294
· Freelance, Assn. of Cda., 8-295
· de manuels scolaires du Qué.,
  Soc. des, 8-295
· and Writers Soc. for Business
  Media, Nat'l (NEWS Business),
  8-295

Edmonton
· Chamber of Commerce, 8-192
· libraries & archives, 8-12—16
· newspapers, 9-14
· Opera, 8-281
· pubn., 8-151
· radio stations, 9-45, -52—3
· Symphony Soc., 8-281
· television stations, 9-57

Education, *see* 7-1—54
· Advanced,
· · Alta. Dept. of, 17-15
· · and Job Training, Dept. of, B.C.,
  17-65
· · Div., Dept. of Education, N.W.T.,
  17-202
· · Div., Dept. of Education, Yukon,
  17-434
· Art, Ont. Soc. for Education
  through, 8-185
· assns., 8-211—218
· · administration, 8-213—215
· · adult, 8-216—217
· · alumni, 8-215—216
· · art, 8-185
· · career, 8-216—217
· · continuing, 8-216—217
· · correspondence schools, 8-216
· · disciplines, 8-217—218
· · guidance & counselling, 8-216,
  -217
· · home & school, 8-215
· · professional, 8-213, -257
· · research, 8-212, -213
· · special, 8-218
· · sports, 8-314
· · student, 8-215—216
· · trustees, 8-213, -214, -215
· Broadcast, Assn. of Cda., 8-188
· Cdn. Broadcasting Corp., (CBC),
  7-5, 9-5—8, 16-41—43
· Cons. supérieur de, 17-353
· Council of Ministers of, Cda.,
  18-3—4
· Dance Teachers Assn., Cdn.,
  8-209
· degrees granted by sex, 7-11
· depts., *see* 7-4
· · Alta., 17-30
· · B.C., 17-73
· · Man., 17-118
· · N.B., 17-153
· · Nfld., 17-180
· · N.W.T., 17-202
· · N.S., 17-222
· · Ont., 17-273
· · P.E.I., 17-318
· · Que., 17-352
· · Sask., 17-402
· · Yukon, 17-434
· Distance, 7-7—8
· · assns., 8-216
· · elementary-secondary level, 7-6—7
· · enrolment statistics, 7-2
· · expenditure, 7-11
· · financing authorities, B.C., 17-77
· · general structure of, 7-2—3
· · government, 7-3—6
· · · federal, 7-4—6; schools, 7-5—6
· · · provincial, 7-3—4
· · Independent School, assns., 8-216
· · Maritime Provinces
· · · Education Fdn., 18-3
· · · Higher Education Commn., 18-3
· · Music assns., 8-280
· · native, 7-5—6
· · N.B. Community Colleges, 17-149,
  7-48
· · N.S. Coun. on Higher, 17-218
· · Northern Studies, Assn. of Cdn.
  Universities for, 8-184
· · Nursing, Cdn. Assn. of University
  Schools of, 8-285
· · post-secondary, 7-11—54
· · pre-school programs, 7-6
· · Programming Service, Cdn., 8-214
· · provincial structure, 7-3
· · pubns., 8-128—129, -169, -170
· · Qualifications Evaluation Coun. of
  Ont., 8-217
· · Relations Commn., Ont., 17-274
· · Scholarship Trust Fdn., Cdn.,
  8-216
· · Special, Atlantic Provinces
  Authority, 18-1—2
· · Statistics Cda., 16-142—145
· · Student Services, Cdn. Assn. of
  College & University, 8-214
· · Talent, Soc. for, 8-282
· · technical & vocational, 7-9—10
· · Women, Cdn. Fed. of University,
  8-350

Educational
· Boundaries Commn., Sask.,
  17-402
· Communications
· · Authority (TVOntario), Ont.,
  17-271
· · Corp., Alta., 17-52
· Credit Inst. Educational Fdn.,
  Cdn., 8-225
· Researchers' Assn., Cdn., 8-213
· Workers, Cdn. Union of, 11-19

Educators, Assn. of N.B.
  Professional, 11-17

Egg
· assns., 8-228, 293
· mktg. bds.,
· · Alta., 17-19
· · B.C., 17-69
· · Man., 17-109
· · Nfld., 17-189
· · P.E.I., 17-317
· · Sask., 17-399

Eldorado Nuclear Ltd., 16-129

Elections, 1-2, -3, -4
· Canada, 16-27
· Chief Electoral Officer, 16-27
· Commissioner of Cda., 16-27
· Finances, Commn. on, Ont.,
  17-251

Electoral
· districts
· · federal, 16-20—23, -27
· · provincial, *see* Legislative
  assemblies
· Officer, Chief, 16-27
· qualifications (federal franchise),
  16-26
· reform, Que., 17-334

Electric
· Energy Mktg. Agency, Alta., 17-50
· Service League of Man., 8-219
· Vehicle Assn. of Cda., 8-186

Electric Power (*see also* Hydro)
· Alta., Energy Resources
  Conservation Bd., 17-33
· Man. Hydro, 17-139
· Nat'l Energy Bd., 16-63
· N.B. Power, 17-166
· Nfld. & Labrador Hydro, 17-192
· N.S. Power Corp., 17-238
· Ont. Hydro, 17-276
· P.E.I., Energy Corp., 17-322
· Que.,
· · Min. de l'Énergie et des
    Ressources, 17-353
· · Hydro-Québec, 17-356
· Sask. Power Corp., 17-417

Electrical
· assns., 8-218—219
· Energy Mktg. Cttee., Man., 17-122
· engineering, assns., 8-221
· equipment, pubns., 8-129
· Installation & Inspection Advisory
  Bd., N.B., 17-156
· pubns., 8-129
· Radio & Machine Workers of Cda.,
  United, 11-29
· Safety Assn. of Ont. Inc., Utilities,
  8-304
· Workers
· · Int'l Brotherhood of, 11-11
· · Interprovincial Brotherhood of,
    11-22
· Yukon Utilities Bd., 17-436

Electricians Licensing Examining
  Bd., Man., 17-134

Electricity, 4-19

Electronic(s)
· assns., 8-218—219
· Electrical, Salaried, Machine and
  Furniture Workers, Int'l Union
  of, 11-13
· pubns., 8-129

Elementary education, 7-6

Elevator
· Bd., Man., 17-134
· Constructors, Int'l Union of, 11-13
· and Escalator Assn., Nat'l, 8-204

Elizabeth Fry Societies, Cdn. Assn.
  of, 8-309

Elks of Cda., Benevolent &
  Protective Order of, 8-231

Elocution & Debate Assn., Sask.,
  8-249

Embalmers & Funeral Directors Act,
  Bd. of Administration under,
  Man., 17-115

Embassies
· Canadian, 16-148—158
· foreign, 16-158—163

Emergencies Act, 1-2

Emergency
· crisis intervention, 8-310
· Health Services Commission, B.C.,
  17-83
· Measures
· · Alta., Public Safety Services,
    17-53
· · B.C., Prov. Emergency Program,
    Min. of Solicitor General,
    17-91

· · Man., 17-126
· · N.B., Dept. of Municipal Affairs,
    17-158
· · Nfld., Dept. of Municipal Affairs,
    17-187
· · N.S., 17-234
· · Ont., Min. of the Solicitor
    General, 17-296
· · Sask., 17-404
· Preparedness Cda., 16-99
· Program—Provincial, 8-304

Empire
· Club of Cda., 8-231
· Loyalists' Assn. of Cda., United,
  8-239

Employees/Employés
· assns.
· · (Marconi), Salaried, 11-27
· · Professional, 11-25
· · St. Mary's of the Lake Hospital,
    11-19
· coiffeurs du Qué., Féd. des., 11-20
· municipaux et scolaires du Qué.,
  Féd. des., 11-20
· Provincial Gov't, Nat'l Union of,
  11-23—24
· Public, Cdn. Union of, 11-19
· de services publics, Féd. des,
  11-20
· Union, N.S. Government, 17-236

Employment
· Alta., Dept. of Career Dev't and,
  17-24
· anti-discrimination legislation,
  11-6—7
· assns., 8-219
· B.C., Min. of Labour & Consumer
  Services, 17-84
· Canada,
· · and Immigration: Advisory Coun.
    (CEIAC), Cda., 16-55; Dept.,
    11-3, 16-52—56
· · Labour Dept., 16-95—97
· · Public Service Commn.,
    16-100—101
· federal gov't, 16-30—31
· Man., Employment Services &
  Economic Security Dept.,
  17-120
· N.B., Dept. of Labour, 17-155
· Nfld., Dept. of Labour, 17-185
· N.W.T., Equal Employment
  Directorate, 17-202
· N.S., Dept. of Labour, 17-227
· Ont., Employment Standards Br.,
  Min. of Labour, 17-288
· P.E.I., Labour Standards Div.,
  Dept. of Labour, 17-320
· Que.,
· · Conseil consultatif du travail et
    de la main-d'oeuvre, 17-382
· · Min. de la Main-d'oeuvre et de la
    Sécurité du revenu, 17-371
· · Min. du Travail, 17-380
· Sask., Dept. of Human Resources,
  Labour & Employment, 17-407
· Standards Bds.
· · N.B., 17-156
· · P.E.I., 17-320
· standards legislation, 11-3

Emunah Women of Cda., 8-193

Énergie et des Ressources, Min. de
  l', Qué., 17-353

Energy
· Alta., Dept. of, 17-31
· Allocation Cttee., Man., 17-122
· assns., 8-219—220
· Atomic Energy of Cda. Ltd., 16-62
· Auth., Man., 17-123
· Bds.,
· · Nat'l, 16-63
· · Ont., 17-275
· B.C. Utilities Commn., 17-77
· Canada, 14-10
· and Chemical Workers Union,
  11-19
· Clean, The Planetary Assn. for,
  8-202
· Corp.: Ont., 17-275; P.E.I., 17-322;
  Yukon, 17-437
· Council, Man., 17-123
· and Forestry, Dept. of, P.E.I.,
  17-318
· industry, 4-17—20
· and Mines, Dept. of
· · Man., 17-122
· · Sask., 17-403
· Mines & Petroleum Resources,
  B.C. Min. of, 17-74
· Mines & Resources Dept.,
  16-56—65
· N.B.,
· · Dept. of Natural Resources &,
    17-159
· · Power, 17-166
· Nfld., Dept. of Energy, 17-181
· N.S., Dept. of Mines & Energy,
  17-230
· Ont. Ministry of, 17-274
· overview, 4-17—18
· primary, 4-18
· pubns., 8-129
· Resources Conservation Bd., Alta.,
  17-33
· and Resources Min., Que., 17-353
· Supplies Allocation Bd., 16-63
· supply & demand, 4-18—20
· Tax Reform Package, 4-18
· Trade Accord, 4-17—18
· trends, 4-18
· Wood Energy Inst., Cdn., 8-351

Engineering
· Agricultural, Cdn. Soc. of, 8-180
· assns., 8-220—222
· Biological, Int'l Fed. for Medical
  and, 8-306
· Forest, Research Inst. of Cda.,
  8-302
· pubns., 8-130, -169
· Safety, Cdn. Soc. of, 8-304
· and Scientific Assns., Fed. of,
  8-306
· technicians & technologists,
  assns., 8-220, -221

Engineers
· Operating, Int'l Union of, 11-13
· Operating, and General Workers,
  Cdn. Union of, 11-19
· Power
· · Advisory Bd., Man., 17-135
· · Bd. of Examiners, P.E.I., 17-321
· Professional
· · assns., 8-220—222
· · and Technical, Int'l Fed. of,
    11-12

Engineers (cont'd)
· Refrigeration Service Engineers
   Soc. Cda., 8-182
· and Scientists' Assn. (Marconi),
   11-20
· Stationary, N.S. Bd., 17-228
· Stationary, Bd. of Examiners for,
   N.B., 17-156

Enseignant(e)s
· de CEGEP, Féd. des, 11-20
· des commissions scolaires,
   Comm. des, 11-19
· franco-ontariens, Assoc. des,
   11-16
· francophones du N.-B., Assoc.
   des, 8-213
· protestants du Qué., Assoc. prov.
   des, 11-25
· du Qué., Féd. nationale des, 11-21

Enseignement
· Comm. d'appel sur la langue d',
   17-353
· Féd. du personnel des
   établissements privés d',
   (FPEPE), 11-21
· privé, Comm. consultative de l',
   17-353
· du Qué., Centrale de
   l'enseignement, (CEQ), 11-8
· supérieur et de la science, Min. de
   l', Qué., 17-358

Enterprise Centre, B.C., 17-80

Entertainment (see also Cinema;
   Film; Music; Television; Theatre;
   etc.)
· home, assns., 8-161—163
· pubns., 8-152—153
· Violence in, Cdns. Concerned
   About, (C-CAVE), 8-206

Entomological Soc. of Cda., 8-306

Environment (see also
   Conservation)
· Board of Negotiation, Ont., 17-277
· The Clean, Commn., Man., 17-124
· Coun. of Alta., 17-35
· depts.,
· · Alta., 17-34
· · B.C., 17-75
· · Cda., 16-65—68
· · Man., 17-123
· · N.B., 17-158
· · Nfld., 17-181
· · N.S., 17-223
· · Ont., 17-276
· · Que., 17-359
· · Sask., 17-403
· Ministers, Cdn. Council of
   Resource and, 18-2
· N.W.T., Dept. of Renewable
   Resources, 17-203
· PCBs phase-out, 1-3
· P.E.I., Environmental Management,
   Dept. of Community & Cultural
   Affairs, 17-318
· protection assns., 8-201—202
· pubns., 8-158—159, -169, -170

Environmental
· Advisory Coun., Cdn., 16-67
· Appeal Bds.,
· · B.C., 17-75
· · Ont., 17-277

· Assessment
· · Ont.: Adv. Cttee., 17-277; Bd.,
   17-277
· · Review Office, Federal,
   16-67—68
· Biologists, Cdn. Soc. of, 8-201
· Compensation Corp., Ont., 17-278
· Control Council, N.S., 17-223
· Councils,
· · Man., 17-124
· · N.B., 17-158
· law, assns., 8-250, -251
· Medicine, Defence & Civil Inst. of,
   8-302
· Research Trust, Alta., 17-34

L'Environnement
· de la Baie-James, Com. consultatif
   de la, Que., 17-361
· Bur. d'audiences publiques sur,
   Qué., 17-360
· Kativik, Cons. consultatif de l',
   Que., 17-360
· Ministère de, 17-359

Envoypost, 9-10

Epilepsy assns., 8-269

Equal Employment Directorate,
   N.W.T., 17-202

Equalization, 15-7—8, -19—20

Equestrian (see also Horses)
· assns., 8-236, -322—323
· pubns., 8-157—158

Equipment
· assns., 8-222
· farm
· · assns., 8-222
· · pubns., 8-166
· Printing & Supply Dealers Assn.,
   8-293
· pubns., 8-130
· recreational pubns., 8-144—145

Equity financing, 13-21—33

Eskimo (see also Inuit; Native
   Peoples)
· Arts Coun., Cdn., 16-86
· Inuit Tapirisat of Cda.,
   Brotherhood, 8-283
· Loan Fund Advisory Bd., N.W.T.,
   17-205

Esperanto Assn., Cdn., 8-249

Estey, Mr. Justice Willard, 1-1

Estonian
· Cdn. History Commn., 8-238
· Central Coun. in Cda., 8-223
· Evangelical Lutheran Church, The,
   6-9
· pubns., 9-41

Établissements de plein air du Qué.,
   Soc. des, 17-371

Ethiopian Jews, Cdn. Assn. for,
   8-192

Ethnic
· assns, 8-223—224
· pubns.
· · consumer, 8-153
· · newspapers, 9-40—44
· (Radio) Broadcasters, Cdn. Assn.
   of, 8-188
· Studies Assn., Cdn., 8-252

Etiquette, forms of address, 2-4—7

European Economic Community,
   14-19, 16-185

L'Évaluation foncière du Qué., Bur.
   de révision de, 17-342

Evangelical assns., 8-300

Examiners
· (Municipal), Bd. of, B.C., 17-87
· Rural Bd. of, Sask., 17-418
· (Urban), Bd. of, Sask., 17-419

Excel Sports Employees Assn.,
   11-20

Exchange rates, U.S.-Cdn., 13-5

Excise, Customs and, 16-103—104

Executive(s)
· Cdn. College Health Services
   Assn., 8-260
· Chamber of Commerce
   Executives, of Cda., 8-191
· Chief, of Large Public Libraries,
   8-254
· Councils,
· · Alta., 17-13
· · B.C., 17-63
· · Man., 17-105
· · N.B., 17-147
· · Nfld., 17-173
· · N.W.T., (Exec. Members of Leg.
   Assembly), 17-199
· · N.S., 17-215
· · Ont., 17-249
· · P.E.I., 17-315
· · Que., 17-331
· · Sask., 17-395
· · Yukon, 17-431
· Fund Raising, Cdn. Soc. of, 8-193
· N.W.T. (Office of the Commr.),
   17-199
· Service Organization, Cdn., 8-257
· Toronto Executives Assn. Inc.,
   8-258

Exhibit & Display Assn. of Cda.,
   8-225

Exhibitions
· assns., 8-224—225
· Pacific National, 17-80

Exploration minière, Soc. qué. d',
   17-357

Export(s)
· Alberta,
· · Market Dev't, Dept. of
   Agriculture, 17-18
· · Trade & Investment Div., Dept. of
   Economic Development &
   Trade, 17-29
· assns., 8-229—230
· B.C., Min. of International
   Business & Immigration, 17-83
· Cda., Dept. of
· · External Affairs, 16-68—72
· · Industry, Science & Technology,
   16-87—92
· Development Corp., 16-135—137
· Man., Dept. of Industry, Trade &
   Tourism, 17-131
· N.B., Dept. of Commerce &
   Technology, 17-151
· N.S., Dept. of Industry, Trade &
   Technology, 17-227
· Ont., Min. of Industry, Trade &
   Technology, 17-285
· pubns., 8-132
· Que., Min. de l'Industrie et du
   Commerce, 17-363
· Review Board, Cdn. Cultural
   Property, 16-43
· Sask., Dept. of Economic
   Development & Tourism, 17-401
· statistics, 14-20

Exposition Mgrs., Cdn. Assn. of,
8-225
Expropriations
· Advisory Officer, N.B., 17-155
· Bd. of Negotiation, Ont., 17-259
· Compensation Bd.: B.C., 17-72,
N.S., 17-220
· Public & Private Rights Bd., Sask.,
17-411
Extend-A-Family, 8-236
Extension, Cdn. Soc. of, 8-181
External Affairs
· Alta., Dept. of Federal &
Intergovernmental Affairs, 17-35
· Canada,
· · Cdn. Int'l Development Agency
(CIDA), 7-5, 16-132—134,
-190—191
· · Dept. of External Affairs, 7-5,
16-68—72
· Que., Min. des Affaires
internationales, 17-341
Eye Bank of Cda., 8-260
Eyesight Universal, Operation, 8-311

F

F.I.S.U. Games (World Student
Games), 8-234
F.K. Morrow Fdn., 8-193
Facsimile transmission, 9-2
Fair assns., 8-224—225
Family
· income, 5-10
· Service, assns., 8-310, -311
· size of, 5-10
· statistics, 5-9—11
· Vanier Inst. of the, 8-302
Family Planning
· Alta., Dept. of Health, 17-37
· assns., 8-286—287
· Birth Control Assn., Calgary, 8-286
· Emergency Pregnancy Centre,
Birthright, 8-286
· Ont., Min. of Health, 17-282
· P.E.I., Dept. of Health & Social
Services, 17-319
· Que., Min. de la Santé et des
Services sociaux, 17-374
· Sask., Dept. of Health, Community
Health Services Br., 17-405
Farm
· assns., 8-180, -181, -182
· Credit Bur., Que., 17-346
· Credit Corp., 16-36—37
· Development Loan Bd., Nfld.,
17-190
· equipment & machinery assns.,
8-222
· Income Stabilization Commn. of
Ont., 17-256
· Interest Rate Reduction Appeal
Bd., Ont. Family, 17-257
· Land Security Board, Sask.,
17-410
· Lands Ownership Bd., Man.,
17-111
· Loan Bd., N.S., 17-219
· Machinery Bds.,
· · Man., 17-110
· · Ont., 17-257
· Ownership Bd., Sask., 17-411

· Pollution Advisory Cttee., Ont.,
17-278
· pubns., 8-165—167
· Safety Assn. Inc., 8-304
· Tax Rebate Appeal Bd., Ont.,
17-257
Farm Products
· Appeal Tribunal, Ont., 17-257
· Corp., Nfld., 17-190
· mktg.
· · Commn., N.B., 17-150
· · Nat'l Council, 16-37
· · Ont., 17-255
Farmers
· Advocate, Alta., 17-21
· aid to, 1-3
· assns., 8-181
Farmworkers Union, Cdn., 11-18
Fashion (see also Footwear; Fur;
Textiles)
· pubns., 8-153
Fasteners Inst., Cdn., 8-259
Fatality Review Board, Alta., 17-23
Faune
· Fdn. de la, du Québec, 17-361
· Syndicat des agents de
conservation de la, du Qué.,
11-27
Federal
· budget, 1-1
· Business Development Bank,
16-91—92
· Court of Cda., 12-7, 16-146
· franchise, 16-26
· government, 16-5—191
· · departments & agencies,
16-32—145
· · and education, 7-4—6
· · employees unions, see Public
Service Alliance of Cda.,
11-25—26
· · employment, 16-30—31
· · organization, 16-29
· · human rights legislation, 12-3—5
· · administrators, 12-5—6
· · and Intergovernmental Affairs,
Alta., Dept. of, 17-35
· · judiciary & judicial officers,
12-6—7, 16-146—148
· · labour legislation, 11-2—3, -6
· · police forces, 12-9—10
· · Public Service employees, number
of,
· · by geographic area & sex, 16-31
· · by type of employment, 16-30
· · Superannuates Nat'l Assn., 8-307
· · taxation, 16-104—106
Federal-Provincial Relations
· Alta., Dept. of Federal &
Intergovernmental Affairs, 17-35
· Cda.,
· · Federal-Provincial Relations
Office, 16-12
· · Health & Welfare,
Intergovernmental & Int'l
Affairs Br., 16-79
· Man., Finance Dept.,
Federal-Provincial Relations &
Research Div., 17-125
· Nfld., Intergovernmental Affairs
Secretariat, 17-174

· N.S., Finance Dept.,
Federal-Provincial Taxation &
Fiscal Relations Div., 17-223
· Ontario,
· · Federal-Provincial Relations Br.,
Min. of Intergovernmental
Affairs, 17-288
· · Budget & Intergovernmental
Finance Br., Min. of Treasury
& Economics, 17-302
· Que., Secrétariat aux affaires
intergouvernementales
canadiennes, 17-333
· Sask., Intergovernmental Affairs,
Office of the Premier, 17-396
· Yukon, Federal Relations Office,
17-431
Federalism, 15-3
Federalists of Cda., World, 8-247
Feed assns., 8-180, -181
Féminine, Secrétariat à la condition,
Qué., 17-333
Feminist pubns., 8-159, -164, -171
Femme, Conseil du statut de la,
Qué., 17-334
Fence Industry Assn., The Cdn.,
8-203
Fencing assns., 8-323
Ferry(ies), 10-12
· Co., Que., 17-380
· Corp., B.C., 17-95
· & Marine Workers' Union, 11-22
Fertilizer assns., 8-190, -191, -196
Fibre optics, 9-4
Field hockey assns., 8-323—324
Figure skating assns., 8-324
Filipino, pubns., 9-41
Film
· assns., 8-197—198
· Bd., Nat'l, 16-46—48
· Classification
· · Bd.: Man., 17-117; N.B., 17-162
· · Div., B.C., 17-91
· · Commn., B.C., 17-84
· · Craftspeople, Assn. of Cdn., 11-17
· · Development Corp., Ont., 17-272
· · pubns., 8-126, -152, -153
Filmmakers assns., 8-197, -198
Finance
· assns., 8-225—226
· Bank of Cda., 13-3—5, 16-74
· Comptroller General of Cda.,
Office of the, 16-125
· depts.,
· · Alta., Treasury Dept., 17-51
· · B.C., 17-75
· · Cda., 16-72—73
· · Man., 17-125
· · N.B., 17-153
· · Nfld., 17-181
· · N.W.T., 17-202
· · N.S., 17-223
· · Ont., 17-302
· · P.E.I., 17-318
· · Que., 17-361
· · Sask., 17-404
· · Yukon, 17-434
· Federal Business Development
Bank, 16-91
· financement, Soc. générale de,
17-365
· foreign chartered banks, 13-10—14

Finance (cont'd)
· P.E.I. Lending Authority, 17-325
· Sask., Crown Mgmt. Bd. of, 17-416
· Treasury Bd., 16-124—125

Finances, Min. des, Qué., 17-361

Financial
· Institutions
· · Min. of, Ont., 17-279
· · Superintendent of, 13-2, 16-73
· · Management Secretariat, N.W.T., 17-202
· pubns., 8-130—131, -153
· · deregulation of, 13-2

Finnish
· Organization of Cda., 8-224
· pubns., 9-41

Fire
· Advisory Cttee., Man., 17-134
· Commr.
· · B.C., Office of the, 17-85
· · Nfld., Provincial, 17-187
· Marshal, N.S., 17-227
· pubns., 8-131
· and Safety Assn., Cdn., 8-304
· Underwriters Survey, 8-244

Fire Prevention
· Alta., Fire Prevention Br., Dept. of Labour, 17-39
· assns., 8-226—227, -304
· Canada,
· · Dept. of Forestry, 16-76
· · Dept. of Labour, Fire Commr. of Cda., 16-96
· Man., Office of the Fire Commr., Dept. of Labour, 17-133
· Nat'l Research Coun. of Cda., Institute for Research in Construction, 16-139
· Ont., Aviation & Fire Mgmt. Ctr., Min. of Natural Resources, 17-293
· Que., Dir. gén. de la prévention des incendies, Min. des Affaires municipales, 17-341
· Sask.,
· · Dept. of Parks, Recreation & Culture, 17-413
· · Fire Commission, Dept. of Environment & Public Safety, 17-404
· Yukon, Fire Marshal, Dept. of Community & Transportation Services, 17-433

Firearms Office, Prov., N.S., 17-231

Firefighters
· assns., 8-226—227
· Assn., Ontario Professional, 11-25
· Cdn. Assn. of, 11-18
· Int'l Assn. of, 11-11

Firemen & Oilers, Int'l Brotherhood of, 11-11

First Interstate Bank of Cda., 13-11

First National Bank of Chicago (Cda.), 13-11

First Nations
· Assembly of, 8-283
· Confederacy Inc., 8-283

Fish
· and Game Assn., Alta., 8-296
· industry assns., 8-227
· Marketing Corp., Freshwater, 16-76

· processing, GATT ruling, 1-1
· Saltfish Corp., Cdn., 16-75

Fisher Gauge Employees Assn., 11-22

Fisheries
· Alta., Fish & Wildlife Div., Dept. of Forestry, Lands & Wildlife, 17-37
· assns., 8-227
· Atlantic coast, 4-12
· B.C., Aquaculture & Commercial Fisheries Br., Min. of Agriculture & Fisheries, 17-69
· Depts.,
· · N.B., 17-154
· · Nfld., 17-182
· · N.S., 17-224
· · P.E.I., 17-319
· · Que., 17-344
· Development Bd., N.B., 17-154
· foreign trade, 4-12
· Freshwater Fish Marketing Corp., 16-76
· industry, 4-11—13, 14-9
· · highlights, 4-12
· inland, 4-13
· int'l organizations, 16-185
· landings, 4-12, -13
· Loan Bds.,
· · Nfld., 17-182
· · N.S., 17-225
· Man., Fisheries Br., Dept. of Natural Resources, 17-137
· and Oceans,
· · Dept. of, Cda., 16-74—76, 17-210, 17-438
· · Research Advisory Council (FORAC), 16-75
· Ont., Fisheries Dir., Min. of Natural Resources, 17-293
· Pacific coast, 4-12
· Prices Support Bd., 16-75—76
· production, 4-12
· pubns., 8-131
· Que., Dir. générale des pêches maritimes, Min. de l'Agriculture, des Pêcheries et de l'Alimentation, 17-345
· Saltfish Corp., Cdn., 16-75
· Sask., Fisheries Br., Dept. of Parks, Recreation & Culture, 17-413
· statistics, 4-12, -13
· Value by Main Species, Nominal Catch & Landed, 4-13

Fishermen & Allied Workers' Union
· Food and, 11-22
· Great Lakes, 1-3, 11-22
· United, 11-29

Fishing
· Cod War, 1-2
· Industry
· · Advisory Bd., Nfld., 17-183
· · Relations Bd., N.B., 17-157
· pubns., 8-153—154
· Vessel Owners Assn. of B.C., 8-227

Fitness
· and Amateur Sport, Nat'l Advisory Council on, 16-81
· Coun., Ont. 8-313

Flag
· Assn., Cdn., 8-238
· Canadian, 2-3

Flax Growers Western Cda., 8-181

Flexible Packaging Inst., Cdn., 8-286

Floor Coverings
· assns., 8-258, -259
· pubns., 8-132

Florists pubns., 8-134

Flour Millers Assn., Ont., 8-229

Flowers Cda., 8-240

Fluid
· Milk Commn., Man., 17-111
· Power Assn., Cdn., 8-219

Fly Bait Casting Assn· , Ont., 8-298

Flying (See Aviation)

Foam Manufacturers' Assn., Cdn. Flexible, 8-233

Folk
· Art, Councils, 8-185
· Music, 8-280

Folklore Cda. Int'l, 8-224

Fonction publique, Qué.,
· Comm. de la, 17-336
· Office des ressources humaines, 17-339

Fonctionnaires provinciaux du Qué., Syndicat des, 11-27

Fondation Université du Québec, 8-214

Food
· Agriculture Cda., Food Production & Inspection Br., 16-33—34
· and Allied Workers Union, Fishermen, 11-22
· assns., 8-227—229
· · agriculture, 8-179—182
· · equipment, 8-222, -228
· and Commercial Workers Union, United, 1-2
· · Int'l Union, 11-14
· Consumer Products Br., Bur. of Consumer Affairs, Consumer & Corporate Affairs Cda., 16-52
· Equipment Fabricators, Cdn. Assn. of, 8-222
· Fisheries & Oceans, Dept. of, 16-74—76
· grocery trade pubns., 8-133
· pubns., 8-131, -135, -154
· Science & Technology, Cdn. Inst. of, 8-305
· Service
· · assns., 8-228, -302—303
· · pubns., 8-135
· Terminal Bd., Ont., 17-258

Football assns., 8-324

Foote, Rev. John Weir, 1-2

Footwear
· assns., 8-229
· pubns., 8-131—132

Forage, statistics, 4-6—7

Forces Bases, Cdn., 16-183

Foreign
· aid, 16-189—191
· Ambassadors & High Commissioners to Cda., 16-158—163
· Chartered Banks, 13-10—14
· Claims Commission, 16-72
· Exchange, 13-6
· investment, 14-5—6, see also Investment Cda., 16-92

Foreign (cont'd)
· representatives in Cda.,
    16-158—163, -163—174
· Service Community Assn., 8-210
· Service Officers, Professional
    Assn. of, 11-25
· trade
· · assns., 8-229—230
· · pubns., 8-132

Forensic
· Psychiatric Servs. Commn., 17-83
· Science, Cdn. Soc. of, 8-306
· Service, Metro Toronto
    (METFORS), 17-260

Forest/Forestry
· assns., 8-230—231
· depts.,
· · Alta., 17-36
· · B.C., 17-79
· · Man., Natural Resources, 17-136
· · N.B., Natural Resources &
        Energy, 17-159
· · Nfld., 17-183
· · N.S., 17-229
· · Ont., Natural Resources, 17-292
· · P.E.I., 17-318
· · Que., Energie et des
        Ressources, 17-353
· depletion, 4-8
· Engineering Research Inst. of
    Cda., 8-302
· Enhancement, N.S., 17-229
· industry, 4-7—11, 14-8
· Inventory, 4-9
· land, 4-8
· and Lumber Industries, 4-8—11
· Products Commn., N.B., 17-165
· pubns., 8-132
· regions, 4-7—8
· statistics, 4-8, -9, -10, -11
· University Forestry Schools of
    Cda., Assn. of, 8-217
· Utilization in Cda., 4-10
· Wardens of Cda., Junior, 8-231

Forest Products
· Accident Prevention Assn., 8-304
· assns., 8-351
· Commn., N.B., 17-165
· Corp., Sask., 17-422
· Mktg. Bd., N.S. Primary, 17-229

Forest Resources
· Alta. Forest Serv., 17-37
· in Cda., 4-7—8
· Canada, Dept. of Forestry, 16-76
· Manfor Ltd., Man., 17-139
· Ont., Forest Resources Group,
    Min. of Natural Resources,
    17-293
· Que., Dir. gén. des forêts, Min. de
    l'Energie et des Ressources,
    17-355
· REXFOR, Que., 17-357
· Sask., Forestry Div., Dept. of
    Parks, Recreation & Culture,
    17-413
· statistics, 4-9
· · export, 4-11
· · wood cut, 4-10

Foresters/Forestiers
· assns., 8-230—231
· Féd. des travailleurs, du Qué.,
    11-21

· du Qué., Soc. de récupération,
    d'exploitation et de
    développement, 17-357
Forêt, Féd. des travailleurs du
    papier et de la, 11-21
Forms of address, 2-4—7
Forty-Plus of Cda., 8-219
Foster Parents Plan of Cda., 8-196
Foundry Assn., Cdn., 8-274
4-H Council, 8-353, -354
Foursquare Gospel Church of Cda.,
    6-9
Fowl (See Poultry)
Franchise, Federal, 16-26
Franchisors, Assn. of Cdn., 8-189
Francisation des entreprises, Comm.
    d'appel de, Qué., 17-336
Franco-manitobain
· Le Centre culturel, 17-117
· La Soc., 8-200
Franco-Ontarian Education, Coun.
    for, 17-274
Francophone Affairs, Ont., 17-250,
    17-262
Fraser Institute, The, 8-211
Fraternal & Social
· assns., 8-231—232
· pubns., 8-154
Fredericton
· Military Compound Bd., 17-161
· Multicultural Assn. of, 8-277
Free trade, 14-22—25
· Agreement, 1-1, -2, -3, -4,
    14-19—21
Freedom
· from Fear Fdn., 8-274
· Party of Ont., 8-290
Freelance Editors Assn. of Cda.,
    8-295
Freight
· assns., 8-346—347
· service, rail, Nfld., 1-2
French Language, Commn. for
    Protection of the, 17-337
Frequency Coordination System
    Assn. (FCSA), 8-341
Freshwater Fish Marketing
    Corporation, 16-76
Friends
· of Boys Town Jerusalem, Cdn.,
    8-353
· of the Earth, 8-201
· of Haifa Univ., Cdn., 8-212
· Service Cttee., Cdn., 8-300
· of SOS—Children's Villages Cda.
    Inc., 8-310
· of Tel-Aviv Univ., Cdn., 8-212
Friendship Centres, Nat'l Assn. of,
    8-283—284
Fruit
· assns., 8-228, -229
· pubn., 8-165
· statistics, 4-6
· and Vegetable Growers Assn.,
    Ont., 8-181
Fuji Bank Cda., 13-11
Funeral(s)
· assns., 8-232—233
· Directors Act, Bd. of Admin. Under
    Embalmers and, 17-115
· pubns., 8-132

Fur industry, 4-14
· assns., 8-233
· pubns., 8-132
Furniture & Furnishings
· assns., 8-233
· pubns., 8-132
Fusion: The Ont. Clay & Glass
    Assn., 8-207
Future Corp., Sask., 17-417

G

GATT
· rulings, 1-1
· meeting, 1-4
· permanent mission, 16-186
GDP statistics, 14-2, -3
Gairdner Fdn., 8-193
Galaxy, 2-14
Gallery
· assns., see Museums & Art
    Galleries, 8-278—279
· of Cda., National, 16-48
· · Friends of the, 8-279
· music, 8-274
Games
· assns., 8-233—234
· Cda. Games Park Commn., Nfld.,
    17-178
· Ski Marathon, Cdn., 8-333
Gaming Commn.,
· Alta., 17-23
· B.C., 17-92
Garde à l'enfance, Office des
    services de, 17-334
Garden (see also Botanical;
    Horticultural)
· pubns., 8-134, -158
Garment Workers of America,
    United, 11-14
Gas
· assns., 8-219, -220, -288—289
· pubns., 8-141
· Régie du gaz naturel, 17-356
Gaspésie, Soc. de conservation de
    la, 8-202
Gay (See Homosexual assns.)
Gazebo Gallery, 8-111
Gelbvieh Assn., Cdn., 8-256
Gemmological Assn., Cdn., 8-277
Genealogy, societies, 8-234
Geneticists, Cdn. College of
    Medical, 8-261
Genetics Soc. of Cda., 8-306
Geographers, Cdn. Assn. of, 8-305
Geographic Names
· Bd., Ont. 17-294
· Cdn. Permanent Cttee. on, 16-63
Geography, 3-1—13
· B.C., Surveys & Resource
    Mapping Br., Min. Crown Lands,
    17-73
· Cda., Energy, Mines & Resources
    Dept., Surveys, Mapping &
    Remote Sensing Sector, 16-58
· Man., Dept. of Natural Resources,
    Surveys & Mapping Br., 17-137
· map of Cda., 3-2—3
· Nat'l Archives of Cda., 16-45
· N.S., Dept. of Lands & Forests,
    Land Services, 17-229
· pubns., 8-155

Geological
· Assn. of Cda., 8-306
· regions of Cda., 3-6—8
· · map of, 3-8
· Soc., Sask., 8-277
· Survey of Cda., 16-58—59
Geology
· Alta., Geological Survey, Alta.
  Research Coun., 17-53
· B.C., Min. of Energy, Mines &
  Petroleum Resources, 17-74
· Cda., Inst. of Sedimentary &
  Petroleum Geology, 16-59
· Man., Dept. of Energy & Mines,
  Mineral Div., 17-122
· N.B., Dept. of Natural Resources &
  Energy, 17-159
· Nfld., Dept. of Mines, 17-182
· N.S., Resource Geology, Dept. of
  Mines & Energy, 17-230
· Ont., Ont. Geological Survey, Min.
  of Northern Development &
  Mines, 17-294
· Que., Dir. gén. de l'exploration
  géologique et minérale, Min. de
  l'Energie et des Ressources,
  17-355
· Sask., Geology & Mines Div., Dept.
  of Energy & Mines, 17-403
Geo-political regions of Cda., 3-4—6
Georgetown Shipyard Inc., P.E.I.,
  17-322
Geoscience Coun., Cdn., 8-305
Geriatrics Research Soc., Cdn.,
  8-307
German
· Canadian
· · Assn. of University Teachers of,
    8-213
· · Business & Prof. Assn., 8-190
· · Historical Assn., 8-238
· · Mardi Gras Assn., 8-208
· Chamber of Industry & Commerce,
  Cdn., 8-229
· Clubs in Cda., Central Org. of
  Sudeten-, 8-223
· Pensioners, Cdn. Soc. of, 8-223
· pubns., 9-41
· Wine Soc., 8-229
Gerontology, Cdn. Assn. on, 8-307
Gideons Int'l in Cda., 8-300
Gift & Tableware Assn., Cdn., 8-303
Gifts, pubns., 8-132
Girl Guides of Cda., 8-354
Gladiolus Soc., Cdn., 8-240
Glass, Molders, Pottery, Plastics &
  Allied Workers Int'l Union, 11-10
Glazing Contractors Assn., 8-203
Glenbow-Alta. Inst., 8-279
Glove Mfrs. Assn., Cdn., 8-259
GO Transit, Ont., 17-301
Goethe Institute, 8-208
Golf
· assns., 8-325
· pubns., 8-161
· Superintendents Assn., Cdn.,
  8-313
Golfers' Assn., Cdn. Prof., 8-313
Goodwill Rehabilitation Services of
  Alta., 8-272
Gospel Churches of Cda.,
  Associated, 6-4

Government(s)
· corporations, defined, 16-28
· employees unions
· · federal, see Public Service
    Alliance of Cda., 11-25—26
· · N.S., 17-236
· · provincial, see National Union of
    Provincial Government
    Employees, 11-23—24
· federal, 16-5—191
· information agencies
· · Alta., Public Affairs Bureau,
    17-54
· · B.C., Min. of Tourism & Prov.
    Secretary, 17-94
· · Man., Citizens' Inquiry Service,
    17-105
· · N.B., Information Service, 17-147
· · Nfld., Information Services,
    17-188
· · N.W.T., Dept. of Culture &
    Communications, 17-201
· · N.S., Information Service, 17-236
· · Ont., Citizens' Inquiry Bureau,
    Ministry of Gov't Services,
    17-248
· · P.E.I., Island Information Service,
    17-323
· · Que., Min. des Communications,
    17-331, -350
· · Sask., Provincial Inquiry Centre,
    17-395, -416
· · Yukon, Gov't Inquiry Centre,
    17-431
· institutions, 15-9—12
· Insurance (SGI), Sask., 17-422
· municipal, 19-1—43
· Parliamentary, 15-2—3
· powers
· · federal, 15-8—9, -22—23
· · provincial, 15-8—9, -22—23
· provincial, 17-10—440
· pubns., 8-132—133
· Purchasing Agency, N.S., 17-236
· Services
· · bilingual, 1-2
· · depts.: B.C., 17-79, Man., 17-125,
    N.W.T., 17-202, N.S., 17-225,
    Ont., 17-280, Yukon, 17-434

Governor General, 15-2, -10, 16-5—6
· list of, since Confederation, 16-6
· Office of the Secretary to the, 16-6
· responsibilities of the, 16-6

Governor-in-Council, 16-10

Grain(s)
· Car Corp., Sask., 17-400
· Commns.,
· · Alta., 17-21
· · Cdn., 16-35—36
· · N.B., 17-151
· · N.S., 17-219
· Corn Coun., Ont., 17-255
· Coun., Cda., 8-180
· Elevator Assn., Western, 8-182
· Elevators Corp., P.E.I., 17-325
· and Feed Dealers Assn., Ont.,
  8-181
· harvested area & production of,
  4-4
· Millers, American Fed. of, 11-9
· and Oilseeds Br., Dept. of Agric.,
  Cda., 16-35

· production of, 4-4
· Services Union, 11-22
· Transportation Agency,
  16-122—123
· Western Grain Stabilization
  Admin., 16-35
Grand Théâtre de Qué., Soc. du,
  17-340
Grant, George, 1-3
Grape Mktg. Bd., B.C., 17-70
Graphic(s)
· assns., 8-293
· Communications Int'l Union, 11-10
· pubns., 8-133, -142
Great Lakes
· Fishermen and Allied Workers
  Union, 1-3, 11-22
· lowlands, 3-7
· Tomorrow, 8-201
· Waterways Dev't Assn., 8-347
Great Plains, 3-7
Greater Winnipeg Bldg.
  Construction Wages Bd., 17-135
Greece (Cda.), Nat'l Bank of, 13-13
Greek
· Community of Metro Toronto,
  8-224
· Orthodox Church, 6-12
· pubns., 9-41
Green Party of Cda., 8-290—291
Greenhouse operations, 4-6
Greenpeace Foundation, 8-201
Gretzky, Wayne, 1-2
Greyhound Racing & Breeders
  Assn., Cdn., 8-297
Grievance Settlement Bd., 17-289
Grocers, Cdn. Fed. of Independent,
  8-303
Grocery
· food pubns., 8-131
· Products Mfrs. of Cda., 8-229
· Trade, pubns., 8-133
Gross Domestic Product, statistics,
  14-2, -3
Grotto (Cerebral Palsy Fdn. Inc.),
  8-236
Guards' Assn., Cdn., 11-18
Guelph
· Trail Club, 8-284
· Univ. of, 7-19—20
Guidance & Counselling Assn.,
  Cdn., 8-216
Guild Soc., 8-342
Gujarati pubn., 9-41
Gymnastics
· assns., 8-325—326
· · Rhythmic, 8-329—330

H

Habitation du Qué., Soc. d', 17-344
Hadassah-WIZO Organization of
  Cda., 8-310
Hail & Crop Insurance Corp., Alta.,
  17-21
Hair pubns., 8-144
Hairdressing Bd. of Examiners,
  Man., 17-134
Halifax
· Business Improvement District
  Commn., Downtown, 8-190
· Infirmary Hospital, 17-234
· libraries & archives, 8-42—44

Hamilton
· Chamber of Commerce, and District, 8-192
· libraries & archives, 8-50—51
· Philharmonic Orch., 8-281

Handbag Mfrs. Coun., Cdn., 8-259

Handball assns., 8-326

Handicapped
· assns, 8-234—237
· · sports assns., 8-314—316
· Fraternal Soc. of the Deaf, Nat'l, 8-232

Hang gliding assns., 8-298

Hanil Bank Cda., 13-12

Hanover Bank of Cda., Manufacturers, 13-12

Hansen, Rick, 1-1

Harbours
· in Cda., 10-11—12, 16-120
· Harbour Place Corp., Cda., 16-121
· Harbourfront Corp., 1-1, 16-130—131

Hardware
· and Housewares Mfrs. Assn., Cdn., 8-259
· pubns., 8-133

Hardwood Plywood Assn., Cdn., 8-351

Hare Krishna Movement, see ISKCON Toronto, 8-300

Harness Horsemen's Assn., Ont., 8-183

Headware, Optical & Allied Workers Union of Cda., United, 11-29

Healing Arts Radiation Protection (HARP) Commn., Ont., 17-284

Health (see also Medicine & Health; Public Health; Social Services)
· assns., 8-270—273
· Boards, N.W.T.
· · Regional, 17-208
· · Territorial, 17-209
· Business Health Research Inst., Cdn., 8-301
· Cdn. Council on Health Facilities, 8-241
· Care Professionals, Man. Assn. of, 11-23
· Centre Bd. of Mgmt., Fort Smith, N.W.T., 17-209
· Centres, Assn. of Ont., 8-271
· Cons. d'évaluation des technologies de la santé, 17-375
· depts. of,
· · Alta., 17-37
· · B.C., 17-81
· · Man., 17-126
· · N.B., 17-154
· · Nfld., 17-183
· · N.W.T., 17-203
· · N.S., 17-225
· · Ont., 17-282
· · P.E.I., 17-319
· · Que., 17-374
· · Sask., 17-405
· · Yukon, 17-435
· Food Assn., Cdn., 8-228
· and Human Resources, Yukon Dept. of, 17-435
· Industry Dev't Initiative, 17-131
· Insurance Bd., Que., 17-384

Labour Relations Assn. of B.C., 8-248
· Physical Education & Recreation, Cdn. Assn. for (CAHPER), 8-312
.Professionals
· · Nfld. & Labrador, Assn. of Allied, 11-16
· · Ont., Assn. of Allied, 11-16
· pubns., 8-133—134, -156
· Research
· · Bd., Sask., 17-406
· · Coun., Man., 17-128
· Sciences
· · assns.: Alta., 11-22; B.C., 11-24; Sask., 11-22
· · Centre, Man., 17-128
· · Communications Assn., (HeSCA), 8-260
· · Service Executives, Cdn. College of, 8-261
· Services
· · Commn.: Emergency, B.C., 17-83; Man., 17-128
· · and Insurance Commn., N.S., 17-226
· · and Social Services, Dept. of, P.E.I., 17-319
· · and Welfare Cda., 16-77—82

Healthcare Volunteer Services, Ont. Assn. of Directors of, 8-241

Hearing (see also Deaf)
· Aid Bd., Man., 17-128
· Handicapped, assns., 8-234, -235
· · Atlantic Provinces Resource Centre for the, 18-2

Heart Foundations, 8-268

Heat & Frost Insulators & Asbestos Workers, Int'l Assn. of, 11-11

Heating
· assns., 8-182
· pubns., 8-120

Heavy Construction Wages Bd., Man., 17-135

Heavy Equipment
· Operators, Union of, 11-28
· Trades, Independent Union of, 11-22

Hébergement du Qué., Corp. d', 17-375

Heirloom of Canada Union, 11-22

Hellenic Community of Vancouver, 8-224

Hematology Soc., Cdn., 8-264

Hemophilia
· Soc., Cdn., 8-268
· World Fed. of, 8-195

Henson College of Public Affairs & Continuing Education, 8-211

Heraldry Soc. of Cda., 8-238

Hereford Assn., Cdn., 8-256

Heritage
· Advisory Bd., Sask., 17-414
· assns., 8-237—239
· Council, Man., 17-118
· foundations,
· · Ont., 17-272
· · P.E.I. Museum and, 17-325
· Man., Dept. of Culture, and Recreation, 17-116
· Musical Heritage Soc., Cdn., 8-280
· N.B., Dept. of Tourism, Recreation and, 17-160

Property Review Bd., Sask., 17-414
· Rivers Bd., Cdn., 18-2—3
· Trust, B.C., 17-88

Hibernia offshore development, 1-2

High Commissioners
· for Cda., 16-148—158
· to Cda., 16-158—163

High school athletic assns., 8-314

Highland Games Coun., Cdn., 8-233

Highway
· Traffic Boards,
· · Man., 17-130
· · Sask., 17-407
· Transport Boards,
· · N.W.T., 17-205
· · Ont., 17-302

Highways
· Dept. of Public Works &, N.W.T., 17-203
· distances between major cities, 10-6
· and transportation,
· · B.C., Min. of, 17-94
· · Man. Dept. of, 17-129
· · Sask. Dept. of, 17-406
· · Yukon, Dept. of Community & Transportation Servs., 17-432

Hiking trail assns., 8-284

Hindi pubn., 9-41

Historic Sites
· Bd., Alta., 17-28
· and Monuments Bd. of Cda., 16-68

Historical
· assns., 8-237—239
· Aviation Historical Soc., Cdn., 8-187
· · pubn., 8-121
· Microreproductions, Cdn. Inst. for, 8-295
· pubns., 8-121, -169, -170
· Resources Fdn., Alta., 17-28
· Sites Div., Provincial Parks, Dept. of Tourism, Recreation & Heritage, N.B., 17-161

History
· Alta., Provincial Archives, Dept. of Culture & Multiculturalism, 17-26
· Man., Provincial Archives, Dept. of Culture, Heritage & Recreation, 17-117
· Museum of Civilization, History Div., 16-49
· Nat'l
· · Archives of Cda., 16-45
· · Library of Cda., 16-47—48
· N.B., Provincial Archives, Dept. of Tourism, Recreation & Heritage, 17-161
· Nfld. & Lab., Provincial Archives of, 8-40, 17-177
· N.S., Public Archives of N.S., 17-240
· Ont., Archives of Ont., Min. of Citizenship & Culture, 17-270
· P.E.I., Public Archives, Dept. of Education, 17-318
· pubns., 8-155, -169, -170, -171
· Que., Archives nationales, Min. des Affaires culturelles, 17-336
· Sask., Dept. of Parks, Recreation & Culture, 17-413

History (cont'd)
· Yukon Archives, Dept. of
    Education, 17-434
Hobbies
· assns. 8-239
· pubns., 8-156—157
Hockey
· assns., 8-317, -326, -323—324
· ball, 8-317
· field, 8-323—324
· League
· Nat'l, 8-313
· Players' Assn., Nat'l, 11-23
· pubns., 8-161
Hog
· Marketing
· · B.C., 17-70
· · Man., 17-109
· · P.E.I., 17-317
· · Sask., 17-399
· Producers' Assn., Ont., 8-257
· pubns., 8-166, -167
Holidays, 2-8—10
Holocaust & Genocide, Cdn. Centre
    for Studies of the, 8-301
Home
· builders assns., 8-242
· Mortgage & Housing Corp., Alta.,
    17-41
· Owners Assn., 8-242
· pubns., 8-157, -164
· & School & Parent-Teacher Fed.,
    8-215
· Schoolers, Cdn. Alliance of, 8-211
· senior citizens, 8-191
· Sewing & Needlecraft Assn., Cdn.,
    8-207
· Special Care, Sask. Assn. of,
    8-261
Home-Care Centres, Que. Corp. of,
    (Corp. d'hébergement du Qué.),
    17-375
Home Economics Assn., Cdn. 8-217
Homemaker Services, Cdn. Coun.
    on, 8-308
Homes, facilities, 8-191
Homosexuals/Homosexuality
· assns., 8-199, 239—240
· ordination in the United Church,
    1-1, -2
Honey
· Coun., Cdn., 8-228
· Producers' Mktg. Bd., Man.,
    17-108
· statistics, 4-6
Hong Kong Trade Dev't Coun.,
    8-230
Hongkong Bank of Cda., 13-12
Horse Racing
· Commn., Man., 17-132
· & Sports Commn., P.E.I., 17-323
Horses (see also Equestrian)
· assns., 8-182, -183
· pubns., 8-157—158
Horseshoe Cda. Assn., 8-298
Horticultural
· Assn., Man., 17-111
· assns., 8-240
· crops, 4-6
· fruits, 4-6
· · greenhouse operations, 4-6
· · honey, 4-6

· · maple products, 4-6
· · nursery trades industry, 4-6
· · vegetables, 4-6
· pubns., 8-134, -158
Hospital
· assns., 8-240—241
· Bd. of Management, N.W.T.,
    Stanton Yellowknife, 17-209
· Employees
· · Assn., St. Mary's of the Lake
    Hospital, 11-19
· · Union, 11-22; Alta., 11-15
· Financing Authorities
· · B.C., 17-77
· · Man., 17-125
· and Health Services Commn.,
    P.E.I., 17-323
· Insurance Services Bd., Territorial,
    (N.W.T.), 17-208
· Nova Scotia, 17-236
· Pharmacists, Cdn. Soc. of, 8-289
· pubns., 8-134
· for Sick Children Fdn., 8-193
· Victoria General, 17-241
Hospitality
· N.B., 8-302
· pubns., 8-135
Hostelling Assn., Cdn., 8-353
Hotel
· assns., 8-241
· Employees & Restaurant
    Employees Int'l Union, 11-10
· pubns., 8-135
House of Commons, 15-10,
    16-17—27
· Members,
· · alphabetical list, 16-23—26
· · constituency list, 16-20—23
· Officers', 16-17
· Parliamentary Secretaries, 16-20
· party leaders & standings, 16-18
· remuneration of members, 16-18
· Standing, Special & Joint
    Committees, 16-26
Households, 5-9—11
· statistics
· · characteristics, 5-9—10
· · income, 5-10
Houseware pubns., 8-132, -133
Housing
· assns., 8-241—242
· Canative Housing Corp., 8-283
· corps.,
· · Alta. Mortgage & Housing Corp.,
    17-41
· · Cda. Mortgage & Housing Corp.,
    16-129—130
· · N.B., 17-165
· · N.W.T., 17-206
· · Ont., 17-284
· · P.E.I., 17-325
· · Que., 17-344
· · Sask., 17-423
· · Yukon, 17-437
· depts.,
· · B.C., Social Services &, 17-90
· · Man., 17-130
· · N.S., 17-226
· · Ont., 17-284
· Economic profile, 14-14—15
· and Employment Development
    Financing Auth., B.C., 17-77

· Handicapped, Soc. of Alta., 8-232
· Management Commn., B.C., 17-91
· Manufactured, Cdn. Inst. 8-237
· and Renewal Corp., Man., 17-131
· Yukon, Dept. of Community &
    Transportation Services, 17-432
Howe Institute, C.D., 8-210
Hudson Bay lowlands, 3-8
Huguenot Soc. of Cda., 8-208
Human
· Ecology Fdn. of Cda., 8-261
· Factors Assn. of Cda., 8-306
Human Resource(s) (see also
    Personnel)
· Dept., Yukon, Health &, 17-435
· Labour & Employment, Dept.,
    Sask., 17-407
· pay, assns., 8-225, -226
· Professionals of Que., Assn. of,
    8-288
· pubns., 8-141
Human Rights (see also
    Ombudsmen)
· administrators of legislation,
    12-5—6
· assns., 8-198—199
· Cda., 12-3—5
· · Secretary of State Cda.,
    16-107—110
· Children, Cdn. Soc. for the
    Prevention of Cruelty to, 8-196
· Commns.,
· · Alta., 12-5, 17-39
· · Cdn., 12-5, 16-93—94
· · Man., 12-5, 17-113
· · N.B., 12-6, 17-157
· · Nfld., 12-6, 17-185
· · N.S., 12-6, 17-234
· · Ont., 12-6, 17-261
· · P.E.I., 12-6, 17-323
· · Que., 17-367
· · Sask., 12-6, 17-411
· Coun. of, B.C., 12-5, 17-85
· Directorate, 12-3
· pubn., 8-159
Humane assns., 8-183, -242—243
· Protection of Fur-Bearing
    Animals, Assn. for the, 8-201
Humanities
· Assn. of Cda., 8-252
· Cdn. Fed. for the, 8-301
Hungarian
· Cdn. Federation, 8-224
· pubns., 8-170, 9-41—42
Hunger Fdn., Cdn., 8-193
Hunting pubns., 8-153—154
Huntington Soc. of Cda., 8-269
Huronia
· Historical Advisory Council, Ont.,
    17-298
· Tourist Assn., 8-345
Hydro
· B.C. Hydro, Management & Prof.
    Employees Soc. of, 11-23
· Man., 17-139
· Nfld. & Lab., 17-192
· Ont., 17-276
· Québec, 17-356
· · International, 17-356
Hydrocephalus (See Spina Bifida)
Hydroelectricity contract, 1-2
Hypnosis, Ont. Soc. of Clinical,
    8-261

I

IAO Research Centre Inc., 8-274
IMA, 8-271
IODE (Imperial Order Daughters of the Empire), 8-350
ISBN Agency, Cdn., 8-295
ITVA Cda., 8-188
IWA—Canada, 11-10
Ice Industries, Cdn. Assn. of, 8-258
Icelandic, pubn., 9-42
Ileitis & Colitis, Cdn. Fdn. for, 8-268
Immersion Teachers, Cdn. Assn. of, 8-213
Immigrant
· aid assns., 8-309, -311
· classification of, 5-12
Immigration, 5-12—13
· Act, 5-12
· Dept.
· · B.C., 17-83
· · Que., 17-349
· & Refugee Board, 16-56
· sources of, 5-13
· statistics, 5-12, -13
Immobilière du Qué., Soc., 17-348
Immunology, Cdn. Soc. for, 8-272
Importers Assn., Cdn., 8-230
Imports
· Alta. Dept. of Economic Development & Trade, 17-28
· B.C., Min. of International Business & Immigration, 17-83
· Cda.,
· · Int'l Trade Div., Business & Trade Statistics Field, Statistics Cda., 16-144
· · Special Trade Relations Bur., External Affairs Dept., 16-69
· Cdn. Import Tribunal, see Cdn. International Trade Tribunal, 16-106—107
· N.B., Dept. of Commerce & Technology, 17-151
· Ont., Min. of Industry, Trade & Technology, 17-285
· Que., Min. du Commerce extérieur, 17-348
· statistics, 14-20, -23
Income
· Assistance, Dept. of, N.B., 17-154
· Domestic, and Gross Domestic Product, 14-3
· payroll deductions, 11-4—5
· statistics, 5-10, 14-3, -4
· · disposition of, 14-4
· · sources of, 14-4
Incorporation of Companies & Associations
· Alta., Corporate Registry, Dept. of Consumer & Corporate Affairs, 17-25
· B.C., Registrar of Companies, Min. of Finance & Corporate Relations, 17-76
· Cda., Corporations Br., Consumer & Corporate Affairs Cda., 16-52
· Man., Companies & Business Names Registration Br., Dept. of Co-operative, Consumer & Corporate Affairs, 17-115
· N.B., Corporate & Trust Affairs Br., Dept. of Justice, 17-155

· Nfld., Registry of Deeds, Companies & Securities, 17-185
· N.S., Registrar of Joint Stock Companies, Dept. of Attorney General, 17-219
· Ont., Companies Br., Min. of Consumer & Commercial Relations, 17-266
· P.E.I., Corporations Div., Dept. of Justice, 17-320
· Que., Enregistrement, Min. de la Justice, 17-367
· Sask., Corporations Br., Dept. of Consumer & Commercial Affairs, 17-401
· Yukon, Consumer & Corporate Affairs Div., Dept. of Justice, 17-436
Independent
· Holiness Church, 6-9
· School, assns., 8-216
· Unions, Cdn. Nat'l Fed. of, 11-8
Indexing & Abstracting Soc. of Cda., 8-243
India (Cda.), State Bank of, 13-13
Indian (see also Native Peoples)
· Affairs and Northern Dev't Dept., 7-5—6, 16-82—87, 17-210, -439
· assns., 8-283—284
· Commission of Ont., 18-4
· Friendship Centres, assns., 8-283—284
· and Native Affairs Secretariat, Sask., 17-420
Industrial
· accident, assns., 8-304
· assns., 8-258—260
· Bank of Japan (Cda.), 13-12
· Commercial & Institutional Accountants, Guild of, 8-178
· design
· · assns., 8-243
· · pubns., 8-135
· Developers Assn. of Cda., 8-243
· development
· · assns., 8-243
· · pubns., 8-135
· Mechanical & Allied Workers, Cdn. Assn. of, 11-18
· Mechanics, Nat'l Assn. of, 11-16
· Pharmacists, Cdn. Soc. of, 8-289
· pubns., 8-135
· relations, 11-2
· · Assn., Cdn., 8-248
· · Bd., N.B., 17-157
· · Coun., B.C., 17-85
· Risks Insurers, Cdn., 8-244
· Roofing Contractors Assn., Ont., 8-204
· Sweetener Users, Cdn., 8-228
· Transportation League, Cdn., 8-347
· Truck Assn. of Cda., 8-348
Industrie(s)
· du Commerce et de la Technologie, Min. de l', Qué., 17-363
· culturelles (SOGIC), Soc. gén. des, 17-341
Industry
· Alberta,
· · Economic Development & Trade, Dept. of, Small Business & Industry Div., 17-29

· · Industrial Technologies, Alta. Research Coun., 17-53
· B.C., Min. of International Business & Immigration, 17-83
· Cdn.,
· · Dept. of Industry, Science and Technology, 16-87
· · outlook, 14-1—25
· · regional analysis of, 14-16—19
· Gov't of Cda. Business Information Centres, 16-89
· Man., Dept. of Industry, Trade & Tourism, 17-131
· N.B., Dept. of Commerce & Technology, 17-151
· Nfld., Dept. of Dev't & Tourism, 17-175
· N.S.,
· · Business Capital Corp., 17-235
· · Dept. of Industry, Trade & Technology, 17-227
· · Research Fdn. Corp., 17-238
· Ont., Min. of Industry, Trade & Technology, 17-285
· P.E.I., Dept. of Industry, 17-319
· profiles, Cdn., 14-7—16
· pubns., 8-135—136
· Que., Min. de l'Industrie, du Commerce et de la Technologie, 17-363
· Sask., Dept. of Economic Development & Tourism, 17-401
Infant Deaths (SIDS Fdn.), Cdn. Fdn. for the Study of, 8-262
Infantry Assn., Cdn., 8-276
Infirmières et infirmiers
· auxiliaires du Qué.
· · Alliance prof. des, 11-16
· · Féd. des syndicats d', 11-21
· du Qué.
· · Féd. des, 11-20
· · Ordre des, 8-285
· de Trois-Riviéres, Syndicat prof. des, 11-28
Information
· Act, Freedom of, 12-5
· Cda., Commissioner, 16-94—95
· Comm. d'accès à l', Qué., 17-350
· Processing
· · assns., 8-200—201
· · pubn., 8-170
· Science
· · assns., (see also Computers), 8-200, -243
· · pubn., 8-169
Informatisation de la production, Centre québécois pour l', 17-358
Inhalothérapeutes du Qué., Assoc. prof. des, 11-17
Initiatives
· agro-alimentaires (SOQUIA), Soc. qué. d', 17-347
· pétrolières, Soc. qué. d' (SOQUIP), 17-357
Injured Workmen of Ont., Assn. of Pensioners and, 8-309
Innovation Ontario Corp., 17-287
Inquiries of the Gov't of Canada, 16-12
Insémination artificielle du Qué., Centre d', 17-346

Insolvency, 13-34
· Assn., Cdn., 8-225

Inspecteur gén. des institutions
  financières, 17-366

Installations olympiques, Régie des,
  17-347

Instituto Nazionale Assistenza
  Sociale (INAS Cda.), 8-310

Insulation & Energy Saving
· Alta., Dept. of Energy, 17-31
· B.C., Min. of Energy, Mines &
  Petroleum Resources, 17-74
· Cda.
· · Energy Sector, Energy Mines &
    Resources Dept., 16-60—61
· · Mortgage & Housing Corp.,
    16-129—130
· Man., Dept. of Energy & Mines,
  17-122
· N.B., Dept. of Natural Resources &
  Energy, 17-159
· Nfld., Dept. of
· · Energy, 17-181
· · Mines, 17-186
· Ont.
· · Development Corp., 17-286
· · Min. of Energy, 17-275
· Que., Hydro-Qué., 17-356
· Sask., Sask. Power Corp., 17-417

Insulation Contractors Assns., B.C.,
  8-203

Insurance
· Accountants Assn., Cdn., 8-177
· assns., 8-243—245
· Automobile (See Automobile
  Insurance)
· Cda., Sup't of Financial Inst.,
  16-73—74
· Corp. of B.C., 17-85
· Coun. of B.C., 17-78
· crop (See Crop Insurance)
· hospital (See Medical Care
  Insurance)
· life, 13-18—19
· property & casualty, 13-19
· pubns., 8-136
· Sask. Govt. (SGI), 17-422
· superintendents, 13-20

Integrated Service Digital Network,
  9-4

Intelligence Service, Cdn. Security,
  16-110—111

Intelpost, 9-9

Inter-American
· Commercial Arbitration Commn.,
  8-248
· Freight Conf., 8-347
· Organizations, 16-185

Inter Pares, 8-247

Inter-Church Cttee. for World
  Education, 8-247

Inter-Port, de Qué., Soc., 17-366

Inter-Varsity Christian Fellowship of
  Cda., 8-300

Intercultural Council, Man., 17-118

Interdepartmental Planning Bd.,
  Man., 17-136

Intergovernmental
· Affairs Dept.
· · N.B., 17-155
· · Ont., 17-288
· agencies, 18-1—5

Cttee. on Urban & Reg'l Research,
  18-4
· Conference Secretariat, Cdn., 18-3
· Relations (See Federal-Provincial
  Relations)

Interior Decor/Design
· assns., 8-245—246
· pubns., 8-136, -157

Interior Plains, 3-7

Interior Systems Mechanics,
  Resilient Floor Layers & Plant
  Workers, Nat'l Union of, 11-28

International
· Corp., Ont., 17-287
· Date Line, 2-21
· Development
· · Agency (CIDA), Cdn., 7-5,
    16-132—134, -190—191
· · Agency for, Alta., 17-30
· · Education: Cttee. of Ont., 8-212;
    Resources Assn., 8-212
· · Research Centre (IDRC), 16-137,
    -190
· education programs, 7-5
· Joint Commn., 16-137
· organizations, 16-184—189

International Relations
· assns., 8-246—247
· UNICEF, 8-195

Interns & Residents
· Cdn. Assn. of, 8-263
· Prof. Assn. of,
· · of B.C., 11-25
· · of Man., 11-25
· · of the Maritime Provinces, 11-25
· · of Nfld., 11-25
· · of Ont., 8-265
· · of Sask., 11-25

Interprovincial Labourers Assn.,
  11-16

Interuniversity Athletic Union, Cdn.,
  8-314

Intramural Recreation Assn., Cdn.,
  8-297

Inuit (see also Native Peoples)
· Alta., Native Services Div., Dept. of
  Municipal Affairs, 17-41
· Canada,
· · Cdn. Museum of Civilization:
    Cdn. Ethnology Service;
    Archaeological Survey of
    Cda., 16-49
· · Indian Affairs & Northern Dev't
    Dept., 16-82—87
· · Native Citizens, Citizenship,
    Secretary of State, 16-108
· Qué., Secrétariat aux Affaires
  autochtones, 17-333

Inventors Assn., 8-206

Investigators & Guard Agencies of
  Ont., Assn. of 8-307

Investment
· assns., 8-247—248
· Dealers, 13-20
· · Assn. of Cda. (IDA), 13-20
· foreign, 14-5—6
· pubns., 8-131, -153

**Investment (Corporate & Capital;
  Industrial & Commercial)** (see
  also Incorporation of
  Companies & Associations;
  Real Estate)

· Alta.,
· · Dept. of Economic Development
    & Trade, Trade and
    Investment Div., 17-29
· · Securities Commn., 17-25
· B.C.,
· · Min. of International Business &
    Immigration, Business &
    Industrial Dev't Div., 17-83
· · Securities Commn., 17-77
· Cda., 16-92
· Man., Dept. of Industry, Trade &
  Tourism, Industry & Trade Div.,
  17-131
· N.B., Dept. of Commerce &
  Technology, 17-151
· Nfld., Dept. of Development &
  Tourism, 17-175
· N.S., Dept. of Industry, Trade &
  Technology, 17-227
· Ont.,
· · Corporations Tax Br., Min. of
    Revenue, 17-295
· · Min. of Industry, Trade &
    Technology, Industry & Trade
    Expansion, 17-285
· P.E.I., Dept. of Industry, 17-319
· Que., Dir. de la promotion des
  investissements, Min. de
  l'Industrie et du Commerce,
  17-363
· Sask., Dept. of Trade &
  Investment, 17-419

Irish
· Benevolent Irish Soc., 8-231
· Cdn. Aid & Cultural Soc. of
  Toronto, 8-208
· Studies, Cdn. Assn. for, 8-251

Irrigation Coun., Alta., 17-21

Irving Bank Cda., 13-12

ISKCON Toronto—Hare Krishna
  Movement, 8-300

Island(s)
· Cdn., 3-9
· Information Service, P.E.I., 17-323
· Trust, B.C., 17-89

Israel
· Cttee., Cda., 8-246
· Cultural Fdn., Cda., 8-208
· Discount Bank of Cda., 13-12

Italian
· Artist's Assn., Cdn., 8-184
· Business & Prof. Assn. of Toronto,
  Cdn., 8-190
· -Canadians, Nat'l Congress of,
  8-224
· Chamber of Commerce
· · Montreal, 8-230
· · of Toronto, 8-230
· Cultural Inst., 8-208
· Pentecostal Church, 6-10
· pubns., 9-42
· Studies, Cdn. Soc. for, 8-252

Italy, Order of Sons of, in Cda.,
  8-224

J

Jack Miner Migratory Bird Fdn.,
  8-349

Jamaican Cdn. Assn., 8-224

James Bay Development Corp.,
    Que., 17-344
James Bay Energy Corp., 17-357
Japan Society of Cda., 8-224
Japanese Cdn.
· Citizens Assn., 8-224
· Cultural Centre, 8-208
· pubns., 9-42
Jaycees
· Cdn., 8-353
· Toronto, 8-354
Jehovah's Witnesses, 6-10
Jesuit
· Fathers of Upper Cda., 8-300
· Missions, Cdn., 8-300
Jewellers and Jewellery
· assns., 8-248
· pubns., 8-136
Jewish
· assns., 8-208, -223, -224, -232
· Community, 6-10
· Family & Child Service of Metro
    Toronto, 8-310
· holidays, 2-10
· New Fraternal, Assn., 8-232
· pubns., 8-153, -168, 9-42
· religion, 6-10
· social services, 8-308, -310, -311,
    -312
· Vegetarian Soc., 8-231
· women, assns., 8-350, -351
Jews, The Cdn. Coun. of Christians
    and, 6-2—3
Jiu-Jitsu Assn., Cdn., 8-326
John Howard Society, 8-311
John Milton Soc. for the Blind in
    Cda., 8-236
Johnson, Ben, 1-3
Joiners, Foresters & Industrial
    Workers, Nat'l Brotherhood of
    Carpenters, 11-22
Journalism
· Programs in Cdn. Universities,
    Assn. of Directors of, 8-214
· pubns., 8-137
Journeymen & Apprentices of the
    Plumbing & Pipe Fitting Ind. of
    the U.S. & Cda., United Assn.
    of, 11-14
Judaism, Cdn. Coun. for
    Conservative, 8-300
Judges (see also Judiciary & judicial
    officers)
· Benefits Bd., Prov., Ont., 17-281
· Cdn. Assn. of Provincial Court,
    8-250
· Coun. of, Que., 17-368
· salaries, allowances & pensions
    of, 12-8
Judicial Coun., Cdn., 16-94
Judiciary & judicial officers (see
    also individual provinces), 15-9
· federal, 12-6—7, 16-146—148
· provincial (see also each
    province), 12-7
· territorial (see also each territory),
    12-7
Judo assns., 8-326—327
Jung Fdn. of the Analytical
    Psychology Soc. of Ont., C.G.,
    8-273

Junior (see Youth & specific subject
    categories)
Jupiter, 2-12
Justice
· Citizens for Public, 8-290
· Commissioner for Federal Judicial
    Affairs, 16-94
· and Corrections, Church Coun.
    on, 8-251
· depts.
· · Cda., 16-92—95
· · N.B., 17-155
· · Nfld., 17-184
· · N.W.T., 17-203
· · P.E.I., 17-320
· · Que., 17-366
· · Sask., 17-409
· · Yukon, 17-435
· Inst. of B.C., 17-93
Juvenile Diabetes Fdn., 8-269

K

Kabalarian(s)
· of Cda., Soc. of, 8-194
· Philosophy, 8-300
Karate assns., 8-327
Kativik, Comité cons. de
    l'environnement, 17-360
Kawartha Festival Fdn., 8-343
Kayak assns., 8-298, -320
Keith, Vicki, 1-2
Kendo Fed., Cdn., 8-327
Kennel Club, Cdn., 8-183
Kerr Addison Employee's Assn.,
    11-22
Kidney Fdn. of Cda., 8-269
Kilometre Guide—Official highway
    distances, 10-6
Kindness Clubs of Cda., 8-242
King's
· College, Univ. of, 7-20
· Landing Historical Settlement,
    N.B., 17-161
Kingston District Chamber of
    Commerce, 8-192
Kinsmen Clubs, Assn. of, 8-231
Kirby House, Iris, 8-350
Kitchen Cabinet Assn., Cdn., 8-259
Kiwanis
· International, 8-311
· Music Festival Assn., 8-281
Knights
· of Columbus, 8-231—232
· of Pythias, 8-232
Korea Exchange Bank of Cda.,
    13-12
Korean
· Businessmen's Assn., Ont., 8-191
· pubns., 9-42

L

Laboratory Technologists, Cdn. Soc.
    of, 8-266
Labour
· assns., 8-248—249
· Bd., Man., 17-134
· Cda., Employment & Immigration,
    Public Affairs Div., 16-54

· Cdn. Fed. of, (CFL), 11-7
· Code, Cda., 11-1—2, -6
· Congress (CLC), Cdn., 11-7—8
· Congresses, central, 11-7—9
· depts., 11-2—3
· · Alta., 17-39
· · B.C., 17-84
· · Cda., 11-2—3, 16-95—97
· · Man., 17-133
· · N.B., 17-155
· · Nfld., 17-185
· · N.S., 17-227
· · Ont., 17-288
· · P.E.I., 17-320
· · Que., 17-380
· · Sask., 17-407
· · Yukon, 17-435
· division of legislative powers,
    11-1—2
· federations (of CLC), provincial,
    11-7—8
· Int'l Labour Organization, 16-185
· legislation, 11-1—7
· · federal, 11-2—3
· · provincial, 11-3—4
· Management
· · Relations Coun., P.E.I., 17-321
· · Review Cttee., Man., 17-134
· organizations, 11-7—29
· pubns., 8-158
· Relations Bds.
· · Alta., 17-40
· · Cda., 16-96
· · Nfld., 17-186
· · N.S., 17-228
· · Ont., 17-289
· · P.E.I., 17-321
· · Sask., 17-408
· Review Board, Adjustment, 16-97
· Standards, 11-3—4
· · Bd., Nfld., 17-186
· · Commn., Que., 17-372
· · N.W.T., 17-205
· · N.S., 17-228
· · Tribunal, Nfld., 17-186
· statistics (see also People
    chapter), 11-2, -4
· unions, 11-2, -7—29
Labour force, 5-11—12
· statistics
· · by age & sex, 5-11
· · by province, 5-12
Labourers' Int'l Union of North
    America, 11-13
Labrador (See Newfoundland &
    Labrador)
Lacrosse assns., 8-327—328
Ladies
· Amateur Radio Assn., Cdn., 8-239
· Garment Workers Union, Int'l,
    11-12
· Orange Benevolent Assn. of Cda.,
    8-232
Lake(s)
· Cda., 3-8
· Erie Fish Packers & Processors
    Assn., 8-227
· of the Woods Control Bd., 18-4—5
Lakehead University, 7-20
Lamp & Fixture Mfrs. Assn., Cdn.,
    8-259

Lampoon Puppet Theatre, 8-343

Land
· claims settlements, 1-2, -3
· Compensation Bd., Alta., 17-23
· Development Corp., P.E.I., 17-325
· Economists, Assn. of Ont., 8-210
· registration
· · and Information Service, 18-3
· · officials, Sask., 17-427
· · Yukon, 17-440
· surveyors, assns., 8-340
· Use
· · Commn., P.E.I., 17-323
· · Planning Commn., N.W.T., 17-207
· · Value Appraisal Commn., Man., 17-126

Land Titles
· Alta.,
· · Dept. of Attorney General, Land Titles Office, 17-22
· · Land Registrars, 17-59
· B.C., Land Title Office, 17-72
· Man., Land Titles Office, Dept. of Attorney General, 17-112
· N.B., Registrars of Deeds, 17-155, -169
· Nfld., Registrar of Deeds, 17-195
· N.W.T., Land Titles/Legal Registries, Dept. of Justice, 17-203
· N.S., Registrars of Deeds, 17-244
· Ont., Registration Div., Min. of Consumer & Commercial Relations, 17-266
· P.E.I., Registrars of Deeds, 17-327
· Sask., Property Registration Branch, Dept. of Justice, 17-409
· Yukon, Land Titles, Dept. of Justice, 17-435

Landlord & Tenant Regulations
· B.C., Residential Tenancies Br., Min. of Labour & Consumer Services, 17-84
· Man., Landlord & Tenant Affairs, Dept. of Housing, 17-131
· N.B., Dept. of Justice, 17-155
· Nfld., Landlord-Tenant Relations, Dept. of Consumer Affairs & Communications, 17-176
· N.S., Rent Review & Residential Tenancies Div., Dept. of Consumer Affairs, 17-222
· Ont., Rent Review Hearing Bd., 17-285
· Qué., Régie du logement du, 17-343
· Sask.,
· · Provincial Mediation Bd./Rentalsman, 17-410
· · Rent Appeal Commn., 17-411

Landrace Swine Breeders Assn., Cdn., 8-256

Lands
· Allocation Appeal Bd., Sask., 17-400
· Dept., Environment and, Nfld., 17-181
· and Forests Dept., N.S., 17-229
· Min. of Crown, B.C., 17-73

Landscaping
· architects, assns., 8-249
· nursery trades, assns., 8-284—285
· pubns., 8-134

Language(s)
· assns., 8-249—250
· Commissioner of Official, 16-134
· distribution in Cda., 5-9
· of Instruction Commn. of Ont., 17-274
· pubns., 8-170

Langue d'enseignement, Commn. d'appel sur la, Qué., 17-353

Langue française
· Assoc. cdne d'éducation de (ACELF), 8-217
· Assoc. cdne de la radio et de la télévision de, (ACRTF), 8-188
· Commn. de protection de la, Qué., 17-337
· Conseil de la, Qué., 17-338
· Office de la, Qué., 17-339

Latvian
· Art Craftsmen in Cda., Assn. of, 8-207
· Business & Prof. Assn., Cdn., 8-190
· pubn., 9-43

Laundry assns., 8-307—308

Laurentian Bank of Cda., 13-10

Laurentian University, 7-21

Laval, Université, 7-21—22

Law
· Artists' Legal Advice Services (ALAS), 8-184
· assns., 8-250—251
· bilingual statutes, 1-1
· civil, 12-1, -2
· common, 12-2
· criminal, 12-2—3
· Fdn.,
· · B.C., 17-72
· · Cdn. Petroleum, 8-288
· · of N.S., 8-251
· Libraries, Cdn. Assn. of, 8-253
· public, 12-1
· Quebec Civil, 12-2
· Reform Commns.,
· · B.C., 17-72
· · Cda., 16-95
· · Man., 17-113
· · Nfld., 17-185
· · N.W.T., 17-206
· · Ont., 17-260
· · Sask., 17-410
· rights of citizens, 12-3—6
· rule of, and the courts, 15-9

Lawn bowling assns., 8-328

Le Dain, Mr. Justice Gerald, 1-4

Leaf Rapids Town Properties Ltd., Man., 17-136

Learned Societies assns., 8-251—252

Learning Disabilities assns., 8-218

Leather
· Goods, Plastics & Novelty Workers' Union, Int'l, 11-12
· pubns., 8-137

La Leche League Cda., 8-196

Legal
· Court Interpreters & Translators, Assn. of, 8-249
· profession, the, 12-8
· pubns., 8-137, -171

Legal Aid, 12-8
· Alta., 17-24
· B.C., 17-72
· Man., 17-113
· N.B., 17-155
· N.S., 17-220
· P.E.I., 17-320
· Que., 17-368
· Sask., 17-419
· Yukon, 17-436

Legal Services, 12-8
· duty counsel, 12-8
· N.W.T., Legal Servs. Bd., 17-206

Legion, Royal Cdn., 8-276

Legislation, bilingual, 1-1, -2

Legislative
· assemblies
· · Alta., 17-13
· · B.C., 17-63
· · Man., 17-105
· · N.B., 17-147
· · Nfld., 17-174
· · N.W.T., 17-201
· · N.S., 17-216
· · Ont., 17-250
· · P.E.I., 17-315
· · Que., 17-331
· · Sask., 17-395
· · Yukon, 17-432
· process, 15-13, 16-13—14

Legislature, The, 16-13—27

Lending Auth., P.E.I., 17-325

Leprosy Mission Cda., The, 8-270

Lethbridge
· Symphony Assn., 8-281
· Univ. of, 7-22

Letter Carriers' Union of Cda., 1-3, 11-22

Leukemia Research Fund, 8-193

Lewis, Lennox, 1-3

Liberal Party
· Alta., Offices of the, 17-15
· of Cda., 8-291

Libérations conditionnelles, Comm. qué. des, 17-377

Libertarian Party
· of Cda., 8-291
· Ont., 8-292

Libraries (see also Archives; Information Processing)
· academic (See public, academic & special)
· Bd., Nfld. Public, 17-178
· Cdn. Assn. of Toy, 8-346
· legislative
· · Alta., 17-15
· · B.C., 17-65
· · Man., 17-107
· · N.B., 17-149
· · N.S., 17-217
· · Ont., 17-253
· · Que., 17-334
· · Sask., 17-397

Libraries (cont'd)
· public, academic & special
· · Alta., 8-7—20
· · B.C., 8-20—28
· · Man., 8-28—34
· · N.B., 8-34—38
· · Nfld., 8-38—40
· · N.W.T., 8-40—41
· · N.S., 8-42—45
· · Ont., 8-45—79
· · P.E.I., 8-79—80
· · Que., 8-80—99
· · Sask., 8-99—104
· · Yukon, 8-104

Library
· assns., 8-252—255
· Bd., Alta., 17-28
· of Cda., Nat'l, 16-47—48
· of Parliament, 16-17
· pubns., 8-137
· Sask., 17-402
· Science, see Information Science, 8-243
· Services, Nfld. Public, 17-178
· Technicians, assns., 8-253, -254, -255
· Trustees, assns., 8-253, -254, -255

License Suspension Appeal Bd.
· N.B., 17-162
· Ont., 17-302

Lieutenant-Governors, 15-2, -10
· Alta., 17-13
· B.C., 17-63
· Man., 17-105
· N.B., 17-147
· Nfld., 17-173
· N.S., 17-215
· Ont., 17-249
· P.E.I., 17-315
· Que., 17-331
· Sask., 17-395

Life
· Alliance for, 8-198
· Saving Soc. Cda., Royal, 8-304—305

Lifeboat Inst., Cdn., 8-304

Lighting pubn., 8-132

Limousin assns., 8-255, -256

Linguistic assns., 8-249

Lions Clubs Int'l, 8-311

Liquid Waste Carriers Assn., Ont., 8-202

Liquor
· Alcohol & Drug Services, Dept. of Health & Human Resources, Yukon, 17-435
· Bd., Sask., 17-423
· Boards Employees' Union, Ont., 11-24
· Commrs., Cdn. Assn. of Prov., 8-228
· Commns.
· · N.W.T., Dept. of Government Services, 17-202
· · N.S., 17-237
· Control & Licensing Br., Min. of Labour & Consumer Services, B.C., 17-84
· Control Boards/Commns.,
· · Alta., 17-47
· · Man., 17-138

· · Ont., 17-266
· · P.E.I., 17-323
· Corps.,
· · N.B., 17-165
· · Nfld., 17-193
· · Yukon, 17-437
· Licensing Bds./Commns.,
· · N.B., 17-164
· · Nfld., 17-193
· · N.W.T., 17-206
· · N.S., 17-237
· · Ont., 17-267
· pricing, GATT ruling, 1-1
· Régie des permis d'alcool du Qué., 17-377

Literacy assns., 8-192, -212, -213

Literary
· Arts, Alta. Fdn. for the, 17-27
· Press Group, 8-294
· pubns., 8-171—172
· Translators Assn., 8-249

Literature
· Children's, Cdn. Research Soc. for, 8-196
· pubns., 8-171—172

Lithuanian
· Cdn. Fdn., 8-193
· pubns., 9-43

Liturgie, Office national de, 8-301

Liver Fdn., Cdn., 8-268

Livestock
· Alta., Animal Industry Div., Dept. of Agriculture, 17-18
· assns., 8-255—257
· Cda., Dept. of Industry, Science & Technology, Food Products, 16-90
· Feed Bd. of Cda., 16-37
· Insurance Commn., N.S. Crop &, 17-219
· Man., Animal Industry Br., Dept. of Agriculture, 17-107
· N.B., Animal Industry Br., Dept. of Agriculture, 17-150
· Nfld., Agriculture Br., Dept. of Rural, Agricultural & Northern Development, 17-189
· N.S., Livestock Services Br., Dept. of Agriculture & Marketing, 17-218
· Ont., Animal Industry Br., Min. of Agriculture & Food, 17-255
· pubns., 8-165—167
· Que., Service des productions animaux, Min. de l'Agriculture, des Pêcheries et de l'Alimentation, 17-345
· Sask., Livestock Br., Dept. of Agriculture, 17-397
· statistics, 4-4—5
· · cattle, 4-4—5
· · pigs, 4-5
· · sheep, 4-5

Lloydminster heavy oil upgrader, 1-3

Lloyds Bank Cda., 13-12

Loans Bd.
· Co-operative
· · and Loans Guarantee, Man., 17-115
· · of Ont., 17-256
· Territorial Business, N.W.T., 17-209

Local Authorities Bd., Alta., 17-43

Locomotive
· Engineers, Int'l Brotherhood of, 11-11
· Vintage Locomotive Soc., 8-239

Logement, Régie du, Qué., 17-343

Logging industry (see also Forest/Forestry; Wood), 4-8

Loisir
· de la Chasse et de la Pêche, Min. du, 17-369
· Féd. du personnel des établissements de, 11-21

London (Ont.)
· Chamber of Commerce, 8-192
· Folk Arts Multicultural Coun., 8-185
· Orchestra, 8-282

Long Point Bird Observatory, 8-349
Long Term Care Facility, Inuvik, N.W.T., 17-209

Longshoremen's
· Assn., Int'l, 11-12
· and Warehousemen's Union, Int'l, 11-12

Loon, 1-2

Lotteries
· Corp.
· · Atlantic, 18-1
· · Interprovincial, 18-4
· · Ont., 17-299
· · Western Cda., 18-5
· Loteries et courses du Qué.,
· · Régie des, 17-374
· · Soc. des, (Loto-Québec), 17-362
· Man., Fdn., 17-140
· N.B., Commn., 17-153
· N.S., Commn., 17-237
· P.E.I., 17-325
· Sask., Dept. of Consumer & Commercial Affairs, 17-401

Low-Income Support Services, Ottawa Coun. for, 8-311

Lower
· Churchill Dev't Corp., Nfld., 17-192
· Red River Valley Water Commn., Man., 17-137

Loyal
· Ont. Group Interested in Computers (LOGIC), 8-200
· Orange Assn., 8-232

Loyola College, see Concordia University, 7-18

Lubicon Cree land claim, 1-3

Luge, 8-318

Lumber
· assns., 8-351
· · and Bldg. Materials Assn. of Ont., 8-205
· Dealers Co-operative (ILDC), Independent, 8-203
· pubns., 8-132

Lumbermen's Assn.,
· Cdn., 8-351
· Western Retail, 8-303

Lung Assns., Cdn., 8-268—269

Lutheran
· Church, 6-10
· College, Camrose, 7-17
· Coun. in Cda., 8-300
· Estonian Evangelical Lutheran Church, 6-9

Lyceum Club & Women's Art Assn. of Cda., 8-350

M

MIM Management Centre, 8-258

MISA Advisory Cttee., Ont., 17-278

M.S.I. Fdn., The, 8-302

M2/W2 Assn. (Christian Volunteers in Corrections), 8-311

Maccabi Cda., 8-234

Macdonald College of McGill University, 7-22

Machine Tool Distributor's Assn., Cdn., 8-348

Machinery
· assns., 8-222
· & Equipment Advisory Board, 16-107
· Institute, Prairie Agricultural, 18-5
· pubns., 8-130

Machinists & Aerospace Workers, Int'l Assn. of, 11-11

MacLaren Advertising, 1-2

Magazine Assn. of Cda. (Magazines Cda.), 8-295

Magazines
· Affaires +, 8-122
· ethnic press, 9-40—44
· pubns., 8-120—176
· · business & professional, 8-120—148
· · consumer, 8-148—165
· · farm, 8-165—167
· · religious, 8-168—169
· · scholarly, 8-169—172
· · university & school, 8-172—176

Magistrature du Qué., Cons. de la, 17-368

Mail, see Postal Information, 9-9—12

Main-d'oeuvre
· Cons. consultatif du travail et de la, 17-382
· et de la Sécurité du revenu, Min. de la, 17-371

Maintenance
· Assn. of Waterloo County Board of Education, Custodians and, 11-19
· of Way Employees, Brotherhood of, 11-10

Major League Baseball Players Assn., 11-13

Malayalam pubns., 9-43

Malta Services Bureau, 8-224

Maltese-Cdn. Soc. of Toronto, The, 8-224

Management
· Accountants, societies, 8-177
· assns. (see also specific topics), 8-257—258
· Bd. of,
· · Cabinet, Ont. 17-291
· · N.B., 17-151
· and Prof. Employees Soc. of B.C. Hydro, 11-23

Managers
· Cdn. Inst. of Certified Administrative, 8-257—258

Manitoba
· agriculture, 4-3, 17-104
· Chamber of Commerce, 8-192
· coat of arms, 17-103
· community colleges, 7-47
· courts, 17-142
· economy, 14-17, 17-104
· education, 7-4, -7, -8, -47
· election, 1-2
· forestry, 4-9, 17-104
· geography, 3-5, 17-104
· government, 1-1, 17-105—141
· Heritage Council, 17-118
· history, 17-103
· income statistics, 5-10
· judicial officers, 17-142
· labour legislation, 11-3, -6
· libraries & archives, 8-28—34
· manufacturing, 17-104
· map, 17-102
· minimum wage rate, 11-4
· mining, 17-104
· motor vehicle regulations, 10-8
· municipal gov't, 19-10
· municipalities, 19-11—13
· newspapers, 9-20—21
· population, 5-2, 17-104
· Provincial Exhibition of, 8-225
· radio stations, 9-46—47, -53
· superintendent of insurance, 13-20, 17-115
· Teachers' Society, 11-23
· television stations, 9-58
· universities,
· · Brandon Univ., 7-14
· · Manitoba, Univ. of, 7-23—24
· · Winnipeg, Univ. of, 7-44
· Vital Statistics, Admin. & Financial Div., Dept. of Community Services, 17-114

Manpower (see also Employment; Labour)
· and Income Security Dept., Que., 17-371

Manufacturers (see also specific categories)
· Assn., Cdn., 8-259

Manufacturing
· Alta., Bur. of Statistics, Treasury Dept., 17-51
· assns., 8-258—260
· B.C., Min. of International Business & Immigration, 17-83
· Cda., Dept. of Industry, Science & Technology, 16-87—92
· Centre, Que. Computer-Assisted, 17-358
· industry profile, Cdn., 14-10—11
· Man., Industry & Trade Div., Dept. of Industry, Trade & Technology, 17-131
· Nat'l Research Coun. Cda., Industry Dev't Office, Industrial Research Assistance Program, 16-139
· N.B., Dept. of Commerce & Technology, 17-151
· Nfld., Dept. of Development & Tourism, 17-178

· N.S.,
· · Business Capital Corp., 17-235
· · Dept. of Industry, Trade & Technology, 17-227
· Ont., Industry & Trade Expansion, Min. of Industry & Trade, Industry, 17-285
· P.E.I., Dept. of Industry, 17-319
· Que., Min. de l'Industrie et du Commerce, 17-363
· Sask., Dept. of Economic Development & Trade, 17-401

Map(s)
· Cda., 3-2—3
· · geological regions, 3-8
· · time zones, 2-21
· Libraries, Assn. of Cdn., 8-253
· provinces, see individual province
· territories, see individual territory

Maple Products, 4-6

Maple Syrup
· assns., 8-229
· statistics, 4-6

Mapping, Cdn. Inst. of Surveying and, 8-340

March of Dimes, 8-237

Marchand, Jean, 1-2

Marchés agricoles du Qué., Régie des, 17-345

Marconi Employees Union, 11-27

Marine
· Atlantic Inc., 16-123
· Engineering, Cdn. Inst. of, 8-221
· Officers' Union, Cdn., 11-18
· pubns., 8-144
· shipping assns., 8-308
· Underwriters, Cdn. Bd. of, 8-244
· Underwriters of B.C., Assn. of, 8-243
· Workers' Fed., 11-23
· Workers' Union, Ferry and, 11-22

Marionnette (UNIMA), Union internat. de la, 8-344

Mariposa Folk Fdn., 8-281

Maritime
· Command, Cdn. Armed Forces, 16-179
· Employers Assn., B.C., 8-248
· Fishermen's Union, 11-23
· Municipal Training & Development Bd., 18-3
· Premiers, Council of, 18-3
· Provinces
· · Education Foundation, 18-3
· · Higher Education Commn., 18-3
· Remote Sensing Cttee. (MRSC), 18-3
· Resource Management Service (MRMS), 18-3

Marketing
· Advertising Assn. of Cda., Specialty, 8-179
· assns., 8-260
· boards (See specific commodity)
· B.C. Bd., 17-69
· Coun., P.E.I., 17-316
· Dept. of Agriculture &, N.S., 17-218
· direct, assn., 8-260
· electronics, 8-219

Marketing (cont'd)
· photo, assn., 8-290
· pubns., 8-120
· Publishers List Owners Assn.,
    8-260

Marriage
· and Family Therapy (OAMFT), Ont.
    Assn. for, 8-311
· statistics, 5-6

Mars, 2-11—12

Masonry assns., 8-203, -204

Masons
· Ancient Free & Accepted, 8-231
· Royal Arch Masons of Cda., 8-232

MATCH—International Centre, 8-350

Mathematical
· pubns., 8-169
· Soc., Cdn., 8-305

Mayflower Handquilters Soc. of
    N.S., 8-207

Max Bell Fdn., 8-193

McDougall, Barbara, 1-4

McGill University, 7-24—26

McMaster University, 7-26

McMichael Collection, Ont., 17-270

McMurray Independent Oil Workers,
    11-23

Meat Council, Cdn., 8-228

Mechanical Contractors Assn. of
    Cda., 8-204

Médecins
· assns., 8-260—273
· de langue française du Cda.,
    Assoc. des, 8-260
· du Qué., Corp. prof. des, 8-265
· résidents et internes du Qué., Féd.
    des, 11-20

Media & Technology in Education,
    Assn. for, 8-211

Media
· Aboriginal Multi-, Soc. of Alta.,
    8-188
· Directors Councils, Cdn., 8-179
· Educational
· · Nfld. Teachers' Assn., Coun.,
    8-213
· · Sask. Assn. of, Specialists, 8-212

Mediation Board
· and Arbitration, (Petroleum &
    Natural Gas Act), B.C., 17-74
· Man., 17-111
· Provincial, Sask., 17-410

Mediawatch, 8-350

Medic-Alert Fdn., Cdn., 8-271

Medical (see also Health Care;
    specific disease or subject)
· Assistance, Int'l
· · IMA, 8-271
· · to Travellers, Assn. for, 8-345
· assns., 8-260—273
· · administrative, 8-262—265
· · condition, 8-266—270
· · disease, 8-266—270
· · education, 8-261—262
· · health & health promotion,
    8-270—273
· · illness, 8-266—270
· · profession, 8-262—265
· · research, 8-261—262, -301
· · technicians, 8-266

· and Biological Engineering Soc.,
    Cdn., 8-305
· Care Commn., Nfld., 17-193
· Council
· · of Cda., 8-265
· · Yukon, 17-436
· libraries, 8-254, -255, -261
· pubns., 8-137—139
· Registration Cttee., N.W.T., 17-206
· Research
· · Alta. Heritage Fdn. for, 8-301
· · Council of Cda., 16-138
· · Dystonia, Fdn., 8-262
· Services,
· · Associated, 8-260
· · Commn., B.C., 17-83

Medical Care Insurance
· Alta., Health Care Insce. Div.,
    Dept. of Health, 17-39
· B.C.,
· · Hospital Programs Div., Min. of
    Health, 17-82
· · Medical Services Commn., 17-83
· Cda., Health Services & Promotion
    Br., Health & Welfare Cda.,
    16-79
· Man. Health Services Commn.,
    17-128
· N.B., Insured Health Benefits Div.,
    Dept. of Health & Community
    Services, 17-154
· Nfld.,
· · Institutional Services Div., Dept.
    of Health, 17-184
· · Medical Care Commn., 17-193
· N.W.T., Health Insce. Admin.,
    Dept. of Health, 17-203
· N.S., Health Services & Insce.
    Commn., 17-226
· Ont., Health Insce. Div. (OHIP),
    Min. of Health, 17-283
· P.E.I., Hospital & Health Services
    Commn., 17-323
· Que., Régie de l'assurance
    maladie du Qué., 17-384
· Sask.,
· · Hospital Services Plan, Dept. of
    Health, 17-406
· · Medical Care Insce. Commn.,
    17-406

Medicine
· Academy of, 8-261
· Environmental, Defence and Civil
    Inst. of, 8-302
· health assns., 8-260—273
· History of, Cdn. Soc. for the, 8-238
· Prices Review Board, Patented,
    16-52
· sports
· · Cdn. Academy of, 8-312
· · Coun. of Cda., 8-314
· · and Safety Advisory Bd., Ont.,
    17-299

Mediterranean Inst., Cdn., 8-252

Meech Lake Accord, 1-2, 15-5,
    -24—26

Meetings, pubns., 8-127

Mellon Bank Cda., 13-12

Members
· of Parliament, list of, 16-20—23,
    -23—26

· of Provincial Legislatures, see
    Legislative Assemblies
· of the Senate, list of, 16-15—16

Memorial (see also Funeral)
· assns. & societies, 8-232—233
· University of Nfld., 7-26—27

Mennonite(s), 6-11
· Brethren Churches, Cdn. Conf. of,
    8-300
· of Cda., Conf. of, 8-300
· pubns., 8-168

Mental Health
· Advisory Council, Prov., Alta.,
    17-39
· Art Therapy Inst., Toronto, 8-184
· Assn., Cdn., 8-273
· Cttee., Que., 17-375
· Fdn., Ont., 17-284
· Ont. Assn. of Children's, Centres,
    8-274

Mental Patients, 1-3
· Assn., 8-274

Mentally Retarded, assns., 8-237

Merchant
· Seamen Compensation Bd., 16-97
· Service Guild, Cdn., 11-18

Merchants Assn. of Cda., Retail
    8-303

Mercury, 2-11

Mernick, Stephen, 1-4

Metal
· Arts Guild, 8-248
· Mining Assn., Que., 8-277
· Polishers, Buffers, Platers & Allied
    Workers Int'l Union, 11-13
· Trades, Mines & Chemical
    Products Democratic Fed.,
    11-20

Métallurgie
· Féd. de la, 11-20
· des mines et des produits
    chimiques, Féd. démocratique
    de la, 11-20

Metallurgy
· assns., 8-276—277
· pubn., 8-144

Metals
· Alta., Natural Resources Div., Alta.
    Research Coun., 17-53
· B.C., Min. of Energy, Mines &
    Petroleum Resources, 17-74
· Cda., Dept. of Energy, Mines &
    Resources, Cda. Centre for
    Mineral & Energy Technology
    (CANMET), 16-57—58
· Man., Mineral Div., Dept. of Energy
    & Mines, 17-122
· N.B., Minerals & Energy Div., Dept.
    of Natural Resources & Energy,
    17-159
· Nfld., Dept. of Mines, 17-186
· N.S., Mineral Resources, Dept. of
    Mines & Energy, 17-230
· Ont., Min. of Natural Resources,
    17-292
· Que., Min. de l'Énergie et des
    Ressources, 17-353
· Sask., Dept. of Energy & Mines,
    17-403

Metalworking
· industries, assns., 8-274—275
· pubns., 8-139

Meteorites, 2-14

Meteorological & Oceanographic Soc., Cdn., 8-305

Meteors, 2-14

Métis (*see also* Native Peoples)
· assns., 8-283, -284
· land claims settlements, 1-2, -3

Metric Assn., Cdn., 8-339

Metropolitan Area Planning Commn., N.S., 17-235

Microbiologists, Cdn. College of, 8-305

Microreproductions, Cdn. Inst. for Historical, 8-243

Microscopal Soc. of Cda., 8-306

Midwifery Task Force, 8-286

Migraine Fdn., 8-270

Migration, internal, 5-5—6

Military
· assns., 8-275—276
  .College
· · of Cda., Royal, 7-34
· · Royal Roads, 7-35
· · de St-Jean, Collège militaire royal, 7-53
· Colleges, 16-183
· Compound Bd., Fredericton, 17-161
· forces, *see* Cdn. Armed Forces, 16-179—183
· Inst., Royal Cdn., 8-276
· Museums of Cda., Org. of, 8-279
· pubns., 8-121, -139
· structure, 16-179—181
· veterans assns., 8-275—276

Milk
· assns., 8-208—209
· Bd., B.C., 17-70
· Control Bd., Sask., 17-398
· mktg. bds.,
· Man., 17-109
· · Nfld., 17-190
· · P.E.I., 17-317

Millers Assn., Cdn. Nat'l, 8-228

Millwork Manufacturers Assn., 8-351

Miltronics Employees Assn., 11-23

Mime Unlimited: The Company, 8-343

Mind Abuse, Council on, 8-199

Mine
· Mill & Smelter Workers Union, Sudbury, 11-27
· Occupational Health & Safety Bd., N.W.T., 17-206
· Workers of America, United, 11-14

Mineral
· Analysts, Cdn., 8-277
· and Energy Technology, Cda. Centre for, (CANMET), 16-57—58
· industry, Cdn., 4-14—17
· · economic outlook, 4-15—17
· · prices & trends, 4-15
· production
· · leading (minerals), 4-16
· · sectors of production, 4-14—15
· Resources Ltd., Man., 17-123
· Rights, Alta., 17-59

Mineralogical Assn. of Cda., 8-277

Minerals in Canada, 14-9

Mines
· assns., 8-276—277
· · accident prevention, 8-304
· depts.
· · Nfld. 17-186
· · N.S., and Energy, 17-230
· · Yukon, and Small Business, 17-433

Miniature Enthusiasts
· (NAME), Nat'l Assn. of, 8-207
· of Toronto, 8-207

Minimum Wage
· Bd./Commn.
· · Man., 17-134
· · N.B., 17-157
· · N.S., 17-228
· · Sask., 17-408
· rates across Cda., 11-4

Mining
· Alta., Energy Resources Conservation Bd., 17-33
· assns., 8-276—277
· B.C., Min. of Energy, Mines & Petroleum Resources, 17-74
· Cda. Centre for Mineral & Energy Technology (CANMET), 16-57—58
· Man.,
· · Minerals Div., Dept. of Energy & Mines, 17-122
· · Mining Bd., 17-123
· N.B., Mines & Energy Div., Dept. of Natural Resources & Energy, 17-159
· Nfld., Dept. of Mines, 17-186
· N.S., Dept. of Mines & Energy, 17-230
· Ont.,
· · Mining & Lands Commr., 17-293
· · Mining Health & Safety Br., Min. of Labour, 17-288
· · Min. of Mines, 17-294
· P.E.I., Energy Br., Dept. of Energy & Forestry, 17-318
· pubns., 8-140
· Que., Min. de l'Énergie et des Ressources, 17-353
· recorders, Ont., 17-311
· Sask., CAMECO, 17-419

Ministries of State, Federal Government Departments and, 16-32—128

Mink Breeders Assn., Cda., 8-233

Mint, Royal Cdn., 16-117—118

Mirabel Ltd., Cda. Lands Co., 16-129

Miramichi Trades & Labour Union, 11-23

Missionary Fellowship, Overseas, 6-12—13

Missions abroad, Cdn. permanent, 16-185—186

Mitsubishi Bank of Cda., 13-12

Mitsui Bank of Cda., 13-12

Model
· Aeronautics Assn. of Cda., 8-239
· Soldier Soc., Ont., 8-239

Modern Pentathlon, assns., 8-328

Molders' & Allied Workers' Union, Int'l, 11-12

Moldmakers (WAMM), Windsor Assn. of, 8-260

Molson Family Fdn., The, 8-193

Monarchist League of Cda., 8-287

Moncton, Université de, 7-28

Monetary system, 13-5—6

Money Soc., Cdn. Paper, 8-239

Montessori Inst., Toronto, 8-215

Montreal
· Chamber of Commerce, 8-191
· City & District Savings Bank, *see* Laurentian Bank of Cda., 13-10
· Convention & Tourism Bur., Greater, 8-345
· Exchange, 13-25—28
· Italian Chamber of Commerce, 8-230
· libraries & archives, 8-85—92
· métro., Centre de services sociaux du, 8-310
· newspapers, 1-1, 9-34—35
· Place des Arts de, Soc. de la, 17-340
· radio stations, 9-50—51, -56
· television stations, 9-59
· Université de, 7-28—29

Moon, 2-11
· phases of, 2-17—19

Morgan Bank of Cda., 13-12

Mormons, *see* The Church of Jesus Christ of Latter-day Saints, 6-8

Mortgage
· Brokers Assn., Ont., 8-226
· companies, 13-17
· Corp., Ont., 17-281
· and Housing Corp.
· · Alta., 17-41
· · Cda., 16-129—130
· rates, bond yield averages & conventional, 13-35

Motel(s)
· assns., 8-241
· pubn., 8-135

Mothercraft, societies, 8-196

Motion picture(s)
· Appeal Bd., B.C., 17-93
· assns., 8-153, -197—198
· Industries Assn., Alta., 8-197
· pubns., 8-126

Motor
· Carrier
· · Bd., N.B., 17-162
· · Commn., B.C., 17-93
· · Dealers, assns., 8-185—187
· Transport
· · assns., 8-346, -347
· · Bds.: Alta., 17-50; Man., 17-130; Yukon, 17-433
· · Industrial Relations Bur. of Ont., 8-249
· · trucks & buses, pubns., 8-146
· Vehicle
· · Manufacturers' Assn., 8-347
· · Regulations, 10-1—2; (table) 10-8—9

Motorcycle
· Assn.
· · B.C., 8-296
· · Cdn., 8-297
· and Moped Industry Coun., 8-347
· pubns., 8-149

Motorsport B.C., 8-298

Mount Allison University, 7-29

Mount Saint Vincent University, 7-29

Mountain(s)
· in Cda., 3-7
· Clubs of B.C., Fed. of, 8-328

Mountaineering assns., 8-328

Movers assns., 8-346, -347

Mulroney, Brian, 1-1, -2, -3, -4

Multicultural
· Advisory Coun., Sask., 17-415
· assns., 8-283
· Commn., Alta., 17-28
· Education, Cdn. Coun. for, and
    Intercultural, 8-212
· Health Coalition, 8-272
· History Soc. of Ont., 8-238
· pubns., 9-43
· Theatre Assn., Nat'l 8-343

Multiculturalism
· Advisory Council Sec't, Cdn.,
    16-110
· Alta., Dept. of Culture and, 17-26
· assns., 8-277
· Minister of State for, see Secretary
    of State Dept., 16-107—110
· Ont. Advisory Coun. on, and
    Citizenship, 17-261
· pubns., 9-40—44

Multiple
· Dwelling Standards Assn., 8-340
· Sclerosis Soc. of Cda., 8-270

Municipal
· Assessors of Ont., Inst. of, 8-296
· assns., 8-277—278
· boards,
· · Man., 17-136
· · N.S., 17-237
· · Ont., 17-261
· · Sask., 17-423
· Capital Borrowing Bd., N.B.,
    17-159
· Employees' Benefits Bd., Man.,
    17-136
· Engineers Assn., 8-222
· financing corps.,
· · Alta., 17-51
· · N.B., 17-153
· · N.S., 17-237
· · Sask., 17-404
· governments, forms of, 19-1—43
· Personnel Assn., Ont., 8-278
· Police Authorities, 8-251
· Social Services Assn., Ont., 8-311

Municipal Affairs depts.
· Alta., 17-40
· B.C., 17-87
· Man., 17-135
· N.B., 17-158
· Nfld., 17-187
· N.W.T., 17-203
· N.S., 17-230
· Ont., 17-292
· P.E.I., Dept. of Community &
    Cultural Affairs, 17-318
· Que., 17-341
· Sask., 17-418, -419

Municipale du Qué., Comm., 17-342

Municipalities, see 19-1—43
· assns., 8-277-278
· unions, 8-278

Muscular Dystrophy Assn. of Cda.,
    8-270

Museum(s)/Musée(s)
· d'art contemporain, 17-339
· Assistance Programmes, 16-40
· assns., 8-278—279
· Bata Shoe, Fdn., 8-229
· of Cda., Nat'l, 16-48—50
· Cdn. Museum of Civilization, 16-49
· de la civilisation, 17-339
· Culture Div., Min. of Culture &
    Communications, Ont., 17-270
· Glenbow, 8-111
· & Heritage Fdn., P.E.I., 17-325
· Man. Museum of Man & Nature,
    17-118
· N.B. Museum, 17-161
· Nfld. Museum, Historic Resources
    Div., Dept. of Culture,
    Recreation & Youth, 17-177
· pubns., 8-143
· du Qué., 17-339
· qué., La Soc. des, 8-279
· Restoration Service, 8-115
· Royal Ont., 17-273
· Sask. Western Development,
    17-415

Mushroom
· Growers' Assn., Cdn., 8-180
· Mktg. Bd., B.C., 17-70

Music
· assns., 8-279—283
· composers, 8-206, -280—282
· copyright, assns., 8-206
· Libraries, Cdn. Assn. of, 8-253
· pubns., 8-140, -158
· Publishers Assn., Cdn., 8-295
· teachers assns., 8-217, -280, -282

Musical
· Reproduction Rights Agency,
    Cdn., 8-206
· Theatre Writers, Guild of Cdn.,
    8-352

Musicians
· American Fed. of, of the U.S. &
    Cda., 11-9
· assns., 8-279—283

Muslim
· Communities of Cda., Coun. of,
    6-9
· Ottawa, Assn., 8-301

Mustard seed statistics, 4-7

N

NATO, 16-184

Narcolepsy, Cdn. Assn. for, 8-267

National
· Arts Centre, 8-343, 16-45—46
· · Orchestra, 8-281
· Bank of Cda./Banque Nationale
    du Cda, 13-9—10
· Training Act, 7-9

Nationality, Dual, 16-177

Nations, Commonwealth of,
    16-186—189

Native (see also Indian; Inuit; Métis)
· Affairs
· · Directorate, Ont., 17-303
· · Secretariat, B.C., 17-96

· assns., 8-283—284
· · broadcasting assns., 8-188, -189
· Brotherhood of B.C., 11-24
· Economic Dev't Advisory Bd.,
    16-92
· education, 7-5—6
· land claims settlements, 1-2, -3
· rights, 15-7, -19, -20
· Services Unit, Alta. Dept. of
    Municipal Affairs, 17-41

Native Peoples (see also Indian;
    Inuit; Métis)
· assns., 8-283—284
· pubn., 9-43
· Secrétariat aux Affaires
    autochtones, 17-333

Natural gas, 4-19
· Assn., Ont., 8-288

Natural Healing, Cdn. College of,
    8-262

Natural History, socs., 8-284

Natural products mktg. councils
· Man., 17-108
· N.S., 17-218
· Sask., 17-398

Natural resources
· Alta.,
· · Dept. of Environment, 17-34
· · Natural Resources Div., Alta.
        Research Coun., 17-53
· Cda.,
· · Energy, Mines & Resources
        Dept., 16-56—65
· · Environment, Dept. of the,
        16-65—68
· Constitutional provisions, 15-7,
    -21—22
· Co-ordinating Coun., Alta., 17-35
· depts.,
· · B.C., 17-74
· · Man., 17-136
· · N.B., 17-159
· · Ont., 17-292
· · Que., 17-353
· energy industry, 4-17—20
· fisheries industry, 4-11—13
· forestry industry, 4-7—11
· fur industry, 4-14
· mineral industry, 4-14—17
· Nfld.,
· · Dept. of Energy, 17-181
· · Dept. of Environment & Lands,
        17-181
· · Dept. of Forestry, 17-183
· · Dept. of Mines, 17-186
· P.E.I., Energy Br., Dept. of Energy
    & Forestry, 17-318
· Que., Min. de l'Énergie et des
    Ressources, 17-353
· Sask.,
· · Dept. of Energy & Mines, 17-403
· · Dept. of Parks, Recreation &
        Culture, 17-413

Natural Sciences
· and Engineering Research Coun.,
    Cda., 16-140
· Nat'l Museum of, 16-48—49

Naturalists
· assns., 8-284
· · Young Naturalist Fdn., 8-354

Nature
· assns., 8-284
· pubns., 8-158—159

Naval
· Assn., Royal Cdn., 8-276
· Benevolent Fund, Royal Cdn., 8-194
· Reserve, 16-179

Navigation System, Air, 10-16

Navy, see Maritime Command, 16-179
· Army, and Air Force Veterans in Cda., 8-275
· League of Cda., 8-276

Nazarene, Church of the, 6-8

Negotiation, Bd. of, Ont., 17-259
· (Environment), 17-277

Neighbourhood Houses of Greater Vancouver, Assn. of, 8-309

Neptune, 2-13

Neptune Theatre Foundation, 8-343

Netball assns., 8-328

Neurological assns., 8-264

Neurotics Anonymous, 8-274

New Age Int'l Fdn., 8-194

New Brunswick
· agriculture, 4-3, 17-146
· archives, 17-161
· coat of arms, 17-145
· community colleges, 7-48
· courts, 17-168
· economy, 14-17, 17-146
· education, 7-4, -7, -8, -48
· fisheries, 17-146
· forestry, 4-9, 17-146
· geography, 3-4, 17-145
· government, 17-147
· history, 17-145
· income statistics, 5-10
· information serv., 17-147
· judicial officers, 17-168
· labour legislation, 11-3, -6
· libraries & archives, 8-34—38
· manufacturing, 17-146
· map, 17-144
· minimum wage rate, 11-4
· mining, 17-146
· motor vehicle regulations, 10-8
· municipal gov't, 19-13
· municipalities, 19-14—15
· newspapers, 1-3, 9-21—22
· population, 5-2, 17-145, -144
· radio stations, 9-47, -53
· superintendent of insurance, 13-20
· television stations, 9-58
· universities,
· · Moncton, Univ. de, 7-28
· · Mount Allison Univ., 7-29
· · N.B., Univ. of, 7-29—30
· · St. Thomas Univ., 7-36
· Vital Statistics, Dept. of Health & Community Servs., 17-154

New Democratic Party, 8-291—292
· B.C., Offices, 17-106
· Leader, Office of the, 16-19
· N.S., Offices, 17-217

New Play Centre, 8-343

Newfoundland
· agriculture, 4-3

· Arts & Culture Centre, 8-342
· coat of arms, 17-171
· community colleges, 7-48
· courts, 17-194
· economy, 14-17—18, 17-172
· education, 7-4, -7, -8, -48
· educational institutes, 7-48
· fishing, 17-172
· forestry, 4-9, 17-172
· geography, 3-4, 17-171
· government, 17-173
· history, 17-171
· hydro, 17-172
· income statistics, 5-10
· judicial officers, 17-194
· labour legislation, 11-3, -6
· libraries & archives, 8-38—40
· map, 17-170
· minimum wage rate, 11-4
· mining, 17-172
· motor vehicle & traffic regulations, 10-8
· municipal government, 19-15—16
· municipalities, 19-16—18
· newspapers, 9-22
· oil & gas, 17-172
· population, 5-2, 17-171, -172
· radio stations, 9-47—48, -54
· rail freight service, 1-2
· superintendent of insurance, 13-20
· television stations, 9-58
· University of, Memorial, 7-26—27
· Vital Statistics, Dept. of Health, 17-184

Newfoundland & Labrador
· Computer Services Ltd., 17-192
· Construction Assn., 8-204
· Hydro, 17-192
· Labrador Affairs, Dept. of, Nfld., 17-186

News
· Cda., 8-120
· pubn., 8-159

Newsletter Assn. (Cdn. Chapter), The, 8-295

Newspaper(s) (see also Ethnic Press, 9-40—44), 1-1, -3, 9-13—39
· Advertising Executive Assn., 8-179
· assns., 8-293, -294, -295
· Children's, Dynamite Write, 8-150
· Guild, Cdn. Region, 11-13
· Marketing Bur., 8-260

Niagara
· Escarpment Commn., 17-292
· Falls, Cda. Visitor & Convention Bureau, 8-345
· Institute, The, 8-211
· & Midwestern Ont. Travel Assn., 8-345
· Parks Commn., Ont., 17-298
· Tourist Coun., Region, 8-345

Nickel Dev't Inst., 8-275

Niska Wildlife Fdn., 8-349

Nobel Peace Prize, 1-3

Non-Smokers' Rights Assn., 8-199

Normes du travail, Commn. des, 17-372

North Atlantic
· Council, 16-184

· Treaty Organization, (NATO), 16-184

North Okanagan Naturalists' Club, 8-284

North Sask. Electric Ltd., Sask. Power Corp., 17-417

North Shore Construction Union Inc., 11-27

North York Symphony Assn., 8-281

Northern
· Affairs
· · Man. Dept. of, 17-137
· · Secretariat, Sask., 17-412
· · Yukon, Dept. of Indian and, 17-439
· Dev't,
· · Dept. of Rural, Agricultural and, Nfld., 17-188
· · Ont.: Min. of, 17-294; Dev't Corp., 17-287
· · Studies, Boreal Inst. for, 8-180

Northland Transportation Commn., Ont., 17-294

Northwest Territories
· Act, 17-199
· agriculture, 4-4, 17-198
· coat of arms, 17-197
· college, 7-48
· courts, 17-211
· economy, 17-198
· education, 7-4, -7, -48
· Exec. Coun. Secretariat, 17-199
· Federal Govt. Directory, 17-210
· fishing & hunting, 17-198
· forestry, 4-9, 17-198
· geography, 3-6, 17-197
· government, 17-199
· · regional offices, 17-200
· history, 17-197
· judicial officers, 17-211
· labour legislation, 11-3, -7
· libraries & archives, 8-40—41
· map, 17-196
· minimum wage rate, 11-4
· mining, 17-198
· motor vehicle regulations, 10-8
· municipal gov't, 19-18
· municipalities, 19-18—19
· newspapers, 9-22
· oil & gas, 17-198
· population, 5-2, 17-197, -198
· radio stations, 9-48, -54
· superintendent of insurance, 13-20
· television stations, 9-58

Northwestern Ont. Municipal Assn., 8-278

Notwithstanding clause, 1-4, 15-6, -19

Novaco Ltd., N.S., 17-239

Nova Scotia
· agriculture, 4-3, 17-214
· coat of arms, 17-213
· College of Art & Design, 7-30
· courts, 17-242
· economy, 14-18, 17-214
· education, 7-4, -7, -8, -10, -48—49
· educational institutes, 7-48
· election, 1-3
· fishing, 17-214

Nova Scotia (cont'd)
· forestry, 4-9, 17-214
· geography, 3-4, 17-213
· government, 17-215
· history, 17-213
· Hospital, 17-236
· income statistics, 5-10
· judicial officials, 17-242
· labour legislation, 11-3, -7
· libraries & archives, 8-42—45
· map, 17-212
· minimum wage rate, 11-4
· mining & energy, 17-214
· motor vehicle regulations, 10-8
· municipal gov't, 19-19
· municipalities, 19-20—21
· newspapers, 9-22—23
· population, 5-2, 17-213, -214
· radio stations, 9-48, -54
· superintendent of insurance, 13-20
· television stations, 9-58
· universities & colleges,
· · Acadia Univ., 7-12
· · Cape Breton, Univ. College of,
    7-17
· · Dalhousie Univ., 7-19
· · King's College, Univ. of, 7-20
· · Mount Saint Vincent Univ., 7-29
· · N.S. College of Art & Design,
    7-30
· · Ste-Anne, Univ., 7-35
· · St. Francis Xavier Univ., 7-35—36
· · St. Mary's Univ., 7-36
· · Technical Univ. of N.S., 7-38
· vocational
· · adult training centres, (AVTC),
    7-49
· · regional schools, (RVS), 7-49

Novelty & Production Workers, Int'l
    Union of Allied, 11-12

Nuclear Energy (see also Atomic
    Energy)
· assns., 8-219—220
· Eldorado Nuclear Ltd., 16-129
· industry, 4-20
· insurance assn., 8-245
· N.B. Power, 17-166
· N.S., Dept. of Mines & Energy,
    17-230
· Ont. Hydro, 17-276

Numismatic Assn., Cdn., 8-239

Nursery Trades (see also Florists;
    Landscape)
· assns., 8-284—285
· pubns., 8-134
· statistics, 4-6

Nurses
· Aides, Prof. Alliance of Quebec,
    11-16
· Aids Unions, Quebec Fed. of,
    11-21
· of Alta., United, 11-29
· assns., 8-285—286
· · of Alberta, Staff, 11-27
· · Ont., 11-25
· · Man. Org. of, 11-23
· dental, 8-210
· Union
· · N.B., 11-24

· · Nfld. & Labrador, 11-24
· · N.S., 11-24
· · P.E.I., 11-25
· · Sask., 11-26

Nursing
· Assistants, Registered
· · Alta. Assn., 11-15
· · Ont. Assn., 8-285
· assns., 8-285—286
· pubns., 8-140
· Research, Alta. Fdn. for, 17-16

Nutritional Sciences, Cdn. Soc. for,
    8-262

O

'O Canada', 2-2

OISE, 7-30

ORADIO, 8-187

Obstetricians & Gynaecologists of
    Cda., Soc. of, 8-265

Occupational
· Health Nurses Assn., Ont., 8-285
· Medical Assn. of Cda., 8-265
· Therapists, Cdn. Assn. of, 8-263

Occupational Health & Safety
· Alta., Dept. of Occupational Health
    & Safety, 17-43
· B.C., Occupational Health & Safety
    Div., Workers' Compensation
    Bd., 17-86
· Cdn. Centre for, 8-304, 16-132
· Commn.,
· · N.B., 17-166
· · Que., 17-381
· Coun.,
· · Alta., 17-39
· · Ont., 17-289
· · P.E.I., 17-321
· Man., Dept. of Environment &
    Workplace Safety & Health,
    17-123
· Nfld., Occupational Health &
    Safety Div., Dept. of Labour,
    17-185
· N.W.T., Bd., Mine, 17-206
· N.S., Occupational Health & Safety
    Div., Dept. of Labour, 17-227
· Ont., Min. of Labour, Occupational
    Health & Safety Div., 17-288
· Policy, Communications &
    Information Br., Health &
    Welfare Cda., 16-77
· P.E.I., Workers Compensation Bd.,
    17-320
· pubns., 8-141
· Que., Commn de la santé et de la
    sécurité du travail, 17-381
· Sask., Occupational Health &
    Safety Br., Dept. of Human
    Resources, Labour &
    Employment, 17-408

Occupational Training
· Alta., Training & Employment
    Services Div., Dept. of Career
    Dev't & Employment, 17-24
· B.C., Job Training Br., Min. of
    Advanced Education & Job
    Training, 17-66

· Cda.,
· · Public Affairs, Employment &
    Immigration Cda., 16-54
· · Training Programs Br., Public
    Service Commn., 16-101
· Man., Post-Secondary Adult,
    Continuing Education Div.,
    Dept. of Education, 17-119
· N.B., Community Colleges, Dept.
    of Advanced Education &
    Training, 17-149
· Nfld., Industrial Training Div.,
    Dept. of Career Dev't &
    Advanced Studies, 17-176
· N.S., Dept. of Advanced Education
    & Job Training, 17-217
· Ont., Min. of Skills Dev't, 17-296
· P.E.I., Apprenticeship & Ind.
    Training, Dept. of Industry,
    17-319
· Que.,
· · Min. de l'Enseignement
    supérieur et de la Science,
    17-358
· · Min. de la Main-d'oeuvre et de la
    Sécurité du revenu, 17-371
· Sask.,
· · Apprenticeship & Trade
    Certification, Dept. of
    Education, 17-402
· · New Careers Corp., 17-414

Oceanographic Soc., Cdn.
    Meteorological and, 8-305

Oddfellows, Independent Order of,
    8-231

Office
· Employees Union, Cdn., 11-27
· equipment, pubns., 8-141
· Machine Dealers Assn., Cdn.,
    8-303
· Products Assn. (COPA), Cdn.,
    8-259
· and Professional Employees Int'l
    Union, 11-13

Official Languages, (see also
    Bilingualism)
· Act, 1-2
· bilingual legislation, 1-1, -2
· Commissioner of, 16-134
· rights, 15-6, -18
· and Translation, Sec. of State
    Dept., 16-109

Official Opposition, Office of the
    Leader, 16-18

Offshore Oil & Gas Bd., Cda.-N.S.,
    16-62

Oil (see also Petroleum)
· assns., 8-201, -288
· crude, 4-18
· exploration, 1-2
· and Natural Gas Conservation Bd.,
    Man., 17-123
· pubns., 8-141
· Sands, 17-32
· upgrader, Lloydminster, 1-3
· Workers,
· · Atlantic, 11-17
· · of Cda., United, 11-28

Oil & Natural Gas
· Alta., Dept. of Energy, 17-31
· B.C., Min. of Energy, Mines & Petroleum Resources, 17-74
· Cda. Oil & Gas Lands Administration, 16-61, -84, 17-204
· Man., Energy Div., Dept. of Energy & Mines, 17-122
· N.B., Mines & Energy Div., Dept. of Natural Resources & Energy, 17-159
· Nfld., Dept. of Energy, 17-181
· N.S., Energy Resources Div., Dept. of Mines & Energy, 17-230
· Ont., Mines & Minerals Div., Min. of Northern Dev't & Mines, 17-294
· P.E.I., Energy Br., Dept. of Energy & Forestry, 17-318
· Que., Min. de l'Énergie et des Ressources, 17-353
· Sask., Dept. of Energy & Mines, 17-403

Oilwell Drilling Contractors, Cdn. Assn. of, 8-288

Okanagan Symphony Soc., 8-281

Old
· Fort William Advisory Cttee., 17-298
· Order Amish Church, 6-11
· Strathcona Fdn., 8-238

Olympics
· Assn., Cdn., 8-233
· Cdn. Special, 8-315
· Calgary winter games, 1-1
· Seoul summer games, 1-3
· Trust of Cda., 8-313

Ombudsmen
· Alta., 12-6, 17-15
· B.C., 12-6, 17-65
· Man., 12-6, 17-107
· N.B., 12-6, 17-149
· Nfld., 12-6, 17-175
· N.S., 12-6, 17-217
· Ont., 12-6, 17-253
· Que., 12-6, 17-334
· Sask., 12-6, 17-397

Omnichild Fdn. Inc., 8-197

ON OUR OWN: Ont. Patients' Self-Help Assn., 8-272

One Parent Families Assn. of Cda., 8-286

Ontario
· agriculture, 4-3, 17-248
· Chamber of Commerce, 8-192
· coat of arms, 17-247
· College of Art, 7-30—31
· community colleges, 7-49—50
· courts, 17-304
· economy, 14-18, 17-248
· education, 7-4, -8, -9, -10, -49—50
· forestry, 4-9, 17-248
· geography, 3-5, 17-247
· government, 17-249
· Hydro Professional & Admin. Employees, Soc. of, 11-26
· income statistics, 5-10
· judicial officers, 17-304

· labour legislation, 11-3, -7
· libraries & archives, 8-45—79
· loon as official bird, 1-2
· manufacturing, 17-248
· map, 17-246
· mining, 17-248
· minimum wage rate, 11-4
· motor vehicle regulations, 10-8
· municipal gov't, 19-21—22
· municipalities, 19-22—29
· newspapers, 9-23—32
· Place Corp., 17-299
· population, 5-2, 17-247
· Provincial Police, 12-9—10, 17-297
· radio stations, 9-48—50, -54—56
· superintendent of insurance, 13-20
· television stations, 9-58—59
· universities & colleges,
· · Brock Univ., 7-15—16
· · Carleton Univ., 7-17—18
· · Dominicain, collège, 7-19
· · Guelph, Univ. of, 7-19—20
· · Lakehead Univ., 7-20
· · Laurentian Univ., 7-21
· · McMaster Univ., 7-26
· · OISE, 7-30
· · Ont. College of Art, 7-30—31
· · Ottawa, Univ. of, 7-31—32
· · Queen's Univ., 7-33
· · Royal Military College of Cda., 7-34
· · Ryerson Polytechnical Inst., 7-35
· · Toronto, Univ. of, 7-38—40
· · Trent Univ., 7-40
· · Waterloo, Univ. of, 7-41—42
· · Western Ont., Univ. of, 7-42—43
· · Wilfrid Laurier Univ., 7-43
· · Windsor, Univ. of, 7-43
· · York Univ., 7-44—45
· vital statistics, Registrar General's Office, 17-266

Open Interest in Contracts, Trading Volume and, 13-33

Opera assns., 8-281

Operation
· Dismantle, 8-247
· Eyesight Universal, 8-311

Operational Research Soc., Cdn., 8-301

Operative Plasterers' & Cement Masons' Int'l Assn. of the U.S. & Cda., 11-13

Ophthalmological Soc., Cdn., 8-264

Opportunity Company, Alta., 17-30

Opposition Leaders
· Alta., 17-15
· B.C., 17-65
· federal, 16-18
· Man., 17-106
· Nfld., 17-175
· N.S., 17-217
· Ont., 17-253
· P.E.I., 17-316
· Que., 17-334
· Sask., 17-397
· Yukon, 17-432

Opticians, Cdn. Guild of Dispensing, 8-264

Optometrists assns., 8-263, -265

Optometry of Cda., Assn. of Schools of, 8-217

Oral & Maxillofacial Surgeons, Ont. Soc. of, 8-210

Orange Headquarters, Cdn., 8-287

Orchestras, 8-280—283

Order-in-Council Review Bd., B.C., 17-93

Organ Donors Cda., 8-261

Organic Growers, Cdn., 8-240

Organists, Royal Cdn. College of, 8-282

Organization
· of American States, 16-186
· for Economic Co-operation & Development, 16-186

Orienteering assns., 8-329

Ornamental Plant Fdn., Cdn., 8-240

Orthodox Churches, 6-11—12

Orthopaedic assns., 8-264, 8-266

Oshawa Symphony Orch., 8-282

Osteopathic assns., 8-272, -273

Osteoporosis Soc. of Cda., 8-270

Otolaryngology, Cdn. Soc. of, 8-265

Ottawa
· libraries & archives, 8-57—62
· newspapers, 9-28—29
· radio stations, 9-49, -55
· Symphony Orch., 8-282
· television stations, 9-58
· Univ. of, 7-31—32

Ottawa-Carleton
· Board of Trade, 8-192
· Safety Coun., 8-304
· Social Planning Coun. of, 8-308

Ouimet, J. Alphonse, 1-4

Outdoor(s)
· Advertising Assn. of Cda., 8-179
· Power Equipment Assn., Cdn., 8-222
· Recreation Coun. of B.C., 8-299
· Unlittered, 8-202

Outward Bound, 8-299

Overeaters Anonymous, 8-273

Overseas
· Bank (Cda.), United, 13-14
· Missionary Fellowship, 6-12—13
· Telecommunications Union, Cdn., 11-18
· Union Bank of Singapore, 13-13

OXFAM Cda., 8-194

Oyster
· Growers' Assn., B.C., 8-228
· Mktg. Bd., B.C., 17-70

P

PACT Communications Centre, 8-343

PCBs phase-out, 1-3

PLAST, 8-354

PLURA, 8-308

Pacific
· Ballet Theatre Society, 8-209
· Cinémathèque Pacifique, 8-198
· coastal waters, 3-9
· fisheries, 4-12
· Lumber Inspection Bureau, 8-351
· Nat'l Exhibition, 17-80

Packaging
. assn. of Cda., 8-286
. pubns., 8-141

Paddling Assn., Man., 8-320

Paediatric assns., 8-264

Paint
. assns., 8-286
. pubns., 8-141

Painters
. and Allied Trades
. . Int'l Brotherhood of, 11-11
. . Nat'l Assn. of, 11-16
. in Water Colour, Cdn. Soc. of,
    8-184

Painting
. contractors, assns., 8-286
. & decorating, assns., 8-246

Pakistani pubn., 9-43

Palais des congrès de Montréal,
    Soc. du, 17-378

Pallet Council, Cdn., 8-228

Palomino Horse Assn., Cdn., 8-183

Pan-Macedonian Assn., 8-224

Paper
. Box Mfrs. Assn., Cdn., 8-286
. Pulp and, Assn., Cdn., 8-351
. Trade Assn., Cdn., 8-351

Paperworkers
. Int'l Union, United, 11-14
. Union, Cdn., 11-18

Papier et de la forêt, Féd. des
    travailleurs du, 11-21

Parachuting assns., 8-329

Paraplegic Assn., Cdn., 8-236

Parc industriel
. du Centre du Qué., Soc. du,
    17-365
. et commercial aéroportuaire de
    Mirabel, Soc. du, 17-365

Parent(s)
. assns., 8-286—287
. Co-operative Preschools Int'l,
    8-215
. Finders Inc., 8-311
. for French, Cdn., 8-283
. pubns., 8-150

Paribas Bank of Cda., 13-13

Parkinson
. Disease Assn., B.C., 8-267
. Fdn. of Cda., 8-270

Park(s)
. Alta., Dept. of Recreation & Parks,
    17-45
. assns., 8-287
. B.C., Recreation & Sport Br., Min.
    of Municipal Affairs, Recreation
    & Culture, 17-90
. Canada, 16-67
. dept., B.C., 17-89
. Man., Dept. of Natural Resources,
    Parks Br., 17-137
. N.B., Sport & Recreation, Dept. of
    Tourism, Recreation & Heritage,
    17-161
. Nfld., Parks Div., Dept. of Culture,
    Recreation & Youth, 17-177
. N.S., Sport & Recreation Commn.,
    17-239
. Ont., Outdoor Recreation Group,
    Min. of Natural Resources,
    17-293

. P.E.I., Dept. of Tourism & Parks,
    17-321
. pubns., 8-143
. Que., Min. du Loisir, de la Chasse
    et de la Pêche, 17-369
. Sask., Parks Br., Dept. of Parks,
    Recreation & Culture, 17-413
. and Wildlife Fdn., Recreation,
    Alta., 17-46
. Yukon, Parks, Resources &
    Regional Planning Br., Dept. of
    Renewable Resources, 17-437

Parliament
. of Canada, 15-9—13; 16-13—27
. . procedures, 15-12—13
. Library of, 16-17

Parliament, protocol, Parliamentary
    procedures
. Alta., Clerk of the Legislative
    Assembly, 17-14
. B.C., Clerk of the Legislative
    Assembly, 17-64
. Canada,
. . Clerk of the House of Commons,
    16-17
. . Clerk of the Senate, 16-15
. Man., Clerk of the Legislative
    Assembly, 17-106
. N.B., Clerk of the Legislative
    Assembly, 17-147
. Nfld., Clerk of the House, 17-174
. N.W.T., Clerk of the Legislative
    Assembly, 17-201
. N.S., Chief Clerk of the House,
    17-216
. Ont., Clerk of the House, 17-250
. P.E.I., Clerk of the Legislative
    Assembly, 17-315
. Que., Secrétaire gén. de
    l'Assemblée nationale, 17-332
. Sask., Clerk of the Assembly,
    17-395
. Yukon, Clerk of the Legislative
    Assembly, 17-432

Parliamentary
. Centre for Foreign Affairs &
    Foreign Trade, 8-230
. Committees, 16-26
. Government, 15-2—3
. Secretaries, 16-20

Parole (see also Prisons)
. Alta., Correctional Services Div.,
    Dept. of Solicitor General, 17-47
. boards,
. . B.C., 17-92
. . Nat'l, 12-13, 16-112—113
. . N.B., 17-160
. . Ont., 17-268
. Comm., Que., 17-377
. Nfld., Adult Corrections, Dept. of
    Justice, 17-185
. Sask., Corrections Div., Dept. of
    Justice, 17-409

Parti québécois, 8-292

Participaction, 8-299

Participation, Dept. of Public, Sask.,
    17-418

Particleboard Assn., Cdn., 8-351

Party leaders & standings (federal),
    16-18

Passport(s)
. Bureau, 16-70
. Cdn., information, 16-175

Pastoral Education, Cdn. Assn. for,
    8-217

Patented Medicine Prices Review
    Board, 16-52

Patents
. assns., 8-206
. and Copyright, Bureau of Corp.
    Affairs, Consumer & Corporate
    Affairs Cda., 16-52
. and Development Ltd., Cdn.,
    16-134

Pathologists, Cdn. Assn. of, 8-264

Patients
. Review Bd., B.C. Order-in-Council,
    17-93
. Rights Assn., 8-261
. Self-Help Assn., Ont., see ON OUR
    OWN, 8-272

Patriotic assns., 8-287

Patronat du Qué., Conseil du, 8-258

Pattern Makers' League of N.A.,
    11-13

Pavilion Corp., B.C., 17-80

Pay television networks, 9-6, -7—8,
    -60

Pay, assns., 8-225

Peace
. assns., 8-246, -247
. Park Assn., Cda., 8-192
. Toronto Assn. for, 8-199

Peacekeeping forces, United
    Nations, 1-3

Pension (see also Superannuation;
    Teachers)
. Appeals Board, 16-141
. commns.,
. . Cdn., 16-127
. . Man., 17-134
. . of Ont., 17-279
. Conf., Cdn., 8-226
. Mgmt., Assn. of Cdn., 8-225
. Plan, Cda., 11-5
. Plan, Sask., 17-405

Pensioners
. Concerned Inc., Cdn., 8-307
. and Injured Workmen of Ont.,
    Assn. of, 8-248
. and Senior Citizens Fed., Nat'l,
    8-307

Pensions
. Alta., Pension Boards, Treasury
    Dept., 17-51
. Advocates, Bur. of, 16-127
. B.C., Superannuation Commn.,
    17-80
. Canada,
. . Cdn. Pension Commn., 16-127
. . Dept. of Employment &
    Immigration, 16-52—56
. . Dept. of Health & Welfare,
    Income Security Programs
    Br., 16-77—78
. Manitoba,
. . Economic Security Div., Dept. of
    Employment Services &
    Economic Security, 17-120
. . Pension Commn., Dept. of
    Labour, 17-134

Pensions (cont'd)
· Nfld., Pension Administration, Dept. of Finance, 17-182
· Ont., Pension Commn. of Ont., 17-279
· Que.,
· · Caisse de dépôt et placement du Qué., 17-362
· · Régie des rentes du Qué., 17-373
· · Que. Pension Commn., 17-383
· Sask., Pensions Br., Dept. of Human Resources, Labour & Employment, 17-408

Pentathlon, Modern, 8-328

Pentecost of Cda. Inc., Apostolic Church of, 6-4

Pentecostal
· Assemblies of Cda., 6-13
· Benevolent Assn. of Ont., 8-194
· Holiness Church of Cda., 6-13
· Italian Pent. Church of Cda., 6-10

People for Sunday Assn. of Cda., 8-301

Performing
· Arts
· · Alta. Fdn. for the, 17-28
· · Publicists Assn., 8-185
· Rights Organization of Cda. Ltd. (PROCAN), 8-206

Periodical(s)
· Distributors of Cda., 8-295
· magazine listings, 8-120—176
· newspapers, 9-13—39
· · ethnic press, 9-40—44
· publishers, assns., 8-295
· Writers Assn. of Cda., 8-352

Permanent
· Cttee. on Geographical Names, Cdn., 16-63
· missions abroad, Cdn., 16-185—186

Perpetual Calendar, see inside back cover

Persephone Theatre, 8-343

Personnel
· Administration Office, Alta., 17-54
· assns., 8-288
· Dept. of, N.W.T., 17-203
· pubns., 8-141

Personnes agées, Comité sur les abus exercés à l'endroit des, Que., 17-375

Pest Management
· Advisory Board, 16-37—38
· Soc., Cdn., 8-180

Pesticides Advisory Cttee., Ont., 17-278

Pet Food Assn. of Cda., 8-229

Peterborough Symphony Orch., 8-282

Petro-Cda., 16-63—64
· Int'l Assistance Corp., 16-64

Petroleum (and natural gas)
· Act, B.C., 17-74
· assns., 8-288—289
· conservation assn., 8-202
· Mktg. Commn., Alta., 17-33
· Mediation & Arbitration Bd., 17-74
· Min. of Energy, Mines & Petroleum Resources, 17-74

· Monitoring Agency, 16-65
· products, 4-18—19
· pubns., 8-141

Pétrolières (SOQUIP), Soc. qué. d'initiatives, 17-357

Pharmaceutical
· assns., 8-289
· pubns., 8-142

Pharmaciens du Qué., Ordre des, 8-283

Pharmacists assns., 8-289

Pharmacological Society of Canada, 8-302

Pharmacologie, Cons. consultatif de, Que., 17-375

Phases of the Moon, 2-17—19

Philanthropy, Cdn. Centre for, 8-192

Philatelic
· Service, Cda. Post, 9-10
· Soc. of Cda., Royal, 8-239

Philosophical Assn., Cdn., 8-252

Philosophy
· pubn., 8-170
· and Social Science, Soc. of, 8-252

Photography
· assns., 8-290
· pubns., 8-142, -159

Photosphere, 2-10

Physical
· Distribution Management, Cdn. Assn. of, 8-257
· Medicine & Rehabilitation, Cdn. Assn. of, 8-271

Physicians
· College of Family, of Cda., 8-262
· of Ont., Assn. of Independent, 8-262
· for Prevention of Nuclear War, Cdn., 8-247
· and Surgeons of Cda., Royal College of, 8-262
· and surgeons, provincial colleges of, 8-262

Physicists, Cdn. Assn. of, 8-305

Physiothérapeutes du Qué.
· Assoc. prof. des, 11-17
· Corp. prof. des, 8-265

Physiotherapists & physiotherapy, assns., 8-262, -265

Phytopathological Soc., The Cdn., 8-180

Picture Pioneers, Cdn., 8-197

Pigs, statistics, 4-5

Pioneer Women's Na'amat, see Na'amat Cda., 8-350

Pipe Line Contractors Assn. of Cda., 8-289

Pipeline Agency, Northern, 16-140—141

Place des Arts de Montréal, Soc. de la, 17-340

Planetarium Assn. of Cda., 8-279

Planets, 2-11—13

Planification et de développement du Qué., Office de, 17-383

Planning
· boards, Alta., 17-42
· Commn., Metropolitan Area, N.S., 17-235
· Cttee., N.B. Prov., 17-159

· and development, community assns., 8-199—200
· Forum, The, 8-258
· and Implementation Commn., Ont., 17-274

Plant Guard Workers of America, Int'l Union, United, 11-12

Plastics assns., 8-125, -126

Plate Printers, Die Stampers & Engravers' Union of North America, Int'l, 11-12

Playground, pubns., 8-143

Playwrights' Union of Cda., 8-352

Plumbers & Pipe Fitters, Nat'l Assn. of, 11-16

Plumbing
· Advisory Bd., N.B., 17-158
· assns., 8-182

Pluto, 2-13

Podiatry assns., 8-262, -263, -265

Poets, League of Cdn., 8-352

Police/Policiers
· Alta., Dept. of the Solicitor General, 17-47
· assns., 8-250, -251
· Cdn.: Nat'l Railways, 11-18; Pacific, 11-18
· · of N.S., 11-25
· B.C. Fed. of Police Officers, 11-17
· commns.,
· · B.C., 17-92
· · Man., 17-113
· · N.B., 17-160, -165
· · N.S., 17-231
· · Ont., 17-297
· · Que., 17-377
· · Sask., 17-412
· Nfld., Dept. of Justice, 17-184
· Ont. Provincial, 11-25, 12-9—10, 17-297
· personnel, (table) 12-9
· P.E.I., Dept. of Justice, 17-320
· pubn., 8-137
· Que.
· · Féd. des, 11-20
· · provinciaux du Qué., Assoc. des, 11-16
· · Sûreté du, 12-10, 17-376
· Royal Cdn. Mounted, 12-9, 16-113—114
· Sask., Policing Br., Dept. of Justice, 17-410
· services in Cda., 12-9—10
· Solicitor General, Dept. of, Cda., 16-110—114

Policy
· Alternatives, Cdn. Centre for, 8-301
· Analysis, Inst. for, 8-211

Polish
· assns., 8-223, -224
· Combatants' Assn. in Cda. Inc., 8-276
· Engineers in Cda., Assn. of, 8-220
· Nat'l Catholic Church, 6-13
· pubns., 9-43
· Research Inst., Cdn., 8-238

Political
· history, 15-13—15
· Involvement, Inst. for, 8-291

Political (cont'd)
· parties, 15-11
· · and assns., 8-290—292
· · leaders & standings (federal), 16-18
· pubns., 8-142, -159

Political Science
· Assn., Cdn., 8-290
· pubns., 8-170

Pollution
· Advisory Cttee., Farm, Ont., 17-278
· assns., see Conservation & Environment, 8-201—202
· Control Equipment Assn., Ont., 8-222

Pompiers professionnels du Qué., Féd. des, 11-20

Poplar Coun. of Cda., 8-240

Population, 5-1—14
· Alta., Bur. of Statistics, Treasury Dept., 17-51
· B.C., Central Statistics Bur., Min. of Finance & Corporate Relations, 17-76
· distribution in Cda., 5-3—6
· · by age, 5-7
· · language, 5-8—9
· · migration, 5-5
· · by province, 5-2
· · by sex, 5-7
· · urban growth, 5-3
· families, 5-9—11
· · income, 5-10
· · size of, 5-10
· growth, 5-1—3
· Man., Bur. of Statistics, 17-121
· of metropolitan areas, 5-3
· mother tongue, 5-9
· of municipalities, 19-1—43
· Nat'l Archives of Cda., 16-45
· N.S., Statistics & Research Services, Dept. of Industry, Trade & Technology, 17-227
· size, quarterly estimates, 5-2
· urban growth, 5-3

Pork
· Coun., Cdn., 8-256
· Producers Marketing Board
· · Alta., 17-19
· · N.S., 8-257
· · Sask., 17-399

Port ferroviaire Baie-Comeau-Hauterive, Soc. du, Qué., 17-380

Portable Appliance Mfrs. Assn., 8-259

Portland Cement Assn., Cdn., 8-203

Ports
· in Cda., 10-11—12
· Corp., Cda., 10-11—12, 16-121

Portuguese
· Cdn. Club, First, 8-224
· pubns., 9-43

Post Corp., Cda., 9-9—12, 16-131

Post-secondary education institutions, 7-10—12, -12—54

Postal
· Code System, 9-10
· History Soc. of Cda., 8-238
· information, 9-9—12

· Museum, Nat'l, 16-49
· Officials of Cda., Assn. of, 11-17
· rates, 9-9
· services, 9-9—10
· Workers, Cdn. Union of, 1-3, 11-19

Postmasters & Assistants Assn., Cdn., 11-18

Potash Corp. of Sask., 17-420

Potato
· Chip Assn., Cdn., 8-228
· Commission, Alta., 8-180
· Mktg. Bd., Alta., 17-19
· Mktg. Bd., P.E.I., 17-317
· statistics, 4-6

Poultry
· Alta., Dept. of Agriculture, Animal Industry Div., 17-18; Animal Health Div., 17-18; Hatching Egg Mktg. Bd., 17-19
· assns., 8-293
· Broiler Hatching Egg: Commn., Man., 17-108; Mktg. Bd., Sask., 17-398
· Cda.,
· · Agriculture Dept., Food Production & Inspection Br., Health of Animals Dir., 16-33
· · Dept. of Industry, Science & Technology, Service Industries & Consumer Goods, Food Products Br., 16-90
· chicken mktg. bds.,
· · Alta., 17-19
· · B.C., 17-69
· · Man., 17-109
· · Nfld., 17-189
· · N.S., 8-293
· · Sask., 17-398
· Man., Animal Industry Br., Dept. of Agriculture, 17-107
· mktg. bd., P.E.I., 17-317
· N.B., Animal Industry Br., Dept. of Agriculture, 17-150
· Nfld., Agriculture Br., Dept. of Rural, Agricultural & Northern Development, 17-189
· N.S., Livestock Services Br., Dept. of Agriculture & Marketing, 17-218
· P.E.I., Dept. of Agriculture, 17-316
· pubn., 8-165
· Que., Service des productions animales, Min. de l'Agriculture, des Pêcheries et de l'Alimentation, 17-345
· statistics, 4-5
· · chicken & fowl, 4-5
· · eggs, 4-5
· turkey mktg. bds.,
· · Alta., 17-20
· · B.C., 17-71
· · Man., 17-109
· · Sask., 17-399

Poverty
· Nat'l Anti-poverty Org., 8-308

Power
· Consumers in Ont., Assn. of Major, 8-219

· corporations,
· · N.W.T., 17-207
· · N.S., 17-238
· · Sask., 17-417
· · Tidal, N.S., 17-240
· Engineers (See Engineers, Power)
· plants, pubn., 8-129
· pubn., 8-130
· and Sail Squadrons, Cdn., 8-297

Prairie
· Agricultural Machinery Inst., 18-5
· Farm Rehabilitation Admin., (PFRA), 16-38
· farmers, aid to, 1-3
· Provinces Water Bd., 18-5
· Theatre Exchange, 8-343

Premier's Advisory Coun. on Science & Technology, 17-67

Premiers
· Alta., 17-15
· B.C., 17-64
· Coun. of Maritime, 18-3
· Man., 17-106
· N.B., 17-148
· Nfld., 17-175
· N.W.T., Gov't Leader, 17-199
· N.S., 17-217
· Ont., 17-252
· P.E.I., 17-316
· Que., 17-333
· Sask., 17-396
· Yukon, Gov't Leader, 17-432

Presbyterian Church, 6-13

Pre-school programs, 7-6

Preservation Technology, Assn. for, 8-237

Press assns., 8-295

Price Indexes, Consumer, 14-6—7

Prime Minister, 15-11, 16-9
· list of, since Confed., 16-9
· Office of the, 16-18

Prince Edward Island
· agriculture, 4-3, 17-314
· coat of arms, 17-313
· community college, 7-50
· courts, 17-327
· economy, 14-18, 17-314
· education, 7-4, -8, -9, -50
· exhibitions, 8-225
· fishing, 17-314
· forestry, 4-9, 17-314
· geography, 3-4, 17-313
· government, 17-315
· history, 17-313
· income statistics, 5-10
· judicial officers, 17-327
· labour legislation, 11-3, -7
· libraries & archives, 8-79—80
· link with the mainland, 1-1, -3
· manufacturing, 17-314
· map, 17-312
· minimum wage rate, 11-4
· motor vehicle regulations, 10-9
· municipal government, 19-29
· municipalities, 19-29—30
· newspapers, 9-32
· population, 5-2, 17-313, -314
· radio stations, 9-50, -56
· superintendent of insurance, 13-20

P.E.I. (cont'd)
· television station, 9-59
· tourism, 17-314
· University of, 7-32
· Vital Statistics Div., Dept. of Health & Social Services, 17-319

Principals' Assn., Ont. 8-215

Print Measurement Bur., 8-179

Printing
· assns., 8-293
· Government Printing Co., Sask., 17-423
· Graphic Communications Int'l Union, 11-10
· Ink Manufacturers Assn., Cdn., 8-195
· pubns., 8-142

Prison
· Arts Fdn., 8-185
· Guards, Union of, 11-28

Prisons (see also Parole Boards)
· Alta., Correctional Services Div., Dept. of the Solicitor General, 17-47
· B.C., Min. of the Solicitor General, 17-71
· Cda.,
· · Correctional Service of Cda., 16-111—112
· · Solicitor General, Dept. of, 16-110—114
· Man., Corrections Div., Dept. of the Attorney General, 17-112
· N.B., Corrections Services Div., Dept. of the Solicitor General, 17-160
· Nfld., Adult Corrections, Dept. of Justice, 17-185
· N.S., Dept. of the Solicitor General, 17-231
· Ont., Min. of Correctional Services, 17-268
· P.E.I., Corrections, Dept. of Justice, 17-320
· Que., Services correctionnels, Min. de la Sécurité publique, 17-376
· Sask., Corrections Div., Dept. of Justice, 17-409
· Yukon, Corrections, Dept. of Justice, 17-435

Privacy
· Act, 12-5
· Commissioner, 16-95
· Cttee. (RTPC), Right to, 8-240

Private
· Colleges Accreditation Bd., Alta., 17-16
· Motor Truck Council of Cda., 8-348

Privatization & Regulatory Affairs, Cda., 16-100

Privy Council
· for Canada, 15-11, 16-6—8
· clerk of the, 16-11
· Office, 16-11
· · Office of the President of the, 16-7

Privy Councillors, list of, 16-7—8

Pro Musica Society of Cda., 8-282

Producteurs agricoles, Union des, 8-182

Production
· Centre qué. pour l'informatisation de la, 17-358
· Employees' Union, Acadia & Quebec, 11-27

Professional
· Dev't Inst., 8-258
· Secretaries Int'l, 8-191
· and Technical
· · Employees, Cdn. Union of, 11-19
· · Engineers, Int'l Fed. of, 11-12

Professionnel(le)s
· des collèges et universités, Féd. des, 11-20
· de commissions scolaires du Qué., Féd. des syndicats de, 11-21
· du gouvernement du Qué., Syndicat de, 11-27
· salariés et des cadres du Qué., Féd. des, 11-21

Professions du Qué., Office des, 17-359

Professors
· for the Gov't of Quebec, Union of, 11-27
· and Lecturers, Fed. of University, 11-20

Profit Sharing Council of Cda., 8-226

Progress
· Charitable Fdn., Cdn., 8-193
· Club, Cdn., 8-231

Progressive Conservative
· assns., 8-291, -292, -354
· Ont., Offices of the, 17-253

Prologue to the Performing Arts, 8-343

Promotion Bd., Co-operative, Man., 17-115

Propagation of the Faith for Cda., The Soc. for the, 8-301

Propane Gas Assn. of Cda., 8-289

Property Tax Agents Assn., Cdn., 8-340

Proprietary Crown corp., defined, 16-28

Prospectors & Developers Assn. of Cda., 8-277

Protecteur du citoyen, Qué., 17-334

Protection
· Civile, Bureau de la, Qué., 17-347
· du territoire agricole, Commn. de, 17-346

Protectionism, U.S., 14-25

Protestant School Boards, Quebec Assn. of, 8-215

Protocol, Cdn., 2-3

Province House Credit Union Ltd., N.S., 17-239

Provincial
· Auditor, Sask., 17-416
· boundaries commissions, B.C., 17-75
· Building & Construction Trades Coun. of Ont., 8-204
· governments, 17-1—440
· · employees unions, see Nat'l Union of Provincial Gov't Employees, 11-23—24
· · powers, 15-8—9

· Holdings Ltd., N.B., 17-152
· Municipal Coun., N.B., 17-159
· Planning Cttee., N.B., 17-159
· population (see also individual provinces)
· · growth, 5-3
· Secretary, Dept. of the, Sask., 17-416
· Secretary, Min. of Tourism &, B.C., 17-94

Psychiatric
· assns., 8-273—274
· Forensic, Services Commn., 17-83
· nurses assns., 8-285, -286

Psychogeriatric Assn., Ont., 8-307

Psychological Research, Inst. of, 8-113

Psychology
· assns., 8-211, -273—274
· pubns., 8-137—139

Psychotherapy Assn., Cdn. Group, 8-273

Public
· Admin. of Cda., Inst. of, 8-278
· Affairs
· · Bur., Alta., 17-54
· · Couchiching Inst. on, 8-212
· Archives Cda., see National Archives of Cda., 16-45
· Archives of N.S., 17-240
· Complaints Commr., Ont., 17-260
· Employees
· · Assn., N.B. 11-24
· · Benefits Agency, Sask., 17-404
· · Cdn. Union of, 11-19
· · N.S. Union of, 11-24
· Health
· · Advisory & Appeal Bd., Alta., 17-39
· · assns., 8-270—273
· holidays, 2-9
· Insurance Corp., Man., 17-140
· Investments Corp., Man., 17-141
· Legal Education Assn. of Sask. Inc., 8-251
· libraries (See Libraries; Library)
· Participation, Dept. of, Sask., 17-418
· Policy
· · assns., 8-211
· · Inst. for Research on, 8-302
· and Private Rights Bd., Sask., 17-411
· Records Cttee., N.W.T., 17-208
· relations
· · assns., 8-179, -293
· · pubn., 8-120
· Safety, Dept. of the Environment and, Sask., 17-403
· Services, Dept. of Safety and, N.W.T., 17-204
· Schools Finance Bd., Man., 17-119

Public Commercial Vehicles ("For Hire" Carriers)
· Alta., Motor Transport Bd., 17-50
· B.C., Motor Carrier Commn., 17-93
· Man., Motor Transport Bd., 17-130
· N.B., Motor Carrier Bd., 17-162
· Nfld., Nfld. Commn. of Public Utilities, 17-193

Public Commercial Vehicles (cont'd)
. N.S., Bd. of Commrs. of Public
    Utilities, 17-233
. Ont.,
. . Highway Traffic Bd., 17-302
. . Transportation Regulation
    Operations Div., Min. of
    Transportation, 17-300
. P.E.I., Public Utilities Commn.,
    17-326
. Que., Comm. des transports du
    Qué., 17-379
. Sask., Highway Traffic Bd., 17-407

Public Entertainment Standards
    Program (Ont.), 17-266

Public Safety Services, Alta., 17-53

Public Service
. Alliance of Cda., 1-3, 11-25—26
. of Cda., Prof. Inst. of, 11-25
. Classification Rating Cttee., Ont.,
    17-289
. commns.,
. . B.C., 17-94
. . Cda., 16-100—101
. . Nfld., 17-188
. . Sask., 17-424
. . Yukon, 17-436
. employees,
. . number of federal, by
    geographic area & sex, 16-31
. . by type of employment, 16-30
. . unions, 11-25—26, see also Nat'l
    Union of Prov. Gov't
    Employees, 11-23—24
. Employment
. . Act, 11-6
. . in Canada, 16-30—31
. Grievance Bd., Ont., 17-290
. Labour Relations
. . Bd., N.B., 17-166
. . Tribunal, Ont., 17-289
. Staff Relations Bd., Cda., 16-141
. Superannuation Bd., Ont., 17-281

Public Utilities
. boards,
. . Alta., 17-24
. . Man., 17-116
. . N.B., 17-163
. . N.W.T., 17-208
. commns.,
. . B.C., 17-74
. . Nfld., 17-193
. . N.S., 17-233
. . P.E.I., 17-326
. Ontario Hydro, 17-276
. Que., Hydro-Qué., 17-356
. Sask.,
. . Power Corp., 17-417
. . Telecommunications, 17-424

Public Works
. depts.,
. . Alta., Supply & Services, 17-44
. . Cda., 16-101—102
. . Nfld., and Services, 17-187
. . N.W.T., and Highways, 17-203
. . P.E.I., 17-321
. Man., Dept. of Government
    Services, 17-125
. N.B., Dept. of Supply & Services,
    17-160

. N.S., Dept. of Government
    Services, 17-225
. Ont., Min. of Government
    Services, 17-280
. Sask., Property Management
    Corp., 17-415
. Yukon, Dept. of Gov't Services,
    17-434

Publishers
. assns., 8-293—295
. book, 8-105—119
. Ethnic Press, 9-40—44
. List Owners Assn., 8-255
. newspaper, 9-13—39
. pubns., 8-121

Publishing
. desktop pubn., 8-126
. industry profile, 14-13

Pubs assns., 8-302—303

Pulp & Paper
. assns., 8-351—352
. exports, 4-11
. industry in Cda., 4-10—11
. Makers Safety Assn., Ont., 8-304
. pubns., 8-132
. Research Inst. of Cda., 8-302
. and Woodworkers of Cda., 11-26

Pulsars, 2-14

Pulse
. Crop Development Bd., Sask.,
    17-399
. statistics, 4-7

Punjabi pubns., 9-43

Puppet Centre, 8-343

Purchasing
. Commn., B.C., 17-80
. Mgmt. Assn. of Cda., 8-258
. pubns., 8-143

Q

Quakers, 6-14

Qualifications Evaluation Council of
    Ont., 8-217

Quasars, 2-14

Quebec
. agriculture, 4-3
. chambre de commerce et
    d'industrie, 8-191
. colleges, 7-50—53
. . CÉGEPs, 7-50—52
. . private, 7-52—53
. . regional admissions service, 7-52
. courts, 17-385
. economy, 14-18, 17-330
. education, 7-4, -8, -9, -10, -50—53
. forestry, 4-9
. geography, 3-4, 17-329
. government, 17-331
. income statistics, 5-10
. judicial officers, 17-385
. labour legislation, 11-3, -7
. libraries & archives, 8-80—99
. map, 17-328
. minimum wage rate, 11-4
. motor vehicle regulations, 10-9
. municipal gov't, 19-30
. municipalities, 19-31—40
. newspapers, 9-32—37

. population, 5-2, 17-319
. radio stations, 9-50—51, -56—57
. senators sworn in, 1-3
. signs, unilingual, 1-4
. superintendent of insurance, 13-20
. Telephone Professional
    Employees Union, 11-27
. television stations, 9-59
. universities,
. . Bishop's Univ., 7-14
. . Concordia Univ., 7-18
. . Laval, Univ., 7-21—22
. . Macdonald College of McGill
    Univ., 7-22
. . McGill Univ., 7-24—26
. . Montréal, Univ. de, 7-28—29
. . Québec, Univ. du, 7-32—33
. . Sherbrooke, Univ. de, 7-37
. . Winter Carnival, 8-225

Queen Crab Assn., Atlantic, 8-227

Queen Elizabeth II, 15-10, 16-5

Queen's
. Printer
. . Nfld., 17-188
. . P.E.I., 17-326
. . Sask., Property Management
    Corp., 17-415
. . Yukon, Dept. of Government
    Services, 17-434
. Privy Council for Cda., 16-6—8

Queen's University, 7-33

Quetico Foundation, 8-202

R

RCMP, see Royal Cdn. Mounted
    Police, 12-9, 16-113—114

Racetracks of Cda. Inc., 8-299

Racing
. commns.,
. . Alta., 17-48
. . B.C., 17-93
. . Man., 17-132
. . N.S., 17-220
. . Ont., 17-267
. . P.E.I., 17-323
. . Que., 17-374
. Drivers Assn., Cdn., 8-186
. Pigeon Union Inc., Cdn., 8-297
. Radio Control Race Car Assn. of
    N.S., 8-299
. Soc. de développement de
    l'industrie des courses de
    chevaux du Qué., 17-362

Racquetball assns., 8-329

Radiation
. Protection
. . Assn., Cdn., 8-304
. . Commission, Healing Arts
    (HARP), Ont., 17-284
. Safety, Cdn. Inst. for, 8-304
. technologists, assns. of medical,
    8-266

Radio
. assns.
. . amateur, 8-239
. . broadcasting, 8-188—189
. in Canada, 9-4, -7, -8
. -Canada, Syndicat des techniciens
    du réseau français de, 11-27

Radio (cont'd)
· Carriers Assn., Cdn. Radio
    Common, 8-341
· cellular, 9-4
· communications, 9-2
· DX Club, Cdn., Int'l, 8-239
· Operators, Cdn. Assn. of Prof.,
    11-18
· Producers' Assn., Nat'l, 11-23
· pubns., 8-122, -161
· -Québec, 17-351
· · Television Broadcast Employees'
    Union, 11-27
· stations, 9-45—57
· · AM, 9-45—52
· · FM, 9-52—57
· statistics, 9-5, -7
· -television & Telecommunications
    Commn. (CRTC), Cdn., 9-2,
    -7—8, 16-43—45
· -Télévision du Qué., Soc. de
    (Radio-Québec), 17-351
· wireless, 9-1

Radiologists, Cdn. Assn. of, 8-264

Ragtime Society Inc., 8-282

Rail
· B.C., Ltd., 17-95
· Cda. Traffic Controllers, Union of,
    11-29
· freight service, Nfld., 1-2

Railroad Historical Assn., Cdn.,
    8-238

Railway(s)
· Assn. of Cda., 8-347
· Cdn. Nat'l, 10-2—3, 16-122
· Carmen of the U.S. & Cda.,
    Brotherhood, 11-10
· companies in Cda., 10-4—5
· Labour Assn., Cdn., 8-248
· Safety Directorate, 10-4
· Transport & General Workers,
    Cdn. Brotherhood of, 11-18

Rainbow Stage, 8-343

Rape Crisis Centres, Ont. Coalition
    of, 8-351

Raspberry Growers' Assn., B.C.,
    8-180

Real Estate (see also Housing)
· Assmt. Review Bd., Que., 17-342
· assns., 8-296
· Coun. of B.C., 17-78
· industry profile, Cdn., 14-14—15
· pubns., 8-143
· Que., Société immobilière, 17-348

Real Estate Regulations
· Alta., Supt. of Real Estate, Dept. of
    Consumer & Corporate Affairs,
    17-25
· Cda.
· · Chief of Registration, Office of
    the Asst. Deputy Registrar
    General, Dept. of Consumer &
    Corporate Affairs, 16-52
· · Mortgage & Housing Corp.,
    16-129—130
· Nfld., Real Estate, Dept. of
    Consumer Affairs &
    Communications, 17-176
· N.S., Consumer & Commercial
    Reations Div., Dept. of
    Consumer Affairs, 17-222

· Ont., Registrar of Real Estate &
    Business Brokers, Min. of
    Consumer & Commercial
    Relations, 17-265
· P.E.I., Dept. of Justice, 17-320
· Que., Soc. immobilière, 17-348
· Sask.,
· · Dept. of Consumer &
    Commercial Affairs, 17-401
· · Farm Ownership Bd., 17-411

Reality & Meaning, The Assn. of
    Concern for, 8-301

Receiverships, 13-34

Recherche
· sur la Culture, Institut québécois
    de, 17-338
· Fonds pour la formation de
    chercheurs et l'aide à la, 17-359
· Industrielle du Qué., Centre de,
    17-364
· en Santé, Fonds de la, Que.,
    17-376
· Sociale, Cons. qué. de la, 17-375

Reconnaissance des associations
    d'artistes, Comm. de, 17-337

Record
· Players, Assn. of Prof., 8-280
· Production Assn., Cdn.
    Independent, 8-280

Recording
· Arts & Sciences, Cdn. Academy
    of, 8-280
· Industry Assn., Cdn., 8-280

Records
· Cttee., Public, N.W.T., 17-208
· Mgrs. & Admin., Assn. of, 8-243

Recours collectifs, Fonds d'aide
    aux, Que., 17-368

Recreation (see also Parks; Sports;
    Tourism)
· Alta.
· · Parks & Wildlife Fdn., 17-46
· · Recreation Development Div.,
    Dept. of Recreation & Parks,
    17-45
· assns., 8-296—299
· automobile, 8-185
· B.C., Recreation & Sport Br., Min.
    of Tourism, Recreation &
    Culture, 17-87
· Canada,
· · Fitness & Amateur Sport, 16-81
· · Parks Cda., 16-67
· · Tourism Cda., 16-90—91
· Centres' Staff, Fed. of, 11-21
· Council, Interprov. Sport and, 18-4
· facilities, 8-287, -296, -297, -299
· Man., Recreation Br., Dept. of
    Culture, Heritage & Recreation,
    17-116
· N.B., Sport & Recreation Div.,
    Dept. of Tourism, Recreation &
    Heritage, 17-161
· Nfld., Community Recreation,
    Dept. of Culture, Recreation &
    Youth, 17-177
· N.W.T., Sport & Recreation Div.,
    Dept. of Municipal & Community
    Affairs, 17-203
· N.S., Sport & Recreation Commn.,
    17-239

· Ont., Recreation Div., Min. of
    Tourism & Recreation, 17-298
· and Parks assns., 8-287
· P.E.I., Youth, Fitness & Recreation
    Unit, Dept. of Community &
    Cultural Affairs, 17-318
· pubns., 8-143, -144
· sports & outdoor activities,
    8-160—161
· Que., Min. du Loisir, de la Chasse
    et de la Pêche, 17-369
· Sask., Dept. of Parks, Recreation
    & Culture, 17-413
· Yukon, Dept. of Community &
    Transportation Servs., 17-432

Recreational Vehicle Assn., Cdn.,
    8-297

Recycling
· Advisory Cttee., Ont., 17-278
· assns. (see also Conservation),
    8-201, -202

Red Cross
· Blood Transfusion Service
    Employees Assn., Cdn., 11-18
· Soc., Cdn., 8-272

Red River Exhibition, 8-225

Reference, Bd. of, Man., 17-119

Reform Rabbis, Cdn. Coun. of,
    8-300

Réforme
· administrative et aux emplois
    supérieurs, Secrétariat à la,
    Que., 17-333
· électorale, Que., 17-334

Refrigerating & Air Conditioning
    Inst. of Cda., Heating, 8-182

Refrigeration
· Air Conditioning & Fire Protection
    Workers, Nat'l Assn. of, 11-16
· Service Engineers Soc. Cda.,
    8-182

Refugee Board, Immigration and,
    16-56

Refugees, 1-1, -4

Regents for Colleges of Applied Arts
    & Technology, Ont. Coun. of,
    17-262

Regina
· Chamber of Commerce, 8-192
· libraries & archives, 8-101—103
· radio stations, 9-52, -57
· Symphony, 8-282
· television stations, 9-59—60
· Univ. of, 7-34

Regional Industrial Expansion, Dept.
    of, see Dept. of Industry,
    Science & Technology,
    16-87—92, 17-439

Regulatory Affairs, Privatization and,
    16-100

Rehabilitation
· Alta., Dept. of Social Services,
    17-46
· Art Therapy Inst., The Vancouver,
    8-274
· B.C., Rehabilitation & Support
    Services Div., Min. of Social
    Services & Housing, 17-90
· Cda., Health & Welfare Cda.,
    Social Service Programs Br.,
    16-78

Rehabilitation (cont'd)
· Disabled, Cdn. Rehabilitation
  Coun. for the, 8-236
· Kinsmen, Fdn. of B.C., 8-237
· Medicine and, Cdn. Assn. of
  Physical, 8-264
· Nfld., Div. of Rehabilitation
  Services, Dept. of Social
  Services, 17-191
· N.S., Rehabilitation & Community
  Services, Dept. of Community
  Services, 17-221
· Ont.,
· · Advisory Council for Disabled
  Persons, 17-252
· · Community Services Div., Min. of
  Community & Social Services,
  17-263
· · Correctional Services, Min. of,
  17-268
· · Office for Disabled Persons,
  17-252
· Personnel, Cdn. Assn. of, 8-264
· P.E.I., Dept. of Health & Social
  Services, 17-319
· Que., Réadaption, Min. de la Santé
  et des Services sociaux, 17-374
· Sask., Dept. of Health, 17-405
· training, Cdn. ORT Organization,
  8-218
· · Women's, 8-218
· University Schools of, Cdn. Assn.
  of, 8-218
· Yukon, Vocational Rehabilitation
  Services, Dept. of Health &
  Human Resources, 17-435

Reinforcing Steel Inst. of Cda.,
  8-204

Religion
· assns., 8-299—301
· Homosexuality and, Coun. on,
  8-240
· statistics
· · churches by denomination, 6-2
· · clergy, 6-2
· · membership, 6-2
· Taskforce on the Churches &
  Corporate Responsibility, 8-301

Religious
· Conference, Cdn. 8-300
· councils, ecumenical, 6-2—3
· denominations, 6-3—16
· education, assns., 8-217, -218
· holidays, 2-9—10
· pubns., 8-168—169
· Society of Friends (Quakers), 6-14

Remote Sensing
· Cda. Centre for, 16-58
· Cttee. (MRSC), Maritime, 18-3

Remotivation Therapists of Cda.,
  Assn. of, 8-273

Rémunération, Inst. de recherche et
  d'information sur la, 17-382

Renaissance
· Int'l, 8-301
· Studies, Cdn. Soc. for, 8-252

Renewable Resources, depts.,
· N.W.T., 17-203
· Yukon, 17-436

Rent
· Appeal Commn., Sask., 17-411
· Review Commn., N.S., 17-222

Rentes, Régie des, Que., 17-373

Reorganized Church of Jesus Christ
  of Latter Day Saints, 6-14

Reporters Assn., Ont., 8-352

Reptile Conservation Soc., Cdn.
  Amphibian and, 8-349

Republic Nat'l Bank of New York
  (Cda.), 13-13

Rescue, Civil Air, 8-187

Research (see also specific fields)
· Advanced, Cdn. Inst. for, 8-301
· assns., 8-301—302
· Council,
· · Alta., 17-53
· · B.C., 8-301, 17-67
· · Employees' Assn., 11-26
· · Nat'l, 16-138—140
· · Que., Social, 17-375
· · Sask., 17-424
· Fonds pour la formation de
  chercheurs et l'aide à la
  recherche, Que., 17-359
· Foundations,
· · N.S., 17-238
· · Ont., ORTECH International,
  17-287
· and Productivity Coun., N.B.,
  17-152
· and Telecommunications, Dept. of
  Technology, Alta., 17-48
· Urban & Regional,
  Intergovernmental Cttee. on,
  18-4

Resident & Ratepayer Assns.,
  Confederation of (CORRA),
  8-200

Residential Tenancies Bd., N.S.,
  17-222

Resilient Flooring Contractors Assn.
  of Ont., 8-205

Resort(s)
· Ont., 8-345
· Timesharing Coun. of Cda., 8-345

Resources
· and Environment Ministers, Cdn.
  Coun. of, 18-2
· Law, Cdn. Inst. of, 8-250
· Ltd., N.S., 17-238
· Railway Corp., Alta., 17-50

Resources Development
· B.C., Min. of Energy, Mines &
  Petroleum Resources, 17-74
· Canada,
· · Energy, Mines & Resources
  Dept.: Energy Sectors,
  16-60—61; Mineral Policy
  Sector, 16-59
· · Fisheries & Oceans, Dept. of,
  16-74—76
· · Indian Affairs & Northern Dev't,
  Dept. of, Natural Resources &
  Economic Dev't Br., 16-83
· · Industry, Science & Technology,
  Dept. of, Resource
  Processing Industries, 16-90

· Man.,
· · Hydro, 17-139
· · Natural Resources, Dept. of,
  17-136
· Maritime Resource Mgmt. Service,
  18-3
· Nat'l Research Coun. Cda.,
  16-138—140
· N.B., Mineral Resources, Dept. of
  Natural Resources & Energy,
  17-159
· Nfld., Dept. of the Environment &
  Lands, 17-181
· N.S., Dept. of Industry, Trade &
  Technology, 17-227
· Ont.,
· · Forest Resources Group, Min. of
  Natural Resources, 17-293
· · Min. of Northern Development &
  Mines, 17-294
· · Northland Transportation
  Commn., 17-294
· P.E.I., Dept. of Industry, 17-319
· Que., Min. de l'Énergie et des
  Ressources, 17-353
· Sask.,
· · Dept. of Energy & Mines, 17-403
· · Dept. of Parks, Recreation &
  Culture, 17-413

Respiratory Therapists, Cdn. Soc.
  of, 8-265

Ressources humaines, Off. des,
  17-339

Restaurant
· assns., 8-302—303
· pubns., 8-131

Restrictive Trade Practices
  Commission, see Competition
  Tribunal, 16-52

Retail
· assns., 8-303
· industry profile, Cda., 14-13
· pubns., 8-143
· Wholesale
· · and Dept. Store Union: 11-13;
  Sask. Joint Board, 11-26
· · Union, 11-26

Retailers, automotive assns., 8-186,
  -187

Retirement
· assns., 8-307
· pubns., 8-160

Retraite et d'assurances, Comm.
  admin. des régimes de, Que.,
  17-383

Revenue
· depts.,
· · Cda., 16-103—107
· · Ont., 17-295
· · Que., 17-373

Rheumatism Assn., Cdn., 8-269

Rhododendron Soc. of Cda., 8-240

Rhythmic Gymnastics assns.,
  8-322—323

Richard III Soc. of Cda., 8-238

Rideau-Trent-Severn CORTS
  Agreement Bd., Cda.-Ont.,
  17-293

Rights (*see also* Civil Liberties & Human Rights)
· assns., 8-198, -199
· Cdn. Charter of Rights & Freedoms, 12-4—5, 15-6—7, -17—19
· Citizens', 12-3—6

Ringette assns., 8-330

Rivers
· Board, Cdn. Heritage, 18-2—3
· of Canada, 3-8—9

Rivet Employees Assn., Thomson Canada, 11-28

Road(s)
· Assn., Ont. Good, 8-347
· Builders
· · assns., provincial, 8-202—205
· · Safety Assn., Sask., 8-305
· Safety Regs., Fed., 10-5
· and Transportation Assn. of Cda., 8-347

Rock Climbing Assn., Ont., 8-299

Roller Skaters assns., 8-297, -298

Roman Catholic (*see also* Catholic)
· Church in Cda., 6-14

Roofing assns., 8-202—205

Rose Soc., Cdn., 8-240

Rotary Club, The, 8-232

Rowing assns., 8-330

Royal
· Agricultural Winter Fair Assn., 8-225
· Bank of Cda., 13-9
· Botanical Gardens, Ont., 17-272
· Cdn.
· · Air Force Benevolent Fund, 8-194
· · Arts, Academy of, 8-185
· · Geographical Soc., 8-252
· · Humane Assn., 8-243
· · Inst., 8-252
· · Legion, 8-276
· · Military Inst., 8-276
· · Mint, 16-117—118
· · Mounted Police, 12-9, 16-113—114
· · Naval: Assn., 8-276; Benevolent Fund, 8-194
· Commission on the Future of the Toronto Waterfront, 16-12
· Commonwealth Soc., 8-287
· Life Saving Soc. of Cda., 8-304—305
· Military College of Cda., 7-34, 16-183
· Roads Military College, 7-35, 16-183
· Soc. of Cda., 8-252

Rubber
· Assn. of Cda., 8-196
· Cork, Linoleum & Plastic Workers of America, United, 11-15

Rugby assns., 8-331

Rural
· Agricultural & Northern Dev't, Dept. of, Nfld., 17-188
· Bldg. Construction Wages Bd., Man., 17-135
· Bd. of Examiners, Sask., 17-418

· Dev't,
· · Act (ARDA) Cttee., Special, 17-209
· · Dept. of, Sask., 17-418
· Education & Dev't Assn., 8-217
· Municipal Administrators, assns., 8-278

Russian
· Cdn. Cultural Aid Society, 8-208
· pubns., 9-43

Ryerson Polytechnical Inst., 7-35

S

SCE Inc., *see* Les Éditions l'étincelle, 8-110

SEVEC — Soc. for Educational Visits & Exchanges in Cda., 8-212

SOGIC, 17-341

SPCA, 8-242—243

Safety
· and Advisory Bd., Ont. Sports Medicine and, 17-299
· assns., 8-303—305
· Dept. of the Environment and Public, Sask., 17-403
· Directorate, Railway, 10-4
· fire prevention assns., 8-226—227
· and Public Services, Dept. of, N.W.T., 17-204

Sailing assns., 8-296, -297, -298, -299

Ste-Anne, Université, 7-35

St. Clair Parkway Commn., Ont., 17-299

St. Elizabeth Visiting Nurses' Assn., 8-286

St. Francis Xavier University, 7-35—36

St. George's Society of Toronto 8-194

St-Jean-Baptiste
· de Montréal, Société, 8-208
· de l'Ontario, Féd. des sociétés, 8-287

St. John Ambulance, 8-261

Saint John (N.B.) Visitor & Convention Bureau, 8-345

St. John's
· Metropolitan Area Bd., Nfld., 17-193
· Tourist Bureau, 8-345

St. Lawrence
· lowlands, 3-7
· Parks Commn., Ont., 17-299
· Seaway, 10-12—13
· · Authority, 16-123

St. Leonard's Soc. of Cda., 8-312

Saint Mary's University, 7-36

St. Thomas University, 7-36

St. Vincent de Paul, Soc. of, 8-312

Salaries, legislative
· Alta., 17-14
· B.C., 17-64
· Cda., 16-16—17, -18
· Man., 17-105
· N.B., 17-147
· Nfld., 17-174

· N.W.T., 17-201
· N.S., 17-216
· Ont., 17-250
· P.E.I., 17-315
· Que., 17-331
· Sask., 17-395
· Yukon, 17-432

Sales (*see also* Advertising; Marketing; Retail; Wholesale)
· pubns., 8-120, -143

Sales taxes
· B.C., Min. of Finance & Corporate Relations, 17-75
· Cda., Revenue Cda., Customs & Excise Div., 16-103—104
· Man., Retail Sales Tax Br., Dept. of Finance, 17-125
· N.B., Tax Administration, Dept. of Finance, 17-153
· Nfld., Tax Compliance, Dept. of Finance, 17-182
· N.S., Provincial Tax Commn., Dept. of Finance, 17-224
· Ont., Tax Revenue & Grants Program, Min. of Revenue, 17-295
· P.E.I., Revenue Div., Dept. of Finance, 17-319
· Que., Min. du Revenu, 17-373
· Sask., Revenue Div., Dept. of Finance, 17-404
· Yukon, Revenue Services, Dept. of Finance, 17-434

Salmon Fed., Atlantic, 8-349

Saltfish Corp., Cdn., 16-75

Salvation Army, 6-14—15, 8-194

Samuel & Saidye Bronfman Family Fdn., The, 8-194

Sanatorium Bd. of Man., 17-141

Sandford Fleming Fdn., 8-194

Sanitarium Assn., Nat'l, 8-194

Sanitation, assns., 8-308

Santé
· Cons. d'évaluation des technologies de la santé, 17-375
· mentale, Comité de la, 17-375
· du Qué., Fonds de la recherche en, 17-376
· du Qué., Syndicat des professionnels et des techniciens de la, 11-27
· et de la sécurité du travail du Qué., Comm. de la, 17-381
· et des services sociaux
· · Féd. du personnel de la, (FPSSS), 11-21
· · Min. de la, Que., 17-374

Sanwa Bank Cda., 13-13

Saskatchewan
· agriculture, 4-3, 17-394
· coat of arms, 17-393
· colleges, 7-53—54
· courts, 17-425
· economy, 14-18—19, 17-394
· education, 7-4, -8, -9, -53—54
· geography, 3-5, 17-393
· history, 17-393
· income statistics, 5-10
· Joint Board Retail, Wholesale & Dept. Store Union, 11-26

· judicial officers, 17-425
· labour legislation, 11-3, -7
· legislation, bilingual, 1-1, -2
· libraries & archives, 8-99—104
· map, 17-392
· minimum wage rates, 11-4
· mining 17-394
· motor vehicle regulations, 10-9
· municipal gov't, 19-40
· municipalities, 19-40—43
· newspapers, 9-37—39
· population, 5-2, 17-393, -382
· Property Management Corp.,
    17-415
· radio stations, 9-51—52, -57
· superintendent of insurance, 13-20
· Teachers' Fed., 11-26
· television stations, 9-59—60
· University of
· · Regina, 7-34
· · Saskatchewan, 7-36—37
· Vital Statistics Div., Dept. of
    Health, 17-405

Saskatoon
· libraries & archives, 8-103—104
· Symphony Soc., 8-282
· Visitor & Convention Bureau,
    8-346

Satellite
· Communications, 9-2, -4
· program, 9-4, -8

Satellites, Anik, 9-2, -4

Saturn, 2-12

Save the Children—Canada, 8-194

Savings Office, Prov. of Ont., 13-14

Scandinavian Fdn., Cdn., 8-208

Schizophrenia Fdn., Cdn., 8-274

Schneider Employees' Assn., 11-26

Scholarship Trust Fdn., Cdn., 8-216

School(s) (see also Universities &
    Colleges, 7-11—54)
· administrators, assns., 8-214, -215
· Agricultural, 7-10
· Athletic assns., provincial, 8-314
· Blind & Deaf, 7-8—9
· Boards Assns., provincial, 8-214,
    -215
· Business
· · Employees' Assn., N.B., 11-24
· · Officials, Ont. Assn. of, 8-215
· Commns. Prof. Employees'
    Unions, Fed. of Quebec, 11-21
· Counsellors' Assn., Ont., 8-217
· Elementary-Secondary, 7-6—9
· enrolment statistics, 7-2
· Library, assns., 8-254, -255
· Native, 7-5—6
· National Defence, 7-6
· Post-Secondary, 7-10—12, -12—54
· Private, 7-7
· Public, Finance Bd., Man., 17-119
· pubns., 8-172—176
· Sports Feds., 8-312
· Separate, 7-6
· Technical & Vocational, 7-9—10
· Trustees, assns., 8-213, -214, -215

Science
· Assn. for the Advancement of, in
    Cda., 8-305

· Cdn. Soc. for the History &
    Philosophy of, 8-252
· Centre, Ont., 17-272
· Councils,
· · B.C., 17-68
· · Cda., 16-141—142
· Education, Cdn. Assn. for, 8-305
· Institute, N.W.T., 17-208
· North, Ont., 17-273
· pubns., research & development,
    8-143

Science & Scientific Research
· Alta. Research Coun., 17-53
· Alcoholism & Drug Addiction
    Research Fdn., 17-283
· Canada,
· · Agriculture Dept., Food
    Production & Inspection Br.,
    16-33
· · Atomic Energy of, Ltd., 16-62
· · Energy, Mines & Resources
    Dept.: Geological Survey of
    Cda., 16-58—59; Cda. Centre
    for Mineral & Energy
    Technology (CANMET),
    16-57—58; Cdn. Centre for
    Remote Sensing, 16-58;
    Office of Energy Research &
    Development, Mineral &
    Energy Technology, 16-57
· · Indian Affairs & Northern Dev't
    Dept., 16-82—87
· · Medical Research Coun. of Cda.,
    16-138
· · Nat'l Gallery of Cda., Restoration
    & Conservation Lab., 16-48
· · Nat'l Museum of Natural
    Sciences, 16-48—49
· · Natural Sciences & Engineering
    Research Coun. of Cda.,
    16-140
· · Science Coun. of Cda.,
    16-141—142
· Cdn.
· · Conservation Inst., 16-40
· · Grain Commn., 16-35
· · Museum of Civilization, 16-49
· · Wildlife Service, Environment
    Cda., 16-66
· Man. Research Coun., 17-132
· N.B., Research & Productivity
    Coun., 17-152
· N.S. Research Fdn. Corp., 17-238
· Ont.
· · Hydro, 17-265
· · ORTECH International, 17-288
· · pubns., 8-143, -160
· Que., Dir. gén. du Centre de
    recherches minérales, Min. de
    l'Énergie et des Ressources,
    17-356

Science & Technology
· B.C. Advanced Systems Fdn.,
    17-66
· Cda.
· · Dept. of Industry, 16-87—92
· · Min. of State for, 16-107
· Nat'l Museum of, 16-49—50
· N.S., Coun. of Applied, 17-234

· Premier's Advisory Coun. on,
    17-67
· Que., Cons. de la science et de la
    technologie, 17-358
· Sask., Dept. of, 17-418

Sciences (acfas), Assoc.
    cdne.-française pour
    l'avancement des, 8-305

Scientific
· assns., 8-305—306
· Experimental Aircraft Assn. of
    Cda., 8-187

Scottish Studies, Cdn. Assn. for,
    8-251

Sculptor's Soc. of Cda., 8-184

Seafarers' Int'l Union of Cda., 11-14

Seafood
· and Allied Workers' Union, Cdn.,
    11-18
· producers, assns., 8-227

Search & Rescue (See Rescue)

Second Language Teachers, Cdn.
    Assn. of, 8-213

Secondary education, 7-7
    Secretaries, Professional, Int'l,
    8-191

Secretary of State Dept., Cda.,
    16-107—110

Sécurité
· du revenu des chasseurs et
    piégeurs cris, Off. de la, 17-372
· dans les sports du Québec, Régie
    de la, 17-370
· publique, Min. de la, 17-376

Securities
· Act, N.B., 17-163
· commns.,
· · Alta., 17-25
· · B.C., 17-77
· · Man., 17-116
· · N.S., 17-220
· · Ont., 17-279
· · Que., 17-383
· · Sask., 17-412
· Inst., Cdn., 8-247—248
· Registration, Corporation, N.B.,
    17-162
· regulation, 1-4, 13-21

Security
· assns., 8-307
· Intelligence Service, Cdn.,
    16-110—111
· Pacific Bank Cda., 13-13
· pubns., 8-144

Seed
· assns., 8-179—182
· Commodity Mktg. Bd., P.E.I.
    Pedigreed, 17-317

Semen Distribution Centre, Man.,
    17-107

Semiotic Assn., Cdn., 8-252

Senate, 15-10, 16-15—17
· Officers' & Members' names,
    16-15—16
· remuneration of Members,
    16-16—17
· senators sworn in, Quebec, 1-3

Senior Citizens (*see also* Aging)
· Advisory Coun. on, Ont., 17-253
· Affairs, Office for, Ont., 17-252
· Alta., Senior Citizens' Secretariat, Minister's Office, Dept. of Social Services, 17-46
· assns., 8-307
· Cda., Health & Welfare Cda., Income Security Programs Br., 16-77
· Man., Income Supplements Program, Employment Services & Economic Security Dept., 17-121
· N.B., Dept. of Health & Community Services, 17-154
· Nfld., Dept. of Social Services, 17-190
· N.W.T., Dept. of Social Services, 17-204
· N.S.,
· · Commn., 17-221
· · Family Benefits Div., Dept. of Community Services, 17-221
· · Secretariat, 17-221
· Ont.,
· · Affairs, Office for, 17-252
· · Guaranteed Income & Tax Credit Br., Min. of Revenue, 17-295
· · Min. of Community & Social Services, 17-263
· P.E.I., Aging & Extended Care Div., Dept. of Health & Social Services, 17-319
· pubns., 8-160
· Que.,
· · Comité sur les abus exercés à l'endroit des personnes agées, 17-375
· · Min. de la Santé et des Services sociaux, 17-374
· Sask. Social Services, 17-418

Serbian
· Orthodox Church, 6-12
· pubns., 9-40

Serena Cda., 8-287

Service(s)
· Employees Int'l Union, 11-14
· essentiels, Cons. des, 17-382
· government, bilingual, 1-2
· Industries, assns., 8-307—308
· juridiques, Comm. des, Qué., 17-368
· social de la province de Québec, Assoc. des employés en, 11-16

Seventh-day Adventist Church in Cda., 6-15

Sewing (*See* Crafts)

Sex Information & Education Council of Cda., 8-212

Sexual Assault Centres, Cdn. Assn. of, 8-350

ShareLife, 8-194

Shastri Indo-Cdn. Inst., 8-302

Shaw Festival Theatre Fdn., 8-343

Sheep
· statistics, 4-5

· and Wool Commns.,
· · Alta., 17-20
· · B.C., 17-70
· · Sask., 17-397

Sheet Metal
· and Air Conditioning Contractors Nat'l Assn., 8-275
· and Air Handling Group, Ont., 8-204
· Assn., B.C., 8-275
· Workers' Int'l Assn., 11-14

Sheet Steel Bldg. Inst., Cdn., 8-274

Sherbrooke, Université de, 7-37

Sheridan Park Assn., 8-302

Sheriffs (Bailiffs), *see* Table of Contents for prov. judiciary listings, 17-1

Shingle & Handsplit Shake Bur., Red Cedar, 8-352

Shippers' Coun., The Cdn., 8-308

Shipping
· assns., 8-308
· pubns., 8-144
· transport industry, 10-11

Shipyard General Workers' Fed. of B.C., 11-26

Shoe assns., 8-229

Shooting assns., 8-331

Shorthorn assns., 8-256—257

Sickle Cell Soc., Cdn., 8-269

SIDBEC-DOSCO, 17-364

Sidereal Time, 2-22

Sierra Club
· of Ont., 8-284
· Western Cda., 8-284

Sign Assn. of Cda., 8-259

Signal & Communications Union, Cdn., 11-18

Signs, Quebec language ban, 1-4

Sikhs, 6-15

Silent Voice Cda. Inc., 8-312

Simmental Assn., Cdn., 8-257

Simon Fraser University, 7-38

Single-parent families, assns., 8-286

Sir George Williams University, *see* Concordia University, 7-18

Sir Joseph Flavelle Fdn., 8-194

Skating, assns.
· figure, 8-324
· speed, 8-334

Ski
· Jumps Ltd., Thunder Bay, 17-300
· Marathon, Cdn., 8-333
· Patrol System, Cdn., 8-313

Skiing
· assns., 8-332
· Biathlon Cda., 8-332
· pubns., 8-161

Skills Dev't, Min. of, Ont., 17-296

Slavists, Cdn. Assn. of, 8-252

Slovak
· League, Cdn., 8-223
· pubns., 9-43

Small business
· Alta., Small Business & Industry Div., Dept. of Economic Development & Trade, 17-29

· Cda., Small Businesses Div., Dept. of Industry, Science & Technology, 16-89
· Cdn. Organization of, 8-190
· depts. of,
· · N.S., 17-230
· · Yukon, 17-433
· Development Corp., N.S., 17-231
· Network, 8-191

Small loans companies, 13-17

Smelter
· and Allied Workers, Cdn. Assn. of, 11-18
· Workers Union, Sudbury Mine, Mill and, 11-27

Smile Theatre Company, 8-343

Smoking
· & Health, Cdn. Coun. on, 8-271
· and human rights, assn., 8-199
· legislation, 1-2

Snowmobile assns., 8-297, -299

Snowshoeing assns., 8-333

Soap & Detergent Assn. of Cda., 8-196

Soaring Assn. of Cda., 8-333

Soccer assns., 8-333—334

Social
· Affairs
· · Commn., Que., 17-372
· · Federation, 11-20
· clubs, 8-231—232
· Credit Party, B.C., 8-290
· Development & planning, assns., 8-308
· Research Council, Que., 17-375
· Science Fed. of Cda., 8-302
· Sciences & Humanities Research Council of Cda., 16-50
· Work, Cdn. Assn. of Schools of, 8-217
· Workers, assns., 8-308, -309, -311

Social Assistance
· Appeal Board
· · Nfld., 17-191
· · N.W.T., 17-208
· Review Board, Ont., 17-264

Social Service(s) (*see also* Charitable organizations)
· Advisory Cttee., Man., 17-122
· assns., 8-308—312
· Council, N.S., 17-221
· depts.
· · Alta., 17-46
· · B.C., 17-90
· · Cda., Health & Welfare Dept., Social Service Programs Br., 16-78
· · Man., Community Services, Dept. of, 17-114
· · N.B., Health & Community Services, 17-154
· · Nfld., 17-190
· · N.W.T., 17-204
· · N.S., 17-220
· · Ont., 17-263
· · P.E.I., 17-319
· · Que., 17-374
· · Sask., 17-418
· · Yukon, 17-432

Social Service (cont'd)
· Employees of the Province of
   Quebec, Assn. of, 11-16
· pubns., 8-160

Social Welfare
· Appeals Bd., N.B., 17-154
· pubns., 8-160

Sociale, Cons. qué. de la recherche,
   17-375

Société
· des alcools du Qué., Syndicat du
   personnel technique et prof. de
   la, 11-27
· Générale (Cda.), 13-13

Sociology & Anthropology
· Assn., Cdn., 8-252
· pubns., 8-169—171

Soft Drink Assn., Cdn., 8-228

Softball assns., 8-334

Soil(s)
· of Cda., 3-12—13
· Science, Cdn. Soc. of, 8-306
· and Water Conservation Soc.,
   8-202

Solar
· energy, assns., 8-220
· system, 2-10—14
· · physical elements, 2-13
· · principal elements, 2-13
· time, 2-20

Solicitor General (see also Attorney
   General)
· depts.,
· · Alta., 17-47
· · B.C., 17-91
· · Canada, 16-110—114
· · N.B., 17-160
· · N.S., 17-231
· · Ont., 17-296
· · Que., 17-375

Souris Basin Dev't Authority, 17-417

Soutien, Féd. du personnel de,
   11-21

Sovereign of Cda., 15-10, 16-5

Soviet
· Jewry, Nat'l Cttee. for, 8-194
· spies, 1-2

Space
· Aeronautics & Space Inst., Cdn.,
   8-187
· Communications
· · Information Services, Dept.,
   16-38
· Energy, Mines & Resources Dept.,
   Cdn. Centre for Remote
   Sensing, 16-58
· Nat'l Defence Dept., Exec.
   Secretariat, Information, 16-97
· Nat'l Research Coun. Cda., Space
   Division, 16-139
· Technology Research Div.,
   Communications Dept., 16-39

Spanish pubns., 9-43—44

Speakers, see prov. Table of
   Contents for legislatures, 17-1
· House of Commons, 15-12, 16-17
· Senate, 15-12, 16-15

Special
· Areas Bd., Alta., 17-43
· assns., see Handicapped,
   8-234—237
· Waste Mgmt. Corp., Alta., 17-34

Speech
· assns., 8-249—250
· · hearing, 8-234—237

Speed skating assns., 8-334—335

Speleological Fed., B.C., 8-297

Spina Bifida & Hydrocephalus Assn.
   of Ont., 8-194

Sport(s)
· Administrators of N.S. (SANS),
   8-313
· Amateur (see also Recreation)
· · Athletics Assn., B.C., 8-312
· · assns., 8-312—339
· · Disabled Support, 8-314—316
· Coun., Alta., 17-46
· Education, 8-314
· Employees Assn., Excel, 11-20
· Halls of Fame
· · B.C., 8-297
· · N.B., 17-162
· Heritage, Cdn. Assn. for, 8-238
· Marketing Coun. (Cda.), 16-82
· Medicine
· · Coun. of Cda., 8-314
· · and Safety Advisory Bd., Ont.,
   17-299
· Museums & Halls of Fame, Assn.
   of, 8-279
· professional & support
   organizations, 8-312—314
· pubns., 8-160—161
· and Recreation Council,
   Interprovincial, 18-4
· Régie de la sécurité dans les, du
   Qué., 17-370
· Sciences
· · Cdn. Assn. of, 8-312
· · Cdn. Journal of, 8-143

Sporting Goods
· Assn., Cdn., 8-303
· and Recreational Equipment,
   pubns., 8-144, -160—161

Sportsmen's Shows, Cdn. Nat'l,
   8-225

Spouses of Gays, 8-240

Sprinkler Assn., Cdn. Automatic,
   8-304

Spying, 1-2

Squash
· assns., 8-335
· pubn., 8-161

Stadium Corp. of Ont. Ltd., 17-302

Staff
· Nurses Assn. of Alberta, 11-27
· Union, Cdn., 11-18

Stained Glass, Artists in, 8-206

Stamps (See Philatelic; Postal
   information)

Standard
· Chartered Bank of Cda., 13-13
· Time Zones, 2-20, -21

Standardization assns., 8-339

Standards
· Assn., Cdn., 8-339
· Cda. Mortgage & Housing Corp.,
   16-129—130
· Cdn. General Standards Bd.
   (CGSB), 16-117
· Council of Cda., 16-142
· Information Service (SIS), 16-142
· Labour Dept., Operations, 16-96
· Measurement Bur., Cdn. Outdoor,
   8-179
· Nat'l Research Council Cda.,
   16-138—140

Standing, Special & Joint
   Committees (federal gov't),
   16-26

Star(s)
· Maps, Quarterly, 2-15—16
· and Stellar Systems, 2-14—17

Stationary Engineers, Bd. of
   Examiners for, N.B., 17-156

Stationery pubns., 8-141

Statistical Soc. of Cda., 8-306

Statistics
· Alta., Bur. of Statistics, Treasury
   Dept., 17-51
· B.C., Central Statistics Bur., Min.
   of Finance & Corporate
   Relations, 17-76
· Canada
· · Bank of Cda., 16-74
· · Cda. Mortgage & Housing Corp.,
   16-129—130
· · Employment & Immigration Cda.,
   Public Affairs Div., 16-54
· · Labour Dept., Communications
   Dir., 16-95
· · Statistics, 16-142—145
· Man., Bur. of Statistics, 17-121
· N.S., Statistics & Research
   Services Br., Dept. of Industry,
   Trade & Technology, 17-227
· Ont., Office of Economic Policy,
   Min. of Treasury & Economics,
   17-302
· P.E.I., Dept. of Finance, 17-318
· Yukon,
· · Bur. of Statistics, 17-431
· · Dept. of Economic Dev't, Mines
   & Small Business, 17-433
· · Vital Statistics, Dept. of Health &
   Human Resources, 17-435

Statutory
· holidays, public, 2-9
· Human Rights Agencies
   (CASHRA), Cdn. Assn. of, 8-198

Steel
· Castings Inst. of Cda., 8-275
· Construction, assns., 8-200
· Erectors, Bldg. Locksmiths &
   Boilermakers, Nat'l Brotherhood
   of Structural, 11-22
· industry
· · profile, Cdn., 14-11
· · Research Assn., Cdn., 8-301
· Reinforcing, Inst. of Cda., 8-204
· Service Centre Inst., Cdn., 8-274

Steelworkers
· of America, United, 11-15
· Interprovincial Brotherhood of
   Structural, 11-22
· Union, Independent Cdn., 11-22

Stock exchanges, 13-22—33
· Alberta, 13-30—32
· · volume & value of trading, 13-30
· Montreal, 13-25—28
· · volume & value of trading, 13-26
· Toronto, 1-1, 13-22—25
· · Equity Market Trading, 13-23
· trading on Cdn., 13-22
· Vancouver, 13-28—30
· · volume & value of trading, 13-29
· Winnipeg, 13-32
· · volume & value of trading, 13-32

Stock Growers Assn., Western,
   8-182

Stock Yards Bd., Ont., 17-258

STOP Inc., 8-202

Storage assn., 8-340

Strategic Studies, The Cdn. Inst. of,
   8-107

Stratford Shakespearean Festival
   Fdn. of Cda., 8-343

Street Haven at the Crossroads,
   8-312

Stress, Cdn. Inst. of, 8-271

Student(s)
· assns., 8-215—216
· Christian Mvmt., Cda., 8-301, -354
· Finance Bd., Alta., 17-17
· Services Personnel, Assn. of,
   11-17

Student Aid
· Alta., Students Finance Bd., Dept.
   of Advanced Education, 17-17
· B.C., Min. of Advanced Education
   & Job Training, 17-65
· Canada,
· · Indian Affairs & Northern Dev't
   Dept., Education Br., 16-83
· · Secretary of State Dept., Student
   Assistance, 16-109
· Man.
· · Student Aid Br., Dept. of
   Education, 17-119
· · Student Aid Appeal Bd., Man.,
   17-120
· Nfld., Student Aid, Dept. of Career
   Dev't & Advanced Studies,
   17-176
· N.W.T., Student Financial
   Assistance Bds., 17-209
· N.S., Finance & Budgeting
   Program, Dept. of Education,
   17-222
· Ont., Student Awards, Min. of
   College & Universities, 17-262
· P.E.I., Personnel & Student Aid,
   Dept. of Education, 17-318
· Que., l'Aide financière aux
   étudiants, Min. de
   l'Enseignement supérieur et de
   la Science, 17-358
· Sask., Student Financial
   Assistance, Dept. of Education,
   17-402

· Yukon, Student Financial Servs.,
   Dept. of Education, 17-434

Subsidies, agricultural, 1-4

Subud Toronto, 8-301

Sudbury
· Chamber of Commerce, 8-192
· Convention & Visitors Services of,
   8-345
· Mine, Mill & Smelter Workers
   Union, 11-27
· Theatre Centre, 8-343

Sudeten-German Clubs in Cda.,
   Central Org. of, 8-223

Sugar Beet
· Growers' Mktg. Bd., Alta., 17-20
· statistics, 4-7

Suicide Prevention, Prov. Advisory
   Cttee. on, Alta., 17-39

Sumitomo Bank of Cda., 13-13

Summerside Waterfront Dev't Corp.,
   P.E.I., 17-326

Summit, economic, 1-2

Sun, 2-10

Superannuated Teachers of Ont.,
   8-213

Superannuates Nat'l Assn., Federal,
   8-307

Superannuation (*see also* Pensions;
   Public Service; Teachers)
· Bds.
· · Civil Service, Man., 17-138
· · Public Service, Ont., 17-281
· Commn., B.C., 17-80

Superintendent(s)
· of Financial Institutions, 13-2,
   16-73—74
· of Insurance, Cda., 13-20

Supernovae, 2-14

Supply & Services
· depts.,
· · Alta., 17-44
· · Canada, 16-114—118
· · N.B., 17-160
· · Que., 17-347
· · Sask., 17-415

Support Staff, Fed. of, 11-21

Supreme Court
· of Canada, 12-7, 16-146
· · rulings, 1-1, -2, -3, -4
· · vacancies, 1-1, -3, -4
· provincial courts, *see* Table of
   Contents for Judiciary, 17-1

Sûreté du Qué., 12-10, 17-376

Surface Rights
· Arbitration Bd., Sask., 17-412
· Bds.,
· · Alta., 17-21
· · Man., 17-136

Surgeons, Paediatric, Cdn. Assn. of,
   8-264

Surveying assns., 8-340

Survival Inst., Nat'l, 8-202

Swedish pubn., 9-44

Swimming
· assns., 8-299, -335
· · synchronized, 8-335—336
· · pubns., 8-161

Swine
· Breeders Assn., Alta., 8-255
· Cttee., R.O.P., Man., 17-111

Swiss
· Bank Corp., 13-13
· Cdn. Chamber of Commerce,
   8-230

Switzerland, Union Bank of, 13-14

Sydney Steel Corp. (SYSCO), N.S.,
   17-240

Symphony orchestras, 8-281, -282,
   -283

Syndicat(s)
· démocratiques (CSD), Centrale
   des, 11-8
· des fonctionnaires provinciaux du
   Qué. inc., 11-27
· hospitaliers de Montréal Inc.,
   Conseil des, 11-19
· nationaux (CSN), Confédération
   des, 11-9
· professionnel des
· · diététistes du Qué., 11-28
· · médecins du gouvernement du
   Qué., 11-28
· · techniciens en radiologie
   médicale du Qué., 11-28

Systems
· Corp., B.C., 17-80
· Mgmt. (Toronto chapter), Assn.
   for, 8-200

T

Table Tennis assns., 8-336

Tae Kwon-Do, assns., 8-336

Taiyo Kobe Bank (Cda.), 13-13

Talent, Soc. for the Recognition of
   Cdn., 8-185

Tamahnous Theatre Workshop,
   8-343

Tanners Assn. of Cda., 8-260

Tantalus Research Ltd., 8-118

Tarentaise Assn., Cdn., 8-257

Tariff Board, *see* Cdn. International
   Trade Tribunal, 16-106—107

Tarragon Theatre, 8-343

Taverns, assns., 8-302—303

Tax
· Court of Cda., 12-7, 16-147—148
· Fdn., Cdn., 8-340

Taxation (*see also* Sales taxes)
· Alta., Treasury Dept., 17-51
· assns., 8-340
· B.C., Revenue Div., Min. of
   Finance & Corporate Relations,
   17-75
· Canada,
· · Finance Dept., 16-72—73
· · Revenue Cda., Taxation,
   16-104—106
· Man., Taxation Div., Dept. of
   Finance, 17-125
· N.B., Taxation & Fiscal Policy,
   Dept. of Finance, 17-153
· Nfld., Fiscal Policy, Dept. of
   Finance, 17-182

Taxation (cont'd)
· N.S., Revenue Div., Dept. of
    Finance, 17-223
· Ont., Min. of Revenue, 17-295
· P.E.I., Revenue Div., Dept. of
    Finance, 17-319
· Que., Min. of Revenue, 17-373
· Sask., Dept. of Finance, 17-404

Taxicab Bd., Man., 17-130

Te Deum Concert Soc., 8-282

Tea & Coffee Assn. of Cda., 8-229

Teacher(s)
· Assn.
· · Alta., 11-15
· · Nfld., 11-24
· · N.W.T., 11-24
· · Ont.: Catholic Occasional, 11-24;
    English Catholic, 11-24
· · Yukon, 11-29
· assns., 8-213
· Certification Bd., N.W.T., 17-208
· Commission, School Board, 11-19
· Education
· · Cdn. Assn. for, 8-213
· · and Certification, Bd. of Man.,
    17-119
· Federations
· · B.C., 11-17
· · of CEGEP, 11-20
· · Canadian, 8-213
· · N.B., 11-24
· · Ont.: 8-213; Public School
    Teachers', 11-25; Secondary
    School Teachers', 11-25
· · P.E.I., 11-25
· · of Provincial Schools Authority
    Teachers, 11-21
· -Librarians' Assn., B.C., 8-253
· music, assns., 8-280, -282
· Pension Commn., N.S., 17-223
· Retirement Allowances Fund Bd.,
    Man., 17-120
· Society, Man., 11-23
· Superannuation Commns.,
· · Ont., 17-275
· · Sask., 17-402
· Union, N.S., 11-24

Team Handball assns., 8-336

Teamsters, Chauffeurs,
    Warehousemen & Helpers of
    America, Int'l Brotherhood of,
    11-11

Technical
· Aids & Systems for the
    Handicapped Inc. (TASH Inc.),
    8-237
· schools, 7-10
· Service Council, 8-219
· University of N.S., 7-38

Technicians (see also Technologists
    & Technicians)
· dental, 8-210
· library, 8-253, -254, -255
· Nat'l Assn. of Broadcast
    Employees and, (NABET), 11-23
· Union, CBC French Network,
    11-27

Technologistes médicaux du Qué.,
    Assoc. prof. des, 11-17

Technologists & Technicians
· assns.
· · architecture, 8-184
· · engineering, 8-220, -221
· · dental, 8-210
· · food, 8-228
· · library, 8-253, -254, -255
· · medical, 8-265—266
· · surveying, 8-340

Technology
· Advanced Technology Assn.,
    Cdn., 8-243
· Alta.
· · Office of Coal Research and,
    17-34
· · Research & Telecomm., Dept. of,
    17-48
· Cda., Dept. of Industry, Science
    and, 16-87
· industry profile, Cdn., 14-12
· Information, Assn. of Cda. (ITAC),
    8-200
· N.B., Dept of Commerce and,
    17-151
· N.S.
· · Coun. of Applied Science and,
    17-234
· · Dept. of Industry, Trade and,
    17-227
· · Transfer Office, 17-240
· Que.
· · Cons. d'évaluation des
    technologies de la santé,
    17-375
· · Min. de l'Industrie, du Commerce
    et de la Technologie, 17-363

Telebook Agency, Cdn., 8-295

Telecaster Cttee. of Cda., 8-189

Telecom Cda., 9-2

Telecommunications
· Agency, Gov't, 16-39
· Alta., Dept. of Technology,
    Research and, 17-48
· assns., 8-340—341
· in Canada, 9-1—5
· carriers, 9-2, -3
· Employees Assn. of Manitoba,
    11-28
· Government, 16-39
· pubns., 8-145
· du Qué., Régie des, 17-351
· SaskTel, 17-424
· Workers Union, 11-28

Tele-Education in Cda. (ATEC),
    Agency for, 8-211

Telefilm Cda., 16-50

Teleglobe Cda., 9-2

Telegraph
· network, 9-1
· Workers, United, 11-15

Telephone, 9-1, -2, -3
· carriers, characteristics of major
    Cdn., 9-3
· Employees
· · Assn., Cdn., 11-19
· · Union, 11-28
· Professional Employees Union,
    Que., 11-27

· Service Commn., Ont., 17-272
· System, Man., 17-140
· systems in Cda., 9-2
· Telecom Cda., 9-2

Telepost, 9-10

Telesat Cda., 9-4

Television
· ACCESS Network, Alta., 17-52
· assns., 8-188, -189
· cable, 9-6, -8, -61—68
· · assns., 8-188
· Cdn. content regulations, 9-7
· educational, 9-6
· Guides, pubns., 8-161—163
· pay, 9-6
· · networks, 9-60
· private, 9-6
· Producers & Directors
· · Assn., Cdn., 11-19
· · Toronto, Assn. of, 11-17
· pubns., 8-188
· and Radio Artists, Alliance of Cdn.
    Cinema (ACTRA), 11-16
· specialty programming services,
    9-8
· stations, 9-57—60
· statistics, 9-5—6
· TV Ontario, 17-271

Telidon, 9-5

Temperance Union, Cdn. Woman's
    Christian, 8-350

Temporary Help Services, Fed. of,
    8-219

Tenants Assns., Fed. of Metro,
    8-242

Tennis
· assns., 8-337
· pubn., 8-161

Terrazzo Tile & Marble Assn. of
    Cda., 8-206

Terrestrial Dynamical Time, 2-22

Territorial
· governments
· · N.W.T., 17-199
· · Yukon, 17-431
· Health Bd., N.W.T., 17-209

Testing assns., 8-341

Textile
· assns., 8-341—342
· and Chemical Union, Cdn., 11-19
· and Clothing Bd., see Cdn.
    International Trade Tribunal,
    16-106—107
· Féd. cdne des travailleurs du,
    11-20
· industry profile, Cdn., 14-12
· Processors, Service Trades,
    Health Care, Professional &
    Technical Employees Int'l
    Union, 11-14
· pubns., 8-145
· Workers
· · of America, United, 11-15
· · Cdn. Fed. of, 11-20

Theatres/Théâtres
· Censorship Bd. of Ont., Theatres
    Br., 17-267
· companies, 8-342—344

Theatre (cont'd)
· Dance, Anna Wyman, 8-209
· pubns., 8-152

Theatrical Stage Employees &
    Moving Picture Machine
    Operators of the U.S. & Cda.,
    Int'l Alliance of, 11-10

Thermal Insulation Assn. of Cda.,
    8-206

Thetis Park Nature Sanctuary Assn.,
    8-349

Thomson Canada Rivet Employees
    Assn., 11-28

Thoracic soc., 8-265

Thoroughbred Horse Soc., Cdn.,
    8-183

Thos. J. Johnston Fdn., 8-194

Thunder Bay
· Multicultural Assn., 8-277
· Ski Jumps Ltd., 17-300
· Symphony Orchestra, 8-282

Thyroid Fdn. of Cda., 8-270

Tibetan Refugee Aid Society (TRAS
    Cda.), 8-195

Tidal Power Corp., N.S., 17-240

Tile Workers & Allied Trades, Union
    of, 11-28

Time, 2-20—22

Time zones, standard, 2-20, -21

Tinsmiths & Tilers, Nat'l Assn. of,
    11-16

Titles, forms of address, 2-3
· academic, 2-7
· diplomatic, 2-6—7
· gov't officials, 2-4
· judicial, 2-4—5
· professional, 2-7
· religious, 2-5—6

Tobacco
· advertising ban, 1-2
· Growers Commodity Bd., P.E.I.,
    17-317
· Mfrs. Coun., Cdn., 8-259
· pubn., 8-165
· statistics, 4-7

Tokai Bank Cda., 13-13

Token Collectors, Cdn. Assn. of,
    8-239

Tooling Mfrs.' Assn., Cdn., 8-259

Toponymie, Comm. de, Qué., 17-337

Toronto
· Art Therapy Inst., 8-184
· Assn. for Peace, 8-199
· Black Watch Assn., 8-276
· Cdn. Club of, 8-231
· Chinese Community Services
    Assn., 8-195
· Clinical Research Soc. of, 8-301
· Consort, 8-282
· Consular Corps. Assn. of, 8-210
· Dance Theatre, 8-209
· Executives Assn. Inc., 8-258
· Film Soc., 8-198
· Historical Bd., 8-239
· Humane Soc., 8-243
· Jewish Congress, 8-301
· Junior Bd. of Trade/Jaycees,
    8-354

· libraries & archives, 8-66—76
· Memorial Society, 8-233
· Mendelssohn Choir, 8-282
· Montessori Inst., 8-215
· Musicians' Assn., 8-282
· newspapers, 9-30—31
· pubns., 8-151
· radio stations, 9-49—50, -55
· Real Estate Bd., 8-296
· St. George's Soc. of, 8-194
· Soc. of Financial Analysts, 8-226
· Stock Exchange, 1-1, 13-22—25
· Symphony, The, 8-282
· television stations, 9-59
· Univ. of, 7-38—40
· Vegetarian Assn., 8-256
· Waterfront, Royal Commn. on the
    Future of the, 16-12
· Workshop Productions, 8-344

Toronto (Metro)
· Apartment Builders Assn., 8-204
· Board of Trade, 8-191
· Building Owners & Managers
    Assn., 8-296
· Cerebral Palsy Inst., Adult, 8-234
· Community
· · Folk Art Coun. of, 8-185
· · Information Centre of, 8-310
· · Living, Assn. for, 8-237
· Convention
· · Centre Corp., 17-298
· · and Visitors Assn., 8-345
· Volunteer Centre of, 8-312

Toronto-Dominion Bank, 13-9

Tourism (see also Travel)
· assns., 8-344—346
· Canada, 16-90—91
· Commr. General for Trade and,
    Alta., 17-30
· depts. of,
· · Alta., 17-48
· · B.C., Recreation & Culture, Min.
    of, 17-94
· · Man., Industry, Trade and,
    17-131
· · N.B., Recreation & Heritage,
    17-160
· · Nfld., Dev't and, 17-178
· · N.W.T., Economic Dev't and,
    17-202
· · N.S., 17-232
· · Ont., 17-297
· · P.E.I., 17-321
· · Que., 17-377
· · Sask., 17-401
· · Yukon, 17-437
· farm vacations, provincial,
    8-344—346
· industry profile, Cdn., 14-15—16
· pubns., 8-145—146
· visitor & convention bureaus,
    municipal, 8-344—346

Toxicology of Cda., Soc. of, 8-252

Toys
· assns., 8-346
· pubns., 8-146

Track & Field assns., 8-337

Tract Soc., Cdn., 8-300

Trade
· Advisory Cttees., Man., 17-135
· Alta., Trade & Investment Div.,
    Dept. of Economic Dev't &
    Trade, 17-29
· areas, principal trading, 14-23
· assns., 8-191—192
· · foreign, 8-229—230
· balance, 14-19—25
· boards of, 8-191—192
· B.C., Min. of International
    Business & Immigration, 17-83
· Canada,
· · Export Development Corp.,
    16-135—137
· · External Affairs Dept., Int'l Trade
    Development Br., 16-70
· · Finance Dept., 16-72—73
· · Industry, Science & Technology,
    Dept. of, Industrial & Trade
    Policy, 16-89
· commissioners, federal,
    16-148—158
· and Convention Centre,
    Vancouver, 17-80
· foreign commissioners in Cda.,
    16-163—174
· free, 14-22—25
· Free Trade Agreement, 1-1, -2, -3,
    -4, 14-22—25
· major commodities, 14-20
· Man., Trade Br., Dept. of Industry,
    Trade & Tourism, 17-131
· N.B., Dept. of Commerce &
    Technology, 17-151
· N.S., Dept. of Industry, Trade &
    Technology, 17-227
· Ont., Min. of Industry, Trade &
    Technology, Trade Div., 17-285
· P.E.I., Dept. of Industry, 17-319
· protectionism, U.S., 14-25
· Que.,
· · Min. de l'Industrie et du
    Commerce, 17-363
· · Min. du Commerce extérieur et
    du Dév. technologique,
    17-348
· Sask., Dept. of Economic
    Development & Tourism, 17-401
· summary, by industrial sector,
    14-21
· surplus, 14-19—21
· Toronto Junior Bd. of, (Jaycees),
    8-354
· and Tourism, Commr. General for,
    Alta., 17-30
· Tribunal, Cdn. Int'l, 16-106
· in Volume & Open Interest in
    Contracts, 13-33

Trade offices
· Alta., 17-36
· B.C., 17-84
· N.S., 17-227
· Ont., 17-285
· Que., 17-348

Trade unions (see also Labour
    Relations; Unions)
· in Canada, 11-7—9; -15—29

Trade unions (cont'd)
· Confederation of Nat'l (CNTU),
   11-9
· international, 11-9—15
· pubns., 8-158

Trademarks, assns., 8-206

Trades Advisory Cttees., N.W.T.,
   17-209

Traducteurs du Qué., Soc. des,
   8-249

Traffic
· Assn., Western Cda., 8-347
· Conf., Ont., 8-347
· Injury Research Fdn. of Cda.,
   8-302
· regulations, 10-5, -8—9
· and Transportation, Cdn. Inst. of,
   8-347

Trail Riders of the Cdn. Rockies,
   8-299

Training
· Advisory Coun., Man., 17-121
· and Dev't, Ont. Soc. for, 8-217

Trans-Cda.
· Advertising Agency Network,
   8-179
· Telephone System, see Telecom
   Cda., 9-2

Transit
· B.C., 17-88
· GO (Ont.), 17-301
· Union
· · Amalgamated, 11-9
· · Independent Cdn., 11-22
· Urban, Cdn., Assn., 8-347

Translation
· Que., Min. des Communications,
   17-350
· Secretary of State Dept., Official
   Languages & Translation,
   16-109

Translators assns., 8-249

Transplant Int'l, 8-262

Transport
· air, 10-14—17
· Boards, provincial motor, 10-7
· Brotherhood of Constables of the
   Que. Dept. of, 11-22
· Cda., Dept. of, 10-1—2,
   16-118—124
· Commn., Cdn., see National
   Transportation Agency, 10-2,
   16-123
· Cttee., Motor Vehicle, 10-7
· of Dangerous Goods, 10-2
· rail, 10-2—5
· road, 10-5—11
· Tariff Bureau Assn., Cdn., 8-347
· 2000 Cda., 8-206
· water, 10-11—13
· Yukon,
· · Motor Transport Bd., 17-433
· · Transport Services, Dept. of
     Community & Transportation
     Services, 17-432

Transportation (see also Freight)
· Alta.,
· · Motor Transport Bd., 17-50
· · Resources Railway Corp., 17-50

· assns., 8-346—347
· air, 8-187
· Authority, N.B., 17-163
· B.C. Ferry Corp., 17-95
· Canada,
· · Cdn. Nat'l Railways, 10-2—3, -4,
     16-122
· · Cdn. Pacific Ltd./CP Rail, 10-3,
     -5
· · -Communications Int'l Union,
     11-14
· · Industry, Science & Technology
     Dept., Surface Transportation
     & Machinery, 16-90
· · Nat'l Aeronautical Establishment,
     Nat'l Research Coun. of Cda.,
     16-139
· · Nat'l Aviation Museum, Nat'l
     Museum of Science &
     Technology, 16-50
· · Nat'l Research Coun., Div. of
     Mechanical Engineering,
     16-139
· · Nat'l Transportation Agency,
     10-2, 16-123
· · Ports Corp., Cda., 16-121
· · P.E.I. link with the mainland, 1-1,
     -3
· · St. Lawrence Seaway Authority,
     10-12—13, 16-123
· · Transport, Dept. of, 16-118—124
· Commn., Ont. Northland, 17-294
· Co., Sask., 17-425
· depts.,
· · Alta., 17-49
· · B.C., 17-94
· · Man., 17-129
· · N.B., 17-162
· · Nfld., 17-191
· · N.W.T., 17-204
· · N.S., 17-232
· · Ont., 17-300
· · P.E.I., 17-321
· · Que., 17-378
· · Sask., 17-406
· · Yukon, 17-432
· Employees, Cdn. Union of, 11-19
· federal regulation of, 10-1—2
· industry profile, Cdn., 14-15
· pubns., 8-146
· Safety Assn. of Ont., 8-305
· Shipping, assns., 8-308
· Trucking Assn., Cdn., 8-348
· Union, United, 11-15

Transports
· Commn. des, du Qué., 17-379
· Min. des, Que., 17-378
· Soc. qué. des, 17-380

Transsexuals, Fed. of American &
   Cdn. (FACT), 8-240

Trapping, Cdn. Assn. for Humane,
   8-242

Travail
· Comm.
· · des normes du, 17-372
· · de la santé et de la sécurité du,
     17-381

· Cons. consultatif du travail et de la
   main-d'oeuvre, 17-382
· Min. du, 17-380

Travel (see also Tourism)
· assns., 8-344—346
· Assurance Bd., B.C., 17-86
· Automobile Assn., Cdn., 8-186
· Bus Assn., Cdn., 8-346
· Convention bureaus, municipal &
   provincial, 8-344—346
· passports & visas, 16-175
· pubns., 8—147, -160—161
· regulations abroad, 16-175—176

Travellers
· Associated Cdn., 8-231
· Int'l Assn. for Medical Assistance
   to, 8-345

Traversiers du Qué., Soc. des,
   17-380

Treasury & Economics, Ont. Ministry
   of, 17-302

Treasury
· boards
· · B.C., 17-63, -78
· · Cda., 16-124—125
· · Man., 17-105
· · Nfld., 17-173
· · P.E.I., 17-315
· · Que., 17-351
· branches, Prov. of Alta., 13-14,
   17-51
· depts.
· · Alta., 17-51
· · Ont., 17-302

Tree Fruit Mktg. Bd., B.C., 17-70

Trent University, 7-40

Trésor, Cons. du, Que., 17-351

Tridon Employees Union, 11-28

Trillium Fdn., Ont., 17-299

Trinity Western University, 7-41

Tropical Medicine & Int'l Health,
   Cdn. Soc. for, 8-272

Trotting Assn., Cdn., 8-257

Trowel Trades Cdn. Assn., 11-16

Truck Loggers' Assn., 8-352

Trucking
· assns., 8-347—348
· industry
· · legislation, 10-5—6
· · structure, 10-11
· pubns., 8-146—147
· regulation of Cdn., 10-5—6, -10
· regulatory agencies, 10-7

Trust
· companies, 13-15—17
· Companies Assn. of Cda., 8-226

Turkey (See Poultry)

TV Ontario (Ont. Educational
   Communications Authority),
   17-271

25th St. Theatre, 8-344

Twin Falls Power Corp., Nfld.,
   17-194

U

UNESCO
· Canada's delegation, 16-186
· Cdn. Commn. for, 7-5, 8-246

UNICEF Cda., 8-195

USSR Assn., Cda.-, 8-246

Ukraine, Cdn. League for the Liberation of, 8-247

Ukrainian(s)
· assns., 8-223, -224, -354
· Orthodox Church, 6-12
· pubns., 9-44

Umpire, Office of the (Cda.), 16-56

Underwater Diving, assns., 8-337

Underwriters
· assns., 8-243—245
· Laboratories of Cda., 8-305

Unemployment Insurance, 11-4—5
· Act, 11-6
· Employment & Immigration Cda., 16-54

Unifarm, 8-182

Unions (*see also* Labour Relations; Trade Unions)
· Confederation
· · of Cdn. (CCU), 11-9
· · of Nat'l Trade Unions (CNTU), 11-9
· Independent, Cdn. Nat'l Fed. of, (CNFIU), 11-8
· labour, 11-2, -9—29
· membership by congress affiliation, 11-2

Unison Soc. of Cape Breton, 8-309

Unitarian
· Church, see Cdn. Unitarian Council, 6-6
· Service Cttee. (USC Cda.), 8-312

United
· Church of Cda., The, 1-1, -2, 6-15
· Empire Loyalists' Assn. of Cda., 8-239
· Way, 8-195
· World Colleges, 8-213

United Kingdom
· Assn. of Ottawa, 8-224
· Freight Conference, Cda., 8-346

United Nations, 16-186
· Assn. in Cda., 8-247
· peacekeeping forces, 1-3
· Security Council, 1-3

Unity, Coun. for Cdn., 8-283

Universal Fellowship of Metro. Community Churches, 6-16

Universités, Cons. des, Que., 17-359

University(ies) 7-11—12, -12—45
· Advisory Coun., B.C., 17-68
· Affairs, Ont. Coun. on, 17-263
· Art Assn. of Cda., 8-252
· assns., see Education, 8-211—218
· Athletic Assn., Ont., 8-314
· and College Employees, Assn. of, 11-17
· Endowment Lands, 17-86
· Grants Commn., Man., 17-120
· Min. of Colleges &, Ont., 17-262
· Music Soc., Cdn., 8-280
· for Northern Studies, Assn. of Cdn., 8-184
· Presses, Assn. of Cdn., 8-294
· Professors & Lecturers, Fed. of, 11-20

· pubns., 8-172—176
· Service
· · of Cda., World, 8-247
· · Overseas, Cdn., (CUSO), 8-246

Unsatisfied Judgment Fund, N.B., 17-163

Upholsterers' Int'l Union of North America, 11-15

Uranium & Nuclear Energy, 4-20

Uranus, 2-12

Urban
· development, assns., 8-200
· Municipalities Assn., Alta., 8-278
· and Regional Research, Intergovernmental Cttee. on, 18-4
· Transit Assn., Cdn., 8-347

Urban Affairs
· Man. Dept. of, 17-138
· Sask. Dept. of, 17-419

Urbanistes du Qué., Corp. prof. des, 8-200

Urdu, pubns., 9-44

Utilities (*see also* Public Utilities)
· Bd., Yukon, 17-436
· Commn., B.C., 17-74
· Dept. of Transportation and, Alta., 17-49

V

Vaccination requirements, travel abroad, 16-176

Valeurs mobilières du Qué., Commn. des, 17-383

Valuation, Bd. of, Ont., 17-260

Vancouver
· libraries & archives, 8-24—26
· newspapers, 9-19
· Opera Assn., 8-282
· pubns., 8-151—152
· radio stations, 9-46, -53
· Stock Exchange, 13-28—30
· television stations, 9-58
· Trade & Convention Centre, 17-80

Vanier Inst. of the Family, 8-302

Vegetable
· Co-operative Assn., B.C. Coast, 8-180
· Fruit and, Growers Assn., Ont., 8-181
· mktg. bds.,
· · Alta., 17-19, -20
· · B.C., 17-71
· · Man., 17-108
· · Sask., 17-399
· and Potato Producers of N.S., 8-182
· statistics, 4-6

Vegetarian Assn., Toronto, 8-261

Vegetation of Cda., 3-12—13

Vehicle Distributors Coun., Cdn. All-Terrain, 8-346

Venture Capital Co., Assn. of Cdn., 8-189

Venus, 2-11

Veterans
· Affairs, Dept. of, Cda., 16-125—128

· Appeal Board, 16-127—128
· assns., 8-275—276

Veterinary
· assns., 8-182—183
· pubns., 8-147

VIA Rail Cda. Inc., 10-3—4, -5, 16-124

Victoria
· Chamber of Commerce, 8-192
· libraries & archives, 8-27—28
· pubns., 8-151
· Real Estate Bd., 8-296
· Symphony Soc., 8-282
· University of, 7-41

Victoria General Hospital, N.S., 17-241

Victorian Order of Nurses for Cda., 8-286

Video
· Exchange Soc., Satellite, 8-185
· pubns., 8-161—163

Videotex, 9-5

Vietnamese assns., 8-224

Vintner's Club, Toronto, 8-239

Visa & entry requirements, 16-175—176

Visiting Homemakers Assn., 8-312

Visual Arts, 8-184—185

Visual Communications Cda., 8-120

Visually Impaired, Atlantic Provinces Resource Centre for the, 18-2

Vital Statistics, see 5-5—7 & individual provinces
· comparison of Cda. with other countries, 5-8

Vocational
· Assn., Cdn., 8-216
· schools, 7-9—10

Volleyball assns., 8-338

Volunteer Int'l Christian Service, 8-312

W

Waferboard Assn., 8-206

Wage
· discrimination, 11-3
· rates, minimum, 11-4

Waldo, Carolyn, 1-3

War
· Amputations of Cda., 8-276
· Graves Commn. (Cda.), Commonwealth, 16-127, -189
· Measures Act, 1-2
· Museum, Cdn., 16-49
· Veterans' Assns., Cdn. Coun. of, 8-276

Warehousing Assn., Cdn., 8-340

Warplane Heritage Museum, Cdn., 8-279

Waste
· assns., 8-201—202
· Management Corp.,
· · Man. Hazardous, 17-124
· · Ont., 17-278
· · pubns., 8-147

Water
· Bds.,
· · N.W.T., 16-86—87, 17-208
· · Prairie Provinces, 18-5
· · Yukon, 16-87
· coastal, Cdn., 3-9
· Commn., Lower Red River Valley,
    Man., 17-137
· Corp., Sask., 17-425
· inland, Cdn., 3-8
· Pollution Research & Control
    (CAWPRC), Cdn. Assn. on,
    8-201
· Resources Br., Dept. of Municipal
    Affairs & Environment, N.B.,
    17-158
· Services Bd., Man., 17-111
· system, assns., 8-348
· and Waste
· · Assn., B.C., 8-201
· · treatment pubns., 8-147
· works Equipment Assn., Ont.,
    8-222

Water polo assns., 8-338

Water skiing assns., 8-338

Waterfront Development Corp. Ltd.,
    N.S., 17-241

Waterloo, Univ. of, 7-41—42

Waterways Dev't Assn., Great Lakes,
    8-347

Weightlifting, assns., 8-339

Weights & Measures
· Legal Metrology Br., Consumer &
    Corporate Affairs Cda., 16-52
· Standards Coun. of Cda., 16-142

Weizmann Inst. of Science, Cdn.
    Soc. for, 8-306

Welding
· Bur., Cdn., 8-203
· Inst. of Cda., 8-275

Welfare
· Alta., Dept. of Social Services,
    17-46
· B.C., Income Assistance Div., Min.
    of Social Services & Housing,
    17-89
· Cda.
· · Dept. of Health & Welfare,
    16-77—82: Income Security
    Programs Br., 16-77—78;
    Policy, Communications &
    Information Br., 16-77; Social
    Service Programs Br.,
    16-78—79
· · Nat'l Coun. of Welfare, 16-81—82
· Man.,
· · Dept. of Community Services,
    17-114
· · Economic Security Div., Dept. of
    Employment Services &
    Economic Security, 17-120
· N.B., Dept. of Income Assistance,
    17-154
· Nfld., Dept. of Social Services,
    17-190
· N.S., Dept. of Community
    Services, 17-220

· Ont., Min. of Community & Social
    Services, 17-263
· P.E.I., Dept. of Health & Social
    Services, 17-319
· Que., Min. de la main-d'oeuvre et
    de la sécurité du revenu, 17-371
· Sask., Income Security Div., Dept.
    of Social Services, 17-418
· Yukon, Dept. of Health & Human
    Resources, 17-435

Well Drilling Advisory Bd., N.B.,
    17-166

West Coast Environmental Law
· Assn., 8-251
· Research Fdn., 8-251

Western
· Bank, Canadian, 13-10
· Barley Growers Assn., 8-182
· Deaf, Inst. for the, 8-237
· Dog Organizations (FIDO), Fed. of
    Individuals and, 8-183
· Economic Diversification, Dept. of,
    16-128
· Fair Assn., 8-225
· Grain
· · Elevator Assn., 8-182
· · Stabilization Admin., 16-35
· Interior Plains, 3-7
· Lumbermen's Assn., Retail, 8-303
· Museums, Sask. Dev't, 17-415
· Music, Bd. of, 8-282
· Stock Growers Assn., 8-182
· Transportation Advisory Coun.,
    8-347

Western Canada
· Concept Party of Alta., 8-292
· Lottery Corp., 18-5
· Summer Games Coun., 8-234
· Theatre Co., 8-344
· Traffic Assn., 8-347
· Water & Wastewater Assn., Cda.,
    8-348

Westminster
· Bank of Cda., Nat'l, 13-13
· Inst. for Ethics & Human Values,
    8-302

Wheat
· Bd., Cdn., 16-36
· Pool, Alta., 8-180

Wheelchair Sports, assns., 8-316

Whistler Conference Centre, 17-81

White Water Canoeing Assn. of
    B.C., 8-320

Wholesale Trade, assns., 8-348

Wigwamen Inc., 8-284

Wilderness Assn., Alta., 8-201

Wildlife
· Alta.
· · Fish & Wildlife Div., Dept. of
    Forestry, Lands & Wildlife,
    17-37
· · Fdn., Recreation, Parks and,
    17-46
· assns., 8-349
· B.C., Wildlife Branch, Min. of
    Environment, 17-75
· Cda., Cdn. Wildlife Service, Dept.
    of the Environment, 16-66

· Conservation Employees' Union,
    Que., 11-27
· Man., Wildlife Br., Dept. of Natural
    Resources, 17-137
· Nat'l Museum of Natural Sciences,
    16-48—49
· N.B., Fish & Wildlife Br., Dept. of
    Natural Resources & Energy,
    17-159
· Nfld., Wildlife Div., Dept. of
    Culture, Recreation & Youth,
    17-177
· N.W.T., Wildlife Management,
    Dept. of Renewable Resources,
    17-203
· Ont., Wildlife Dir., Min. of Natural
    Resources, 17-293
· Que.,
· · Dir. gén. de la ressource
    faunique, Min. du Loisir, de la
    Chasse et de la Pêche,
    17-369
· · Fdn. de la faune du Québec,
    17-370
· Sask., Wildlife Br., Dept. of Parks,
    Recreation & Culture, 17-413
· Yukon, Fish & Wildlife Br., Dept. of
    Renewable Resources, 17-437

Wilfrid Laurier Univ., 7-43

Willow Society, 8-184

Wilson, Michael, 1-1

Window & Door Mfrs. Assn., Cdn.,
    8-259

Windsor
· libraries & archives, 8-78
· Symphony Orchestra, 8-282
· Univ. of, 7-43

Wine
· assns., 8-227—229
· · hobbies, 8-239
· pubns., 8-154

Winnipeg
· Ballet, Royal, 8-209
· Building Construction Wages Bd.,
    Greater, 17-135
· Chamber of Commerce, 8-192
· Commodity Exchange, 13-33
· Convention & Visitors Bureau,
    8-346
· Fdn., The, 8-195
· libraries & archives, 8-30—34
· newspapers, 9-21
· radio stations, 9-47, -53
· Real Estate Bd., 8-296
· Stock Exchange, 13-32—33
· Symphony Orchestra Inc., 8-283
· television stations, 9-58
· Univ. of, 7-44

Wolf Damage Assessment Bd., Ont.,
    17-258

Women (see also specific
    categories)
· agriculture, 8-182
· assns., 8-349—351
· Condition féminine, Que., 17-333

Women (cont'd)
· Councils on Status of (see also
    Women, status of)
· · Cdn., 8-351, 16-131—132, -145
· · Man., 17-121
· · N.B., 17-148
· · N.W.T., 17-206
· · N.S., 17-233
· · P.E.I., 17-324
· · Que., 17-334
· Employment Equity Br., Dept. of
    Employment & Immigration,
    Cda., 16-53
· in Information Processing, 8-201
· Medical Women of Cda., Fed. of,
    8-265
· pubns., 8-164, -169, -170
· · consumers, 8-164
· in Science & Technology, Soc. for
    Cdn., 8-306
· Teachers' Assns. of Ont., Fed. of,
    11-21

Women's (see also specific
    categories)
· Advertising Club of Toronto, 8-179
· Art Assn. of Cda., Lyceum Club &,
    8-350
· assns., 8-349—351
· Athletic Assn. (OWIAA), Ont.
    Women's Intercollegiate, 8-314
· Directorate,
· · Man., 17-121
· · Ont., 17-303
· · Yukon, 17-437
· Inter-Church Coun. of Cda., 8-301
· Issues, Ont. Adv. Council on,
    17-303
· Legal Education & Action Fund
    (LEAF), 8-251
· Mining Industry of Cda., Assn. of
    the, 8-277
· Native Women's assns., 8-283,
    -284
· pubns., 8-164
· Secretariat
· · Alta., 17-54
· · B.C., 17-68

Wood
· assns., 8-351—352
· buffalo, 1-2
· Carvers Assn., Ont., 8-207
· industry in Cda., 4-8—4-10
· pubns., 8-147—148
Woodlot Owners Inc., N.B. Fed of,
    8-231
Woodwork
· Mfrs. Assn., Cdn., 8-351
· · Architectural, 8-206
· pubns., 8-147

Woodworkers Fed., Que., 11-21
Wool
· Bureau of Cda., 8-342
· Growers Ltd., Cdn. Co-operative,
    8-180
· pubn., 8-165
Workers
· Appeal Bd., N.S., 17-228
· Compensation
· · Boards: 11-5—6; Alta., 17-55;
    B.C., 17-86; Man., 17-124;
    N.B., 17-157; Nfld., 17-194;
    N.W.T., 17-210; N.S., 17-228;
    Ont., 17-290; P.E.I., 17-326;
    Que., 17-381; Sask., 17-409;
    Yukon, 17-438
· Review Bd., B.C., 17-86
· · Educational Assn. of Cda., The,
    8-213
Workplace Safety & Health, Adv.
    Coun. on, Man., 17-124
World
· Energy Conf., Cdn. Nat'l Cttee. of,
    8-219
· Literacy of Cda., 8-213
· Trade & Convention Centre, (N.S.),
    17-241
· Vision Cda., 8-195
Wrestling assns., 8-339
Writers
· assns., 8-352
· Researchers & Composers, Soc.
    of, 11-26

X

Xavier College, Sydney, see St.
    Francis Xavier University,
    7-35—36

Y

YMCAs of Cda., Nat'l Coun. of,
    8-298
YWCA of Cda., 8-299
Yachting
· assns., 8-339
· pubns., 8-149
Yellowknife Chamber of Commerce
    8-192
York
· Pioneer & Historical Soc., 8-239
· University, 7-44—45
· · Staff Assn., 11-29
Young Offenders Act, 12-11—12
Young People's Theatre, 8-344

Youth (see also specific categories)
· Advisory Coun.,
· · B.C., 17-67
· · Nfld. & Lab., 17-178
· assns., 8-352—354
· Bowling Coun., 8-319
· for Christ/Cda., 8-301
· Coun. of N.B., 17-149
· Employment Services Br., Min. of
    Skills Development, 17-296
· Farmers, assns., 8-181
· Forest Wardens of Cda., 8-231
· Music, assns., 8-280, -281
· Nfld., Dept. of Culture, Recreation
    & Youth, 17-177
· pubns., 8-164—165
· Science Fdn., 8-306

Yukon (see also B.C. & Yukon)
· Act, 17-431
· agriculture, 4-4
· coat of arms, 17-429
· college, 7-54
· Commissioner, 17-431
· Communities, Assn. of, 8-278
· courts, 17-440
· economy, 17-430
· education, 7-4, -8
· Federal Gov't Directory, 17-438
· forestry, 4-9
· geography, 3-6, 17-429
· gov't, 17-431
· history, 17-429
· judicial officers, 17-440
· labour legislation, 11-3, -7
· libraries & archives, 8-104
· local gov't, 19-43
· map, 17-428
· minimum wage rate, 11-4
· mining, 17-430
· motor vehicle regulations, 10-9
· municipalities, 19-43
· native land claims, 1-2, -3
· newspapers, 9-39
· population, 5-2, 17-429, -430
· radio stations, 9-52, -57
· superintendent of insurance, 13-20
· television station, 9-60
· Vital Statistics, Health Services,
    Dept. of Health & Human
    Resources, 17-435

Z

Zionist Fed., Cdn., 8-223
Zoological, societies, 8-182, -183
Zoologists, Cdn. Soc. of, 8-306